UCSMP
Secondary Component

The University of Chicago School Mathematics Project

Functions, Statistics, and Trigonometry

Second Edition
Teacher's Edition
Part 2, Chapters 7-13

About the Cover The three curves shown on the cover represent the major themes of UCSMP *Functions, Statistics, and Trigonometry*. This text integrates algebraic and trigonometric functions with data analysis and probability explorations, using modeling throughout. More advanced statistical concepts and some discrete mathematics topics are also included.

Authors

Sharon L. Senk   Steven S. Viktora   Zalman Usiskin
Nils P. Ahbel   Virginia Highstone   David Witonsky
Rheta N. Rubenstein   James E. Schultz   Margaret Hackworth
John W. McConnell   Dora Aksoy   James Flanders   Barry Kissane

Scott Foresman
Addison Wesley

Editorial Offices: Glenview, Illinois • Menlo Park, California
Sales Offices: Reading, Massachusetts • Duluth, Georgia • Glenview, Illinois
Carrollton, Texas • Menlo Park, California
http://www.sf.aw.com

Contents
of Teacher's Edition

The complete Table of Contents for the Student Edition begins on page vi.

Your UCSMP Professional Sourcebook is found at the back of Part 1, starting on page T20.

ISBN: 0-673-45928-4

CONTENTS

CHAPTER 1   4

EXPLORING DATA

CHAPTER 2   80

FUNCTIONS AND MODELS

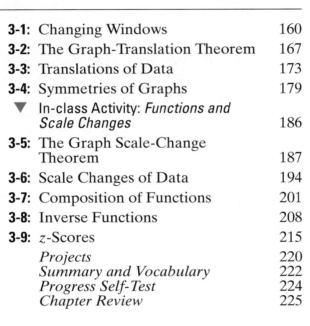

TRANSFORMATIONS OF GRAPHS AND DATA

CIRCULAR FUNCTIONS

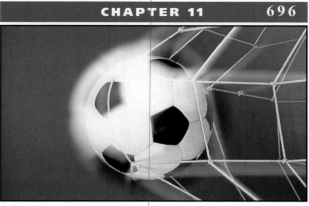
x

Adapting to Individual Needs

The student text is written for the vast majority of students. The chart at the right suggests two pacing plans to accommodate the needs of your students. Students in the Full Course should complete the entire text by the end of the year. Students in the Minimal Course will spend more time when there are quizzes and more time on the Chapter Review. Therefore, these students may not complete all of the chapters in the text.

Options are also presented to meet the needs of a variety of teaching and learning styles. For each lesson, the Teacher's Edition provides a section entitled *Adapting to Individual Needs*. This section regularly includes **Optional Activities, Challenge** problems, **English Language Development** suggestions, and suggestions for providing **Extra Help.** The Teacher's Edition also frequently includes an **Error Alert,** an **Extension,** and an **Assessment** alternative. The options available in Chapter 7 are summarized in the chart below.

Chapter 7 Pacing Chart

Day	Full Course	Minimal Course
1	7-1	7-1
2	7-2	7-2
3	7-3	7-3
4	Quiz*; 7-4	Quiz*; begin 7-4.
5	7-5	Finish 7-4.
6	7-6	7-5
7	Quiz*; 7-7	7-6
8	7-8	Quiz*; begin 7-7.
9	Self-Test	Finish 7-7.
10	Review	7-8
11	Test*	Self-Test
12		Review
13		Review
14		Test*

*in the Teacher's Resource File

In the Teacher's Edition...

Lesson	Optional Activities	Extra Help	Challenge	English Language Development	Error Alert	Extension	Cooperative Learning	Ongoing Assessment
7-1	●	●	●	●	●	●	●	Oral
7-2	●	●	●		●	●		Written
7-3	●	●	●		●	●		Quiz
7-4	●	●	●		●	●		Written
7-5	●	●	●	●	●	●		Written
7-6	●	●	●			●	●	Quiz
7-7	●	●	●	●	●	●	●	Written
7-8	●	●	●		●	●	●	Written

Chapter 7 Block Schedule

Day	Recommended Pacing
1	Lessons 7-1, 7-2
2	Lesson 7-3
3	Lessons 7-4, 7-5
4	Lesson 7-6
5	Lesson 7-7
6	Lesson 7-8, Self-Test, Chapter Review
7	Chapter Review, Chapter Test

In the Additional Resources...

Lesson	In the Teacher's Resource File							Explorations Software
	Lesson Masters	Teaching Aids*	Answer Masters	Technology Sourcebook	Assessment Sourcebook	Visual Aids**	Technology	
7-1	7-1	62, 65	7-1			62, 65, AM		
7-2	7-2	62, 66	7-2			62, 66, AM		
7-3	7-3	62	7-3	Calc 6	Quiz	62, AM		
7-4	7-4	63	7-4			63, AM		
7-5	7-5	63, 67, 68	7-5			63, 67, 68, AM		
7-6	7-6	64	7-6	Calc 6	Quiz	64, AM		
In-class Activity			7-7			AM		7-7
7-7	7-7	64, 69	7-7			64, 69, AM		
7-8	7-8	64, 70	7-8	Comp 8		64, 70, AM	BASIC	7-8
End of chapter					Tests			

*Teaching Aids are pictured on pages 424C and 424D.

**Visual Aids provide transparencies for all Teaching Aids and all Answer Masters.

Also available is the Study Skills Handbook which includes study-skill tips related to reading, note-taking, and comprehension.

Integrating Strands and Applications

	7-1	7-2	7-3	7-4	7-5	7-6	7-7	7-8
Mathematical Connections								
Number Sense	●					●		
Algebra	●	●	●	●	●	●	●	●
Geometry	●	●				●		
Logic and Reasoning	●	●	●	●	●	●	●	●
Probability	●	●	●	●	●	●	●	●
Statistics/Data Analysis						●		
Patterns and Functions	●	●	●	●		●		●
Discrete Mathematics	●	●	●	●	●	●	●	●
Interdisciplinary and Other Connections								
Art			●	●				
Science	●				●	●	●	●
Social Studies	●	●			●	●		
Multicultural				●	●	●	●	
Technology			●	●				●
Consumer	●	●	●	●	●		●	

Teaching and Assessing the Chapter Objectives

Chapter 7 Objectives (Organized into the SPUR categories—Skills, Properties, Uses, and Representations)	Lessons	Progress Self-Test Questions	Chapter Review Questions	Chapter Test, Forms A and B	In the Teacher's Resource File — Chapter Test, Forms C	In the Teacher's Resource File — Chapter Test, Forms D
Skills						
A: List sample spaces and events for probabilistic experiments.	7-1	1	1-6	2	1	✓
B: Compute probabilities.	7-1, 7-2, 7-3	1, 2, 3	7-12	1, 2, 3	1	✓
C: Find the number of ways of selecting or arranging objects.	7-3, 7-4	4	13-16	6	5	
D: Evaluate expressions using factorials.	7-3, 7-4	5, 6	17-24	4, 5	2	
Properties						
E: State and use properties of probabilities.	7-1, 7-2, 7-5	7	25-30	7	1	✓
F: Determine whether events are mutually exclusive, independent, or complementary.	7-2, 7-5	8	31-38	9, 10	4	
G: Solve equations using factorials.	7-4	9	39-42	8		
Uses						
H: Calculate probabilities in real situations.	7-1, 7-2, 7-5	10	43-46	11	4	✓
I: Use counting principles and theorems to find the number of ways of arranging objects.	7-3, 7-4	11, 12	47-52	12, 13	5	
J: Design and conduct simulations without technology.	7-7	13, 14	53-56	14		✓
K: Design and conduct simulations using technology.	7-8	15	57-60	15	3	✓
Representations						
L: Construct, graph, and interpret probability distributions.	7-6	16	61-65	16		✓

Multidimensional Assessment
Quiz for Lessons 7-1 through 7-3
Quiz for Lessons 7-4 through 7-6
Chapter 7 Test, Forms A–D
Chapter 7 Test, Cumulative Form

 Quiz and Test Writer

Teaching Aids

Warm-up
Lesson 7-1

A drawer contains *r* red socks, *b* blue socks, and *w* white socks. Assume that you draw a sock randomly from the drawer.

1. What is the probability that the sock is red?

2. What is the probability that the sock is not white?

3. What is the probability that the sock is green?

Warm-up
Lesson 7-2

How many positive integers less than or equal to 1000 satisfy each condition?

1. Divisible by 5

2. Divisible by 7

3. Divisible by 5 or 7

Warm-up
Lesson 7-3

1. How many sets of answers are possible if a true-false test has:
   a. 1 question?   b. 2 questions?
   c. 4 questions?   d. 10 questions?

2. State a generalization about the number of sets of answers that are possible for a true-false test.

Warm-up
Lesson 7-4

At least twelve permutations of the letters AEPRS are legal words in the game of Scrabble®. In fact, no other set of five letters forms as many legal Scrabble words as these five letters.

1. Name as many as you can.

2. If the letters AEPRS are ordered at random, what is the probability that the ordering forms a legal word in Scrabble?

Warm-up
Lesson 7-5

Suppose the probability that a boy is born in a family is .49 and that a family has three children of different ages.

1. What is the probability that the oldest two children are boys?

2. What is the probability that the youngest child is a girl?

3. What is the probability that the oldest two children are boys and the youngest child is a girl?

4. Are the events of Questions 1 and 2 independent?

Warm-up
Lesson 7-6

Think of rolling two dice.

1. Which sum is most likely to occur?

2. Which two sums are least likely to occur?

3. Which is more likely, a sum of 3 or a sum of 11?

4. Name the other pairs of sums that are equally likely to occur.

Warm-up
Lesson 7-7

Pick three digits at random from 0 to 9 using any means you wish. Then, when your teacher calls your name, record your number on the chalkboard. After everyone has written his or her number on the chalkboard, discuss what these numbers represent.

Warm-up
Lesson 7-8

Work in groups. Each group will need a calculator with a random number generator.

1. Generate 5 simulations like the one in Example 2 on page 474 of the Student Edition.

2. For each simulation, determine the number of reservations needed.

3. Put all of your results together to give relative frequencies for each number of reservations needed.

4. How many reservations do you think the airline should accept?

Lesson 7-1

Sample Space for Tossing Two Dice

Lesson 7-2

Addition Counting Principles and Basic Theorems

Addition Counting Principle (Mutually Exclusive Form)
If two finite sets A and B are mutually exclusive, then

$$N(A \cup B) = N(A) + N(B).$$

Theorem (Probability of the Union of Mutually Exclusive Events)
If A and B are mutually exclusive events in the same finite sample space, then

$$P(A \cup B) = P(A) + P(B).$$

Addition Counting Principle (General Form)
For any finite sets A and B,

$$N(A \cup B) = N(A) + N(B) - N(A \cap B).$$

Theorem (Probability of a Union of Events—General Form)
If A and B are any events in the same finite sample space, then

$$P(A \text{ or } B) = P(A \cup B) = P(A) + P(B) - P(A \cap B).$$

Theorem (Probability of Complements)
If A is any event, then $P(\text{not } A) = 1 - P(A)$.

Lesson 7-5

Sample Spaces of Socks

With Replacement

1 1	1 2	1 3	1 4	1 1	1 2
2 1	2 2	2 3	2 4	2 1	2 2
3 1	3 2	3 3	3 4	3 1	3 2
4 1	4 2	4 3	4 4	4 1	4 2
1 1	1 2	1 3	1 4	1 1	1 2
2 1	2 2	2 3	2 4	2 1	2 2

Without Replacement

1 2	1 3	1 4	1 1	1 2
2 1	2 3	2 4	2 1	2 2
3 1	3 2	3 4	3 1	3 2
4 1	4 2	4 3	4 1	4 2
1 1	1 2	1 3	1 4	1 2
2 1	2 2	2 3	2 4	2 1

Lesson 7-5

Sample Spaces

Example 1

Example 2

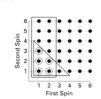

Lesson 7-7

Random Number Table

24130	48360	22527	97265	76393	64809
15179	24830	49340	32081	30680	19655
63348	58629	42167	93093	06423	61680
17856	16376	39440	53537	71341	57004
00849	74917	97758	16379	37570	39975
81837	16656	06121	91782	60468	81305
49684	60672	14110	06927	01263	54613
77921	06907	11008	42751	27756	53498
18602	70659	90655	15053	21916	81825
44394	42880	99562	72905	56420	69994
98872	31016	71194	18738	44013	48840
63213	21069	10634	12952	96301	91977
05463	07972	18876	20922	94595	56869
69014	60045	18425	84903	42508	32307

Airplane Reservations Simulations

Trial 1:	71194	18738	44013	48840	6321
Trial 2:	94595	56869	69014	60045	1842
Trial 3:	57740	84378	25331	12566	5867
Trial 4:	38867	62300	08158	17983	1643
Trial 5:	56865	05859	90106	31595	7154
Trial 6:	18663	72695	52180	20847	1223

Trial	Reservations						Needed
	Simulated (0 means no-show)						
1	24130	48360	22527	97265	76393	6	26
2	42167	93093	06243	61680	37856	16	27
3	37570	39975	81837	16656	06121	9	26
4	77921	06907	11008	42751	27756	534	28
5	09429	93969	52636	92737	88974		25
6	10365	61129	87529	85689	48237		25
7	07119	97336	71048	08178	77233	13	27
8	51085	12765	51821	51259	77452		25
9	82368	21382	52474	60268	89368		25
10	01001	54092	33362	94904	31273	04147	30

Chapter Opener

CHAPTER 7

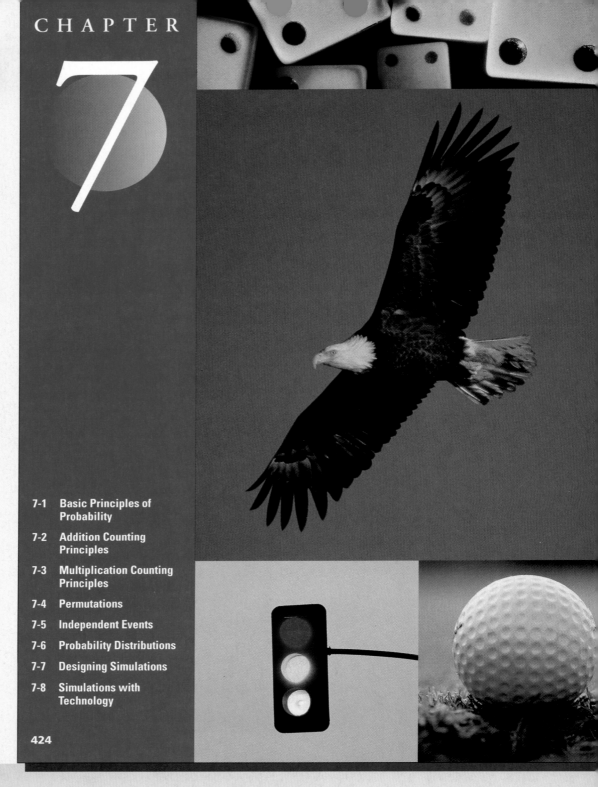

Pacing

All lessons in this chapter are designed to be covered in one day. At the end of the chapter, you should plan to spend 1 day to review the Progress Self-Test, 1–2 days for the Chapter Review, and 1 day for a test. You may wish to spend a day on projects, and possibly a day is needed for quizzes and the In-class Activity. This chapter should therefore take 11–14 days. Spending more than 15 days on this chapter is not recommended; there is ample opportunity to review ideas in later chapters.

Using Pages 424–425

The point to make is that probabilities are of critical importance in many different activities. This chapter covers the basic ideas of probability and simulation, ideas that are extended in Chapters 8 and 10.

424

Chapter 7 Overview

This chapter has as its main themes probability, counting, and simulation. The intent is to review certain concepts, tackle some important types of questions of counting and probability, and prepare students for the study of binomial and normal distributions in Chapters 8 and 10.

A typical sequence in chapters that discuss counting and probability is to begin with counting, discuss permutations and combi-

nations, and then cover probability. Instead, we begin with probability, as it provides the rationale for many of the counting situations to follow. We also delay the discussion of combinations for the next chapter, so students do not confuse them with permutations.

In Lessons 7-2 and 7-3 we present the basic properties of counting, which should be familiar to most students, but may be new to some even at this level. The

Multiplication Counting Principle flows naturally into the discussion of permutations in Lesson 7-4. These counting techniques enable the theory of independent events to be verified with examples in Lesson 7-5.

Lesson 7-6 serves as a review of much of the previous lessons, putting together the calculations of probability with the study of probability distributions and the calculation of expected value. The last two lessons

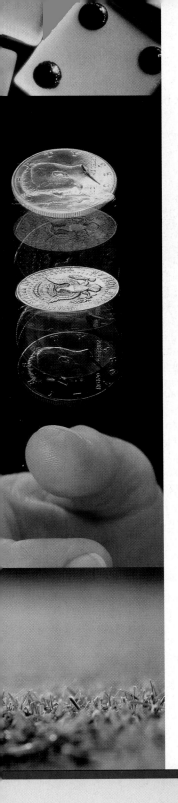

PROBABILITY AND SIMULATION

Many situations in life involve uncertainty. Will it rain on the day of the class picnic? Will there be enough people at a student council meeting to have a quorum? Can you expect to win a lottery once in your life if you play each week? Answers to these questions involve *probabilities*, numbers which measure the likelihood of an event.

The mathematics of probability theory is usually considered to have begun in a series of letters between the French mathematicians Pascal and Fermat in 1654 concerning dice games. Nowadays, probability theory has many applications beyond the analysis of games of chance, including setting insurance rates, weather forecasting, and political polling.

The simplest of probability questions can be answered by direct counting. Sometimes the situations can be pictured and probabilities calculated by comparing lengths of segments or areas of regions. In complicated situations, theorems are applied to calculate the number of ways in which things can happen. Probabilities arising from still more complex situations, such as weather forecasting, cannot be calculated directly, but they can be estimated from *simulations* of the situation.

In this chapter, you will study a broad range of situations involving probability, from counting to simulation.

Photo Connections

The photo collage makes real-world connections to the content of the chapter: probability and simulation.

Dice: Many situations involving dice appear throughout Chapter 7. Dice in games of chance go back at least 5000 years.

Eagle: For a while some species of eagles were thought to be endangered, but because of diligent conservation efforts, their numbers are now increasing. In Lesson 7-5, **Question 10**, students determine the probability of seeing an eagle in a wildlife reservation park.

Coin Toss: Many interesting experiments with probability can be conducted by flipping one or more coins. Coins were first used as a medium of exchange in Asia Minor, as early as the eighth century B.C.

Stop Light: Some drivers may think they are lucky when they hit several green lights in a row. Actually stop lights are often timed to allow for more orderly traffic flow. In the language of probability, these lights are not independent of each other. In Lesson 7-5, dependent and independent events are discussed.

Golf Ball: Just because a golfer has never made a hole in one does not mean it is impossible for the golfer to do so. Such a situation can be discussed in terms of relative frequency and probability. These topics are introduced in Lesson 7-1.

Chapter 7 Projects

At this time, you might want to have students look over the projects on pages 478–479.

---

introduce probability simulations. Such simulations require the concept of randomness, which is studied in some detail in Lesson 7-7. A particular type of simulation, the Monte Carlo simulation, is also discussed in Lesson 7-7.

Functions underlie much of the discussion. The notations $P(\ )$ and $N(\ )$ are used from the first lesson on, even though probability distributions are not explicitly discussed until

the sixth lesson. Multiple representations of distributions are used throughout the chapter, including graphs, tables, and equations.

Students who have studied from UCSMP *Transition Mathematics* and *Algebra* will have encountered the basics of probability and counting and permutations, so much of Lessons 7-1 through 7-4 will be review for them. If your students have no background in probability, you may need to spend an

extra day here and do Project 1 on page 478 as an In-class Activity.

Objectives

A List sample spaces and events for probabilistic experiments.
B Compute probabilities.
E State and use properties of probabilities.
H Calculate probabilities in real situations.

Resources

From the Teacher's Resource File
■ Lesson Master 7-1
■ Answer Master 7-1
■ Teaching Aids
 62 Warm-up
 65 Sample Space for Tossing Two Dice

Additional Resources
■ Visuals for Teaching Aids 62, 65

Teaching Lesson 7-1

Warm-up

A drawer contains *r* red socks, *b* blue socks, and *w* white socks. Assume that you draw a sock randomly from the drawer.
1. What is the probability that the sock is red? $\frac{r}{r+b+w}$
2. What is the probability that the sock is not white? $\frac{r+b}{r+b+w}$
3. What is the probability that the sock is green? 0

LESSON 7-1

Basic Principles of Probability

Weather or Not. *A precipitation probability is determined by mathematical models based upon what has happened in the past.*

Probability theory is the branch of mathematics that studies chance. In your earlier mathematics courses, you have calculated probabilities of some events. In this course, you will study probability in more detail, and in later chapters you will see connections to polynomials and even to the number *e*, the base of natural logarithms. To begin this study we define some of the basic vocabulary you should be certain to know.

The Outcomes and Sample Space of an Experiment

Probabilities occur when something happens and various results are possible. That "something" is called an *experiment*. Specifically, an **experiment** is a situation that has several possible results. The results are called **outcomes**. Here are some familiar experiments and outcomes.

Experiment	Outcomes
tossing a coin	heads, tails
tossing a coin twice	HH, HT, TH, TT
rolling a die	1, 2, 3, 4, 5, 6
rolling two dice and considering the sum of the numbers on the top faces	2, 3, 4, 5, 6, 7, 8, 9, 10, 11, 12

The set of possible outcomes of an experiment is the **sample space** for the experiment. For the experiment "tossing a coin," the usual sample space is {heads, tails}, or $\{H, T\}$ for short. For "rolling two dice and considering the sum of the numbers on the top faces," the natural sample space is the set of integers from 2 to 12. But if you were interested in all possible results of rolling two dice, then you might consider a different sample space, as is done in Example 1.

426

Lesson 7-1 Overview

Broad Goals This lesson introduces the basic vocabulary and principles of probability. Probabilities are calculated for events in which the sample space is small and finite and the outcomes are equally likely. Similarities are drawn between the ideas of relative frequency and probability, and the basic properties of a probability function *P* defined on the events and outcomes of a sample space are established.

Perspective Throughout UCSMP texts, we are careful to distinguish between *relative frequencies*, which are ratios calculated from data, and *probabilities*, which are values hopefully close to relative frequencies that are either
1. hypothesized on the basis of an educated guess,
2. calculated on the basis of some assumptions such as randomness or equal likelihood, or

3. estimated from known relative frequencies.

We do not use the term "experimental probability" for "relative frequency" because it disguises the origin of the number.

The language of set theory is particularly appropriate for studying probability. The sample space is the set of possible outcomes of an experiment; an event is a

Example 1

Two different dice (red and white) are rolled and the numbers that appear are recorded. Describe an appropriate sample space.

Solution

There are 6 ways that each die might land. So there are 6 · 6 = 36 ways two dice can come up. All the possible outcomes of this experiment are shown below.

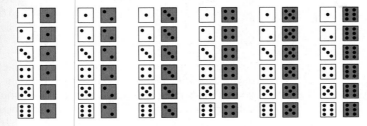

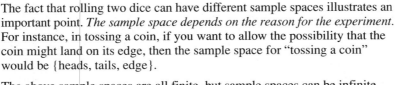

The fact that rolling two dice can have different sample spaces illustrates an important point. *The sample space depends on the reason for the experiment.* For instance, in tossing a coin, if you want to allow the possibility that the coin might land on its edge, then the sample space for "tossing a coin" would be {heads, tails, edge}.

The above sample spaces are all finite, but sample spaces can be infinite. For instance, if a dart is thrown at a dartboard, we can think of the sample space as being the set of points on the board.

Events and Probabilities

In the dartboard at the left, you might be particularly interested in the *bull's eye.* This is an example of an *event.* In general, an **event** is any subset of the sample space of an experiment.

Example 2

For the experiment of tossing two dice, list the outcomes in the event "doubles," that is, getting the same number on each die.

Solution

The event "doubles" consists of the outcomes (1, 1), (2, 2), (3, 3), (4, 4), (5, 5), and (6, 6). You could write

Doubles = {(1, 1), (2, 2), (3, 3), (4, 4), (5, 5), (6, 6)}.

The *probability of an event* is a number from 0 to 1 that measures the likelihood that the event will occur. Probabilities may be written in any way that numbers are written. An event which is expected to happen one-quarter of the time has a probability which can be written as $\frac{1}{4}$ or $\frac{2}{8}$ or .25 or 25%, and so on.

Have students record the results of the **Activity** for use with **Question 8** on page 431.

If your students have not studied probability before, you might wish to separate the class into groups to do Project 1, *Fair Dice?,* on page 478.

The sample space of an experiment is not always unique. For instance, in tossing a die, one could make the case that the sample space consists of the 36 ordered pairs (1, 1) through (6, 6). However, since the sum of the numbers is recorded and the dice are not distinguishable, if you were interested in the sum, you could choose to consider the 11 sums as the sample space. In **Examples 1–3,** the sample space is viewed as having 36 outcomes, because it is easier to calculate the probability when the outcomes are equally likely. **Teaching Aid 65** is provided so that you do not have to list the 36 possibilities.

You may need to stress that a sample space can be an infinite set. For example, the dartboard on page 427 represents an infinite set of points because an area is the measure of an infinite set (of points). The bull's eye is a subset of the infinite set.

Example 4 can be used to illustrate the difference between a relative frequency and a probability. In this example we *assume* that the sexes are equally likely even though it is known from birth certificate data that the relative frequencies are significantly different from $\frac{1}{2}$.

Optional Activities

subset of the sample space. There is a nice analogy with geometry: the sample space is the entire space; an outcome is a point; an event is a figure.

Cooperative Learning
Materials: Pennies or other coins

You might use this activity to introduce the lesson. Have students **work with a partner** and use a penny (or other coin). Have them toss the coin 30 times and record the number of heads and number of tails. It is helpful for students to shake the penny in their hands before tossing, as if they were throwing a die. They should calculate the relative

frequency of heads and tails. It is very likely that in just 30 tosses they will not find exactly 15 heads and 15 tails. Ask them whether they think their coin is fair. [Some students may say that the fairness of the coin cannot be determined from only 30 tosses. Ask them how many tosses they'd need to make a conclusion.] This quick experiment further emphasizes the difference between a probability and a relative frequency.

The distinction between a relative frequency and a probability may be represented graphically. Suppose a coin is flipped 1, 2, 3, ..., n times and $P(n)$ represents the relative frequency of heads. The graph of the pairs $(n, P(n))$ should theoretically approach (from both directions) the line $y = p$ as an asymptote, where p is the probability that the coin lands heads up. With each toss, the relative frequency changes a little bit, but the probability remains the same.

Regarding the Properties of Probabilities on page 430, it may seem as if (ii) and (iii) could both be written as "if and only if" statements. The question is whether one wishes to allow impossible outcomes in the sample space. For instance, one could ask, "What is the probability of getting a 13 as the sum of numbers in the tosses of two dice?" While 13 is not a possible outcome, it could be given as an outcome in the sample space. Then we would have $P(\{13\}) = 0$, but $\{13\}$ is not the null set. It is for this reason that we do *not* write the statements in if-and-only-if form.

In function terms, the Properties of Probabilities are properties of the domain and range of a probability function P. The fact that the independent variable in this function (an event) may be the occurrence of one *or more* of the outcomes listed in the domain makes a probability function more complicated than most of the functions students have studied up to this point. For this reason we do not discuss P as a function in this lesson, but use the notation in anticipation of discussing *probability distribution* functions in Lesson 7-6.

Let $N(E)$ be the number of elements in a set E, and S be a sample space. For the experiment "rolling a die," $S = \{1, 2, 3, 4, 5, 6\}$, and $N(S) = 6$. If $E =$ "rolling an even number with a die," $E = \{2, 4, 6\}$ and $N(E) = 3$. So if all outcomes were equally likely, you would expect to roll an even number half the time. This idea is generalized in the definition of probability.

> **Definition**
> Let E be an event in a finite sample space S. If each outcome in S is equally likely, then the **probability that E occurs**, denoted **$P(E)$**, is given by
> $$P(E) = \frac{\text{number of outcomes in the event}}{\text{number of outcomes in the sample space}}.$$

Note that in order to apply this definition, each element in the sample space must be *equally likely*. You must pay attention to this requirement when you set up or interpret sample spaces. For example, if you toss two fair coins, and record all possible orders of heads and tails, there are four equally likely outcomes in the sample space: HH, HT, TH, and TT.

Thus, $P(HH) = P(HT) = P(TH) = P(TT) = \frac{1}{4}$.

Now suppose you were interested in the number of *heads* that come up when you toss two fair coins. You might pick the sample space to be $\{2 \text{ heads}, 1 \text{ head}, 0 \text{ heads}\}$. There are three outcomes, but they are not equally likely because

$$P(1 \text{ head}) = \frac{2}{4} = \frac{1}{2}, \text{ whereas } P(2 \text{ heads}) = P(0 \text{ heads}) = \frac{1}{4}.$$

If a sample space has n outcomes all of which are equally likely, then the experiment is called **fair** or **unbiased** and each outcome has probability $\frac{1}{n}$. The outcomes are said to occur *at random* or *randomly*.

Example 3

Suppose two fair dice are rolled.
a. Find $P(\text{sum of dice} = 7)$.
b. Find $P(\text{sum of dice} < 10)$.
c. Find $P(\text{sum of dice} = 1)$.
d. Find $P(\text{sum of dice} < 50)$.

▶

Adapting to Individual Needs

Extra Help
Some students might be confused about how to choose an appropriate sample space. Often, the sample space that lists equally likely outcomes is appropriate because of the definition of probability given on page 428. For example, consider **Example 3, part a**. A student might choose the sample space first described on page 426: the set of integers from 2 to 12, $\{2, 3, 4, 5, 6, 7, 8, 9, 10, 11, 12\}$.

Stress that this sample space is not as useful here because each of its elements is not equally likely.

Solution

The sample space, first shown on page 427, is repeated here. $N(S) = 36$. Because the dice are fair, each outcome is equally likely.

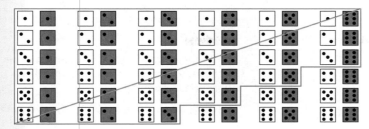

a. Let $E =$ "sum of dice = 7." The outcomes in E are identified above by the orange line through them. $N(E) = 6$. So $P(E) = \frac{N(E)}{N(S)} = \frac{6}{36} = \frac{1}{6}$.

b. Let $E =$ "sum of dice < 10." E consists of 30 outcomes outlined above by the blue polygon. $P(E) = \frac{N(E)}{N(S)} = \frac{30}{36} = \frac{5}{6}$.

c. Let $E =$ "sum of dice = 1." There are no outcomes in E. So $E = \emptyset$, and $N(E) = 0$. Thus $P(E) = \frac{N(E)}{N(S)} = \frac{0}{36} = 0$.

d. Let $E =$ "sum of dice < 50." Every outcome of S is also in E. So $N(E) = 36$. Thus $P(E) = \frac{N(E)}{N(S)} = \frac{36}{36} = 1$.

Part **c** illustrates that in a finite sample space, if an event is impossible, then its probability is 0. Part **d** illustrates that if an event must happen, then it will contain all the possible outcomes in the sample space, and so $N(E) = N(S)$. Then $P(E) = \frac{N(E)}{N(S)} = 1$. So the probability of a "sure thing" is 1.

Relative Frequencies and Probabilities

Probabilities are determined in a variety of ways. When tossing a coin, you might assume that heads and tails are equally likely. From this assumption, it follows that the probability of a head is $\frac{1}{2}$ and the probability of a tail is $\frac{1}{2}$. In 2500 tosses of the coin you would expect about 1250 heads. If you do not wish to toss the coin so many times, you might simulate the tossing with a computer or calculator. In contrast, if you have some reason to expect that a particular coin is unbalanced, you might toss the coin a large number of times and take the long-term relative frequency of heads as an estimate of the probability. For instance, if it comes up heads 1205 times in 2500 tosses, then the relative frequency of heads is $\frac{1205}{2500} = 48.2\%$, and you might pick 48% as the probability of getting a head for that coin.

History Connection The word coin comes from the Latin *cuneus*, meaning wedge (from *cuneiform* writing). The early dies for stamping out coins were wedge shaped, but the meaning evolved to refer to the coins themselves.

Additional Examples

1. A test is given with five possible grades: A, B, C, D, and F.
   a. Give the sample space for the experiment. **{A, B, C, D, F}**
   b. Identify the event "passing." **{A, B, C, D}**
2. Suppose two fair dice are rolled. What sum has the highest probability of occurring? What is its probability? **$7; \frac{1}{6}$**
3. Persons A, B, and C were playing a game and needed to decide who would go first. Person A suggested tossing two dice. If a 3, 6, 9, or 12 appeared, person A would go first. If a 2, 5, 8, or 11 appeared, person B would go first. If a 1, 4, 7, or 10 appeared, person C would go first. Is this fair? Why or why not? **If the dice are fair, each event has probability $\frac{1}{3}$, so it is fair to decide this way.**
4. If births of boys and girls are assumed equally likely, what is the probability that a family with four children has all girls? **$\frac{1}{16}$**

Adapting to Individual Needs

English Language Development
The language of probability can be confusing because all the terms involve words such as *experiment*, *trial*, *sample*, *space*, and *event* that have other meanings to students. Be careful to clarify the meanings of these terms.

Question 12 While this question may seem contrived, it is not at all. Often from sampling one has an idea of the relative frequency of an event (for instance, the relative frequency of a disease). Then, if the size of the population is known, one can estimate the actual frequency of the event (e.g., the number of cases of the disease in a particular city).

Question 14 This question asks for the probability of the complement of the event {A, B, O}. This calculation is formalized in Lesson 7-2.

Question 15 Some students may be confused about which face to read when a tetradedral die is tossed. Point out that using the face on which the die rests (the base) avoids such confusion.

Example 4

A researcher is studying the number of boys and girls in families with three children. Assume that the birth of a boy or a girl is equally likely. Find the probability that a family of three children has exactly one boy.

Solution

Let B represent a boy, G a girl, and a triple of letters, the genders of the children from oldest to youngest. List the outcomes. Then an appropriate sample space is

{BBB, BBG, BGB, BGG, GBB, GBG, GGB, GGG}.

Three outcomes have exactly one boy. Thus, the probability of exactly one boy in a three-child family is $\frac{3}{8}$. So P(one boy) = $\frac{3}{8}$.

Activity

Find the probability that a family of three children has exactly two girls. $\frac{3}{8}$

Actually, more boys than girls are born. In the U.S. the relative frequency of the birth of a boy in a single birth is closer to 51%. So the assumption in Example 4 is a little off. Later in this chapter you will see how to calculate probabilities when the outcomes are not equally likely.

Relative frequencies and probabilities have important similarities and differences. For example, both yield values from 0 to 1. However, the meanings of the two values differ. A relative frequency of 0 means an event *has not occurred*; for example, the relative frequency of snow on July 4 in Florida since 1900 is 0. In contrast, a probability of 0 in a finite sample space means the event is *impossible*. For example, the probability of tossing a sum of 17 with two normal dice is 0. A relative frequency of 1 means that an event *has occurred* in each known trial. In contrast, a probability of 1 means that an event *must always occur*. For example, the probability is 1 that the toss of a single die gives a number less than 7. Notice that this event consists of the whole sample space of the experiment. These properties are summarized below.

Theorem (Basic Properties of Probability)
Let S be the sample space associated with an experiment, and let $P(E)$ be the probability of E. Then:

(i) $0 \le P(E) \le 1$.
(ii) If $E = S$, then $P(E) = 1$.
(iii) If $E = \emptyset$, then $P(E) = 0$.

Adapting to Individual Needs

Challenge
Have students consider a sample space consisting of equally likely outcomes. Suppose event E consists of x of these outcomes and there are y outcomes in the sample space that are in E', the set of outcomes not in E. Then the odds in favor of E are $\frac{x}{y}$ and the odds against E are $\frac{y}{x}$. Have students explore the relationship between odds and probability with the following questions.

1. Give a formula for odds in favor of an event E in terms of $P(E)$ and $P(E')$. $\left[\frac{P(E)}{P(E')}\right]$

2. Give a formula for odds against an event E in terms of $P(E)$ and $P(E')$. $\left[\frac{P(E')}{P(E)}\right]$

Covering the Reading

1. Which mathematicians are credited with beginning the study of probability? **Pascal and Fermat**

2. Define *experiment*. **An experiment is a situation that has several possible results.**

3. To test a new package design, a carton of a dozen eggs is dropped from a height of 18 inches. The number of broken eggs is counted. Determine a sample space for this experiment. **The sample space is the set of possible numbers of broken eggs: {0, 1, 2, . . . , 12}**

In 4–7, suppose two fair dice are rolled. **a.** List the outcomes of the named event. **b.** Give the probability of the event.

4. The sum is 11. a) {(6, 5), (5, 6)}   b) $\frac{1}{18}$

5. The absolute value of the difference of the numbers shown on the dice is 1. **See left**.

6. At least one die shows a 3. **See left**.

7. The product of the numbers shown on the dice is 7. a) $\varnothing$ b) 0

8. Give the answer to the Activity. $\frac{3}{8}$

9. Consider the experiment of tossing 3 fair coins.
   a. Give a sample space for the experiment. **See left**.
   b. Find P(2 heads). **See left**.
   c. *True or false.* P(3 heads) = P(0 heads) **True**
   d. Find P(at least 2 heads). $\frac{1}{2}$

10. State the difference between a probability of zero and a relative frequency of zero. **A probability of 0 means the event is impossible; a relative frequency of 0 means an event has not occurred.**

11. Give an example different from the one in the lesson of an event V such that $P(V) = 1$. **Sample: The probability that the name of the day of the week ends in "y."**

12. In 1994, 483,000 of the 1,678,000 men and women in the U.S. armed forces were in the Navy. What was the relative frequency of Navy personnel in the armed forces in 1994? $\frac{483000}{1678000} \approx 28.78\%$

Sidebar answers

5a) {(1, 2), (2, 3), (3, 4), (4, 5), (5, 6), (6, 5), (5, 4), (4, 3), (3, 2), (2, 1)}
 b) $\frac{5}{18}$

6a) {(3, 1), (3, 2), (3, 3), (3, 4), (3, 5), (3, 6), (1, 3), (2, 3), (4, 3), (5, 3), (6, 3)}
 b) $\frac{11}{36}$

9a) {HHH, HHT, HTH, HTT, THH, THT, TTH, TTT}
 b) $\frac{3}{8}$

Applying the Mathematics

13. Let A be an event. If $P(A) = .25$ and there are 200 equally likely outcomes in the sample space, how many outcomes are in A? **50**

14. All human blood can be typed as one of O, A, B, or AB, but the distribution of the blood type varies with race. Among African Americans, 49% have type O, 27% have type A, and 20% have type B. What is the probability that an African American has type AB blood? **4%**

15. Consider a fair tetrahedral die with faces numbered 1, 3, 5, 7. Two of these dice are tossed. Find each probability.
   a. P(sum is even)   b. P(sum is odd)   c. P(sum is 8)
      1   0 $\frac{1}{4}$

Notes on Questions

Questions 17–18 As an extension of these questions, see the Challenge in *Adapting to Individual Needs*, on page 430.

Follow-up for Lesson 7-1

Practice

For more questions on SPUR Objectives, use **Lesson Master 7-1** (shown on page 429).

Assessment

Oral Communication Write a problem like **Example 3** on the chalkboard. Have each student explain orally how to find each answer, referring to the sample space pictured on page 427 (or **Teaching Aid 65**) as necessary. [Students explain how to compute probabilities.]

Extension

Ask the following: Is it possible to number the faces of two fair dice so that each of the sums from 2 to 12 is equally likely? Allow the possibility that two faces on the same die could have the same numbers. [No, there are 11 sums; each cannot occur the same number of times in 36 tosses.]

Then point out that it is possible to have each of the sums from 1 to 12 be equally likely and challenge students to find out how. [Number one die with 3 sides of 1 and 3 sides of 2; number the faces of a second die 0, 2, 4, 6, 8, and 10.]

Project Update Project 1, *Fair Dice?*, on page 478, relates to the content of this lesson.

---

16. The definition of probability can be extended to infinite sample spaces. If every outcome in an infinite sample space is equally likely, and E is an event in that space, then

$$P(E) = \frac{\text{measure of event}}{\text{measure of sample space}},$$

where the measure may be length, area, volume, and so on.

a) $\frac{1}{12}$

   a. Due to a storm, the electricity went out at 2:13, so both hands of a clock stopped between 2 and 3. If all times are equally likely, what is the probability that both hands would be between the same two consecutive numbers on the face of the clock?
   b. Think of the minute hand as a spinner. If the dial is fair and the minute hand spun, what is the probability it lands between 6 and 8? $\frac{1}{6}$

In 17 and 18, if the *odds against* an event are x to y, the probability of the event is $\frac{y}{x + y}$.

17. If the odds against winning a wager are 5 to 1, what is the probability of winning? $\frac{1}{6}$

18. Suppose the probability of having exactly one boy in a family of three children is $\frac{3}{8}$. What are the odds against having exactly one boy in a family of three children? **5 to 3**

19. A baseball player with a batting average of .318 for the first 85 at-bats gets up to bat for the 86th time.
   a. Estimate the probability that this batter gets a hit. $\approx$ **0.318**
   b. Suppose the batter gets a hit. What is the new batting average? **.326**

Review

cabin

133°

dock

44°

100 m

22) If the graphs are reflection images of each other over the *y*-axis, then for all *x*, *f*(*x*) should equal *g*(-*x*). However, $f(1) = 6^1 = 6$ but $g(-1) = (-1)^6 = 1$.

20. From the town dock and another point 100 m away, Mr. Wu sights his cabin and takes angle measures as indicated on the drawing. Find the distance from the cabin to the dock. *(Lesson 5-4)* $\approx$ **1330 meters**

21. If the half-life of a drug in the body is 10 hours, what percent of the drug remains after the given amount of time?
   a. 10 hours **50%**   b. 24 hours *(Lesson 2-5)* $\approx$ **18.95%**

22. *True or false.* The graphs of $f(x) = 6^x$ and $g(x) = x^6$ are reflection images of each other over the *y*-axis. Explain why or why not. *(Lessons 2-4, 3-4)* **False. See left.**

23. Evaluate $\sum_{k=1}^{10} k$. *(Lesson 1-3)* **55**

Exploration

24. Simulate the experiment of Example 4 by tossing three coins. Call one side of each coin a boy and the other side a girl. Repeat the experiment a large number of times. How close is the relative frequency of "one boy" that you find to the probability calculated in the example? **Answers will vary, but the relative frequency should be close to 37.5%.**

Setting Up Lesson 7-2

Question 15 can be used to set up the idea that the probability of a union of mutually exclusive events is the sum of the probabilities.

Point out that: $P(\text{sum is even}) = P(\text{sum is 2}) + P(\text{sum is 4}) + P(\text{sum is 6}) + P(\text{sum is 8}) + P(\text{sum is 10}) + P(\text{sum is 12})$.

Also, $P(\text{sum is odd}) = 1 - P(\text{sum is even})$, illustrating the Probabilities of Complements Theorem.

Addition Counting Principles

Because probabilities are often calculated by dividing one count by another, being able to count elements of sets is an important skill. This and the next lesson cover the fundamental principles of counting.

Recall that $A \cup B$, the **union** of sets A and B, contains all elements that are either in A or in B. If A and B have no elements in common, they are called **disjoint** or **mutually exclusive**. If two events are not mutually exclusive, then they *overlap*. Recall that the **intersection** $A \cap B$ of two sets A and B is the set of elements in both A and B.

The *Venn diagrams* below show $A \cup B$ for two types of events: mutually exclusive, and not mutually exclusive.

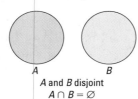
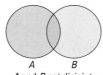

A B
A and *B* disjoint
$A \cap B = \varnothing$

A B
A and *B* not disjoint
$A \cap B \neq \varnothing$

Probability of the Union of Mutually Exclusive Sets

The first counting principle is a restatement of the Putting-Together Model for addition that you first learned in elementary school.

> **Addition Counting Principle (Mutually Exclusive Form)**
> If two finite sets A and B are mutually exclusive, then
> $$N(A \cup B) = N(A) + N(B).$$

Now think of A and B as events in a finite sample space S. Divide both sides of the equation in the Addition Counting Principle by $N(S)$.

$$\frac{N(A \cup B)}{N(S)} = \frac{N(A)}{N(S)} + \frac{N(B)}{N(S)}$$

A basic theorem about probability is obtained.

> **Theorem (Probability of the Union of Mutually Exclusive Events)**
> If A and B are mutually exclusive events in the same finite sample space, then
> $$P(A \cup B) = P(A) + P(B).$$

Objectives

B Compute probabilities.
E State and use properties of probabilities.
F Determine whether events are mutually exclusive, independent, or complementary.
H Calculate probabilities in real situations.

Resources

From the **Teacher's Resource File**
■ Lesson Master 7-2
■ Answer Master 7-2
■ Teaching Aids
  62 Warm-up
  66 Addition Counting Principles and Basic Theorems

Additional Resources
■ Visuals for Teaching Aids 62, 66

Teaching Lesson 7-2

Warm-up

How many positive integers less than or equal to 1000 satisfy each condition?
1. Divisible by 5   **200**
2. Divisible by 7   **142**
3. Divisible by 5 or 7
  200 + 142 − 28 = 314 (subtract those divisible by 35 from the answers to 1 and 2)

Lesson 7-2 Overview

Broad Goals This lesson presents the Addition Counting Principle and uses it to develop theorems for finding probabilities of unions of events (mutually exclusive or not), and probabilities of complementary events. Students should be able to compute the number of elements in a union of sets, and apply the theorems appropriately.

Perspective From (assumed) probabilities, other probabilities can be calculated using

basic counting principles. Again the language of set theory is most useful. Let A and B be events in a finite sample space S. Then in general, $N(A \cup B) = N(A) + N(B) - N(A \cap B)$, from which $P(A \cup B) = P(A) + P(B) - P(A \cap B)$.

If A and B are complements, then $A \cup B = S$, from which $P(A \cup B) = 1$, and so $P(A) = 1 - P(B)$. These ideas are found in many of the previous UCSMP courses.

Have students record the results of the **Activity** for use with **Question 5** on page 437.

This lesson is review for students who have taken UCSMP courses previously. Probably the most imposing thing about it is the number of definitions and the cryptic formulas. Don't let students be dissuaded by this. There are two Addition Counting Principles and two Probability Theorems in this lesson. The two principles and two theorems are listed on **Teaching Aid 66**. They differ only in that one deals with mutually exclusive events, the other does not. The more complicated Addition Counting Principle simply says that to get the total number of things in two sets all you have to do is add the number in each set and subtract the number you counted twice. If the sets represent events, then divide this total by the number of outcomes in the sample space and you have a probability of either event occurring. If you can identify the events as mutually exclusive, then the process simplifies. If the events are complementary, you can compute probabilities in your head.

Every year teachers who use UCSMP textbooks are invited to a two-day conference at the University of Chicago.

Example 1

If two fair dice are tossed, what is the probability of a sum of 7 or 11?

Solution 1

Let A = "tossing a 7" and B = "tossing an 11." You might wish to refer to the list of outcomes in the previous lesson. There are 6 outcomes in A and 2 outcomes in B. A and B are mutually exclusive, so there are 8 outcomes in $A \cup B$. Because there are 36 outcomes in the sample space, $N(S) = 36$.

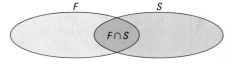

$$P(A \cup B) = \frac{N(A \cup B)}{N(S)} = \frac{8}{36} \approx 0.22$$

Solution 2

Let A and B be defined as in the first solution.

$$P(A) = \frac{N(A)}{N(S)} = \frac{6}{36} \quad \text{and} \quad P(B) = \frac{N(B)}{N(S)} = \frac{2}{36}$$

Because A and B are mutually exclusive,

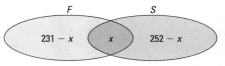

$$P(A \cup B) = P(A) + P(B) = \frac{6}{36} + \frac{2}{36} = \frac{8}{36} \approx 0.22.$$

Probability of the Union of Any Two Sets

Consider the following situation. Participants at a two-day conference could register for only one of the days or both. There were 231 participants on Friday; 252 on Saturday. The total number of people who registered for the conference was 350. Because $231 + 252 \neq 350$, there must have been people who attended both days.

Symbolically, if F is the set of Friday attendees and S is the set of Saturday attendees, then $N(F) = 231$, $N(S) = 252$, and $N(F \cup S) = 350$.

Let x be the number of people who registered for both days. Then the number of people who registered only for Friday is $231 - x$, and the number of people who registered only for Saturday is $252 - x$. Thus,

$$N(F \cup S) = (231 - x) + x + (252 - x)$$
$$= 483 - x.$$

Because $N(F \cup S) = 350$,
$$350 = 483 - x.$$

So, $x = 133$. Thus, there were 133 people who registered for both days.

434

Refer students to **Question 17**. Given the constraints in the problem, ask students to answer the following questions.

1. How many points is a dart player most likely to earn from throwing one dart? [20 points, with a probability of about 0.415]

2. Is a dart player more likely to score 10 points or 30 points on a given throw? [10 points; the probability of 10 points is 0.215, while the probability of 30 points is about 0.208.]

3. Is a dart player more likely to score 30 points or 40 points on a given throw? [30 points; getting a score of 40 has a probability of about 0.136]

This situation is a special case of a more general result. If $N(A \cap B) = x$, then the number of elements in A which are not in the intersection is $N(A) - x$. Similarly, there are $N(B) - x$ elements in B which are not in the intersection, as shown below. Then

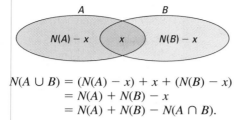

$$N(A \cup B) = (N(A) - x) + x + (N(B) - x)$$
$$= N(A) + N(B) - x$$
$$= N(A) + N(B) - N(A \cap B).$$

This proves the following theorem.

Addition Counting Principle (General Form)
For any finite sets A and B,

$$N(A \cup B) = N(A) + N(B) - N(A \cap B).$$

If A and B are two events in the same finite sample space S, then dividing by $N(S)$ yields

$$\frac{N(A \cup B)}{N(S)} = \frac{N(A)}{N(S)} + \frac{N(B)}{N(S)} - \frac{N(A \cap B)}{N(S)}.$$

The fractions all stand for probabilities, identified in the next theorem.

Theorem (Probability of a Union of Events—General Form)
If A and B are any events in the same finite sample space, then

$$P(A \text{ or } B) = P(A \cup B) = P(A) + P(B) - P(A \cap B).$$

Example 2

The name of a participant in the conference described on page 434 is drawn for a door prize. What is the probability that this person attended on both days?

Solution 1

Use the definition of probability. Since 133 of the 350 participants attended both days,

$$P(\text{winner attended both days}) = \frac{133}{350} = 0.38.$$

▶

While the distinction between mutually exclusive events and not mutually exclusive events is easy to make in the examples of this lesson, it seems that many people do not make the distinction so easily. For example, the number of people reported as having learning disorders or physical disabilities, or being afflicted with a disease, is sometimes overestimated because the estimator does not take into account the possibility that the same individual could have more than one disorder. The amounts of time people spend watching television is often inflated because other simultaneous activities are overlooked.

History Connection Venn diagrams, which picture relations between sets, are named after John Venn, a British mathematician who lived between 1834 and 1923. Although Venn is best known for Venn diagrams, he also worked with George Boole's symbolic logic and the frequency theory of probability.

Adapting to Individual Needs

Extra Help
Some students might benefit from an alternate approach to dice problems. Have the class collect statistics on eye and hair color and calculate, for example, the probability that a randomly chosen student is a brunette with blue eyes.

---

1. If two fair dice are tossed, what is the probability that the sum is a 2 or a 3? $P(2 \text{ or } 3) =$ $P(2) + P(3) = \frac{3}{36} = \frac{1}{12}$

2. Thirteen of the 50 states include territory that lies west of the continental divide. Forty-two states include territory that lies east of the continental divide. Is this possible? Explain your answer. **If 5 states include territory on both sides of the continental divide, then this is possible. (This is the case; the 5 states are Montana, Wyoming, Colorado, New Mexico, and a small corner of Alaska.)**

3. Three fair coins are tossed. What is the probability that *not all* the coins show the same face? $P(1 \text{ head}) + P(2 \text{ heads}) = \frac{3}{4}$

4. Use complementary events to answer Additional Example 3. $P(3 \text{ heads}) + P(3 \text{ tails}) =$ $\frac{1}{8} + \frac{1}{8} = \frac{1}{4}$; $P(\text{not all the same})$ $= 1 - \frac{1}{4} = \frac{3}{4}$.

Solution 2

Use the Probability of a Union of Events Theorem. $P(A) = \frac{231}{350}$ and $P(B) = \frac{252}{350}$. *Because everyone who attended the conference attended on either Friday or Saturday* $P(A \cup B) = 1 = \frac{350}{350}$.

By the above theorem,

$$P(A \cup B) = P(A) + P(B) - P(A \cap B).$$
$$\frac{350}{350} = \frac{231}{350} + \frac{252}{350} - P(A \cap B)$$
$$-\frac{133}{350} = -P(A \cap B)$$

So $\qquad P(A \cap B) = \frac{133}{350} = 0.38.$

Activity

In Example 2, find the probability that the winner attended only on Saturday.

$$\frac{119}{350} = 0.34$$

Example 3

A pair of dice is thrown. What is the probability that the dice show doubles or a sum over 7?

Solution

Use the sample space shown on page 427 for a pair of dice. Find the probability of each event.

$$P(\text{doubles}) = \frac{6}{36},$$
$$P(\text{sum over 7}) = \frac{15}{36}, \text{ and}$$
$$P(\text{doubles and sum over 7}) = \frac{3}{36} \text{ (double 4's, 5's, or 6's)}$$

Now compute the probability of their union using the theorem on page 435.
So, $P(\text{doubles or sum over 7}) = P(\text{doubles}) + P(\text{sum over 7}) - P(\text{both})$

$$= \frac{6}{36} + \frac{15}{36} - \frac{3}{36}$$
$$= \frac{18}{36} = \frac{1}{2}.$$

Notice that the Probability of the Union of Mutually Exclusive Events Theorem on page 433 is a special case of the Probability of a Union of Events Theorem. When A and B are mutually exclusive events, $A \cap B = \emptyset$ and so $P(A \cap B) = 0$. Then

$$P(A \cup B) = P(A) + P(B) - P(A \cap B)$$

reduces to $\qquad P(A \cup B) = P(A) + P(B).$

436

Adapting to Individual Needs

Challenge
Materials: Dice and coins

1. Have students consider tossing a fair coin and rolling a fair die. Ask them to write out the sample space and find each of the following probabilities.
   a. Getting a head on the coin and a six on the die. $[\frac{1}{12}]$
   b. Getting a head on the coin or a six on the die. $[\frac{7}{12}]$

2. Ask students to perform the experiment by tossing a coin and rolling a die 100 times. Then have them compute these relative frequencies.
   a. Getting a head on the coin and a six on the die. [Answers will vary.]
   b. Getting a head on the coin or a six on the die. [Answers will vary.]

3. Compare your answers to Questions 1–2. [Answers will vary.]

Complementary Events

In the next example, the events are mutually exclusive and their union is the entire sample space. Such events are called **complementary events**. The complement of an event A is called **not A**.

Example 4

Two dice are tossed. Find the probability of each event.

a. Their sum is seven. **b.** Their sum is *not* seven.

Solution

a. Use the diagram of the two-dice experiment on page 427. There are 6 possibilities on the diagonal from lower left to upper right.

So $$P(\text{sum is } 7) = \frac{6}{36} = \frac{1}{6}.$$

b. You could count again. Or you could recognize that "sum is 7" and "sum is not 7" are mutually exclusive events whose union is the entire sample space. Then

$$P(\text{sum is 7 or sum is not 7}) = P(\text{sum is 7}) + P(\text{sum is not 7}).$$

So, $$1 = P(\text{sum is 7}) + P(\text{sum is not 7}),$$

or $$P(\text{sum is not 7}) = 1 - P(\text{sum is 7})$$

$$= 1 - \frac{1}{6}.$$

Thus, the probability that the sum of two dice is not seven is $\frac{5}{6}$.

The reasoning in Example 4 leads to the following general theorem.

Theorem (Probability of Complements)

If A is any event, then $P(\text{not } A) = 1 - P(A)$.

QUESTIONS

Covering the Reading

In 1 and 2, suppose two fair dice are rolled. **a.** State whether X and Y are mutually exclusive. **b.** Find $N(X \cup Y)$. **c.** Find $N(X \cap Y)$.

1. $X =$ The first die shows 6. $Y =$ The sum of the dice is 10.
a) No   b) 8   c) 1

2. $X =$ The first die shows 5. $Y =$ The sum of the dice is 3.
a) Yes   b) 8   c) 0

In 3 and 4, refer to the sample space for tossing two fair dice on page 427.

3. What is the probability that white shows an even number or red shows a multiple of 3? $\frac{2}{3}$

4. What is the probability that at least one of the dice shows a 4? $\frac{11}{36}$

5. Give your answer to the Activity. $\frac{119}{350} = 0.34$

Lesson 7-2 *Addition Counting Principles* **437**

Notes on Questions

Questions 1–2 You might also ask these questions. In general, given two sets X and Y:
a. when will $N(X \cup Y) = N(X \cap Y)$?
[When $X = Y$]
b. when will $N(X \cup Y) = N(X)$?
[When Y is a subset of X]
c. when will $N(X \cap Y) = N(X)$?
[When X is a subset of Y]

Question 7 Ask students how we know there must be at least three candidates? [Because 0.4 + 0.5 < 1.]

Question 13 The events in **Question 7** could be the answer.

Question 16 If you give more questions of this type, there is a general pattern that students might know or discover. The probability that a number from 1 to m is divisible by n is $\frac{\lfloor \frac{m}{n} \rfloor}{m}$. For example, the probability that a number from 1 to 300 is divisible by 7 is $\frac{42}{300}$.

Question 21 Error Alert Some students may not realize that x is a variable here but just think that it means we do not know the probability. The probabilities for red, green, and orange are assumed here to be identical.

Question 25 This is an important question to discuss in class; all students should realize the ideas of the lesson extend to more than two events.

12) **Sample:** Let a = the number of elements in A and s = the number of elements in the entire sample space. Then $s - a$ is the number of elements not in A. Therefore, $P(\text{not } A) = \frac{s - a}{s} = \frac{s}{s} - \frac{a}{s} = 1 - P(A)$.

6. Suppose that the probability that a manufactured computer chip is usable is 0.993. What is the probability that it is not usable? **0.007**

7. The probability that Carol wins the election for the Student Government presidency is 0.4 and the probability that Carl wins is 0.5.
   a. What is the probability that Carol or Carl will win? **0.9**
   b. What is the probability that Carl will not win? **0.5**
   c. What is the probability that neither Carl nor Carol will win? **0.1**

In 8–10, assume that A and B are in the same sample space. Under what conditions are the following true?

8. $P(A \text{ or } B) = P(A) + P(B) - P(A \cap B)$ **all conditions**

9. $P(A \text{ or } B) = P(A) + P(B)$ **A and B are mutually exclusive**

10. $P(\text{not } A) = 1 - P(A)$ **all conditions**

11. *True or false.* Complementary events are a special case of mutually exclusive events. **True**

12. Write an argument explaining why $P(\text{not } A) = 1 - P(A)$. **See left.**

Applying the Mathematics

13. Give an example of two mutually exclusive events that are not complementary. **Sample: The temperature is above 90°; the temperature is below 40°.**

14. Name a sport in which "win the game" and "lose the game" are not complementary events. **Sample: golf**

15. The manager of a little league baseball team contacted the local meteorological office regarding the likely weather for the opening day of the season, and was given the table of probabilities below.

	Wind Speed (mph)		
	Less Than 10	10–30	More Than 30
Sunny	0.30	0.16	0.08
Partly cloudy	0.14	0.08	0.06
Overcast	0.09	0.06	0.03

   a. What is the probability that opening day will be sunny? **0.54**
   b. What is the probability that the wind speed will be 30 mph or less?
   c. What is the probability that the weather will be overcast or the wind speed will be greater than 30 mph? **0.32**
   d. What is the probability that the weather will not be overcast and the wind speed will be less than 10 mph? **0.44**
   b) **0.83**

16. A whole number from 1 to 300 is chosen at random. Find the probability of each event.
   a. The number is divisible by 3. $\frac{1}{3}$ b) $\frac{1}{4}$
   b. The number is divisible by 4.
   c. The number is divisible by 3 or by 4. $\frac{1}{2}$

17a) $\frac{25\pi}{484} \approx 0.162$

b) $1 - \frac{57\pi}{484} \approx 0.630$

17. Consider the dartboard pictured here. The radii of the concentric circles are 2", 6", 10", and 11". You get 10, 20, 30, 40, or 50 points if your dart lands in the regions as indicated. Suppose you always hit the interior of the square when you throw, you are equally likely to hit any point within the square, and you cannot land on a boundary. Determine the probability of each event.
  a. Your score is over 30 points.
  b. Your score is under 30 points. **a, b) See left.**

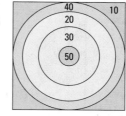

In 18 and 19, refer to the probabilities in the Venn diagram of events A and B at the right.

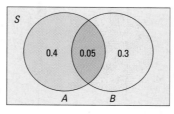

18. Are A and B mutually exclusive? Why or why not? **No; A and B have elements in common.**

19. Calculate the following probabilities.
  a. $P(A \cap B)$ **0.05**   **b.** $P(A)$ **0.45**
  c. $P(A \cup B)$ **0.75**   **d.** $P(\text{not } B)$ **0.65**

Review

20. A basketball player shoots two free throws. Each is either made or missed. Determine the sample space for the experiment under each circumstance.
  a. You record the result of each shot in order.
  b. You count the number of baskets made.   *(Lesson 7-1)* **{0, 1, 2}**
  a) {(0, 0), (0, 1), (1, 0), (1, 1)}

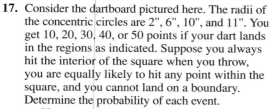

Michael Jordan has made about 85% of his free throws.

21. The table below estimates the probability that a randomly chosen M&M® peanut candy is a particular color.

Color	Brown	Red	Yellow	Green	Orange	Blue
Probability	.2	x	.2	x	x	.3

If no other color is possible, find the value of x.   *(Lesson 7-1)* **0.1**

22. If a whole number from 1 to 50 is picked at random, what is the probability that it is a perfect square?   *(Lesson 7-1)* $\frac{7}{50}$

23. Give an equation for the parabola at the left.   *(Lessons 2-6, 3-2)*
  $y = -x^2 + 4x$

24. Solve $t^2 - 100t = 21$.   *(Previous course)* $t = 50 \pm \sqrt{2521}$

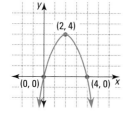

Exploration

25. a. Draw a Venn diagram for $A \cup B \cup C$.
  b. Extend the Probability of a Union of Events Theorem to cover any 3 events in the same sample space. That is, give a formula for $P(A \cup B \cup C)$.
  c. Give an example of the use of the formula you find in part **b.**
  a–c) See margin.

Practice
For more questions on SPUR Objectives, use **Lesson Master 7-2** (shown on page 435).

Assessment
Written Communication Have students make up two probability problems and solve them. One should involve mutually exclusive events and the other should not. [Students demonstrate understanding of mutually exclusive events and find the probability of the union of events.]

Extension
Have students continue the **Activity** on page 436 and find the probability that the winner attended the conference only on Friday. [0.28]

Additional Answers
25. a. Sample:

b. $P(A \cup B \cup C) = P(A) + P(B) + P(C) - P(A \cap B) - P(B \cap C) - P(A \cap C) + P(A \cap B \cap C)$

c. Sample:
Let S = {students in your high school},
  A = {students enrolled in an English course},
  B = {students enrolled in a math course},
  C = {students enrolled in a social studies course}.
$P(A \cup B \cup C)$ is the probability that a student in your school is enrolled in an English, math, or social studies course.

Objectives

B Compute probabilities.
C Find the number of ways of selecting or arranging objects.
D Evaluate expressions using factorials.
I Use counting principles and theorems to find the number of ways of arranging objects.

Resources

From the *Teacher's Resource File*
- Lesson Master 7-3
- Answer Master 7-3
- Teaching Aid 62: Warm-up
- Assessment Sourcebook: Quiz for Lessons 7-1 through 7-3
- Technology Sourcebook Calculator Master 6

Additional Resources
- Visual for Teaching Aid 62

Teaching Lesson **7-3**

Warm-up

1. How many sets of answers are possible if a true-false test has:
   a. 1 question? 2
   b. 2 questions? 4
   c. 4 questions? 16
   d. 10 questions? 1024

2. State a generalization about the number of sets of answers that are possible for a true-false test.
   If there are n questions, there are 2^n possible answers.

The Multiplication Counting Principle

Pete Seria decided to offer a special on his famous pizza pies. He limited the special to cheese pizzas with or without pepperoni and with a choice of thin crust, thick crust, or stuffed. Pete wondered how many different versions of pizza were possible, so he sketched this *tree diagram*.

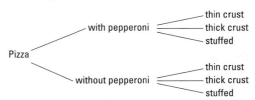

Counting the paths, Pete saw there were only six different possible pizzas, and thought that offer wasn't attractive enough. So he decided to advertise that each pizza came in one of four sizes: individual, small, medium, and large. Rather than continuing with the tree (since he'd run out of room on his paper), Pete noticed that for each of 2 choices about pepperoni there were 3 choices of crust and $2 \cdot 3 = 6$ possible pizzas. And for each of these there were 4 possible sizes; so that gave $6 \cdot 4 = 24$ total choices.

Pete did not have to diagram or list all the possible choices because he knew a fundamental use of multiplication.

> **The Multiplication Counting Principle**
> Let A and B be any finite sets. The number of ways to choose one element from A and then one element from B is $N(A) \cdot N(B)$.

The Multiplication Counting Principle has an obvious extension to choices made from more than two sets. The number of ways to choose one element from set A_1, one element from set A_2, ..., and one element from set A_k is $N(A_1) \cdot N(A_2) \cdot \ldots \cdot N(A_k)$.

Selections with Replacement

Example 1

a. How many ways are there of answering a test having 5 true-false questions?
b. If you guess on each question, what is the probability of answering all 5 questions correctly?

Lesson 7-3 Overview

Broad Goals If the first component of an ordered pair must come from a set with x elements and the second component comes from a set with y elements, then there are xy different ordered pairs possible. In this lesson, that idea is generalized to deduce the number of possible arrangements of r objects from n with replacement (n^r) and the number of arrangements of n objects from n without replacement ($n!$).

Perspective We would hope that students would have seen the Multiplication Counting Principle as early as 4th grade. UCSMP students have seen it in *Transition Mathematics*, where it is used to count elements of arrays, and in *Algebra*, where it is used to count permutations of 2 objects from n both with and without replacement.

Tree diagrams that show visually all possible arrangements and the logic supporting the Multiplication Counting Principle are useful for small numbers, as at the beginning of the lesson, but they become less practical as the number of arrangements increases. In UCSMP *Precalculus and Discrete Mathematics*, tree diagrams are employed to represent situations of conditional probability.

Solution

a. There are two ways to respond to each of the five questions. Think of each response as a choice from a set with 2 elements in it, T or F. $A_1 = \{T, F\}$, $A_2 = \{T, F\}$, $A_3 = \{T, F\}$, $A_4 = \{T, F\}$, and $A_5 = \{T, F\}$. The number of ways to answer the test equals
$$N(A_1) \cdot N(A_2) \cdot N(A_3) \cdot N(A_4) \cdot N(A_5) = 2 \cdot 2 \cdot 2 \cdot 2 \cdot 2 = 2^5 = 32.$$

b. When you guess, all outcomes are equally likely. One of those 32 outcomes is "all answers correct," so **the probability of answering all questions correctly is** $\frac{1}{32}$, **or about 3%.**

Check

a. Below is a list of the 16 possible ways to answer the 5 questions if the first is answered T.

TTTTT	TTFTT	TFTTT	TFFTT
TTTTF	TTFTF	TFTTF	TFFTF
TTTFT	TTFFT	TFTFT	TFFFT
TTTFF	TTFFF	TFTFF	TFFFF

In the Questions you are asked to list the other 16.

© 1968 United Feature Syndicate, Inc.

❶ The situation in Example 1 is an instance of making 5 choices *with replacement* from a set, here the set $\{T, F\}$. That is, you may give the same response as many times as you wish. Each way of answering the 5 questions gives rise to an **arrangement** of the 2 symbols T and F. Two choices for each of 5 questions gives 2^5 arrangements. In general:

❷ **Theorem (Selections with Replacement)**

Let S be a set with n elements. Then there are n^k possible arrangements of k elements from S with replacement.

Proof

Use the Multiplication Counting Principle. Here $N(S) = n$, so the number of possible ways to choose one element from S, each of k times, is
$$\underbrace{N(S) \cdot N(S) \cdot \ldots \cdot N(S)}_{k \text{ times}} = \underbrace{n \cdot n \cdot \ldots \cdot n}_{k \text{ factors}} = n^k.$$

❶ We treat the terms *arrangement* and *permutation* as synonyms. The latter word is introduced in Lesson 7-4. In Chapter 8, when combinations are introduced, then the distinction between permutations (order matters) and combinations (order does not matter) will be made.

❷ Some people like the phrase "with repetition" where we use "with replacement." However, "with repetition" gets confusing when the original set contains repeated elements. Suggest that students (1) decide if the given situation is one with replacement or without, and (2) show their calculations with their answers.

Most students will have seen the factorial symbol before; if not in a mathematics course, then on their calculator keyboard. There are ways of dealing with factorials higher than those most calculators will estimate. In later lessons, students will learn to write the factors and then, when possible, divide out common factors.

Higher factorials can also be approximated using Stirling's formula, $n! \approx \sqrt{2n\pi}\left(\frac{n}{e}\right)^n$, where e is the base of natural logarithms, or with a simple program like the one below.

```
20    INPUT N
30    F = 1
40    FOR X = 1 TO N
50    F = F*X
60    NEXT X
70    PRINT N;"! = "; F
80    END
```

Optional Activities

Activity 1 Technology Connection You might wish to assign *Technology Sourcebook, Calculator Master 6* with Lessons 7-3 and 7-6. In this activity, students use a programmable calculator to enter and run a program that gives the sample space and probability distribution for the sum of three dice.

Activity 2 Have students write their own situation that illustrates the Multiplication Counting Principle. Have them draw a tree diagram with at least three levels of branches and indicate how the diagram reveals the multiplication necessary to compute total number of outcomes. [For example, students might show the number of different T-shirts available in a mail-order catalog.]

Do not sell the tree diagram that opens this lesson as a way to count the number of arrangements. It is too inefficient! Tree diagrams are designed (1) to emphasize the order in which selections are made when using the Multiplication Counting Principle; (2) to show that the principle is derived from the notion of multiplication as repeated addition; and (3) to introduce a representation that can be applied in situations of conditional probability.

As you go through the questions, it is useful to identify the situation as one with replacement or without, and give the calculations used to obtain the answer, as we have done with the Additional Examples that follow.

Additional Examples

1. A quiz has 10 questions, each of which can be answered "always," "sometimes," or "never." If you guess on each question, what is the probability of answering all questions correctly?
$(\frac{1}{3})^{10} \approx .000017$

2. How many license plates are possible with 4 letters from A to Z (except O and I) followed by two digits from 0 through 9?
$24^4 \cdot 10^2 = 33,177,600$

3. How many orders of finish are possible in a 7-horse race?
$7! = 5040$

Example 2

There are two multiple-choice parts to the mathematics section of the PSAT (Preliminary Scholastic Aptitude Test). One has 25 multiple-choice questions with 5 options each, and the other has 15 multiple-choice questions with 4 options each. How many ways are there to answer the multiple-choice parts of the PSAT mathematics section?

Solution

First, determine how many ways there are of answering each part of the test. 5 choices for 25 questions gives 5^{25} possible arrangements on the first part, and 4 choices for 15 questions gives 4^{15} arrangements on the second part. Now use the Multiplication Counting Principle again. There are $5^{25} \cdot 4^{15}$, or $3.2 \cdot 10^{26}$ different ways of answering these two parts of the PSAT mathematics section.

Selections Without Replacement

Example 3 illustrates that when repeated choices from a set are made *without replacement*, the Multiplication Counting Principle can still be applied.

Example 3

Susita decides to rank order the five colleges to which she plans to apply. How many rankings can she make?

Solution

For her first choice there are 5 possibilities. For her second choice there are 4 remaining colleges. For her third choice there remain 3 colleges. There are 2 colleges left for the fourth choice, and 1 school is left for fifth. Altogether there are $5 \cdot 4 \cdot 3 \cdot 2 \cdot 1 = 120$ possible rankings.

The answer to Example 3 is often denoted as 5!, read "five *factorial*."

> **Definition**
> For n a positive integer, n **factorial** is the product of the positive integers from 1 to n. In symbols, $n! = n \cdot (n-1) \cdot (n-2) \cdot (n-3) \cdot \ldots \cdot 3 \cdot 2 \cdot 1$.

Most scientific and graphing calculators have a factorial function. Check yours and find out how to use it to calculate factorials.

The result of Example 3 can easily be generalized.

> **Theorem (Selections without Replacement)**
> Let S be a set with n elements. Then there are $n!$ possible arrangements of the n elements *without replacement*.

442

Adapting to Individual Needs

Extra Help
Note the difference between arrangements with replacement and arrangements without replacement. Ask: How many 4-letter arrangements are there from the letters A, B, C, D, E, and F. Students will probably in turn ask: Can we repeat letters? You could then suggest that they do it both ways [With replacement, there are $6^4 = 1296$ arrangements; without replacement, there are $6 \cdot 5 \cdot 4 \cdot 3 = 360$ arrangements.]

Students should know but not have to memorize the general formulas here; they can be derived quickly from the Multiplication Counting Principle.

Challenge
Ask students to simplify each of following expressions.
1. $(k+1)! - k!$ $[k \cdot k!]$
2. $\frac{(k+1)! - k!}{k!}$ $[k]$
3. $\frac{(k+1)! + k!}{(k+1)! - k!)}$ $[\frac{k+2}{k}]$
4. $\frac{1}{k!} - \frac{1}{(k+1)!}$ $[\frac{k}{(k+1)!}]$

442

QUESTIONS

Covering the Reading

1. If each of Pete Seria's pizzas came in only 3 sizes, how many different specials would he have had? **18**

2. In how many ways can a sample of two children (one boy and one girl) be chosen from a class of 12 boys and 14 girls? **168**

3. A diner serves a bargain breakfast which includes eggs (over-easy, poached, or scrambled); pancakes or toast; and juice (orange, tomato, or grapefruit). A breakfast must include eggs and one selection from each of the other categories. **See margin.**
   a. Draw a tree diagram showing the different possible breakfasts.
   b. How many possible breakfasts are there?

4. Refer to Example 1, part **a**. Write the other 16 ways to answer the test. **See left.**

5. A test has 10 true-false questions. If you know three answers and guess on seven, what is the probability that you will get them all correct? **1/128 ≈ 0.0078**

6. How many ways are there of answering a test (assuming you answer all items) if the test has 10 multiple-choice questions, each with 4 choices? $4^{10} = 1,048,576$

7. How many ways are there of answering a test with 10 true-false and 20 multiple-choice questions, each with 5 choices, if you must answer each question? $2^{10} \cdot 5^{20} \approx 9.8 \cdot 10^{16}$

8. Refer to Example 2. The PSAT mathematics section has a penalty for guessing, so if you don't know an answer you should leave the question blank. Each five-option multiple-choice question therefore really has six possible responses (A, B, C, D, E, or blank), and each four-option multiple-choice question has five possible responses (A, B, C, D, or blank). Write an expression for the number of ways of answering the multiple-choice part of the PSAT mathematics section. $6^{25} \cdot 5^{15} \approx 8.7 \cdot 10^{29}$

9. Evaluate 6! without using a calculator. **720**

10. Evaluate 12! using a calculator. **479,001,600**

Applying the Mathematics

11. In how many ways can the batting order of a 10-person softball team be set? $10! = 3,628,800$

12. The spinner at the left has 6 congruent regions.
    a. If it is spun twice, list the possible outcomes. **See margin.**
    b. If it is spun 10 times, how many possible outcomes are there?
    c. If the spinner is fair, what is the probability of ten 1s in a row?
    b) $6^{10} = 60,466,176$ c) $1/6^{10} \approx 1.7 \cdot 10^{-8}$

13. An 18-speed bicycle gets its 18 speeds by selecting one gear from each of two sets of gears. The front set has three gears. How many gears does the rear set have? **6**

Lesson 7-3 *Multiplication Counting Principles* **443**

Nite Owl Diner,
Fall River, MA

4) FTTTT   FTFTT
FTTTF   FTFTF
FTTFT   FTFFT
FTTFF   FTFFF

FFTTT   FFFTT
FFTTF   FFFTF
FFTFT   FFFFT
FFTFF   FFFFF

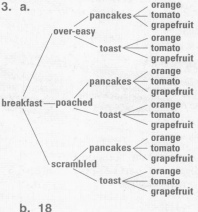

Additional Answers
12. a. {(1, 1), (1, 2), (1, 3), (1, 4), (1, 5),
(1, 6), (2, 1), (2, 2), (2, 3), (2, 4),
(2, 5), (2, 6), (3, 1), (3, 2), (3, 3),
(3, 4), (3, 5), (3, 6), (4, 1), (4, 2),
(4, 3), (4, 4), (4, 5), (4, 6), (5, 1),
(5, 2), (5, 3), (5, 4), (5, 5), (5, 6),
(6, 1), (6, 2), (6, 3), (6, 4), (6, 5),
(6, 6)}

Question 2 The word *sample* here suggests a subset, signaling that the order of selection of the boy or girl does not matter. If the sample did not have to have two children of different genders, then the answer is $26 \cdot 25$ when the order makes a difference (for instance, a winner and a runner-up) and $26 \cdot \frac{25}{2}$ when the order does not matter. This is the distinction between permutations and combinations, to be discussed later in this chapter and in Chapter 8.

Question 5 Error Alert Some students might think that the number ten somehow plays into the solution. In fact, the only pertinent information is that you are guessing on seven true-false questions.

Additional Answers
3. a.

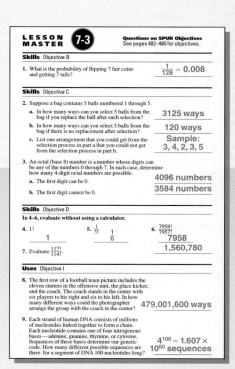

b. **18**

15. Consider $\frac{n!}{r!} = 72$, where n and r are positive integers.

   a. To find all possible solutions (n, r), how many different pairs of numbers must you check if $10 \geq n \geq 6$ and $8 \geq r \geq 5$? **20**

   b. Solve $\frac{n!}{r!} = 72$, where n and r satisfy the conditions of part **a**.

                                           n = 9, r = 7

16. Evaluate $\frac{10000!}{9998!}$ without using a calculator.

   99,990,000

Review

17. A record store receives a new shipment of albums. Of these, r can be cataloged as rock, c can be cataloged as country, and b can be cataloged as either rock or country. How many records are in the shipment? *(Lesson 7-2)*
r + c − b

18. Of the 37 books on a bookstore shelf labeled "Photography & Painting," 18 books contain chapters on photography, and 23 books have chapters on painting. What is the probability that a randomly selected book has chapters both on photography and painting? *(Lesson 7-2)* $\frac{4}{37} \approx 0.11$

19. a. What is the probability of rolling a sum of 10 with two fair dice?

   b. What are the odds against rolling a sum of 10 with two fair dice?
   (Lesson 7-1) **11 to 1**
  a) **1/12 ≈ 0.08**

In 20 and 21, give exact values without using a calculator. *(Lessons 5-3, 5-6)*

20. $\tan^{-1} 1$ $\frac{\pi}{4}$

21. $\cos^{-1}\left(\frac{-\sqrt{2}}{2}\right)$ $\frac{3\pi}{4}$

22. Refer to the graph below. *(Lessons 2-1, 4-6)*

   a. What are the domain and range of f? **See left.**

   b. Give the maximum and minimum values of f. **See left.**

   c. What is the period of f? **4**

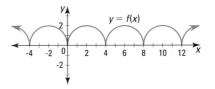

Exploration

23. a. What is the largest factorial your calculator can display without going into scientific notation? **13! on many calculators**

   b. What is the largest factorial your calculator can estimate in scientific notation? **69! on many calculators**

Ansel Adams (1902–1984), renowned wilderness photographer, increased public acceptance of photography as an art. At the California School of Fine Arts, he established the first academic department to teach photography as a profession.

22a) domain: set of all real numbers; range: {$y: 0 \leq y \leq 2$}
b) maximum value = 2; minimum value = 0

7-4

Permutations

Northridge	Northridge	Northridge	Northridge
Sacramento	Sacramento	Sacramento	Sacramento
E. Washington	E. Washington	E. Washington	E. Washington
Idaho State	Idaho State	Idaho State	Idaho State
Montana	Montana	Montana	Montana
Montana State	Montana State	Montana State	Montana State
N. Arizona	N. Arizona	Portland State	Portland State
Portland State	Weber State	N. Arizona	Weber State
Weber State	Portland State	Weber State	N. Arizona

Permutations of *n* Objects Taken *n* at a Time

In 1996, the Big Sky Basketball Conference had nine teams: California State Northridge, California State Sacramento, Eastern Washington, Idaho State, Montana, Montana State, Northern Arizona, Portland State, and Weber State. Assuming no ties, how many different possible standings could result?

The answer is given by the Selections without Replacement Theorem from the last lesson; for the nine teams, the number of different standings is

$$9! = 9 \cdot 8 \cdot 7 \cdot 6 \cdot 5 \cdot 4 \cdot 3 \cdot 2 \cdot 1 = 362,880.$$

Each different arrangement of a set of objects is called a **permutation**. Four of the 362,880 possible permutations of the teams in the Big Sky Conference are listed above. In general, the Selections without Replacement Theorem can be restated as a theorem about permutations.

> **Permutation Theorem**
> There are *n*! permutations of *n* different elements.

Permutations of *n* Objects Taken *r* at a Time

Similar reasoning can be used when not all of the *n* original objects are selected for arrangement.

Example 1

Seven horses are in a race at Churchill Downs. You want to predict which horse will finish first, which second, and which third (called *win*, *place*, and *show*, respectively). How many different predictions are possible?

Solution

Unlike the standings situation, only three of the seven horses are selected. Use the Multiplication Counting Principle.

	win	place	show
Any of the 7 horses can be first.	7		
For each of these, 6 horses can be second.	7 ·	6	
For each of these, 5 horses can be third.	7 ·	6 ·	5

So **there are 7 · 6 · 5 = 210 possible predictions.**

Lesson 7-4 *Permutations* **445**

Objectives

C Find the number of ways of arranging objects.
D Evaluate expressions using factorials.
G Solve equations using factorials.
I Use counting principles and theorems to find the number of ways of arranging objects.

Resources

From the *Teacher's Resource File*
■ Lesson Master 7-4
■ Answer Master 7-4
■ Teaching Aid 63: Warm-up

Additional Resources
■ Visual for Teaching Aid 63

Teaching 7-4
Lesson

Warm-up

At least twelve permutations of the letters AEPRS are legal words in the game of Scrabble®. In fact, no other set of five letters forms as many legal Scrabble words as these five letters.

1. Name as many as you can.
   APERS, APRES (meaning after), ASPER (a Turkish money of account), PARES, PARSE, PEARS, PRASE (a mineral), PRESA (a musical symbol), RAPES, REAPS, SPARE, SPEAR

2. If the letters AEPRS are ordered at random, what is the probability that the ordering forms a legal word in Scrabble?
   $\frac{12}{120} = \frac{1}{10}$

Lesson 7-4 Overview

Broad Goals In this lesson, the most general type of permutation without replacement is covered, and the familiar formulas are presented.

Perspective Students will have had practice with factorials and expressions containing factorials before this lesson, so the difficulty of learning the notation *and* the concept of permutations at the same time is avoided.

Two types of permutation problems have been covered in Lesson 7-3 as simpler applications of the Multiplication Counting Principle. Here the most general type of permutation without replacement is covered, and the familiar formulas for $_nP_r$ are generated.

We prefer $_nP_r$ to $P(n, r)$ notation here because it is easier to translate into words.

445

In permutation problems, all of the objects may be arranged, as with the basketball teams, or just some of the objects may be arranged, as in **Example 1,** where not all of the seven horses can finish first, second, or third.

Point out that in all the counting problems of this lesson, *the order of the elements being counted matters.* If the 4, 6, and 1 horses finished first, second, and third, this is different than if the order of the finish had been 6, 4, and 1. If we were counting combinations, these would not be distinct. This illustrates the difference between permutations and combinations, which is the topic of Lesson 8-6.

❶ Note that the Permutation Theorem is a special case of the formula for $_nP_r$. Let $r = n$ in that theorem and the formula becomes $_nP_n = n(n-1)(n-2) \cdot \ldots \cdot (n-n+1)$. Since each factor is one less than the preceding, and the last factor is 1, $_nP_n = n!$.

❷ It is universal to define $0! = 1$ because otherwise a number of formulas would fail. For instance $0! = 1$ is consistent with the formula for $_nP_r$. This value for $0!$ is also the only value that satisfies the criterion that $n! = n(n-1)!$ for $n = 1$. Specifically, one would need $1! = 1 \cdot 0!$, from which $1 = 1 \cdot 0!$, from which $0! = 1$. It is also the only value that works in formulas for $_nC_r$.

Multicultural Connection. Some African nations mark birth by the "outdooring ceremony." In Ghana, babies are 8 days old when first brought outside and presented to family and community.

Thus, in Example 1, if you picked the horses blindly, the probability of predicting the first, second, and third place finishers correctly is $\frac{1}{210}$.

When the order of the subjects is taken into account, the number of ways of arranging 3 objects out of a set of 7 objects is referred to as the number of permutations of 7 objects taken 3 at a time. In general, the number of permutations of **n objects taken r at a time** is denoted $_nP_r$ and can be calculated by multiplying n by the consecutive integers less than itself, until r factors have been taken. The second factor is $n - 1$, the third factor is $n - 2$, and so on. So the rth factor is $n - (r - 1)$, which equals $n - r + 1$.

❶ **Theorem (Formula for $_nP_r$)**
The number of permutations of n objects taken r at a time is

$$_nP_r = n(n-1)(n-2) \cdot \ldots \cdot (n-r+1).$$

Notice that $7 \cdot 6 \cdot 5 = \frac{7 \cdot 6 \cdot 5 \cdot 4 \cdot 3 \cdot 2 \cdot 1}{4 \cdot 3 \cdot 2 \cdot 1} = \frac{7!}{4!}$, and $4 = 7 - 3$. In a similar way, any product of consecutive integers can be written as a quotient of factorials. This provides an alternate way of calculating $_nP_r$.

Theorem (Alternate Formula for $_nP_r$)

$$_nP_r = \frac{n!}{(n-r)!}$$

Example 2
How many different five-letter words can be formed from the word BIRTHDAY? (The words do not have to make sense in English or any other language.)

Solution 1
One such word is BIRTH. Other words are RABID and YDRIA. The question essentially asks for the number of permutations of 8 objects taken 5 at a time. Use the first formula for $_nP_r$.

$$_8P_5 = \frac{8 \cdot 7 \cdot 6 \cdot 5 \cdot 4}{5 \text{ factors}} = 6720 \text{ words}$$

Solution 2
Use the Alternate Formula for $_nP_r$.

$$_8P_5 = \frac{8!}{(8-5)!} = 6720 \text{ words}$$

When all n objects are selected, the alternate formula for $_nP_r$ gives $_nP_n = \frac{n!}{(n-n)!} = \frac{n!}{0!}$. Because $_nP_n$ should be $n!$, $0!$ is defined to equal 1.

❷ **Definition**

$$0! = 1$$

446

Optional Activities

Activity 1 After discussing **Example 2,** some students may enjoy trying to find 5-letter permutations from BIRTHDAY that are words in the English language. [Here are 19 of them:

AIRTH	DIARY	HYDRA	THIRD
BAITH	DIRTY	RABID	TRIAD
BIRTH	HABIT	RHYTA	YAIRD
BRAID	HAIRY	TABID	YIRTH]
DAIRY	HARDY	TARDY	

Activity 2 After discussing **Question 12** you might have students answer the following questions.
1. What is the probability that the ID number formed is divisible by 5? $[\frac{1}{6}]$
2. What is the probability that the ID number formed is divisible by 2? $[\frac{1}{2}]$
3. What is the probability that the ID number formed is a number 5000 or greater? $[\frac{1}{3}]$

Example 3

Solve $_nP_5 = 7 \cdot {_nP_4}$.

Solution 1

Use the Formula for $_nP_r$.

$$n(n-1)(n-2)(n-3)(n-4) = 7n(n-1)(n-2)(n-3)$$

Divide each side of the equation by $n(n-1)(n-2)(n-3)$.

$$n - 4 = 7$$
$$n = 11$$

Solution 2

Use the Alternate Formula for $_nP_r$.

Rewrite.

$$\frac{n!}{(n-5)!} = 7\frac{n!}{(n-4)!}$$

Divide by $n!$ and multiply means by extremes.

$$(n-4)! = 7(n-5)!$$

A key step is to use the fact that $n! = n(n-1)!$, or, more generally, $(n-a)! = (n-a)(n-a-1)!$

Rewrite.

$$(n-4)(n-5)! = 7(n-5)!$$
$$n - 4 = 7$$
$$n = 11$$

Check

Find the $_nP_r$ function on your calculator. Then compute $_{11}P_5 = 55440$, $_{11}P_4 = 7920$, and $7 \cdot {_{11}P_4} = 55440$. So $_{11}P_5 = 7 \cdot {_{11}P_4}$.

QUESTIONS

Covering the Reading

1. List all the permutations of the letters in USA.
   USA, UAS, SUA, SAU, AUS, ASU
2. Doc, Grumpy, Happy, Sleepy, Bashful, Sneezy, and Dopey go to work whistling in a different order each day. How many days can they go without repeating an order? **5,040**

Adapting to Individual Needs

Extra Help
Point out to students that there are many situations in which the number of permutations is very large and calculators are essential. In many cases some arithmetic rewriting can speed calculation, and in some cases such rewriting is necessary. For example, $_{100}P_3$ cannot be computed on most calculators in the form $\frac{100!}{97!}$, because both 100! and 97! are too large. However, the alternative $_{100}P_3 = 100 \cdot 99 \cdot 98$, is easily computed.

Additional Examples

1. In a 4-person relay race, the fastest runner typically is the last person to run for the relay team. If that place is set, how many different orders are there for the other runners? $3! = 6$
2. How many different four-letter words can be formed from the letters in the word EQUATIONS? (The words do not have to make sense.) $_9P_4 = 3024$
3. Solve: $_xP_{10} = 20(_xP_8)$.
   $\frac{(x!}{(x-10)!} = \frac{20x!}{(x-8)!}$, so $20(x-10)! = (x-8)!$, from which $20 = (x-8)(x-9)$. Solving the quadratic yields $x = 4$ or $x = 13$, of which only $x = 13$ is in the domain of the original equation.

Notes on Questions

Question 2 The wording of the question is ambiguous. Do the seven dwarfs whistle in a different order each day, or do they go to work in a different order each day? However, it makes no difference; the answer is the same either way.

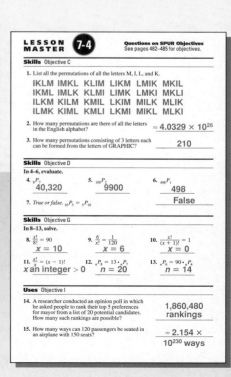

Notes on Questions

Question 3a Error Alert Some students might not be sure when to stop writing factors. Point out that when $_nP_r$ is written as a product of factors, there are r factors.

Question 16 The skill of rewriting factorials is needed in proofs, particularly those involving combinations in the next chapter.

Question 17 Point out that the pronunciation of the word entrée is "on´-tray."

Question 26 This exploration is placed here because the given equation can be rewritten as $_7P_3 = {}_{15}P_2$. Have students convert each of the equations they find to the language of permutations.

8a) n
b) If 1 item is picked from n, there are n possibilities.

9a) $n!$
b) If you order all the items from a set of n items, your ordering can be any of the $n!$ permutations of the n items.

10) According to the formula, $_nP_n = \frac{n!}{(n-n)!} = \frac{n!}{0!}$. But we know $_nP_n = n!$, so $\frac{n!}{0!}$ should equal $n!$, from which 0! must be 1.

16a) $_6P_4 = \frac{6!}{(6-4)!} = \frac{6!}{2!} = \frac{6 \cdot 5!}{2!} = \frac{6 \cdot 5!}{(5-3)!} = 6 \cdot {}_5P_3$

b) $_nP_r = \frac{n!}{(n-r)!} = \frac{n \cdot (n-1)!}{((n-1)-(r-1))!} = n \cdot {}_{n-1}P_{r-1}$

---

3. Write $_{11}P_3$ in each way.
   a. as a product of integers
   $11 \cdot 10 \cdot 9$
   b. as a ratio of two factorials
   $\frac{11!}{8!}$

In 4 and 5, evaluate.

4. $_{12}P_5$ **95,040**

5. $_7P_2$ **42**

6. Refer to the 9 teams in the Big Sky Basketball Conference. In how many ways can the first 5 positions in the standings be filled? **15,120**

7. **a.** How many permutations consisting of two letters each can be formed from the letters of UCSMP? **20**
   b. List them all. **UC, US, UM, UP, CU, CS, CM, CP, SU, SC, SM, SP, PU, PC, PS, PM, MU, MC, MS, MP.**

In 8 and 9, an expression is given. **a.** Evaluate it. **b.** Explain your answer to part **a** in terms of choosing items from a set. **See left.**

8. $_nP_1$

9. $_nP_n$

10. Explain why 0! is defined to equal 1. **See left.**

11. Solve for n: $_nP_3 = 5 \cdot {}_nP_2$. **n = 7**

Applying the Mathematics

12. **a.** How many ID numbers are there consisting of a permutation of four of the digits 1, 2, 3, 4, 5 and 6? **360**
    b. If one of the ID numbers is chosen at random, what is the probability that it is 3416? $\frac{1}{360} \approx 0.003$

13. An exhibition hall has eight doors. In how many ways can you enter and leave the hall through different doors? **56**

14. Each row of an aircraft has three seats on each side of the aisle. In how many different ways can a woman, her husband, and four children occupy a row of seats if the two parents sit in the aisle seats? **48**

15. A curator at a museum wants to hang six portraits and four landscapes in a line on a wall.
    a. In how many ways can the paintings be arranged?
    b. In how many ways can the paintings be arranged if the portraits are kept together and the landscapes are kept together?
    a) $10! = 3,628,800$ b) $2(6! \cdot 4!) = 34,560$

16. **a.** Show that $_6P_4 = 6 \cdot {}_5P_3$.
    b. Prove that $_nP_r = n \cdot {}_{n-1}P_{r-1}$ for all integers n and r with $1 \le r \le n$.
    a, b) See left.

Adapting to Individual Needs

Challenge
Ask students to order the following from least to greatest, without any calculations.

$_{17}P_{15}, {}_{18}P_{16}, {}_{17}P_{16},$ and $_{18}P_{15}$

[$_{17}P_{15}, {}_{17}P_{16}, {}_{18}P_{15}, {}_{18}P_{16}$; Possible thought process: $_{17}P_{15}$ is less than $_{17}P_{16}$ —they both start with the factor 17, but the first has 15 factors and the second 16 factors. $_{17}P_{16}$ is less than $_{18}P_{16}$ since they each have 16 factors but the latter starts at the higher number. Similarly, $_{18}P_{15}$ is between $_{17}P_{15}$ and $_{18}P_{16}$. So the question is, which is larger, $_{18}P_{15}$ or $_{17}P_{16}$. Do not compute, but write out the factors of each and cancel the common factors to show that $_{18}P_{15}$ is larger.]

17b)

In 17–19, consider Chuck's Restaurant, which has the following items on its menu. *(Lesson 7-3)*

lunch specials

BEVERAGES
Coffee   Tea   Milk
Orange Juice

ENTRÉES
Hamburger
Tuna Sandwich
Fried Chicken
Vegetarian Delight

DESSERTS
Cheese Cake
Apple Pie
Brownie
Ice Cream

17. a. If you order milk, an entrée, and a dessert, how many possible orders are there? **16**
   b. Show them in a tree diagram. **See left.**

18. How many ways are there to order an entrée, beverage, and dessert? **64**

19. If you cannot eat either hamburger or chicken, how many ways are there to order an entrée, beverage, and dessert? **32**

In 20 and 21, evaluate. *(Lesson 7-3)*

20. $6 \cdot 5!$ **720**

21. $\frac{395!}{392!}$ **61,162,590**

22) Mutually exclusive sets do not intersect, so $P(A \cap B) = 0$. Since A and B are nonempty, $P(A) > 0$ and $P(B) > 0$, and so $P(A) + P(B) > 0$.

22. *True or false.* If A and B are nonempty mutually exclusive events, then $P(A \cap B) = P(A) + P(B)$. Explain your reasoning. *(Lesson 7-2)*
False. See left for reasoning.

23. There are nine felt-tip and nine ball-point pens in a box, with three red, three blue, and three black of each kind. A pen is selected at random from the box. What is the probability that it is black or has a ball-point? *(Lessons 7-1, 7-2)* $\frac{2}{3}$

24. If x is randomly chosen from the set $\{1, 2, 3, \ldots , 50\}$ of integers, what is the probability that $\log_2 x$ is an integer? *(Lessons 6-3, 7-1)* $\frac{6}{50} = 0.12$

25a)

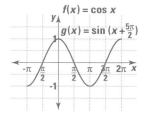

$f(x) = \cos x$
$g(x) = \sin\left(x + \frac{5\pi}{2}\right)$

25. a. Graph $f(x) = \cos x$ and $g(x) = \sin\left(x + \frac{5\pi}{2}\right)$, for $-\pi \le x \le 2\pi$, on the same axes. **See left.**
   b. *True or false.* For all x, $\sin\left(x + \frac{5\pi}{2}\right) = \cos x$. *(Lesson 4-8)*
   True

26. $7 \cdot 6 \cdot 5 = 15 \cdot 14$. Find two other sets of consecutive integers greater than 1 whose products are equal.
Sample: $7 \cdot 8 \cdot 9 \cdot 10 = 2 \cdot 3 \cdot 4 \cdot 5 \cdot 6 \cdot 7$ and $8 \cdot 9 \cdot 10 = 2 \cdot 3 \cdot 4 \cdot 5 \cdot 6$

Lesson 7-4 *Permutations* **449**

Follow-up for Lesson 7-4

Practice
For more questions on SPUR Objectives, use **Lesson Master 7-4** (shown on page 447).

Assessment
Written Communication Have students use one of the formulas for $_nP_r$ to determine how many one-letter words, four-letter words, and nine-letter words can be formed from the word EDUCATION. (The words do not have to make sense.) Then ask students to check their work using the other formula. [Students find the number of permutations of n objects taken r at a time.]

Extension
Have students show that
$_nP_r - \,_nP_{r-1} = (n - r)_nP_{r-1}.$
$[_nP_r - \,_nP_{r-1} = \frac{n!}{(n-r)!} - \frac{n!}{(n-r+1)!}$
Multiply the first term by $\frac{n-r+1}{n-r+1}$ and factor out $n!$ in the numerator:
$= \frac{n!(n-r+1-1)}{(n-r+1)!} = \frac{n!(n-r)}{(n-r+1)!} = (n-r)_nP_{r-1}.]$

Project Update Project 3, *The Birthday Problem*, and Project 4, *Seating Arrangements*, on pages 478–479, relate to the content of this lesson.

Objectives

E State and use properties of probabilities.

F Determine whether events are mutually exclusive, independent, or complementary.

H Calculate probabilities in real situations.

Resources

From the Teacher's Resource File
- Lesson Master 7-5
- Answer Master 7-5
- Teaching Aids
  63 Warm-up
  67 Sample Spaces of Socks
  68 Sample Spaces

Additional Resources
- Visuals for Teaching Aids 63, 67, 68

Teaching Lesson 7-5

Warm-up

Suppose the probability that a boy is born in a family is .49 and that a family has three children of different ages.

1. What is the probability that the oldest two children are boys? $.49^2 = .2401$

2. What is the probability that the youngest child is a girl? 0.51

3. What is the probability that the oldest two children are boys and the youngest child is a girl? $\approx .122$

4. Are the events of Questions 1 and 2 independent? Yes

LESSON 7-5

Independent Events

Sure Thing. *Whether they are made of wool, cotton, or polyester, socks are ususally stored in pairs so the probability of selecting a matching pair is one.*

What Are Independent Events?

When you flip a fair coin twice, the result of the first flip has no bearing on the result of the second flip. This is sometimes expressed by saying "the coin has no memory." Thus *if a coin is fair*, even if 10 heads have occurred in a row, the probability of heads on the 11th toss is still $\frac{1}{2}$. The tosses of the coin are called *independent events* because the result of one toss does not affect the results of other tosses.

Similarly, selections with replacement are considered to be independent events because later selections do not remember what happened with earlier selections. For instance, suppose that six socks are in a drawer: four of them orange, two blue. We name them 1 2 3 4 1 2. If a first sock is blindly taken, put back, and then a second sock is taken, what is the probability that both are blue?

Let A be the event that the first sock is blue, and B be the event that the second sock is blue. Thus $A \cap B$ is the event that both socks are blue. Since in each selection there are 2 blue socks among the 6, $P(A) = \frac{2}{6}$ and $P(B) = \frac{2}{6}$. To calculate $P(A \cap B)$, a rectangular array can be drawn as was done for the dice in Lesson 7-1. Each pair in the array is an outcome of the event $A \cap B$. For instance, 4 1 means that the orange sock #4 is the first sock and blue sock #1 is the second sock.

Sample Space with Replacement

1 1	1 2	1 3	1 4	1 1	1 2
2 1	2 2	2 3	2 4	2 1	2 2
3 1	3 2	3 3	3 4	3 1	3 2
4 1	4 2	4 3	4 4	4 1	4 2
1 1	1 2	1 3	1 4	1 1	1 2
2 1	2 2	2 3	2 4	2 1	2 2

Lesson 7-5 Overview

Broad Goals In this lesson, students are asked to determine whether events are independent, and to calculate probabilities if independence is known.

Perspective We define the events A and B to be independent if and only if $P(A \cap B) = P(A) \cdot P(B)$. There is another definition of independence based on conditional probability—A and B are independent if and only if $P(B$ given $A) = P(B)$—but the definition we use here directly relates to the Multiplication Counting Principle and lends itself to binomial experiments.

In 4 of the 36 pairs, both socks are blue. So $P(A \cap B) = \frac{4}{36}$. This is the product of $P(A)$ and $P(B)$.

More generally, if S_1 is the sample space for the first event A, and S_2 is the sample space for the second event B, and the events are independent, then an array formed like the one above will have $N(S_1) \cdot N(S_2)$ elements, of which $N(A) \cdot N(B)$ are in $A \cap B$. So

$$P(A \cap B) = \frac{N(A) \cdot N(B)}{N(S_1) \cdot N(S_2)} = \frac{N(A)}{N(S_1)} \cdot \frac{N(B)}{N(S_2)} = P(A) \cdot P(B).$$

This relationship between the probabilities of A, B, and $A \cap B$ is taken as the definition of independent events.

Definition
Events A and B are **independent events** if and only if $P(A \cap B) = P(A) \cdot P(B)$.

Example 1

The circular region around a fair spinner is divided into six congruent sectors and numbered as shown at the right. Consider spinning it twice. (Suppose the spinner cannot stop on a boundary line.) Define two events as follows.
   A: The first spin stops on an even number.
   B: The second spin stops on a multiple of 3.
Decide whether or not events A and B are independent.

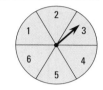

Solution

A and B are independent if $P(A \cap B) = P(A) \cdot P(B)$.

$$P(A) = \frac{3}{6} = \frac{1}{2}$$

$$P(B) = \frac{2}{6} = \frac{1}{3}$$

$P(A \cap B)$ can be obtained from the sample space illustrated at the right. The six circled points represent those for which both A and B are true.

So $P(A \cap B) = \frac{6}{36} = \frac{1}{6}.$

Because $P(A) \cdot P(B) = \frac{1}{2} \cdot \frac{1}{3} = \frac{1}{6} = P(A \cap B)$, events A and B are independent.

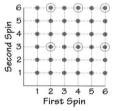

First Spin

Check

Because the spinner does not have a memory, the outcome of the first spin does not influence the second spin. Thus, we would expect the events to be independent.

What Are Dependent Events?

Now examine what happens if two socks are blindly taken *without replacement* from a drawer with four orange socks and two blue socks. $P(A)$, the probability that the first sock is blue, is still $\frac{2}{6}$. But $P(B)$, the probability that the second is blue, depends on whether the first one taken was blue or was orange. If the first one taken was blue, then there are four orange socks and one blue sock left, so the probability that the second is blue is $\frac{1}{5}$. If the first one taken was orange, then there are three orange and two blue socks left, so the probability that the second sock is blue is $\frac{2}{6}$.

The value of $P(B)$ depends on the outcome of event A. For this reason, selections without replacement are considered to be *dependent events*.

It is possible to calculate $P(A \cap B)$ even when A and B are dependent.

At the right is a listing for the sock experiment without replacement. These outcomes consist of all those in the independent case except those with the same sock selected twice. Thus there are only 30 outcomes. In only two are both socks blue, so $P(A \cap B) = \frac{2}{30}$. This confirms that in this case, $P(A \cap B) \neq P(A) \cdot P(B)$, because $P(A) \cdot P(B) = \frac{2}{6} \cdot \frac{2}{6} = \frac{4}{36}$.

Sample Space without Replacement

12	13	14	11	12
21	23	24	21	22
31	32	34	31	32
41	42	43	41	42
11	12	13	14	12
21	22	23	24	21

Example 2

Consider spinning the spinner in Example 1 twice. Define the events
  A: the first spin shows a number less than 3;
  B: the sum of the spins is less than 5.
Decide whether events *A* and *B* are independent.

Solution

We need to determine whether $P(A \cap B) = P(A) \cdot P(B)$. The sample space has the 36 elements shown in the solution to Example 1, and copied at the left.

A consists of the 12 outcomes inside the orange rectangle.

So, $$P(A) = \frac{12}{36} = \frac{1}{3}.$$

B is the set of outcomes {(1, 1), (1, 2), (1, 3), (2, 1), (2, 2), (3, 1)} inside the green triangle.

So, $$P(B) = \frac{6}{36} = \frac{1}{6}.$$

The five circled points represent $A \cap B$.

So, $$P(A \cap B) = \frac{5}{36}.$$

In this case, $$P(A) \cdot P(B) = \frac{1}{3} \cdot \frac{1}{6} \neq P(A \cap B).$$

So, the events A and B are not independent.

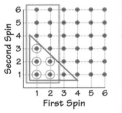

Second Spin / First Spin

Adapting to Individual Needs

▶ **Check**

The event B requires small numbers on both spins, so if event A occurs, B seems more likely to occur. This makes us expect that B is dependent on A.

An Example from Aviation

The notion of independence can be extended to more than two events. Consider this true story.

In May, 1983, an airline jet carrying 172 people between Miami and Nassau lost its engine oil, power, and 12,000 feet of altitude over the Atlantic Ocean before a safe recovery was made. When the warning lights indicating low oil pressure on all three engines lit up at nearly the same time, the crew's initial reaction was that something was wrong with the warning system, not the oil pressure. As one person stated in *The Miami Herald* of May 5, 1983,

"They considered the possibility of a malfunction in the indication system because it's such an unusual thing to see all three with low pressure indications. The odds are so great that you won't get three indications like this. The odds are way out of sight, so the first thing you'd suspect is a problem with the indication system."

Example 3

Aviation records show that for the most common engine on a Boeing 727 airliner, there is an average of 0.04 "inflight shutdowns" per 1000 hours of running time. So the probability of an engine's failure in a particular hour is about 0.00004. Suppose the failures of the three engines were independent. What is the probability of three engines failing in the same hour?

Solution

Let A, B, and C be the engines. If they are independent events,
$$P(A, B \text{ and } C \text{ fail}) = P(A \text{ fails}) \cdot P(B \text{ fails}) \cdot P(C \text{ fails})$$
$$= (0.00004) \cdot (0.00004) \cdot (0.00004)$$
$$= 6.4 \times 10^{-14}.$$

Boeing 727 cockpit

The number 6.4×10^{-14} is the sort of "out of sight" probability the writer of the article mentioned. This probability could be interpreted that *if* failures were independent, then about once in every 16,000,000,000,000 hours of flight would all three engines fail simultaneously.

After the incident, it was discovered that a mechanic doing routine maintenance on the plane had failed to install six tiny rubber seals on the engines' oil plugs. The gaps this error created allowed all the oil to leak out when the engines were fired up.

Lesson 7-5 *Independent Events* **453**

Additional Examples

1. Imagine that a fair coin is tossed 4 times. Let A = getting all heads and B = getting all tails. Are A and B independent or dependent? Why or why not?
$P(A) = \frac{1}{16} = P(B)$; $P(A \cap B) = 0$, so $P(A \cap B) \neq P(A) \cdot P(B)$ and the events are dependent.

2. Two normal dice are tossed. Let C = the sum is 7 and D = the first die shows a 5. Are C and D dependent or independent?
$P(C) = \frac{6}{36}$, $P(D) = \frac{1}{6}$, and $P(C \cap D) = \frac{1}{36}$, so $P(C) \cdot P(D) = P(C \cap D)$, so the events are independent. This result may come as a surprise. However, regardless of what the first die shows, there is still a $\frac{1}{6}$ chance of getting a 7 for the sum. This is not true for any other sum.

3. A coach keeps records on the basketball team. When a team member shoots two free throws, 65% of the time the first free throw is made and 70% of the time the second free throw is made. What percent of the time do both free throws need to be made in order for these events to be independent? $.65 \cdot .7 = 45.5\%$

Note that despite what some people might call "streaks," there is reasonable evidence that the making of free throws in basketball games is independent of the time in the game.

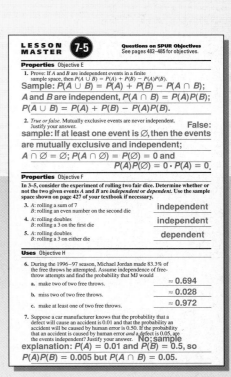

LESSON MASTER 7-5

Questions on SPUR Objectives
See pages 482–485 for objectives.

Properties Objective E

1. Prove: If A and B are independent events in a finite sample space, then $P(A \cup B) = P(A) + P(B) - P(A)P(B)$.
Sample: $P(A \cup B) = P(A) + P(B) - P(A \cap B)$; A and B are independent, $P(A \cap B) = P(A)P(B)$; $P(A \cup B) = P(A) + P(B) - P(A)P(B)$.

2. *True or false.* Mutually exclusive events are never independent. Justify your answer. **False:** sample: If at least one event is $\varnothing$, then the events are mutually exclusive and independent; $A \cap \varnothing = \varnothing$; $P(A \cap \varnothing) = P(\varnothing) = 0$ and $P(A)P(\varnothing) = 0 \cdot P(A) = 0$.

Properties Objective F

In 3–5, consider the experiment of rolling two fair dice. Determine whether or not the two given events A and B are *independent* or *dependent*. Use the sample space shown on page 427 of your textbook if necessary.

3. A: rolling a sum of 7
B: rolling an even number on the second die — **independent**

4. A: rolling doubles
B: rolling a 3 on the first die — **independent**

5. A: rolling doubles
B: rolling a 3 on either die — **dependent**

Uses Objective H

6. During the 1996–97 season, Michael Jordan made 83.3% of the free throws he attempted. Assume independence of free-throw attempts and find the probability that MJ would
a. make two of two free throws. ≈ 0.694
b. miss two of two free throws. ≈ 0.028
c. make at least one of two free throws. ≈ 0.972

7. Suppose a car manufacturer knows that the probability that a defect will cause an accident is 0.01 and that the probability an accident will be caused by human error is 0.50. If the probability that an accident is caused by human error *and* a defect is 0.05, are the events independent? Justify your answer. **No; sample explanation:** $P(A) = 0.01$ and $P(B) = 0.5$, so $P(A)P(B) = 0.005$ but $P(A \cap B) = 0.05$.

Adapting to Individual Needs

English Language Development
Discuss with students how words used in mathematics generally have meanings which are more precise than their definitions in everyday usage. For example, consider the word *independent*. A person is thought to act independently when he or she does not worry about what others do or think; two events are independent if the probability of one does not influence the probability of the other. Thus events from repeated trials with replacement can be independent because you do not know what transpired, but events from repeated trials without replacement are not independent because the first event affects what is possible for the second.

Question 1 In general, selections with replacement are independent events unless the situation changes; selections without replacement are often dependent events.

Question 10 This question could be turned around. If 2% of the visitors observe both hawks and eagles on a given day, and the probability of observing an eagle is .21, what would be the probability of observing a hawk if the events are independent? ($\frac{.02}{.21} \approx 9.5\%$) There is also a question of rounding here; the 2% probability might be anything from 1.5% to 2.5%.

Question 11 On roads with many traffic lights, the lights are often set up to be dependent so that, in light traffic, motorists will need to stop only occasionally.

Question 12 With real data, the variability of data needs to be taken into account. If $P(A) \cdot P(B)$ were close to $P(A \cap B)$, we might say that the events seem to be independent. Here, however, $P(A) \cdot P(B)$ is quite different from $P(A \cap B)$.

(Notes on Questions continue on page 456.)

2) independent;
$P(A) = \frac{1}{5}, P(B) = \frac{1}{6}$,
$P(A \cap B) = \frac{1}{30} = \frac{1}{5} \cdot \frac{1}{6}$

3) not independent;
$P(A) = \frac{1}{5}, P(B) = \frac{1}{2}$,
$P(A \cap B) = \frac{2}{15} \neq \frac{1}{5} \cdot \frac{1}{2}$

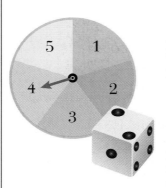

The crew members assumed that oil pressure problems in the three engines were independent events. Had this in fact been the case, they would have been correct in their assumption that the probability of all three engines failing simultaneously was extremely small. But the three failures were all due to one cause, a mechanic's error. So the failures were dependent events, and the event was not as unlikely as the crew thought.

Can Events Be Independent and Mutually Exclusive?

Suppose that A and B are two events which have a nonzero probability of occurring, that is, $P(A) > 0$ and $P(B) > 0$. If the events are independent, then $P(A \cap B) = P(A) \cdot P(B)$, and so $P(A \cap B) > 0$. For the events to be mutually exclusive, $A \cap B = \emptyset$, and so $P(A \cap B) = P(\emptyset) = 0$. This proves that events which have a nonzero probability of occurring cannot be both independent and mutually exclusive.

As an example, consider two candidates running for the office of President of the United States, one a Republican and one a Democrat. Because they cannot both win the election, the event of the Republican winning and the event of the Democrat winning are mutually exclusive. Yet, these two events are clearly not independent of one another.

QUESTIONS

Covering the Reading

1. A drawer contains five socks, three red and two blue.
   a. If you pick a sock randomly, replace it, and pick another, what is the probability that both socks are red? **9/25 = 0.36**
   b. If you pick two socks randomly without replacing the first, what is the probability that both are red? **6/20 = 0.3**
   c. If F = the first sock is red, and S = the second sock is red, in which of parts **a** and **b** are F and S independent events? **part a**

In 2 and 3, suppose you have a spinner with five congruent areas and a die, both fair. Decide whether or not the two events are independent. Justify your answer.

2. A = the spinner shows 4. B = the die shows 4. **See left.**

3. A = the spinner shows 4. B = the sum of the spinner and die is over 6. **See left.**

4. When are three events A, B, and C independent? **when $P(A \cap B \cap C) = P(A) \cdot P(B) \cdot P(C)$**

In 5 and 6, refer to the reporting of the airline incident. Suppose the failure rate per hour of each engine is 0.0005, and assume failures of the engines are independent events.

5. What is the probability that all three engines fail at the same time? $(0.0005)^3 = 1.25 \times 10^{-10}$

6. What is the probability that none of the engines fails? $(0.9995)^3 \approx 0.9985$

7. Give an example of two events different from the ones in the text which have nonzero probabilities and are not both independent and mutually exclusive. **See margin.**

Adapting to Individual Needs

Challenge
Have students do the following experiment.
1. Write the letters M, A, T, and H on separate cards. Draw out the cards, one at a time, without replacement, and write down the letter.
   a. Are the drawings independent? [No]
   b. How many different "words" can be formed? [24]

c. What is the probability of spelling the word "MATH?" $[\frac{1}{24}]$
d. Conduct the experiment 40 times. How many times did you spell the word MATH? [Answers will vary.]

Additional Answers
7. Sample: Consider tossing a quarter and a dime. If A is the event that the quarter lands heads up and B is the event that the dime lands heads up, A and B are independent, but they are not mutually exclusive.

Applying the Mathematics

8. Two fair dice are tossed. Use the definition of independence to classify the following pairs of events as independent, mutually exclusive, or neither.
   a. One die shows 2. The other die shows 3. **independent**
   b. One die shows 2. The same die does not show 3. **neither**
   c. One die shows 2. The same die shows 3. **mutually exclusive**

9. A fair coin is tossed three times. Consider the events:
   > *A:* at most one head occurs;
   > *B:* heads and tails occur at least once.

   Are *A* and *B* independent? Justify your answer using the definition of independence. **See left.**

9) Yes; $P(A) = \frac{1}{2}$,
$P(B) = \frac{3}{4}$,
$P(A \cap B) = \frac{3}{8} = \frac{1}{2} \cdot \frac{3}{4}$

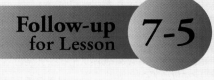

African fish eagle in Okavango, Botswana

10. The information booklet about a wildlife reservation park states that the probability of observing an eagle on a given day is 0.21, and the probability for a hawk is 0.17. The booklet also indicates that, based on records, 2% of the visitors observe both of these birds of prey on the same day. In this park, are observing an eagle and observing a hawk independent events? Explain your answer.
    No;   P(eagle) · P(hawk) = 0.21 · 0.17 = 0.0357 ≠ 0.02

11. A motorist has recorded some data while commuting on a section of road with five traffic lights. In 50 trips on this road, the five lights stopped the motorist 20, 22, 25, 19, and 24 times, respectively. The five lights all stopped the motorist once. Do you think the lights are operating independently? Explain your reasoning. **See left.**

11) We cannot answer this with certainty. If the relative frequencies represent the probabilities that the lights stop the motorist, and all the events are independent, then the probability of all happening is
$\frac{20}{50} \cdot \frac{22}{50} \cdot \frac{25}{50} \cdot \frac{19}{50} \cdot \frac{24}{50}$,
or about .016. This would suggest that in 50 trips, on average about 0.8 times all the lights would come on. That rounds to 1, suggesting that the lights are operating independently.

12. An auto manufacturer buys plastic molded parts from two companies: Ace and Best. Here is the frequency distribution of parts by quality that the auto company has received.

	Ace	Best
Excellent	60	24
Acceptable	272	20
Unacceptable	16	8

   a. What is the probability that a randomly selected part is from Ace?
   b. What is the probability that a randomly selected part is excellent?
   c. What is the probability that a randomly selected part is both from Ace and excellent? **0.15**
   d. Are the quality of parts and their sources independent? **No**

   a) 0.87   b) 0.21

13. A roulette wheel in Europe has 37 compartments numbered 0, 1, 2, . . . , 36. Find the probability that the number 29 will come up at least once in each case.
    a. a single spin ≈ 0.027
    b. two successive spins ≈ .0533
    c. three successive spins ≈ .0789

Practice
For more questions on SPUR Objectives, use **Lesson Master 7-5** (shown on page 453).

Assessment
Written Communication Have students write a paragraph explaining the difference between independent and dependent events, giving an example of each situation. Ask them to calculate probabilities in each situation to verify that the events are independent or dependent. [Students use probabilities to determine if events are independent.]

Extension
A group of students could mount an experiment using two local traffic signals, like that described in **Question 11**. First have students calculate the probability that each signal is red. Then have someone drive a car and see how often both signals are red. This should be done when there is very little traffic. The experiment could be done by different groups with the car in each group traveling at a different fixed (legal) speed. It could be extended into a chapter project.

Project Update Project 2, *Insurance Rates*, on page 478, relates to the content of this lesson.

Notes on Questions

Question 14 When the question asks how many ways the members can "line up," this implies the students are in a straight row. Project 4, *Seating Arrangements*, on page 479 deals with an alternative arrangement.

Question 22 It is common for sportscasters to say that a baseball player who has been hitting poorly is due for a hit. We seldom hear them say about players who have been playing well that they are due to play poorly. If a coin lands on heads 9 times in a row, it is more reasonable to say either that the coin is more likely to land on heads the next time (because perhaps the coin is weighted) or the coin is equally likely to land on heads or tails (because the coin is fair), than to say that the coin is due to land on tails.

KAUAI
OAHU
MOLOKAI
LANAI
MAUI
HAWAII

14a) $23! \approx 2.5852 \cdot 10^{22}$

b) $_{23}P_4 = \frac{23!}{19!} = 212,520$

14. **a.** In how many ways can the 23 members of a club line up for a photo?
    b. In how many ways can four of these people be chosen to be president, vice president, secretary, and treasurer of the club? *(Lesson 7-4)*
    a, b) See left.

15. Suppose you wish to visit all six large islands in the state of Hawaii: Hawaii, Kauai, Lanai, Maui, Molokai, and Oahu. If you are to visit each island once, in how many different orders might you travel? *(Lesson 7-4)*
    $6! = 720$

16. Solve for n: $17! = n \cdot 16!$. *(Lesson 7-4)* $n = 17$

17. Solve for n and r: $_nP_r = 600$. *(Lesson 7-4)*
    $n = 25$ and $r = 2$ or $n = 600$ and $r = 1$

18. When one coin is tossed there are two possible outcomes—heads or tails. How many outcomes are possible when the following numbers of coins are tossed? *(Lesson 7-3)*
    a. 2 $2^2 = 4$ **b.** 5 $2^5 = 32$ **c.** 8 $2^8 = 256$ **d.** n 2^n

19. Suppose a basketball player has a free throw shooting average of 0.75. What is the probability that the player will not make his next free throw? *(Lesson 7-2)* **0.25**

In 20 and 21, two bags each contain five slips of paper. An angle has been drawn on each slip. The measures of the angles on the slips in each bag are 10°, 30°, 45°, 60°, and 90°. Let a and b be the measures of the angles drawn from bags 1 and 2, respectively. *(Lessons 4-3, 7-1)*

20. Find $P(a + b \geq 90°)$.
    $\frac{15}{25} = 0.6$

21. Find $P(\sin(a + b) \geq \sin 90°)$.
    $\frac{3}{25} = 0.12$

22. The so-called "Law of Averages" is often used to lead people to expect that if event E occurs often, then its complement E' is more likely to occur the next time the experiment is undertaken. Test this "law." Toss a coin at least 200 times and record each result. Count the number of times that each of the following occurs: *HH, HT, TH, TT*. (In the sequence *HHHT*, you would count *HH* twice and *HT* once.) Does your data suggest more switches than would be expected? **Answers will vary.**

Setting Up Lesson 7-6

Consider **Question 18b.** Take the 32 outcomes and group them by the number of tails. Then make a table:

Tails	0	1	2	3	4	5
Outcomes	1	5	10	10	5	1

Note that *if* the coins were fair, the probabilities are easy to calculate. From these we get a probability distribution; we distribute the total probability of 1 over these 6 events. This is the idea studied in Lesson 7-6.

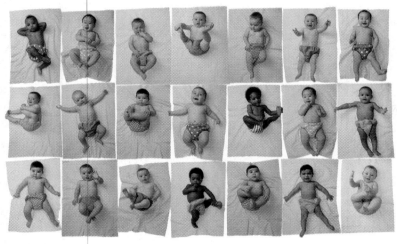

*Observation shows that births of boys and girls are not equally likely although we
often assume that they are. See Example 2.*

What Is a Probability Distribution?

In Lesson 7-1, the 36 possible outcomes for the tossing of two dice are
listed. If the dice are fair, then the probabilities of obtaining each possible
sum are given in the table below. Check that the sum of the probabilities is
1, so no possible outcome has been excluded.

x (sum of dice)	2	3	4	5	6	7	8	9	10	11	12
$P(x)$ (probability of outcome)	$\frac{1}{36}$	$\frac{2}{36}$	$\frac{3}{36}$	$\frac{4}{36}$	$\frac{5}{36}$	$\frac{6}{36}$	$\frac{5}{36}$	$\frac{4}{36}$	$\frac{3}{36}$	$\frac{2}{36}$	$\frac{1}{36}$

In this situation, let $x =$ the sum of the top faces of two dice. Then x is
a *random variable*. In general, a **random variable** is a variable whose
values are numbers determined by the outcome of an experiment. The
pairs of numbers in the table above represent a *probability distribution*. A
probability distribution is a function which maps each value of a random
variable onto its probability.

The probability distribution P for the sum
of two dice is graphed at the right. From
both the table and the graph, you can see
that the domain of P is the set of integers
from 2 to 12; the range is the set

$$\left\{\frac{1}{36}, \frac{2}{36}, \frac{3}{36}, \frac{4}{36}, \frac{5}{36}, \frac{6}{36}\right\}.$$

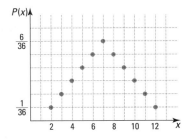

Lesson 7-6

Objectives

L Construct, graph, and interpret
probability distributions.

Resources

From the *Teacher's Resource File*
- Lesson Master 7-6
- Answer Master 7-6
- Assessment Sourcebook: Quiz
  for Lessons 7-4 through 7-6
- Teaching Aid 64: Warm-up
- Technology Sourcebook
  Calculator Master 6

Additional Resources
- Visual for Teaching Aid 64

Teaching 7-6
Lesson

Warm-up

Think of rolling two dice.
1. Which sum is most likely to
   occur? **7**
2. Which two sums are least likely
   to occur? **2 and 12**
3. Which is more likely, a sum of 3
   or a sum of 11? **Both are
   equally likely.**
4. Name the other pairs of sums
   that are equally likely to occur.
   4 and 10, 5 and 9, 6 and 8

Lesson 7-6 Overview

Broad Goals The purpose of this lesson is
to introduce probability distributions well in
advance of the more in-depth study of them
in Chapter 10.

Perspective A probability distribution is a
function which pairs the mutually exclusive
outcomes of a sample space (the domain)
with their probabilities of occurrence. When
statisticians search for mathematical models to describe patterns in experimental

data, they assume or test the existence of
an underlying probability distribution based
on calculations or expectations of how the
data are expected to behave.

Probability distributions are theoretical,
whereas relative frequency distributions
(that one often sees in reports and other
writing) are based on actual data. The mean
of the relative frequency distribution has as
its counterpart (but not necessarily its

equal) the expected value of the probability
distribution. This discussion of probability
distributions could have been presented
immediately after Lesson 7-2, but we chose
to provide students with more time to
become comfortable with probability
concepts before connections with functions
were made.

Our use of the term *random variable* to refer to the domain variable of a probability distribution does not represent uniform usage. Often, the probability distribution itself is called a random variable. That is, you may see in other books that a random variable is not a variable, but a function. That unusual use of the word *variable* can cause confusion, which is why we avoid it.

The distributions on pages 457–458 help illustrate that a relative frequency distribution will tend not to have the regularity of the corresponding probability distribution. For the dice example, the text explains that the observed mean $\bar{x} \approx 7.06$ while the expected mean for fair dice $\mu = 7$.

In **Example 1b** the percent error between $\bar{x}$ and μ is less than 1%. Caution: A quick reading may lead students to believe that the percent error is 86%, not 0.86%.

Emphasize that the domain of a probability distribution function consists of *all* the mutually exclusive outcomes of an experiment.

A finite probability distribution can be displayed as a scatterplot of possible outcomes versus their probabilities. If the graph is similar to that of a known function, then it is possible to find an equation for the distribution. Notice that the graph on page 457 is the image of the graph of the function $y = |x|$ reflected over the x-axis, stretched by a magnitude of $\frac{1}{36}$, and translated so that the vertex is the point $(7, \frac{1}{6})$. The resulting graph has the equation $P(x) = -\frac{1}{36}|x - 7| + \frac{1}{6}$. This is a briefer description of the distribution than that in **Question 10c.**

Now compare this probability distribution with the distribution of relative frequencies you might get if you performed an experiment. In an experiment, two dice were tossed 78 times and the sum of the numbers on the top faces was found. Below is a table of the relative frequencies of each sum.

x (sum of dice)	2	3	4	5	6	7	8	9	10	11	12
R(x) (relative frequency)	$\frac{2}{78}$	$\frac{4}{78}$	$\frac{6}{78}$	$\frac{6}{78}$	$\frac{13}{78}$	$\frac{12}{78}$	$\frac{14}{78}$	$\frac{11}{78}$	$\frac{5}{78}$	$\frac{2}{78}$	$\frac{3}{78}$

At the right is a graph of the relative frequencies. The graph of the relative frequencies resembles the graph of the probability distribution. Each graph shows that for $x = 2$ or 12 both $P(x)$ and $R(x)$ are small; and for $x = 6, 7,$ or 8 both $P(x)$ and $R(x)$ are relatively large.

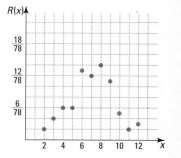

Expected Value

The distributions can be compared further by calculating their means. To find the mean sum $\bar{x}$ resulting from the experiment, add all 78 outcomes and divide by 78. There were two 2s, four 3s, six 4s, etc., so the total is

$$2 \cdot 2 + 3 \cdot 4 + 4 \cdot 6 + 5 \cdot 6 + 6 \cdot 13 + 7 \cdot 12 + 8 \cdot 14 + 9 \cdot 11 + 10 \cdot 5 + 11 \cdot 2 + 12 \cdot 3 = 551.$$

Thus, the mean sum is $\bar{x} = \frac{551}{78} \approx 7.06$.

Alternatively, you could divide each outcome by 78 before adding. Then the mean sum is

$$\bar{x} = 2 \cdot \frac{2}{78} + 3 \cdot \frac{4}{78} + 4 \cdot \frac{6}{78} + 5 \cdot \frac{6}{78} + 6 \cdot \frac{13}{78} + 7 \cdot \frac{12}{78} + 8 \cdot \frac{14}{78} + 9 \cdot \frac{11}{78} +$$
$$10 \cdot \frac{5}{78} + 11 \cdot \frac{2}{78} + 12 \cdot \frac{3}{78}$$
$$= \frac{551}{78} \approx 7.06.$$

Think of the 11 possible values of the random variable x as $x_1, x_2, \ldots, x_{11}$. This way of calculating the mean generalizes to the following formula for computing the mean $\bar{x}$ of n numbers x_i, if the relative frequency $R(x_i)$ of each x_i is known.

$$\bar{x} = x_1 \cdot R(x_1) + x_2 \cdot R(x_2) + \ldots + x_n \cdot R(x_n) = \sum_{i=1}^{n} (x_i \cdot R(x_i))$$

The *mean* or *expected value of a probability distribution* is found by using the probability $P(x_i)$ instead of the relative frequency $R(x_i)$. The expected value of the probability distribution is usually denoted by μ, the lowercase Greek letter mu (pronounced "mew").

458

Cooperative Learning
Materials: Dice

You may wish to divide the class into groups and give each group some dice. Have them toss the dice 36 times and find the mean and percent error from the expected value if the dice were fair. The question of when the difference between the observed mean and expected value is large enough is basic to statistics. Have each group decide what

difference seems sufficient to cause them to believe the dice are not fair. Have each group share its conclusion and encourage the class to come to an agreement.

Definition
Let $\{(x_1, P(x_1)), (x_2, P(x_2)),..., (x_n, P(x_n))\}$ be a probability distribution. The **mean** or **expected value** μ of the distribution is

$$\mu = \sum_{i=1}^{n} (x_i \cdot P(x_i)).$$

The mean of the probability distribution is also called the mean or expected value of the random variable. It indicates the average value of the random variable you may expect as an experiment is repeated. As with a probability, an expected value is a fixed theoretical value which is not necessarily obtained every time an experiment is repeated.

Example 1

Consider the experiment of rolling two dice and adding the numbers on the top faces.
a. Calculate the expected value of the probability distribution.
b. What is the percent error between the mean sum $\overline{x}$ of the relative frequencies, calculated on page 458, and the expected value?

Solution

a. Refer to the table of values of x_i and $P(x_i)$ at the beginning of the lesson. The expected value

$\mu = \sum_{i=1}^{11} (x_i \cdot P(x_i))$

$= 2 \cdot \frac{1}{36} + 3 \cdot \frac{2}{36} + 4 \cdot \frac{3}{36} + 5 \cdot \frac{4}{36} + 6 \cdot \frac{5}{36} + 7 \cdot \frac{6}{36} + 8 \cdot \frac{5}{36} +$

$\quad 9 \cdot \frac{4}{36} + 10 \cdot \frac{3}{36} + 11 \cdot \frac{2}{36} + 12 \cdot \frac{1}{36}$

$= \frac{2}{36} + \frac{6}{36} + \frac{12}{36} + \frac{20}{36} + \frac{30}{36} + \frac{42}{36} + \frac{40}{36} + \frac{36}{36} + \frac{30}{36} + \frac{22}{36} + \frac{12}{36}$

$= 7.$

b. The mean sum for the experiment at the beginning of the lesson is 7.06. This differs by only 0.06 from the expected value, so **the percent error from the expected value is** $\frac{0.06}{7} \approx 0.0086 = 0.86\%$**, less than 1%.**

A probability distribution is a function. So it can be described by identifying its domain and by giving a table or rule for the function. Frequently, a probability distribution is graphed as a histogram. It is common in such cases to center a bar of width 1 over the individual value of the random variable. The height of each bar is the corresponding probability.

The probability distribution of **Example 2** is an example of a binomial probability distribution. These distributions are discussed in some detail in Chapter 10.

LESSON MASTER **7-6**

Questions on SPUR Objectives
See pages 482–485 for objectives.

Representations Objective L

1. *Multiple choice.* In which table is P *not* a probability distribution?   **c**

(a)
x	1	2	3
P(x)	$\frac{1}{3}$	$\frac{1}{3}$	$\frac{1}{3}$

(b)
x	1	2	3
P(x)	$\frac{1}{2}$	$\frac{1}{2}$	0

(c)
x	1	2	3
P(x)	$\frac{1}{4}$	$\frac{1}{2}$	$\frac{1}{3}$

(d)
x	1	2	3
P(x)	$\frac{3}{8}$	$\frac{7}{24}$	$\frac{1}{3}$

2. A researcher collects the following data about the incubation time of a certain disease.

x = Number of days	1	2	3	4	5	6	7
P(x)	$\frac{1}{14}$	$\frac{3}{28}$	$\frac{3}{14}$	$\frac{1}{28}$	$\frac{1}{7}$	$\frac{2}{7}$	$\frac{1}{7}$

a. What is the random variable?   **incubation time**

b. Find the mean incubation time.   **4.5 days**

3. Consider the experiment of rolling two fair 6-sided dice.

a. Construct a probability distribution table in which the value of the random variable is calculated by subtracting the value showing on the second die from the value showing on the first die.

x	-5	-4	-3	-2	-1	0	1	2	3	4	5
P(x)	$\frac{1}{36}$	$\frac{2}{36}$	$\frac{3}{36}$	$\frac{4}{36}$	$\frac{5}{36}$	$\frac{6}{36}$	$\frac{5}{36}$	$\frac{4}{36}$	$\frac{3}{36}$	$\frac{2}{36}$	$\frac{1}{36}$

b. Graph the distribution in part a as a scatterplot.

c. Find the expected value of the probability distribution.

____0____

Adapting to Individual Needs

Extra Help
If students have difficulty making comparisons between the graph of a probability distribution and a graph of relative frequencies, use the same scales on each. For example, in the graphs on pages 457 and 458, rewrite the y-scale showing the probabilities as decimals. Suggest that students do the same in **Questions 11–12.**

Additional Examples

1. Just for these notes, an author rolled two normal dice 9 times with the following sums: 6, 10, 11, 10, 9, 9, 12, 7, 9.
   a. Give the mean of these numbers. Mean $\frac{83}{9} \approx 9.2$
   b. Give the percent error between the mean and the expected value for the distribution, assuming the dice are fair. Percent error $\frac{20}{63} \approx 32\%$ (This percent error is quite high, so one wonders if the underlying distribution is correct. That is, perhaps the dice are not fair or the tosses were not independent.)

2. Repeat **Example 2** for a family with 5 children.
   a. There may be 0, 1, 2, 3, 4, or 5 boys, so the random variable takes on values 0, 1, 2, 3, 4, or 5.
   b. Let x = number of boys. Then $P(0) = \frac{1}{32}$, $P(1) = \frac{5}{32}$, $P(2) = \frac{10}{32}$, $P(3) = \frac{10}{32}$, $P(4) = \frac{5}{32}$, and $P(5) = \frac{1}{32}$.
   c.
   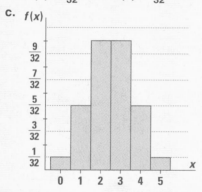
   d. 2.5

Example 2

Consider a family with three children. Assume that births of boys and girls are equally likely. Let the random variable of the distribution stand for the number of boys.
   a. Give the domain of the random variable.
   b. Find the probability for each value of the random variable.
   c. Construct a histogram of the probability distribution.
   d. Find the expected value of the distribution.

Solution

   a. There may be 0, 1, 2, or 3 boys, so the random variable takes on the values 0, 1, 2, and 3.
   b. The sample space consists of 8 outcomes, the ordered triples BBB, BBG, BGB, BGG, GBB, GBG, GGB, and GGG.
   Since each outcome is equally likely, we use $\frac{N(E)}{N(S)}$ to determine each probability.

x = number of boys	0	1	2	3
$P(x)$	$\frac{1}{8}$	$\frac{3}{8}$	$\frac{3}{8}$	$\frac{1}{8}$

   c. Graph with bars centered over the values of x.

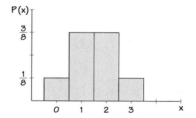

   d. Use the definition of expected value. Here x_i is the event "having i boys."
   $$\mu = \sum_{i=0}^{3}(x_i \cdot P(x_i)) = 0 \cdot \frac{1}{8} + 1 \cdot \frac{3}{8} + 2 \cdot \frac{3}{8} + 3 \cdot \frac{1}{8}$$
   $$= \frac{12}{8}$$
   $$= 1.5 \text{ boys}$$

Check

For part **d**, if the births of boys and girls are equally likely, they each happen half of the time. In a family of three children, $\frac{1}{2}$ of 3 *is* 1.5, the expected value calculated in part **d**.

Look back at the histogram above. Notice that each bar has an area of $1 \cdot P(x_i) = P(x_i)$. So the area of each bar is the probability of the event to which it corresponds; and thus the sum of the areas of the bars is 1. This property is true for *all* probability distributions, and will be applied in Chapter 10.

Adapting to Individual Needs

Challenge

A raffle sells only 1000 tickets at $1 each. There is a first prize of $400, two second prizes of $100 each, and six third prizes of $10 each. Have students answer the following questions.

1. Give the probability distribution for the net earnings of a single ticket. [See chart below.]

x	399	99	9	-1
$P(x)$	$\frac{1}{1000}$	$\frac{1}{500}$	$\frac{3}{500}$	$\frac{991}{1000}$

2. Find the expected winnings of one ticket. [-.34]

3. Explain how the expected value is found by using ordinary averages (mean). [Add 1000 numbers, of which 991 are -1's, 6 are 9's, 2 are 99's, and 1 is 399. Divide the sum by 1000.]

Covering the Reading

7a) {(GGGG), (GGGB), (GGBG), (GGBB), (GBGG), (GBGB), (GBBG), (GBBB), (BGGG), (BGGB), (BGBG), (BGBB), (BBGG), (BBGB), (BBBG), (BBBB)}

b) $\left(0, \frac{1}{16}\right)$, $\left(1, \frac{4}{16}\right)$, $\left(2, \frac{6}{16}\right)$, $\left(3, \frac{4}{16}\right)$, $\left(4, \frac{1}{16}\right)$

c)

1. What is a *random variable*? a variable whose values are determined by the outcome of an experiment

2. What is a *probability distribution*? a function that maps each value of a random variable onto its probability

3. *True or false.*   In a probability distribution, each element in the range must be a number between 0 and 1, inclusive. True

In 4 and 5, explain why the given table does not define a probability distribution.

4.

x	3	4	5	6	7
$f(x)$	$\frac{1}{16}$	$\frac{11}{16}$	$-\frac{1}{16}$	$\frac{2}{16}$	$\frac{3}{16}$

$-\frac{1}{16}$ is not a probability because it is not between 0 and 1.

5.

x	0	1	2	3
$f(x)$	$\frac{1}{4}$	$\frac{2}{4}$	$\frac{3}{4}$	$\frac{1}{4}$

The sum of the $f(x)$ values is not 1.

6. Find the expected value of the following probability distribution.

x	5	6	7	8	9	10
$P(x)$	$\frac{1}{15}$	$\frac{2}{15}$	$\frac{3}{15}$	$\frac{4}{15}$	$\frac{4}{15}$	$\frac{1}{15}$

$\frac{116}{15} \approx 7.73$

7. Consider a family with four children. a–c) See left.
   a. List all possible outcomes in the sample space.
   b. Let $x =$ the number of girls in the family. Find the probability for each value of the random variable assuming that births of boys and girls are equally likely.
   c. Make a histogram of the probability distribution.
   d. Find the expected value of x. 2

8. What is the total area of the bars in a histogram for a probability distribution? 1 square unit

9. *True or false.*   The mean of a probability distribution is always a value of the random variable of the experiment. False

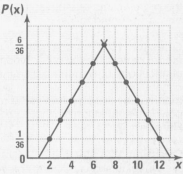

The British royal family in the 1970s: Queen Elizabeth, Prince Philip, and their children, Charles, Anne, Andrew, and Edward.

Applying the Mathematics

10. Copy the graph of the probability distribution on page 457 associated with rolling two dice and recording the sum. See margin.
   a. Superimpose two lines which contain the points of the graph.
   b. Show that the area enclosed by the x-axis and the two lines in part **a** is 1 square unit.
   c. Determine the equations for the two lines in part **a**.

Notes on Questions

Question 7 This question extends **Example 2** to 4 children; Additional Example 2 deals with 5 children. All of these are useful preparation for the binomial distributions to be discussed in Chapter 10.

Question 10c See the *Notes on Reading* on page 458 for a derivation of an absolute value function that contains all the points.

Additional Answers
10. a.

$P(x)$ graph with points forming a triangle peaking at $\frac{6}{36}$

b. It is a triangle with base 12 units and height $\frac{6}{36}$ units. The area is $\frac{1}{2}bh = \frac{1}{2}(12)\left(\frac{6}{36}\right) = 1$.

c. $y = \frac{1}{36}x - \frac{1}{36}$ and $y = -\frac{1}{36}x + \frac{13}{36}$

Question 12 The probability distribution can be pictured by referring to the array of 36 outcomes shown in Lesson 7-1, graphing the ordered pairs, and looking at the diagonals with slope 1. All outcomes on the same diagonal have the same difference.

Question 13 For many people, the loss of $.20 per ticket on the average (calculated from the expected value) is not enough to deter them from the slim chance that they could win. Yet the more tickets one buys, the more one is expected to lose.

Question 15 This absolute value model generalizes to other binomial distributions only in the sense that a distribution with $2n$ points can be modeled by the absolute value of a polynomial function of degree $n - 1$. Here, $n = 2$.

Question 16 Later in the program the wheel is slightly different. If you have any aficionados of the program in your class, you might ask them to invent reasonable questions about that wheel.

11a)

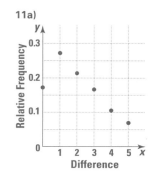

Difference

13a) It represents a loss; it is negative because $1 must be paid for the ticket.

15a)
$f(0) = -\frac{1}{4}|0 - \frac{3}{2}| + \frac{1}{2} = \frac{1}{8};$

$f(1) = -\frac{1}{4}|1 - \frac{3}{2}| + \frac{1}{2} = \frac{3}{8};$

$f(2) = -\frac{1}{4}|2 - \frac{3}{2}| + \frac{1}{2} = \frac{3}{8};$

$f(3) = -\frac{1}{4}|3 - \frac{3}{2}| + \frac{1}{2} = \frac{1}{8}$

b) Substituting

$x - \frac{3}{2}$ for x

and $\dfrac{y - \frac{1}{2}}{-\frac{1}{4}}$ for y

in $y = |x|$ results in

$\dfrac{y - \frac{1}{2}}{-\frac{1}{4}} = |x - \frac{3}{2}|$ or

$y = -\frac{1}{4}|x - \frac{3}{2}| + \frac{1}{2}.$

In 11 and 12, an experiment involves rolling two dice and recording the absolute value of the difference between the numbers showing on the two dice. For example, if you roll a 4 and a 6, the outcome is $|4 - 6| = 2$.

11. The following table of relative frequencies was formed after 360 trials.

Difference	0	1	2	3	4	5
Relative frequency	$\frac{62}{360}$	$\frac{98}{360}$	$\frac{77}{360}$	$\frac{60}{360}$	$\frac{38}{360}$	$\frac{25}{360}$

a. Make a scatterplot of these data. **See left.**
b. Find the mean difference. $\frac{709}{360} \approx 1.97$

12. Let X = the absolute value of the difference between the numbers showing on two dice. **a, b) See margin.**
a. Make a table of values of the probability distribution for X.
b. Make a scatterplot of the distribution.
c. Find the expected value of X. $\mu = 70/36 \approx 1.94$
d. What is the percent error between the mean difference in Question 11, part **b** and the expected value of X? $\approx 1.5\%$

13. In a lottery, the *value* of a ticket is a random variable, defined to be the amount of money you win less the cost of playing. Suppose that in a lottery with 125 tickets, each ticket costs $1. First prize is $50, second prize is $30, and third prize is $20. Then the possible values of the random variable are $49, $29, $19, and -$1.
a. Why is one of the values negative? **See left.**
b. The probability of winning first prize is $\frac{1}{125}$. The same probability holds for second and third prizes. Find the probability of winning nothing. $122/125 = 0.976$
c. Find the expected value of a ticket. $-\frac{25}{125} = $-$0.20 or -20¢

14. An ecologist collected the data shown in the table below on the life span of a species of deer. Based on this sample, what is the expected life span of this species? **about 4.6 years**

Age at death (years)	1	2	3	4	5	6	7	8
Number	2	30	86	132	173	77	40	10

15. The dot frequency graph at the right is of the probability function in Example 2. The graph of $f(x) = -\frac{1}{4}|x - \frac{3}{2}| + \frac{1}{2}$ is superimposed. **See left.**
a. Verify that each of the four points $(x_i, P(x_i))$ is on the graph of f.
b. Verify that the equation above for f is produced from $y = |x|$ by the rubberband transformation $L(x, y) = (x + \frac{3}{2}, -\frac{1}{4}y + \frac{1}{2}).$

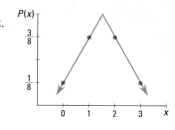

12. a.

Difference	0	1	2	3	4	5
Probability	$\frac{6}{36}$	$\frac{10}{36}$	$\frac{8}{36}$	$\frac{6}{36}$	$\frac{4}{36}$	$\frac{2}{36}$

b.

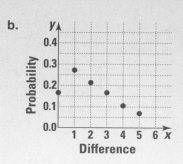

Difference

Review

16. The wheel on the TV program *Wheel of Fortune* is first divided equally into 24 compartments with one labeled "Lose A Turn." Find the probability that the wheel stops at "Lose A Turn" for each of the following.
    a. a single spin $1/24 \approx 0.042$
    b. two successive spins $(1/24)^2 \approx 0.0017$
    c. three successive spins   *(Lesson 7-5)* $(1/24)^3 \approx 7.2 \cdot 10^{-5}$

17. Consider the experiment of tossing a fair coin five times.
    a. Determine the probability of at least one tail. $31/32 = 0.96875$
    b. Determine the probability of exactly two heads. $10/32 = 0.3125$
    c. *True or false.*   The two events in parts **a** and **b** are independent.
       (Lessons 7-1, 7-2, 7-3, 7-5) **False**

18. In how many different ways can a class with 18 students be seated in a room containing 24 desks?   *(Lesson 7-4)* $_{24}P_{18} \approx 8.6 \times 10^{20}$

19. Write $\frac{(n+2)!}{n!}$ as a polynomial in n.   *(Lesson 7-3)*
    $(n+2)(n+1) = n^2 + 3n + 2$

20. The *Statistical Abstract of the United States 1996* states that in 1991 there were 31,041,000 freshwater anglers and 8,885,000 saltwater anglers. The total number of anglers, however, is 35,578,000.
    a. How many anglers in 1991 were in both categories?   **4,348,000**
    b. If there were 252,131,000 people in the U.S. in 1991, determine the probability of randomly picking a person in the population who fished in saltwater but not in freshwater.   *(Lesson 7-2)*
       $4,537,000/252,131,000 \approx 0.018$

21. A person recorded the following scores on an electronic game: 810, 670, 630, 820, 710, 590, 6450, 920, 610, 770.
    a. Find the mean of these scores.   **1298**
    b. Find the median score.   **740**   **c) See left.**
    c. Which is the better measure of center—the mean or the median? Why?
    d. Find the standard deviation of the scores.   **about 1813**
    e. How does the score of 6450 affect the size of the standard deviation of the scores?   *(Lessons 1-3, 1-7)* **It has a great effect. If that score is removed, the standard deviation changes from about 1813 to 112.**

21c) Sample: median; the median is not affected by the unusually high score of 6450.

Exploration

22. a. Find the life expectancy for a person of your age and sex.
    b. Find out how life expectancies are determined.
       a, b) Answers will vary.

Practice
For more questions on SPUR Objectives, use **Lesson Master 7-6** (shown on page 459).

Assessment
Quiz A quiz covering Lessons 7-4 through 7-6 is provided in the *Assessment Sourcebook.*

Extension
Have students in the class list the number of people in their immediate family (the number of people they live with on a daily basis). Make a table of the different outcomes and frequencies and have the class compute their relative frequencies. Then have the class make a probability distribution and calculate the mean number of people in a family for the class.

Project Update Project 1, *Fair Dice?*, and Project 2, *Insurance Rates*, on page 478, relate to the content of this lesson.

Setting Up Lesson 7-7
Do the In-class Activity on page 464.

In-class Activity

Resources

From the Teacher's Resource File
■ Answer Master 7-7

Additional Resources
■ Exploration 7-7

Marilyn vos Savant posed this probability problem in her "Ask Marilyn" column in *Parade Magazine.* Judging from the mail she received, the problem confounded many people, including several mathematicians. This activity simulates the situation.

Here is the theoretical solution to the problem. The probability of winning if you do not switch is $\frac{1}{3}$. Your probability of winning if you switch is $\frac{2}{3}$.

Rationale: Suppose these are the doors.

Prize	Goat	Goat
1	2	3

If you pick Door 1, the host will show you door 2 or 3. Either way, if you switch, you will lose. If you pick Door 2, the host will show you door 3. If you switch, you win. If you pick Door 3, the host will show you door 2, and if you switch, you win. Hence, when you switch, you win 2 out of 3 times.

The Monty Hall Problem

IN-CLASS
ACTIVITY

Work with a partner on this problem. You will need three playing cards, two of one color and a third of a different color.

Monty Hall was the host of the TV game show called *Let's Make a Deal!* Contestants were told that behind each of three doors was a prize, not all of which were considered desirable. The contestant was asked to pick a door, and then Monty Hall would offer money to the contestant, who could take it or choose what was behind the door, sight unseen.

Here is a variation of that game. Suppose that behind two of the doors is a goat and behind the third door is a new car. You are the contestant and you pick one door, say Door Number 2. The host, *who knows what is behind each door*, then opens one of the other two doors and shows you a goat. The host now asks you, "Do you want to stay with the door you chose or do you wish to choose the other unopened door?" The problem is to determine whether it is to your advantage to switch.

1 Decide who will play the role of the host, and who will play the contestant. Let the two cards of the same color represent the goats, and the card with the unique color represent the car.

2 The host should shuffle the cards, place them face down without the other person's watching, and remember which card represents the car.

3 The contestant will then choose one of the cards. The host will not turn over that card, but the host will turn over a remaining card which represents a goat.

4 The contestant will then decide to keep the first choice or to switch. Then the host will turn over the final choice to see if the contestant won the game (got the car) or lost the game (got a goat).

5 Play the game (that is, repeat steps 2–4) 15 times. Keep a tally on a chart similar to the one below. Then reverse roles and play the game 15 more times, and record your results on the same tally chart.

Contestant's Strategy	Number of Wins	Number of Losses
Keeps the Original Card		
Switches Cards		

6 On the basis of your data, what should the strategy of the contestant be?

7 Under the direction of your teacher, incorporate your data with that of the rest of the class. On the basis of the class data, what should be the strategy of the contestant?
6, 7) See margin.

Technology Connection
Materials: Explorations software

Students may use *Exploration 7-7, The Monty Hall Problem,* to do this In-class Activity. Students play a computer version of the classic TV game show *Let's Make a Deal!* Students record their results in a table so they can decide whether it is a mathematical advantage to keep their first choice or change.

Additional Answers
6, 7. The students should recognize that a strategy of switching doors will more likely reveal the car. Let $P(1)$ = probability that the car is behind door number 1, $P(2)$ = probability that it is behind door 2, and $P(3)$ = probability that it is behind door 3. Notice that $P(1) = P(2) = P(3)$, that $P(1) + P(2) + P(3) = 1$, and therefore $P(1) = P(2) = P(3) = \frac{1}{3}$.

However, when the contestant switches, the probability of winning must be $P(\text{not } 2) = \frac{2}{3}$ since no other options are available. This result is explained by taking a close look at the cases when the car is behind door 1 and when it is behind door 3. In each of these equally likely cases Monty will steer the contestant to the car by revealing the goat behind the other of the two doors.

The In-class Activity on the preceding page is a *simulation* of what happened on the TV show. A **simulation** of a real situation is an experimental model of the situation that attempts to capture all aspects of the situation that affect the outcomes. Simulations appear in all areas of our lives. They are used by car manufacturers to test safety features in cars, by governments to examine procedures in the case of major emergencies, by toymakers to estimate how long a toy will last. A poll before an election is a simulation of the election. A fire drill in a school is a simulation; not only does a fire drill alert you to what to do in case of fire, but it also provides an estimate of how long it takes to evacuate the school. The PSAT exam is a simulation of the SAT; the PLAN exam is a simulation of the ACT.

When it is possible, people repeat simulations so that probabilities of the various outcomes can be estimated. When an experiment is repeated, the repetitions are called **trials**. In the Monty Hall situation, you were asked to perform 30 trials, that is, 30 simulations of the same real situation. By combining your data with the data of others, hundreds of simulations could be run. It is possible to compute the probability of choosing the door with the car behind it, but the repeated trials provide a relative frequency that may be a fairly good estimate of that probability without using any laws of probability.

Monte Carlo Simulations

The use of relative frequencies obtained from repeated trials to answer a mathematical problem is often called a **Monte Carlo method**, named after the well-known Monte Carlo Casino in the principality of Monaco. Monte Carlo methods were pioneered by John von Neumann (1903–1957), one of the inventors of modern computer programming. These methods make it possible to estimate solutions to a variety of problems.

There are three steps to the Monte Carlo method.

1. Determine how the situation will be simulated.
2. Define what constitutes a single trial and what data will be recorded.
3. Specify the number of trials that will be run and how the estimated answer will be obtained.

We first use a Monte Carlo method to simulate a problem for which you already know the answer.

Lesson 7-7

Objectives
J Design and conduct simulations without technology.

Resources
From the *Teacher's Resource File*
■ Lesson Master 7-7
■ Answer Master 7-7
■ Teaching Aids
   64 Warm-up
   69 Random Number Table

Additional Resources
■ Visuals for Teaching Aids 64, 69

Teaching 7-7
Lesson

Warm-up

Activity Pick three digits at random from 0 to 9 using any means you wish. Then, when your teacher calls your name, record your number on the chalkboard. After everyone has written his or her number on the chalkboard, discuss what these numbers represent. **This activity is a crude way of attempting to create a random number table. Generally, students will pick fewer 0s and 9s than would be expected, and more numbers in the middle. This is why tables are used and not merely numbers "picked" out of the air.**

Lesson 7-7 Overview

Broad Goals In this lesson, students use a random number table to generate pseudo-random numbers, that is, numbers that behave much like random numbers. They are shown how to simulate experiments by generating random numbers to fall within specific intervals.

Perspective No method for actually generating random numbers is known. In fact, it is not known if it is theoretically possible to generate such numbers. Until recent times, if random numbers were desired, one would look in a table for them. (That is hardly random. Two different people might use identical tables and start at the same place.)

A Monte Carlo simulation is simply the use of random numbers to simulate an event. Monte Carlo methods are an outgrowth of the ability of computers to perform calculations very quickly. However, in this lesson, random number tables are used instead of computers.

Notes on Reading

Have students record the results of the **Activity** for use with **Question 2** on page 468.

When students think of simulation, they may think of simulating accidents, or people learning to fly by using "simulators," or computer simulations of various kinds of terrain. They may not be aware of simulations that are probabilistic in nature.

In order to simulate an experiment in which there is an underlying (assumed) probability distribution, since the domain variable in that distribution is a random variable, the domain values must be found by some random process. A spinner, die, or coin could be used to generate the domain values, but here we focus on the use of random numbers. The reason is that such numbers can simulate whatever probabilities we need. For instance, if we want to simulate the days of the week occurring randomly, we would need 7 outcomes that occur with equal frequency. This is difficult with a coin or die and few spinners have 7 sectors, but a random number table can do it. (Note that **Teaching Aid 69** provides a random number table.) Also, a BASIC function can be defined to do it.

History Connection John von Neumann was one of the most versatile and innovative mathematical theorists of the 20th century. He was born in Budapest, Hungary, and taught in Germany before coming to the United States in the 1930s to teach at Princeton University. He created game theory and laid the ground work for the design of the computer.

Example 1

A researcher is studying the number of boys and girls in families with three children. Assume that the birth of a boy or a girl is equally likely. Design a simulation with 100 trials to estimate the probability that a family of three children has exactly one boy. (This is the situation of Example 4 of Lesson 7-1.)

Solution 1

Follow the three steps on page 465.
1. *To simulate the situation, flip a coin. If the coin comes up heads, call it a boy. If it comes up tails, call it a girl.*
2. *A trial is to flip the coin three times and count the number of heads.*
3. *Repeat the trial 100 times. Calculate the percent of trials in which exactly one head occurs.*

Solution 2

1. *Use a die. If it comes up 1, 2, or 3, call it a boy. If it comes up 4, 5, or 6, call it a girl.*
2. *A trial is to roll the die three times and count the number of times a 1, 2, or 3 occurs.*
3. *Repeat the trial 100 times. Calculate the percent of trials in which exactly one of the three throws shows a 1, 2, or 3.*

Activity

Run one of these simulations to estimate the probability of having exactly one boy in a family with three children.
Answers may vary. $P(\text{exactly one boy}) = \frac{3}{8}$

Using Random Numbers for Simulation

A set of numbers is **random** if each number has the same probability of occurring, each pair of numbers has the same probability of occurring, each triple of numbers has the same probability of occurring, and so on. A fair die is a device for generating random numbers from $\{1, 2, 3, 4, 5, 6\}$, and for this reason dice are used for playing games in which you want everyone to have the same chance. However, cards, coins, and dice are often not efficient for running a simulation. Using random numbers takes less time and energy.

The Table of Random Numbers in Appendix C is such a set of numbers. It was constructed so that each digit from 0 to 9 has the same probability of being selected, each pair of digits from 00 to 99 has the same probability of being selected, each triple of digits from 000 to 999 has the same probability of being selected, and so on.

To use a Table of Random Numbers, you must start randomly as well. One way to do this is to close your eyes, point to a pair of digits on the page, and use that pair as the row. Then close your eyes again, point to a pair of digits on the page, and use that pair as the column. For instance, if you

Optional Activities

Have students design a simulation for winning the lottery in **Question 13** of Lesson 7-6. [The probability of winning is $\frac{1}{125}$ or 0.008. One way to run the simulation is to look at three digits in the Table of Random Numbers. If the digit is 001, 002, 003, ... , 008, then winning occurs. If the digit is 009, 010, ... , 998, 999 or 000, then winning does not occur.] To extend this idea, you could ask students to design a simulation for winning *some* money in the lottery. That probability is $\frac{3}{125}$ or 0.024. [Use the same strategy as above but the numbers from 001 to 024 indicate winning some money; 025 to 999 or 000 indicate winning no money (and in fact losing money, if money was spent on a ticket!)]

point to 03 and then to 12, start at the 3rd row, 12th column. Then choose to go up, down, right, or left—perhaps by rolling a die. If you point to a pair of digits which does not refer to a row or column, point again.

Example 2

A researcher is studying the number of boys and girls in families with three children. Assume that the birth of a boy or a girl is equally likely. Use the Table of Random Numbers to estimate the probability that a family of three children has exactly one boy.

Solution

1. To simulate the sex of a child, read a single digit in the table. **Let an even number represent the birth of a boy and an odd number represent the birth of a girl.**
2. The table starting at row 3 is shown below. A trial is to read three consecutive digits and to count the number of even numbers. For instance, if you started at row 3, column 12 and read to the right, the digits 196 would represent the first trial, a family with two girls and one boy.

Begin

24130	48360	22527	97265	76393	64809	15179	24830	49340	32081	30680	19655	63348	58629
42167	93093	06423	61680	17856	16376	39440	53537	71341	57004	00849	74917	97758	16379
37570	39975	81837	16656	06121	91782	60468	81305	49684	60672	14110	06927	01263	54613
77921	06907	11008	42751	27756	53498	18602	70659	90655	15053	21916	81825	44394	42880
99562	72905	56420	69994	98872	31016	71194	18738	44013	48840	63213	21069	10634	12952
96301	91977	05463	07972	18876	20922	94595	56869	69014	60045	18425	84903	42508	32307

End

3. Repeat the trial 100 times, and record your results. Some of the trials are shown below.

Trial	Digit Simulating Births	Number of Boys (evens)	Exactly 1 Boy
1	196	1	Yes
2	556	1	Yes
3	334	1	Yes
4	858	2	No
5	629	2	No
6	421	2	No
7	679	1	Yes
⋮	⋮	⋮	⋮
17	405	2	No
18	353	0	No
⋮	⋮	⋮	⋮
99	296	2	No
100	301	1	Yes

There are 47 trials with exactly 1 boy. So, the relative frequency is $\frac{47}{100}$ = .47.

Lesson 7-7 *Designing Simulations* **467**

Adapting to Individual Needs
Extra Help
Some students have difficulty accurately reading a table of random digits. You might want to point out that in a situation like **Example 2**, where three consecutive digits are read at a time, students could use just the first three digits in each group of five and skip over the remaining two.

Additional Examples

1. Four darts are thrown randomly at a coordinate plane and the quadrants in which they land are recorded. (If a dart lands on an axis, it is thrown again.) It is desired to simulate the probability that all four darts land in at most two of the quadrants. (For instance, if 1 dart lands in quadrant 1 and 3 darts land in quadrant 4, then there is a success.) Design a simulation with 50 trials to estimate this probability. **Sample: Toss two dice: If the sum of the numbers showing is 2, 3, 6, or 12, call it quadrant 1; if the sum is 4 or 7, call it quadrant 2; if the sum is 5 or 8, call it quadrant 3; if the sum is 9, 10, or 11, call it quadrant 4. Call four tosses of the two dice a trial, and run 50 trials.**

2. Explain how to use a table of random numbers to simulate the trials in Additional Example 1. **Sample: Look at two digits at a time. If the digits are 00 to 24, quadrant 1; if 25 to 49, quadrant 2; if 50 to 74, quadrant 3; if 75 to 99, quadrant 4.**

(Additional Examples continue on page 468.)

LESSON MASTER 7-7

Questions on SPUR Objectives
See pages 482–485 for objectives.

Vocabulary

1. What is a Monte Carlo method? **Sample: a method of using repeated random trials of an experiment to find relative frequencies and estimate probabilities.**

Uses Objective J

2. Suppose a basketball player makes free-throw shots $\frac{5}{6}$ of the time.
   a. Design a simulation using a fair 6-sided die which will estimate the probability that the basketball player will make at least 2 free throws in 3 attempts. Be sure to define a trial. **Sample: Let rolling a 1–5 be a free throw made and rolling a 6 a free throw missed. A trial is 3 rolls of the die. Calculate the % of trials in which 2 or 3 of the 3 rolls result in 1, 2, 3, 4, or 5.**
   b. Use 25 trials to calculate the estimated probability of making at least 2 of 3 free throws. **Answers will vary.**
   c. The actual probability of making at least 2 free throws in 3 attempts is about 0.93. How could you increase the accuracy of your estimation? **Sample: Increase the number of trials**

3. A conservationist is attempting to repopulate a lake with trout. Each fish released has a 0.4 chance of surviving. Five fish are released at a time.
   a. Use the Table of Random Numbers in the Appendix of your textbook to design a simulation to estimate the probability that all 5 fish in a release will survive. Be sure to define a trial. **Sample: Let 0, 1, 2, 3 represent fish living and 4, 5, 6, 7, 8, 9 represent fish dying. Choose a random spot in the table and move in some direction. A trial is to read five consecutive digits. Calculate the percent of trials in which all five digits are numbers from 0 to 3.**
   b. Use 50 trials to estimate the probability that all 5 fish in a release will survive. (The actual probability is close to 0.01.) **Answers will vary.**

Run one of the simulations for Additional Example 1 or 2. We ran two simulations beginning with row 10, column 10, fourth and fifth digits (83), so we need 8 digits for each trial. In our first simulation, 18 of the 50 trials had all darts landing in two of the quadrants, for an estimated probability of .36. In our second simulation, 16 of the 50 trials were successes, for an estimated probability of .32. **The theoretical probability is $\frac{3}{8}$.**

Notes on Questions

Questions 6–7 Error Alert Ask for a variety of answers. Check that students do not think there is only one way to use the Table of Random Numbers.

Question 8 The key point is that when events are independent and have certain probabilities, one does not always get the same results. In considering a large number of patients, 70% of the patients will recover, but a random sample of the patients can vary quite a bit around that 70%. In Lesson 10-7 students will see that, when the sample size is large enough, the variation in percentage lies in a normal distribution centered around 70%.

Question 9 Again stress the variability, as in **Question 8**.

Question 10 This explanation, even when done carefully, will still not be clear to all students. It is a very tricky problem; as we point out in the notes to the In-class Activity on page 464, even some mathematicians were confused by it.

As you know from Example 4 in Lesson 7-1, the probability in the situation of Examples 1 and 2 is $\frac{3}{8}$ =.375. We would usually want a closer estimate than .47, and probably should have done a larger simulation, but with 100 trials, even being off by 10% is not a rare event. For this reason, simulations like the ones above typically involve thousands of trials and require programming a calculator or computer. These ideas are discussed in the next lesson.

Entire probability distributions can be estimated by considering the relative frequencies of all possible events in a simulation. For instance, in the simulation of Example 2, it happens that 10 trials yield 0 boys, 47 trials yield 1 boy (as we stated earlier), 30 trials yield 2 boys, and 13 trials yield 3 boys. We compare the relative frequencies of these events with their probabilities when boys and girls are equally likely.

Number of Boys	0	1	2	3
Relative Frequency from Simulation	.10	.47	.30	.13
Probability	$\frac{1}{8}$ = .125	$\frac{3}{8}$ = .375	$\frac{3}{8}$ = .375	$\frac{1}{8}$ = .125

A Table of Random Numbers can be used to simulate any event with a known probability.

Example 3

Explain how to use a Table of Random Numbers for an event that has the given probability.

a. 0.2   **b.** 0.25

Solution

a. We want to assign 0.2 of the possible digits to the event. Choose two of the digits from 0 to 9 to represent the event occurring, and the other eight to represent the event not occurring. One way to do this is to examine single digits in the table of random numbers. If the digit is:

    0 or 1   *the event occurs;*
    2, 3, 4, 5, 6, 7, 8, or 9   *the event does not occur.*

b. Because the probability involves hundredths, use the 100 pairs of digits from 00 to 99. One way to do the simulation is to examine pairs of digits in the table of random numbers. If the pair is:

    00, 01, 02, …, 23, or 24   *the event occurs;*
    25, 26, 27, …, 98, or 99   *the event does not occur.*

QUESTIONS

Covering the Reading

1) an experimental model of a real situation that attempts to capture all aspects which affect the outcomes

1. Define *simulation*. See left.

2. What are the results that you obtained in the Activity? See page 466.

Adapting to Individual Needs

English Language Development
A popular meaning of random is "haphazard," but this is not the mathematical meaning of the term. Point out to students that a random phenomenon must have some aspect of equal probabilities with it.

3. Explain how to use a regular tetrahedral die to run a Monte Carlo simulation of the situation of Example 1. **Sample: If the die comes up 1 or 2, call it a girl. Otherwise, call it a boy.**

4. When using the Table of Random Numbers, how should the user decide where to start? **Specific answers may vary, but one must start randomly.**

5a) {(GBG), (GBB), (BBG), (BGB), (BBG), (GBG), (BGB), (GGB), (GGB)}

5. a. Give the results for trials 8–16 of Example 2. **See left.**
  b. Graph the relative frequencies from trials 1–25 to estimate the probability distribution for this example. **See margin.**

In 6 and 7, explain how to define a trial using the Table of Random Numbers for an event that has the given probability.

6. 0.6 **Choose six digits from 0 to 9 to represent the event occurring and the other four to represent the event not occurring.**

7. 0.57 **See left.**

7) Choose 57 two-digit numbers from 00 to 99 to represent the event occurring, and the other 43 to represent the event not occurring.

Applying the Mathematics

8. Suppose a person with a certain medical condition has probability 0.7 of recovering fully, if the person undergoes surgery. Also suppose that 100 surgeries for this condition are performed.
  a. Design a simulation for this situation. **See left.**
  b. Run the simulation to estimate the number of patients who underwent surgery and recovered fully. **Answers will vary.**

8a) Sample: Use random digits and a choice of 7 digits from 0 to 9 to represent full recovery, and the other three to represent not full recovery. Continue this for 100 sets of ten digits, and record the results.

9. A softball player has a batting average of .300. This means

$$\frac{\text{number of hits}}{\text{number of official at-bats}} = .300.$$

  a. Design a simulation to illustrate the next ten at-bats of this player without using the Table of Random Numbers. Run this simulation.
  b. Design a simulation for the next ten at-bats using the Table of Random Numbers. Run this simulation.
  c. Run 100 trials of the simulation for ten at-bats using either method.
  a–c) Designs will vary, but results should approximate .300.

10. Without using a simulation, explain why, in the Monty Hall problem, the probability of the contestant winning is $\frac{2}{3}$ if he or she switches doors.
  (Hint: Remember that the host always knows what is behind the first door chosen and then shows a different door with a goat behind it.)
  See margin.

Review

11. The distribution of family sizes in a small village is given in the table below. **See margin.**

S = family size	2	3	4	5	6	7	8
$R(S)$ = relative frequency	$\frac{2}{87}$	$\frac{9}{87}$	$\frac{19}{87}$	$\frac{31}{87}$	$\frac{15}{87}$	$\frac{8}{87}$	$\frac{3}{87}$

Village of Foroglio in Switzerland

  a. Graph this distribution.
  b. How can this be considered as a probability distribution?
  c. What is the average size of a family in this village? *(Lesson 7-6)*

Additional Answers
5. b.

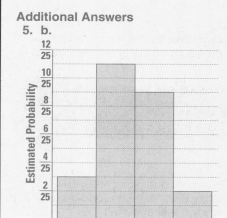

10. Let $P(1)$ = probability that the car is behind door number 1, $P(2)$ = probability that it is behind door 2, and $P(3)$ = probability that it is behind door 3. Notice that $P(1) = P(2) = P(3)$, that $P(1) + P(2) + P(3) = 1$, and therefore $P(1) = P(2) = P(3) = \frac{1}{3}$. However, when the contestant switches, the probability of winning must be $P(\text{not } 2) = \frac{2}{3}$ since no other options are available. This result is explained by taking a close look at the cases when the car is behind door 1 and when it is behind door 3. In each of these equally likely cases Monty will steer the contestant to the car by revealing the goat behind the other of the two doors. (From In-class Activity before 7-7)

11. a.

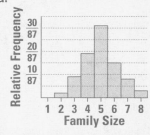

  b. The relative frequencies can be considered as the probability of randomly choosing a family of the given size from all the families in the village.
  c. $\frac{432}{87} \approx 4.97$

469

Question 18 Students should use **part b** as an aid in answering **part c**.

Practice
For more questions on SPUR Objectives, use **Lesson Master 7-7** (shown on page 467).

Assessment
Written Assessment Have students write a paragraph explaining how the Table of Random Digits can be used to simulate an event. [Students explain how random digits can be used to run simulations.]

Extension
Students can **work in groups** and invent a simulation like that in **Example 1**. Then they should carry out their simulation with technology or using a random number table and write up the results they get.

Project Update Project 5, *Probabilistic Analysis of Functions*, on page 479, relates to the content of this lesson.

12c) Sample: When one engine shuts down, the other is put under greater strain and may be more likely to shut down.

17b) $\dfrac{576}{27,907,200} \approx 2.1 \cdot 10^{-5}$

18c) $x = \dfrac{7\pi}{6} + 2k\pi$ or $x = -\dfrac{\pi}{6} + 2k\pi$ (k is an integer)

12. On January 8, 1989, a two-engine plane crashed in England after both engines shut down. Reporters quoted experts as saying that the probability of both engines failing was 10^{-6}. Assume the engines' performances are independent. *(Lesson 7-5)*
   a. What is the probability of one engine failing? **0.001**
   b. Are the engines on this plane more or less reliable than the ones described in Lesson 7-5? **less reliable**
   c. Give a reason why the engine failures may *not* have been independent events. **See left.**

In 13–15, identify the events as independent, mutually exclusive, complementary, or none of these. *(Lessons 7-1, 7-2, 7-5)*

13. One student is chosen from a class, then another student is chosen. **none of these (assumes first student is not replaced)**
14. Fumbling in the dark, a person tries one key from his key ring, drops the ring, then tries a key again. **independent**
15. Kevin is early for class; Kevin is late for class. **mutually exclusive (assumes another possibility: Kevin arrives exactly on time.)**
16. Consider eight athletes in a 100 m dash heat as shown at left. *(Lessons 7-3, 7-4)*
   a. In how many ways can the runners finish the race? **8! = 40,320**
   b. If three of the athletes are neck and neck at the finish line, in how many ways might the eight finish? **3! · 5! = 720**
17. A kindergarten teacher has 20 felt-tip pens, which are evenly divided among the colors yellow, green, red, blue, and purple. Find the probability that the first six pens chosen by the children have the following characteristics. *(Lessons 7-1, 7-3)*
   a. Each pen has a color different from the others. **0**
   b. Three pens are red and the other three are blue. **See left.**
18. *Skill sequence.* Solve for x. *(Previous course, Lesson 5-7)*
   a. $2x - 5 = 3$ b. $2x^2 - 5x = 3$ c. $2\sin^2 x - 5\sin x = 3$
      $x = 4$ $x = 3, -1/2$ **See left.**
19. a. Evaluate $\lfloor 3x \rfloor$ for $x = 0, 0.25, 0.5,$ and 0.75. **0, 0, 1, 2**
   b. For what values of x is $1 \le \lfloor 3x \rfloor < 2$? *(Lesson 2-7)*
      $\dfrac{1}{3} \le x < \dfrac{2}{3}$

Exploration

20. Find three different tables of random numbers.
   a. Select three samples of 100 consecutive digits (horizontally, vertically, or diagonally) in each table. Calculate the relative frequency of the digits 0 through 9 in each sample.
   b. Discuss the differences and similarities between the frequencies you calculated in part **a**.
   a, b) Answers will vary.

Setting Up Lesson 7-8
Any of the simulations that are done with random numbers will be tedious. Let students know that in Lesson 7-8 they will see how to run simulations using computer programs or calculator random number generators.

As you saw in the last lesson, running a simulation can be very tedious, even if you use a table of random numbers. Fortunately, technology makes it easier and more efficient to obtain random numbers.

There is no known way to generate a set of random numbers. Computers and graphics calculators can generate numbers that are close to random. For this reason, the numbers generated are called *pseudo-random*. ("Pseudo" means "false" or "pretended".) However, we will use the convention of talking about random numbers even though we know they are pseudo-random.

Generating Random Numbers with Technology

In BASIC, pseudo-random numbers with decimal values between 0 and 1 can be obtained using the RND function. In some versions of BASIC, this function always has an argument, usually 1. In other versions the argument may be optional. The computer program below will print ten random numbers, with a different set printed each time it is run.

```
10 FOR I = 1 TO 10
20 PRINT RND(1)
30 NEXT I
40 END
```

In some versions of BASIC it is necessary to *seed* the random number generator first, in order to avoid getting the same numbers every time RND is used. In this case, add the line

```
5 RANDOMIZE
```

to the program above and provide a seed value when the computer asks

```
RANDOM NUMBER SEED (-32768 TO 32767)?
```

We assume that a seed is either not needed or has already been given for the programs in the rest of this lesson.

Many calculators can generate random numbers. The function on your calculator might be called **rand**, **RANDOM**, or something similar. As in BASIC, the range of this function is $0 \le y < 1$. In this text, **rand** will be used to denote this function.

Objectives

K Design and conduct simulations using technology.

Resources

From the *Teacher's Resource File*
- Lesson Master 7-8
- Answer Master 7-8
- Teaching Aids
  64 Warm-up
  70 Airplane Reservation
     Simulations
- Technology Sourcebook
  Computer Master 8

Additional Resources
- Visuals for Teaching Aids 64, 70
- Exploration 7-8

Teaching 7-8
Lesson

Warm-up

Cooperative Learning Have students **work in groups.** Each group will need a calculator with a random number generator.
1. Generate 5 simulations like the one in **Example 2** on page 474.
2. For each simulation, determine the number of reservations needed.
3. Put all of your results together to give relative frequencies for each number of reservations needed.
4. How many reservations do you think the airline should accept?
   Answers will vary.

Lesson 7-8 Overview

Broad Goals This lesson is designed to show the power of simulation.

Perspective Three different types of simulations are described. In a medical situation, students see the variability of results without having to look at actual data. In an airplane reservation situation and the finding of the area under a parabola, simulation substitutes for an exact answer whose derivation requires college level mathematics.

Notes on Reading

This is an appropriate lesson to begin with an open discussion (assuming students have done the reading and questions first). Ask students to summarize the major points. Go over questions that relate to the points of their summary as they mention them. Split the discussion into three parts; how to generate random numbers, the airline and similar problems, and area problems.

Note that **Teaching Aid 70** provides the two airplane reservation simulations relating to **Example 2.**

Students may be bothered by the fact that airlines accept more reservations than seats, but point out that the alternative is to tell prospective travelers that the plane is full when the likelihood is that there will be a small number of seats available. For instance, if the company were only to accept 200 reservations on a jet seating 200 passengers, and if 95% of the people showed up, there would be 10 empty seats. It is worth the risk of not satisfying a passenger with a reservation to have the opportunity to satisfy 10 more customers. Besides, if a person will be "bumped" because of overbooking (that is, not able to fly on a flight for which the person has a reservation) but must fly on the flight, then the airline offers to pay other people to get off the flight. Usually the airline will provide a free ticket or a significant discount on a future flight.

It may be necessary to seed your calculator. Find out how to do that. In the rest of this lesson we shall assume that your calculator does not need a seed or has been seeded.

Simulating a Probability

Once you have learned how to generate random integers with your technology, you can perform simulations, as the following example shows.

Example 1

A new operation to restore eyesight is thought to be successful 85% of the time when performed well on appropriate patients. Explain how to use technology to generate data to simulate the results of 60 operations.

Solution

Use the three steps of the Monte Carlo method.
1. **Use a graphics calculator as the tool.** **rand** will generate random numbers y such that $0 \leq y < 1$. **round** can be used to round to the nearest hundredth. On some calculators the key sequence **round (rand**, 2), will randomly generate a number in the set {.00, .01, .02, .03, …, .98, .99}.
2. A trial can be run by pressing [ENTER]. If the trial gives .00 to .84, call it a success. If the trial gives .85 to .99, call it a failure.
3. Repeat for 60 trials.

Check

Here are the data from a simulation on one calculator.

.96	.31	.28	.08	.73	.02	.67	.05	.75	.81
.77	.4	.21	.96	.91	.01	.02	.79	.96	.04
.28	.22	.48	.7	.58	.35	.84	.65	.96	.97
.88	.9	.7	.47	0	.09	.78	.24	.09	.19
.72	.64	.58	.15	.16	.89	.9	.71	.05	.54
.76	.66	.68	.64	.29	.48	.52	.75	.85	.18

49 of the results are from 0 to .84, and $\frac{49}{60} \approx 82\%$. The simulation seems to be generating a random sample.

Generating Random Integers

The range of the **rand** function is $0 \leq y < 1$. This is a convenient range if the function is used to simulate an event with a certain probability, as in Example 1. If you need a different range, you can use the floor function and transformations to generate random numbers within an appropriate range.

Suppose, for instance, you want to select numbers randomly from the set {1, 2, 3}. The value of **rand** will lie in each of the equal-sized intervals $0 \leq y < \frac{1}{3}$, $\frac{1}{3} \leq y < \frac{2}{3}$, and $\frac{2}{3} \leq y < 1$ about one-third of the time. So 3 * **rand** will lie in each of the intervals $0 \leq y < 1$, $1 \leq y < 2$, and $2 \leq y < 3$ about one-third of the time. Now apply the floor function.

Optional Activities

Activity 1 Technology Connection
Materials: Explorations software

You may use *Exploration 7-8, Use Probability to Find Area Under a Curve*, as an alternative discussion of simulations for purely mathematical problems. The computer generates random points in a unit square on the coordinate grid, determines whether these points lie beneath the curve, and calculates the ratio of "yes" points to the total.

Activity 2
Have students write a BASIC program to simulate 100 trials of a car approaching a red light when the probability that the light is red is .40.

```
[10   FOR I = 1 TO 100
 20   LET X = ND(1)
 30   IF X < 0.40 THEN PRINT "RED"
      ELSE PRINT "GREEN"
 40   NEXT I
 50   END]
```

Activity 3 Technology Connection
In *Technology Sourcebook, Computer Master 8*, students use BASIC programs to generate pseudo-random numbers and simulate dice-tossing experiments.

INT (3 * **rand**) will generate each of the integers 0, 1, and 2 about one-third of the time. Finally, **INT** (3 * **rand**) + 1 will generate the correct integers 1, 2, and 3 with the appropriate frequencies. The following table summarizes this reasoning.

Function	Range	Graph
rand	$\{y: 0 \leq y < 1\}$	
3 * rand	$\{y: 0 \leq y < 3\}$	
INT(3 * rand)	$\{0, 1, 2\}$	
INT(3 * rand) + 1	$\{1, 2, 3\}$	

The procedure can be generalized to any set of the form $\{1, 2, \ldots, n\}$.

Using Random Integers for Simulations

It is a common practice for airline companies to accept more reservations than there are available seats, to compensate for the fact that many people do not show up for their scheduled flights. If the airline accepts too many reservations, it is likely that some passengers will not be able to travel, despite having reserved seats. If they accept too few reservations, many flights will depart with empty seats. Neither situation is desirable from the company's viewpoint.

Suppose that an airline has a small commuter aircraft with a 24-seat capacity. How many reservations should it accept for each flight?

The company could solve this problem by experimenting with accepting different numbers of reservations. However, they may find this too expensive if too many planes depart with empty seats. If too many planes are overbooked, the company may lose many future customers. So, a simulation is a good idea here.

Suppose, based on past records, that the probability of arrival for each passenger is 0.9 and further that each passenger acts without regard to what other passengers do. That is, assume the events are independent.

A means of simulating a probability of .9 is needed. One way to do this is to generate random integers from 0 to 9. This can be done by using a BASIC program or **INT**(10 * **rand**) on a calculator. We generated 24 random numbers, and let '0' represent a no-show. (A no-show could be coded with any digit since each has a 0.1 probability of appearing, the same as that of a passenger failing to show up for a flight.) We ran the experiment 6 times.

Trial 1:	71194	18738	44013	48840	6321
Trial 2:	94595	56869	69014	60045	1842
Trial 3:	57740	84378	25331	12566	5867
Trial 4:	38867	62300	08158	17983	1643
Trial 5:	56865	05859	90106	31595	7154
Trial 6:	18663	72695	52180	20847	1223

Lesson 7-8 *Simulations with Technology* **473**

Hotels use the same idea in booking more rooms than they have. This seems to cause problems at conventions of mathematics teachers; mathematics teachers seem to carry through on their reservations at a much higher rate than the general public!

On the flights themselves, airlines use Monte Carlo methods to determine how many meals of particular kinds to have. For instance, if the entrées are chicken and beef, they estimate the percent that might choose chicken and try to have enough more to take the random variability into account.

The use of Monte Carlo methods to estimate area is perhaps conceptually easier to understand than its use to simulate airplane reservations, even though in this situation, probability is calculated from a sample space with an infinite number of points. If calculus were not available, this might be the most common way to calculate area.

Adapting to Individual Needs
Extra Help
If students have difficulty understanding the discussion about finding the area under a curve, you might want to provide a large graph of $y = x^2$ for $0 < x < 1$. Then for each point given in the table on page 475, have students calculate x^2 and decide if $y < x^2$ is true or false. Explain that true or false is recorded in the table by using 1 or 0. Verify the result by plotting the point on the graph.

Additional Examples

1. A particular state lottery has a game in which a winner receives $10 for a $1 entry, but only 3 in 50 entries win. Explain how to use technology to simulate the results of 100 bets. **Generate random two-digit decimals between 0 and 1. On some calculators, the key sequence** `round` (`rand`, 2) **will pick a random number. Run this 100 times. If the decimal is from .00 to .05, call it a success. If the decimal is from .06 to .99, call it a failure. At the end, multiply the number of successes by $10 and then subtract this number from $100.**

2. Some Boeing 747 airplanes have a capacity of 420 passengers. If past performance shows that on the average 90% of individuals with reserved seats show up, work with classmates to run a simulation to estimate how many seats the airline could sell and be reasonably certain of not overbooking. **Answers will vary. The airline could sell 450 seats and be quite safe.**

The results, if only 24 reservations are accepted, are shown at the right. This suggests that the airline might reasonably accept 25 reservations and seldom be overbooked. But how often is seldom? The following shows a way to find out.

trial	arrived	not arrived (no-shows)
1	22	2
2	21	3
3	23	1
4	21	3
5	21	3
6	22	2

Example 2

Run 10 simulations to estimate how many reservations are needed to fill the plane.

Solution

Use the same plan as just described, except now generate random integers until all 24 seats are full. Our results are shown below.

Trial	Simulated (0 means no-show)						Needed
1	24130	48360	22527	97265	76393	6	26
2	42167	93093	06243	61680	37856	16	27
3	37570	39975	81837	16656	06121	9	26
4	77921	06907	11008	42751	27756	534	28
5	09429	93969	52636	92737	88974		25
6	10365	61129	87529	85689	48237		25
7	07119	97336	71048	08178	77233	13	27
8	51085	12765	51821	51259	77452		25
9	82368	21382	52474	60268	89368		25
10	01001	54092	33362	94904	31273	04147	30

Accepting less than 25 reservations will leave empty seats. Accepting 26 reservations may lead to overbooking in some cases but will fill the plane most of the time.

By using a computer, thousands of trials can be run and the probability of people with no seat estimated rather closely. The company then has the information it needs to decide how many reservations to accept.

This same idea is used by hotels in deciding how many reservations they can accept.

Simulation Used for Purely Mathematical Problems

A problem of great importance in mathematics is that of finding the area enclosed by curves on the coordinate plane. The great mathematician Archimedes (287–212 B.C.) was the first to solve the problem of finding the area of the region under the parabola $y = x^2$ between $x = 0$ and $x = 1$, shown shaded in the graph at the right.

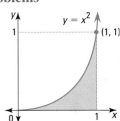

Adapting to Individual Needs

Challenge

Some calculators will generate a random matrix of any specified size. For instance, the `randM(` function on the TI-82 will give a matrix with random integer entries from -9 to 9. After the `randM(` function, type in `M` `,` `N` `)` `ENTER`, where *M* and *N* are the dimensions of the matrix and can be any integers from 1 to 99. Have students answer the following.

1. Use a random 99 × 3 matrix to estimate the probability that a family of 3 has exactly 1 boy. Explain how to interpret the numbers within the matrix. [Sample: use the `abs` key before the `randM(` function. Let each row in the matrix stand for a family of 3 children where the even numbers represent a girl and the odd numbers represent a boy.]

2. Compare your answer above with **Example 2** in Lesson 7–7 and **Question 15** in Lesson 7–8. [Answers will vary.]

At first, this may not look like a problem which can be approached by a simulation. However, it can be done! The idea is that if a point is randomly selected in the unit-square region bounded by $(0, 0)$, $(0, 1)$, $(1, 1)$, and $(1, 0)$, then the probability it lies in the shaded area is the ratio of the shaded area to the area of the square:

$$P(\text{point is in the shaded area}) = \frac{\text{shaded area}}{\text{area of square}}.$$

Notice that in the shaded area, $y < x^2$. Using this fact, it is possible to use a spreadsheet or a graphics calculator with a spreadsheet feature to conduct a Monte Carlo simulation. Randomly select a large number n of points at random in the unit-square region and test whether $y < x^2$. If c of the points lie in the shaded area, then a good estimate of $P(\text{point is in the shaded area})$ is $\frac{c}{n}$. Because the area of the square is known to be 1, the shaded area under the parabola is easily estimated.

One way to do this is to use the **rand** function to assign 100 random numbers to column L1 and 100 random numbers to column L2. The numbers in column L1 are the x-values and those in column L2 are the y-values of 100 random points in the unit-square region. Have the spreadsheet or the calculator test when the numbers in column L2 are smaller than the squares of the numbers in column L1. When this is so, let 1 be the result. When this is not so, let the result be 0. Store these answers in column L3. The sum of the numbers in column L3 is the number c of points in the shaded area. Below are the first seven points of our output for one trial.

L1	L2	L3
.81957	.61630	1
.77186	.87352	0
.42401	.62674	0
.53215	.70656	0
.91212	.35701	1
.96849	.54378	1
.04107	.07178	0

The table shows that 3 of the first 7 randomly chosen points were in the shaded region.

We ran this simulation 100 times (thus randomly choosing $100 \cdot 100 = 10,000$ points in the unit square). The number of times our point was in the shaded region was 3282. Thus, an estimate for the area is $\frac{3282}{10000} = .3282$.

Using calculus, it can be shown that the area under the parabola between $x = 0$ and $x = 1$ is exactly $\frac{1}{3}$. Thus our simulation is accurate to within about .005. In any simulation, you need to conduct a large number of trials to obtain accurate results.

Notes on Questions

Question 8 Error Alert Students may incorrectly think that using a 4 should make no difference in the decision regarding the number of reservations to accept. It will probably make a slight difference in the results that lead to the decision.

Questions 10–11 The answers are so different because only a few points have been selected.

Question 23 Since the integral of $f(x) = x^n$ is $g(x) = \frac{x^{n+1}}{n+1}$, the area under the curve from $x = 0$ to $x = 1$ is $\frac{1}{n+1}$. If the simulation is run thousands of times, the pattern might be seen.

Covering the Reading

1) Pseudo-random numbers are the nearly random numbers generated by computers and calculators.

3) If the trial gives 0.00 to 0.89, call it a success. If the trial gives 0.90 to 0.99, call it a failure.

14) Answers will vary, but in each adaptation the random coordinates should be generated within the intervals $0 \le x < 2$ and $0 \le y < 4$, and the area should be approximated by multiplying the proportion of points under the curve by 8, the area of the sample space. The actual area is $\frac{8}{3}$.

1. Explain the meaning of *pseudo-random numbers*. **See left.**

2. What function on your calculator yields random numbers between 0 and 1? **Answers will vary. The key or command may be abbreviated "RAND."**

3. Suppose in Example 1 the probability of success was .9. Modify the procedure to run the simulation. **See left.**

In 4–7, give the range of possible values of the calculator key sequence.

4. 12 * **rand** {x: $0 \le x < 12$}

5. **INT** (2 * **rand**) 0, 1

6. **INT** (**rand**) + 1 1

7. **INT** (2 * **rand**) + 1 1, 2

8. Refer to the six trials of the airline reservations problem before Example 2. Suppose that 4 is used instead of a 0 to represent a no-show. What difference does this make in the results? **It does not change the resulting number of reservations to be accepted.**

9. Refer to Example 2. Run the simulation for five more trials. Comment on any differences in the results. **Answers will vary, but should support the trend in nearly all cases.**

In 10–13, suppose that a simulation is run to find the area under the parabola $y = x^2$ between $x = 0$ and $x = 1$. What is the approximation produced if the following points are chosen?

10. (0.3, 0.8), (0.6, 0.2), (0.4, 0.1), (0.9, 0.5) $\frac{3}{4} = 0.75$

11. (0.16, 0.74), (0.77, 0.68), (0.88, 0.96), (0.04, 0.71), (0.85, 0.37), (0.2, 0.01) $\frac{2}{6} \approx 0.33$

12.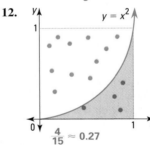
$\frac{4}{15} \approx 0.27$

13.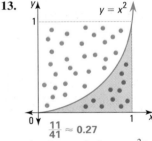
$\frac{11}{41} \approx 0.27$

14. Adapt the simulation to find the area under the parabola $y = x^2$ between $x = 0$ and $x = 2$ using 1000 points. **See left.**

15) Answers will vary.
Note that the
command "ROUND
(RAND, 3)" will
provide 3 random
digits on some
calculators.

16) Answers will
vary, but in each
simulation the
random coordinates
should be generated
within the ranges
$0 \leq x \leq \pi$ and
$0 \leq y \leq 1$, and
the area should
be approximated
by multiplying the
proportion of points
under the curve by
π, the area of the
sample space. The
actual area is 2.

18a) Designs may vary,
but all should
choose a starting
point on the table
and designate digits
to be discarded.
(Sample: Use 1
through 6 and
discard 7, 8, 9,
and 0.)

Applying the Mathematics

15. Run a simulation of Example 2 of Lesson 7-7 using technology.
See left.

16. Run a simulation to approximate the area bounded by the graphs of
$y = \sin x$, $x = 0$, $x = \pi$, and the x-axis. **See left.**

17. Suppose that a manufacturer knows that 2% of the nails he makes are
defective. Design and run a simulation to determine how many nails his
company should put in each box in order to have at least 100 good nails
in a box. **Answers will vary, but repeated valid simulations would
reveal that 102 nails would be adequate in most cases, and 103 nails in
almost all cases.**

Review

18. a. Use the Table of Random Numbers to simulate rolling two dice
100 times. **See left.**
  b. What fraction of the time did a sum of 7 occur? *(Lesson 7-7)*
  Multiple observations will reveal a frequency approaching $\frac{1}{6}$.

19. A bag contains 5 black, 4 orange, and 3 green marbles. Three marbles are
drawn in succession, each marble being replaced before the next one is
drawn. What is the probability of drawing a black, then an orange, and
then a green marble? *(Lessons 7-1, 7-5)*
$\frac{5}{144} \approx 0.035$

20. a. How many four-letter permutations can be made using the letters in
the word COMPANY? $_7P_4 = 840$
  b. List five of these permutations which have a meaning in English.
  (Lesson 7-4) **Answers will vary. Samples: CAMP, COMA, MANY,
  MOAN, PONY**

21. a. Show that $_8P_5 = 56 \cdot {_6P_3}$. $_8P_5 = 8 \cdot {_7P_4} = 8 \cdot 7 \cdot {_6P_3} = 56 \cdot {_6P_3}$
  b. Prove that $_nP_r = (n^2 - n) \cdot {_{n-2}P_{r-2}}$. *(Lesson 7-4)*
  See margin.

22. Consider the experiment of tossing a fair coin four times. *(Lessons 7-1, 7-2)*
  a. Determine the probability of at least two heads. $11/16 \approx 0.69$
  b. Determine the probability of exactly one head. $4/16 \approx 0.25$
  c. *True or false.* The two events in parts **a** and **b** are complementary
  events. Justify your answer.
  False. $P(a) + P(b) = \frac{15}{16} \neq 1$

Exploration

23. a. Use a simulation to approximate the area under the curve $y = x^n$ from
$x = 0$ to $x = 1$ for $n = 3$, 4, and 5.
  b. Make a conjecture for the area under the curve $y = x^n$ from $x = 0$ to
$x = 1$ for positive integers n.
  a, b) See margin.

Practice
For more questions on SPUR
Objectives, use **Lesson Master 7-8**
(shown on page 473).

Assessment
Written Communication Refer
students to **Example 2**. Have students use technology to complete
the example for an aircraft that has
a 20-seat capacity. Then have students discuss their results in **small
groups**. [Students conduct a simulation using technology and interpret
the results.]

Extension
An enterprising student or students
might call a local hotel to determine
how many reservations (if any) the
hotel will take over its capacity. It is
possible that such information is considered confidential and would not
be divulged. Even so, the number of
hotel rooms could be found, and students might ask what is the percentage of people with reservations who
actually use them. From that data,
students can do simulations that
could be used to advise the hotel
regarding the number of reservations
it should accept. This activity could
be a used as a project.

Project Update Project 2,
Insurance Rates, and Project 5,
Probabilistic Analysis of Functions,
on pages 478–479, relate to the
content of this lesson.

Additional Answers
21. b. $_nP_r = n \cdot {_{n-1}P_{r-1}} = n \cdot (n - 1) \cdot$
$_{n-2}P_{r-2} = (n^2 - n) \cdot {_{n-2}P_{r-2}}$
23. a. Answers will vary, but all should
approximate $\frac{1}{4}$ for $n = 3$, $\frac{1}{5}$ for $n = 4$,
and $\frac{1}{6}$ for $n = 5$.
  b. Answers will vary, but should
approximate $\frac{1}{n+1}$.

477

Chapter 7 Projects

The projects relate chiefly to the content of the lessons of this chapter as follows:

Project	Lesson(s)
1	7-1, 7-6
2	7-5, 7-6, 7-8
3	7-3, 7-4
4	7-3, 7-4
5	7-7, 7-8

1 Fair Dice? This is a classic exercise. Students who do not readily grasp the ideas of Lesson 7-1 might benefit from the opportunity to do this project early in the chapter.

2 Insurance Rates This is the most open-ended of the projects. If a student owns a car, the student could begin by exploring the variables that are considered when determining how much insurance must be paid.

3 The Birthday Problem This is an exceedingly famous problem. The calculations are messy but doable with a calculator. It generally surprises people that the smallest value of *k* is 23; that is, in a group with 23 or more people, there is a better than even chance that two people have the same birthday.

4 Seating Arrangements This is a standard counting problem, not particularly difficult. The answer is divided by 2 if reflection images are also regarded to be the same.

A project presents an opportunity for you to extend your knowledge of a topic related to the material of this chapter. You should allow more time for a project than you do for a typical homework question.

PROJECTS 7 CHAPTER SEVEN

1 Fair Dice?
Obtain a pair of dice distinguishable from each other (for instance, two dice of different sizes or colors).
a. Throw the dice fifty times, recording the results of each die on each throw.
b. Construct a relative frequency distribution for each of the two dice separately.
c. Construct a relative frequency distribution for the sum of the two dice.
d. Repeat steps **a–c** at least three more times. Calculate the total relative frequency distribution for the sum of the two dice.
e. For a larger number of tosses, describe how close the relative frequencies of occurrence of the numbers 1 to 6 on a single die and of the sums from 2 to 12 on the pair of dice are to their probabilities. Do your dice seem to be fair? Why or why not?

478

2 Insurance Rates
Statistics and probability are used in determining insurance premiums (the amounts that people pay for insurance). Pick a type of insurance (for example, automobile or life).

a. Find out all the variables that affect the premiums you would have to pay if you wanted this type of insurance and what it would cost you to obtain this type of insurance.
b. Write an essay summarizing how insurance companies use statistics and probability to determine these rates.

3 The Birthday Problem
a. Calculate the probability that *n* people have *n* different birthdates, for *n* = 2, 3, 4, and *k*.
b. What is the smallest value of *k* for which this probability is less than .5? (This is known as the **birthday problem**.)
c. Test the result of part **b** on a group of people or with a set of birthdays of famous people.

Responses, page 478
1. **a.** Answers will vary.
   b. Answers will vary. The frequency distribution should be close to uniform. Each frequency should be about $\frac{1}{6}$.
   c. Answers will vary. The frequency distribution should be close to the one discussed in the chapter for the sum of two dice. In other words, the frequency for a sum of 2 or 12 should be about $\frac{1}{36}$; the frequency for a sum of 3 or 11 should be about $\frac{2}{36}$; etc.
   d. Answers will vary.
   e. Answers will vary. For a large number of tosses, the relative frequencies should be close to the probabilities. If this is not the case, the dice might not be fair.
2. Answers will vary.

3. **a.** To simplify the problem, assume that it is equally likely for someone to have a birthday on any of the 366 possible days of the year. For *n* = 2, the probability is $\frac{365}{366}$, or about 0.997. For *n* = 3, the probability is $\frac{365 \times 364}{366^2}$, or about 0.992. Using the same method, the probability for *n* = 4 is about 0.984 . The probability for

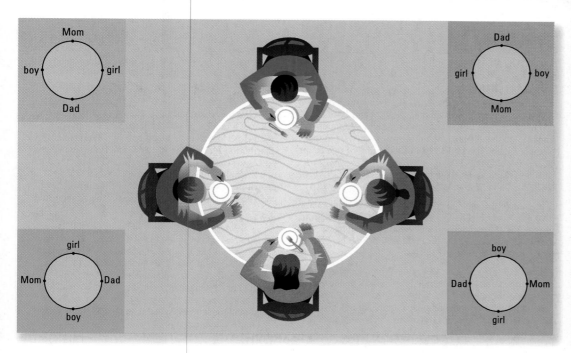

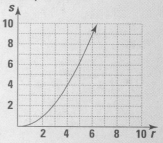

4 Seating Arrangements

a. The Grump family, consisting of two parents and two children, are about to sit down together at a circular table with four seats. In how many different ways can they do this if rotation images as shown in the corners above are regarded as the same?

b. Generalize your answer to part **a**. That is, in how many different ways can *n* people be seated at a circular table? Make drawings and write mathematical arguments to support your answer.

5 Probabilistic Analysis of Functions

Investigate the following situation. If *r* and *s* are numbers from 0 to 9, what is the probability *P* that the function $f(x) = x^2 + rx + s$ has real roots?

a. Consider the case where *r* and *s* are integers, and conduct an experiment. Randomly choose 20 pairs (r, s) of integers from 0 to 9, calculate the relative frequency of the number of functions having real roots, and estimate *P*. Repeat the experiment and revise your estimate as necessary.

b. Calculate the probability of having real roots if *r* and *s* are integers from 0 to 9. (Hint: There are 100 outcomes in the sample space.)

c. Assume *r* and *s* are real numbers from 0 to 9. Modify the method of Lesson 7-8 to estimate the probability that *f* has real roots.

d. Repeat parts **b** and **c** allowing *r* and *s* to lie in the interval from -10 to 10. Compare the probabilities you get with those found in parts **b** and **c**.

The domain for *r* and *s* can be expanded. Certainly it is reasonable to allow *r* and *s* to be negative, so you might pick numbers between -9 and 9, perhaps avoiding 0. Students might also solve the quadratics to see how often the solution is rational. They would learn that even if *r* and *s* are selected to be "nice numbers," only a small percentage of quadratics factor into polynomials with rational coefficients. This is the reason that factoring is not a widely applicable method for solving quadratics.

Additional Answers
5. **a.** Answers will vary.
   b. $f(x)$ will have real roots whenever $r^2 - 4s \geq 0$ or equivalently when $\frac{1}{4}r^2 \geq s$. Graph $s = \frac{1}{4}r^2$ and count the the lattice points between the graph and the *r*-axis. (Graph is shown below)

(0, 0), (1, 0), (2, 0), (2, 1), (3, 0), (3, 1), (3, 2), (4, 0), (4, 1), (4, 2), (4, 3), (4, 4), (5, 0), (5, 1), (5, 2), (5, 3), (5, 4), (5, 5), (5, 6), and all points for which $r = 6, 7, 8,$ or 9 and *s* is between 0 and 9 satisfy the inequality. The total number of points is 59. Since there are 100 outcomes in the sample space, the probability that $f(x)$ has real roots is 0.59 .

   c. In each simulation random coordinates should be generated within the range from 0 to 9 for both *r* and *s*. The probability is estimated by the proportion of points under the $s = \frac{1}{4}r^2$ curve.
   d. Answers will vary.

$n = k$ is $\frac{_{365}P_{k-1}}{366^{k-1}}$.

b. The smallest value for which this probability is less than .5 is $n = 23$.
c. Answers will vary.
4. **a.** 6
   b. Since rotation images are regarded as the same, we can seat a person and regard that person as the "starting point." There are now

$(n - 1)$ people that can be seated to the left of this person. After the second person is seated, there are $(n - 2)$ people remaining who can sit to the left of that person, and so on. So the number of ways that *n* people can sit around a table is $(n - 1)(n - 2)(n - 3) \cdot \ldots \cdot 1 = (n - 1)!$.

Summary

The Summary gives an overview of the entire chapter and provides an opportunity for students to consider the material as a whole. Thus, the Summary can be used to help students relate and unify the concepts presented in the chapter.

Vocabulary

Terms, symbols, and properties are listed by lesson to provide a checklist of concepts a student must know. Emphasize to students that they should read the vocabulary list carefully before starting the Progress Self-Test. If students do not understand the meaning of a term, they should refer back to the indicated lesson.

SUMMARY

Probabilities of events in finite sample spaces can be calculated using counting and an approach similar to calculating relative frequencies. If all outcomes in a sample space are equally likely, the probability of an event is the ratio of the number of individual outcomes making up the event to the number of outcomes in the sample space. The probability of the union of two events A and B satisfies $P(A \cup B) = P(A) + P(B) - P(A \cap B)$. If A and B are mutually exclusive, $P(A \cup B) = P(A) + P(B)$. If A and B are complementary, $P(B) = 1 - P(A)$.

The number of ways to choose one element from each of two sets A and B is $N(A) \cdot N(B)$. This leads to the definition that A and B are independent events (the occurrence of one does not change the probability for the other) if and only if $P(A \cap B) = P(A) \cdot P(B)$.

From the Multiplication Counting Principle, the number of arrangements of n different items is $n!$ The number of arrangements of r of n items *with* replacement is n^r. The number of arrangements of r items out of a given set of n *without* replacement (called a permutation of r

out of n things) is denoted $_nP_r$.

$$_nP_r = n(n - 1) \ldots (n - r + 1) = \frac{n!}{(n - r)!}.$$

A probability distribution is a function which maps each value of a random variable (determined by the outcome of an experiment) onto its probability. The probability distribution for an experiment with a finite number of outcomes can be represented by a table, a scatterplot, or a histogram. The mean, or the expected value, of a probability distribution is the sum of the products of each possible outcome with its respective probability;

that is, $\mu = \sum\limits_{i=1}^{n} (x_i \cdot P(x_i))$.

Randomness can be approximated manually (such as by throwing dice) or by using technology-generated pseudo-random numbers. By proper coding of experiments or events with random numbers, it is possible to simulate many real-life situations such as the number of people who will appear at an event, or estimations in mathematical situations such as the area under a curve.

VOCABULARY

Below are the most important terms and phrases for this chapter. You should be able to give a general description and a specific example of each and a precise definition for those marked with an asterisk (*).

Lesson 7-1
probability theory, experiment
outcome, *sample space
event
*probability of an event
fair, unbiased, at random, randomly
Basic Properties of Probability
    Theorem

Lesson 7-2
union of sets
*disjoint sets, mutually exclusive sets
intersection of sets, Venn diagram
Addition Counting Principle (mutually
    exclusive form; general form)
Probability of a Union Theorem (for
    mutually exclusive events; general
    form)
complementary events, not A
Probability of Complements
    Theorem

Lesson 7-3
tree diagram
Multiplication Counting Principle
arrangement
Selections with Replacement
    Theorem
*n factorial, $n!$
Selections without Replacement
    Theorem

Lesson 7-4
*permutation
Permutation Theorem
*permutations of n objects taken r at
    a time, $_nP_r$
Formula for $_nP_r$ Theorem
Alternate Formula for $_nP_r$ Theorem

Lesson 7-5
*independent events
dependent events

Lesson 7-6
random variable
probability distribution
*mean of a probability distribution
expected value of a
    probability distribution

Lesson 7-7
simulation
trial
Monte Carlo method
*random numbers

Lesson 7-8
pseudo-random numbers
rand

480

PROGRESS SELF-TEST

1a, 8a, b, 11, 13, 14, 15, 16a–c) See margin.

Take this test as you would take a test in class. Then check the test yourself using the solutions at the back of the book.

1. Assume that each of the two spinners shown below is equally likely to land in each of the three regions.

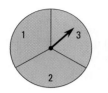

   a. Give the sample space for the result of spinning *both* spinners.

   b. What is the probability that the sum of the two spinners is greater than 4? **3/9 ≈ 0.33**

2. When two fair dice of different colors are rolled, what is the probability that the red die will show an odd number and the green die will show an even number? **1/2 · 1/2 = 0.25**

3. Suppose $P(A \cap B) = 0.5$, $P(A) = 0.6$, and $P(B) = 0.8$. Find $P(A \cup B)$. **0.9**

4. a. Determine the number of permutations of the letters in the word MASTER. **6! = 720**

   b. How many of these permutations begin with A and end with T? **4! = 24**

In 5 and 6, evaluate.

5. $\frac{9!}{3!}$ **60,480**

6. $_5P_3$ **60**

7. *True or false.*   If an event A contains all the possible outcomes of an experiment, then $P(A) = 1$. **True**

8. Consider the events of scoring under 50 and scoring from 50 to 100 on a test. Determine if the events are mutually exclusive, complementary, or both, if the maximum possible score on the test is the following.

   a. 100   **b.** 120

9. Solve $_nP_4 = 56 \,_nP_2$. **n = 10**

10. A consumer protection group reports that 25% of 5-lb bags of sugar of a certain brand are underweight. Three bags of sugar are selected at random. Assume that the report is correct.

   a. What is the probability that all three bags are underweight? $(0.25)^3 \approx 0.016$.

   b. What is the probability that none of the bags is underweight? $(0.75)^3 \approx 0.42$

11. If you have three pairs of jeans, two pairs of sneakers, and five sweatshirts, how many different outfits consisting of jeans, a sweatshirt, and sneakers can you make?

12. A test contains 10 true-false questions and 5 multiple-choice questions, each with four choices. Assuming a student answers all questions, how many different answer sheets are possible? $2^{10} \cdot 4^5 = 2^{20} = 1{,}048{,}576$

13. Susie Shoorschott makes $\frac{1}{3}$ of her three-point shots in basketball. Design a simulation which does not use random digits to estimate how many three-point shots she would make if she shot 100 times.

14. It is known that the probability of contracting a certain children's disease by coming into contact with an infected person is 0.12. Use the random number table in Appendix C to estimate the probability that if all five children in a family come in contact with their infected cousin, at least two of the children in the family will get the disease from the cousin. Conduct 25 trials.

15. Explain how to use technology to approximate the area between the graph of $y = \cos x$ and the x-axis from $x = 0$ to $x = \frac{\pi}{2}$.

16. a. Verify that the table below shows a probability distribution.

x	1	2	3	4	5
$P(x)$	.03	.47	.22	.05	.23

   b. Graph the probability function in part **a.**

   c. Calculate the mean of the distribution.

Additional Answers

1. a. Each outcome can be represented by a pair of numbers, one for each spinner. So $S = \{(1, 1), (1, 2), (1, 3), (2, 1), (2, 2), (2, 3), (3, 1), (3, 2), (3, 3)\}$

8. a. The events are mutually exclusive and complementary.

   b. The events are mutually exclusive but not complementary.

11. 30

13. Designs will vary. Sample: A die thrown 100 times counting rolls of 1 and 2 as shots made, and 3, 4, 5, and 6 as shots not made.

14. Answers will vary depending on table starting point but infections should number 2 to 4 of the 25 trials in most cases.

Progress Self-Test

For the development of mathematical competence, feedback and correction, along with the opportunity to practice, are necessary. The Progress Self-Test provides the opportunity for feedback and correction; the Chapter Review provides additional opportunities and practice. We cannot overemphasize the importance of these end-of-chapter materials. It is at this point that the material "gels" for many students, allowing them to solidify skills and understanding. In general, student performance should be markedly improved after these pages.

Assign the Progress Self-Test as a one-night assignment. Worked-out *solutions* for all questions are in the Selected Answers section of the student book. Encourage students to take the Progress Self-Test honestly, grade themselves, and then be prepared to discuss the test in class.

Advise students to pay special attention to those Chapter Review questions (pages 482–485) that correspond to questions missed on the Progress Self-Test.

15. Answers will vary, but random coordinates should be generated with the range 0 to $\frac{\pi}{2}$ for *x*, and 0 to 1 for *y*, and the area should be estimated by multiplying the resulting proportion of points below the line by $\frac{\pi}{2}$. The actual area is 1.

16. a. Each value of $P(x)$ satisfies $0 \le P(x) \le 1$ and their sum is 1.

   b.

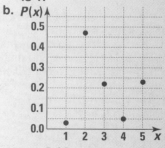

   c. $\mu = 2.98$

Chapter 7 Review

Resources

From the **Teacher's Resource File**
- Answer Master for Chapter 7 Review
- Assessment Sourcebook: Chapter 7 Test, Forms A-D Chapter 7 Test, Cumulative Form

Additional Resources
- Quiz and Test Writer

The main objectives for the chapter are organized in the Chapter Review under the four types of understanding this book promotes—Skills, Properties, Uses, and Representations.

Whereas end-of-chapter material may be considered optional in some texts, in *UCSMP Functions, Statistics, and Trigonometry* we have selected these objectives and questions with the expectation that they will be covered. Students should be able to answer these questions with about 85% accuracy after studying the chapter.

You may assign these questions over a single night to help students prepare for a test the next day, or you may assign the questions over a two-day period. If you work the questions over two days, then we recommend assigning the *evens* for homework the first night so that students get feedback in class the next day, then assigning the *odds* the night before the test, because answers are provided to the odd-numbered questions.

It is effective to ask students which questions they still do not understand and use the day or days as a total class discussion of the material which the class finds most difficult.

Additional Answers
2. {HTT, THT, TTH, TTT}
4. {i, iii, v, vii, ix, 1, 3, 5, ..., last odd page in book}

CHAPTER REVIEW

Questions on SPUR Objectives

SPUR stands for **S**kills, **P**roperties, **U**ses, and **R**epresentations. The Chapter Review questions are grouped according to the SPUR Objectives for this chapter.

SKILLS DEAL WITH THE PROCEDURES USED TO GET ANSWERS.

Objective A: *List sample spaces and events for probabilistic experiments.*   *(Lesson 7-1)*

In 1–3, consider the experiment of tossing three different coins. **1) See below.**

1. Write the sample space for the experiment.

2. List the outcomes in the event "at least two tails show up." **2, 4) See margin.**

3. *True or false.*   The event "no tails show up" consists of a single outcome. **True**

In 4–6, assume that a right-hand page of this book is picked at random and the page number if it has one is recorded.

4. What is the sample space for this experiment?

5. Write the set of outcomes in the event "the page is the first page of a chapter." ∅

6. *True or false.*   The event "the page has an even number" is the empty set. **False**
1) {HHH, HHT, HTH, HTT, THH, THT, TTH, TTT}

Objective B: *Compute probabilities.*
(Lessons 7-1, 7-2, 7-3)

In 7 and 8, consider rolling two fair dice, and recording the numbers on the top faces. Find each probability.

7. P(each die is even) $\frac{1}{4} = 0.25$

8. P(the sum is even) $\frac{1}{2} = 0.5$

9. Consider the experiment of tossing a coin and a fair die. The coin is marked "1" (heads) and "2" (tails). Find the probability that the sum is less than 5. $\frac{5}{12} \approx 0.417$

In 10 and 11, let x be a randomly selected number from {1, 2, 3, 5, 8, 13, 21, 34, 55, 89}. Calculate the probability.

10. $P(x$ is even or $x < 2^5)$ $\frac{8}{10} = 0.8$

11. $P(x$ is even and $x < 2^5)$ $\frac{2}{10} = 0.2$

12. When two fair dice are tossed, what is the probability the first is a 3 or the second is odd? $\frac{21}{36} \approx 0.583$ **15a, b) See below.**

Objective C: *Find the number of ways of selecting or arranging objects.*   *(Lessons 7-3, 7-4)*

13. A coin is tossed seven times. How many possible outcomes are there? **128**

14. List all the permutations of the digits 4, 0, and 7. **407, 470, 047, 074, 740, 704**

15. **a.** Determine the number of permutations of the letters of the word NUMBER.

    b. How many of these permutations end in BER?

16. **a.** How many permutations consisting of four letters each can be formed from the letters of DINOSAUR? **1680**

    b. How many of the permutations in part **a** end in R? **210**

    c. How many of the permutations in part **a** start with D and end in *R*? **30**

15a) 720   b) 6

Objective D: *Evaluate expressions using factorials.*   *(Lessons 7-3, 7-4)*

In 17–19, evaluate without using a calculator. 21

17. 7! **5040**   18. 0! **1**   19. $\frac{21!}{20!}$

20. Write $\frac{16!}{12!}$ as a product of integers.
                                              $16 \cdot 15 \cdot 14 \cdot 13$
21. Evaluate $\frac{120!}{116!}$. **197,149,680**

22. *True or false.* $\frac{12!}{6!6!} = \frac{12!}{8!4!}$ **False**

In 23 and 24, evaluate.

23. $_{10}P_4$ **5040**   24. $_5P_5$ **120**

PROPERTIES DEAL WITH THE PRINCIPLES BEHIND THE MATHEMATICS.

Objective E: *State and use properties of probabilities.* *(Lessons 7-1, 7-2, 7-5)*

25. If $P(A) = .23$ in an experiment, determine $P(\text{not } A)$. **0.77**

26. Explain why $P(E) = 1.5$ cannot be a correct statement for any event E. **P(E) is always from 0 to 1.**

In 27–30, *true or false*.

27. If A and B are mutually exclusive events, and $P(A) = .7$, then $P(B) = .3$. **False**

28. If A and B are complementary events and $P(A) = k$, then $P(B) = 1 - k$. **True**

29. If A and B are independent events, then $P(A \text{ or } B) = 1$. **False**

30. If the sample space of A is $\varnothing$, then $P(A) = 0$. **True**

Objective F: *Determine whether events are mutually exclusive, independent, or complementary.* *(Lessons 7-2, 7-5)*

In 31 and 32, determine if the pair of events are mutually exclusive.

31. Scoring an 80 on a test and scoring a 95 on the same test. **mutually exclusive**

32. Throwing a sum of 9 on two dice and throwing a 2 on at least one die. **mutually exclusive**

33) **False**   34) **No, a TV viewer could be a child.**

33. *True or false.* Selecting a king from a deck of cards and then picking a king from the remaining cards are two independent events.

34. In selecting a TV viewer, are "finding an adult" and "finding a teenager" complementary events? Explain your reasoning.

In 35–38, you are given information about the probabilities of events A and B. Deduce which (if any) of the terms below apply to the events.

  (a) mutually exclusive

  (b) complementary

  (c) independent

35. $P(A) = .5, P(B) = .2, P(A \cup B) = .6$ **c**

36. $P(A) = .5, P(B) = .2, P(A \cup B) = .7$ **a**

37. $P(A) = .4, P(B) = .6, P(A \cup B) = 1$ **a, b**

38. $P(A) = .33, P(B) = .3, P(A \cup B) = .099$ **none**

Objective G: *Solve equations using factorials.* *(Lesson 7-4)*

In 39–42, solve.

39. $\frac{x!}{56} = 6!$ $x = 8$

40. $\frac{t!}{(t-1)!} = 19$ $t = 19$

41. $_nP_5 = 12 \,_nP_4$ $n = 16$

42. $_5P_c = \,_6P_3$ $c = 4$ or $c = 5$

USES DEAL WITH APPLICATIONS OF MATHEMATICS IN REAL SITUATIONS.

Objective H: *Calculate probabilities in real situations.* *(Lessons 7-1, 7-2, 7-5)*

In 43 and 44, consider the following situation. An ornithologist feeds a special nutrient to 26 of the 257 pelicans in a bird sanctuary and tags them. A week later, she captures a pelican in the sanctuary. Assume the special nutrient does not affect the behavior of the birds.

43. What is the probability that the pelican is a tagged one? **26/257 ≈ 0.1012**

44. If the pelican is not tagged, what is the probability that the next one she catches will be tagged if she **b) 26/256 ≈ 0.1016**

  a. releases the first bird? **26/257 ≈ 0.1012**

  b. does not release the first bird?

Additional Answers

53. Answers may vary. Sample: Use 100 small pieces of paper numbered from 1 to 100. If a piece of paper is numbered less than 26, call it damaged; otherwise, call it undamaged. Randomly choose 16 pieces of paper from the 100, and record the number of pieces of paper numbered less than 26. Repeat that 5 times and get 5 samples. Our result shows the percentage of corn damaged in each sample as follows: .25, .375, .5625, .12, and .3125.

54. Answers may vary. Sample: Use a die. If it comes up with 1 or 2, call it correct; otherwise, call it wrong. A trial is to roll the die 15 times and count the number of times a 1 or 2 occurs. Repeat the trial 10 times and find how many trials there are with the number of times being correct not less than 7. Our result shows the estimated probability is .1. (The actual probability is .203.)

55. Answers may vary. Sample: Choose a triple of digits from 000 to 999, and if it is from 000 to 324, John gets a hit; if it is from 325 to 999, he does not get a hit. Run it 10 times and record the number of times with 4 or more hits. Repeat the above procedure a certain number of times (e.g., 10 times). Our result shows the estimated probability is .4 . (The actual probability is .418.)

56. Answers may vary. Sample: Choose a pair of digits from 00 to 99, and if it is from 00 to 02, it is defective; if it is from 03 to 99, it is good. Run it enough times until there are 50 good washers. Record the number of times. Repeat the above procedure a number of times (e.g., 10 times). Our result shows that 54 washers should be put in each box to have at least 50 good ones.

In 45 and 46, consider a business which needs computer diskettes. Of the two independent suppliers they usually use, U has a .4 probability and C has a .7 probability of filling any given order in three days. They order diskettes from both suppliers.

45. What is the probability that both U and C will fill the order in 3 days? **0.28**

46. What is the probability that the order will be filled by at least one of the suppliers in 3 days? **0.82**

Objective I: *Use counting principles and theorems to find the number of ways of arranging objects.* *(Lessons 7-3, 7-4)*

47. How many different ways can a student answer 20 multiple-choice questions, each of which has four choices? $4^{20} \approx 1.1 \times 10^{12}$

48. Susan has a choice of n math classes, five science classes and two history classes. In how many ways can she select one of each of the three kinds of classes? **10n**

49. In how many ways can the starting five on a basketball team line up in a row? **120**

50. A committee of two students is to be chosen from a school with 340 juniors and 330 seniors. In how many ways can the committee be chosen to include both a junior and a senior?

51. How many automobile license plates consisting of two letters followed by four digits are there if repetitions of letters or digits are allowed?
$26^2 \cdot 10^4 = 6{,}760{,}000$

50) 112,200

484

52. A certain car seats five people, two in front and three in back.

  a. In how many ways can a family of five be seated in the car? **120**

  b. In how many ways can a family of five be seated in the car for a trip if only two of the family members have driver's licenses? **48**

Objective J: *Design and conduct simulations without technology.* *(Lesson 7-7)*

In 53–54, design and conduct a simulation without using a random number table or technology.

53. Simulate selecting 5 samples of 16 corn stalks each from a field which is estimated to be 25% damaged because of a drought. What percentage of corn in each sample is damaged?

54. Manuel doesn't have any idea how to answer 15 questions on a multiple-choice test for which there are 3 possible choices for each question. Simulate his answering these questions by guessing, running 10 trials. What is the estimated probability that he gets 7 or more correct?

In 55–56, design and conduct a simulation using a random number table to answer each question.

55. John has a batting average of .325. What is the estimated probability of his getting 4 or more hits in his next 10 at-bats?

56. A washer manufacturer knows that 3% of the washers made are defective. How many washers should be put in each box sold to have at least 50 good washers in each box?

53–56) See margin.

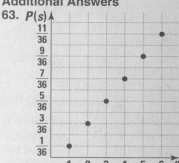
Objective K: *Design and conduct simulations using technology.*   *(Lesson 7-8)*

57. Design and conduct an experiment to simulate rolling three dice 1000 times. What is your experimental probability that the sum is greater than or equal to 15?

58. Suppose that in a lacrosse playoff series of 5 games, team *A* has a .6 probability of winning the game over team *B*. Design and conduct a simulation of 1000 such series between the two teams. About how many times does *A* win the series?

In 59–60, estimate the area between the graph of the function and the *x*-axis.

59. $f(x) = x^2 + 3$ from $x = 0$ to $x = 1$

60. $f(x) = \sin x + \cos x$ from $x = 0$ to $x = \frac{\pi}{2}$

57–60) Answers will vary but should be close to: 57) 0.06   58) 3   59) $\frac{10}{3}$ 60) 2

REPRESENTATIONS DEAL WITH PICTURES, GRAPHS, OR OBJECTS THAT ILLUSTRATE CONCEPTS.

Objective L: *Construct, graph, and interpret probability distributions.*   *(Lesson 7-6)*

61. On a fair die, the faces contained 0, 1, 2, 1, 2, and 4 dots.

  a. Find the probability of each of the outcomes 0, 1, 2, and 4. $\frac{1}{6}, \frac{1}{3}, \frac{1}{3}, \frac{1}{6}$

  b. Graph the distribution as a histogram. c) $\frac{5}{3}$

  c. Find the mean of the probability distribution.

62. Tell why this table does *not* show a probability distribution. **See below right.**

x	−1	0	1	4
$P(x)$	$\frac{1}{2}$	$\frac{1}{4}$	$\frac{1}{8}$	$\frac{1}{5}$

63. Construct a graph of the probability distribution for the function P where $P(s)$ is the probability that when two fair dice are rolled, the number s showing on one die is greater than or equal to the number showing on the other die. **See margin.**

61b)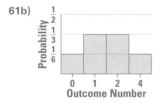

64. In a lottery, 120 tickets are sold at $1 each. First prize is $50 and second prize is $20. Find the expected value of a ticket. $\approx$ -41.7¢

x = profit in dollars	-1	19	49
$P(x)$	$\frac{118}{120}$	$\frac{1}{120}$	$\frac{1}{120}$

65. The clerk in charge of textbooks took a sample of books that were returned at the end of the year and judged whether they were reusable. Here is the distribution of books that were not reusable.

x = age of book in years	1	2	3	4	5	6
Number destroyed	3	10	10	12	20	30

On the basis of this data, what is the expected life span of a book?

$\frac{381}{85} \approx 4\frac{1}{2}$ years

62) The sum of the $P(x)$ values is $\frac{43}{40}$, which does not equal 1.

Chapter 7   *Chapter Review*   **485**

Chapter **8** Planner

Adapting to Individual Needs

The student text is written for the vast majority of students. The chart at the right suggests two pacing plans to accommodate the needs of your students. Students in the Full Course should complete the entire text by the end of the year. Students in the Minimal Course will spend more time when there are quizzes and more time on the Chapter Review. Therefore, these students may not complete all of the chapters in the text.

    Options are also presented to meet the needs of a variety of teaching and learning styles. For each lesson, the Teacher's Edition provides a section entitled *Adapting to Individual Needs*. This section regularly includes **Optional Activities, Challenge** problems, **English Language Development** suggestions, and suggestions for providing **Extra Help.** The Teacher's Edition also frequently includes an **Error Alert,** an **Extension,** and an **Assessment** alternative. The options available in Chapter 8 are summarized in the chart below.

Chapter 8 Pacing Chart

Day	Full Course	Minimal Course
1	8-1	8-1
2	8-2	8-2
3	8-3	8-3
4	Quiz*; 8-4	Quiz*; begin 8-4.
5	8-5	Finish 8-4.
6	8-6	8-5
7	Quiz*; 8-7	8-6
8	8-8	Quiz*; begin 8-7.
9	8-9	Finish 8-7.
10	Self-Test	8-8
11	Review	8-9
12	Test*	Self-Test
13		Review
14		Review
15		Test*

*in the Teacher's Resource File

In the Teacher's Edition...

Lesson	Optional Activities	Extra Help	Challenge	English Language Development	Error Alert	Extension	Cooperative Learning	Ongoing Assessment
8-1	●	●	●	●	●	●	●	Written
8-2	●	●	●	●	●	●		Oral
8-3	●	●	●	●	●	●		Quiz
8-4	●	●	●		●	●	●	Group
8-5	●	●	●		●	●	●	Written
8-6	●	●	●	●		●		Quiz
8-7	●	●	●			●		Written
8-8	●	●	●		●	●	●	Oral
8-9	●	●	●		●	●		Written

Chapter 8 Block Schedule

Day	Recommended Pacing
1	Lesson 8-1
2	Lesson 8-2
3	Lesson 8-3
4	Lessons 8-4, 8-5
5	Lesson 8-6
6	Lessons 8-7, 8-8
7	Lesson 8-9, Self-Test, Chapter Review
8	Chapter Review, Chapter Test

In the Additional Resources...

Lesson	Lesson Masters	Teaching Aids*	Answer Masters	Technology Sourcebook	Assessment Sourcebook	Visual Aids**	Technology	Explorations Software
				In the Teacher's Resource File				
8-1	8-1	71	8-1			71, AM		
8-2	8-2	71, 74	8-2			71, 74, AM		8-2
8-3	8-3	71	8-3	Calc 7	Quiz	71, AM		
8-4	8-4	72	8-4			72, AM		
In-class Activity			8-5			AM		8-5
8-5	8-5	72, 75	8-5			72, 75, AM		
8-6	8-6	72	8-6		Quiz	72, AM		
8-7	8-7	73, 76	8-7			73, 76, AM		
8-8	8-8	73, 77	8-8			73, 77, AM		
8-9	8-9	73, 78	8-9	Comp 9		73, 78, AM	Spreadsheet	8-9
End of chapter					Tests			

*Teaching Aids are pictured on page 486C.

**Visual Aids provide transparencies for all Teaching Aids and all Answer Masters.

Also available is the Study Skills Handbook which includes study-skill tips related to reading, note-taking, and comprehension.

Integrating Strands and Applications

	8-1	8-2	8-3	8-4	8-5	8-6	8-7	8-8	8-9
Mathematical Connections									
Number Sense		●						●	
Algebra	●	●	●	●	●	●	●	●	●
Geometry	●	●	●	●		●	●		
Logic and Reasoning	●	●	●	●	●	●	●	●	●
Patterns and Functions	●	●	●	●	●	●	●	●	●
Discrete Mathematics	●	●	●	●	●	●	●	●	●
Interdisciplinary and Other Connections									
Art				●			●		
Music		●		●					
Science	●		●		●				●
Social Studies			●	●			●	●	●
Multicultural				●			●	●	●
Technology	●	●	●	●	●	●		●	●
Consumer	●		●	●					●
Sports	●		●		●	●			●

Teaching and Assessing the Chapter Objectives

Chapter 8 Objectives (Organized into the SPUR categories—Skills, Properties, Uses, and Representations)	Lessons	Progress Self-Test Questions	Chapter Review Questions	Chapter Test, Forms A and B	Chapter Test, Forms C	Chapter Test, Forms D
Skills						
A: Find terms of sequences from explicit or recursive formulas.	8-1	2	1-4	1	1	✓
B: Find explicit or recursive formulas for the nth term of an arithmetic or geometric sequence.	8-1	3, 4	5-8	7, 8	1	✓
C: Evaluate arithmetic or geometric series.	8-3, 8-4	9, 10	9-14	3, 4	2	✓
D: Expand binomials.	8-8	13, 14	15-20	9, 10	4	
Properties						
E: Determine whether a sequence is arithmetic or geometric.	8-1	1	21-26	2	1	✓
F: Determine limits of certain sequences.	8-2	6	27-32	5, 6	3	
G: Tell whether an infinite series converges. If it does, give the limit.	8-5	8	33-37	13, 14	2	✓
H: Prove and apply properties involving combinations.	8-7	12	38-41	15, 16	5	
Uses						
I: Solve problems involving arithmetic and geometric sequences and series.	8-1, 8-3, 8-4, 8-5	5, 7, 11	42-46	17, 18		✓
J: Use combinations to compute the number of ways of selecting objects.	8-6	15	47-51	19, 20		
K: Determine probabilities in situations involving binomial experiments.	8-9	16	52-56	21	6	
Representations						
L: Locate numerical properties represented by the patterns in Pascal's Triangle.	8-7	17	57-60	11, 12	4	

In the Teacher's Resource File

Multidimensional Assessment
Quiz for Lessons 8-1 through 8-3
Quiz for Lessons 8-4 through 8-6

Chapter 8 Test, Forms A–D
Chapter 8 Test, Cumulative Form

Quiz and Test Writer

Teaching Aids

Warm-up   Lesson 8-1

Write the first six terms the sequence with the given formula.

1. $\begin{cases} a_1 = 2 \\ a_n = a_{n-1} + 2n - 1 \end{cases}$

2. $a_n = n^2 + 1$

3. What do you notice about your answers to Questions 1 and 2?

Warm-up   Lesson 8-2

Estimate the millionth term of each sequence to the nearest integer, if possible.

1. The sequence defined by $a_n = \frac{3n-2}{n+1}$ for all positive integers n.

2. The sequence defined by $b_1 = 400$, $b_n = 0.9b_{n-1}$ for all integers $n > 1$.

3. The sequence defined by $b_1 = 6$, $b_n = \frac{3}{2} b_{n-1}$ for all integers $n > 1$

Warm-up   Lesson 8-3

1. Find the sum of the first 100 terms of the arithmetic sequence 3, 7, 11, ...

2. Find the sum of the first 101 terms of this sequence.

Warm-up   Lesson 8-4

1. a. Find a formula for the sum S_n of the first n terms of the geometric series $1 + 3 + 9 + \ldots$.

    b. Use this formula to determine the sum of the first 10 terms of the series.

Warm-up   Lesson 8-5

1. Explain why $1 + \frac{1}{2} + \frac{1}{4} + \ldots + \frac{1}{2^{n-1}} + \ldots = 21$.

2. Explain why $a + \frac{a}{2} + \frac{a}{4} + \ldots + \frac{a}{2^{n-1}} \ldots = 2a$

Warm-up   Lesson 8-6

1. List all permutations of 3 letters taken from the 5 letters R, I, N, S, E.

2. Group the permutations found in the answer above so that those permutations that use the same letters, such as EIN and NIE, are in the same group. How many groups are there?

Warm-up   Lesson 8-7

Give the number of subsets of the set of letters {A, E, I, O, U, Y} that have the given number of elements.

1. 1 element   **2.** 2 elements

3. 3 elements   **4.** 4 elements

5. 5 elements   **6.** 0 elements

Warm-up   Lesson 8-8

1. Multiply $x^2 + 2xy + y^2$ by $x + y$.

2. Multiply your answer to Question 1 by $x + y$.

Warm-up   Lesson 8-9

1. Write all the possible permutations of heads and tails when a coin is tossed three times.

2. If the probability of heads is .6, find the probability of each outcome.

Lesson 8-2

Graphs of Sequences

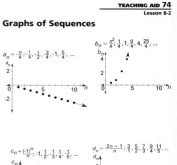

Lesson 8-5

The Jumping Flea

Number of Jumps	Total Distance Jumped	
1	$S_1 = \frac{1}{2}$	$= \frac{1}{2}$
2	$S_2 = \frac{1}{2} + \frac{1}{4}$	$= \frac{3}{4}$
3	$S_3 = \frac{1}{2} + \frac{1}{4} + \frac{1}{8}$	$= \frac{7}{8}$
4	$S_4 = \frac{1}{2} + \frac{1}{4} + \frac{1}{8} + \frac{1}{16}$	$= \frac{15}{16}$
.		
.		
.		
n	$S_n = \frac{1}{2} + \frac{1}{4} + \ldots + \frac{1}{2^n}$	$= 1 - \left(\frac{1}{2}\right)^n$

NUMBER OF JUMPS	DISTANCE JUMPED
1	0.5
2	0.75
3	0.875
.	.
.	.
6	0.984375
7	0.9921875
8	0.9960938
.	.
14	0.999939
15	0.9999695
.	.
23	0.9999999
24	0.9999999
25	1
26	1

Lesson 8-7

Pascal's Triangle (12 rows)

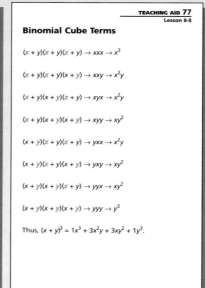

Lesson 8-8

Binomial Cube Terms

$(x + y)(x + y)(x + y) \rightarrow xxx \rightarrow x^3$

$(x + y)(x + y)(x + y) \rightarrow xxy \rightarrow x^2y$

$(x + y)(x + y)(x + y) \rightarrow xyx \rightarrow x^2y$

$(x + y)(x + y)(x + y) \rightarrow xyy \rightarrow xy^2$

$(x + y)(x + y)(x + y) \rightarrow yxx \rightarrow x^2y$

$(x + y)(x + y)(x + y) \rightarrow yxy \rightarrow xy^2$

$(x + y)(x + y)(x + y) \rightarrow yyx \rightarrow xy^2$

$(x + y)(x + y)(x + y) \rightarrow yyy \rightarrow y^3$

Thus, $(x + y)^3 = 1x^3 + 3x^2y + 3xy^2 + 1y^3$.

Lesson 8-9

Outcomes for a Binomial Experiment with 4 Trials

exactly 0 successes	exactly 1 success	exactly 2 successes	exactly 3 successes	exactly 4 successes
FFFF	FFFS	FFSS	FSSS	SSSS
	FFSF	FSFS	SFSS	
	FSFF	FSSF	SSFS	
	SFFF	SFFS	SSSF	
		SFSF		
		SSFF		

Chapter Opener

Pacing

All lessons in this chapter are designed to be covered in one day. At the end of the chapter, you should plan to spend 1 day to review the Progress Self-Test, 1–2 days for the Chapter Review, and 1 day for a test. You may wish to spend a day on projects, and possibly a day is needed for quizzes and the In-class Activity. This chapter should therefore take 12–15 days. We recommend that you not spend more than 16 days on this chapter. There is ample opportunity to review ideas in later chapters.

Using Pages 486–487

If your students studied probability in their biology classes in connection with genetics, they were applying the binomial theorem and binomial probabilities. Specifically, if two organisms, each having a dominant gene G and a recessive gene g, mate, then their offspring will have $\frac{1}{4}$ probability of having each of the following genes: GG, Gg, gG, and gg. An offspring with GG does not exhibit the recessive trait and cannot pass it on to the next generation. Offspring with Gg, or gG, are "carriers" of the recessive trait (they do not exhibit it but can pass it on to another generation), and an offspring with gg exhibits the recessive trait. These possibilities are like the terms in the expansion of $(G + g)^2$.

486

Chapter 8 Overview

Sequences are fundamental to mathematics; they occur whenever we wish to study the change in a quantity over time, to examine a pattern, or simply to list some data.

This chapter begins by reviewing the basic notation and properties of arithmetic and geometric sequences, which are defined simply as functions having as domain the set of integers greater than a given integer. Without formally defining *limit*, students study the limiting behavior of sequences in order to determine whether the sequences converge or diverge, using a calculator or computer and available analytic techniques to generate terms and make judgments. We consider an intuitive background to the study of limits to be essential for the more formal treatment of the concept later in calculus.

Series are indicated sums of terms of sequences. Thus any summation Σ is a series. Most of the important applications of series occur when the terms are values of a function whose formula is known.

Series are the primary topic of Lessons 8-3 through 8-5. Classic algorithms for finding the sums S_n of arithmetic and geometric series are presented and used to prove theorems for finding S_n explicitly. The theorems, in turn, provide formulas for quick solutions to applications involving series.

SEQUENCES, SERIES, AND COMBINATIONS

Although few hereditary diseases can be cured at present, tests have been developed to detect carriers of many genetic disorders. By assessing the probabilities that various genetic diseases will arise in their family, couples can make informed decisions concerning their future.

For instance, suppose that Mr. and Mrs. Washington each had siblings with cystic fibrosis, a disease now known to be hereditary. If the Washingtons have two children, what is the probability that one will have the disease? This situation can be analyzed as a *binomial experiment*, a type of situation which you will study in this chapter.

Probabilities in binomial experiments can be calculated from just a few pieces of information. In the case of cystic fibrosis, two out of three people who have siblings with cystic fibrosis are carriers of the disease. Also, the probability that two carriers of the disease have an afflicted child is 25%. From this information, it can be found that if Mr. and Mrs. Washington have two children, then the probability that at least one has the disease is about 21%. (Of course, if detection tests show that either Mr. or Mrs. Washington is not a carrier, the probability is drastically reduced.)

Binomial experiments such as this one appear in business, politics, and sports, as well as medicine, and they require a knowledge of counting techniques. In this chapter, these techniques are developed through a discussion of sequences, series, and combinations.

In the specific example on this page, since both Mr. and Mrs. Washington had siblings with cystic fibrosis, then we know each of them either has Gg, gG, or GG, with equal probability. This is why each has $\frac{2}{3}$ chance of carrying the gene for cystic fibrosis. For a child to have the disease, both parents must be carriers, so the probability that both are carriers is $\frac{4}{9}$. Since the probability is $\frac{1}{4}$ that a child has the disease, given that both parents are carriers, in this case the probability is $\frac{1}{4} \cdot \frac{4}{9}$, or $\frac{1}{9}$ that a particular child has the disease. Thus there is a $\frac{1}{9} + \frac{1}{9} - \frac{1}{81}$ or $\frac{17}{81}$ probability that at least one of two children has cystic fibrosis, and $\frac{17}{81} \approx 20.99\%$.

Photo Connections
The photo collage makes real-world connections to the content of the chapter: sequences, series, and combinations.

Car: Arithmetic and geometric sequences are discussed in Lesson 8-1. The value of a car after n years if it depreciates the same percent each year can be found using a geometric sequence.

Hot Air Balloon: A geometric sequence can be used to find how long it will take a hot air balloon to reach a specific height.

Chess Piece and Wheat: A legendary story including chess, wheat, and the finite geometric series,
$$S_{64} = \sum_{n=1}^{64} 2^{n-1},$$ is told in Lesson 8-4.

Bee: A female bee has both female and male parents; but a male bee has only a female parent. In Lesson 8-1 students are asked to write a recursive formula for the number of bees in the nth generation of both the male's and female's ancestral tree.

Chapter 8 Projects
At this time, you might want to have students look over the projects on pages 546–547.

Lessons 8-6 through 8-9 deal with combinations and their application to the powers of binomials and to binomial probabilities. First, counting problems leading to combinations are considered. Pascal's triangle is introduced as a way of representing combinations. Then it is shown that Pascal's Triangle also contains the coefficients of the powers of the binomial $a + b$. Finally, the binomial coefficients are related to the calculation of probabilities in certain situations.

Throughout the chapter calculators having keys for calculating combinations will come in handy. Calculators or computers are also helpful in showing how sequences and finite series approach limits.

Objectives

A Find terms of sequences from explicit or recursive formulas.
B Find explicit or recursive formulas for the nth term of an arithmetic or geometric sequence.
E Determine whether a sequence is arithmetic or geometric.
I Solve problems involving arithmetic and geometric sequences.

Resources

From the *Teacher's Resource File*
■ Lesson Master 8-1
■ Answer Master 8-1
■ Teaching Aid 71: Warm-up

Additional Resources
■ Visual for Teaching Aid 71

Teaching Lesson 8-1

Warm-up

Write the first six terms the sequence with the given formula.

1. $\begin{cases} a_1 = 2 \\ a_n = a_{n-1} + 2n - 1 \end{cases}$

   2, 5, 10, 17, 26, 37
2. $a_n = n^2 + 1$
   2, 5, 10, 17, 26, 37
3. What do you notice about your answers to Questions 1 and 2?
   The answers are the same. Given are recursive and explicit formulas for the same sequence.

LESSON

8-1

Formulas for Sequences

In a *Nauts*hell. *The shell of a chambered nautilus maintains its shape as it grows along a logarithmic spiral. The sizes of the chambers, shown in this cross section, form a sequence which is closely related to the Fibonacci sequence.*

What Is a Sequence?

Consider the following example. Let R_n be the number of dots in a rectangular array of dots with n columns and $n + 1$ rows.

$R_1 = 2 \qquad R_2 = 6 \qquad R_3 = 12 \qquad R_4 = 20 \qquad R_5 = 30$

In general, the nth array has n dots in each of $n + 1$ rows, so $R_n = n(n + 1)$.

$R_n = n(n + 1)$ is a formula that pairs each positive integer n with the corresponding number R_n. Specifically, the function R contains the ordered pairs (1, 2), (2, 6), (3, 12), (4, 20), (5, 30), and so on. It is an example of a type of function called a *sequence*.

❶ **Definition**
A **sequence** is a function whose domain is a set of consecutive integers greater than or equal to k.

Each element in the range of a sequence is called a **term** of the sequence. The corresponding positive integer in the domain is its **position** in the sequence. Often, the letter n is used to denote the position of a term, and a subscripted variable such as R_n or a_n is used to denote the term itself.

A formula such as $R_n = n(n + 1)$, which shows the nth term of a sequence in terms of n, is called an **explicit formula**. In contrast, a **recursive**

Lesson 8-1 Overview

Broad Goals This lesson focuses on arithmetic and geometric sequences in preparation for the arithmetic and geometric series to be discussed in Lessons 8-3 and 8-4.

Perspective The terms "arithmetic progression" and "geometric progression" were once commonly used to identify arithmetic and geometric sequences; those terms are generally not used very much these days because they mistakenly suggest that these

sequences are qualitatively different from other sequences. Alternate terms that suggest the underlying functions are *linear sequence* and *exponential sequence*.

Recursively, an arithmetic sequence is any sequence in which, for all n, the $(n + 1)$st term is found by adding a fixed constant d (the first letter of "difference" due to the constant difference) to the nth term. Because sequences are functions, we use one letter

to name them. If the terms of an arithmetic sequence are $a_1, a_2, a_3, \ldots$, then an explicit formula is $a_n = a_1 + (n - 1)d$, and we call the sequence a.

Geometric sequences are to arithmetic sequences as multiplication is to addition. A geometric sequence is a sequence in which, for all n, the $(n + 1)$st term is found by multiplying the nth term by a constant. If g is a geometric sequence, then an explicit

formula is one in which the first term or first few terms are given, and then the *n*th term is expressed using the preceding term(s).

For the sequence *R* on page 488, notice that each term other than the first is the sum of the previous one and some even number.

$$\begin{aligned} R_2 &= 6 = 2 + 4 = R_1 + 4 \\ R_3 &= 12 = 6 + 6 = R_2 + 6 \\ R_4 &= 20 = 12 + 8 = R_3 + 8 \\ R_5 &= 30 = 20 + 10 = R_4 + 10 \end{aligned}$$

❷ In each case the even number added is twice the subscript of R_n. That is, $R_n = R_{n-1} + 2n$. So a recursive formula for this sequence is

$$\begin{cases} R_1 = 2 \\ R_n = R_{n-1} + 2n, \text{ for all integers } n > 1. \end{cases}$$

The pattern in the recursive formula can be pictured.

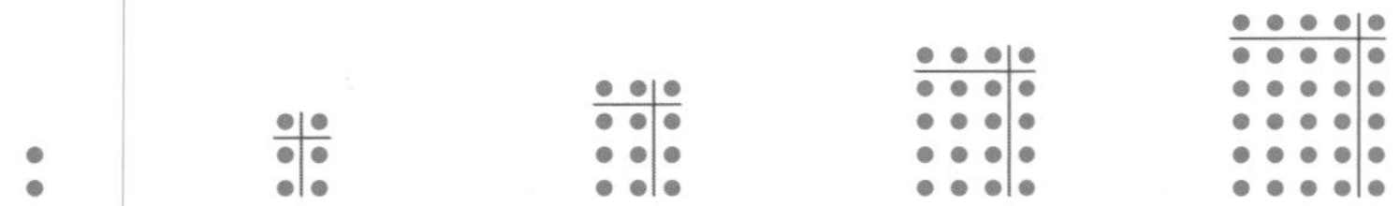

$R_1 = 2$ $R_2 = R_1 + 2 \cdot 2$ $R_3 = R_2 + 2 \cdot 3$ $R_4 = R_3 + 2 \cdot 4$ $R_5 = R_4 + 2 \cdot 5$

Example 1

a. Calculate R_6 using the explicit formula.
b. Assume R_5 is known. Calculate R_6 using the recursive formula.
c. Find R_{14} using either formula.

Solution

a. Use the explicit formula $R_n = n(n + 1)$.

$$R_6 = 6(6 + 1) = 6 \cdot 7 = 42$$

b. Use the recursive formula $R_n = R_{n-1} + 2n$.

$$\begin{aligned} R_6 &= R_{6-1} + 2 \cdot 6 \\ &= R_5 + 12 \\ &= 30 + 12 \\ &= 42 \end{aligned}$$

c. To use the recursive formula, you would need to know R_{13}. So use the explicit formula.

$$\begin{aligned} R_{14} &= 14(14 + 1) \\ &= 14 \cdot 15 = 210 \end{aligned}$$

Check

a. and **b.** Draw an array. As shown at the right, $R_6 = 42$.
c. Find the first 13 terms: 2, 6, 12, 20, 30, 42, 56, 72, 90, 110, 132, 156, 182. So $R_{13} = 182$. Now use the recursive definition. $R_{14} = R_{13} + 2 \cdot 14$. So $R_{14} = 182 + 28 = 210$. It checks.

Notes on Reading

This lesson assumes that students have studied arithmetic and geometric sequences before. If your students have no background with sequences or recursion, plan on spending two days on this lesson.

Emphasize the difference between a recursive formula for a sequence and an explicit formula. With a recursive formula, every term but the first (or first few) is found by using previous terms. With an explicit formula, any term can be found without using the previous ones.

❶ Our definition of sequence allows sequences to begin at any integer *k* because it is convenient at times to start a sequence with a 0th term. (This happens with the sequence of rows in Pascal's Triangle.) Sometimes it is helpful to begin a sequence with an integer greater than 1, such as often happens with sequences of years. However, unless otherwise indicated, sequences defined in terms of *k* begin with $k = 1$.

❷ The recursive formulas in this lesson give the *n*th term in terms of the previous term. This enables us to compare the recursive formula with the explicit formula for the *n*th term. It is also common to give the $(n + 1)$st term in terms of the previous terms. For the sequence at the beginning of this lesson, one would have $R_1 = 2$ and $R_{n+1} = R_n + 2n$ for all integers $n > 1$.

formula is $g_n = g_1 r^{n-1}$, and we call *r* the *constant ratio.*

These sequences are important because many applications of linear and exponential functions can evolve into applications of sequences.

Optional Activities

Activity 1 As an extension of **Question 18** ask students whether any of them have seen the sequence in this problem before. [It is the Fibonacci sequence: 1, 1, 2, 3, 5, 8, 13, 21, ...] Have students research other instances of the Fibonacci sequence. Some other instances are the patterns of cells on the outside of pineapples and certain sums of diagonals in Pascal's Triangle.

Error Alert In **Example 2**, students may not immediately recognize that the sequence is arithmetic because it is not written in the form of the explicit definition in the theorem preceding the example. Point out that a_1 and d in the theorem are constants (similar to m and b in the slope-intercept form of a line), and so a_n is a linear function of n.

In **Example 4**, you might start the sequence with $g_0 = \$14,800$. Then g_n stands for its value n years after purchase. (As is, g_{n+1} stands for this value, since the sequence begins with g_1.) This example is an application of exponential modeling. You may wish to relate it back to Lesson 2-5.

Additional Examples

1. **a.** What is the 9th term of the sequence 2, 4, 6, 8, … ? Without being given one type of formula or the other, you cannot be certain what the 9th term is. For instance, this sequence might be 2, 4, 6, 8, 0, 2, 4, 6, 8, 0, … , the sequence of last digits of the even positive integers; in this case the 9th term is 8. But we expect most students will think that this is the increasing sequence of positive even integers, so that they will respond 18.

Arithmetic Sequences

Two important types of sequences are *arithmetic* and *geometric* sequences. An **arithmetic sequence** is one in which the difference between consecutive terms is constant. For example, the sequence with first term equal to -7 and a constant difference of 3 is an arithmetic sequence whose first six terms are

$$-7, -4, -1, 2, 5, 8.$$

Each term beyond the first is three more than the previous term. Each term is also equal to -7 plus some number of 3s. If the nth term of this sequence is called a_n, then

$$a_n = -7 + 3 \cdot (n - 1).$$

In general, any arithmetic sequence can be generated both explicitly and recursively.

> **Theorem**
> Let n be a positive integer and a_1 and d be constants. The formulas
> $$a_n = a_1 + (n - 1)d \quad \text{and} \quad \begin{cases} a_1 \\ a_n = a_{n-1} + d, n > 1 \end{cases}$$
> generate the terms of the arithmetic sequence with first term a_1 and constant difference d.

The explicit formula in the theorem shows that arithmetic sequences are linear functions of n. Given such a function as an explicit formula, you can find a recursive formula.

Example 2

Write the first three terms, and give a recursive formula for the sequence whose nth term is $a_n = 27 - 4n$.

Solution

The formula for a_n is linear, so from the previous theorem it generates an arithmetic sequence. The first term is $a_1 = 27 - 4(1) = 23$. The second term is $a_2 = 27 - 4(2) = 19$. The third term is $a_3 = 27 - 4(3) = 15$. The constant difference confirms that the sequence is linear. The constant difference is $d = a_2 - a_1 = 19 - 23 = -4$. So a recursive formula is

$$\begin{cases} a_1 = 23 \\ a_n = a_{n-1} - 4, \text{ for all integers } n > 1. \end{cases}$$

Check

Find the first few terms, using both the explicit and recursive definitions. For both methods, you get 23, 19, 15, 11, 7, ...

Optional Activities

Activity 2 Have students graph the sequences in **Examples 2 and 4**. They could do so by hand on graph paper or with an automatic grapher that will graph sequences (discrete points, not a continuous curve). Students will quickly see that the sequence in **Example 2** falls on a line, as all arithmetic sequences do, and that the sequence in **Example 4** falls on an exponential decay curve; all geometric sequences lie on exponential curves.

In an explicit formula for an arithmetic sequence, if any three of the numbers d, n, a_1, and a_n are known, the fourth can always be found.

Example 3

What position does 127 have in the arithmetic sequence below?
16, 19, 22, . . . , 127, ...

Solution

The constant difference d is 3, $a_1 = 16$, and $a_n = 127$. Substitute into the explicit formula from the preceding theorem and solve for n.

$$a_n = a_1 + (n-1)d$$
$$127 = 16 + (n-1)3$$
$$127 = 3n + 13$$
$$n = 38$$

127 is the 38th term of the sequence.

Check

Find the 38th term directly from the formula. $a_{38} = 16 + (38 - 1)3 = 127$. It checks.

Geometric Sequences

A **geometric sequence** is one in which the *ratio* of consecutive terms is constant. For instance, in the geometric sequence $3, \frac{3}{2}, \frac{3}{4}, \frac{3}{8}, \ldots$, the constant ratio is $\frac{1}{2}$. Below at the left is an explicit formula for the nth term of this sequence; at the right is a recursive formula.

$$g_n = 3\left(\tfrac{1}{2}\right)^{n-1} \qquad \begin{cases} g_1 = 3 \\ g_n = \frac{1}{2}g_{n-1}, \text{ for all integers } n > 1 \end{cases}$$

Generalizing for any geometric sequence gives the following.

Theorem
Let n be a positive integer and g_1 and r be constants. The formulas

$$g_n = g_1 r^{n-1} \quad \text{and} \quad \begin{cases} g_1 \\ g_n = rg_{n-1},\ n > 1 \end{cases}$$

generate the terms of the geometric sequence with first term g_1 and constant ratio r.

Notice that geometric sequences are exponential functions if $r > 0$ and $r \neq 1$.

b. Did you use an explicit formula or a recursive formula to get the 9th term in part a. If students repeatedly added 2 to get the term 18, then they are using recursive thinking. If they doubled 9 to get 18, they are using an explicit formula.

2. Give a recursive formula for the increasing sequence of positive odd numbers.
$\begin{cases} a_1 = 1 \\ a_n = a_{n-1} + 2 \text{ for } n > 1 \end{cases}$

3. Which term is 344 in the arithmetic sequence 8, 15, 22, 29, ... ? 49th

4. Suppose a model train collection valued now at \$2000 increases 5% in value each year.

a. Give its value next year. \$2100

b. Give the value of the collection n years from now. $\$2000(1.05)^n$

c. What will its value be 10 years from now? $\$2000(1.05)^{10}$, or about \$3258

Adapting to Individual Needs

Extra Help

Some students might benefit from a discussion of how d and r affect arithmetic sequences and geometric sequences respectively. Point out that in an arithmetic sequence, the terms increase if d is positive and decrease if d is negative. In a geometric sequence, if $|r| > 1$, then the absolute values of the terms increase, while if $0 < |r| < 1$, the absolute values of the terms decrease. If r is positive, the terms all have the same sign, but if r is negative, the terms have alternating signs.

► **LESSON MASTER 8-1** *page 2*

Properties Objective E

In 10–15, identify the sequences in Exercises 1–6, respectively, as *arithmetic*, *geometric*, or *neither*.

10. geometric
11. arithmetic
12. neither
13. neither
14. neither
15. arithmetic

Uses Objective I

16. Cynthia is to begin training for a long-distance bicycle ride. Her plan is to ride every day, starting with 25-km rides the first week and increasing her distance by 7 km each subsequent week.

a. What is the distance of Cynthia's rides in the second week of her training? 32 km

b. Write a recursive formula for the distance of Cynthia's training rides in the nth week. $\begin{cases} d_1 = 25 \\ d_n = d_{n-1} + 7, \text{ for } n \geq 2. \end{cases}$

c. Write an explicit formula for the distance of Cynthia's training rides in the nth week. $d_n = 25 + 7(n-1)$

d. In what week will the distance of Cynthia's training rides be 102 km? week 12

17. A particular high-powered personal home computer system costs about \$3,000 new. However, due to rapid advances in technology, it depreciates in value by 35% each year.

a. How much will the computer be worth in its second year? \$1950

b. Write a recursive formula for the value of the computer in its nth year. $\begin{cases} V_1 = 3000 \\ V_n = 0.65V_{n-1}, \text{ for } n > 1. \end{cases}$

c. Write an explicit formula for the value of the computer in its nth year. $V_n = 3000(0.65)^{n-1}$

d. In what year will the value of the computer first drop below \$500? year 6

Example 4

A particular car depreciates 25% in value each year. Suppose the original cost is $14,800.
   a. Find the value of the car in its second year.
   b. Write an explicit formula for the value of the car in its nth year.
   c. In how many years will the car be worth about $1000?

Solution

a. Let g_n = the amount the car is worth in dollars in year n. So, the initial amount $g_1 = 14800$. In year 2, it is worth 75% of the previous amount, so $g_2 = 14800(.75) = 11100$.

b. The situation generates a geometric sequence. Find g_n when $g_1 = 14800$ and $r = .75$.

$$g_n = 14800(0.75)^{n-1}$$

c. Find n so that
$$g_n \approx 1000.$$
$$14800\,(.75)^{n-1} = 1000$$
$$(.75)^{n-1} \approx 0.06757.$$
Take the logarithm of each side.
$$(n-1)\,\log.75 \approx \log 0.06757$$
$$n - 1 \approx 9.37$$
$$n \approx 10.37$$

That is, in year 10, the car will be worth about $1000.

Some calculators have a SEQUENCE mode that allows you to generate sequences either recursively or explicitly. On these calculators, the terms of the geometric sequence in Example 4 might be generated by inputting either of the following formulas.

Recursive Formula	Explicit Formula
$U_n = .75 * U_{n-1}$	$U_n = U_n\text{Start} * (.75)^{\wedge}(n-1)$

At the right is the output from a calculator when the window variables $U_n\text{Start} = 14800$ and $n\text{Start} = 1$. The variable $n\text{Start}$ sets the value of n at which the calculation begins, and the variable $U_n\text{Start}$ sets the value of U_n when $n = n\text{Start}$.

n	U_n
1	14800
2	11100
3	8325
4	6243.75
5	4682.813
6	3512.109
7	2634.082
8	1975.562
9	1481.671
10	1111.253
11	833.440

The 10th and 11th terms of the sequence provide a check to the work in part **c** of Example 4.

Explicit formulas are useful because they allow you to calculate values directly. There are, however, several reasons for using recursive formulas.

492

First, sometimes an explicit formula cannot be found. Second, some biological processes, such as the genetic instructions for the spiral growth of certain shells, work recursively. Third, calculator and computer programs often run faster using recursive rather than explicit formulas, particularly when the number of terms generated is large. Throughout this chapter, you will need to find many terms of a sequence quickly. You should learn to use programs or to use list features of a calculator to generate sequences.

QUESTIONS

Covering the Reading

In 1 and 2, refer to the sequence R in the lesson.

1. What is the 7th term? **56**

2. Find R_{30}. **930**

In 3 and 4, *true or false*.

3. The domain of every sequence is the set of positive numbers. **False**

4. The terms of a sequence are elements of its range. **True**

5. If t_n is a term in a sequence, what is the following term? t_{n+1}

In 6–8, an explicit or recursive formula for a sequence is given. **a.** Determine the first three terms of the sequence. **b.** Identify the sequence as arithmetic, geometric, or neither.

6. $\begin{cases} C_1 = 2 \\ C_n = C_{n-1} - 2, \text{ for all integers } n > 1 \end{cases}$ a) 2, 0, -2   b) arithmetic

7. $b_n = \frac{n(n+1)}{2}$ a) 1, 3, 6   b) neither

8. $d_n = -(1.05)^{n-1}$ a) -1, -1.05, -1.1025   b) geometric

9. Find the first term and the constant difference of the arithmetic sequence defined by $k_n = \frac{4-n}{2}$. $k_1 = \frac{3}{2}, d = -\frac{1}{2}$

10. What is the position of 3282 in the arithmetic sequence 6, 18, 30, ..., 3282, ...? **the 274th term**

11. Consider the sequence generated by the following.

$$\begin{cases} t_1 = 18 \\ t_n = \frac{1}{2}t_{n-1}, \text{ for all integers } n > 1 \end{cases}$$

11b) $t_n = 18\left(\frac{1}{2}\right)^{n-1}$

c) $\frac{18}{2^{19}} \approx 3.4 \times 10^{-5}$

   a. Write the first four terms of the sequence. 18, 9, $\frac{9}{2}$, $\frac{9}{4}$
   b. Write an explicit formula for t_n.
   c. Find t_{20} using either the explicit or recursive formula.
   b, c) See left.

12. Suppose a car bought for $25,000 depreciates 20% per year.
   a. Find the value of the car in its 3rd year. $25{,}000\,(.8)^2 = \$16{,}000$
   b. In what year will the value of the car first fall below $5000?
   in the 8th year

Lesson 8-1   *Formulas for Sequences*   **493**

Notes on Questions
Question 5 This is an important question to generalize. Ask: What is the previous term? $[t_{n-1}]$ What is the term after the next term? $[t_{n+2}]$

Question 12 Certain types of depreciation are allowed for income tax purposes. One is linear, one is exponential.

Adapting to Individual Needs

Challenge
Identify each of the following as geometric, arithmetic, or neither. If arithmetic, give the common difference and an explicit formula; if geometric, give the common ratio and an explicit formula; if neither, give a recursive formula.

1. $\log x, \log x^2, \log x^3, \log x^4, \ldots$
   [Arithmetic; $d = \log x$; $a_n = n \log x$]
2. $\ln 2, \ln 4, \ln 8, \ln 16, \ln 32, \ldots$
   [Arithmetic; $d = \ln 2$; $a_n = n \ln 2$]

3. $1, x, \frac{x^2}{2!}, \frac{x^3}{3!}, \frac{x^4}{4!}, \ldots$ [Neither; $a_1 = 1$;
   $a_n = \left(\frac{x}{n-1}\right)a_{n-1}$ for $n > 1$]
4. $1, 1, 2, 3, 5, 8, 13, 21, \ldots$
   [Neither; $a_1 = 1$; $a_2 = 1$;
   $a_n = a_{n-1} + a_{n-2}$ for $n > 2$]
5. $\ln 3, \ln 9, \ln 81, \ln 6561, \ldots$
   [Geometric; $r = 2$; $a_n = \ln 3 \cdot 2^{n-1}$]
6. $e^2, e^4, e^6, e^8, e^{10}, \ldots$
   [Geometric; $r = e^2$;
   $a_n = e^2(e^2)^{n-1} = (e^2)^n$]

493

Questions 16–17 Students might find this formula two ways. One way is to see that the rectangles are 1×3, 2×4, 3×5, and 4×6. The pattern is then rather easy to generalize. Another way is to see that the sequence 3, 8, 15, 24, … is quadratic and to fit a quadratic model to the terms using ideas from Lesson 2-6. That is, this function contains (1,3), (2,8), (3,15), (4,24), … .

Question 18 This recursive formula begins with two terms because two terms are needed to get the next term. Many students may recognize the sequence as the Fibonacci sequence.

Question 24 This question reviews skills that are important for Lesson 8-2.

Additional Answers

18. **c.**

d.
$$\begin{cases} b_1 = 1 \\ b_2 = 2 \\ b_n = b_{n-1} + b_{n-2} \text{ for } n \ge 3 \end{cases}$$

13b) 36, 24, 16, 10.67, 7.11, 4.74, 3.16, 2.11, 1.40, 0.936, 0.624, 0.416, 0.277, 0.185, 0.123, 0.082, 0.055, 0.037, 0.024, 0.016

18a)
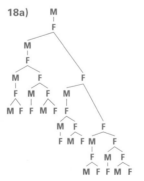

Applying the Mathematics

13. **a.** Complete the lines below so that a calculator in SEQUENCE mode will generate the geometric sequence 36, 24, 16, … recursively.

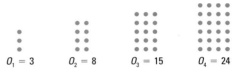

$U_n =$ _?_ $(2 \div 3)* U_{n-1}$ or $36\left(\frac{2}{3}\right)^{n-1}$

U_nStart = _?_ 36

nStart = _?_ 1

   b. Use a calculator to find the first twenty terms of the sequence in part **a**. See left.

14. How many terms are in the finite geometric sequence 6, 12, 24, … , 768?
8

15. Several long distance runners are on a special ten-day exercise program. They are to run three miles on the first day, and on each successive day of the program they are to increase their distance by 10% over the previous day's distance. How far must they run on the sixth day?
$3 \cdot (1.10)^5 \approx 4.8$ miles

In 16 and 17, consider the following sequence of dots in rectangular arrays.

$O_1 = 3$ $O_2 = 8$ $O_3 = 15$ $O_4 = 24$

16. *Multiple choice.* Recall that n is the index of O_n. Which of the following describes those rectangles? **c**
   (a) The width and length equal the index.
   (b) The width equals the index and the length is one more than the index.
   (c) The width equals the index and the length is two more than the index.

17. **a.** Write an explicit formula for O_n. $O_n = n(n+2)$
   b. What is O_{100}? **10,200**

18. A female bee has both female and male parents; but a male bee has only a female parent.
   a. At the left is part of the ancestral tree of a male bee. The number of bees in consecutive generations are 1, 1, 2, 3. Continue the ancestral family tree for the male bee for three more generations. **See left.**
   b. Complete the recursive formula for the number of bees in the nth generation of the male's ancestral tree.

$$\begin{cases} b_1 = 1 \\ b_2 = 1 \\ b_n = \underline{} \quad b_{n-1} + b_{n-2} \text{ for } n \ge 3 \end{cases}$$

   c. Make an ancestral tree for 3 generations of a female bee.
   d. Write a recursive formula for the number of bees in the nth generation of the female's ancestral tree.
   c, d) See margin.

19. **a.** Use a calculator or computer to generate the first 20 terms of the arithmetic sequence with $a_1 = -97$ and $d = 4$. **See below.**
   b. Which term of this sequence is the number –1? **the 25th**
   a) –97, –93, –89, –85, –81, –77, –73, –69, –65, –61, –57, –53, –49, –45, –41, –37, –33, –29, –25, –21

20. *Multiple choice.* Refer to the graph below. Which can be an equation for the graph? *(Lesson 4-8)* **d**

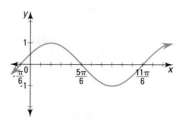

(a) $y = \cos\left(x - \frac{\pi}{6}\right)$

(b) $y = \cos\left(x + \frac{\pi}{6}\right)$

(c) $y = \sin\left(x - \frac{\pi}{6}\right)$

(d) $y = \sin\left(x + \frac{\pi}{6}\right)$

In 21 and 22, find x. *(Lessons 5-2, 5-4)*

21.

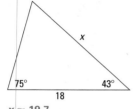

$x \approx 19.7$

22.

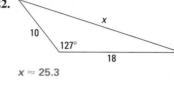

$x \approx 25.3$

23. **a.** Give an equation for a function that has a horizontal asymptote and draw its graph. **See left.**

b. What is an equation for that asymptote? *(Lesson 3-1)*
Sample: **y = 3**

24. *Skill sequence.* Simplify. *(Previous course)*

a. $\dfrac{\frac{2}{x}}{\frac{3}{x}} \quad \frac{2}{3}$

b. $\dfrac{\frac{1}{n} - 4}{\frac{3}{n} + 6} \quad \frac{1 - 4n}{3 + 6n}$

23a) Sample: $y = \dfrac{3x}{x + 1}$

25b) By the Pythagorean Theorem,
$a^2 + (a + d)^2 = (a + 2d)^2$. **So** $a^2 + a^2 + 2ad + d^2 = a^2 + 4ad + 4d^2$;
$2a^2 + 2ad + d^2 = a^2 + 4ad + 4d^2$;
$a^2 - 2ad - 3d^2 = 0$.
Factoring, we get $(a - 3d)(a + d) = 0$, **but** $a + d \neq 0$ **because** $a + d$ **is the length of one side. Then** $a - 3d = 0$, **or** $a = 3d$.

Exploration

25. Consider the right triangle with sides 3, 4, and 5. Notice that the lengths of the sides form an arithmetic sequence.
   a. Determine three other right triangles with side lengths in arithmetic sequence. **Samples: {6, 8, 10}, {9, 12, 15}, {12, 16, 20}**
   b. Let the sides of a right triangle be a, $a + d$, and $a + 2d$ units long. Use the Pythagorean Theorem to determine a relation between a and d.
   c. Based on the result in part **b**, make a general statement about all the right triangles whose sides form an arithmetic sequence.
   b) See left. **c)** If $a = 3d$, the three sides are {$3d$, $4d$, $5d$} for any number $d > 0$, so all the right triangles whose sides form an arithmetic sequence are similar to a 3, 4, 5 right triangle.

Practice

For more questions on SPUR Objectives, use **Lesson Master 8-1** (shown on pages 490–491).

Assessment

Written Communication Have students **work in pairs**. Ask each student to write several consecutive terms of an arithmetic sequence. Have students exchange papers and give both a recursive formula and explicit formula for their partner's sequence. Repeat the activity with a geometric sequence. [Students write recursive formulas and explicit formulas for arithmetic and geometric sequences.]

Extension

Pose the following question to students. Are there any right triangles whose sides are three consecutive terms of a geometric sequence? [Yes; suppose a, b, and c are sides of a right triangle, $b = ar$, and $c = ar^2$. Then, from the Pythagorean Theorem, $a^2 + (ar)^2 = (ar^2)^2$. Dividing both sides by a^2, $r^4 = 1 + r^2$. So $r^2 = \dfrac{1 + \sqrt{5}}{2}$, from which $r = \sqrt{\dfrac{1 + \sqrt{5}}{2}}$.]

Project Update Project 3, *A Prime Number Sieve*, and Project 5, *Recursively Defined Curves* on pages 546–547, relate to the content of this lesson.

Setting Up Lesson 8-2

Go over **Question 24** so that students regain facility with complex fractions.

Objectives

F Determine limits of certain sequences.

Resources

From the _Teacher's Resource File_
- Lesson Master 8-2
- Answer Master 8-2
- Teaching Aids
  71 Warm-up
  74 Graphs of Sequences

Additional Resources
- Visuals for Teaching Aids 71, 74
- Exploration 8-2

Teaching Lesson 8-2

Warm-up

Estimate the millionth term of each sequence to the nearest integer, if possible.
1. The sequence defined by $a_n = \frac{3n-2}{n+1}$ for all positive integers n. **3**
2. The sequence defined by $b_1 = 400$, $b_n = 0.9b_{n-1}$ for all integers $n > 1$ **0**
3. The sequence defined by $b_1 = 6$, $b_n = \frac{3}{2}b_{n-1}$ for all integers $n > 1$ **It is a very large number that overflows any calculator we have; it has about 155,000 digits.**

LESSON

8-2

Limits of Sequences

Each image of the boy is half the height of the previous one. The limit of the sequence of images is a single point. The height of any image is the sum of the heights of the smaller images.

Notation for Limits

In Lesson 6-4, we defined the number e as the _limiting value_ of the sequence

$$s_n = \left(1 + \tfrac{1}{n}\right)^n.$$

That is, e is the number to which $\left(1 + \tfrac{1}{n}\right)^n$ gets closer and closer as n increases. At that time, you were asked to calculate s_n for various values of n. Here are some other values of the sequence.

n	s_n
10	$\left(1 + \tfrac{1}{10}\right)^{10} = 1.1^{10} \approx 2.593742460\ldots$
100	$\left(1 + \tfrac{1}{100}\right)^{100} = 1.01^{100} \approx 2.704813829\ldots$
1000	$\left(1 + \tfrac{1}{1000}\right)^{1000} = 1.001^{1000} \approx 2.716923932\ldots$
10000	$\left(1 + \tfrac{1}{10000}\right)^{10000} = 1.0001^{10000} \approx 2.7181459268\ldots$

The limiting value, to 13 decimal places, is 2.7182818284590. We write

$$\lim_{n\to\infty}\left(1 + \tfrac{1}{n}\right)^n = e,$$

read "the limit of $\left(1 + \tfrac{1}{n}\right)$ to the nth power, as n approaches infinity, is e."

The sequence for e is a complicated sequence, and so we have to _tell_ you it has a limiting value because proving that fact is beyond the scope of this course.

Lesson 8-2 Overview

Broad Goals This lesson informally presents the limit of a sequence and the ideas of convergent and divergent sequences. Students should be able to graph sequences in the coordinate plane and decide whether a sequence seems to have a limit or find the limit by using algebra and applying properties of limits.

Perspective Treated as a function, a sequence $a_1, a_2, a_3, \ldots, a_n$ has a limit if its graph has a horizontal asymptote as $n \to \infty$. Arithmetic sequences do not have a limit unless the common difference is 0, in which case they are constant. Geometric sequences have the limit 0 if the constant ratio r satisfies $|r| < 1$. However, other sequences have interesting limits. In this lesson, the notion of a limit is introduced intuitively, and students see how computer programs enable a person to make educated guesses as to the limiting behavior of a sequence. From the fact that $\lim_{n\to\infty} \frac{1}{n} = 0$, fundamental properties of limits, and some algebraic manipulation, students can deduce limits of sequences with rational formulas. In _Precalculus and Discrete Mathematics_, the ideas are carried further in a detailed discussion of the end behavior of rational functions.

Divergent Sequences

A description of what happens to the values t_n of a sequence as n gets very large is called the **end behavior** of the sequence. Examine the following two sequences and the graphs of their first few terms. There are important similarities in the end behaviors of these sequences.

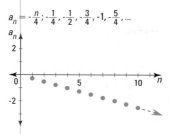

$a_n = -\frac{n}{4}: -\frac{1}{4}, -\frac{1}{2}, -\frac{3}{4}, -1, -\frac{5}{4}, \ldots$

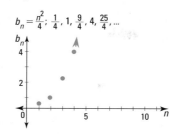

$b_n = \frac{n^2}{4}: \frac{1}{4}, 1, \frac{9}{4}, 4, \frac{25}{4}, \ldots$

The sequence with terms $a_n = -\frac{n}{4}$ is an arithmetic sequence whose terms decrease steadily as n increases. Each term is $\frac{1}{4}$ less than its predecessor; the points all lie on a line. The terms of $b_n = \frac{n^2}{4}$ increase as n increases; all points of the graph lie on a parabola. Sequence a has a maximum value but no minimum value. Sequence b has a minimum value but no maximum value. As n increases, the terms in the former decrease without bound and those in the latter increase without bound.

Because neither sequence a nor b approaches a constant value as n increases, neither sequence has a limit as n approaches infinity. Another way of saying this is "the limit does not exist." This is consistent with the lack of horizontal asymptotes to the graphs of a and b. A sequence which does not have a finite limit is said to be **divergent** or to **diverge**. Sequences a and b are divergent.

The Harmonic Sequence

A sequence which has a finite limit L is said to be **convergent** or to **converge to L**. In this book, we do not give an algebraic definition of the limit of a sequence. Usually such a definition is studied in calculus. But we assume some properties of limits from which it can be determined whether some sequences are divergent or convergent.

The sequence of reciprocals of the positive integers, $1, \frac{1}{2}, \frac{1}{3}, \frac{1}{4}, \ldots$, sometimes called the **harmonic sequence**, is convergent.

Limit Property 1

(1) $\lim\limits_{n \to \infty} \left(\frac{1}{n}\right) = 0$

The limit of the harmonic sequence is 0.

Notes on Reading
A major purpose of this lesson is to provide students with background experience before they encounter a more formal treatment of limits in a later course. Thus we do not give a formal "epsilon-delta" (ε-δ) definition of a limit. Likewise, we have avoided an explicit definition of ∞. Still, you might give a verbal description of these ideas:
1. The limit of a sequence is L if and only if, no matter how close to L you decide to be, after a certain point in the sequence all terms are at least that close to L.
2. The limit of a sequence is ∞ if and only if no matter how large a number you pick, after a certain point in the sequence all terms of the sequence are larger than that number.
3. Analogously, the limit of a sequence is -∞ if and only if no matter how small a number you pick, after a certain point in the sequence all terms of the sequence are smaller than that number.

Technology Technology can be used to help build intuition about limits in two ways. The apparent convergence or divergence of a sequence can be seen dynamically when large numbers of terms of the sequence are generated. The other way that technology can help is with graphs of sequences. The behavior of these functions as $n \to \infty$ can be a signal to the divergence or convergence of a sequence. Graphs of sequences can be found on **Teaching Aid 74.**

Why does the harmonic sequence converge to 0? Because no matter how small a number near zero you might pick, after a while the terms of the harmonic sequence are all nearer 0 than your number. This is what we mean by the phrase "getting closer and closer" to 0.

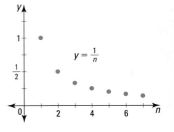

Graphically, the terms of the harmonic sequence lie on one branch of the hyperbola $y = \frac{1}{n}$. That 0 is the limit is geometrically represented by the fact that $y = 0$ is an asymptote to this graph. In general, graphs of convergent sequences have horizontal asymptotes.

❶ The Alternating Harmonic Sequence

The **alternating harmonic sequence** with terms $c_n = \frac{(-1)^n}{n}$ is like the harmonic sequence, but every other term is negative. For example, $c_{99} = \frac{(-1)^{99}}{99} = -.\overline{01}$ and $c_{100} = \frac{(-1)^{100}}{100} = 0.01$. Although the terms alternate between positive and negative values, this sequence also has a limit of 0. Its graph has $y = 0$ as a horizontal asymptote, as shown at the right.

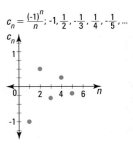

$$c_n = \frac{(-1)^n}{n}; \ -1, \frac{1}{2}, -\frac{1}{3}, \frac{1}{4}, -\frac{1}{5}, \ldots$$

More Properties of Limits

Consider the three sequences defined by

$$e_n = 2, \qquad f_n = \frac{2}{n}, \qquad \text{and} \qquad d_n = \frac{2n+1}{n},$$

for all integers $n \geq 1$. The sequence e has all terms equal to 2, so $\lim_{n\to\infty} e_n = 2$. The sequence f is just twice the harmonic sequence, so its limit is twice the limit of the harmonic sequence; that is, $\lim_{n\to\infty} f_n = 0$.

The first few terms of the sequence defined by $d_n = \frac{2n+1}{n}$ are $\frac{3}{1}, \frac{5}{2}, \frac{7}{3}, \frac{9}{4}, \ldots$. To find out if $\lim_{n\to\infty}\left(\frac{2n+1}{n}\right)$ exists, you can rewrite $\frac{2n+1}{n}$ as a sum of fractions and simplify.

$$\frac{2n+1}{n} = \frac{2n}{n} + \frac{1}{n}$$
$$= 2 + \frac{1}{n}$$

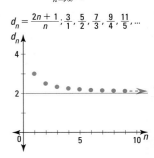

$$d_n = \frac{2n+1}{n}; \ \frac{3}{1}, \frac{5}{2}, \frac{7}{3}, \frac{9}{4}, \frac{11}{5}, \ldots$$

So each term of this sequence is 2 more than the corresponding term of the harmonic sequence. So its limit is 2 more than 0, or 2.

Adapting to Individual Needs

Extra Help

Point out to students that unless an arithmetic sequence has a constant difference of 0, an arithmetic sequence does not have a limit. When the constant difference is 0, then the sequence simply has all terms equal, and the limit is equal to any of the terms.

In general, limits possess the following properties.

From Limit Properties 2 and 4, we can deduce two more properties. Suppose that a sequence b is convergent and that $\lim_{n\to\infty} b_n \neq 0$.

$$\lim_{n\to\infty} b_n \cdot \lim_{n\to\infty}\left(\frac{1}{b_n}\right) = \lim_{n\to\infty}\left(b_n \cdot \frac{1}{b_n}\right) \qquad \text{Limit Property 4}$$
$$= \lim_{n\to\infty} 1$$
$$= 1 \qquad \text{Limit Property 2}$$

Dividing both sides of the equation by $\lim_{n\to\infty} b_n$ gives

$$\lim_{n\to\infty}\left(\frac{1}{b_n}\right) = \frac{1}{\lim_{n\to\infty} b_n}.$$

This proves Limit Property 6. The proof of Limit Property 7 is left for the Questions.

Limit Properties 6 and 7

If $\lim_{n\to\infty} a_n$ and $\lim_{n\to\infty} b_n$ exist and $\lim_{n\to\infty} b_n \neq 0$, then:

(6) $\lim_{n\to\infty}\left(\frac{1}{b_n}\right) = \frac{1}{\lim_{n\to\infty} b_n}$

The limit of a reciprocal is the reciprocal of the limit.

(7) $\lim_{n\to\infty}\left(\frac{a_n}{b_n}\right) = \frac{\lim_{n\to\infty} a_n}{\lim_{n\to\infty} b_n}$

The limit of a quotient is the quotient of the individual limits.

In the following example, the limit is found by rewriting the expression in terms of $\frac{1}{n}$ and then applying Property 7.

Question 5 Error Alert If students use an automatic grapher to graph the function with equation $f(x) = \frac{3x + 2}{2x - 1}$ and are unable to restrict the domain, they will have to ignore all the extra points the grapher gives them. The sequence, a subset of the function, exhibits much simpler behavior than the function: it has no zeros and no vertical asymptotes.

Question 6 Note that the calculator does not provide a proof, but we know enough about the expressions in the numerator and denominator of these fractions to believe that the behavior of the sequence will not be unusual. This gives us confidence in what the calculator signals.

Question 13 This question can be answered by using the techniques of the next lesson. In fact, students may have used that technique in the past to rewrite repeating decimals as fractions. If they know it, fine. But if they do not know the technique, we suggest putting off instructions until the next lesson. At this point, appeal to students' memories and common sense: where have they seen this decimal before? Suggest that they use a calculator and trial and error if necessary.

Question 14c This kind of thinking is needed in formal approaches to the idea of limit.

(Notes on Questions continue on page 502.)

Example

Find $\lim_{n \to \infty} \left(\frac{2 - n}{4 - 3n} \right)$.

Solution

Rewrite the expression after dividing numerator and denominator by n.

$$\lim_{n \to \infty} \left(\frac{2 - n}{4 - 3n} \right) = \lim_{n \to \infty} \left(\frac{\frac{2}{n} - 1}{\frac{4}{n} - 3} \right)$$

$$= \lim_{n \to \infty} \left(\frac{2\left(\frac{1}{n}\right) - 1}{4\left(\frac{1}{n}\right) - 3} \right) = \frac{\lim_{n \to \infty} \left(2\left(\frac{1}{n}\right) - 1 \right)}{\lim_{n \to \infty} \left(4\left(\frac{1}{n}\right) - 3 \right)} \quad \text{Limit Property 7}$$

Now use Limit Properties 3, 5, 1 and 2.
So, the limit is $\frac{2(0) - 1}{4(0) - 3} = \frac{-1}{-3} = \frac{1}{3}$.

Check

Substitute some large values for n. For instance, if $n = 1000$, $\frac{2 - n}{4 - 3n} = \frac{2 - 1000}{4 - 3000} = \frac{-998}{-2996} \approx 0.3331 \approx \frac{1}{3}$.

QUESTIONS

Covering the Reading

1) The end behavior is a description of what happens to the values t_n of a sequence as n gets very large.

1. What is the *end behavior* of a sequence? **See left.**

2. Consider the five sequences a, b, c, d, and the harmonic sequence in this lesson.
   a. Which have limits?   **b.** Which converge?
   a, b) harmonic sequence, sequence c, sequence d

In 3 and 4, *true or false*.

3. If each term in a sequence is less than the preceding term, the sequence has a limit. **False**

4. If a sequence has a limit, then the graph of the sequence has a horizontal asymptote. **True**

5. Consider the sequence s
   $$\frac{5}{1}, \frac{8}{3}, \frac{11}{5}, \frac{14}{7}, \ldots, \text{ where } s_n = \frac{3n + 2}{2n - 1}.$$
   a. Find the tenth term of the sequence. Write it as a fraction and as a decimal. **32/19 ≈ 1.684**
   b. Evaluate s_{100} and s_{1000} to three decimal places. **1.518; 1.502**
   c. Graph the sequence. **See margin.**
   d. Does the graph appear to have a horizontal asymptote? If so, what is its equation? **Yes; $y = 3/2$**
   e. Find the limit of the sequence using the idea of the Example.
   $$\lim_{n \to \infty} s_n = \lim_{n \to \infty} \frac{3 + 2\left(\frac{1}{n}\right)}{2 - \left(\frac{1}{n}\right)} = \frac{3}{2}$$

Additional Answers

5. c.

6a)

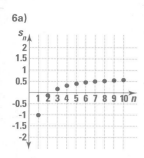

6. **a.** Graph the sequence with nth term $\frac{3n-7}{4n}$. **See left.**

   b. Is the sequence convergent or divergent? If it is convergent, give its limit. **convergent;** $\frac{3}{4}$

7. Does the sequence generated by $t_n = \frac{n^2+3}{n^2+1}$ converge or diverge? If it converges, state its limit.
   It converges; 1

In 8 and 9, decide whether the sequence is convergent or divergent. If it is convergent, give its limit.

8. $-1, 1, \frac{3}{7}, \frac{2}{7}, \ldots, \frac{n}{n^2-2}, \ldots$
   convergent; 0

9. $0, \frac{6}{4}, \frac{24}{9}, \frac{60}{16}, \ldots, \frac{n^3-n}{n^2}, \ldots$
   divergent

In 10–13, find the limit by using properties of limits.

10. $\lim_{n\to\infty} \left(\frac{3}{n}\right)$ **0**

11. $\lim_{n\to\infty} \left(\frac{11-5n}{6n+23}\right)$ $-\frac{5}{6}$

12. the constant sequence 8, 8, 8, 8, ... **8**

13. the sequence of decimals formed by an increasing number of 3s: 0.3, 0.33, 0.333, 0.3333, 0.33333, ... $\frac{1}{3}$

Applying the Mathematics

14. Let $t_n = \frac{24,000}{n}$.

    a. Find $t_1, t_2, t_3, t_4,$ and $t_{10,000}$. **24,000; 12,000; 8000; 6000; 2.4**
    b. This sequence has a limit L. Use the theorems in the lesson to determine L. **$L = 0$**
    c. Find a number x such that for all $n > x$, t_n is within 0.1 of L.
    Sample: x = 240,000

15e) If $|r| < 1$, $\lim_{n\to\infty} r^n = 0$.
If $|r| > 1$, $\lim_{n\to\infty} r^n$ does not exist.

15. In parts **a–d**, tell whether the limit exists. If it does, state it.

    a. $\lim_{n\to\infty} \left(\frac{2}{3}\right)^n$ **exists; 0**
    b. $\lim_{n\to\infty} \left(\frac{3}{2}\right)^n$ **does not exist**
    c. $\lim_{n\to\infty} (-4)^n$ **does not exist**
    d. $\lim_{n\to\infty} (-0.99)^n$ **exists; 0**
    e. Make a conjecture about $\lim_{n\to\infty} r^n$. **See left.**

16c) Sample: The horizontal asymptote of the equation $y = \frac{a}{x} + b$ is $y = b$, and b is also the limit, as $n \to \infty$, of $\frac{a}{n} + b$.

16. **a.** Find $\lim_{n\to\infty} \left(\frac{1}{n} - 5\right)$. **-5**

    b. Give an equation of the horizontal asymptote to the graph of $y = \frac{1}{x} - 5$. **b) $y = -5$**
    c. How are the answers to parts **a** and **b** related?
    See left.

17. Assume $\lim_{n\to\infty} a_n$ and $\lim_{n\to\infty} b_n$ exist and $\lim_{n\to\infty} b_n \neq 0$. Provide the justifications for Steps 2–4 in the proof of Limit Property 7 below.

Conclusions		Justifications
Step 1: $\lim_{n\to\infty}\left(\frac{a_n}{b_n}\right) = \lim_{n\to\infty}\left(a_n \cdot \frac{1}{b_n}\right)$		Algebraic Definition of Division
Step 2: $= \lim_{n\to\infty} a_n \cdot \lim_{n\to\infty}\left(\frac{1}{b_n}\right)$	?	**Limit Property 4**
Step 3: $= \lim_{n\to\infty} a_n \cdot \frac{1}{\lim_{n\to\infty} b_n}$	?	**Limit Property 6**
Step 4: $= \frac{\lim_{n\to\infty} a_n}{\lim_{n\to\infty} b_n}$	?	**Algebraic Definition of Division**

Practice

For more questions on SPUR Objectives, use **Lesson Master 8-2** (shown on page 499).

Assessment

Oral Communication Have students show their work and explain orally how they applied the appropriate Limit Properties in **Question 14b** to determine the limit. [Students use Limit Properties to determine the limit of a sequence.]

Extension

Ask students to do the following.

1. Find the limits as $n \to \infty$ of each of these sequences:
   $a_n = \frac{1}{n^2}$; $b_n = \frac{1}{n^3}$; $c_n = \frac{1}{n^4}$; $d_n = \frac{1}{n^{-2}}$; $e_n = \frac{1}{n^{-3}}$; $c_n = \frac{1}{n^{-4}}$. [a, b, and c have limits of 0; d, e, and f are divergent.]

2. Make a generalization about the limit as $n \to \infty$ of the sequence $\frac{1}{n^k}$, where k is an integer. [For $k < 0$, the sequence diverges; for $k > 0$, the sequence has a limit of zero; for $k = 0$, the sequence has a limit of 1.]

Project Update Project 6, *A Test for Convergence*, on page 547, relates to the content of this lesson.

Adapting to Individual Needs

Challenge

1. In each of the following functions, describe the end behavior $x \to \infty$.

   a. $f(x) = 2x + 1$ $[f(x) \to \infty]$
   b. $f(x) = \frac{1}{2} \cdot 3^x$ $[f(x) \to \infty]$
   c. $f(x) = \left(\frac{1}{4}\right)^x$ $[f(x) \to 0]$
   d. $f(x) = \frac{x+1}{x}$ $[f(x) \to 1]$

2. Describe the end behavior of each of the following sequences.

   a. $a_n = 2n + 1$ [Diverges]
   b. $a_n = \frac{1}{2} \cdot 3^{n-1}$ [Diverges]
   c. $a_n = \left(\frac{1}{4}\right)^{n-1}$ [Converges to 0]
   d. $a_n = \frac{n+1}{n}$ [Converges to 1]

3. How do the functions in Question 1 relate to the sequences in Question 2? [For a given function f, in these cases, $y = f(x)$ and $a_n = f(n)$ have the same end behaviors.]

Question 21 It may be easier to prove the general theorem: If g_n are in a geometric sequence, then the sequence defined by $h_n = \log g_n$ is an arithmetic sequence. Proof: Since g_n are in a geometric sequence, $g_n = g_1 r^{n-1}$. So $\log g_n = \log g_1 + \log r^{n-1} = \log g_1 + (n-1)\log r = \log g_1 - \log r + n\log r$, which defines an arithmetic sequence with constant difference $\log r$.

Question 24 This is important review for Lesson 8-3.

Additional Answers

22. $m\angle A \approx 60°02'$,
    $m\angle B \approx 94°18'$,
    $b \approx 23$ or
    $m\angle A \approx 119°58'$,
    $m\angle B \approx 34°22'$,
    $b \approx 13$

23. a. $\displaystyle\sum_{i=1}^{4} a_i$

    b. $\displaystyle\sum_{n=2}^{10} b_n$

    c. $\displaystyle\sum_{j=1}^{n} m_j$

25. a. $\displaystyle\lim_{n\to\infty} \left(1 + \tfrac{1}{n}\right)^n \approx 2.718$

    $\displaystyle\lim_{n\to\infty} \left(1 + \tfrac{3}{n}\right)^n \approx 20.086$

    $\displaystyle\lim_{n\to\infty} \left(1 + \tfrac{8}{n}\right)^n \approx 2980.958$

    b. $\displaystyle\lim_{n\to\infty} \left(1 + \tfrac{1}{n}\right)^n = e$

    $\displaystyle\lim_{n\to\infty} \left(1 + \tfrac{3}{n}\right)^n = e^3$

    $\displaystyle\lim_{n\to\infty} \left(1 + \tfrac{8}{n}\right)^n = e^8$

    In general,
    $\displaystyle\lim_{n\to\infty} \left(1 + \tfrac{x}{n}\right)^n = e^x.$

18a) $g_n = \dfrac{100}{(-2)^{n-1}}$

b) $\begin{cases} g_1 = 100 \\ g_n = \left(-\tfrac{1}{2}\right)\cdot g_{n-1} \end{cases}$
(for all integers $n > 1$)

21a) $t_n = 5(3)^{n-1}$
b) $\log 5 \approx .70$,
$\log 15 = 1.18$,
$\log 45 \approx 1.65$,
$\log 135 \approx 2.13$,
$\log 405 \approx 2.61$
c) $t_n = 5 \cdot (3)^{n-1}$
so $\log t_n =$
$\log (5 \cdot 3^{n-1}) =$
$\log 5 + \log 3^{n-1} =$
$\log 5 + (n-1) \log 3$.
Therefore, the terms of $\log t_n$ form an arithmetic sequence with first term $\log 5$ and constant difference $\log 3$.

Review

18. For the geometric sequence $100, -50, 25, -12.5, \ldots$, write each.
    a. an explicit formula
    b. a recursive formula *(Lesson 8-1)*
    a, b) See left.
19. For the arithmetic sequence $3x + 2y, 4x + y, 5x, \ldots$, find each.
    a. the constant difference $x - y$
    b. the 50th term *(Lesson 8-1)* **$52x - 47y$**
20. What is the position of 105 in the arithmetic sequence $10, 15, 20, \ldots, 105, \ldots$? *(Lesson 8-1)* **20th term**
21. Consider the geometric sequence with terms $5, 15, 45, 135, 405, \ldots$.
    a. Find a formula for t_n, the nth term.
    b. Write the log of the first five terms in the geometric sequence.
    c. Prove that the numbers found in part **b** form an arithmetic sequence. *(Lessons 6-3, 8-1)*
    a–c) See left.
22. Find the other measures of the sides and angles of two non-congruent triangles in which $a = 20$, $m\angle C = 25°40'$, and $c = 10$. *(Lesson 5-4)*
    See margin.
23. *Skill sequence.* Represent using summation notation. See margin.
    a. $a_1 + a_2 + a_3 + a_4$
    b. $b_2 + b_3 + b_4 + \ldots + b_{10}$
    c. $m_1 + m_2 + m_3 + \ldots + m_n$ *(Lesson 1-3)*
24. Evaluate $\dfrac{2(2^{13} - 1)}{2 - 1}$. *(Previous course)* $2^{14} - 2 = 16382$

Exploration

25. Consider the sequences whose terms are defined by $\left(1 + \tfrac{r}{n}\right)^n$, where r is a constant. See margin.
    a. Use a computer or calculator to estimate, to the nearest thousandth, the limit of the sequence when $r = 1, 3,$ and 8.
    b. Each of the limits in part **a** is related to a power of e. Determine the relation and generalize what you observe.

Setting Up Lesson 8-3
Be certain to discuss **Question 24**.

A **series** is an indicated sum of terms of a sequence. If the number of terms added is infinite, the resulting series is an **infinite series**. If a finite number of terms is added, the resulting series is called a **finite series**.

For example, consider the sequence t with $t_n = \frac{1}{n!}$. Then

$$\sum_{n=1}^{5} t_n = \frac{1}{1!} + \frac{1}{2!} + \frac{1}{3!} + \frac{1}{4!} + \frac{1}{5!}$$

is a finite series, while

$$\sum_{n=1}^{\infty} t_n = \frac{1}{1!} + \frac{1}{2!} + \frac{1}{3!} + \ldots$$

is an infinite series.

If $a_1, a_2, a_3, \ldots, a_n$ are terms in an arithmetic sequence, then

$$S_n = a_1 + a_2 + a_3 + \ldots + a_n = \sum_{i=1}^{n} a_i$$

is called a **finite arithmetic series**, or simply, an **arithmetic series**.

Examples of Arithmetic Series

Suppose a child builds a figure with colored blocks in stages as illustrated below.

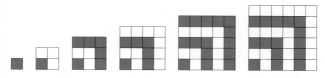

The number of blocks set down in each stage is a term in the arithmetic sequence of odd numbers $1, 3, 5, \ldots$. The final pattern consists of a 6×6 square of 36 blocks. So the number of blocks in the sixth pattern is the sum of the first six odd numbers.

$$1 + 3 + 5 + \ldots + 11 = 36$$

If a_n is the number of blocks added in the nth stage and S_n is the total number of blocks in the nth figure, then

$$S_6 = a_1 + a_2 + a_3 + \ldots + a_6 = \sum_{n=1}^{6} a_n.$$

Recall that an explicit formula for the nth odd number is $a_n = 2n - 1$. So

$$S_6 = \sum_{n=1}^{6} (2n - 1).$$

Lesson 8-3 Overview

Broad Goals A series is the sum of a finite number of terms of a sequence; an arithmetic series is derived from an arithmetic sequence. The two common formulas for finding the sum of arithmetic series are given here.

Perspective The series in this lesson serve as an introduction to the greater variety of series that are seen in the next two lessons. Although simple programs to add successive

terms of an arithmetic sequence might be written, we have avoided doing so. It is usually much more efficient to use the algebraic formulas than to use a program to deal with these situations.

To evaluate this expression, replace n with each of the integers 1 through 6, and add the resulting terms.

$$\sum_{i=1}^{6}(2n-1) = (2\cdot 1 - 1) + (2\cdot 2 - 1) + (2\cdot 3 - 1) + (2\cdot 4 - 1) +$$
$$(2\cdot 5 - 1) + (2\cdot 6 - 1)$$
$$= 1 + 3 + 5 + 7 + 9 + 11$$
$$= 36$$

Note the importance of the parentheses in $\sum_{i=1}^{6}(2n-1)$. In the expression $\sum_{i=1}^{6} 2n - 1$, the 1 is not part of the summation, and a different sum is indicated.

Example 1

Evaluate $\sum_{n=1}^{6} 2n - 1$.

Solution

Each of the six terms is of the form $2n$. Add them and then subtract one from the result.

$$\sum_{n=1}^{6} 2n - 1 = \left(\sum_{n=1}^{6} 2n\right) - 1$$
$$= (2(1) + 2(2) + 2(3) + 2(4) + 2(5) + 2(6)) - 1$$
$$= (2 + 4 + 6 + 8 + 10 + 12) - 1$$
$$= 41$$

❶ **A Story about Gauss**

To find the sum of the terms of a finite arithmetic sequence, one method is to add every term. Another way was discovered by the great mathematician Carl Friedrich Gauss (1777–1855) while he was in the third grade. As punishment for misbehavior, everyone in his class was asked to add the integers from 1 to 100. Here is what Gauss did.

Carl Friedrich Gauss as a youth was specially tutored in advanced mathematics and supplied with hard-to-get texts such as the algebra book shown above.

Suppose S_{100} represents the sum of the first 100 integers. So
$$S_{100} = 1 + 2 + 3 + \ldots + 99 + 100.$$
He rewrote the series beginning with the last term.
$$S_{100} = 100 + 99 + 98 + \ldots + 2 + 1$$
Then he added the two equations.
$$2S_{100} = 101 + 101 + 101 + \ldots + 101 + 101$$
The right side of the equation has 100 terms, each equal to 101. Thus
$$2S_{100} = 100(101).$$
He divided each side of the equation by 2.
$$S_{100} = 5050.$$

It is said that Gauss wrote nothing but the answer of 5050 on his slate, having done all the previous work in his head. Imagine the reaction of his teacher, who thought this would take a long time!

504

❷ A Formula for the Sum of Any Arithmetic Series

Gauss's strategy can be used to find a formula for the sum S_n of any arithmetic series. First, write S_n starting with the first term a_1 and successively add the constant difference d. Second, write S_n starting with the last term a_n and successively subtract the constant difference d.

$$S_n = a_1 + (a_1 + d) + (a_1 + 2d) + \ldots + (a_1 + (n-1)d)$$
$$S_n = a_n + (a_n - d) + (a_n - 2d) + \ldots + (a_n - (n-1)d)$$

Now add the two preceding equations.

$$2S_n = \underbrace{(a_1 + a_n) + (a_1 + a_n) + (a_1 + a_n) + \ldots + (a_1 + a_n)}_{n \text{ terms}}$$

The right side has n terms each equal to $a_1 + a_n$.

$$2S_n = n(a_1 + a_n)$$

Divide both sides by 2. $S_n = \frac{n}{2}(a_1 + a_n)$

This formula for S_n is useful if you know the first and nth terms of the series. If you do not know the nth term, you can find it using $a_n = a_1 + (n-1)d$ from Lesson 8-1. This leads to an alternative formula which you are asked to prove in the Questions.

Theorem

The sum $S_n = a_1 + a + \ldots + a_n$ of an arithmetic series with first term a_1 and constant difference d is given by

$$S_n = \frac{n}{2}(a_1 + a_n) \qquad \text{or} \qquad S_n = \frac{n}{2}(2a_1 + (n-1)d).$$

Uses of Arithmetic Series

Example 2

A student borrowed $4000 for college expenses. The loan was repaid over a 100-month period, with monthly payments as follows:

$$\$60.00, \$59.80, \$59.60, \ldots, \$40.20.$$

How much did the student pay over the life of the loan?

Solution

Find the sum $60.00 + 59.80 + 59.60 + \ldots + 40.20$. Because the terms show a constant difference $(d = 0.20)$, this sum is an arithmetic series with $a_1 = 60.00$, $n = 100$, and $a_{100} = 40.20$.

Use the formula $S_n = \frac{n}{2}(a_1 + a_n)$.

So $S_{100} = \frac{100}{2}(60.00 + 40.20)$
$$= 5010.$$

The student paid back a total of $5010.

Lesson 8-3   *Arithmetic Series*   **505**

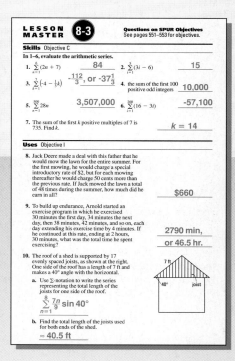

Example 3

In training for a marathon, an athlete runs 7500 meters on the first day, 8000 meters the next day, 8500 meters the third day, each day running 500 m more than on the previous day. How far will the athlete have run in all at the end of thirty days?

Solution

The distances form an arithmetic sequence, with $a_1 = 7500$ and $d = 500$. Because the final term is not known, use the second formula in the theorem.

$$S_{30} = \frac{30}{2}(2a_1 + (30-1)d)$$
$$= \frac{30}{2}(2(7500) + (30-1)500)$$
$$= 442{,}500 \text{ m}$$

The athlete runs 442.5 km in thirty days.

The formulas for S_n are also useful if S_n is known and you must find one of a_1, a_n, n, or d, as shown in Example 4.

Example 4

A woman is building a log playhouse for her children, with the design at the left for part of the roof. How should she cut a ten-foot log to get the five logs needed, if each log is to be eight inches longer than the one before it?

Solution

The lengths of the logs form an arithmetic sequence. You have $n = 5$, $d = 8$, and $S_5 = 120$. If you knew a_1, you would know how to cut the logs. Substitute into the formula for S_n and solve for a_1.

$$S_5 = \frac{5}{2}(2a_1 + (5-1)8)$$
$$120 = \frac{5}{2}(2a_1 + 32)$$
$$120 = 5a_1 + 80$$

Thus, $a_1 = 8$.

She should cut the top log 8 inches long. The other logs should be 16, 24, 32 and 40 inches long.

Check

$8 + 16 + 24 + 32 + 40 = \frac{5}{2}(8 + 40) = 120$

Adapting to Individual Needs

English Language Development
In common usage, the word "series" is often a synonym for sequence. For instance, we may speak of a series of lights, or the world series (a sequence of games). The mathematical use of the word "series" is different in that it refers to a sum.

Covering the Reading

In 1 and 2, refer to the child's pattern of blocks at the start of the lesson.

1. *Multiple choice.* Which expression represents the number of green blocks in the 6 × 6 square? **c**

   (a) $\sum_{n=1}^{3} (2n - 1)$ (b) $\sum_{n=1}^{3} (4n - 1)$

   (c) $\sum_{n=1}^{3} (4n - 3)$ (d) $\sum_{n=0}^{3} (2n + 1)$

2. Suppose the pattern is continued to form a 10 × 10 square.
   a. How many blocks are green?   **b.** How many blocks are white?
   45   **55**

3. What is the main difference between a sequence and a series?
   A series is an indicated sum of the terms of a sequence.

In 4 and 5, evaluate.

4. **a.** $\sum_{n=1}^{5} (2n + 1)$ **35**   **b.** $\sum_{n=1}^{5} 2n + 1$ **31**

5. **a.** $\sum_{n=1}^{5} (2^n + 3)$ **77**   **b.** $\sum_{n=1}^{5} 2^n + 3$ **65**

6. Find the sum of the first one thousand positive integers. **500,500**

7. A woman borrowed $6000 for 5 years. Her monthly payments were
   $145, $144.25, $143.50, $142.75, ... , $100.75.
   a. How much did she pay over the life of the loan? **$7372.50**
   b. How much interest did she pay on this loan? **$1372.50**

8. Refer to Example 3. How far will the athlete have run after two weeks?
   150.5 km

9. Refer to Example 4. How should a 12-foot log be cut to get five logs whose lengths form an arithmetic sequence with constant difference equal to 8 in.? **12.8 in., 20.8 in., 28.8 in., 36.8 in., 44.8 in.**

Applying the Mathematics

In 10 and 11, evaluate.

10. $\sum_{p=1}^{7} \left((-1)^p p\right)$ **-4**   11. $\sum_{p=1}^{7} p^p$ **873,612**

12) $S_n = \frac{n}{2}(a_1 + a_n)$. Since $a_n = a_1 + (n-1)d$, $S_n = \frac{n}{2}(a_1 + a_1 + (n-1)d)$; $S_n = \frac{n}{2}(2a_1 + (n-1)d)$.

12. Use the formulas $S_n = \frac{n}{2}(a_1 + a_n)$ and $a_n = a_1 + (n-1)d$ to prove that the sum of the first n terms of an arithmetic series with first term a_1 and constant difference d can also be written $S_n = \frac{n}{2}(2a_1 + (n-1)d)$.
    See left.

In 13 and 14, suppose a display of cans in a supermarket is built with one can on top, two cans in the next row, and one more can in each succeeding row.

13. If there are 12 rows of cans, how many cans are in the display? **78**

14. If 200 cans are available to be displayed, how many rows are needed, and how many cans will be left over? **19 rows, 10 left over**

Notes on Questions
Question 4–5 Error Alert Students who miss these questions may need reminding of the significance of parentheses or lack of parentheses in indicating a sum.

Question 7 A decreasing payment loan like the one discussed here is rare. Most loans require the same amount to be paid back each month.

Questions 13–14 These questions use a special case of the formula for an arithmetic series:
$$\sum_{i=1}^{n} i = \frac{n(n + 1)}{2}.$$

Adapting to Individual Needs

Challenge
If the measures of the angles of a convex pentagon (no interior angle is greater than 180°) form an arithmetic sequence, what are the greatest and least measures each angle can have? [Let the measures be a_1, a_2, a_3, a_4, and a_5 in increasing order. Since the sum is 540, $a_3 = 108$.

All else is determined by a_5. $a_4 = \frac{a_3 + a_5}{2}$, $a_2 = 216 - a_4$, and $a_1 = 216 - a_5$. Since a_5 must be less than 180, $108 < a_5 < 180$; and thus $108 < a_4 < 144$; $72 < a_2 < 108$, and $36 < a_1 < 108$.]

Practice
For more questions on SPUR Objectives, use **Lesson Master 8-3** (shown on page 505).

Assessment
Quiz A quiz covering Lessons 8-1 through 8-3 is provided in the *Assessment Sourcebook.*

Extension
To allow practice with manipulating the formulas, have students answer the following questions. The first answer involves solving a system, the second a quadratic.
1. The sum of the first seventeen terms of an arithmetic series is 493. The third term is 11. Find the first term and the seventeenth term. [5; 53]
2. The sum of the first n terms of an arithmetic series is -51. The series has a constant difference of -1.5 and a first term of 4. Find the number of terms in the sum. [12]

Project Update Project 3, *A Prime Number Sieve*, on page 546, relates to the content of this lesson.

19a) $\dfrac{\sqrt{3}}{2}, \dfrac{1}{2}, 0, -\dfrac{1}{2}, -\dfrac{\sqrt{3}}{2}$

20) $20\left(10^{\frac{1}{5}}\right) \approx 32$ mg;
$20\left(10^{\frac{2}{5}}\right) \approx 50$ mg;
$20\left(10^{\frac{3}{5}}\right) \approx 80$ mg;
$20\left(10^{\frac{4}{5}}\right) \approx 126$ mg

21a) $\begin{cases} a_{1996} = 206.6 \\ a_n = 1.015a_{n-1} \\ \text{for } n > 1996 \end{cases}$
b) $206.6(1.015)^{14} \approx$ 254.5 million

---

15. As part of a sales promotion, a large flag was made by attaching strips of plastic ribbon three inches wide to a pole. If the first strip is six inches long and each successive strip is four inches longer than the previous one, how many strips were cut from a roll of plastic ribbon 966 inches long? **21**
16. Write an expression for the sum of the first k terms of an arithmetic sequence with first term f and kth term m.
$S_k = \dfrac{k}{2}(f + m)$

Review

In 17 and 18, decide whether the sequence is convergent or divergent. If it is convergent, give its limit. *(Lesson 8-2)*
17. $\dfrac{8}{3}, \dfrac{11}{15}, \dfrac{16}{35}, \ldots, \dfrac{n^2 + 7}{4n^2 - 1}, \ldots$ **convergent;** $\dfrac{1}{4}$
18. $\dfrac{8}{3}, \dfrac{11}{7}, \dfrac{16}{11}, \ldots, \dfrac{n^2 + 7}{4n - 1}, \ldots$ **divergent**
19. Let $t_n = \cos\left(\dfrac{\pi}{6}n\right)$. **a) See left.**
    a. Write the first five terms of the sequence generated by this formula.
    b. State whether the sequence is arithmetic, geometric, or neither.
    c. Does $\lim\limits_{n \to \infty} t_n$ exist? If so, what is it? *(Lessons 4-5, 8-1, 8-2)*
    b) neither   **c) This limit does not exist.**
20. Life scientists often test animals' responses to doses of drugs or nutrients in amounts that form a geometric sequence. To test the content of vitamin A in carrots, pieces are fed to rats. Six dosage levels are arranged in a geometric sequence. If the lowest dose is 20 mg and the highest is 200 mg, find the other four doses. *(Lesson 8-1)* **See left.**
21. According to the U.S. Bureau of the Census's International Data Base, the population of Indonesia was estimated to be 206.6 million in 1996, and the annual growth rate was 1.5%. **a, b) See left.**
    a. Use this information to write a recursive formula for the sequence of annual Indonesian populations.
    b. Estimate the population of Indonesia in the year 2010.
    c. Give two reasons why the annual growth rate may not, in fact, remain constant. *(Lesson 8-1)* **Samples: Immigration may increase. The birth rate may change.**
22. Solve $3^x = 120$. *(Lesson 6-6)*
    $\dfrac{\log 120}{\log 3} \approx 4.358$

Exploration

23. Consider the arithmetic sequence of positive odd integers, $1, 3, 5, 7, \ldots$, and the new sequence formed by adding consecutive terms of the sequence
$$S_1 = \sum_{n=1}^{1} a_n = 1,$$
$$S_2 = \sum_{n=1}^{2} a_n = 1 + 3 = 4,$$
$$S_3 = \sum_{n=1}^{3} a_n = 1 + 3 + 5 = 9, \text{ and so on.}$$
    a. Determine S_4, S_5, and S_6. **16; 25; 36**
    b. Based on the results in part **a**, write a rule for the sum of the first n odd integers S_n. $S_n = n^2$
    c. Deduce your rule in part **b** from the general formula $S_n = \dfrac{n}{2}(a_1 + a_n)$. **See margin.**

Additional Answers
23. c. $S_n = \dfrac{n}{2}(a_1 + a_n) = \dfrac{n}{2}(1 + 2n - 1) = \dfrac{n}{2} \cdot 2n = n^2$

Royal Game. *Chess originated in India or China. When an opponent's king is about to be captured, the winning player declares "checkmate", which comes from the Persian words* shāh *"king" and* māt *"dead."*

An Example of Geometric Series

The story about Gauss in Lesson 8-3 is generally considered to be a true story. The example that begins this lesson is legend.

❶ The game of chess was invented between 1500 and 2500 years ago. A story is told that the king of Persia, after learning how to play, offered the game's inventor a reward. Clearing a chessboard, the inventor asked for one single grain of wheat on the first square, twice that on the second square, twice that again on the third, twice that again on the fourth, and so on for the whole board. The king, ready to give jewelry, gold, and other riches, thought that this was a modest request, easily granted. Was it?

The numbers of grains on the squares are $2^0, 2^1, 2^2, \ldots, 2^{63}$. They form a geometric sequence with $g_1 = 1$ and $r = 2$, and so the nth term is $g_n = 2^{n-1}$. Representing the total award for the entire chessboard by S_{64},

$$S_{64} = \sum_{n=1}^{64} 2^{n-1} = 1 + 2 + 4 + 8 + \ldots + 2^{63}.$$

S_{64} is a *finite geometric series*, analogous to the finite arithmetic series of the previous lesson.

To evaluate S_{64} without adding every term, you can use an approach similar to the one used for arithmetic series. First, write the series and then multiply each side of the equation by the constant ratio, 2.

$$S_{64} = 1 + 2 + 4 + \ldots + 2^{62} + 2^{63}$$

So, $\quad 2S_{64} = 2 + 4 + \ldots + 2^{62} + 2^{63} + 2^{64}$

Then, subtract the second equation from the first, term by term.

$$S_{64} - 2S_{64} = 1 + (2-2) + (4-4) + \ldots + (2^{62} - 2^{62}) + (2^{63} - 2^{63}) - 2^{64}$$

Lesson 8-4 *Geometric Series* **509**

Lesson 8-4 Overview

Broad Goals This lesson is to geometric series as the previous lesson was to arithmetic series. Given appropriate information about a geometric sequence, students should be able to find the sum of the first n terms using a formula.

Perspective When the constant ratio $r > 1$, then as n increases, both sequences and series can grow quite large rather

quickly. The case where $|r| < 1$ leads into the next lesson.

Lesson 8-4

Objectives
C Evaluate geometric series.
I Solve problems involving geometric series.

Resources
From the *Teacher's Resource File*
■ Lesson Master 8-4
■ Answer Master 8-4
■ Teaching Aid 72: Warm-up

Additional Resources
■ Visual for Teaching Aid 72

Teaching 8-4
Lesson

Warm-up

1. **a.** Find a formula for the sum S_n of the first n terms of the geometric series $1 + 3 + 9 + \ldots$. $S_n = \frac{3^n - 1}{2}$

   b. Use this formula to determine the sum of the first 10 terms of the series. **29,524; Note: If students have not read the lesson, have them write down the terms of the geometric sequence, calculate the first few terms of the series, and then double those terms. A pattern emerges.**

Notes on Reading

❶ This lesson begins with a classic story with a geometric sequence imbedded in it. The total number of grains of wheat is astonishingly huge, yet students may not be able to appreciate its magnitude. Therefore, you might wish to discuss **Question 24** during class.

❷ **Consumer Connection** The total world wheat production in 1995 was 541,120,000 metric tons, which is equivalent to approximately .58 cubic kilometers.

Error Alert You may find that even students who have had little trouble with summation notation get a bit confused when the index is in the exponent, as it is with

$$S_n = \sum_{i=1}^{n} a_1 r^{i-1}$$ For this reason,

Example 1 and **Questions 4–6** are important. For additional practice with the notation, you might want to have students write out the 8 terms of the sum in **Example 2**.

Because students know how to solve exponential equations, solving a problem like **Example 3** can be routine. Still, the list of values of the geometric series shows the growth in these values better than a simple computation of the answer.

Simplify.

$$-S_{64} = 1 - 2^{64}$$

So, $S_{64} = 2^{64} - 1.$

❷ Thus the total number of grains of wheat on the chessboard is $2^{64} - 1$, or 18,446,744,073,709,551,615. If you assume that each grain has the volume of a 4 mm $\times$ 1 mm $\times$ 1 mm rectangular box, the total volume of wheat would be about 74 cubic kilometers, many many times the amount of wheat in the world! Various versions of the story exist—what do you think happened to the inventor?

A Formula for the Sum of Any Geometric Series

In general, a **geometric series** is an indicated sum of terms of a geometric sequence. Suppose the sequence has first term g_1 and constant ratio r. The sum S_n of the first n terms of the sequence is called the **nth partial sum** and is written

$$S_n = g_1 + g_1 r + g_1 r^2 + \ldots + g_1 r^{n-1}$$
$$= \sum_{i=1}^{n} g_1 r^{i-1}$$

The procedure used to find S_{64} can be generalized.

$$S_n = g_1 + g_1 r + g_1 r^2 + \ldots + g_1 r^{n-1}$$
$$rS_n = g_1 r + g_1 r^2 + \ldots + g_1 r^{n-1} + g_1 r^n \qquad \text{Multiply } S_n \text{ by } r.$$
$$S_n - rS_n = g_1 - g_1 r^n \qquad \text{Subtract the preceding equations.}$$

$$(1 - r)S_n = g_1(1 - r^n) \qquad \text{Factor each side.}$$
And, if $r \neq 1$, $S_n = \frac{g_1(1 - r^n)}{1 - r}$ \qquad \text{Divide each side by } 1 - r.

This proves the following theorem.

Theorem

The sum $S_n = g_1 + g_2 + \ldots + g_n$ of the finite geometric series with first term g_1 and constant ratio $r \neq 1$ is given by

$$S_n = \frac{g_1(1 - r^n)}{1 - r}.$$

Example 1

Evaluate $\sum_{i=1}^{7} 18\left(\frac{1}{3}\right)^{i-1}$.

▶

510

Optional Activities

Activity 1 You might want to have students compare the opening geometric series with an arithmetic series. Suppose, instead, that 1 grain of wheat was put on the first square, 2 grains on the second, 3 on the third, and so on, with n grains on the nth square. Have students find the total number of grains on the entire chessboard. [2080 grains]

Activity 2 Social Studies Connection
In conjunction with **Question 21**, you might have interested students determine if any other countries have flags with three stripes of equal width which utilize the same colors. [Possible answers: Guinea and Mali (green, yellow, red vertical stripes); Netherlands, Yugoslavia and Russia (red, dark blue, and white horizontal stripes). Source: *The World Almanac and Book of Facts 1997*.]

Solution 1

This sum is a geometric series with $g_1 = 18$, $r = \frac{1}{3}$, and $n = 7$. Use the theorem on page 510.

$$S_n = \frac{g_1(1 - r^n)}{1 - r}$$

Substitute:

$$S_n = \frac{18\left(1 - \left(\frac{1}{3}\right)^7\right)}{1 - \frac{1}{3}}$$

$$= \frac{18\left(1 - \frac{1}{2187}\right)}{\frac{2}{3}}$$

$$= \frac{2186}{81}$$

$$= 26\frac{80}{81}$$

Solution 2

Evaluate each term and add them.

$$18 + 6 + 2 + \frac{2}{3} + \frac{2}{9} + \frac{2}{27} + \frac{2}{81} = 26\frac{80}{81}$$

Uses of Geometric Series

If you multiply the numerator and denominator of the formula for the sum of a geometric series by -1, you get an equivalent formula useful for situations where $r > 1$.

$$S_n = \frac{g_1(r^n - 1)}{r - 1}$$

Example 2

The set of a music show includes a backdrop in a design of nested triangles; the first four are shown at the left. The innermost triangle is the first built, having a perimeter of 0.55 meters. Each successive triangle has perimeter twice the previous one. What is the sum of the perimeters of the first eight nested triangles?

Solution

The sum begins $0.55 + 2 \cdot 0.55 + 4 \cdot 0.55 + \ldots$. Thus, the sum is the value of the finite geometric series g with $g_1 = 0.55$, $r = 2$, and $n = 8$.

$$S_n = \sum_{n=1}^{8} (0.55 \cdot 2^{n-1}),$$

Use the alternative formula for S_n.

$$S_n = \frac{g_1(r^n - 1)}{r - 1}$$

$$= \frac{0.55(2^8 - 1)}{2 - 1}$$

$$= 0.55(256 - 1)$$

$$= 140.25$$

The sum of the perimeters is 140.25 meters.

Adapting to Individual Needs

Extra Help

If students have trouble following the evaluation of S_{64} begun at the bottom of page 509, rewrite the equations for S_{64} and $2S_{64}$, writing the terms of $2S_{64}$ directly under those that match in S_{64}. Then, when the equations are subtracted, students will easily see that $S_{64} - 2S_{64} = 1 - 2^{64}$. Use this same strategy of aligning matching terms in the generalization for finding S_n on page 510.

Additional Examples

1. Evaluate $\sum_{i=1}^{6} 10(0.75)^{i-1}$.

   32.88085938

2. In a set of 10 Russian nesting dolls, each doll is $\frac{5}{6}$ the height of the taller one. If the height of the first doll is 15 cm, what is the total height of the dolls?

   $90(1 - \left(\frac{5}{6}\right)^{10}) \approx$ **75 cm**

3. Suppose you have two children who marry and each of them has two children. Each of these offspring has two children, and so on. If all of these progeny marry but none marry each other, and all have two children, in how many generations will you have a thousand descendants? Count your children as Generation 1. **10**

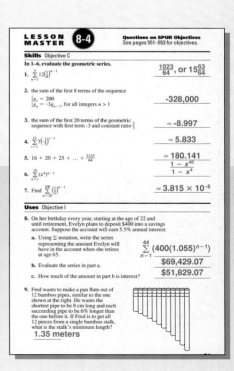

Notes on Questions

Question 2 This answer is not at all obvious. You may wish to compare the sum at each square with the number of grains on the next square.

Question 7 An extension is to ask students on which day the doubling process would have to end for the $1,000,000 to be the more valuable prize? [July 26]

(Notes on Questions continue on page 514.)

Great-Great-. . . Great-Grandparents. *About 19 generations ago, Pieter Bruegel depicted family gatherings in many of his paintings. Shown is a detail from* Peasant Wedding, *painted in 1565.*

Example 3

The maximum number of natural ancestors that you could have are 2 parents, 4 grandparents, 8 great-grandparents, and so on. Assuming that no one appears twice in your ancestral tree, in the last n generations you have S_n natural ancestors, where $S_n = 2 + 4 + 8 + \ldots + 2^n$. How many generations must you go back before you have a million natural ancestors, assuming that no one appears twice?

Solution

Use the alternate formula for S_n. Here $g_1 = 2$, $r = 2$, and n is unknown.

Solve
$$1,000,000 = \frac{2(2^n - 1)}{2 - 1}.$$
$$1,000,000 = 2(2^n - 1)$$
$$500,000 = 2^n - 1$$
$$2^n = 500,001$$
$$n = \frac{\ln 500,001}{\ln 2}$$
$$\approx 18.9$$

So, assuming no one appears twice on your ancestral tree, if you go back 19 generations, you have over a million ancestors.
(It is almost certain that many people have appeared twice on your tree.)

Check

Use a calculator or computer. The left column is the number of generations back. The right column is the maximum number of ancestors. So it checks.

1	2
.	.
.	.
.	.
17	262142
18	524286
19	1048574
20	2097150

QUESTIONS

Covering the Reading

In 1 and 2, refer to the chessboard story at the beginning of the lesson.

1. Explain why the numbers of grains on the squares of the chessboard form a geometric sequence. **The ratio between consecutive terms is constant (in this case, 2).**
2. *True or false.* The total number of grains on the first 63 squares of the chessboard is about half that on all 64 squares. **True**

3. *Multiple choice.* The expression $\sum_{i=1}^{n} a_1 r^{i-1}$ equals **b**

   (a) $\frac{a_1(1 - r)^n}{1 - r}$.   (b) $\frac{a_1(1 - r^n)}{1 - r}$.

   (c) $\frac{a_1(1 - r)^n}{r - 1}$.   (d) $\frac{a_1(1 - r^n)}{r - 1}$.

Adapting to Individual Needs

Challenge

Have students determine all right triangles whose side lengths form a geometric sequence.

$\left[a, \sqrt{\frac{1 + \sqrt{5}}{2}}\, a, \frac{1 + \sqrt{5}}{2}\, a \right.$ where a is the shortest side; or $a, \sqrt{\frac{-1 + \sqrt{5}}{2}}\, a, \frac{-1 + \sqrt{5}}{2}\, a$ where a is the longest side.$]$

4. **a.** Write the first six terms of the geometric sequence with first term -2 and constant ratio 3. **-2, -6, -18, -54, -162, -486**

   b. Evaluate $\sum_{i=1}^{6}(-2)3^{i-1}$ by adding the numbers in part **a**. **-728**

   c. Evaluate $\sum_{i=1}^{6}(-2)3^{i-1}$ using the theorem in the lesson. **-728**

In 5 and 6, find the sum.

5. $\sum_{n=1}^{8}3(0.5)^{n-1}$ **5$\frac{125}{128} \approx 5.98$**

6. $\sum_{i=1}^{20}10(1.5)^{i-1}$ $\approx$ **66,485.13**

7. As first prize winner in a lottery, you are offered a million dollars in cash, or a prize consisting of one cent on July 1, two cents on July 2, four cents on July 3, and so on, with the amount doubling each day until the end of July. Which prize is more valuable? Justify your choice.
The latter prize, because it is worth about 21.5 million dollars.

8. Refer to Example 2.
   a. What is the sum of the perimeters of the first seven triangles?
   b. Use your answer in part **a** to give the perimeter of the eighth triangle.
   a) 69.85 m   b) 70.4 m

9. **a.** At most, how many different natural ancestors does a person have 5 generations ago? **32**
   b. At most, how many different natural ancestors does a person have in the last 5 generations? **62**

10. How many generations must you go back before you have 10,000 ancestors assuming that no one appears twice? **13 generations**

11. Consider the geometric sequence 32, 24, 18, ...
   a. Use logarithms to find how many terms must be added to give a sum of more than 127. **17 terms**
   b. Check with a computer or a calculator. $S_{17} \approx$ **127.037831**

Applying the Mathematics

12a) $\sum_{n=1}^{k}pm^{n-1}$

b) $\frac{p(1 - m^k)}{1 - m}$

12. Consider the expression $p + mp + m^2p + \ldots + m^{k-1}p$.
   a. Rewrite the expression using Σ-notation.
   b. Write the sum as a single fraction.
   a, b) See left.

In 13 and 14, find the sum of the geometric series.

13. $3200 + 800 + 200 + \ldots + 3.125$ **4265.625**

14. $8 + -12 + \ldots + -60.75$ **-33.25**

15a) Samples: 1, 1, 1, 1, . . . 1; c, c, c, . . c.

b) Sample: $\frac{1(1 - 1^n)}{1 - 1}$ is not equal to the sum since the denominator is zero.

15. **a.** Give an example of a geometric sequence with common ratio one.
   b. Explain why the theorem for finding the sum of the first n terms of a geometric sequence does not apply to your answer in part **a**.
   c. Give the sum of the first n terms of your answer to part **a**.
   a, b) See left.   c) Samples: n; cn

16. Find an explicit formula for the nth term of a geometric sequence with common ratio 1.5 for which the sum of the first four terms is 65.
$g_n = 8(1.5)^{n-1}$

Practice

For more questions on SPUR Objectives, use **Lesson Master 8-4** (shown on page 511).

Assessment

Group Assessment Have students **work in small groups.** Refer to the story about the king of Persia on page 509. Ask students to determine how many grains of wheat would be awarded on the first eight squares, the second eight squares, and so on. Have them discuss the results. [Students evaluate geometric series.]

Extension

Cooperative Learning The following problem introduces a geometric sequence requiring difficult computation. You might have students **work in groups** on the solution. The earth's population, which passed 5 billion in 1987, has been growing at a rate at which it doubles about every 40 years. If this continues, how long would it be before there is a person for every square foot on the planet? For simplicity of calculation, you might suggest that students assume the population is 6 billion in the year 2000 and that the population were to continue to double every 40 years. Then assume the earth is a sphere with a radius of about 4000 miles. [About the year 2800]

Project Update Project 5, *Recursively Defined Curves* on page 547, relates to the content of this lesson.

Question 17 Error Alert A common error is to ignore the distance traversed as the ball bounces up. The sum of the distances the ball travels upward is the sum of the 8 distances the ball travels downward less 10 feet for the first drop, so students who ignore distances up get an incorrect answer of about 26 feet.

Question 21 If you have students who are fascinated by this question, see Activity 2 in *Optional Activities*, on page 510.

Question 22 This question is important review for Lesson 8-6.

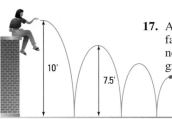

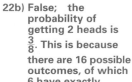

20a) $2, \frac{4}{3}, \frac{8}{7}, \frac{16}{15}, \frac{32}{31}$

22b) False; the probability of getting 2 heads is $\frac{3}{8}$. This is because there are 16 possible outcomes, of which 6 have exactly 2 heads.

Ireland

Ivory Coast

17. A Superball bounces to three-quarters of the height from which it falls. What is the total distance traversed by a Superball dropped nearly vertically from 10 feet above the ground before it hits the ground for the eighth time? (The actual bounce would be closer to vertical. The bounces are shown spread out to help you visualize the problem.) **about 62 ft**

Review

18. Consider these sums: $\sum_{i=1}^{10} (2i + 1)$ and $\sum_{i=1}^{10} (2i - 1)$.
Which is larger, and by how much? (Try to answer without calculating the value of either series.) *(Lesson 8-3)* $\sum_{i=1}^{10} (2i + 1)$ **is larger by 20.**

19. A new graduate accepts a job as a data processing clerk at a starting salary of $18,500 per annum, with an annual increment of $750. Suppose he stays in the job for ten years.
 a. How much will he earn in the 10th year? **$25,250**
 b. How much will he earn in total after ten years? *(Lessons 8-1, 8-3)* **$218,750**

20. Let $t_n = \frac{2^n}{2^n - 1}$.
 a. Write the first five terms of the sequence generated by t_n. **See left.**
 b. Does $\lim_{n \to \infty} t_n$ exist? If so, what is it? *(Lessons 8-1, 8-2)* **yes; 1**

21. Some countries have flags consisting of three stripes of different colors. The flags of Ireland and the Ivory Coast use the same colors, but in a different order. How many different flags can be designed consisting of three congruent stripes, either horizontal or vertical, where one is orange, one is white, and one is green? *(Lesson 7-4)* **12**

22. Imagine tossing a fair coin four times and recording heads or tails each time.
 a. How many elements are there in the sample space? **16**
 b. *True or false.* $P(2 \text{ heads}) = \frac{1}{2}$. Explain your answer. *(Lesson 7-1)* **See left.**

23. Let $f(x) = \frac{1}{x + 8} + 5$. *(Lessons 3-1, 3-2)*
 a. What transformation maps the graph of $y = \frac{1}{x}$ to the graph of $y = f(x)$?
 b. Give equations for the asymptotes of the graph of $y = f(x)$.
 a) $(x, y) \to (x - 8, y + 5)$ b) $x = -8, y = 5$

Exploration

24. Refer to the chessboard story at the start of this lesson.
 a. Express the volume for a single grain of wheat in terms of cubic kilometers, and explain how the approximate volume 74 km³ was obtained. **See margin.**
 b. If 74 cubic kilometers of wheat were spread evenly over the area of the 50 states of the United States, how deep would the wheat be? **See margin.**

Additional Answers
24. a. 4 mm × 1 mm × 1 mm
= $(4 \times 10^{-6}$ km$)(1 \times 10^{-6}$ km$)(1 \times 10^{-6}$ km$)$
= 4×10^{-18} km³ is the volume of 1 grain.
The volume of all the grain is the number of grains multiplied by the volume per grain:
$(1.85 \times 10^{19}$ grains$)(4 \times 10^{-18}$ km³/grain$) \approx$
7.4×10 km³ = 74 km³
b. The area of the U.S. is almost 3.54×10^6 mi² or about 9.17×10^6 km², so the wheat would be about 8.1 mm deep.

Setting Up Lesson 8-5

Use **Question 17** to ponder how far, in theory, the ball bounces before it stops. Ask how many students think the total distance traveled is infinite and how many think the total distance traveled is finite. Point out that the answer is given in Additional Example 2 in Lesson 8-5.

IN·CLASS
ACTIVITY

Exploring Infinite Series

You will need a graphing calculator or a computer for this activity.

1) See margin.

1 Consider the sequence $4, -\frac{4}{3}, \frac{4}{5}, -\frac{4}{7}, \frac{4}{9}, \ldots$ and the *partial sums* that result from adding the first n terms of the sequence.

n	S_n
1	4
2	$4 - \frac{4}{3} \approx 2.666666667$
3	$4 - \frac{4}{3} + \frac{4}{5} \approx 3.466666667$
4	$4 - \frac{4}{3} + \frac{4}{5} - \frac{4}{7} \approx 2.895238095$
5	$4 - \frac{4}{3} + \frac{4}{5} - \frac{4}{7} + \frac{4}{9} \approx 3.33968254$

a. Calculate S_n for $n = 6$ to 10.

b. What pattern(s) do you notice in the *sequence of partial sums*?

c. Do you think the sequence of partial sums converges? Why or why not? If the sequence converges, its limit is considered to be the sum of the *infinite series*

$$4 - \frac{4}{3} + \frac{4}{5} - \frac{4}{7} + \frac{4}{9} - \ldots$$

Do you think this sequence has a limit?

In 2 and 3, an infinite series is given. **a.** Find the first six partial sums for the infinite series. **b.** Make a conjecture about whether the infinite series converges or diverges.

2 $\sum_{i=0}^{\infty} 1.5^i = 1 + 1.5 + (1.5)^2 + (1.5)^3 + (1.5)^4 + \ldots$

3 $\sum_{i=0}^{\infty} 12 \cdot 0.5^{i-1} = 24 + 12 + 6 + 3 + \frac{3}{2} + \frac{3}{4} + \ldots$

2a) 1, 2.5, 4.75, $8\frac{1}{8}$, $13\frac{3}{16}$, $20\frac{25}{32}$
  b) Sample: The series seems to diverge.

3a) 24, 36, 42, 45, 46.5, 47.25
  b) Sample: The series seems to converge.

Technology Connection
Materials: Explorations software

Students may use *Exploration 8-5, Infinite Series*, to do this In-class Activity. Students explore different series by defining the *n*th term of the sequence. The computer will calculate and display the partial sums of the sequence in the table and on a graph.

In-class Activity

Resources
From the *Teacher's Resource File*
■ Answer Master 8-5

Additional Resources
■ Exploration 8-5

The series in Task 1 is called an *alternating series* because the additions and subtractions alternate. All alternating series in which the limit of the *n*th term is 0 are convergent. But this series converges very slowly. You can see this by noting that the 100th term of the series is $\frac{4}{199}$, which is greater than .02. Students might realize that it has a limit because the numbers being added and subtracted get smaller and smaller, but they should not at all anticipate that its limit is π.

In all the tasks, students should not be penalized for conjectures which do not happen to be true. Use conflicting conjectures to establish the need for more in-depth study of these series.

Additional Answers
1. a. $S_6 \approx 2.976046176$
     $S_7 \approx 3.283738484$
     $S_8 \approx 3.017071817$
     $S_9 \approx 3.252365935$
     $S_{10} \approx 3.041839619$
   b. Samples: The even terms of the series are less than the odd terms of the series. The odd terms decrease; the even terms increase.
   c. Answers will vary.

Objectives

G Tell whether an infinite series converges. If it does, give the limit.
I Solve problems involving infinite geometric series.

Resources

From the *Teacher's Resource File*
■ Lesson Master 8-5
■ Answer Master 8-5
■ Teaching Aids
  72 Warm-up
  75 The Jumping Flea

Additional Resources
■ Visuals for Teaching Aids 72, 75

Teaching Lesson **8-5**

Warm-up

1. Explain why
$$1 + \frac{1}{2} + \frac{1}{4} + \ldots + \frac{1}{2^{n-1}} + \ldots = 2.$$
There are many possible answers. Sample: The nth partial sum is
$$\frac{1 - (\frac{1}{2})^n}{1 - \frac{1}{2}} = 2 - (\frac{1}{2})^{n-1}.$$

2. Explain why
$$a + \frac{a}{2} + \frac{a}{4} + \ldots + \frac{a}{2^{n-1}} \ldots = 2a$$
The partial sums are a times those of Question 1, so if that limit is 2, this limit is $a \cdot 2$ or $2a$.

Infinite Series

What Is an Infinite Series?

In general, an *infinite series* is a sum that can be expressed in the form

$$\sum_{i=1}^{\infty} a_i = a_1 + a_2 + a_3 + \ldots$$

In the preceding In-class Activity you encountered three infinite series. As you saw in the In-class Activity, an important question about infinite series is whether the sum of the series exists. And if the sum does exist, what is it? These questions can be answered by looking at the sequence S_n of partial sums of the series, where the nth partial sum is given by $S_n = a_1 + a_2 + \ldots + a_n$. That is,

$$S_1 = a_1$$
$$S_2 = a_1 + a_2$$
$$S_3 = a_1 + a_2 + a_3$$
$$S_4 = a_1 + a_2 + a_3 + a_4$$
$$\vdots$$
$$S_n = a_1 + a_2 + \ldots + a_n$$

If the sequence $S_1, S_2, S_3, \ldots, S_n$ converges, then its limit $\lim_{n\to\infty} S_n$, written S_∞, is called *the sum of the series*.

> **Definition**
> The **sum S_∞** of the infinite series $\sum_{i=1}^{\infty} a_i$ is the limit of the sequence of partial sums S_n of the series, provided the limit exists and is finite. In symbols,
>
> if $\quad\quad\quad\quad\quad\quad S_n = \sum_{i=1}^{n} a_i,$
>
> then $\quad\quad\quad\quad S_\infty = \sum_{i=1}^{\infty} a_i = \lim_{n\to\infty} S_n = \lim_{n\to\infty} \sum_{i=1}^{n} a_i.$

If $\lim_{n\to\infty} S_n$ exists, the series is called **convergent** and its sum is S_∞. If the limit does not exist, the series is **divergent**. In the preceding In-class Activity you should have found two convergent and one divergent series.

Lesson 8-5 Overview

Broad Goals This lesson concentrates primarily on infinite geometric series because they can be studied analytically using the theorem from Lesson 8-4.

Perspective In a geometric series, if the constant ratio r satisfies $|r| < 1$, then as n increases, the sequence approaches 0 and the corresponding series also seems to approach a limit. The expression for that

limit, $\frac{g_1}{1-r}$, is wonderfully simple. The limits of other convergent infinite series are not so easy to obtain, but can be estimated with a calculator or computer.

Example 1

Consider the infinite geometric series $\sum_{i=1}^{\infty} \dfrac{3^{i-1}}{2}$. Find the first five partial sums.

Does the sequence of partial sums seem to converge? If so, what is the sum of the series?

Here are the first five terms: $\dfrac{1}{2} + \dfrac{3}{2} + \dfrac{9}{2} + \dfrac{27}{2} + \dfrac{81}{2} + \ldots$

Solution

$$S_1 = \dfrac{1}{2}$$

$$S_2 = \dfrac{1}{2} + \dfrac{3}{2} = 2$$

$$S_3 = \dfrac{1}{2} + \dfrac{3}{2} + \dfrac{9}{2} = \dfrac{13}{2} = 6.5$$

$$S_4 = \dfrac{1}{2} + \dfrac{3}{2} + \dfrac{9}{2} + \dfrac{27}{2} = \dfrac{40}{2} = 20$$

$$S_5 = \dfrac{1}{2} + \dfrac{3}{2} + \dfrac{9}{2} + \dfrac{27}{2} + \dfrac{81}{2} = \dfrac{121}{2} = 60.5$$

The sequence of partial sums appears to increase without a limit. So the infinite series diverges.

Example 2

With advanced mathematics it can be proved that the infinite series

$$\dfrac{1}{1^4} + \dfrac{1}{2^4} + \dfrac{1}{3^4} + \dfrac{1}{4^4} + \ldots$$

is convergent. Approximate its sum to the nearest thousandth.

Solution

Generate the sequence of partial sums. Examine the sums until several consecutive terms are the same. Our calculator gives the following output.

n	S_n
1	1
2	$1 + \dfrac{1}{16} = 1.0625$
3	$1 + \dfrac{1}{16} + \dfrac{1}{81} \approx 1.0748$
4	$1 + \dfrac{1}{16} + \dfrac{1}{81} + \dfrac{1}{256} \approx 1.0788$
5	$1 + \dfrac{1}{16} + \dfrac{1}{81} + \dfrac{1}{256} + \dfrac{1}{625} \approx 1.0804$
$\vdots$	
10	$\approx 1.0820\ldots$
$\vdots$	
100	$\approx 1.0823\ldots$

An approximation to S_∞ is about 1.082.

❶ Recall that the harmonic series $\dfrac{1}{1} + \dfrac{1}{2} + \dfrac{1}{3} + \ldots + \dfrac{1}{n} + \ldots$ is the sum of the terms of the sequence of reciprocals of the natural numbers. Although the partial sums of the harmonic series change slowly for large values of n,

Error Alert Caution students not to assume that the converse of the situation in **Example 1** is true. In **Example 1**, the terms of the sequence do not approach 0, so the series diverges. But some series, such as the harmonic series, diverge even though the terms of the sequence *do* approach 0, as discussed on page 518. Since this is not at all obvious to students, it is important that **Question 11** be discussed.

At this point in their mathematical careers, since students do not have calculus, a computer or calculator program is indispensable for analyzing infinite series which are not geometric.

❶ You may wish to refer interested students to Project 6, *A Test for Convergence*, on page 547 at this time.

Optional Activities

Cooperative Learning Have students **work in groups** and look back through Lesson 8-4, extending all geometric series in that lesson so that they are infinite. Have them classify each geometric series as either convergent or divergent. If convergent, have them give the sum. [Divergent: Example on p. 509, Example 2, Example 3, Questions 4, 6, 7, 14, 15, 16

Convergent:
Example 1, $S = 27$; Question 5, $S = 6$;
Question 11, $S = \dfrac{128}{3}$;
Question 13, $S = 12{,}800$;
Question 17, $S = 70$ feet]

❷ Fleance's fanciful situation is similar to one of Zeno's paradoxes, namely that a person can never get from point A to point B because to get to B, first the person must get halfway, and then the person must get halfway of the remainder, and halfway of the remainder, and so on. Here the flea will never get to the ring because we tacitly assume that each jump takes the same amount of time. Of course, people do get from A to B because the amount of time to traverse the halves is also being halved. So both sequences converge to a limit.

❸ **Technology** Technology is a great tool for helping to decide whether infinite series seem to diverge or not, and to what limit they converge if that is the case. It helps a great deal to work through an example or two, as is done here and in **Questions 11 and 24**. **Teaching Aid 75** contains the data on the jumping flea, so that you can compare values found from the formula with values found by computer.

Science Connection Jean Foucault (1819–1868) used a pendulum to provide the first direct proof that the Earth rotates on its axis. At the Pantheon in Paris, he suspended an iron ball that had a spike at the bottom from a steel wire that was more than 60 meters long. As the pendulum swung, the spike made marks in the sand on the floor. As time passed, the marks changed direction. Knowing that a swinging pendulum remains in the same plane, Foucault showed that the Earth moved beneath the pendulum.

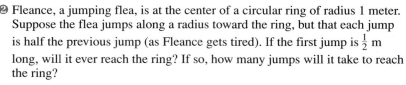

they *do* continue to grow larger than any integer as n gets larger. That is, the series is divergent, and has no sum. Because partial sums may increase slowly, you should be careful and not leap to the conclusion that a series has converged just from examining the partial sums.

To analyze most infinite series thoroughly, more advanced mathematics is needed. However, you can analyze infinite *geometric* series thoroughly.

An Example of an Infinite Geometric Series

❷ Fleance, a jumping flea, is at the center of a circular ring of radius 1 meter. Suppose the flea jumps along a radius toward the ring, but that each jump is half the previous jump (as Fleance gets tired). If the first jump is $\frac{1}{2}$ m long, will it ever reach the ring? If so, how many jumps will it take to reach the ring?

The jumps form a geometric sequence $\frac{1}{2}, \frac{1}{4}, \frac{1}{8}, \frac{1}{16}, \ldots$.

The total distance jumped equals $\frac{1}{2} + \frac{1}{4} + \frac{1}{8} + \ldots$.

The table at the right shows the total distances S_n after various numbers of jumps.

Number of Jumps	Total Distance Jumped	
1	$S_1 = \frac{1}{2}$	$= \frac{1}{2}$
2	$S_2 = \frac{1}{2} + \frac{1}{4}$	$= \frac{3}{4}$
3	$S_3 = \frac{1}{2} + \frac{1}{4} + \frac{1}{8}$	$= \frac{7}{8}$
4	$S_4 = \frac{1}{2} + \frac{1}{4} + \frac{1}{8} + \frac{1}{16}$	$= \frac{15}{16}$
⋮	⋮	
n	$S_n = \frac{1}{2} + \frac{1}{4} + \ldots + \frac{1}{2^n}$	

The total distances $S_1, S_2, S_3, S_4, \ldots, S_n$ form a new sequence, $\frac{1}{2}, \frac{3}{4}, \frac{7}{8}, \frac{15}{16}, \ldots$. In the case of the flea jumps, the original sequence is geometric with first term $\frac{1}{2}$ and common ratio $\frac{1}{2}$. So you can find a formula for the partial sum S_n using the theorem proved in Lesson 8-4 for the sum of a geometric series.

$$S_n = \frac{\frac{1}{2}\left(1 - \left(\frac{1}{2}\right)^n\right)}{1 - \frac{1}{2}}$$

$$= 1 - \left(\frac{1}{2}\right)^n$$

To find out the number of jumps needed to reach the edge of the ring, you need to know the smallest positive integer n such that $S_n \geq 1$.

Substitute $1 - \left(\frac{1}{2}\right)^n$ for S_n and solve.

If $\qquad\qquad\qquad\qquad 1 - \left(\frac{1}{2}\right)^n \geq 1,$

then $\qquad\qquad\qquad\qquad -\left(\frac{1}{2}\right)^n \geq 0.$

518

Adapting to Individual Needs

Extra Help
Some students may still be confusing sequences and series. Writing out the partial sums should be helpful. Students are asked to do this in **Questions 1–2**.

Challenge
Have students use the formula for the sum of a geometric series to show that $.\overline{9} = 1$.

$$\left[.9999 \ldots = \sum_{n=1}^{\infty} 9(.1)^n = \frac{.9}{1 - .1} = 1\right]$$

Notice that the left side of the inequality is always negative. So the sentence $S_n \geq 1$ has no real solution. This means that Fleance never reaches the ring.

❸ You can also use a computer or calculator to study $\lim_{n \to \infty} S_n$. At the left are some lines of output from a program that prints terms of the sequence generated by the formula $S_n = 1 - \left(\frac{1}{2}\right)^n$, where S_n represents the total distance jumped after n jumps.

NO. OF JUMPS	DISTANCE JUMPED
1	0.5
2	0.75
3	0.875
·	·
·	·
·	·
6	0.984375
7	0.9921875
8	0.9960938
·	·
·	·
14	0.9999390
15	0.9999695
·	·
·	·
23	0.9999999
24	0.9999999
25	1
26	1

From this output, you can see that although the flea never actually gets to the ring, it gets close enough for all practical purposes. Note that after 7 jumps, it is within 0.01 m of the ring; after 14 jumps it is within 0.0001 m and after 23 jumps, it is within 0.0000001 m of the ring. After 25 or more jumps, it is even closer than this, and the computer rounds off the total to 1, correct to 7 decimal places. This confirms that the sequence $\frac{1}{2}, \frac{3}{4}, \frac{7}{8}, \frac{15}{16}, \ldots$ of partial sums of the infinite series $\frac{1}{2} + \frac{1}{4} + \frac{1}{8} + \frac{1}{16} + \ldots$ converges to 1. That is,

$$\lim_{n \to \infty} \sum_{i=1}^{n} \frac{1}{2^i} = 1.$$

Thus, the total distance traveled by Fleance in a horizontal direction is 1 meter.

A Test for Convergence of Any Geometric Series

To examine infinite geometric series in general, consider the geometric sequence

$$g_1, g_1 r, g_1 r^2, \ldots, g_1 r^{n-1}, \ldots.$$

For large values of n, $|g_1 r^{n-1}|$ is large if $|r| > 1$, and $|g_1 r^{n-1}|$ is small if $|r| < 1$. This suggests that the convergence or divergence of the geometric series depends on the absolute value of the common ratio r.

The sum of the first n terms of the geometric sequence with first term g_1 and common ratio r is

$$S_n = \frac{g_1(1 - r^n)}{1 - r},$$

or

$$S_n = \frac{g_1 - g_1 r^n}{1 - r}.$$

For $|r| < 1$, r^n is very close to zero for very large values of n. In fact, it can be proved that

$$\lim_{n \to \infty} r^n = 0 \text{ whenever } |r| < 1.$$

So $\displaystyle \lim_{n \to \infty} S_n = \lim_{n \to \infty} \frac{g_1(1 - r^n)}{1 - r} = \frac{g_1}{1 - r} \lim_{n \to \infty}(1 - r^n)$ Limit Property 5

$\displaystyle = \frac{g_1}{1 - r}\left(\lim_{n \to \infty} 1 - \lim_{n \to \infty} r^n\right)$ Limit Property 3

$\displaystyle = \frac{g_1}{1 - r}(1 - 0)$ Limit Property 2
and $\lim_{n \to \infty} r^n = 0$

Thus $\displaystyle S_\infty = \frac{g_1}{1 - r}.$

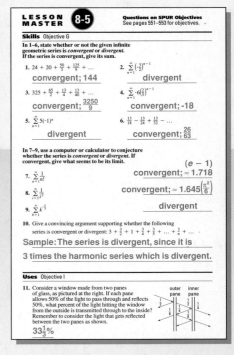

519

When $|r| > 1$, the term $g_1 r^n$ is farther from zero for every successive value of n, and the infinite series is divergent. For $|r| = 1$, the sequence is either $g_1, g_1, g_1, \ldots$, for which $S_n = ng_1$, or the sequence is $g_1, -g_1, g_1, -g_1, \ldots$, for which S_n is either 0 or g_1; in each case, the series is divergent. The following theorem summarizes these results.

Theorem
Consider the infinite geometric series
$$g_1 + g_1 r + g_1 r^2 + \ldots + g_1 r^{n-1} + \ldots, \text{ with } g_1 \neq 0.$$

a. If $|r| < 1$, the series converges and $S_\infty = \dfrac{g_1}{1 - r}$.

b. If $|r| \geq 1$, the series diverges.

Note that in the total distance of Fleance's jumps, $g_1 = \frac{1}{2}$ and $r = \frac{1}{2}$, so the series converges and $S_\infty = \dfrac{\frac{1}{2}}{1 - \frac{1}{2}} = 1$. In contrast, in Example 1, $g_1 = \frac{1}{2}$ and $r = 3$, so the series diverges.

Example 3

Because of air resistance, the length of each swing of a certain pendulum is 95% of the length of the previous swing. If the first swing has length 40 cm, find the total length the pendulum will swing before coming to rest.

Solution

The lengths of successive swings, measured in cm, form a geometric sequence.
$$40, 40(0.95), 40(0.95)^2, \ldots$$
To find the sum of the series
$$40 + 40(0.95) + 40(0.95)^2 + \ldots,$$
where $g_1 = 40$ and $r = 0.95$, use the theorem above. **Because $|r| < 1$, the sum exists.**

$$S_\infty = \frac{g_1}{1 - r}$$
$$= \frac{40}{1 - 0.95}$$
$$= 800 \text{ cm}$$

The pendulum swings through 800 cm, or 8 m.

A Swinging Time. *This Foucault pendulum in Chicago's Museum of Science and Industry is set in motion by burning a string which holds it stationary at night. It is in motion for the entire day.*

$\mathcal{Q}$UESTIONS

Covering the Reading

In 1 and 2, an infinite series is given. **a.** Write the first five partial sums. **b.** Does the sequence of partial sums appear to converge? If yes, what appears to be the sum of the series? If no, why do you think the series diverges?

1a) $\dfrac{1}{2}, \dfrac{7}{6}, \dfrac{23}{12}, \dfrac{163}{60}, \dfrac{213}{60}$

b) No. Sample: The sequence of partial sums appears to increase without limit.

1. $\dfrac{1}{2} + \dfrac{2}{3} + \dfrac{3}{4} + \ldots + \dfrac{n}{n + 1} + \ldots$
See left.

2. $\dfrac{1}{1^3} + \dfrac{1}{2^3} + \dfrac{1}{3^3} + \dfrac{1}{4^3} + \ldots + \dfrac{1}{n^3} + \ldots$
See margin.

In 3–5, refer to the series modeling the flea's jumps.

3. How far has the flea gone after 6 jumps? $\frac{63}{64} = .984375$ m

4. What is the smallest value of n so that Fleance is within 0.001 m of the edge of the ring? **10**

5. How close to the edge of the ring is the flea after 100 jumps? $\frac{1}{2^{100}} \approx 8 \times 10^{-31}$ m

6. Consider $\frac{1}{3} + \frac{1}{9} + \frac{1}{27} + \dots$
   a. Write the first three terms of the sequence of partial sums of this series. **1/3, 4/9, 13/27**
   b. Write an explicit formula for the nth partial sum. **See left.**
   c. Does the series converge? If so, what is its sum? **Yes;** $\frac{1}{2}$

6b) $\dfrac{1 - \left(\frac{1}{3}\right)^n}{2}$

In 7–9, state whether or not the geometric series is convergent. If the series is convergent, give its sum. **7) not convergent**

7. $3 - \frac{9}{2} + \frac{27}{4} - \frac{81}{8} + \dots$

8. $5 + 4 + 3.2 + 2.56 + \dots$ **convergent; 25**

9. $16 - 12 + 9 - 6.75 + \dots$ **convergent; $64/7 \approx 9.14$**

10. Refer to Example 3. How far would the pendulum travel if the length of each swing is 85% of the length of the previous swing?
    $266\frac{2}{3}$ cm

Applying the Mathematics

11a) $1 + \frac{1}{2} + \frac{1}{3} + \frac{1}{4} + \frac{1}{5}$

11. a. Write the first five terms of the harmonic series. **See left.**
    b. Use a calculator or a computer to find how many terms of the harmonic series must be added for the sum to exceed each of the following.
       i. 3 **b) 11**   ii. 5 **b) 83**
    c. *True or false.* The harmonic series is divergent. **True**

12. Consider a pile driver driving a 3-meter pile into the ground. The first hit drives the pile in 50 cm, the second hit drives the pile in 40 cm further, and successive distances driven form a geometric sequence.
    a. How far will the pile be driven into the ground if the pile driver is allowed to run forever? **250 cm**
    b. What percent of the total distance driven is reached after 20 hits? **≈ 98.85%**

13. a. Under what condition(s) will the following geometric series converge?
    $$b + \frac{b^2}{4} + \frac{b^3}{16} + \frac{b^4}{64} + \dots \quad |b| < 4$$
    b. Under the condition(s) in part **a**, what is $\lim_{n \to \infty} \sum_{i=1}^{n} \frac{b^i}{4^{i-1}}$? $\dfrac{4b}{4 - b}$

14. Find $\sum_{i=1}^{\infty} a_i$ for the sequence defined by
    $$\begin{cases} a_1 = 3 \\ a_n = (0.6)a_{n-1}, \text{ for all integers } n \geq 2. \end{cases} \quad 7.5$$

15. A ball dropped 60 feet rebounds on each bounce to $\frac{3}{4}$ of the distance from which it fell. How far will it travel before coming to rest? **420 ft**

16. Find the sum of the series $S = 1 + 3x + 5x^2 + 7x^3 + \dots$, given that $|x| < 1$. (*Hint:* Consider $S - Sx$.) $\dfrac{1 + x}{(1 - x)^2}$

Lesson 8-5 *Infinite Series* **521**

Question 11 Technology You may wish to do this question in class as part of the discussion of the last paragraph of the lesson and the notion that the terms of a sequence can converge to 0 while the corresponding series diverges. You can speed up the running of the program for large values of S_n by including an IF … THEN statement such as the one in line 40 below. The number 5 is the value asked for in **Question 11b(ii)**.

```
10   N = 1
20   SUM = 0
30   SUM = SUM + (1/N)
40   IF SUM > 5 THEN GOTO 70
50   N = N + 1
60   GOTO 30
70   PRINT N, SUM
```

Before you demonstrate the use of this program in class, you may want to test its execution time. On some machines it is painfully slow, so it may be necessary to start running the program before class.

Question 15 Students can compare this with **Question 17** about the Superball in Lesson 8-4.

Question 16 This is a difficult question. Give plaudits to anyone who can do it.

Notes on Questions

Question 24 This is the Taylor series expansion for sin *x*. Students who take calculus should encounter not only this series but many other like it.

Practice

For more questions on SPUR Objectives, use **Lesson Master 8-5** (shown on page 519).

Assessment

Written Communication Have students **work in pairs**. Ask students to define a geometric series with $|r| < 1$. Then students should find S_∞ for their partner's series. [Students give the limit of an infinite series.]

Extension

It can be shown that $0.333 \ldots = \frac{1}{3}$ using geometric series. Explain to students that 0.333 ... can be written as an infinite geometric series:
$0.3 + 0.03 + 0.003 + 0.0003 + \ldots$, with first term 0.3 and common ratio 0.1. Have them find the following.
1. The sum of this series in *fraction* form
$[\frac{0.3}{1 - .1} = \frac{0.3}{0.9} = \frac{3}{9} = \frac{1}{3}]$
2. The exact fractions for 0.444 ..., 0.272727..., and 0.324324324 ...
$[\frac{4}{9}, \frac{3}{11}, \frac{12}{37}]$

Project Update Project 2, *Infinity in Art*, Project 5, *Recursively Defined Curves*, and Project 6, *A Test for Convergence,* on pages 545–546, relate to the content of this lesson.

24a) $s(1) \approx .841471$;
$s(\frac{\pi}{2}) \approx 1.0000035$

17. A hot air balloon rises 60 ft in the first minute after launching. In each succeeding minute, it rises 80% as far as in the previous minute.
(Lessons 8-1, 8-4)
   a. How far does it rise during the sixth minute after launching? ≈ **19.7 ft**
   b. How far will it have risen after 10 minutes? ≈ **268 ft**
   c. How long will it take to reach a height of 260 feet?
   about 9 minutes

18. Prove that the sum of the integral powers of 2 from 2^0 to 2^{n-1} is $2^n - 1$.
(Lesson 8-4) $1 + 2 + 4 + 8 + \ldots + 2^{n-1} = \frac{1(1 - 2^n)}{1 - 2} = 2^n - 1$

In 19 and 20, evaluate. *(Lessons 8-3, 8-4)*

19. $\sum_{k=1}^{6} 3^k$ **1092**

20. $\sum_{k=1}^{6} (3 - k)$ **-3**

21. Find the first positive term of the arithmetic sequence $-101, -97, -93, \ldots$. *(Lesson 8-1)* **3**

22. *Skill sequence.* *(Lesson 7-4)*
   a. How many permutations are there of the letters in FLEAS? **120**
   b. How many of the permutations in part **a** begin with the letter A? **24**
   c. How many of them begin with A and end with S? **6**

23. *True or false.* For $n \geq 1$, $n! = n \cdot (n - 1)!$ *(Lesson 7-3)* **True**

24. Consider the function defined by the infinite series **a) See left.**

$$s(x) = x - \frac{x^3}{3!} + \frac{x^5}{5!} - \ldots + \frac{(-1)^{n-1}x^{2n-1}}{(2n - 1)!} + \ldots$$

   a. Approximate $s(1)$ and $s(\frac{\pi}{2})$ using the first five terms in the definition.
   b. Write a computer or calculator program which accepts as input positive integers *x* and *n*, and produces as output $s(x)$ approximated by the *n*th partial sum of the series. **See margin.**
   c. This series converges to $\sin(x)$ for any real value of *x*. Use the program you wrote in part **b** to determine how many terms of the series are needed to obtain an accuracy of three decimal places for all values of *x* in the interval $-\pi \leq x \leq \pi$.
   For 3 digits, 7 terms are needed.

Additional Answers
24. b. Sample:

```
10   INPUT "ENTER THE NUMBER OF TERMS",N
20   INPUT "ENTER X",X
30   TERM = X
40   SUM = TERM
50   FOR I = 2 TO N
60   TERM = (-1)*TERM*X*X/((2*I − 1)*(2*I − 2))
70   SUM = SUM + TERM
80   NEXT I
90   PRINT SUM
100  END
```

LESSON 8-6

Combinations

Using Series to Solve Counting Problems

Sequences and series can be used to solve certain counting problems. Consider the following situation. Six friends, June, Kevin, Luis, Maria, Noor, and Olivia, leave a restaurant. Each person says good-bye to each of the others with a handshake. How many handshakes are needed?

To answer this question, you might consider one person at a time. Suppose June starts by shaking hands with each of the others: Kevin, Luis, Maria, Noor, and Olivia. Then, since Kevin and June have already said good-bye to each other, Kevin shakes hands with each of Luis, Maria, Noor, and Olivia. The following pattern develops:

J	shakes hands with *K, L, M, N,* and *O*;
K	shakes hands with *L, M, N,* and *O*;
L	shakes hands with *M, N,* and *O*;
M	shakes hands with *N* and *O*;
and *N*	shakes hands with *O*.

Thus, the number of handshakes is $5 + 4 + 3 + 2 + 1 = 15$.

The number of handshakes can also be determined using the Multiplication Counting Principle. There are six choices for the first person in the pair and five choices for the second, so there are $6 \cdot 5 = 30$ ordered pairs of people. This set of thirty pairs are permutations of 2 objects chosen from 6. But the thirty pairs contain *JK* and *KJ, NO* and *ON*, and so on. Thus, the actual number of handshakes is only $\frac{1}{2}$ of 30, or 15.

Lesson 8-6 Overview

Broad Goals A combination is a subset of a set, and counting these subsets is surprisingly useful. The first task of this lesson is to exhibit situations where combinations are desired. Then, a formula for the number of combinations of *n* things taken *r* at a time is derived.

Perspective The different common notations that exist for the number of combinations of *n* things taken *r* at a time, $_nC_r$, $C(n,r)$, and $\binom{n}{r}$ are an indication of the importance and breadth of this concept. We use the $_nC_r$ notation most often in this book. The $C(n,r)$ notation, which we do not use, emphasizes that combinations are functions of two variables. The $\binom{n}{r}$ notation is perhaps the most commonly used notation in advanced courses, but students often confuse it with fractions.

523

Combinations and permutations are quite different. Emphasize: that *permutations are arrangements,* and *combinations are subsets.* In permutations, order matters; in combinations, order does not matter. But they are both names given to objects in counting problems, and since $_nP_r$ is used to derive the formula for $_nC_r$, it is difficult to cover combinations without bringing permutations into the discussion.

❶ It is useful to compare similar combination and permutation problems, as is done after **Example 2**.

As with permutations, calculating combinations involving large numbers may require students to do some arithmetic *before* they can use their calculators. Have students verify the answer to **Example 3** by considering the fraction $\frac{48 \cdot 47 \cdot 46 \cdot 45 \cdot 44 \cdot 43}{6 \cdot 5 \cdot 4 \cdot 3 \cdot 2 \cdot 1}$, simplifying it by removing common factors to $47 \cdot 46 \cdot 3 \cdot 44 \cdot 43$, and multiplying these numbers. Students will be surprised that every factor in the denominator has a corresponding factor in the numerator. Remind students that because the value of the fraction is an integer, this must always happen!

Pacing Although you may not cover all this lesson has to offer in a single day, the next lesson does not consider new types of problems, so it is possible to move on and finish discussion then.

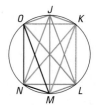

Each of the above solutions is pictured at the left. The five blue segments, with J as an end-point, represent June's handshakes. The five segments with endpoint K, one blue and four orange, represent Kevin's handshakes, and so forth. The segments (5 blue, 4 orange, 3 green, 2 black, and 1 purple) represent $5 + 4 + 3 + 2 + 1$ handshakes. You can also count five segments ending or beginning at each of the six points. You might think there are 30 segments in all, but if you count them, you will see that there are only 15, because you have counted each segment twice.

The methods used to solve the preceding problem can be generalized.

Example 1

Suppose that n people meet at a wedding, and each person greets each of the others with a hug. How many hugs take place?

Solution 1

Consider the number of people each person hugs. No person greets himself or herself. So, **the first person hugs n − 1 people; the second person, having already greeted the first, hugs each of the n − 2 other people; the third person then hugs each of the n − 3 others, etc. So the number of hugs is (n − 1) + (n − 2) + (n − 3) + . . . + 1, an arithmetic series with first term n − 1, last term 1, and n −1 terms. So the sum is** $\left(\frac{n-1}{2}\right)((n - 1) + 1) = \left(\frac{n-1}{2}\right)n.$

Solution 2

There are n(n − 1) ordered pairs of two people chosen from n people. So the number of unordered pairs, corresponding to the number of hugs, is $\frac{n(n-1)}{2}$**.**

What Is a Combination?

The preceding problems involve *combinations*. A **combination** is a collection of objects in which the order of the objects does not matter.

Example 2

Multiple choice. Which of the following situations involves a combination?
(a) Twenty students are semi-finalists for three scholarships—one for $1500, one for $1000, and one for $500. In how many different ways can the scholarships be awarded?
(b) Twenty students are semi-finalists for three $1000 scholarships. In how many different ways can the scholarships be awarded?

Solution

For choice (a), the amounts awarded are different, so the order of the winning students matters. For choice (b), the scholarships are equal, so the order of the winning students does not matter. The situation of choice (b) is a combination.

❶ The answer to the question in choice (a) of Example 2 is the number of *permutations* of 20 things taken 3 at a time. In contrast, the answer to choice (b) is called the number of *combinations* of 20 people taken 3 at a time, written $_{20}C_3$. To calculate $_{20}C_3$, note that for any one of these combinations of 3 students, say A, B, and C, there are $3! = 6$ possible permutations: $A\,B\,C$, $A\,C\,B$, $B\,A\,C$, $B\,C\,A$, $C\,A\,B$, and $C\,B\,A$.

Thus, $3! \cdot {_{20}C_3} = {_{20}P_3} = 6840$. So $_{20}C_3 = \frac{6840}{3!} = 1140$. Thus there are 1140 different ways to award three $1000 scholarships when choosing from 20 students.

In general, the **number of combinations of *n* things taken *r* at a time** is written $_nC_r$ or $\binom{n}{r}$. Some people read this as "*n* choose *r*." A formula for $_nC_r$ can be derived from the formula for $_nP_r$ by generalizing the argument in the previous paragraph. Each combination of r objects can be arranged in $r!$ ways.

So $r! \, {_nC_r} = {_nP_r}$.

Thus, $_nC_r = {_nP_r} \cdot \frac{1}{r!}$.

$_nC_r = \frac{n!}{(n-r)!} \cdot \frac{1}{r!}$ Substitute from the Formula for $_nP_r$ Theorem.

So $_nC_r = \frac{n!}{(n-r)!\,r!}$.

Theorem (Formula for $_nC_r$)

For all whole numbers n and r, with $r \leq n$,

$$_nC_r = \frac{1}{r!} \cdot {_nP_r} = \frac{n!}{(n-r)!\,r!}.$$

Example 3

A menu at a Chinese restaurant contains 48 main dishes. A group of friends chooses 6 different dishes. In how many different ways can they do this?

Solution

There are 48 dishes, from which 6 are to be chosen. Since the order in which the dishes are chosen does not matter, you want $_{48}C_6$. Use the Formula for $_nC_r$.

$$_{48}C_6 = \frac{48!}{42!\,6!}$$

A calculator gives $_{48}C_6 = 12{,}271{,}512$.

There are over 12 million different meals possible!

Lesson 8-6   *Combinations*   **525**

Adapting to Individual Needs

Extra Help

Some students may need extra help in understanding the difference between combinations and permutations. Use the *Warm-up* for this lesson to reinforce this concept.

English Language Development

You might help with the distinctions between the words "permutation" and "combination" by noting that when things are combined, we seldom are concerned with the order.

Activity

Graphics calculators usually have a built-in function for calculating $_nC_r$, which can be more convenient to use than the above formula. On some, you enter n first, then select the $_nC_r$ feature, and then enter r. On others you select the $_nC_r$ feature first.

a. Find out how the $_nC_r$ feature works on your calculator and use it to check Example 3.

b. If the restaurant adds two new dishes to its menu, how many more ways are there to choose six dishes? **3,619,188**

Sometimes numbers resulting from computing a combination are too large for a calculator's memory. Or the display may only give you an approximate answer, because scientific notation has been used. In such cases, it may be necessary to do some calculation by hand first, as Example 4 shows.

Example 4

A football team with a roster of 60 players randomly selects 7 players from the roster for drug testing. What is the probability that its star quarterback and its star middle linebacker are both selected?

Solution

There are $_{60}C_7$ combinations of 7 players that could be picked. To determine how many of these combinations include the two star players, note that each such combination includes 5 players from the remaining 58 on the roster. There is only one way to select the star quarterback and linebacker ($_2C_2 = 1$) and there are $_{58}C_5$ ways to select the other 5 players. Thus, the probability that these two stars are selected, assuming randomness, is

$$\frac{_2C_2 \cdot {}_{58}C_5}{_{60}C_7} = \frac{1 \cdot \frac{58!}{53!5!}}{\frac{60!}{53!7!}} = \frac{58!7!}{60!5!} = \frac{7 \cdot 6}{60 \cdot 59} \approx 0.012.$$

QUESTIONS

Covering the Reading

In 1–3, suppose the 26 students in a class each shake hands once with each other.

1. Use an arithmetic series to calculate the number of handshakes that take place. $25 + 24 + \ldots + 1 = \frac{25}{2}(25 + 1) = 325$

2. Use the Multiplication Counting Principle to calculate the number of handshakes that take place. $\frac{26 \cdot 25}{2} = 325$

3. *True or false.* The number of handshakes that takes place is $_{26}C_2$. **True**

Adapting to Individual Needs

Challenge

Have students answer the following questions

1. Let S be a set with 4 elements.
 a. Complete the table.

r	0	1	2	3	4
# of subsets of size r	[1]	[4]	[6]	[4]	[1]
$_4C_r$	[1]	[4]	[6]	[4]	[1]

b. What conclusion do you draw from the table in part a? [The number of subsets of size r from a set of size n is $_nC_r$.] What makes your conclusion reasonable? [Subsets are unordered collections; i.e. combinations.]

2. Let S be a set with n elements.
 a. Complete the table. Include the empty set and S itself as subsets.

n	1	2	3	4	5
# of subsets of any size	[2]	[4]	[8]	[16]	[32]

b. What conclusion do you draw from the table? [A set of size n has 2^n subsets.]

4. Match each item on the left with its description on the right.
   a. combination **ii**   (i) an arrangement of objects in order
   b. permutation **i**   (ii) a selection of objects without regard to order

5. a. How many combinations of the letters UCSMP taken two at a time are possible? **10**
   b. List them all. **UC, US, UM, UP, CS, CM, CP, SM, SP, MP**

In 6–8, evaluate.

6. $_{18}C_3$ **816**   **7.** $_{14}C_1$ **14**   **8.** $_{103}C_0$ **1**

9. In how many ways can a person order eight different dishes from a list of 48? **377,348,994**

10. What is your answer to part **b** of the Activity in the lesson? **See page 526.**

11. Suppose 13 players from a track squad of 52 are chosen for drug testing.
   a. What is the number of combinations of players that could be chosen?
   b. How many of these combinations include both of the captains?
   c. What is the probability that both captains are chosen? ≈ **0.059**
   a) **635,013,559,600**   b) **37,353,738,800**

Applying the Mathematics

In 12–14, evaluate the expression.

12. $_nC_n$ **1**   **13.** $_nC_1$ **n**   **14.** $_nC_0$ **1**

15. When $r > 1$, which is larger, $_nC_r$ or $_nP_r$? Justify your answer. **See left.**

16. A lottery which requires guessing 6 numbers out of 50 in any order sells $1 tickets. A group of people decides to buy 12,000,000 tickets. Can they ensure that they win? Justify your answer. **No. Sample:** $_{50}C_6 =$ **15,890,700 tickets. Their chance of winning is about 76%.**

17. Six points are in a plane so that no three are collinear, as shown at the left.
   a. How many triangles can be formed having these points as vertices?
   b. Generalize your result in part **a** to the case of n noncollinear points.
   a) **20**   b) **See left.**

18. In the situation of Example 3, suppose that the 48 dishes are equally divided into seafood, meat, and vegetable. How many different meals are possible if the friends want two dishes from each group? **1,728,000**

19. A standard deck of playing cards has 52 different cards: 13 each of clubs, diamonds, hearts, and spades. **See left.**
   a. How many different five-card hands are possible?
   b. How many of the hands in part **a** contain only spades?
   c. What is the probability of getting a five-card hand that is all spades?

20. a. Evaluate each expression.
   i. $_9C_4$ **126**
   ii. $_9C_5$ **126**
   iii. $_8C_2$ **28**
   iv. $_8C_6$ **28**
   b. Find a value of k other than 3 for which $_{10}C_3 = _{10}C_k$. **7**
   c. Generalize the pattern observed in parts **a** and **b**.
   d. Prove that your generalization is true.
   c) $_nC_{n-r} = {}_nC_r$ d) **See margin.**

Lesson 8-6 *Combinations* **527**

---

15) $_nP_r$ is larger. Sample:

$$\frac{_nP_r}{_nC_r} = \frac{\dfrac{n!}{(n-r)!}}{\dfrac{n!}{r!(n-r)!}} =$$

$r! > 1$, so $_nP_r > {}_nC_r$

17b) $_nC_3 = \dfrac{n!}{3!(n-3)!}$

19a) $_{52}C_5 = 2{,}598{,}960$
   b) $_{13}C_5 = 1287$
   c) $\dfrac{1287}{2{,}598{,}960} \approx$
   $0.0005 \approx \dfrac{1}{2000}$

Notes on Questions
Questions 12–14 and 20 These questions are relevant to the properties of Pascal's Triangle, discussed in the next lesson. **Question 12** gives the numbers in the right diagonal; **Question 14** gives the numbers in the left diagonal; **Question 13** gives the second diagonal to the left; and **Question 20** shows the symmetry of each row to the middle.

Question 16 If your state has a lottery, some of your students are likely to know quite a few of the details. You might wish to localize this question to deal with your own situation.

Question 19 In our testing of previous versions of this book, we found that the number of students who have a working knowledge of a standard deck of playing cards seems to be decreasing with time. Thus you may need to teach the names and colors of the four suits, and the names of the ranks of cards.

Additional Answers
20. d. $_nC_{n-r}$
$$= \frac{n!}{(n-r)![n-(n-r)]!}$$
$$= \frac{n!}{(n-r)!\,r!}$$
$$= {}_nC_r$$

Practice

For more questions on SPUR
Objectives, use **Lesson Master 8-6**
(shown on page 525).

Assessment

Quiz A quiz covering Lessons 8-4
through 8-6 is provided in the
Assessment Sourcebook.

Extension

Generalize **Question 17**. Suppose
n points are in space, no three are
collinear and no four of them are
coplanar. How many tetrahedra can
be formed with these points as vertices? $[_nC_4]$

Project Update Project 4, *Probabilities and the Lottery*, on page 547,
relates to the content of this lesson.

*The Chicago Bulls won the
1997 NBA championship
with a series of the form
XXYYXX.*

Review

21. **a.** Determine the sum of the infinite geometric series
$$1 - \tfrac{1}{4} + \tfrac{1}{16} - \tfrac{1}{64} + \dots + \left(-\tfrac{1}{4}\right)^{n-1} + \dots \quad \textbf{0.8}$$
   b. Based on the result in part **a**, determine the sum $\sum_{i=1}^{\infty}\left(b\left(-\tfrac{1}{4}\right)^{i-1}\right)$, where b
   is any real number. *(Lessons 8-2, 8-5)* **0.8b**

22. **a.** Evaluate, giving your answer as a fraction.
$$\frac{3\left(1 - \left(\tfrac{1}{3}\right)^6\right)}{1 - \tfrac{1}{3}} \quad \frac{364}{81}$$
   b. Write a geometric series having the value in part **a** as a sum.
   (Lesson 8-4) $\sum_{i=1}^{6} 3\left(\tfrac{1}{3}\right)^{i-1}$ or $3 + 1 + \tfrac{1}{3} + \tfrac{1}{9} + \tfrac{1}{27} + \tfrac{1}{81}$

23. Solve $6 \cdot {}_nP_2 = {}_9P_4 + 12$. *(Lesson 7-4)* $n = 23$

24. A test has 10 multiple-choice questions with five choices, 15 true-false
   questions, and 5 questions which require matching from a list of
   6 choices. In how many ways can you answer the test in each situation?
   a. You must answer each question. $(5^{10})(2^{15})(6!) = 2.304 \times 10^{14}$
   b. You must answer the matching questions, but you have the option of
   leaving some true-false or multiple-choice questions blank. *(Lesson 7-3)*
   $(6^{10})(3^{15})(6!) \approx 6.247 \times 10^{17}$

Exploration

25. In professional baseball, basketball, and ice hockey the championship is
   determined by two teams playing a best of seven series. (The first team to
   win four games wins the series.) Call the two teams X and Y.
   a. In how many different ways can the series occur if team X wins?
   For instance, two different 6-game series are $XXYXYX$ and $XYYXXX$.
   (Hint: Determine the different numbers of 4-game series, 5-game series,
   6-game series, and 7-game series.)
   b. There is a ${}_nC_r$ with n and r both less than 10 which equals the answer
   for part **a**. Find n and r. $n = 7$, $r = 4$ or $n = 7$, $r = 3$
   c. Explain why the combination of part **b** answers the question of part **a**.
   a) ${}_3C_3 + {}_4C_3 + {}_5C_3 + {}_6C_3 = 35$
   c) Sample: ${}_7C_4$ gives the number of ways X can win exactly 4 out
   of 7 games. A series of fewer than 7 games can be thought of as
   a 7-game series in which X loses all games after its fourth victory.
   Therefore, ${}_7C_4$ counts all the possible series.

LESSON

8-7

Pascal's Triangle

The combinations of Lesson 8-6 came from counting problems but have important applications to powers of binomials and to probability. You will encounter these applications in the next two lessons. For this reason, it is helpful to know how combinations are related to each other. Many of the relationships among combinations can be seen in the array of numbers known as *Pascal's Triangle*.

What Is Pascal's Triangle?

For a given value of n, you can calculate ${}_nC_0, {}_nC_1, {}_nC_2, \dots, {}_nC_n$, a total of $n + 1$ calculations. For instance, for $n = 4$, the 5 values are

$${}_4C_0 = 1 \quad {}_4C_1 = 4 \quad {}_4C_2 = 6 \quad {}_4C_3 = 4 \quad {}_4C_4 = 1.$$

When the values of ${}_nC_r$ are displayed systematically, a beautiful pattern emerges. Below, the values of ${}_nC_r$ with values of n and r from 0 to 6 are arranged in an array in the form of a right triangle. In the Western world this array is called **Pascal's Triangle**, after Blaise Pascal (1623–1662), a French mathematician and philosopher. Notice that the numbering starts with row 0 at the top.

n \ r	0	1	2	3	4	5	6
0	**1**						
1	**1**	**1**					
2	**1**	**2**	**1**				
3	**1**	**3**	**3**	**1**			
4	**1**	**4**	**6**	**4**	**1**		
5	**1**	**5**	**10**	**10**	**5**	**1**	
6	**1**	**6**	**15**	**20**	**15**	**6**	**1**

The isosceles triangle form of Pascal's Triangle is shown below.

row 0 → **1**
row 1 → **1 1**
row 2 → **1 2 1**
row 3 → **1 3 3 1**
row 4 → **1 4 6 4 1**
row 5 → **1 5 10 10 5 1**
row 6 → **1 6 15 20 15 6 1**
⋮

The arrays we call Pascal's Triangle were known to mathematicians long before Pascal studied them. They seem to have first appeared in the works

Lesson 8-7

Objectives

H Prove and apply properties involving combinations.
L Locate numerical properties represented by the patterns in Pascal's Triangle.

Resources

From the ***Teacher's Resource File***
- Lesson Master 8-7
- Answer Master 8-7
- Teaching Aids
  73 Warm-up
  76 Pascal's Triangle

Additional Resources
- Visuals for Teaching Aids 73, 76

Teaching Lesson 8-7

Warm-up

Give the number of subsets of the set of letters {*A, E, I, O, U, Y*} that have the given number of elements.

1. 1 element 6
2. 2 elements 15
3. 3 elements 20
4. 4 elements 15
5. 5 elements 6
6. 0 elements 1

Notes on Reading

Point out that Pascal's Triangle displays a set of numbers, just as a graph does. For this reason, one objective relating to Pascal's Triangle is included under *Representations* in the Chapter Review.

Lesson 8-7 Overview

Broad Goals In this lesson and the next students study the two most important (and quite different) meanings for the numbers in the array known in the West as Pascal's Triangle: (1) as a display of combinations and (2) as a display of binomial coefficients.

Perspective It is possible that your students have seen Pascal's Triangle before, perhaps while studying powers of binomials, perhaps in a previous encounter with combinations, or perhaps merely as an array of numbers with some very nice patterns. Probe this so that you can take advantage of what they know.

There are a number of ways to define Pascal's Triangle. For young children, it is usually defined as a triangular array in which the terms of each succeeding row are sums of terms of the preceding row. Formally, that means that Pascal's Triangle has been defined recursively as a two-dimensional sequence. In algebra, it is often defined as an array of binomial coefficients. Here we define it as an array of combinations and point out its recursive nature. In Lesson 8-8 the connection is made with binomial coefficients.

Blaise Pascal

of Abu Bakr al-Karaji, an Islamic mathematician, and Jia Xian, a Chinese mathematician, in the 11th century. The Persian mathematician and poet Omar Khayyam (c. 1048–1122) used them around the year 1100, and they were written about by the Chinese mathematician Chu Shih-Chieh, in books published in 1299 and 1303. Pascal wrote extensively about this triangular array of numbers and its properties in a 1653 publication, *Treatise on the Arithmetic Triangle.* It is for this reason that the triangle has his name.

Entries in Pascal's Triangle can be identified by row number (n) and column number (r), and so the terms can be considered as a 2-dimensional sequence. The following definition provides an explicit formula for the terms in the nth row, where n can be any whole number. It is an algebraic definition of the triangle.

> **Definition**
> Let n and r be nonnegative integers with $r \le n$. The **(r + 1)st term in row n of Pascal's Triangle** is $_nC_r$.

Example 1

Find the first four terms in row 7 of Pascal's Triangle.

Solution

By the definition of Pascal's Triangle, the first term of row 7 is $_7C_0$, the second term is $_7C_1$, the third term is $_7C_2$, and the fourth term is $_7C_3$.

From the formula for $_nC_r$, these are $\frac{7!}{7!0!}$, $\frac{7!}{6!1!}$, $\frac{7!}{5!2!}$, and $\frac{7!}{4!3!}$, or 1, 7, 21, and 35.

❶ Properties of Pascal's Triangle

Look closely at Pascal's Triangle. In its rows and columns and along the diagonals are many types of sequences, and many interesting patterns. Here are some properties which appear to be true for every row of Pascal's Triangle. The properties are described both in words and in symbols.

1. The first and last terms in each row are ones.
   That is, for each whole number n, $_nC_0 = {_nC_n} = 1$.

2. The second and next-to-last terms in the nth row equal n.
   For each whole number n, $_nC_1 = {_nC_{n-1}} = n$.

3. Each row is symmetric.
   For any whole number n, $_nC_r = {_nC_{n-r}}$.

4. The sum of the terms in row n is 2^n.
   For any whole number n, $\sum_{r=0}^{n} {_nC_r} = 2^n$.

You are asked to verify Property 1 in the Questions. Properties 2 and 3 are proved in Examples 2 and 3, respectively. You are asked to prove Property 4 in the next lesson.

530

Example 2

Prove that the second and next-to-last terms in the nth row of Pascal's Triangle equal n.

Solution

For any row n, the second entry is $_nC_1$.

$$_nC_1 = \frac{n!}{(n-1)!1!} = \frac{n!}{(n-1)!} = \frac{n(n-1)(n-2)\dots1}{(n-1)(n-2)\dots1} = n$$

The next-to-last entry in the nth row is $_nC_{n-1}$.

$$_nC_{n-1} = \frac{n!}{(n-(n-1))!(n-1)!} = \frac{n!}{(n-n+1)!(n-1)!}$$

$$= \frac{n!}{1!(n-1)!} = n$$

So $\quad _nC_1 = {_nC_{n-1}} = n$.

Example 3 is a generalization of the result and proof of Example 2.

Example 3

Prove that for whole numbers n and r, where $r \le n$, $_nC_r = {_nC_{n-r}}$.

Solution

Use the Formula for $_nC_r$ Theorem.

$$_nC_r = \frac{n!}{(n-r)!r!}$$

$$_nC_{n-r} = \frac{n!}{(n-(n-r))!(n-r)!}$$

$$= \frac{n!}{(n-n+r)!(n-r)!}$$

$$= \frac{n!}{r!(n-r)!}$$

So for whole numbers n and r, where $r \le n$, $_nC_r = {_nC_{n-r}}$.

Another property not so easily seen, but easily checked, is the following:

5. Each element in Pascal's Triangle is the sum of the two elements nearest it in the preceding row. Specifically, for any whole numbers n and r with $1 \le r \le n$, $_nC_{r-1} + {_nC_r} = {_{n+1}C_r}$. For example, the 4 and 6 in row 4 generated by $_4C_1$ and $_4C_2$ add to 10, which is the entry just below in row 5 generated by $_5C_2$, as shown below.

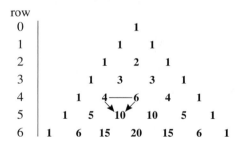

```
row
 0                      1
 1                   1     1
 2                1     2     1
 3             1    3     3     1
 4          1    4———6     4     1
 5       1    5   10    10    5     1
 6    1    6   15   20   15    6     1
```

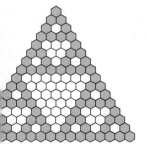

Pascal's Triangle, with the shaded hexagons representing odd numbers.

Lesson 8-7 *Pascal's Triangle* **531**

Adapting to Individual Needs

Extra Help

Students should be able to generate the first 10 rows of Pascal's Triangle quickly by hand. That is, they should know these numbers well enough not to have to painstakingly add to get the new ones. Therefore, you may wish to write down the triangle, having students call out numbers one by one as quickly as they can until the rows are filled.

Students should also be able to prove the properties of Pascal's Triangle. We provide proofs for some of the properties and ask students for proofs of others. Here is where the proofs are found in this lesson and the next.

Property	Proof Location
1	Question 6
2	Example 2
3	Example 3
4	Lesson 8-8 (Question 17)
5	Question 14

The proofs of Properties 1–3 and 5 use the definition of the triangle in terms of $_nC_r$. The proof for Property 4 is delayed until Lesson 8-8. because it utilizes the Binomial Theorem. However, we ask students to verify particular instances of Property 4 in **Questions 8b and 9c**.

❷ The proof of Property 3 repeats the generalization that students were asked to prove in **Question 20d** of Lesson 8-6.

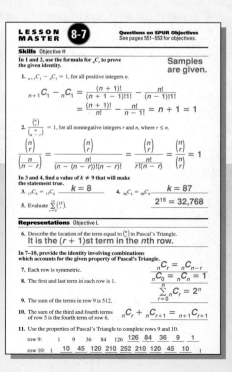

531

1. Use the formula for $_nC_r$ to find the first four terms in row 9 of Pascal's Triangle. $_9C_0 = 1$, $_9C_1 = 9$, $_9C_2 = 36$, $_9C_3 = 84$

2. Give a polynomial formula for the third term in the nth row of Pascal's Triangle. $\frac{n(n-1)}{2} = \frac{1}{2}n^2 - \frac{1}{2}n$ (More generally, the rth term in the nth row has a polynomial formula of degree $r - 1$.)

3. Prove that for all positive integers n and r with $r \le n$,
$$_nC_{r+1} = \frac{n-r}{r+1}\,_nC_r.$$
$$_nC_{r+1} = \frac{n!}{(r+1)!(n-r-1)!} =$$
$$\frac{n!(n-r)}{(r+1)r!(n-r)!} = \frac{n-r}{r+1}\,_nC_r.$$

4. Here are the first 6 terms of row 11 of Pascal's Triangle: 1, 11, 55, 165, 330, 462. Use them to construct row 12. 1, 12, 66, 220, 495, 792, 924, 792, 495, 220, 66, 12, 1; Since the rows are symmetric, the last six terms of row 11 are the same numbers in reverse order. After noting that 1 is the first and last term of row 12, add consecutive terms to get the others.

Notes on Questions

Question 12 This question provides a lead-in to Lesson 8-8.

Question 13 Discuss this question. You never know when a student may find a non-trivial pattern in the triangle. New properties of Pascal's Triangle have been discovered even in recent years. (See Activity 2 in *Optional Activities* on page 530.) You may want to use **Teaching Aid 76** with this question.

(Notes on Questions continue on page 534.)

You are asked to prove this property algebraically in Question 14. Here is an argument using combinations that shows why the property works for a specific case. Suppose you wish to find $_7C_3$, the number of combinations of 7 objects taken 3 at a time. Call the objects $A, B, C, D, E, F,$ and G. Now we split the problem into two parts. First, how many of these combinations contain G? We pick G and 2 objects from the remaining 6, so $_6C_2$ combinations contain G. Second, how many do not contain G? We pick all 3 objects from the remaining 6, so $_6C_3$ do not contain G. In this way, $_7C_3 = _6C_2 + _6C_3$.

Example 4

Use Properties 1, 3, and 5 to construct row 7 in Pascal's Triangle.

Solution

Start by copying row 6 from above. For row 7, Property 1 states that its first and last entries are 1. To find the second, third, and fourth entries in row 7, add consecutive pairs of terms in row 6 as described in Property 5; the results are $1 + 6 = 7$, $6 + 15 = 21$, and $15 + 20 = 35$. Use the symmetry property (or continue adding consecutive pairs of terms of row 6) to find the rest of the terms. Below is the result.

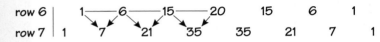

Check 1

Do the entries equal in order $_7C_0, _7C_1, _7C_2, \ldots$? In Example 1, it was shown that $_7C_0 = 1, _7C_1 = 7, _7C_2 = 21,$ and $_7C_3 = 35$.

Check 2

Use Property 4.
Does $1 + 7 + 21 + 35 + 35 + 21 + 7 + 1 = 128 = 2^7$? Yes.

QUESTIONS

Covering the Reading

1. Refer to row 6 of Pascal's Triangle.
   a. How many terms are in the row? **7**
   b. The third term is $_6C_r$. What is the value of r? **2**
   c. The middle term is $_6C_s$. What is s? **3**
   d. What is the sum of the numbers in this row? **64**
   e. Express your answer to part **d** as a power of 2. 2^6

2. *True or false.* Blaise Pascal was the first person to study the triangle that now bears his name. **False**

Adapting to Individual Needs

Challenge
Pascal wrote his "arithmetic triangle" as the rectangular array shown here.

1	1	1	1	1	1	...
1	2	3	4	5	6	...
1	3	6	10	15	21	...
1	4	10	20	35	56	...
1	5	15	35	70	126	...
1	6	21	56	126	252	...

Find a pattern for the value of a_{mn}, the term in row m column n.
$$\left[a_{mn} = \frac{(n+m-2)!}{(m-1)!(n-1)!}\right.$$
$$= _{n+m-2}C_{m-1}$$
$$= _{n+m-2}C_{n-1}\Big]$$

533

6) $_nC_0 = \dfrac{n!}{0!(n-0)!} =$

$\dfrac{n!}{0!n!} = \dfrac{n!}{1 \cdot n!} =$

$1 = \dfrac{n!}{(n-n)!n!} = {_nC_n}$

7) For $n = 8$, $r = 6$,

$_{n+1}C_r = {_9C_6} = \dfrac{9!}{6!3!} =$

84; $_nC_{r-1} + {_nC_r} =$

$_8C_5 + {_8C_6} = \dfrac{8!}{5!3!} +$

$\dfrac{8!}{6!2!} = 56 + 28 = 84$

8b) $1 + 8 + 28 + 56 +$
$70 + 56 + 28 + 8 +$
$1 = 256 = 2^8$

12ai) $x + y$
aii) $x^2 + 2xy + y^2$
aiii) $x^3 + 3x^2y +$
$3xy^2 + y^3$
b) The coefficients of
$(x + y)^n$ are the entries
of the nth row of
Pascal's Triangle.

13) Sample: the "hockey
stick" pattern. With
any number of terms
in the "handle" but
only one in the
"blade," the sum
of the terms in the
handle is equal to
the term in the
blade. For example,
$1 + 3 + 6 + 10 = 20$.

In 3–5, match the English description of the pattern in Pascal's Triangle to the description using combination notation.
(a) For each n, $_nC_1 = {_nC_{n-1}}$.
(b) For each n and each r ($r \le n$), $_nC_r = {_nC_{n-r}}$.
(c) For each n, $_nC_0 = {_nC_n} = 1$.

3. Each row in the isosceles triangle is symmetric to a vertical line. **b**

4. The second and next-to-last entries in each row are equal. **a**

5. The first and last entries in a row are 1. **c**

6. Prove that for all whole numbers n, $_nC_0 = {_nC_n} = 1$. **See left.**

7. Verify the property $_{n+1}C_r = {_nC_{r-1}} + {_nC_r}$ for $n = 8$, $r = 6$.
See left.

8. a. Give the entries in row 8 of Pascal's Triangle.
b. Check your answer to part **a** by showing the entries add to 2^8.
a) 1, 8, 28, 56, 70, 56, 28, 8, 1   b) See left.

9. The first eight entries of row 14 of Pascal's Triangle are

$$1, 14, 91, 364, 1001, 2002, 3003, 3432.$$

a. How many other entries are there in row 14? **7**
b. List the remaining entries. **3003, 2002, 1001, 364, 91, 14, 1**
c. What is the sum of the entries in row 14? $2^{14} = 16{,}384$
d. List the entries in row 15.
1, 15, 105, 455, 1365, 3003, 5005, 6435, 6435, 5005, 3003, 1365, 455, 105, 15, 1

Applying the Mathematics

10. Find the first three numbers in the 100th row of Pascal's Triangle.
1, 100, 4950
11. What are the last two terms in the row of Pascal's Triangle whose terms add to 2^{27}? **27, 1**

12. a. Expand the following.
i. $(x + y)^1$ **ii.** $(x + y)^2$ **iii.** $(x + y)^3$
b. Relate the coefficients of the results in part **a** to Pascal's Triangle.
a, b) See left.
13. Find a pattern in Pascal's Triangle that is not mentioned in this lesson.
See left.
14. Prove Property 5 in the lesson, which states that any entry in Pascal's Triangle is the sum of the two entries directly above it. That is, show that for all positive integers r and n with $1 \le r \le n$, $_{n+1}C_r = {_nC_{r-1}} + {_nC_r}$.
See margin.

Review

15. A soccer league which has grown to include 22 teams is to be broken into two 11-team divisions. In how many ways can this be done? *(Lesson 8-6)*
$_{22}C_{11} = 705{,}432$
16. Each year a company consisting of a president, vice-president, sales manager, financial manager, and 96 other employees holds a drawing in which four employees get a paid vacation to the South Pacific. What is the probability that the four employees chosen are the four executives?
(Lesson 8-6)
$\dfrac{1}{3{,}921{,}225}$

Practice

For more questions on SPUR Objectives, use **Lesson Master 8-7** (shown on page 531).

Assessment

Written Communication Have students determine the terms in the 12th row of Pascal's Triangle using the definition and Properties 1–3. Then have them verify Property 4 for this row and use Property 5 to determine the terms of the 13th row. [Students determine terms in Pascal's Triangle and demonstrate understanding of numerical properties of the triangle.]

(Follow-up continues on page 534.)

Additional Answers
14. $_nC_{r-1} + {_nC_r}$

$= \dfrac{n!}{(r-1)!(n-(r-1))!} + \dfrac{n!}{r!(n-r)!} = \dfrac{r\,n!}{(n-r+1)!r!} + \dfrac{n!(n-r+1)}{(n-r+1)!r!} =$

$= \dfrac{n!(r+n-r+1)}{(n-r+1)!r!} = \dfrac{n!(n+1)}{(n-r+1)!r!} = \dfrac{(n+1)!}{(n-r+1)!r!} = \dfrac{(n+1)!}{r!(n+1-r)!}$

$= {_{n+1}C_r}$

Extension

To find more patterns in Pascal's Triangle, students could transform the triangle and look for patterns in the image.

1. For one transformation, rewrite an entry as 0 if the entry is even and 1 if it is odd. The first ten rows of the image are shown below, but you may wish to encourage students to write 20 rows to see the patterns.

```
              1
             1 1
            1 0 1
           1 1 1 1
          1 0 0 0 1
         1 1 0 0 1 1
        1 0 1 0 1 0 1
       1 1 1 1 1 1 1 1
      1 0 0 0 0 0 0 0 1
     1 1 0 0 0 0 0 0 1 1
    1 0 1 0 0 0 0 0 1 0 1
```

2. A similar transformation is to replace each element in the triangle with its remainder when divided by 3.

3. Still another exploration could use a completely different triangle. For instance, what patterns can be found in the familiar multiplication table when it is represented as a triangle? Here are the first 8 rows.

```
              1
             2  2
           3  4  3
          4  6  6  4
        5  8  9  8  5
      6 10 12 12 10  6
    7 12 15 16 15 12  7
  8 14 18 20 20 18 14  8
```

Notes on Questions

Question 17 These Russian nesting dolls are sometimes called Babushka dolls or Matryoshka dolls and have been made both with religious and secular themes. There exist stores that specialize in these dolls; one is in the Mall of America near Minneapolis.

Russian Matryoshka dolls

23b) the first or last entries in the rows
c) Sample: The sum of any two adjacent terms is equal to the term directly above the two terms. For example, $\frac{1}{4} + \frac{1}{12} = \frac{1}{3}$.

17. Consider a collection of Russian dolls of similar shapes and descending in size so that they fit into each other. Assume that each doll has $\frac{3}{4}$ the height of the next bigger one. *(Lessons 8-4, 8-5)*
   a. What is the ratio of the volumes of two consecutive dolls? **27/64**
   b. If the biggest doll requires a wooden piece of 1400 cm^3, how much wood would be needed to carve out the given number of dolls?
      i. 10 dolls ≈ **2421.19 cm³**
      ii. infinitely many dolls ≈ **2421.62 cm³**

In 18 and 19, a restaurant offers pizza with thick or thin crust, and with or without any of the following toppings: anchovies, mushrooms, onions, peppers, pepperoni, sausage. *(Lessons 7-3, 8-6)*

18. How many different kinds of pizza can be made? $2^7 = $ **128**

19. How many thin crust pizzas can be made with exactly two toppings? **15**

20. The first three terms of a sequence are 4, x, and $\frac{3}{2}x$.
   a. Find x if the sequence is arithmetic. **8**
   b. Find x if the sequence is geometric. *(Lesson 8-1)* **6**

21. *Skill sequence.* Find the exact volume. *(Previous course)*

   a.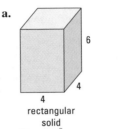
   rectangular solid
   96 units³

   b. right circular cylinder
   24π units³

   c. right circular cone
   diameter = 4
   8π units³

22. Of 210 horses in a herd, 48% are mares and 67% are brown. At least how many mares are brown? At most how many mares are brown? *(Previous course)* **30; 100**

Exploration

23. a. Use the definition $\begin{bmatrix} n \\ k \end{bmatrix} = \dfrac{1}{(n+1)\binom{n}{k}} = \dfrac{k!(n-k)!}{(n+1)!}$ to evaluate each term in the first four rows of the following triangle.

$$\begin{bmatrix} 0 \\ 0 \end{bmatrix}$$

$$\begin{bmatrix} 1 \\ 0 \end{bmatrix} \quad \begin{bmatrix} 1 \\ 1 \end{bmatrix}$$

$$\begin{bmatrix} 2 \\ 0 \end{bmatrix} \quad \begin{bmatrix} 2 \\ 1 \end{bmatrix} \quad \begin{bmatrix} 2 \\ 2 \end{bmatrix}$$

$$\begin{bmatrix} 3 \\ 0 \end{bmatrix} \quad \begin{bmatrix} 3 \\ 1 \end{bmatrix} \quad \begin{bmatrix} 3 \\ 2 \end{bmatrix} \quad \begin{bmatrix} 3 \\ 3 \end{bmatrix}$$

```
                1
              1/2  1/2
           1/3  1/6  1/3
        1/4  1/12  1/12  1/4
```

   b. This triangular array is called Leibniz's Harmonic Triangle. Where in the triangle does the harmonic sequence appear? **See left.**
   c. Describe some other pattern in this triangle. **See left.**

Setting Up Lesson 8-8

Be certain to discuss **Question 12**.

You saw in the previous lesson that Pascal's Triangle arises from evaluating $_nC_r$ for whole numbers n and r, $r \le n$. This lesson examines the connections between $(x + y)^n$ and Pascal's Triangle, as well as some applications of those connections.

To *expand* means to write a product of polynomials or a power of polynomials as a sum. Here are the *expansions* of $(x + y)^n$, for $n = 0, 1,$ and 2.

$$(x + y)^0 = 1$$
$$(x + y)^1 = 1x + 1y$$
$$(x + y)^2 = 1x^2 + 2xy + 1y^2$$

Notice that the coefficients of the terms in the expansions are the entries in the 0th, 1st, and 2nd rows of Pascal's Triangle.

This pattern continues to hold. To see why, consider $(x + y)^3 = (x + y)(x + y)(x + y)$. You can find this product by multiplying each x and y term of the first factor by an x or y term of each of the other factors and then adding those partial products. In all, eight different partial products are computed and then added. These are highlighted in blue below.

Choice of Factors (in blue)	Partial Product
$(x + y)(x + y)(x + y)$	$\rightarrow xxx \rightarrow x^3$
$(x + y)(x + y)(x + y)$	$\rightarrow xxy \rightarrow x^2y$
$(x + y)(x + y)(x + y)$	$\rightarrow xyx \rightarrow x^2y$
$(x + y)(x + y)(x + y)$	$\rightarrow xyy \rightarrow xy^2$
$(x + y)(x + y)(x + y)$	$\rightarrow yxx \rightarrow x^2y$
$(x + y)(x + y)(x + y)$	$\rightarrow yxy \rightarrow xy^2$
$(x + y)(x + y)(x + y)$	$\rightarrow yyx \rightarrow xy^2$
$(x + y)(x + y)(x + y)$	$\rightarrow yyy \rightarrow y^3$

Thus, $(x + y)^3 = 1x^3 + 3x^2y + 3xy^2 + 1y^3$. The coefficients are the entries in the third row of Pascal's Triangle.

To see why each coefficient is a combination, examine the eight partial products. The result x^3 occurs when x is used as a factor three times and y is used as a factor zero times. There are $_3C_0$ ways to choose 0 ys from the three y terms, so x^3 occurs in $_3C_0 = 1$ way. That is, x^3 occurs once, so its coefficient in the expansion is 1. The product x^2y occurs when x is chosen from two of the three factors and y from one. There are three y terms from which to choose, so this can be done in $_3C_1 = 3$ ways. So x^2y occurs three times and its coefficient in the expansion is 3. Similarly, xy^2 occurs when x

Objectives

D Expand binomials.

Resources

From the *Teacher's Resource File*
- Lesson Master 8-8
- Answer Master 8-8
- Teaching Aids
  73 Warm-up
  77 Binomial Cube Terms

Additional Resources
- Visuals for Teaching Aids 73, 77

Teaching **8-8**
Lesson

Warm-up

1. Multiply $x^2 + 2xy + y^2$ by $x + y$.
   $x^3 + 3x^2y + 3xy^2 + y^3$
2. Multiply your answer to Question 1 by $x + y$.
   $x^4 + 4x^3y + 6x^2y^2 + 4xy^3 + y^4$

Notes on Reading

This should not be a difficult lesson for students due to their extensive practice with combinations and Pascal's Triangle during the last couple of days. However, the notations in the Binomial Theorem may be intimidating, so sufficient time should be spent on verifying expansions of $(x + y)^n$ for particular values of n. **Teaching Aid 77** contains an expansion of $(x + y)^3$. **Questions 1–8** can be used to guide class discussion.

Lesson 8-8 Overview

Broad Goals In this lesson, the connections between combinations, Pascal's Triangle, and binomial coefficients are explained and the Binomial Theorem is used to solve certain counting problems in preparation for the next lesson.

Perspective It is one of the wonderful interrelationships in mathematics that the combinations of n things taken r at a time are the entries on the nth row of Pascal's

Triangle and the coefficients in the expansion of $(x + y)^n$.

A proof of the Binomial Theorem, under today's standards of rigor, requires mathematical induction. That is, Omar Khayyam's proof would not be considered a rigorous proof under today's standards. Consequently, we must leave the proof for *Precalculus and Discrete Mathematics*. Still, the connection can be strongly made with combinations.

The algebraic manipulation in expansions like **Example 2** is not easy for most students; it requires very careful writing. Encourage students to be systematic, to write down the form of the Binomial Theorem for the particular value of *n* if needed, and then, directly under that form, do the substitutions. Also encourage students to check their work.

The application of the Binomial Theorem to the coin-tossing problem in **Example 3** is quite elegant in that the powers of the variables *H* and *T* serve double duty as indices. For example, $H^3 T^2$ represents an instance of getting 3 heads and 2 tails in a flip of five coins. Order does not matter, so the coefficient $_5C_2$ counts the number of possible combinations of 3 heads and 2 tails.

As is shown in the solution to **Example 3**, the compact notation allows for a quick solution to the problem of how many tosses have *at least* two heads. Students generally have difficulty with these types of problems at first, but they will see others in the next lesson.

is chosen from one factor and *y* from two. There are three *y* terms from which to choose so this can be done in $_3C_2 = 3$ ways. So the coefficient of xy^2 in the expansion is 3. Finally, y^3 occurs when all three *y* terms are chosen, and this occurs in $_3C_3 = 1$ way. Thus

$$(x + y)^3 = x^3 + 3x^2y + 3xy^2 + y^3.$$

Using the language of combinations, we can write

$$(x + y)^3 = {_3C_0}x^3 + {_3C_1}x^2y + {_3C_2}xy^2 + {_3C_3}y^3.$$

What Is the Binomial Theorem?

In general, the expansion of $(x + y)^n$ has $_nC_0x^n = x^n$ as its first term and $_nC_ny^n = y^n$ as its last. The second term is $_nC_1x^{n-1}y = nx^{n-1}y$, and the second from the last is $_nC_{n-1}xy^{n-1} = nxy^{n-1}$. The sum of the exponents in each term is *n*, and the coefficient of $x^{n-k}y^k$ is $_nC_k$. These results are found in the following important theorem known to Omar Khayyam.

Omar Khayyam (1048–1122)

> **Binomial Theorem**
> For any nonnegative integer *n*,
>
> $$(x + y)^n = {_nC_0}x^n + {_nC_1}x^{n-1}y + {_nC_2}x^{n-2}y^2 + \ldots + {_nC_k}x^{n-k}y^k + \ldots + {_nC_n}y^n$$
>
> $$= \sum_{k=0}^{n} {_nC_k}x^{n-k}y^k.$$

For example,

$$(x + y)^4 = (x + y)(x + y)(x + y)(x + y)$$
$$= {_4C_0}x^4 + {_4C_1}x^3y + {_4C_2}x^2y^2 + {_4C_3}xy^3 + {_4C_4}y^4$$
$$= x^4 + 4x^3y + 6x^2y^2 + 4xy^3 + y^4.$$

Because of their application in this theorem, the combinations $_nC_k$ are sometimes called **binomial coefficients**.

Some Uses of the Binomial Theorem

The Binomial Theorem can be used to expand the power of any binomial.

Example 1

Find the coefficient of x^2y^3 in $(x + y)^5$.

Solution

From the five factors of $(x + y)^5$, y is to be chosen three times and x twice. This can be done in $_5C_3 = 10$ ways, so the coefficient of x^2y^3 is 10.

Check
$$(x + y)^5 = x^5 + 5x^4y + 10x^3y^2 + \mathbf{10x^2y^3} + 5xy^4 + y^5$$

536

Example 2

Expand $(2v - 3)^4$.

Solution

Use the Binomial Theorem with $n = 4$.
$$(x + y)^4 = x^4 + 4x^3y + 6x^2y^2 + 4xy^3 + y^4$$
Substitute $2v$ for x, and -3 for y.
$$(2v - 3)^4 = (2v)^4 + 4(2v)^3(-3) + 6(2v)^2(-3)^2 + 4(2v)(-3)^3 + (-3)^4$$
$$= 16v^4 + 4(8)(-3)v^3 + 6(4)(9)v^2 + 4(2)(-27)v + 81$$
$$= 16v^4 - 96v^3 + 216v^2 - 216v + 81$$

Check

Let $v = 2$. The power $(2v - 3)^4 = (2 \cdot 2 - 3)^4 = 1^4 = 1$. For $v = 2$, the series expansion has the value
$$16(2^4) - 96(2^3) + 216(2^2) - 216(2) + 81 = 256 - 768 + 864 - 432 + 81$$
$$= 1.$$
It checks.

The Binomial Theorem can also be used to solve counting problems involving experiments with only two outcomes.

Example 3

A coin is flipped five times. How many of the possible outcomes have at least two heads?

Solution

Substitute H for x, T for y, and 5 for n in the Binomial Theorem.
$$(H + T)^5 = {}_5C_0H^5 + {}_5C_1H^4T + {}_5C_2H^3T^2 + {}_5C_3H^2T^3 + {}_5C_4HT^4 + {}_5C_5T^5$$
$$= 1H^5 + 5H^4T + 10H^3T^2 + 10H^2T^3 + 5HT^4 + 1T^5$$

The coefficients correspond to the number of ways of obtaining 5 heads, 4 heads and 1 tail, ..., and 5 tails, respectively. Thus, 5 heads can occur in 1 way, 4 heads and 1 tail can occur in 5 ways, and so on. The number of ways in which at least two heads occur is therefore $1 + 5 + 10 + 10 = 26$.

Check

Of the total $2^5 = 32$ outcomes, 1 has no heads and 5 have one head, so 6 have fewer than 2 heads. That leaves $32 - 6 = 26$ outcomes with at least 2 heads. It checks.

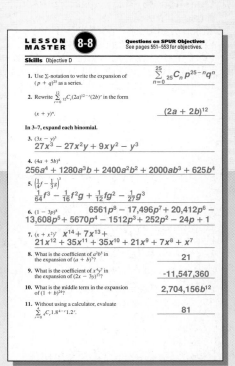

QUESTIONS

Covering the Reading

2) $a^5 + 5a^4b + 10a^3b^2 + 10a^2b^3 + 5ab^4 + b^5$

3) $a^6 + 6a^5b + 15a^4b^2 + 20a^3b^3 + 15a^2b^4 + 6ab^5 + b^6$

1. a. In the product $(x + y)(x + y)(x + y)$ what is the coefficient of x^2y? **3**
   b. Why can this coefficient be derived from a combination problem?
   It is the number of ways of choosing 2 x-terms from 3.

2. Expand $(a + b)^5$.
   See left.

3. Expand $(a + b)^6$.
   See left.

Lesson 8-8   *The Binomial Theorem*   **537**

Additional Examples

1. Give the coefficient of a^9b^2 in $(a + b)^{11}$. **55**

2. a. Expand $(4x + 5y)^5$.
   $1024x^5 + 6400x^4y + 16{,}000x^3y^2 + 20{,}000x^2y^3 + 12{,}500xy^4 + 3125y^5$

   b. Expand $(4x^2 + 5y)^5$.
   $1024x^{10} + 6400x^8y + 16{,}000x^6y^2 + 20{,}000x^4y^3 + 12{,}500x^2y^4 + 3125y^5$

3. A coin is flipped 6 times. How many of the possible outcomes have at least 3 heads? **42**

LESSON MASTER	8-8	Questions on SPUR Objectives
		See pages 551–553 for objectives.

Skills Objective D

1. Use Σ-notation to write the expansion of $(p + q)^{25}$ as a series. $\sum_{n=0}^{25} {}_{25}C_n\, p^{25-n}q^n$

2. Rewrite $\sum_{r=0}^{12} {}_{12}C_r(2a)^{12-r}(2b)^r$ in the form $(x + y)^n$. $(2a + 2b)^{12}$

In 3–7, expand each binomial.

3. $(3x - y)^3$ $27x^3 - 27x^2y + 9xy^2 - y^3$

4. $(4a + 5b)^4$ $256a^4 + 1280a^3b + 2400a^2b^2 + 2000ab^3 + 625b^4$

5. $\left(\frac{1}{4}f - \frac{1}{3}g\right)^3$ $\frac{1}{64}f^3 - \frac{1}{16}f^2g + \frac{1}{12}fg^2 - \frac{1}{27}g^3$

6. $(1 - 3p)^8$ $6561p^8 - 17{,}496p^7 + 20{,}412p^6 - 13{,}608p^5 + 5670p^4 - 1512p^3 + 252p^2 - 24p + 1$

7. $(x + x^2)^7$ $x^{14} + 7x^{13} + 21x^{12} + 35x^{11} + 35x^{10} + 21x^9 + 7x^8 + x^7$

8. What is the coefficient of a^2b^3 in the expansion of $(a + b)^5$?   21

9. What is the coefficient of x^4y^7 in the expansion of $(2x - 3y)^{11}$?   -11,547,360

10. What is the middle term in the expansion of $(1 + b)^{24}$?   2,704,156b^{12}

11. Without using a calculator, evaluate $\sum_{r=0}^{4} {}_4C_r\, 1.8^{4-r}1.2^r$.   81

Adapting to Individual Needs

Extra Help

Many students find it useful to reinforce the concepts of the lesson with what they have learned about Pascal's Triangle. Continue to encourage students to be familiar with the terms of the first 10 rows, as suggested in the *Extra Help* for Lesson 8-7. Attainment of this quick recall is rewarded by easy determination or check of the coefficients in many binomial expansions. Point out, too, that just as the nth row of Pascal's Triangle has $n + 1$ terms, the nth power of $a + b$ has $n + 1$ terms in the expanded form.

Question 9 Students can list how many possible outcomes of 5 tosses have 0 heads, 1 head, 2 heads, 3 heads, 4 heads, and 5 heads. Make the row in Pascal's Triangle explicit. Then the question is very easy to answer.

Question 10 Error Alert Check that students understand that flipping four fair coins is equivalent to flipping one fair coin four times.

Questions 11–13 Students often guess on these when they do not know how to find the answer. You might suggest the following method of solution: Pick a value of n, say 3. Then let $p = 2$, $q = 1$. This forces $k = 3$. Now check the various equations.

Question 14 You might suggest that students begin by expanding $(a - b)^4$. Then substitute x^3 for a and y^2 for b.

Question 17 This proof is so elegant that students do not think it is a proof. Point out that not all proofs have to be long! The key is that the Binomial Theorem not only holds for any integer n, but also for all values of x and y. And since it holds for all values, it must hold for specific values.

Question 18 This formula can be proved: By the Binomial Theorem, for all n, $a_n = (1 - 1)^n = 0^n = 0$.

Question 26 This question presents a use of the Binomial Theorem which was much more important in the days before calculators. Students who are interested might be encouraged to practice the skill. It is possible to do such approximations mentally.

6) $x^6 - 6x^5 + 15x^4 - 20x^3 + 15x^2 - 6x + 1$

7) $1 - 10q + 40q^2 - 80q^3 + 80q^4 - 32q^5$

8) $1000p^3 + 600p^2 + 120p + 8$

14) $x^{12} - 4x^9y^2 + 6x^6y^4 - 4x^3y^6 + y^8$. $(2^3 - 3^2)^4 = (8 - 9)^4 = 1$ and $2^{12} - 4 \cdot 2^9 \cdot 3^2 + 6 \cdot 2^6 \cdot 3^4 - 4 \cdot 2^3 \cdot 3^6 + 3^8 = 1$. It checks.

17) $2^n = (1 + 1)^n$
$= \sum_{k=0}^{n} {}_nC_k (1)^{n-k}1^k$
$= \sum_{k=0}^{n} {}_nC_k$

20b) 1, 11, 55, 165, 330, 462, 462, 330, 165, 55, 11, 1

538

---

4. What is the coefficient of x^2y^4 in the expansion of $(x + y)^6$? **15**

In 5–8, expand. **6–8) See left.**

5. $(v + 2)^3$ $v^3 + 6v^2 + 12v + 8$ **6.** $(x - 1)^6$

7. $(1 - 2q)^5$ **8.** $(10p + 2)^3$

9. How many of the possible outcomes of 5 tosses of a coin have the following?
  a. exactly 3 tails **10**   **b.** at least 3 tails **16**

10. Use the Binomial Theorem to determine the number of ways 1, 2, 3, and 4 heads can occur when four fair coins are flipped. **4, 6, 4, and 1, respectively**

Applying the Mathematics

In 11–13, suppose kx^py^q is a term in the series expansion of $(x + y)^n$. *True or false.*

11. $p + q = n$ **True**   **12.** $k = {}_nC_q$ **True**   **13.** $k = {}_nC_p$ **True**

14. Expand $(x^3 - y^2)^4$ and check by letting $x = 2$ and $y = 3$. **See left.**

15. Mr. and Mrs. Ippy hope to have four children. Assuming that boys and girls are equally likely, what is the probability they will have at least two girls? **11/16 = 68.75%**

16. Rewrite $\sum_{i=0}^{7} \binom{7}{i} a^{7-i}5^i$ in the form $(x + y)^n$. $(a + 5)^7$

17. Use the Binomial Theorem to prove that $\sum_{k=0}^{n} {}_nC_k = 2^n$. (This is Property 4 from Lesson 8-7.) Hint: Let $2^n = (1 + 1)^n$. **See left.**

18. Alternately add and subtract the entries in the rows of Pascal's triangle as follows.

$$a_1 = 1 - 1$$
$$a_2 = 1 - 2 + 1$$
$$a_3 = 1 - 3 + 3 - 1$$
$$a_4 = 1 - 4 + 6 - 4 + 1$$

Give an explicit formula for a_n. $a_n = 0$ for all n

Review

In 19 and 20, refer to the numbers below, which are the first six terms of row 10 of Pascal's Triangle. *(Lesson 8-7)*

$$1 \quad 10 \quad 45 \quad 120 \quad 210 \quad 252$$

19. Which term represents ${}_{10}C_4$? **210**

20. a. Write the rest of row 10. **210, 120, 45, 10, 1**
  b. Write row 11 in full. **See left.**
  c. Write row 9 in full. **1, 9, 36, 84, 126, 126, 84, 36, 9, 1**

Adapting to Individual Needs

Challenge
Expanding a trinomial, $(x + y + z)^n$, gives terms of the form $x^ry^sz^t$ where $r + s + t = n$ and with a coefficient of $\frac{n!}{r!s!t!}$. Have students answer the following questions.

1. Use this pattern to expand $(x + y + z)^3$. [$x^3 + y^3 + z^3 + 3xy^2 + 3xz^2 + 3yx^2 + 3yz^2 + 3zy^2 + 3zx^2 + 6xyz$]

2. Find the sum of the coefficients in the expansion of $(x + y + z)^n$. (Hint: Let $x = y = z = 1$.) [3^n]

Paris, France

24b) If $x = 0$, then the sum is 0; if $x \neq 0$ and $|y| < 1$, the sum is $\dfrac{xy^2}{1 - y}$.

In 21 and 22, suppose that the names of four people in a baking competition are to be chosen from among a list of 100 finalists. **a.** Tell whether the situation represents a combination or permutation. **b.** State the number of possible outcomes.   *(Lessons 7-4, 8-6)*

21. The first receives a $10,000 prize, the second receives $5,000, the third $1,000, and the fourth $500. **a) permutation**   **b) 94,109,400**

22. All four people receive identical prizes: a trip to Paris, France.
a) combination   **b) 3,921,225**

23. Three integers from 1 to 100 are chosen at random. What is the probability that they are three consecutive integers?   *(Lessons 7-1, 8-6)*
98/161700 ≈ 0.000606

24. a. Under what conditions does the following infinite series have a sum?
$$\sum_{n=2}^{\infty} xy^n = xy^2 + xy^3 + xy^4 + xy^5 + \ldots$$
$x = 0$ or $|y| < 1$
b. What is that sum, if it exists?   *(Lesson 8-5)*
See left.

25. Before 1994, in all area codes, the first digit could not be a 0 or 1, the second digit had to be a 0 or 1, and the third digit could not be a 0 or 1. How many area codes were possible with these restrictions?   *(Lesson 7-3)*
128

Exploration

26. a. Expand $(1 + .001)^5$ to obtain the decimal for 1.001^5. **See below.**
b. How many terms of the expansion are needed to get an estimate of 1.001^5 accurate to the nearest thousandth? **2**
c. Use your results from parts **a** and **b** to determine how many terms of the expansion of $(1 + .003)^8$ are needed to estimate 1.003^8 to the nearest millionth. **3**
d. Give the complete decimal expansion of 1.003^8. **See below.**
e. How close is your calculator value of 1.003^8 to the value of your answer in part **d**?
Answers will vary. Sample: A TI-92 in approximate mode yields 1.02425351768, a difference of $3.628429502561 \times 10^{-13}$.
a) $1 + 5 \times 10^{-3} + 10 \times 10^{-6} + 10 \times 10^{-9} + 5 \times 10^{-12} + 10^{-15} = 1.005010010005001$
d) 1.024253517683628429502561

Practice
For more questions on SPUR Objectives, use **Lesson Master 8-8** (shown on page 537).

Assessment
Oral Communication Ask students to refer to **Question 9** on page 533 in Lesson 8-7 and then state the expansion of $(x + y)^{14}$. [Students use Pascal's Triangle and the Binomial Theorem to expand a binomial.]

Extension
Refer to **Question 15**. Ask students to find the probability the Ippy's have exactly 2 girls out of 4 children. [0.375] Then ask students if the same probability will result for having exactly 3 girls out of 6 children, exactly 4 girls out of 8 children, exactly 5 girls out of 10 children. [No, the probability decreases: 0.3125, 0.2734, 0.2461]

Project Update Project 1, *The Binomial Theorem for Rational Exponents*, on page 546, relates to the content of this lesson.

LESSON 8-9

Binomial Probabilities

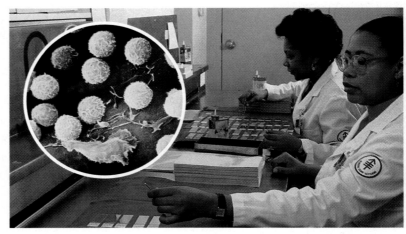

Looking for Signs. *The number of people whose cancer remains in remission follows a binomial distribution model. The inset shows a characteristic of leukemia: immature white blood cells in the bone marrow. See Example 1.*

What Is a Binomial Experiment?

In Example 3 of the preceding lesson, the expansion of $(H + T)^5$ helped to find how many ways 2 heads could occur in 5 tosses of a coin. This situation is an example of a *binomial experiment*, because, as you will learn later in this lesson, a formula for calculating the probabilities associated with such an experiment is related to the Binomial Theorem. A **binomial experiment** has the following features:

1. There are repeated situations, called *trials*.
2. There are only two possible outcomes, often called *success* (*S*) and *failure* (*F*), for each trial.
3. The trials are independent.
4. Each trial has the same probability of success.
5. The experiment has a fixed number of trials.

Listed below are all the possible outcomes for a binomial experiment with four trials.

Outcomes for a Binomial Experiment with 4 Trials				
exactly 0 successes	exactly 1 success	exactly 2 successes	exactly 3 successes	exactly 4 successes
FFFF	FFFS	FFSS	FSSS	SSSS
	FFSF	FSFS	SFSS	
	FSFF	FSSF	SSFS	
	SFFF	SFFS	SSSF	
		SFSF		
		SSFF		

Notice that the number of ways with exactly k successes among the 4 trials is $_4C_k$. That is, the number of outcomes in the columns above, 1, 4, 6, 4, 1, are precisely the numbers from row 4 of Pascal's Triangle.

Lesson 8-9 Overview

Broad Goals A binomial experiment is one in which there is a fixed number of independent trials, each with two possible outcomes A and B that have fixed probabilities p and $q = 1 - p$ of occurrence, respectively. From this definition, it can be deduced that the probability that A occurs k times in n trials is $_nC_k p^k q^{n-k}$. The purpose of this lesson is to show why this formula works and to apply it to a variety of situations.

Perspective The power of the binomial theorem combined with the applicability of combinations enables probabilities to be calculated for events students might not expect to be amenable to mathematical treatment. The outcomes do not have to be equally likely, yet their probabilities can be calculated.

The phrase "binomial experiment" is fancy and may lead students to think at first that such experiments are rare. In fact, they are common, applying to any situation in which a situation that has known outcomes is repeated again and again, independently. They do not apply to weather, since what happens one day can affect the next, so the weather for a given day is not independent of the weather for other days. But they do apply quite well to medical situations in which there is a probability of survival, games of chance, polling, situations subject

The chart on page 540 should look familiar. It has 16 outcomes, similar to tossing four fair coins. However, in general, the 16 outcomes may not be equally likely, because the probability of success and the probability of failure may not be equal.

Example 1

Suppose that the probability for a certain cancer to remain in remission (undetectable) for at least one year after chemotherapy is 0.7 for all patients with that cancer.

a. Find the probability that exactly two of four patients currently being monitored are able to keep the cancer in remission for at least one year after chemotherapy.

b. Find the probability that two or three patients are able to sustain remission for at least one year.

Solution

a. For each patient, $P(\text{success}) = 0.7$; so $P(\text{failure}) = 1 - 0.7 = 0.3$. Use the table on page 540. As listed in the column labeled *exactly 2 successes*, there are 6 combinations in which exactly 2 of the 4 patients sustain remission. The probability of each of these outcomes is $(0.7)^2(0.3)^2$. So

$$P(\text{exactly 2 successes in 4 trials}) = 6(0.7)^2(0.3)^2$$
$$= 6(0.0441)$$
$$= 0.2646.$$

b. Because the outcomes are mutually exclusive,
$$P(\text{2 or 3 successes}) = P(\text{exactly 2 successes}) +$$
$$P(\text{exactly 3 successes}).$$
From part a, $P(\text{exactly 2 successes}) = 0.2646$.
There are 4 ways to have exactly 3 successes. Each has probability $(0.7)^3(0.3)$. So
$$P(\text{exactly 3 successes}) = 4(0.7)^3(0.3)$$
$$= 0.4116.$$
Thus, $$P(\text{2 or 3 successes}) = 0.2646 + 0.4116$$
$$= 0.6762.$$

The results of Example 1 can be generalized. In a binomial experiment, if the probability of success is p, the probability of failure is $1 - p = q$. Then the probability of exactly 2 successes in 4 trials is $_4C_2q^2p^2 = 6q^2p^2$, and the probability of exactly 3 successes in 4 trials is $_4C_3qp^3 = 4qp^3$.

The General Binomial Experiment

These ideas can be generalized still further.

Binomial Probability Theorem
Suppose that in a binomial experiment with n trials the probability of success is p in each trial, and the probability of failure is q, where $q = 1 - p$. Then

$$P(\text{exactly } k \text{ successes}) = {}_nC_k \cdot p^k q^{n-k}.$$

Teaching Aid 78 contains the outcomes for a binomial experiment with 4 trials.

A possible lesson plan follows: Begin with **Questions 1–5**, which relate to the discussion on page 540. State the theorem on page 541. Then go through **Example 1**, followed by **Questions 6–7**. Finally, go through **Example 2** and **Questions 8–9**. **Example 3** wraps this all up and is a prelude to Chapter 10, where binomial probability distributions are discussed in more detail.

In **Example 1**, since the given probability is to only one decimal place, we might round all the answers to one decimal place also.

In **Example 3**, you might note that even though the expected number of successes is 3.5, the most common number of successes to expect is not shared equally by 3 and 4, but is 4. The difference here is that 3.5 is the *mean* number of successes, while 4 is the *mode*.

Optional Activities

to random fluctuations such as people who do not show up for hotel or airline reservations. Examples of all these types are found in this lesson and later in Chapter 10.

Activity 1 Technology Connection
Materials: Explorations software

Students may use Exploration *8-9, Binomial Probability Distribution,* as an alternative to **Example 3** in this lesson. Students choose the number of trials in the probability experiment as well as the probability of successes. The probability of *x* exact successes will be displayed in a table. The binomial distribution is also shown on a graph.

Activity 2 Technology Connection
You may wish to use *Technology Sourcebook, Computer Master 9.* Students use a spreadsheet program to calculate, graph, and compare binomial probability distributions. Have students save this spreadsheet as it will be helpful for their work in Chapter 10.

Additional Examples

1. The probability of getting a sum of 7 in a toss of two fair die is known to be $\frac{1}{6}$.
   a. What is the probability of getting exactly two 7s in 5 tosses? $\frac{625}{3888} \approx 0.16$
   b. What is the probability of getting at least two 7s in 5 tosses? ≈ 0.20 (See Additional Example 3 below.)

2. What is the probability of getting at least 8 of 10 questions on a test correct, if you feel you have an 80% chance of answering each individual question correctly? $\approx .68$

3. Determine the probability distribution from the binomial experiment of Additional Example 1. Let x be the number of 7s in 5 tosses of two fair die.

x	$P(x)$
0	.4019
1	.4019
2	.1608
3	.0322
4	.0032
5	.0001

Example 2

A quiz has eight multiple-choice questions, each with four alternatives. If a student guesses randomly on every question, what is the probability of getting five or more correct?

Solution

This is a binomial experiment. Answering each question is a trial; so **there are n = 8 trials. The probability of success (getting a single question correct) is 0.25; the probability of failure is 0.75.** Getting 5 or more correct is equivalent to the mutually exclusive events of getting exactly 5 or exactly 6 or exactly 7 or exactly 8 correct. So the desired probability is

$P(5 \text{ or better})$
$= P(\text{exactly } 5) + P(\text{exactly } 6) + P(\text{exactly } 7) + P(\text{exactly } 8)$
$= {}_8C_5\,(.25)^5(.75)^3 + {}_8C_6\,(.25)^6(.75)^2 + {}_8C_7\,(.25)^7(.75) + {}_8C_8(.25)^8$
$\approx 56(.000412) + 28(.000137) + 8(.000046) + 1(.000015)$
$\approx .027291.$

So, sheer random guessing on a 8-item multiple-choice quiz yields a probability of less than 3% of getting 5 or more items correct. (Chances improve substantially with study!)

Binomial Probability Distributions

The probability distribution generated from the probability of x successes in a binomial experiment is called a **binomial probability distribution**. Here is an example.

Example 3

In a binomial experiment, suppose that the probability of success is 0.7. Determine and graph the probability distribution for the number of successes in five trials.

Solution

Let x be the number of successes. Then x can be any integer from 0 to 5. **Let $P(x) =$ the probability of exactly x successes.** By the preceding theorem, $P(x) = {}_5C_x\,p^x q^{5-x}$, where $p = 0.7$ and $q = 1 - p = 0.3$. Evaluate $p(x)$ for each possible value of x. The probability distribution is represented on page 543 in a table and with a graph.

Adapting to Individual Needs

Extra Help

Some students might misinterpret the fourth item in the list of features of binomial experiments given on page 540. Explain that stating that each trial has the same probability of success does *not* mean that the two possible outcomes in the experiment are equally likely (although this could be the case). The statement means that the probability for each possible outcome remains the same from one trial to another.

x	P(x)	
0	$q^5 = (.3)^5$	$= .00243$
1	$5pq^4 = 5(.7)(.3)^4$	$= .02835$
2	$10p^2q^3 = 10(.7)^2(.3)^3$	$= .1323$
3	$10p^3q^2 = 10(.7)^3(.3)^2$	$= .3087$
4	$5p^4q = 5(.7)^4(.3)$	$= .36015$
5	$p^5 = (.7)^5$	$= .16807$

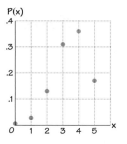

Check

The sum of the probabilities should be 1. You should check this.

Notes on Questions
Questions 1–10 These questions can be used to guide the class discussion. See the *Notes on Reading*.

QUESTIONS

Covering the Reading

1) **Sample: There are repeated situations, called trials. There are only 2 possible outcomes. The trials are independent. Each trial has the same probability of success.**

8a) **The student guesses randomly on each question.**
b) **The answer to any question is not affected by the answer to any other question.**

1. State four characteristics of a binomial experiment. **See left.**

In 2–5, state whether or not the experiment is a binomial experiment. If not, identify the missing property or properties.

2. A die is rolled seven times. Success is rolling a 3. **Yes**

3. Four cards are selected from a standard deck (of 52 cards) without replacement. Success is selecting an ace.
   No;   the trials are not independent.

4. A bag contains two red, three green, and five blue marbles. The bag is shaken, a marble is selected, its color is recorded, and it is replaced. This is repeated five times. **No;   there are three outcomes.**

5. One hundred people are selected at random and asked if they voted in the last presidential election. Success is if the person voted. **Yes**

In 6 and 7, suppose, as in Example 1, that the probability of keeping a certain cancer in remission is 0.7.

6. What is the probability that all four of the patients will stay well?
   0.2401
7. What is the probability that at least two of the four will stay well?
   0.9163
8. Refer to Example 2.
   a. What is a trial in this situation? **See left.**
   b. How do we know the trials are independent? **See left.**
   c. Where in the solution is the requirement of independent events applied? **when the binomial formula is used**
   d. Where in the solution is the fact that events are mutually exclusive applied?
      when the probabilities of 5, 6, 7, and 8 correct are added
9. Suppose a multiple-choice quiz has ten questions, each with five alternatives. If a student answers by random guessing, what is the probability that at least seven questions are answered correctly?
   ≈ .00086

Have slogan, will campaign. *Campaign buttons with names or catchy slogans remind adults of their right and responsibility to vote.*

Lesson 8-9   *Binomial Probabilities*   **543**

Adapting to Individual Needs

Challenge

Suppose a manufacturer of transistors believes that, on the average, one defective transistor occurs in every 100 transistors.
a. Find the probability that a batch of 20 transistors has 2 defectives.
   [0.01586]
b. Find the probability that a batch of 20 transistors has at most 2 defectives.
   [0.998996]

c. Suppose a batch of 20 transistors had 2 defectives. If you were the quality control supervisor, what would you conclude? [Something is probably wrong.]

Notes on Questions

Questions 11–12 Mastery is not expected at this time, but it is important for students to be familiar with the idea of distributions, and it helps in putting the individual answers to other questions in perspective.

Question 16 This question is similar to the airline reservation situation studied in Lesson 7-8. One might wonder how many small cars should a company have in order to be able to satisfy these customers? Car rental companies avoid these kinds of problems by keeping more big cars on hand than they need. Then, when a renter comes in and desires a small car, if they have no small car, they offer the bigger car at no extra cost. Airlines cannot do this since everyone comes at once for a particular flight, but sometimes they upgrade their best customers to first class.

Question 18 Error Alert Be sure students write the exponents after the trigonometric function, not after θ (unless they also use parentheses). That is, the first term should be 8 $\sin^3 \theta$, not 8 $\sin \theta^3$.

Question 19 If your state has a lottery, you may wish to adapt this question to your state lottery. For example, in Illinois, a person must pick 6 numbers correctly out of 54. But the bettor gets to pick two sets of 6 numbers on each $1 ticket. What is the probability of winning on one $1 ticket? $[\frac{1}{12913582.5} \approx 7.74 \times 10^{-8}]$

10)
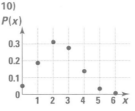

12b)
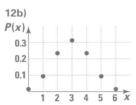

13c)
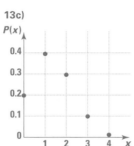

544

10. In a binomial experiment, suppose that the probability of success is 0.4. Determine and graph the probability distribution for the number of successes in 6 trials. **See left for graph.**

Number of successes	0	1	2	3	4	5	6
Probability	.047	.187	.311	.276	.138	.037	.004

Applying the Mathematics

11. For the distribution of Example 3, give each.
   a. mode **4**
   b. expected value **3.5**

12. Consider tossing a fair coin six times.
   a. Construct a probability distribution for this experiment, where x is the number of heads that occurs. **See margin.**
   b. Graph the probability distribution. **See left.**
   c. Find the probability of getting two or three heads. **0.546875**
   d. Find the probability of getting at least one head. **0.984375**

13. Refer to the drawing below with six congruent sectors. On any one spin, the spinner is equally likely to land in any of the six sectors.
   a. What is the probability of the spinner landing in a green sector? **1/3**
   b. Suppose a trial is a single spin, and that "success" means the spinner lands in a green sector. Complete the following probability distribution for the number of successes in four spins.

Probability Distribution of x Successes in 4 Spins

x = exact number of successes	0	1	2	3	4
P(x)	.198	.395	.296	.099	.012

   c. Graph the distribution in part **b.** **See left.**
   d. Find P(at least 3 successes). **0.111**
   e. Find P(at least 1 success). **0.802**

14. A baseball player has a batting average of .250. This can be interpreted to mean that the probability of a hit is $.250 = \frac{1}{4}$. Some people think this means that in 4 times at bat, the batter is *sure* to get a hit. Give the probability that this batter gets the following number of hits in 4 at-bats.
   a. exactly 1 hit
      27/64 ≈ 0.42
   b. at least 1 hit
      175/256 ≈ 0.68

15. Suppose that in a binomial experiment P(success on one trial) = a.
   a. Express P(failure on one trial) in terms of a. **(1 − a)**
   b. Find P(success on exactly 3 of 7 trials).
      (35) $a^3 (1 - a)^4$

16. A car rental company finds that, on the average, 86% of renters want small cars. Suppose 10 people at random come to rent cars.
   a. Find the probability that exactly 7 of them want small cars.
   b. Find the probability that no more than 3 of them want big cars.
      $_{10}C_7 (0.86)^7(0.14)^3 + 45(0.86)^8(0.14)^2 + 10(0.86)^9(0.14)^1 + 1(0.86)^{10} \approx 0.96$
   a) $_{10}C_7(0.86)^7(0.14)^3 \approx 0.115$

Additional Answers

12. a.

Number of Heads	Probability
0	0.015625
1	0.09375
2	0.234375
3	0.3125
4	0.234375
5	0.09375
6	0.015625

544

Review

17) $a^6 + 12a^5b + 60a^4b^2 + 160a^3b^3 + 240a^2b^4 + 192ab^5 + 64b^6$

18) $8 \sin^3\theta - 12 \sin^2\theta \cos\theta + 6 \sin\theta\cos^2\theta - \cos^3\theta$

19) $\frac{1}{{}_{55}C_6} = \frac{1}{28989675} \approx 3.4 \times 10^{-8}$

In 17 and 18, expand.   *(Lesson 8-8)* See left.

17. $(a + 2b)^6$

18. $(2 \sin \theta - \cos \theta)^3$

19. In a particular state lottery, you must pick 6 numbers correctly (in any order) out of 55. What is your probability of winning?   *(Lesson 8-6)*
See left.

20. Solve ${}_{n+5}C_1 = {}_nC_2$.   *(Lesson 8-6)* $n = 5$

21. An integer from 1 to 1000 is chosen at random. What is the probability that it is divisible by 7 or 11?   *(Lessons 7-2, 8-3)* 0.220

22. Describe the end behavior of the sequence generated by $t_n = \frac{\sqrt{n}}{3 + \sqrt{n}}$.   *(Lesson 8-2)* $\lim_{n\to\infty} t_n = 1$

23. Transliterated into English, the Hawaiian language has only the following letters: A, E, H, I, K, L, M, N, O, P, U, W. Every Hawaiian word and syllable ends with a vowel, and some words have no consonants. Two consonants never occur without a vowel between them. How many four-letter words are possible?   *(Lessons 7-3, 7-4)* 4475

24. *Skill sequence.*   Solve for x.   *(Lesson 6-6)*
  a. $.2^x = .05$ $x \approx 1.86$
  b. $1 - .4^x = .95$ $x \approx 3.27$
  c. $1 - p^x = a, p > 0, a < 1$ $x = \dfrac{\log (1 - a)}{(\log p)}$

Exploration

25. Binomial trials are sometimes called *Bernoulli trials*.
  a. Who was Bernoulli?
  b. What work of Bernoulli is related to binomial probabilities?
  Jakob Bernoulli wrote *Ars Conjectandi*, the first significant book on probability. In this work, the theorem that is in this book appeared for the first time. It sometimes is still called Bernoulli's theorem.
  a) **There are many Bernoullis. No less than eight brilliant mathematicians were produced by the family. Jakob Bernoulli (1654–1705) made important contributions in probability theory. His brother Johann (1667–1748) did important work in the theory of functions. He coined the term *functio*, the root of the present term *function*, in 1714.**

Lesson 8-9   *Binomial Probabilities*   **545**

Question 23 Multicultural Connection Do your students know any Hawaiian words or names? Some of the most common ones are the song *Aloha oe* ("Greetings to you"), *hula, poi, luau, Honolulu,* and the names of the major islands: *Oahu, Maui, Kauai, Hawaii, Lanai, and Molokai.* Together, these words and names use all the letters in the Hawaiian alphabet.

Follow-up for Lesson 8-9

Practice
For more questions on SPUR Objectives, use **Lesson Master 8-9** (shown on page 543).

Assessment
Written Communication Refer to **Example 3**. Change the probability of success to 0.8 and the number of trials to 6. Have students complete the problem using this new information. [Students determine binomial probabilities and graph the related probability distribution.]

Extension
Suppose a situation has three possible outcomes with probabilities a, b, and c of occurrence. Then $a + b + c = 1$. Then, if the situation is repeated n times, the probability that a occurs k_1 times and b occurs k_2 times is given by

$${}_nC_{k_1} \cdot {}_{(n - k_1)}C_{k_2} a^{k_1} b^{k_2} c^{(n - k_1 - k_2)}.$$

1. Show that this probability relates to the coefficients of $(a + b + c)^3$.

$$[{}_3C_{k_1}a^{k_1} \cdot {}_{3 - k_1}C_{k_2}b^{k_2} \cdot $$
$$_{3 - k_1 - k_2}C_{(3 - k_1 - k_2)}c^{(3 - k_1 - k_2)}$$

$$= \frac{3!}{k_1!(3 - k_1)!}a^{k_1} \cdot \frac{(3 - k_1)!}{k_2!(3 - k_1 - k_2)!}b^{k_2} \cdot$$
$$c^{(3 - k_1 - k_2)}$$

$$= \frac{3!}{k_1!k_2!(3 - k_1 - k_2)!} a^{k_1}b^{k_2}c^{(3 - k_1 - k_2)}]$$

2. Describe a situation in which this formula might be applied. [Sample: Polling where responses might be "yes," "no," or "undecided."]

Chapter 8 Projects

The projects relate chiefly to the content of the lessons of this chapter as follows:

Project	Lesson(s)
1	8-7, 8-8
2	8-5
3	8-1, 8-3
4	8-6
5	8-1, 8-4, 8-5
6	8-2, 8-5

1 The Binomial Theorem for Rational Exponents Material for this project can be found in many calculus textbooks.

2 Infinity in Art A student doing this project might start with Escher drawings with "infinity" in their title.

3 A Prime Number Sieve This project has more meaning if the student is aware that there is no polynomial formula that will generate all of the primes.

4 Probabilities and the Lottery A growing number of states in the United States support lotteries. We include the caveat about purchasing tickets because we do not wish to encourage experimental approaches to this project. If anything, the results of doing the project should discourage participation in lotteries.

5 Recursively Defined Curves This project involves geometric sequences because each part is a factor times a preceding part.

A project presents an opportunity for you to extend your knowledge of a topic related to the material of this chapter. You should allow more time for a project than you do for a typical homework question.

PROJECTS 8 CHAPTER EIGHT

1 The Binomial Theorem for Rational Exponents
Isaac Newton generalized the Binomial Theorem to all rational exponents. That is, he derived series expansions for such expressions as $(x + y)^{-3}$, $(x + y)^{2/3}$, and $(x + y)^{-5/6}$. What did Newton find? What are the first four terms of the series expansions of the binomials above? How can this extended Binomial Theorem be used to aid in calculations?

2 Infinity in Art
The concept of infinity has intrigued people throughout history. In the last 100 years several artists and mathematicians have created spectacular works of art based on the infinite repetition of geometric

forms. The Dutch artist Maurits Escher is probably most noted for his *tessellations*, which are tilings of the plane with congruent objects. Tessellations can be thought of as providing a finite pattern for covering the infinite plane. In other works of art, such as Square Limit, Escher represented infinite divisions within a finite space. Investigate Escher's use of mathematics in the representation of infinity.

---

3 A Prime Number Sieve
In 1934, a young Indian student named Sundaram devised the following "sieve" to identify some prime numbers. Here is the beginning of his table, in which each row (and column) is an arithmetic sequence.

4	7	10	13	16	19	22	...
7	12	17	22	27	32	37	...
10	17	24	31	38	45	52	...
13	22	31	40	49	58	67	...
16	27	38	49	60	71	82	...

Sundaram's table has the following properties: If N occurs in the table, then $2N + 1$ is not a prime number; if N does not occur in the table, then $2N + 1$ is a prime number.
a. Verify the first property for three numbers in the table and the second property for three numbers that are not (and never will be) in the table.
b. Identify the common difference d for each row. What is the pattern in these common differences as you read down the table?
c. Write an explicit formula for the kth term in the nth row. Use this result to prove that if N occurs in the table, then $2N + 1$ is composite.
d. Prove that if $2N + 1$ is not prime, then N is in the table. (This is the contrapositive of the second property stated above.)
e. Can all prime numbers be found by using Sundaram's table? Why or why not?

Possible Responses
1. Newton stated, but never proved, that the binomial expansion held for fractional and negative n. To understand this, we must first rewrite the binomial expansion shown at the right.

$$(x + y)^n = x^n + nx^{n-1}y + \frac{n(n-1)}{1 \cdot 2} x^{n-2}y^2 + \ldots + \frac{(n(n-1) \ldots n - r + 1)}{1 \cdot 2 \cdot 3 \cdot \ldots \cdot r} x^{n-r} y^r + \ldots + y^n.$$

Notice that, when n is an integer, these coefficients are $_nC_r = \binom{n}{r}$, and the expansion is equivalent to the binomial expansion in the text. Newton claimed that this expansion holds even when n is negative or a fraction. In these cases, the expansion is an infinite series.

$$(x + y)^{-3} = x^{-3} - 3x^{-4}y - 6x^{-5}y^2 - 10x^{-6}y^3 + \ldots$$

$$(x + y)^{\frac{2}{3}} = x^{\frac{2}{3}} + \frac{2}{3}x^{-\frac{1}{3}}y - \frac{1}{9}x^{-\frac{4}{3}}y^2 + \frac{4}{81} x^{-\frac{7}{3}}y^3 + \ldots$$

$$(x + y)^{\frac{-5}{6}} = x^{\frac{-5}{6}} - \frac{5}{6}x^{\frac{-11}{6}} y + \frac{55}{72}x^{\frac{-17}{6}}y^2 - \frac{935}{1296} x^{\frac{-23}{6}}y^3 + \ldots$$

4 Probabilities and the Lottery

a. Obtain the rules, entry sheets, and an information sheet for a lottery. Use this information to find the number of different entries possible for each game, the probability that you will win first prize with a single entry, and the probability of winning *any* prize with a single entry. Would you advise someone to buy lottery tickets? Why or why not?

b. Repeat the steps in part **a** for another lottery. In which lottery does the person have a better chance of winning? Suggest some reasons why a particular game might be played.

(*Note:* Do not attempt to buy a ticket in your local Lotto competition without first checking that it is legal for you to do so. All states restrict sales to persons over a certain age.)

5 Recursively Defined Curves

Many interesting curves can be created by recursive definitions. For instance, begin with a square with a given side, say —————. At each stage, replace each side of the square with this shape:

————— . The original square and

subsequent stages leading to a limit curve, sometimes called the *dragon curve,* are shown below.

a. Determine the perimeter, area, and dimension of the dragon curve. To determine the dimension, you will need to learn something about *fractals.*

b. Find out about other curves that are defined recursively. Some famous ones are called snowflake curves and space-filling curves.

c. Design your own curve.

6 A Test for Convergence

If an infinite series containing only positive terms is to converge, it is necessary that the terms approach 0 as n approaches infinity. However, this is not sufficient; the text points out that the harmonic series diverges even though the terms approach 0.

a. Explain why the following series diverges.

$$A = 1 + \frac{1}{2} + \underbrace{\frac{1}{4} + \frac{1}{4}}_{2 \text{ terms}} + \underbrace{\frac{1}{8} + \frac{1}{8} + \frac{1}{8} + \frac{1}{8}}_{4 \text{ terms}} +$$

$$\underbrace{\frac{1}{16} + \frac{1}{16} + \frac{1}{16} + \frac{1}{16} + \frac{1}{16} + \frac{1}{16} + \frac{1}{16} + \frac{1}{16} + \cdots}_{8 \text{ terms}}$$

b. Show that each term of the harmonic series

$$H = 1 + \frac{1}{2} + \frac{1}{3} + \frac{1}{4} + \frac{1}{5} + \frac{1}{6} + \cdots$$

is greater than or equal to the corresponding term of series A. Explain how this result shows that the harmonic series diverges.

c. The following variation of the harmonic series, the *alternating harmonic series*, converges.

$$B = 1 - \frac{1}{2} + \frac{1}{3} - \frac{1}{4} + \frac{1}{5} - \frac{1}{6} + \cdots$$
$$+ (-1)^{n+1} \frac{1}{n} + \cdots$$

Use a calculator or computer to approximate B to six decimal places.

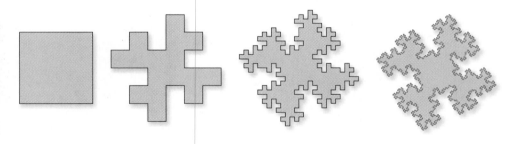

6 A Test for Convergence

Given in the text is the classic proof as to why the harmonic series diverges. A different proof was recently given by Michael Ecker of Pennsylvania State University (*The College Mathematics Journal*, May 1997). It is indirect. Suppose the harmonic series had a sum S. Then split the sum into the sum S_{odd} of the unit fractions with odd denominators and the sum S_{even} of the unit fractions with even denominators. The terms of S_{odd} are greater than the corresponding terms of S_{even}, so $S_{odd} > S_{even}$. But, factoring out $\frac{1}{2}$ from the terms of S_{even} shows that $S_{even} = \frac{1}{2} S$. So $S_{odd} > \frac{1}{2} S$. Consequently $S_{even} + S_{odd} > S$, which is impossible, showing that the original supposition is false, and the harmonic series cannot have a sum S.

3. a. **Sample: We verify the first property for 4, 22, and 31. $2 \cdot 4 + 1 = 9$, $2 \cdot 22 + 1 = 45$ and $2 \cdot 31 + 1 = 63$ which are not prime numbers. We verify the second property for 5, 20, and 21. $2 \cdot 5 + 1 = 11$, $2 \cdot 20 + 1 = 41$, and $2 \cdot 21 + 1 = 43$ which are all prime numbers.**

b. **The values of d for the first five rows are 3, 5, 7, 9, and 11 in that order. In general, if n is the number of the row, the common difference is $d = 2n + 1$.**

c. **The kth term in the nth row is $2nk + n + k$. If N is the kth term in the nth row in the table, $2N + 1 = 2(2nk + n + k) + 1 = 4nk + 2n + 2k + 1 = (2n + 1)(2k + 1)$. Since $2n + 1$ and $2k + 1$ are integers greater than 1, $2N + 1$ is not a prime.**

d. **If $2N + 1$ is not a prime, then it is the product of two integers x and y such that $x > 1$ and $y > 1$. Since $2N + 1$ is odd, x and y must also be odd. Thus $x = 2a + 1$ and $y = 2b + 1$ for $a > 0$ and $b > 0$. So $2N + 1 = xy = (2a + 1)(2b + 1) = 4ab + 2a + 2b + 1$. That implies that $2N = 4ab + 2a + 2b$ and $N = 2ab + a + b$. So N is the bth term in the ath row of the table.**

e. **No, 2 is prime, but 2 cannot be written as $2N + 1$ for any integer N.**

(*Responses continue on page 548.*)

2. **Sample: Escher was able to create the illusion of an infinite two-dimensional space by tessellating or repeating a motif on the surface of a bounded three-dimensional object, such as a sphere, cylinder, or Möbius strip, so that when rotated, the image repeated itself indefinitely. This is well exemplified in his wood carving *Heaven and Hell*. In a two-dimensional medium, Escher was able to make spaces appear infinite by reproducing a motif in the plane, keeping its shape similar but diminishing its size as it approaches some boundary or point on the plane. This can be seen in such works as *Path of Life I*, *Whirlpools*, *Circle Limit III*, and *Smaller and Smaller*.**

Summary

The Summary gives an overview of the entire chapter and provides an opportunity for students to consider the material as a whole. Thus, the Summary can be used to help students relate and unify the concepts presented in the chapter.

Additional responses, pages 546–547

4. **a.** Sample: The Big Game is designed to include a population of 50 million. The probability of winning first prize with 1 ticket is about 1 in 53 million, and the probability of winning any prize is $\frac{1}{24.4} \approx .041$. The expected value of a \$1 ticket when the jackpot is 34 million dollars is shown below.

$34 million $\left(\frac{1}{52.969}\text{ million}\right)$

$+ (\$150,000) \left(\frac{1}{2.207}\text{ million}\right)$

$+ (\$5,000) \left(\frac{1}{235417.8}\right)$

$+ (\$150) \left(\frac{1}{98091}\right)$

$+ (\$100) \left(\frac{1}{5350.4}\right) + (\$5) \left(\frac{1}{222.9}\right)$

$+ (\$5) \left(\frac{1}{373.3}\right) + (\$2) \left(\frac{1}{71.1}\right)$

$+ (\$1) \left(\frac{1}{43.4}\right) = \$0.85$

(This value is high, because it assumes there can be only 1 winner and that the amounts are paid in lump sums.) We would not advise someone to buy a lottery ticket, because the expected value is less than 1.

b. Sample: The POWERBALL® has a base of 21 states and the District of Columbia. The probability of winning is 1 in about 55 million. The probability of winning any prize is $\frac{1}{36}$ or about .028. The expected value of a ticket with a 60 million dollar jackpot is shown at the right.

$60 million $\left(\frac{1}{54.979\text{ million}}\right)$

$+ (\$100,000) \left(\frac{1}{1,249,526}\right)$

$+ (\$5,000) \left(\frac{1}{274,896}\right)$

$+ (\$100) \left(\frac{1}{6248}\right)$

$+ (\$100) \left(\frac{1}{7049}\right) + (\$5) \left(\frac{1}{160}\right)$

$+ (\$5) \left(\frac{1}{556}\right) + (\$2) \left(\frac{1}{120}\right)$

$+ (\$1) \left(\frac{1}{84}\right) = \$1.29.$

SUMMARY

A sequence is a function whose domain is the set of consecutive integers greater than or equal to k. An explicit formula allows you to find any specified term efficiently. A recursive formula describes each term in terms of previous ones and is often more efficient for generating the terms.

Two important kinds of sequences are arithmetic and geometric sequences. For an arithmetic sequence, the difference between successive terms is a constant, the constant difference. In a geometric sequence, the ratio of successive terms is a constant, the constant ratio. If an arithmetic sequence has first term a_1 and constant difference d, the nth term $a_n = a_1 + (n - 1)d$. If a geometric sequence has first term g_1 and constant ratio r, the nth term $g_n = g_1 r^{n-1}$.

Some infinite sequences converge to a limit while others diverge. A computer or calculator is useful for deciding whether or not a sequence is convergent, but it is not an infallible tool. Limits of some sequences can be found by applying properties of limits.

A series is the sum of the terms of a sequence. Explicit formulas for sums of arithmetic and geometric series exist. The sum S_n of the first n terms of an arithmetic sequence is given by $S_n = \frac{n}{2}(2a_1 + (n - 1)d)$ or $S_n = \frac{n}{2}(a_1 + a_n)$.

For a geometric series with $r \neq 1$, $S_n = \frac{g_1(1 - r^n)}{1 - r}$. To examine infinite series, it is useful to form a sequence $S_1, S_2, \ldots$ of partial sums. An infinite series may have a limit; some do not. For an infinite geometric series with first term g_1 and constant ratio r, the limit exists when $|r| < 1$; $S_\infty = \frac{g_1}{1 - r}$.

The number of ways to select r unordered items from a set of n elements is $_nC_r = \frac{_nP_r}{r!} = \frac{n!}{(n - r)!r!}$. Each selection is called a combination. A famous configuration of combinations is called Pascal's Triangle. Each row of Pascal's Triangle gives coefficients of terms in the expanded form of the power of a binomial. In particular, for all positive integers n,

$(x + y)^n = {_nC_0}x^n + {_nC_1}x^{n-1}y + {_nC_2}x^{n-2}y^2 + \ldots + {_nC_n}y^n.$

A binomial experiment has a fixed number of trials, each with only two possible outcomes (success and failure), the probabilities of which are fixed and sum to 1. In a binomial experiment with n trials and probability of success p, the probability of exactly k successes is $_nC_k p^k(1 - p)^{n-k}$. By the Binomial Theorem, this is the $(k + 1)$st term in the expansion of $(x + y)^n$, where $x = p$ and $y = 1 - p$.

548

Since the expected value is greater than 1 we might assume that a jackpot worth 60 million dollars is worth risking the 1 dollar for the ticket. This lottery seems better than the Big Game, although the probability of winning is less. People play these games because the jackpot is large and the price of a ticket is small. However, these costs can sum to larger amounts over time. Another factor to consider is the real value of the jackpot. Because the jackpot is not paid in a lump sum, inflation makes the jackpot worth less. Taxes would also decrease winnings by nearly one half.

(Responses continue on page 549.)

VOCABULARY

Below are the most important terms and phrases for this chapter. You should be able to give a general description and a specific example of each and a precise definition for those marked with an asterisk (*).

Lesson 8-1
*sequence, term, position
explicit formula, recursive formula
*arithmetic sequence
*geometric sequence

Lesson 8-2
limiting value, $\lim_{n \to \infty} s_n$
end behavior of a sequence
*divergent
*convergent, convergent to L
*harmonic sequence
alternating harmonic sequence

Lesson 8-3
*series
infinite series, finite series
arithmetic series

Lesson 8-4
*geometric series
nth partial sum

Lesson 8-5
sequence of partial sums
sum of an infinite series, S_∞
convergent, divergent series

Lesson 8-6
*combination, combinations of n things taken r at a time
$_nC_r, \binom{n}{r}$
Formula for $_nC_r$ Theorem

Lesson 8-7
Pascal's Triangle
$(r + 1)$st term in row n of Pascal's Triangle

Lesson 8-8
expansion of $(x + y)^n$
Binomial Theorem
binomial coefficients

Lesson 8-9
*binomial experiment, success, failure
Binomial Probability Theorem
binomial probability distribution

Vocabulary

Terms, symbols, and properties are listed by lesson to provide a checklist of concepts a student must know. Emphasize to students that they should read the vocabulary list carefully before starting the Progress Self-Test. If students do not understand the meaning of a term, they should refer back to the indicated lesson.

Additional responses, page 547
5. a. If a square with sides of length 1 is considered the first stage of the dragon curve, then at the nth stage the dragon curve has perimeter $4 \cdot 2^{(n-1)}$ and area 1.

b. The snowflake curve called the Koch curve results from the following process: Begin with an equilateral triangle. To create the $(n + 1)$th figure, take each segment of the nth figure, trisect it, and replace it with this pattern.

It progresses as pictured below.

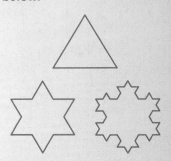

The limit of this curve is a fractal.

c. Sample:

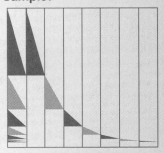

(Responses continue on page 553.)

Progress Self-Test

For the development of mathematical competence, feedback and correction, along with the opportunity to practice, are necessary. The Progress Self-Test provides the opportunity for feedback and correction; the Chapter Review provides additional opportunities and practice. We cannot overemphasize the importance of these end-of-chapter materials. It is at this point that the material "gels" for many students, allowing them to solidify skills and understanding. In general, student performance should be markedly improved after these pages.

Assign the Progress Self-Test as a one-night assignment. Worked-out *solutions* for all questions are in the Selected Answers section of the student book. Encourage students to take the Progress Self-Test honestly, grade themselves, and then be prepared to discuss the test in class.

Advise students to pay special attention to those Chapter Review questions (pages 551–553) that correspond to questions missed on the Progress Self-Test.

Additional Answers

6. a.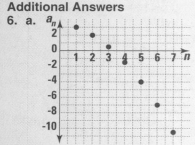

PROGRESS SELF-TEST

6a, 12, 13a, 13b, 17) See margin.

Take this test as you would take a test in class. You will need a calculator. Then check the test yourself using the solutions at the back of the book.

In 1 and 2, consider this formula for a sequence.

$$\begin{cases} g_1 = 0 \\ g_n = g_{n-1} + n^2, \text{ for all integers } n > 1 \end{cases}$$

1. Is the sequence arithmetic, geometric, or neither? **neither**

2. Find the first four terms of the sequence. **2) 0, 4, 13, 29**

3. The first term of an arithmetic sequence is -12 and the constant difference is d. Find the 15th term. **$-12 + 14d$**

4. Consider the geometric sequence that begins $9, 3, \ldots$. Find the 7th term of the sequence. **4) $\frac{1}{81}$**

5. An employee begins a job paying \$19,000 per year with the guarantee of a 5% increase in salary each year.

   a. What is the employee's salary during the fourth year? **$\approx$ \$21,994.88**

   b. What is the employee's salary during the nth year? **$S_n = 19,000(1.05)^{n-1}$**

6. Consider the sequence given by

$$\begin{cases} a_1 = 3 \\ a_n = a_{n-1} - \frac{1}{2}n, n \geq 2. \end{cases}$$

   a. Sketch a graph of this sequence.

   b. Is the sequence convergent? If so, find its limit. **not convergent**

7. On each swing, a certain pendulum swings 70% of the length of its previous swing. How far will the pendulum swing before coming to rest if its first swing is 75 cm? **250 cm**

8. Estimate $\sum_{i=1}^{\infty} \frac{3}{i^3}$ correct to three decimal places. **3.606**

9. Find the sum of all the integers from 100 to 200. **15,150**

10. Find $\sum_{i=1}^{10} 7\left(\frac{3}{4}\right)^i$ to the nearest ten-thousandth. **19.8174**

11. Lillian has begun running every day for exercise. The first day she ran 0.5 miles. The 12th day she ran 3.25 miles. If each day she increased her distance by a constant amount, how many total miles did she run in all 12 days combined? **22.5 miles**

12. Prove that for all integers n greater than or equal to 1, $_nC_2 = {_nC_{n-2}} = \frac{n(n-1)}{2}$.

13. a. Expand $(x + y)^3$.

    b. Explain how your answer to part **a** is related to Pascal's Triangle.

In 14 and 15, *multiple choice*.

14. The first term in the binomial expansion of $(2c - b)^{10}$ is $(2c)^{10}$. What is the 4th term? **d**
    (a) $(2c)^7$
    (b) $(2c)^7(-b)^3$
    (c) $10 \cdot 9 \cdot 8(2c)^7(-b)^3$
    (d) $\frac{10 \cdot 9 \cdot 8}{3!}(2c)^7(-b)^3$

15. In a talent contest with 50 finalists (one from each state), the top three winners will be given identical prizes. How many different sets of possible winners are there? **d**
    (a) 3^{50} (b) 50^3
    (c) $50 \cdot 49 \cdot 48$ (d) $\frac{50 \cdot 49 \cdot 48}{3!}$

16. Suppose the probability that a randomly selected heart transplant patient will survive more than one year is 0.86. Find the probability that at least 4 of 5 randomly selected heart patients will survive for longer than a year. **$\approx$ 0.85**

17. Show three places in Pascal's Triangle where the following property is displayed.
$$_nC_0 + {_nC_2} + {_nC_4} + \ldots + {_nC_{n-1}} =$$
$$_nC_1 + {_nC_3} + {_nC_5} + \ldots + {_nC_n}.$$

$$100 + 101 + 102 + 103 + \ldots + 200$$

550

12. $_nC_2 = \frac{n!}{(n-2)!2!} = \frac{n(n-1)(n-2)!}{(n-2)!2} = \frac{n(n-1)}{2}$;

$_nC_{n-2} = \frac{n!}{(n-n+2)!(n-2)!} = \frac{n!}{2!(n-2)!} = \frac{n(n-1)}{2}$.

So $_nC_2 = {_nC_{n-2}} = \frac{n(n-1)}{2}$.

13. a. $(x + y)^3 = x^3 + 3x^2y + 3xy^2 + y^3$
    b. The coefficients are the terms in row 3 of Pascal's Triangle.

17. Sample:
    In row 1, $_1C_0 = {_1C_1} = 1$.
    In row 3, $_3C_0 + {_3C_2} = 1 + 3 = 3 + 1 = {_3C_1} + {_3C_3}$.
    In row 4, $_4C_0 + {_4C_2} + {_4C_4} = 1 + 10 + 5 = 4 + 4 = {_4C_1} + {_4C_3}$.

CHAPTER REVIEW

Questions on SPUR Objectives

SPUR stands for **S**kills, **P**roperties, **U**ses, and **R**epresentations. The Chapter Review questions are grouped according to the SPUR Objectives for this chapter.
2–6, 8, 17, 18) See margin.

SKILLS DEAL WITH THE PROCEDURES USED TO GET ANSWERS.

Objective A: *Find terms of sequences from explicit or recursive formulas.* (*Lesson 8-1*)

In 1–4, a sequence is described. **a.** Find the first 5 terms. **b.** Find the 12th term.

1. $R_n = n^2 - n$ 2. $\begin{cases} B_1 = -6 \\ B_n = B_{n-1} + 3n, n \geq 2 \end{cases}$

3. $t_n = 3 \cdot 2^{n-1}$ 4. $q_n = -10 + 3(n - 1)$

1a) 0, 2, 6, 12, 20   b) 132

Objective B: *Find explicit or recursive formulas for the nth term of an arithmetic or geometric sequence.* (*Lesson 8-1*)

5. The first four terms of an arithmetic sequence are 84, 67, 50, 33. Find each.
   a. the 50th term   **b.** the nth term

6. The first three terms of a geometric sequence are 24, -84, 294. Find each.
   a. the 15th term   **b.** the nth term

7. Give an explicit formula for the sequence defined by
   $\begin{cases} k_1 = 22{,}000 \quad k_n = 22{,}000(0.8)^{n-1} \\ k_n = 0.8k_{n-1}, \text{ for all integers } n \geq 2. \end{cases}$

8. Give a recursive formula for the sequence defined by $A_n = 32 - 5n$.

Objective C: *Evaluate arithmetic or geometric series.* (*Lessons 8-3, 8-4*)

In 9–12, evaluate the arithmetic or geometric series given.

9. $103 + 120 + 137 + 154 + \ldots + 290$ **2358**

10. $(5u - v) + (4u + v) + (3u + 3v) + \ldots + (23v - 7u)$ **143v − 13u**

11. $1 + 3 + 9 + 27 + \ldots + 3^{14}$ **7,174,453**

12. $x + x^2y + x^3y^2 + \ldots + x^{21}y^{20}$ $\dfrac{x - x^{22}y^{21}}{1 - xy}$

13. Evaluate $\sum_{k=1}^{100} (4k - 13)$. **18,900**

14. Evaluate $\sum_{n=1}^{20} 10(0.6)^{n-1}$. ≈ 24.999

Objective D: *Expand binomials.* (*Lesson 8-8*)

In 15–18, expand. 15) $a^3 + 3a^2b + 3ab^2 + b^3$

15. $(a + b)^3$ 16. $(x - y)^6$ **See below.**

17. $(2x - 5)^4$ 18. $\left(\frac{p}{2} + 2q\right)^5$

19. Find the second term in the binomial expansion of $(x - y)^{12}$. **-12x^{11}y**

20. Find the middle term in the binomial expansion of $(p + q)^{10}$. **252p^5q^5**

16) $x^6 - 6x^5y + 15x^4y^2 - 20x^3y^3 + 15x^2y^4 - 6xy^5 + y^6$

PROPERTIES DEAL WITH THE PRINCIPLES BEHIND THE MATHEMATICS.

Objective E: *Determine whether a sequence is arithmetic or geometric.* (*Lesson 8-1*)

In 21–26, classify the sequence as possibly or definitely arithmetic, possibly or definitely geometric, or definitely neither.

21. 13, 24, 35, 46, . . . **possibly arithmetic**

22. 44, 50, 57, 65, . . . **definitely neither**

possibly arithmetic
23. $3u, u + v, 2v - u, 3v - 3u, \ldots$

24. $\begin{cases} a_1 = -2 \\ a_n = (a_{n-1})^2 + 1, \text{ for all integers } n > 1 \end{cases}$ **definitely neither**

25. $t_n = -8(-0.7)^n$ **definitely geometric**

26. $\begin{cases} a_1 = x \\ a_n = y - a_{n-1}, \text{ for all integers } n \geq 2 \end{cases}$ **definitely neither**

Additional Answers
2. a. -6, 0, 9, 21, 36
   b. 225
3. a. 3, 6, 12, 24, 48
   b. 6144
4. a. -10, -7, -4, -1, 2
   b. 23
5. a. -749
   b. $a_n = 84 - 17(n - 1)$
6. a. $\approx 993{,}490{,}829.369$
   b. $g_n = 24(-3.5)^{n-1}$

8. $\begin{cases} A_1 = 27 \\ A_n = A_{n-1} - 5 \text{ for all integers } n > 1 \end{cases}$

17. $16x^4 - 160x^3 + 600x^2 - 1000x + 625$
18. $\frac{p^5}{32} + 5(\frac{p^4}{8})q + 5p^3q^2 + 20p^2q^3 + 40pq^4 + 32q^5$

Chapter 8 Review

Resources
From the *Teacher's Resource File*
■ Answer Master for Chapter 8 Review
■ Assessment Sourcebook:
Chapter 8 Test, Forms A-D
Chapter 8 Test, Cumulative Form

Additional Resources
■ Quiz and Test Writer

The main objectives for the chapter are organized in the Chapter Review under the four types of understanding this book promotes—Skills, Properties, Uses, and Representations.

Whereas end-of chapter material may be considered optional in some texts, in *UCSMP Functions, Statistics, and Trigonometry* we have selected these objectives and questions with the expectation that they will be covered. Students should be able to answer these questions with about 85% accuracy after studying the chapter.

You may assign these questions over a single night to help students prepare for a test the next day, or you may assign the questions over a two-day period. If you work the questions over two days, then we recommend assigning the *evens* for homework the first night so that students get feedback in class the next day, then assigning the *odds* the night before the test, because answers are provided to the odd-numbered questions.

It is effective to ask students which questions they still do not understand and use the day or days as a total class discussion of the material which the class finds most difficult.

551

Assessment

Evaluation The *Assessment Sourcebook* provides six forms of the Chapter 8 Test. Forms A and B present parallel versions in a short-answer format. Forms C and D offer performance assessment. The fifth test is Chapter 8 Test, Cumulative Form. About 50% of this test covers Chapter 8, 25% of it covers Chapter 7, and 25% of it covers earlier chapters.

For information on grading, see *General Teaching Suggestions; Grading* in the *Professional Sourcebook*, which begins on page T20 in the Teacher's Edition.

Feedback After students have taken the test for Chapter 8 and you have scored the results, return the tests to students for discussion. Class discussion of the questions that caused trouble for the most students can be very effective in identifying and clarifying misunderstandings. You might want to have them write down the items they missed and work, either in groups or at home, to correct them. It is important for students to receive feedback on every chapter test, and we recommend that students see and correct their mistakes before proceeding too far into the next chapter.

Objective F: *Determine limits of certain sequences.* *(Lesson 8-2)*

In 27–30, decide whether the sequence has a limit, and if it does, determine the limit.

27. the geometric sequence 80, 60, 45, 33.75, …

28. the arithmetic sequence 80, 60, 40, 20, …

29. $h_n = \frac{7}{n}$ **yes; 0**

30. $\begin{cases} v_1 = 1 \text{ **no limit**} \\ v_n = (-1)^n \cdot v_{n-1}, \text{ for all integers } n > 1 \end{cases}$

31. Use a calculator or computer to evaluate terms of the sequence   **a) Yes**   **b)** $\frac{3}{2}$

$$-\frac{19}{69}, -\frac{22}{67}, -\frac{25}{65}, \ldots, \frac{3n+16}{2n-71}, \ldots$$

  a. Does the sequence seem to converge?

  b. If the sequence is convergent, give its limit. If it is divergent, explain how you can tell.

32. Use a computer or calculator to decide whether the sequence below is convergent or divergent. If the sequence converges, give its limit as a fraction in lowest terms.

$$1, \frac{11}{16}, \frac{16}{24}, \frac{23}{32}, \ldots, \frac{n^2+7}{8n}, \ldots \text{ **divergent**}$$

27) yes; 0   28) no limit

Objective G: *Tell whether an infinite series converges. If it does, give the limit.* *(Lesson 8-5)*

In 33–35, for the geometric series shown, state whether or not the series is convergent. If the series is convergent, give its sum.

33. $8 - \frac{40}{3} + \frac{200}{9} - \frac{1000}{27} + \ldots$ **not convergent**

34. $7 + 5.6 + 4.48 + \ldots$ **convergent; 35**

35. $a - \frac{a}{5} + \frac{a}{25} - \frac{a}{125} + \ldots$ **convergent;** $\frac{5}{6}a$

36. Use a computer or calculator to conjecture whether the series below is convergent. If it seems to be convergent, give what seems to be its limit.

  $\frac{1}{1^5} + \frac{1}{2^5} + \frac{1}{3^5} + \frac{1}{4^5} + \ldots$ **convergent; about 1.0369**

37. **a.** Under what condition does the following geometric series have a sum?

    $a^3b^2 + a^3b^4 + a^3b^6 + a^3b^8 + \ldots$

  b. Give an expression for the sum, when it exists.

  a) when $b^2 < 1$ **b)** $\frac{a^3b^2}{1-b^2}$

Objective H: *Prove and apply properties involving combinations.* *(Lesson 8-7)*

In 38–40, prove the given identity.

38. $_nC_r = {_nC_{n-r}}$ for all positive integers n and r, $r \leq n$

39. $_nC_1 = {_nC_{n-1}} = n$

40. $_nC_r = {_{n-1}C_r} + {_{n-1}C_{r-1}}$

41. *True or false.* For all positive integers n and r such that $r \leq n$, $_nP_r > {_nC_r}$. **False**

38–40) See margin.

USES DEAL WITH APPLICATIONS OF MATHEMATICS IN REAL SITUATIONS.

Objective I: *Solve problems involving arithmetic and geometric sequences and series.* *(Lessons 8-1, 8-3, 8-4, 8-5)*

42. One sunflower produces 500 seeds. Each seed produces a flower which produces 500 seeds, and so on. Let a_n = the number of seeds after n generations. **a, b) See margin.**

  a. Write an explicit formula for a_n.

  b. Write a recursive formula for a_n.

  c. Assuming no losses, how many sunflower seeds are produced at the end of five generations, starting with a first generation of 100 sunflowers? **3.125 × 10^{15}**

43. The coach of a soccer team rewards the players on the team by putting stars on jerseys. Every time the coach increases the number of stars by two. For the first win, the coach gives 3 stars.

  a. Determine how many times the team has won if each jersey has 17 stars. **8**

  b. Determine the least number of wins needed in order to have 100 stars on each jersey. **50**

44. In mid-1996, the population of Iraq was about 21.4 million, with an average annual growth rate of 3.7%. Estimate the population in the middle of the year 2000, assuming that the population grows geometrically and the growth rate does not change. **≈ 24.7 million**

Additional Answers

38. $_nC_r = \frac{n!}{r!(n-r)!}$;

  $_nC_{n-r} = \frac{n!}{(n-n+r)!(n-r)!}$

  $= \frac{n!}{r!(n-r)!}$

39. $_nC_1 = \frac{n!}{1!(n-1)!} = \frac{n(n-1)!}{(n-1)!} = n$;

  $_nC_{n-1} = \frac{n!}{(n-1)!(n-n+1)!}$

  $= \frac{n(n-1)!}{(n-1!)}$

  $= n$

40. $_{n-1}C_r + {_{n-1}C_{r-1}}$

  $= \frac{(n-1)!}{r!(n-1-r)!} + \frac{(n-1)!}{(r-1)!(n-1-r+1)!}$

  $= \frac{(n-1)!}{r!(n-r-1)!} \cdot \frac{n-r}{n-r} + \frac{(n-1)!}{(r-1)!(n-r)!} \cdot \frac{r}{r}$

  $= \frac{(n-r)(n-1)!}{r!(n-r)!} + \frac{r(n-1)!}{r!(n-r)!} = \frac{(n-1)!(n)}{r!(n-r)!}$

  $= \frac{n!}{r!(n-r)!}$

  $= {_nC_r}$

42. **a.** $a_n = 500(500)^{n-1}$

  b. $\begin{cases} a_1 = 500 \\ a_n = 500 \cdot a_{n-1} \text{ for } n > 1 \end{cases}$

a) $692.67   b) about $96,113

45. In a certain housing complex, rents are increased by 4% every year. Consider a family which has been living at this complex for 15 years and assume that they paid $400 per month in the first year.

  a. Determine the rent they are paying this year.

  b. At the end of this year, how much will the family have paid during their 15 years of residency? (Hint: Consider the total rent the family has paid in each complete year.)

46. The tracks on an LP record can be approximated as concentric circles (rather than a continuous spiral) with a difference of .3 mm between the radii of consecutive circles. If the grooves on a record start 15 cm away from the center and end 3 cm away from it. What is the distance covered by the needle of a record player in one playing of this LP?
  $\approx$ 22,676 cm

Objective J: *Use combinations to compute the number of ways of selecting objects.* (Lesson 8-6)

47. A committee of three is to be chosen from a faculty of 13 math teachers. How many ways of choosing the committee are there? **286**

48. There are 20 members of a tennis club. If each must play the others exactly once in a tennis match, how many games must be played? **190**

49. A euchre hand consists of five cards from a deck of 32 different cards. Half the cards are red, the other half are black.
  201,376

  a. How many different euchre hands are there?

  b. How many euchre hands contain only red cards? **4368**

76,904,685

50. In how many ways can a DJ select eight hits from the top 40 to play in the next half hour?

51. A catering service can prepare 6 soups, 8 salads, 8 vegetables, and 10 entrees. In how many different ways can you select 1 soup, 3 salads, 4 vegetables, and 2 entrees?
  1,058,400

Objective K: *Determine probabilities in situations involving binomial experiments.* (Lesson 8-9)

In 52 and 53, Mrs. McDonnell knows that each of her five children likes roughly 80% of the suppers she serves. Assume that the children's likes and dislikes are independent.

52. What is the probability that all five children will like a given supper? $\approx$ **.32768 $\approx$ 33%**

53. What is the probability that at least one person will dislike supper? $\approx$ **.67232 $\approx$ 67%**

54. If Mr. and Mrs. Washington both have siblings with cystic fibrosis, the probability that any given child born to them has the disease is $\frac{1}{9}$. If they have two children, what is the probability that at least one will have cystic fibrosis? $\approx$ **.20988 $\approx$ 21%**

55. Fifteen percent of a certain species of young trees die during their first winter. A homeowner wants to plant a hedge with this species. If the homeowner plants 12 such trees, what is the probability that at least 10 will survive?

56. What is the probability that a student will get a perfect score by random guessing on an exam with 17 multiple-choice questions each of which has four options? $(.25)^{17} \approx 5.8 \times 10^{-11}$

55) $\approx$ .73582 $\approx$ 74%

REPRESENTATIONS DEAL WITH PICTURES, GRAPHS, OR OBJECTS THAT ILLUSTRATE CONCEPTS.

Objective L: *Locate numerical properties represented by the patterns in Pascal's Triangle.* (Lesson 8-7)

In 57–60, show three places in Pascal's Triangle where the given property is represented.

```
              1
            1   1
          1   2   1
        1   3   3   1
      1   4   6   4   1
    1   5   10  10  5   1
```

58) Every element off the border. Each is the sum of the two elements above it.

57. $_nC_r = {_nC_{n-r}}$ **True of every row**

58. $_nC_r = {_{n-1}C_r} + {_{n-1}C_{r-1}}$ **See below.**

59. $\sum_{i=0}^{n}((-1)^i \cdot i \cdot {_nC_i}) = 0$ **See below.**

60. $\sum_{i=0}^{n}(i \cdot {_nC_i}) = n \cdot 2^{n-1}$
  True in every row

59) True in every row except row 1

Additional responses, page 547

6. a. The first term is 1, term 2 is $\frac{1}{2}$, the sum of terms 3 and 4 is $\frac{1}{2}$, the sum of terms 5, 6, 7, and 8 is $\frac{1}{2}$, the sum of terms 9 through 16 is $\frac{1}{2}$, and so on. So at any point in the series, we can add $\frac{1}{2}$ by grouping together more terms. This sequences cannot have a limit. If it did, when the sequence approached this limit, we could add $\frac{1}{2}$, again by grouping together more terms.

  b. $1 = 1, \frac{1}{2} = \frac{1}{2}, \frac{1}{3} > \frac{1}{4}, \frac{1}{4} = \frac{1}{4}, \frac{1}{5} > \frac{1}{8}$, and so on. Since every term of the harmonic series is greater than the corresponding term of series *A*, any partial sum of the harmonic series is greater than the corresponding partial sum of series *A*. Since the sequence of partial sums for *A* does not have a limit, neither does the sequence of partial sums for the harmonic series. Thus the harmonic series diverges.

  c. Here's a BASIC program to use for calculating the sum of the series:

```
10 N = 1
20 SUM = 0
30 SUM = SUM + (-1) ^
         (N + 1) / N
40 PRINT N, SUM
50 N = N + 1
60 GOTO30
```

  A computer using this program gives a sum of $B \approx 0.693148$ for $N \approx 2,450,000$. (Warning: An Apple IIE took about 42 hours to print the sixth digit "8" repeatedly.)

Adapting to Individual Needs

The student text is written for the vast majority of students. The chart at the right suggests two pacing plans to accommodate the needs of your students. Students in the Full Course should complete the entire text by the end of the year. Students in the Minimal Course will spend more time when there are quizzes and more time on the Chapter Review. Therefore, these students may not complete all of the chapters in the text.

   Options are also presented to meet the needs of a variety of teaching and learning styles. For each lesson, the Teacher's Edition provides a section entitled *Adapting to Individual Needs*. This section regularly includes **Optional Activities, Challenge** problems, **English Language Development** suggestions, and suggestions for providing **Extra Help.** The Teacher's Edition also frequently includes an **Error Alert,** an **Extension,** and an **Assessment** alternative. The options available in Chapter 9 are summarized in the chart below.

Chapter 9 Pacing Chart

Day	Full Course	Minimal Course
1	9-1	9-1
2	9-2	9-2
3	9-3	9-3
4	Quiz*; 9-4	Quiz*; begin 9-4.
5	9-5	Finish 9-4.
6	9-6	9-5
7	9-7	9-6
8	Quiz*; 9-8	9-7
9	9-9	Quiz*; begin 9-8.
10	9-10	Finish 9-8.
11	Self-Test	9-9
12	Review	9-10
13	Test*	Self-Test
14	Comprehensive Test*	Review
15		Review
16		Test*
17		Comprehensive Test*

*in the Teacher's Resource File

In the Teacher's Edition...

Lesson	Optional Activities	Extra Help	Challenge	English Language Development	Error Alert	Extension	Cooperative Learning	Ongoing Assessment
9-1	●	●	●		●	●	●	Written
9-2	●	●	●		●	●	●	Group
9-3	●	●	●		●	●	●	Quiz
9-4	●	●	●		●	●	●	Written/Oral
9-5	●	●	●		●	●	●	Oral
9-6	●	●	●		●	●	●	Oral/Written
9-7	●	●	●		●	●	●	Quiz
9-8	●	●	●		●	●	●	Written
9-9	●	●	●		●	●	●	Oral/Written
9-10	●	●	●			●	●	

Chapter 9 Block Schedule

Day	Recommended Pacing
1	Lessons 9-1, 9-2
2	Lesson 9-3
3	Lessons 9-4, 9-5
4	Lesson 9-6
5	Lesson 9-7
6	Lesson 9-8
7	Lesson 9-9
8	Lesson 9-10, Self-Test, Chapter Review
9	Chapter Review, Chapter Test or Comprehensive Test

In the Additional Resources...

Lesson	Lesson Masters	Teaching Aids*	Answer Masters	Technology Sourcebook	Assessment Sourcebook	Visual Aids**	Technology	Explorations Software
				In the Teacher's Resource File				
9-1	9-1	79	9-1			79, AM		
In-class Activity			9-2			AM		9-2
9-2	9-2	79, 82	9-2	Calc 8		79, 82, AM		
9-3	9-3	79	9-3		Quiz	79, AM		9-3
9-4	9-4	80	9-4			80, AM		9-4
9-5	9-5	80	9-5			80, AM		
9-6	9-6	80, 83	9-6			80, 83, AM		
9-7	9-7	81, 84	9-7		Quiz	81, 84, AM		
9-8	9-8	81	9-8	Calc 9		81, AM		
9-9	9-9	81	9-9			81, AM		
9-10		81, 85	9-10			81, 85, AM		
End of chapter					Tests			

*Teaching Aids are pictured on page 554C.

**Visual Aids provide transparencies for all Teaching Aids and all Answer Masters.

Also available is the Study Skills Handbook which includes study-skill tips related to reading, note-taking, and comprehension.

Integrating Strands and Applications

	9-1	9-2	9-3	9-4	9-5	9-6	9-7	9-8	9-9	9-10
Mathematical Connections										
Number Sense				●	●	●	●			
Algebra	●	●	●	●	●	●	●	●	●	●
Geometry	●	●	●		●	●			●	●
Logic and Reasoning	●	●	●	●	●	●	●	●	●	●
Probability			●			●		●	●	●
Statistics/Data Analysis	●						●			
Patterns and Functions	●	●	●	●	●	●	●	●	●	●
Discrete Mathematics	●		●		●	●			●	●
Interdisciplinary and Other Connections										
Literature							●			
Science		●						●		●
Social Studies						●	●	●		●
Multicultural				●	●					
Technology		●	●	●	●			●	●	●
Consumer	●	●	●	●						
Sports					●				●	

Teaching and Assessing the Chapter Objectives

Chapter 9 Objectives (Organized into the SPUR categories—Skills, Properties, Uses, and Representations)	Lessons	Progress Self-Test Questions	Chapter Review Questions	Chapter Test, Forms A and B	Chapter Test, Forms	
					C	D
Skills						
A: Use finite differences and systems of equations to determine an equation for a polynomial function from data points.	9-3	1	1-4	1	3	
B: Calculate or approximate zeros and relative extrema of polynomial functions.	9-2	2	5-8	4	2	✓
C: Divide polynomials.	9-4	3	9-12	2	4	
D: Factor polynomials and solve polynomial equations using the Factor Theorem, sums or differences of powers, grouping terms, or trial and error.	9-5, 9-6, 9-8, 9-9	4, 5	13-20	5, 6, 7	6	✓
E: Perform operations with complex numbers.	9-6	7	21-26	7, 9, 10	5	
Properties						
F: Apply the vocabulary of polynomials.	9-1, 9-2, 9-7	8, 9	27-30	13, 14, 15	2	✓
G: Apply the Remainder Theorem, Factor Theorem, and Factor-Solution-Intercept Equivalence Theorem.	9-4, 9-5	6, 10	31-34	3	2, 4	
H: Apply the Fundamental Theorem of Algebra and Conjugate Zeros Theorem.	9-7	11, 12	35-39	11		
Uses						
I: Construct and interpret polynomials that model real situations.	9-1, 9-3	13	40-44	16		
Representations						
J: Represent two- or three-dimensional figures with polynomials.	9-1	14, 16	45-47	12	1	
K: Relate properties of polynomial functions and their graphs.	9-2, 9-5, 9-7	15	48-54	8	2	✓

In the Teacher's Resource File

Multidimensional Assessment
Quiz for Lessons 9-1 through 9-3
Quiz for Lessons 9-4 through 9-7

Chapter 9 Test, Forms A–D
Chapter 9 Test, Cumulative Form

Comprehensive Test, Chapters 1–9

Quiz and Test Writer

Teaching Aids

Warm-up — Lesson 9-1

Find the surface area and volume of a box with one edge of unknown length, a second edge one unit longer, and a third edge one unit shorter. Write your answers as a polynomial.

Warm-up — Lesson 9-2

1. Graph $f(x) = x^4 - 2x^2 - 1$.

2. At what value(s) of x does the function f attain its minimum value? What is this value?

3. At what value(s) of x does this function attain a relative maximum value? What is this value?

Warm-up — Lesson 9-3

Solve the following system.
$d = 43$
$c - d = 12$
$2b + 3c - 4d = 201$
$3a + b = -40$

Warm-up — Lesson 9-4

1. Divide $12x^4$ by $3x^3$. Check your answer by substituting 5 for x.

2. Divide $12x^4 - 6x^3$ by $3x^3$. Check your answer by substituting 2 for x.

3. If $a^3 - 8a^2 + 19a - 12 = (a - 3)f(a)$, what is $f(a)$?

Warm-up — Lesson 9-5

Let $f(x) = 3x^2 - 40x + 48$.
1. Which of the given polynomials is a factor of $f(x)$?
   (a) $x - 2$ (b) $x - 3$
   (c) $x - 4$ (d) $x - 6$
   (e) $x - 12$ (f) $x - 24$

2. Which of the given values equals 0?
   (a) $f(2)$ (b) $f(3)$
   (c) $f(4)$ (d) $f(6)$
   (e) $f(12)$ (f) $f(24)$

Warm-up — Lesson 9-6

Use the binomial theorem to calculate $(2 + 2i)^4$.

Warm-up — Lesson 9-7

Find a value of k so that the graph of $P(x) = 2x^4 - 5x^2 + k$ intersects the x-axis in the indicated number of points.

1. 1   2. 2   3. 3
4. 4   5. 0

Warm-up — Lesson 9-8

Factor $x^4 - 1$ over the set of polynomials with the indicated coefficients.

1. Real coefficients

2. Complex coefficients

Warm-up — Lesson 9-9

1. Factor $2x^3 + 3x^2 + x$.

2. Factor $2x^3 + 2x^2 + x^2 + x$.

Warm-up — Lesson 9-10

Find the two solutions to $14x^2 + 50x - 39 = 0$. Then find the sum of the solutions and the product of the solutions.

Extrema of Functions

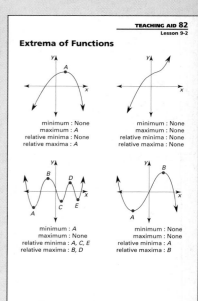

minimum : None
maximum : A
relative minima : None
relative maxima : A

minimum : None
maximum : None
relative minima : None
relative maxima : None

minimum : A
maximum : None
relative minima : A, C, E
relative maxima : B, D

minimum : None
maximum : None
relative minima : A
relative maxima : B

The Complex Number System

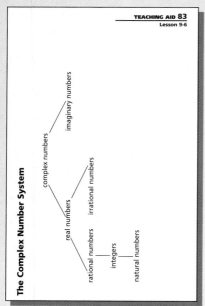

Zeros of Quadratic Functions

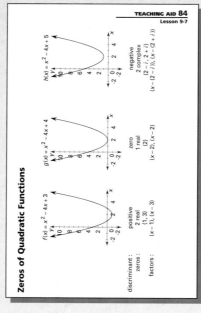

Theorems for Roots and Coefficients

Theorem
For the quadratic equation $x^2 + bx + c = 0$, the sum off the roots is $-b$ and the product of the roots is c.

Theorem
For the cubic equation $x^3 + bx^2 + cx + d = 0$, the sum of the roots is $-b$, the sum of the products of the roots two at a time is c, and the product of the three roots is $-d$.

Theorem
For the polynomial equation
$$x^n + a_1x^{n-1} + a_2x^{n-2} + \ldots + a_{n-1}x + a_n = 0.$$
the sum of the roots is $-a_1$, the sum of the products of the roots two at a time is a_2, the sum of the products of the roots three at a time is $-a_3$, ..., and the product of all roots is $\begin{cases} a_n \text{ if } n \text{ is even,} \\ -a_n \text{ if } n \text{ is odd.} \end{cases}$

Chapter Opener

CHAPTER 9

Pacing

All lessons in this chapter are designed to be covered in one day. At the end of the chapter, you should plan to spend 1 day to review the Progress Self-Test, 1–2 days for the Chapter Review, and 1 day for a test. You may wish to spend a day on projects, and possibly a day is needed for quizzes and the In-class Activities. Therefore, this chapter should take 13–16 days. Spending more than 17 days on this chapter is not recommended; there is ample opportunity to review ideas in later chapters.

Using Pages 554–555

Engage students in an informal question-and-answer session to find out what they know about factoring, about complex numbers, about operations with polynomials (including long division), and about graphing functions of the type found on this page. Almost all students should have familiarity with some of these ideas. This will enable you to determine in advance where students may have trouble and where you should plan to focus class time.

554

Chapter 9 Overview

Polynomial functions are important for a variety of reasons. Linear, quadratic, and power functions, important in their own right, are all classes of polynomial functions. Any finite set of points with no two on the same vertical line can be modeled by a polynomial function. Our base 10 numeration system denotes integers as polynomials with base 10. Some important applications, such as annuities and binomial probability distributions, involve polynomials.

Even a function that is not a polynomial function, if it satisfies certain broad conditions, can be approximated by a polynomial function.

So there are many reasons to learn about polynomials. And, since the mathematical theory is exquisite, there are some very nice and some quite startling results to encounter along the way.

This chapter has three themes. Modeling is the topic of the first three lessons. Applications to annuities and volume are used to introduce the terminology and basic properties of polynomials in Lesson 9-1. Lesson 9-2 discusses the various shapes of polynomial function graphs, thus providing some intuition for the types of data that might be modeled by these functions. Lesson 9-3 covers the fitting of polynomial functions to a finite number of data points.

POLYNOMIAL FUNCTIONS

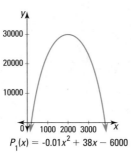

$$P_1(x) = -0.01x^2 + 38x - 6000$$

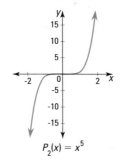

$$P_2(x) = x^5$$

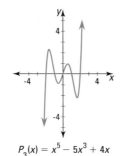

$$P_3(x) = x^5 - 5x^3 + 4x$$

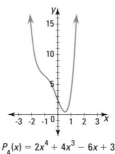

$$P_4(x) = 2x^4 + 4x^3 - 6x + 3$$

A polynomial function P_1 above could be used to model the shape of the nose of the space shuttle on the facing page.

A *polynomial* in one variable is a sum of multiples of nonnegative integer powers of that variable. The quadratic function P_1 and power function P_2 graphed above are examples of *polynomial functions*. Other polynomial functions such as P_3 and P_4 exhibit more complicated behavior.

The variety of polynomial functions makes them candidates for modeling many real-world situations. Some they model exactly and others they approximate. In this chapter, you will see applications of polynomial functions and their graphs in agriculture, economics, and other fields. You will also see some of the beautiful mathematical properties these functions possess. The theory underlying these properties involves complex numbers, division, and factoring.

The second theme is division and factoring, the process of breaking up a polynomial into constituent parts. This theme is found in the Lessons 9-4 and 9-5, in which the general theory is established through the Remain-der and Factor Theorems, and again in Lessons 9-8 and 9-9, in which techniques for factoring are described and practiced.

The third theme is finding the zeros of poly-nomial functions. The major result, whose proof is beyond the scope of this course, is the Fundamental Theorem of Algebra found in Lesson 9-7. For this, complex numbers are reviewed in Lesson 9-6. The relationships between the zeros and the coefficients of a polynomial are discussed in Lesson 9-10.

Before automatic graphers, much of the theory of polynomial functions was em-ployed to determine the properties of the graph. Nowadays, the reverse is possi-ble and few people graph polynomial func-tions by hand. Students need this technolo-gy throughout the chapter.

Objectives

F Apply the vocabulary of polynomials.

I Construct and interpret polynomials that model real situations.

J Represent two- or three-dimensional figures with polynomials.

Resources

From the Teacher's Resource File
- Lesson Master 9-1
- Answer Master 9-1
- Teaching Aid 79: Warm-up

Additional Resources
- Visual for Teaching Aid 79

Teaching Lesson 9-1

Warm-up

Find the surface area and volume of a box with one edge of unknown length, a second edge one unit longer, and a third edge one unit shorter. Write your answers as a polynomial. **Surface area:**
$2x(x - 1) + 2x(x + 1) + 2x(x - 1)(x + 1) = 6x^2 - 2$;
volume: $x(x - 1)(x + 1) = x^3 - x$

Uses of Paper. *In 1996, the U.S. paper industry produced enough paper for 2 billion books, 24 billion newspapers, and 372 billion square feet of corrugated cardboard.*

❶ A Polynomial Model for Volume

A company has pieces of cardboard that are 60 cm by 80 cm. They want to make boxes from them (without a top) to hold equipment. Squares with sides of length x are cut from each corner and the resulting flaps are folded to make an open box as shown. In the language of geometry, this box is a right rectangular prism without one face, and its volume $V = \ell wh$.

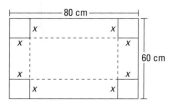
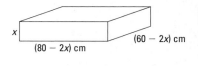

Is there a formula for the volume of the resulting box in terms of x? The cardboard has an original length of 80 cm. By cutting 2 corners, the length of the box is $(80 - 2x)$ cm. Similarly, the width of the box is $(60 - 2x)$ cm. When the flaps are folded to form the box, the height of the box is x cm. To find a formula for the volume of the box in terms of x, substitute these expressions for length, width, and height, respectively.

$$\text{Volume} = \ell wh$$
$$V = (80 - 2x)(60 - 2x)(x)$$
$$= (4800 - 280x + 4x^2)(x)$$
$$= 4800x - 280x^2 + 4x^3$$

The expression $4800x - 280x^2 + 4x^3$ is an instance of a *polynomial in the variable x*.

Lesson 9-1 Overview

Broad Goals In this lesson, annuities and volume situations are employed to review the language and multiplication of polynomials.

Perspective We pick the two applications of this lesson for different reasons. The first application, to volume, is chosen because the use of multiplication to calculate volume is so familiar, and because the particular example, with a folded-up box, is classic.

The second example, to annuities, is chosen because in annuity situations each coefficient and exponent of the polynomial has a meaning that can be traced back to the original situation. Specifically, an *annuity* is a sum of money payable at regular intervals. If the amount of money is a constant M, and is multiplied by the scale factor x in that interval, then the total amount paid after $n + 1$ payments is $Mx^n + Mx^{n-1} + Mx^{n-2} + \ldots + Mx + M$.

This sum can be calculated as the sum of a finite geometric series to be $M \frac{x^{n+1} - 1}{x - 1}$. If the amount paid at the time of payment k is not necessarily constant but called a_{n-k}, then the total amount paid after $n + 1$ payments is $a_n x^n + a_{n-1} x^{n-1} + a_{n-2} x^{n-2} + \ldots + a_1 x + a_0$. This is the general polynomial in x of degree n. Its description in this way (which is a generalization of **Example 2**)

Terminology Associated with Polynomials

The **general form** of a polynomial in one variable is given in the following definiton.

> **Definition**
> A **polynomial in *x*** is an expression of the form
> $$a_n x^n + a_{n-1}x^{n-1} + a_{n-2}x^{n-2} + \ldots + a_1 x + a_0$$
> where n is a nonnegative integer and $a_n \neq 0$.

The number n is the **degree** of the polynomial and the numbers a_n, a_{n-1}, a_{n-2}, ..., a_0 are its **coefficients**. The number a_n is called the **leading coefficient** of the polynomial. You might think that the leading coefficient of $4800x - 280x^2 + 4x^3$ is 4800, because it is the first coefficient, but it is not. For a polynomial in one variable, the leading coefficient comes first only when the terms of the polynomial are written in descending order of their exponents, as they are in the definition. This is called **standard form.** When the polynomial is written in standard form, $4x^3 - 280x^2 + 4800x$, the leading coefficient, 4, is the first coefficient and the degree, 3, is the first exponent. Note that all the exponents in a polynomial must be nonnegative integers.

The volume of the box depends on the length x of the side of the cut-out square, so the volume can be considered as a *polynomial function of x*.

$$V(x) = 4x^3 - 280x^2 + 4800x$$

In general, a **polynomial function** is a function whose rule can be written as a polynomial. In Lesson 9-2, you will see how to use this function to determine the value of x that gives the maximum volume of the box.

Example 1

If $V(x) = 4x^3 - 280x^2 + 4800x$, find $V(10)$ and state what it represents.

Solution

Substitute 10 for x in the formula for $V(x)$.

$$V(10) = 4(10)^3 - 280(10)^2 + 4800(10)$$
$$= 24{,}000$$

When the length of the side of the cut-out square is 10 cm, the volume of the box is 24,000 cm^3.

A Polynomial Model for an Annuity

An annuity is an investment involving money which is periodically deposited or withdrawn. Annuities give rise to polynomials.

Notes on Reading

You may wish to teach this lesson and Lesson 9-2 together, particularly for strong classes.

❶ A possible way to introduce this lesson follows: Go through the polynomial model for volume on page 556 line by line, asking students after each sentence if they follow what was being done. Continue with the discussion of **Example 2**. A calculator may be used to do the calculations in **Example 2**, putting 1.07 in storage and retrieving it as it is needed.

enough application to cover polynomials of any degree. This application should be familiar to students who have studied UCSMP *Algebra* or *Advanced Algebra*.

❷ Students may wonder if there are special names for polynomials with four terms, five terms, and so on. There are no such names in common use, though quadrinomials (4 terms) can be found in some older texts. This is quite similar to the situation with polygons, where there are no special names for polygons with more than 10 sides (decagons), but there exist older names (undecagons and duodecagons) for polygons with 11 and 12 sides. Just as we call the general polygon an *n*-gon, we refer to the general polynomial as the polynomial of degree *n*.

In **Example 3,** note that each term of the answer has degree 3. This should be expected, since the answer stands for volume, and the dimension of volume is 3.

Example 2

Tamara is saving her summer earnings for college. The table below shows the amount of money saved each summer.

After grade	Amount saved
8	$ 600
9	$ 900
10	$1100
11	$1500
12	$1600

At the end of each summer, she put her money in a savings account with an annual yield of 7%. How much will be in her account when she goes to college, if no additonal money is added or withdrawn, and the interest rate remains constant?

Solution

Recall the compound interest formula, $A = P(1 + r)^t$ which gives the value of P dollars invested at an annual rate r after t years. The money Tamara put in the bank after grade 8 earns interest for 4 years. It is worth $600(1.07)^4$ when Tamara enters college. Similarly, the amount saved at the end of grade 9 is worth $900(1.07)^3$. Adding the values from each summer gives the total amount in the bank account.

$$600(1.07)^4 + 900(1.07)^3 + 1100(1.07)^2 + 1500(1.07) + 1600$$

| from summer after grade 8 | from summer after grade 9 | from summer after grade 10 | from summer after grade 11 | from summer after grade 12 |

Evaluating this expression shows that **Tamara will have about $6353 when she goes to college.**

The amount Tamara has when she enters college depends on the interest rate she can get. Let her annual yield be r and $x = 1 + r$. Then her savings $A(x)$ is a polynomial function of x.

$$A(x) = 600x^4 + 900x^3 + 1100x^2 + 1500x + 1600$$

In the function A above, the coefficients of the terms of the polynomial represent the amount invested each successive year. The exponents represent the number of years each amount is on deposit. The value $A(x)$ of the function is the amount Tamara has when the annual interest rate is $x - 1$.

❷ The Degree of a Polynomial

Recall that a **monomial** is a polynomial with one term; a **binomial** is a polynomial with two terms; and a **trinomial** is a polynomial with three terms. Monomials, binomials, and trinomials may be of any degree. For instance, the trinomial $4x^2 - 5x + 1$ is of degree 2, while $a^{10} - a^{20} + a^{30}$ is of degree 30.

558

Optional Activities
When **Question 16** on page 561 is assigned, you may wish to have students write a polynomial in x for the surface area of the box in this question.
$[S(x) = -2x^2 - 250x + 37500]$

Polynomials may also involve several variables. For instance, each of the following is a *polynomial in x and y*.

$$x^2y^3 - 3y^3 + 2x^2 - 6$$
$$x^3 + x^2y^2 + y^5$$

The **degree of a polynomial in more than one variable** is the largest sum of the exponents of the variables in any term. Each of the preceding two polynomials in x and y has degree 5.

Example 3

a. Express the surface area and volume of a cube with sides of length $a + b$ in terms of a and b.
b. State the degree of each polynomial.

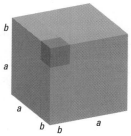

Solution

a. The surface area S is six times the area of one face of the cube.
$$S = 6(a + b)^2$$
Use the Binomial Theorem to expand $(a + b)^2$.
$$S = 6(a^2 + 2ab + b^2)$$
$$S = 6a^2 + 12ab + 6b^2$$
The volume is the length of an edge cubed.
$$V = (a + b)^3$$
Use the Binomial Theorem to rewrite the right side.
$$V = a^3 + 3a^2b + 3ab^2 + b^3$$

b. For surface area, the largest sum of the exponents of the variables in any term is 2, so S has **degree 2.** For volume, the largest sum of the exponents of the variables in each term is 3, so V has **degree 3.**

Check

a. As illustrated in the figure above, the volume of the cube equals the sum of the volumes of 8 rectangular solids. In the top layer are two boxes with volumes equal to b^2a, and one each of volumes b^3 and a^2b. In the bottom layer, two of the visible boxes have volume a^2b, and the third has volume b^2a. The box hidden from view has volume a^3. So the total volume is
$$V = (2b^2a + b^3 + a^2b) + (2a^2b + b^2a + a^3)$$
$$= b^3 + 3b^2a + 3a^2b + a^3.$$

b. The polynomial for the volume of the cube, a 3-dimensional measure, is degree 3, and the polynomial for the surface area, a 2-dimensional measure, is degree 2.

Notes on Questions

Question 6 Technically, students do not know enough mathematics to show that the expressions in **parts b and d** cannot be written as polynomials. So this question has to be answered on faith; if it does not look as if it can be placed in polynomial form relatively easily, then it probably does not represent a polynomial. The division of polynomials in Lesson 9-4 can be used to show that the expression of **part f** cannot be written as a polynomial.

Question 9 Error Alert Some students may use 0.075 instead of 1.075 for x. Remind them that $x = 1 + r$, where r is the annual yield.

Questions 17–19 and 22 These questions review ideas that are needed for Lesson 9-3.

(Notes on Questions continue on page 562.)

3) $V(20) = 132,000$; when the side length of the cut-out square is 20 cm, the box's volume is 132,000 cm³.

10b) summer after grade 11
c) $S(1.0575) \approx 5582.67$; this is the amount available when John enters college if the money is invested in a savings account with an annual yield of 5.75%.

Covering the Reading

In 1–3, refer to the description of making a box from a flat piece of cardboard. Another box is to be made from a 150-cm-by-100-cm piece of cardboard, by cutting squares of side x cm from the corners.

1. What are the length, width, and height of the box?
   length $= 150 - 2x$ cm; width $= 100 - 2x$ cm; height $= x$ cm
2. Write a polynomial function in x for the volume V of the box.
   $V = 4x^3 - 500x^2 + 15,000x$
3. Evaluate $V(20)$ and state what it represents. **See left.**

4. Consider the polynomial $3p^2 - 5p^6$.
   a. What is its degree? **6**   b. What is its leading coefficient? **-5**
   c. *True or false.*   The polynomial is a binomial. **True**

5. Let $p(x) = 6x^8 + 12x^5 - 4x^2 + 9$. If $p(x)$ is of degree n, state the value of each of the following.
   a. n **8**   b. a_n **6**   c. a_0 **9**   d. a_2 **-4**   e. a_{n-1} **0**

6. Determine whether each expression can be written as a polynomial.
   a. $3x^2$ **Yes**   b. 5^x **No**   c. $2x - 5$ **Yes**
   d. $x^{1/2}$ **No**   e. $\frac{x^2 + x}{2}$ **Yes**   f. $\frac{x^2 + x}{x - 1}$ **No**

In 7 and 8, write the general form.

7. a 4th degree polynomial in y $a_4y^4 + a_3y^3 + a_2y^2 + a_1y + a_0$

8. an nth degree polynomial in x $a_nx^n + a_{n-1}x^{n-1} + \ldots + a_1x + a_0$

9. Refer to Example 2. Suppose Tamara can invest her earnings at a 7.5% annual yield. Determine her savings when she enters college. $\approx$ **$6403**

10. John saved his earnings for several summers just as Tamara did. A polynomial for his savings is
$$S(x) = 1000x^4 + 1250x^3 + 1300x^2 + 1400.$$
   a. What did John deposit in the bank the first summer he saved? **$1000**
   b. One summer John did not save any money. Which summer was this?
   c. Evaluate $S(1.0575)$ and explain what it represents.
   b, c, see left.

11. Give the degree of the polynomial $7x^3y + 8y^2x^9$. **11**

12. a. Find a polynomial for V, the volume of a cube with sides of length $x + 2y$. $x^3 + 6x^2y + 12xy^2 + 8y^3$
   b. State the degree of the polynomial. **3**

Applying the Mathematics

In 13 and 14, give an example, if possible, of each of the following.

13. a binomial in three variables, with degree 5 **Sample: $x^3yz + xyz$**

14. a trinomial in two variables, of degree 4 **Sample: $x^2y^2 + x^3y + xy$**

Adapting to Individual Needs

Extra Help
Some students may need a more detailed discussion of the multiplication at the bottom of page 556. Remind them that by the Associative Property of Multiplication, we can multiply any two factors and then multiply that product by the third factor. Explain that the FOIL algorithm was used to multiply the first two binomials. Then the product was multiplied by x.

Challenge
Refer students to the 60-cm by 80-cm piece of cardboard described on page 556. Then have them answer the following questions.
1. Write a polynomial for the surface area of the open-topped box.
   [$S = -4x^2 + 4800$]
2. How does the real-world domain of this surface area function compare with the mathematical domain of this polynomial? [The mathematical domain is the set of all real numbers, but the only real-world values of x that make sense are those satisfying $0 < x < 30$.]
3. What values of x give a box with the greatest surface areas? [Values close to 0]
4. What values of x give a box with the least surface areas? [Values close to 30]

15. The expression $\sum_{i=0}^{n} c_i x^i$ is a polynomial. Give its leading coefficient and its degree. **leading coefficient: c_n; degree: n**

16. A box with a top is constructed from a piece of cardboard 150 cm by 250 cm. The shaded regions are cut out and the flaps are folded to make a box, as in the diagram below. Write a polynomial in x for the volume of the box. $2x^3 - 400x^2 + 18{,}750x$

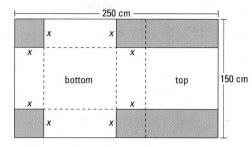

19) $t(n) + t(n + 1)$
$= \frac{1}{2} n(n + 1) +$
$\quad \frac{1}{2} (n + 1)(n + 2)$
$= \frac{1}{2} (n + 1)(n + (n + 2))$
$= \frac{1}{2} (n + 1)(2n + 2)$
$= \frac{1}{2} (n + 1) \cdot 2(n + 1)$
$= (n + 1)^2 = s(n + 1)$

20a, b)

In 17–19, recall that the **square numbers**, 1, 4, 9, 16, 25, . . . , are the values of the function $s(n) = n^2$, when n is a positive integer. The **triangular numbers** $t(n) = \frac{1}{2}n(n+1)$ are the number of dots in shapes like those pictured below.

$t(1) = 1 \qquad t(2) = 3 \qquad t(3) = 6 \qquad t(4) = 10$

17. *True or false.* $s(n)$ is a polynomial function of n of degree 2. **True**

18. *True or false.* $t(n)$ is a polynomial function of n of degree 1. **False**

19. Prove: For all positive integers n, $s(n+1) = t(n) + t(n + 1)$. **See left.**

Review

20. The following table gives the average number of minutes of TV viewing per household per day. **a, b) See left.**
   a. Make a scatterplot of the data. Use the number of years since 1985–86 as the independent variable.
   b. Use a quadratic regression to find a quadratic model for the data. Sketch a graph of the model on the scatterplot.
   c. Is the model a theory-based model? **No**
   (Lesson 2-6)
   b) $y \approx 1.2597x^2 - 8.5446x + 430.62$

Year	Minutes/Day
1985-86	430
1986-87	425
1987-88	415
1988-89	422
1989-90	415
1990-91	416
1991-92	424
1992-93	437
1993-94	441

Source: *1996 Information Please Almanac*

Practice

For more questions on SPUR Objectives, use **Lesson Master 9-1** (shown on page 559).

Assessment

Written Communication Have students **work in pairs**. Ask each student to write several different polynomial expressions in one or more variables, not necessarily in standard form. Have students exchange papers. Each student should give the degree and the leading coefficient for their partner's polynomials. Suggest that students write the polynomial in standard form, if possible. [Students correctly apply the vocabulary of polynomials.]

Extension

1. Suppose you can earn $\frac{1}{2}$% interest compounded each month (6% per year), paid at the end of the month. If you deposit $100 at the beginning of each month from January through December, use geometric series to determine how much will be in the account on January 1st of the next year. $[100(1.005^{12} + 1.005^{11} + \ldots + 1.005 + 1) = 100(\frac{1.005^{13} - 1}{0.005}) \approx \$1339.72]$

2. Generalize the situation in Question 1 for any monthly interest rate r. $[100(\frac{(1 + r)^{13} - 1}{r})]$

Project Update Project 1, *Completing the Pattern,* on page 617, relates to the content of this lesson.

Notes on Questions

Questions 23–24 These questions review a skill that is particularly useful in Lesson 9-9, but at this time point out that the process of multiplication and the process of factoring undo each other.

Question 26 Consumer Connection CD rates tend to be higher if more money is invested, but not necessarily higher when they are longer term. Penalties for early withdrawal can be severe.

Additional Answers

21. b. Sample: In general, drama clubs have a higher ineligibility rate than other activities. Half of the schools declared at least 30% of drama-club members ineligible, and at least one school declared all drama-club members ineligible. On the other hand, yearbook enjoys the lowest median ineligibility rate, with baseball a close second. Band and track are in the middle with median ineligibility rates of about 22% and 25%, respectively. Yearbook displays the widest diversity among many schools with $\frac{3}{4}$ of the schools declaring from 0% to 38% of the yearbook staff ineligible. In contrast, baseball has the least diversity among schools while having a median ineligibility rate only slightly higher than yearbook. Half of the schools declared from 10% to 20% of baseball players ineligible.

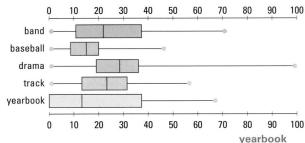

25a)

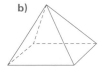
b)

21. In a certain school, following a Board of Education policy, students must maintain a C average and have no failing grades to participate in extracurricular activities. The box plots below represent the percentage of students at 49 city high schools who were declared ineligible in five activities. *(Lesson 1-4)*

a. Which activity has the lowest median rate of ineligibility?
b. Write a paragraph or two comparing and contrasting the rates of ineligibility in these five activities. **See margin.**

22. Solve the system. *(Previous course, Lesson 2-6)*
$(x, y, z) = (1, 2, -3)$

$$\begin{cases} x + y + z = 0 \\ 9x + 3y + z = 12 \\ x - y + z = -4 \end{cases}$$

In 23 and 24, expand. *(Previous course)*

23. $(x + 3)(3x + 5)$ $3x^2 + 14x + 15$ **24.** $(x - 2y)(2x + 8y)$ $2x^2 + 4xy - 16y^2$

25. Draw an example of each geometric solid. **See left.**
a. a regular tetrahedron
b. a pyramid with a square base *(Previous course)*

Exploration

26. a. Find the current annual yield on a certificate of deposit (CD) at a local bank. **Sample: 5.75 on a 1-year CD**
b. Are the rates different for CDs depending on how long you invest the money? Are the rates different for the amount of money invested?
c. What are the penalties for early withdrawal and how do they work?
b) **Yes, under usual circumstances**
c) **Sample: One loses 90 days' interest.**

Setting Up Lesson 9-2
Do the In-class Activity on page 563.

Finding Some Key Points of a Polynomial Function

IN-CLASS
ACTIVITY

Use an automatic grapher.

In Lesson 9-1, a box was made from a 80-cm-by-60-cm piece of cardboard. The volume as a function of the length of a side of a cut-out square was found to be

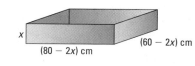
$$V(x) = 4x^3 - 280x^2 + 4800x.$$

In order to utilize most of the cardboard, the company is interested in finding the maximum volume a box can have starting with cardboard 80 cm by 60 cm.

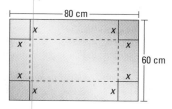

1 On what interval of *x*-values does the function *V* have meaning in this situation? $0 \le x \le 30$

2 Make a table of values of ordered pairs on that interval. **See margin.**

3 What are the minimum and maximum values of the dependent variable in the table? **Sample: 0; 24,192**

4 Use the results of Steps 1 and 3 to set the window on your automatic grapher. Make a sketch of the function. **See margin.**

5 Find the maximum point of the graph. Mark it on the sketch along with its coordinates. **(11.3, 24,258)**

6 State the meaning of the coordinates of the maximum point relative to the problem. **When the side length of the cut-out square is ≈ 11 cm, the box's maximum possible volume will be ≈ 24,250 cm³.**

563

Technology Connection
Materials: Explorations software

Students may use *Exploration 9-2, Key Points of Polynomial Functions*, to do this In-class Activity. Students can define a polynomial function *V*(*x*). A table of values and a graph of the function are shown. The program will show areas where the graph increases or decreases, and give the relative maximum or minimum, if they exist.

In-class Activity
Resources
From the *Teacher's Resource File*
■ Answer Master 9-2

Additional Resources
■ Exploration 9-2

Notes on Reading
This brief activity provides an example that students will need to have in order to answer **Questions 1–3** of Lesson 9-2. It continues the classic use of a polynomial function to determine the maximum volume of a box that can be made from a particular rectangular piece of cardboard.

One message to be sent by this activity is that if a person tries to graph the function *V* on a typical automatic grapher's default window, no graph will be seen. The thinking in Steps 1–3 in this Activity is necessary to determine that window.

Additional Answers
2. Sample:

x	V(x)
0	0
3	11,988
6	19,584
9	23,436
12	24,192
15	22,500
18	19,008
21	14,364
24	9,216
27	4,212
30	0

4., 5.

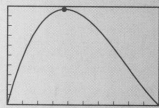

$0 \le x \le 30$,   *x*-scale = 3
$0 \le y \le 25000$, *y*-scale = 2500

Objectives

B Calculate or approximate zeros and relative extrema of polynomial functions.
F Apply the vocabulary of polynomials.
K Relate properties of polynomial functions and their graphs.

Resources

From the Teacher's Resource File
■ Lesson Master 9-2
■ Answer Master 9-2
■ Teaching Aids
　79 Warm-up
　82 Extrema of Functions
■ Technology Sourcebook
　Calculator Master 8

Additional Resources
■ Visuals for Teaching Aids 79, 82

Warm-up

1. Graph $f(x) = x^4 - 2x^2 - 1$.

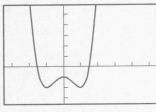

$-4 \le x \le 4$, 　x-scale = 1
$-3 \le y \le 5$, 　y-scale = 1

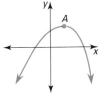

I.

minimum : None
maximum : A
relative minima : None
relative maxima : A

II.
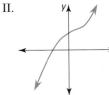

minimum : None
maximum : None
relative minima : None
relative maxima : None

III.
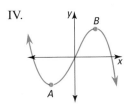

minimum : A
maximum : None
relative minima : A, C, E
relative maxima : B, D

IV.

minimum : None
maximum : None
relative minima : A
relative maxima : B

You are familiar with graphs of polynomial functions of degree 1 or 2. You know that the graph of every 1st degree polynomial is a line, and the graph of every quadratic function is a parabola. The graphs of higher degree polynomials do not have special names; nor do all polynomial functions of the same degree have graphs of the same shape. However, graphs of some higher degree polynomials do show a certain regularity, and like linear and quadratic functions, they can be described using key points and intervals.

Extrema of Functions

Recall that the range of a function is the set of possible values for the dependent variable. The **maximum value** of a function is the largest value in its range. Similarly, the **minimum value** of a function is the smallest value in its range. These are the **extreme values** or **extrema** of the function.

In figure I, the y-coordinate of A is the maximum value of the function. In Figures II and IV, the function has neither a maximum nor a minimum value. In Figure III, the y-coordinate of point A is the minimum value of the function, and there is no maximum value.

A **relative extremum** is a maximum or minimum value on an open interval $\{x: a < x < b\}$ of the function. Relative extrema are values at "turning points" of the function, as in Figures I, III and IV above. Specifically, a value M of a function f is a **relative maximum** for f if there is an open interval

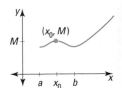

Lesson 9-2 Overview

Broad Goals This lesson covers two aspects of polynomial functions that are the subject of differential calculus: the determination of maxima and minima, and the identification of intervals on which a function is increasing or decreasing.

Perspective The big ideas in this lesson will be review for students who have already considered extrema and intervals on which the function is increasing or decreasing for trigonometric functions. The major difference here is that polynomial functions come in many more shapes, and their ranges are often not easily determined from their formulas.

$\{x: a < x < b\}$ in the domain of f containing a number x_0 such that $f(x_0) = M$ and for all other x in that interval, $f(x) \le M$.

Every maximum value of a function on an open interval is a relative maximum, so in Figure I, the y-coordinate of A is a relative maximum. But in Figure III, the y-coordinates of B and D are relative maxima but not maxima.

Similarly, a value m of a function f is a **relative minimum** for f if there is an open interval $\{x: a < x < b\}$ in the domain of f containing a number x_0 such that $f(x_0) = m$ and for all other x in that interval, $f(x) \ge m$. Figure III has three relative minima, the y-coordinates of A, C, and E. The y-coordinate of A is the minimum value of the function.

Zeros of Polynomial Functions

Recall that the x-intercepts of the graph of a function are the *zeros* of the function itself. Given a polynomial function p with $p(x) = a_n x^n + a_{n-1} x^{n-1} + \ldots + a_1 x + a_0$, the **zeros** or **roots of the polynomial function p** are all values of x such that $p(x) = 0$.

You already know how to find the exact zero of a polynomial of degree 1. This is a **linear polynomial function**, of the form $p(x) = ax + b$, and its zero is $\frac{-b}{a}$. A polynomial of degree 2, of the form $p(x) = ax^2 + bx + c$, is a **quadratic polynomial function**. Using the Quadratic Formula, you can also find its zeros exactly.

Though exact formulas for the zeros of polynomial functions of degrees 3 and 4 do exist, they are quite complicated, and there are no general formulas for finding the zeros of all polynomial functions of degree higher than 4. To find these zeros exactly, algebraic techniques, such as factoring, can sometimes be used. Algebraic techniques are discussed in Lessons 9-8 through 9-10.

To estimate the real zeros of a polynomial function, graphs and tables can be used. Consider a sketch and table of values of $f(x) = -x^3 + 5x + 2$ below.

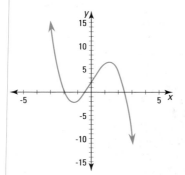

x	f(x)
-3	14
-2.5	5.125
-2	0
-1.5	-2.125
-1	-2
-.5	-0.375
0	2
.5	4.375
1	6
1.5	6.125
2	4
2.5	-1.125
3	-10

2. At what value(s) of x does the function f attain its minimum value? What is this value?
   $x = -1$ or $x = 1$; -2
3. At what value(s) of x does this function attain a relative maximum value? What is this value?
   $x = 0$; -1

Notes on Reading

Teaching Aid 82 contains extrema of polynomial functions.

❶ Because graphs of quadratic functions turn only once, there is only one extreme value of a quadratic function. Note that the graph of the cubic polynomial function f with $f(x) = -x^3 + 5x + 2$ turns twice, and the graph of the quartic function g in the **Example** on page 566 turns three times. These are the maximum number of turns that functions of these degrees can have, and in general a polynomial function of degree n can turn at most $n - 1$ times. Put another way, a polynomial function of degree n has at most $n - 1$ extrema. Proving this result requires calculus.

Optional Activities

Activity 1 Technology Connection
You may wish to use this Activity after discussing the **Example** on page 566. Suggest that students use the minimum and maximum features of a graphing calculator to approximate to the nearest hundredth, the relative maximum and minimum points of each of the following functions:
1. $f(x) = 3x^3 + 2x^2 - 3x + 1$
   [rel. min. (0.40, 0.31);
   rel. max. (-0.84, 3.15)]

2. $f(x) = 2x^3 + 4x^2 - 6x + 2$
   [rel. min. (0.54, 0.24);
   rel. max. (-1.87, 14.13)]
3. $f(x) = x^4 - 3x^3 + 4x$
   [rel.min. (-0.59, -1.62) and (2, 0);
   rel. max. (0.84, 2.08)]

Activity 2 Technology Connection
In *Technology Sourcebook, Calculator Master 8*, students use a graphics calculator to examine the zeros and extrema of cubic polynomials.

Additional Examples

1. Graph the function
$p(x) = -x^3 + 4x + 3$. What zero
can you identify exactly from the
graph? Find the other two zeros
to the nearest tenth. Use the
zeros to determine the intervals
on which the function is positive
and the intervals on which the
function is negative.

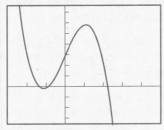

$-3 \le x \le 5, \quad x\text{-scale} = 1$
$-3 \le y \le 7, \quad y\text{-scale} = 1$

-1 (exactly); other zeros are
approximately -1.3, 2.3;
function is positive when
$x < -1.3$ or $-1 < x < 2.3$;
function is negative when
$-1.3 < x < -1$ or $x > 2.3$

2. Approximate (to the nearest
hundredth) the coordinates of
the relative maximum point of
the function p from Additional
Example 1. (The exact coordinates can be found by using
calculus.) (1.15, 6.08)

On the graph, you can see the x-intercepts by finding points where the
graph crosses the x-axis. Notice that -2, an x-intercept on the graph, is
verified by $x = -2, f(x) = 0$ in the table. There are no other places in the
table where $f(x) = 0$, yet the graph clearly shows two other x-intercepts.
Notice as x increases from -0.5 to 0, $f(x)$ increases from -0.375 to 2.
Therefore, there exists a zero of the function between -0.5 and 0. Likewise,
as x increases from 2 to 2.5, $f(x)$ decreases from 4 to -1.125. Another zero
can be found between 2 and 2.5.

Intervals Where a Function Is Positive/Negative or Increasing/Decreasing

So far this lesson has focused on some key points of a polynomial function.
The rest of this lesson focuses on what happens between key points. A
function is **positive** on an interval when the values of the dependent
variable are positive and **negative** on an interval when the values of the
dependent variable are negative. A function is **increasing** on an interval
if, for any two points on that interval, the slope between them is positive.
A function is **decreasing** on an interval if, for any two points on that
interval, the slope between them is negative.

Example

Consider the graph of $g(x) = \frac{1}{2}x^4 - 2x^3 + 3x - 4$ below. The x-coordinates
of all key points (except the y-intercept) are labeled with a letter.

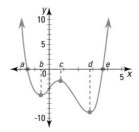

Use the letter labels to describe the interval(s) on which g satisfies the
following conditions.
a. g is positive.   b. g is negative.
c. g is increasing.   d. g is decreasing.
e. Estimate the coordinates of the zeros and extrema to the nearest tenth.
   Redraw the graph with the coordinates of these key points.

Solution

a. The function g is positive when its graph is above the x-axis. This occurs
   when $x < a$ or $x > e$.
b. g is negative when its graph is below the x-axis. This occurs when
   $a < x < e$.
c. g is increasing when the graph goes up as you go to the right. This
   occurs when $b < x < c$ or $x > d$.

▶

566

2.
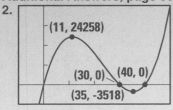

(11, 24258)

(30, 0) (40, 0)

(35, -3518)

$-10 \le x \le 50, \quad x\text{-scale} = 10$
$-10000 \le y \le 40000, \quad y\text{-scale} = 10000$

3. When the side length of the cut-out
square is 30 cm, the volume of the
box is 0 cm³. A square of this size
will not create any flaps to fold up.

5. Sample:

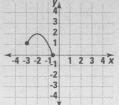

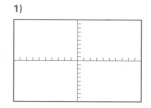
1)

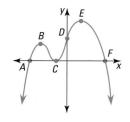

$-10 \le x \le 10$, x-scale = 1
$-10 \le y \le 10$, y-scale = 1

It is not possible to see the graph of the function on this window because the function is well above $y = 10$ for most values $0 < x \le 10$ and well below $y = -10$ for most values $-10 \le x < 0$. Because it increases so rapidly about $x = 0$, the graph appears to be a vertical line at $x = 0$.

d. g is decreasing when the graph goes down as you go to the right. This occurs when $x < b$ or $c < x < d$.

e. Tracing on the graph shows $a \approx -1.5$, $b \approx -0.6$, $c \approx 0.8$, $d \approx 2.8$, and $e \approx 3.7$. The corresponding values of the function are shown on the graph at the right.

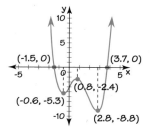

Notice that the description of where a function is positive/negative or increasing/decreasing is an interval of x-values and therefore only x-coordinates are needed.

QUESTIONS

Covering the Reading

In 1–3, refer to the In-class Activity on page 563.

1. Graph $V(x) = 4x^3 - 280x^2 + 4800x$ on the default window of your automatic grapher. Describe what you see and why. **See left.**

2. Graph V again for $-10 < x < 50$ and $-10{,}000 < y < 40{,}000$. Label all intercept points, zeros, and relative extrema. Give coordinates to the nearest integer. **See margin.**

3. Explain what $V(30) = 0$ means in this context. **See margin.**

4. Examine the graph at the left of a 4th degree polynomial with key points labeled. Classify each point as a zero, minimum, maximum, relative minimum, relative maximum, or none of the above. **See left.**

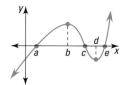

5. Draw a sketch of a polynomial function which has a minimum, but no relative minimum. **See margin.**

6. The table at the left gives values of a polynomial function.
   a. Plot these points and sketch a possible graph of $y = f(x)$. **See margin.**
   b. Between which pairs of consecutive integers must the zeros of f occur?
   -2 and -1, -1 and 0, 1 and 2

x	f(x)
-2	7
-1	-1
0	3
1	7
2	-1
3	-33

7. In this lesson a table of values for $f(x) = -x^3 + 5x + 2$ showed that there was a zero between 2.0 and 2.5. Make another table for x equal to 2.0, 2.1, 2.2, 2.3, 2.4, and 2.5. Between which two values of x in this table must a zero exist? Explain why. **See margin.**

4) A: zero; B: relative maximum; C: zero, relative minimum; D: none of the above; E: relative maximum, maximum; F: zero

8. At the right is a graph of f with various x-coordinates labeled. In what interval(s) does f satisfy the following conditions?
   a. f is positive. $a < x < c$ or $x > e$
   b. f is negative. $x < a$ or $c < x < e$
   c. f is increasing. $x < b$ or $x > d$
   d. f is decreasing. $b < x < d$

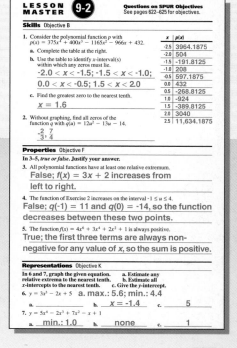

Lesson 9-2 *Graphs of Polynomial Functions* **567**

6. a. **Sample:**

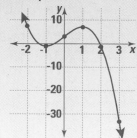

7. **A zero must exist between 2.4 and 2.5 because the values of the function change from positive to negative.**

x	y
2.0	4.0
2.1	3.239
2.2	2.352
2.3	1.333
2.4	0.176
2.5	-1.125

Notes on Questions
Question 4 Error Alert Remind students that the maximum associated with point E is also a relative maximum.

Question 6 From the given data, differences can be taken to determine an equation of the polynomial function of lowest degree that fits these points. $[f(x) = -2x^3 + 6x + 3]$ You might have students try to determine the equation after they have studied Lesson 9-3, or use it as a motivator for that lesson.

Question 11 The students know more powerful techniques for finding the maximum point and zeros of the function h, namely, using the quadratic formula. These techniques can be used to check (or be checked by) the graphing techniques of this lesson.

Questions 12–15 The "advanced mathematics" needed to prove this is covered in *Precalculus and Discrete Mathematics*. As $x \to \infty$ and as $x \to -\infty$, the end behavior of a given 4th degree polynomial function is the same. This can happen if there is one change in direction, as in the function *f* of **Question 12**. More generally, at any relative maximum or minimum point the function changes direction, so there must be an odd number of changes of direction.

Question 16 Students should be able to answer these questions for any polynomial function.

Questions 24–25 These questions continue the review of polynomial operations.

Follow-up for Lesson 9-2

Practice
For more questions on SPUR Objectives, use **Lesson Master 9-2** (shown on page 567).

9b)
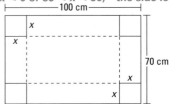

$-10 \le x \le 60$, x-scale = 10
$-20000 \le y \le 50000$, y-scale = 10000

12)
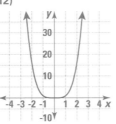

13)
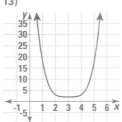

14)
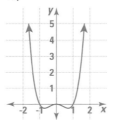

2 rel. min., 1 rel. max.

15)
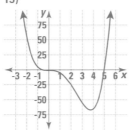

568

Applying the Mathematics

9. An open box is constructed by cutting squares of side x cm from the corners of a 100-cm-by-70-cm sheet of cardboard. **a)** $V = 4x^3 - 340x^2 + 700$
   b) see left.   **c)** $x < 0$ or $35 < x < 50$;   the side length of the square cannot be within these intervals because the volume must be positive.

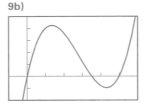

   a. Write a polynomial function for the volume of the box.
   b. Graph the function.
   c. When is the function negative? What does this tell you?
   d. Find the coordinates of the maximum of the function. $\approx$ (13.5, 42,377)
   e. For what size square does the maximum volume occur? $\approx$ 13.5 cm
   f. What is the maximum volume the box can have? $\approx$ 42,377 cm^3

10. Match each function with a characteristic.
    a. $A(x) = 4 - x^2 - x$ II   I. no relative extrema
    b. $B(x) = (x - 2)^3$ I   II. one relative maximum
    c. $C(x) = 7x - 9$ I   III. one relative minimum
    d. $D(x) = (x - 5)^2 - 6$ III   IV. both a relative maximum
    e. $E(x) = x^3 - 5x$ IV   and a relative minimum

11. A missile is fired from 10 ft above the ground with an initial velocity of 500 ft per sec and follows a projectile path. A function describing its height (vertical displacement) h at time t in seconds is $h(t) = -16t^2 + 500t + 10$. $\approx$ 8 sec and $\approx$ 23 sec
    a. After how many seconds will the missile be 3000 ft above the ground?
    b. What will be the maximum height of the missile? $\approx$ 3916 ft
    c. How many seconds after launching will the missile hit the ground? $\approx$ 31 sec

In 12–15, use this information. It can be proved using calculus that every polynomial function of degree 4 has either one or three relative extrema. Sketch a graph of each function and tell how many relative maxima and relative minima the function has. See left.

12. $f(x) = x^4$ 1 rel. min.   13. $g(t) = (t - 3)^4 + 2$ 1 rel. min.

14. $h(x) = x^4 - x^2$ 15. $j(x) = x^4 - 5x^3 - 1$ 1 rel. min.
    a, d–f, See margin.
16. Consider the function G, where $G(x) = x^3 - 8x + 1$.
    a. Sketch a graph of G using an automatic grapher.
    b. Identify and verify the y-intercept of G. $G(0) = 0^3 - 8(0) + 1 = 1$
    c. Estimate the zero(s) of G to the nearest tenth. -2.9, 0.1, and 2.8
    d. Estimate the coordinates of the relative extrema of G to the nearest hundredth.
    e. In what interval(s) is G positive? negative?
    f. In what interval(s) is G increasing? decreasing?

Adapting to Individual Needs

Extra Help
Some students may be confused about the difference between the maximum value of a function and a relative maximum of the function. Explain that the maximum value of the function is the largest value of the range; a relative maximum is a value of the function that is greater than the values of the function near it. Point out that every maximum is a relative maximum, but that a relative maximum may or may not be the maximum value of a function. An analogous difference holds between minima and relative minima.

Challenge
Have students use a calculator to sketch the graph of the function $f(x) = x^4 - 3x^3 + 4x^2 - 5x + 2$. Then have them **work in groups** to solve the following.
1. $x^4 - 3x^3 + 4x^2 - 5x + 2 = 0$
   [{0.5698, 2}]
2. $x^4 - 3x^3 + 4x^2 - 5x + 2 > 0$
   [{x: x < 0.5698 or x > 2}]
3. $x^4 - 3x^3 + 4x^2 - 5x + 2 < 0$
   [{0.5968, 2}]

18b) $100x^7 + 200x^6 + 400x^5 + 800x^4 + 1600x^3 + 3200x^2 + 6400x + 12,800$

d) 100; it represents the amount first deposited.

19c)

h^2	xh	h
yh	xy	y
h	x	

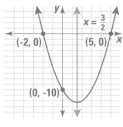

22d)

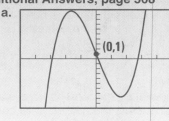

23) $x = \dfrac{^-b \pm \sqrt{b^2 - 4ac}}{2a}$

Review

17. The geometric series $g_1 + g_1r + g_1r^2 + \ldots + g_1r^{n-1}$ is a polynomial in the variable __a.__ of degree __b.__ . *(Lesson 9-1)* a) r b) $n - 1$

18. Isaiah M. Rich started saving on his 14th birthday. On that day he set aside $100. On each successive birthday he has added to his account twice the amount that he deposited the previous birthday. His money is invested at 8% compounded annually and he makes no additional deposits or withdrawals.
 a. How much money will he have in his account after making the deposit on his 21st birthday? **$27,624.90**
 b. Write a polynomial in x to represent Isaiah's savings, where $x = 1 + \frac{r}{100}$ if the account pays $r\%$ interest. **See left.**
 c. What is the degree of the polynomial in part **b**? **7**
 d. What is the leading coefficient of the polynomial in part **b** and what does it represent? *(Lesson 9-1)* **See left.**

19. Rose Gardner is expanding her garden. The original length and width of the rectangular plot were x meters and y meters. She is now adding h meters to each dimension. *(Lesson 9-1)*
 a. Write a product of two binomials to express the area of her new garden. $A = (x + h)(y + h)$
 b. Expand the product. $A = xy + xh + yh + h^2$
 c. Make a diagram of the original plot and the expansion. Identify each of the areas represented by the terms in part **b**. **See left.**

In 20 and 21, give the degree of the polynomial. *(Lesson 9-1)*

20. $(a - 5)(a - 2)^3$ **4**

21. $(x^2 - 5y)^3$ **6**

22. Consider the quadratic function $f(x) = x^2 - 3x - 10$.
 a. Identify its y-intercept. **-10**
 b. Identify its x-intercepts. **-2 and 5**
 c. Identify its line of symmetry. $x = \frac{3}{2}$
 d. Sketch the graph from the information above. **See left.**
 e. Use the results of part **b** to factor $f(x)$. $f(x) = (x + 2)(x - 5)$
 (Previous course, Lesson 2-6)

23. Give the zeros of the function $f: x \rightarrow ax^2 + bx + c$. *(Previous course)* **See left.**

In 24 and 25, factor each expression. *(Previous course)*

24. $x^2 - 10x + 25$ $(x - 5)^2$

25. $x^2 - 11x + 30$ $(x - 6)(x - 5)$

Exploration

26. Create some quintic (5th degree) polynomials of your own. Find functions fitting these criteria.
 a. A quintic with exactly one real zero. **Sample:** $y = x^5 + 3$
 b. A quintic with exactly three real zeros. **See below.**
 c. A quintic with exactly five real zeros. **See below.**
 b) **Sample:** $y = x(x - 1)(x - 2)(x^2 + 1) = x^5 - 3x^4 + 3x^3 - 3x^2 + 2x$
 c) **Sample:** $y = x(x - 1)(x - 2)(x + 1)(x + 2) = x^5 - 5x^3 + 4x$

Assessment

Group Assessment Have each student use an automatic grapher to sketch a graph of the function $G(x) = 2x^3 - 20x + 3$. Then ask students to volunteer answers to the following questions. Have another member of the class state why he or she agrees or disagrees with the given answer. Be sure that all students have an opportunity to respond to a question, or comment on the response.
1. Identify the y-intercept of G. [3]
2. Estimate the zeros of G to the nearest tenth. [-3.2, 0.2, 3.1]
3. Estimate the coordinates of the relative extrema of G to the nearest tenth. [(-1.8, 27.3) and (1.82, -21.34)]
4. In what interval(s) is G positive? [-3.23 $< x <$ 0.15 and $x >$ 3.08]
5. In what interval(s) is G negative? [0.15 $< x <$ 3.08 and $x <$ -3.23]
6. In what interval(s) is G increasing? [$x <$ -1.8 and $x >$ 1.82]
7. In what intervals is G decreasing? [-1.8 $< x <$ 1.82]

Extension

Have students **work in groups** to explore the various shapes of 5th degree polynomials with real coefficients, trying to determine the possible numbers of zeros, relative minima, and relative maxima. [There are from one to five real zeros, and zero to four relative extrema.]

Project Update Project 4, *Properties of Cubics*, on page 618, relates to the content of this lesson.

Setting Up Lesson 9-3

You might use **Question 6** on page 567 as motivation. Is there any way we could find a formula for a polynomial function that fits all these points? [It might be a cubic, since its graph looks a little like the graph of the cubic in the lesson. If it has the form $f(x) = ax^3 + bx^2 + cx + d$, then since $f(0) = 3$, we must have $d = 3$. So certain things can be determined without reading Lesson 9-3.

Additional Answers, page 568

16. a.

$-5 \leq x \leq 5$, x-scale = 1
$-10 \leq y \leq 10$, y-scale = 1

d. relative maximum: (-1.63, 9.71)
 relative minimum: (1.63, -7.71)
e. G is positive in the intervals -2.9 $< x <$ 0.1 or $x >$ 2.8
 G is negative in the intervals $x <$ -2.9 or 0.1 $< x <$ 2.8
f. G is increasing in the intervals $x <$ -1.63 or $x >$ 1.63
 G is decreasing in the intervals -1.63 $< x <$ 1.63

Objectives

A Use finite differences and systems of equations to determine an equation for a polynomial function from data points.
I Construct and interpret polynomials that model real situations.

Resources

From the *Teacher's Resource File*
■ Lesson Master 9-3
■ Answer Master 9-3
■ Assessment Sourcebook: Quiz for Lessons 9-1 through 9-3
■ Teaching Aid 79: Warm-up

Additional Resources
■ Visual for Teaching Aid 79
■ Exploration 9-3

Teaching Lesson **9-3**

Warm-up

Solve the following system.
$$\begin{cases} d = 43 \\ c - d = 12 \\ 2b + 3c - 4d = 201 \\ 3a + b = \text{-}40 \end{cases}$$
$a = \text{-}48$, $b = 104$, $c = 55$, $d = 43$

Finding Polynomial Models

Fruit is sometimes displayed in layers of triangular numbers as shown above. The result is a *tetrahedral* array. The total number of points in a 3-dimensional tetrahedral array is called a **tetrahedral number**.

Below are the four smallest tetrahedral numbers and the arrays that give rise to them.

$T(1) = 1 \qquad T(2) = 4 \qquad T(3) = 10 \qquad T(4) = 20$

Notice that each tetrahedral number beyond the first is the sum of the previous tetrahedral number and a triangular number. For instance, the 3rd tetrahedral number is the sum of the 2nd tetrahedral number and the 3rd triangular number.

$$T(3) = 4 + 6 = 10$$

In general, if $T(n)$ represents the nth tetrahedral number, and $t(n)$ is the nth triangular number, a recursive formula for the nth tetrahedral number is

$$\begin{cases} T(1) = 1 \\ T(n) = T(n-1) + t(n), \text{ for all integers } n > 1. \end{cases}$$

Suppose that for the 25th anniversary of a store, the owner wants to arrange apples in a tetrahedral stack 25 rows high. The owner would like to know how many apples are needed.

Lesson 9-3 Overview

Broad Goals In Chapter 2, students were shown how to determine linear and quadratic models by solving a system of equations. This lesson extends the idea to polynomials of higher degree.

Perspective All continuous functions on closed intervals and many other functions can be approximated by polynomial functions to as close a degree of accuracy as desired (a theorem known as the Weierstrass

Approximation Theorem, whose proof is beyond the scope of this course). Thus there is never a question whether given data points can be approximated by a polynomial model. The only question is how high a degree you wish to allow the polynomial to have.

To obtain a polynomial that fits given data exactly, first is the determination of the (smallest) degree of the polynomial. This is

done by taking successive differences of values of the polynomial until a constant is reached. Then, once the degree n is established, solving a system of $n + 1$ equations in $n + 1$ unknowns determines the coefficients.

The Polynomial Difference Theorem is a theorem of discrete mathematics. Its continuous analog is that the nth derivative of a polynomial function is a constant nonzero

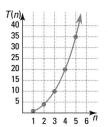

The owner would like an explicit formula for $T(n)$ and begins by graphing known values to see what kind of curve they suggest. At the left is a graph. This graph is clearly not linear. Is it a parabola? Is it part of a higher-degree polynomial? Or is it a part of an exponential curve?

The family of polynomial functions in one variable has a special property that enables you to predict from a table of values whether or not a function is polynomial, and if so, the degree of the polynomial. To examine this property, consider first some polynomials of small degree evaluated at consecutive integers. For instance, consider the first degree polynomial $f(x) = 5x + 3$.

Observe that the differences between consecutive values of $f(x)$, calculated as right minus left, are constant.

x	0		1		2		3		4		5
$f(x) = 5x + 3$	3		8		13		18		23		28
differences		5		5		5		5		5	

Notice that the constant difference is equal to the slope of the function $f(x) = 5x + 3$.

For second degree polynomial functions the differences in function values are not equal, but differences of these differences are constant. Here are the results when $f(x) = x^2 + x + 3$ is evaluated at integers from -1 to 5.

x	-1		0		1		2		3		4		5
$f(x) = x^2 + x + 3$	3		3		5		9		15		23		33
1st differences		0		2		4		6		8		10	
2nd differences			2		2		2		2		2		

Consider now a cubic polynomial, say $f(x) = 2x^3 + x - 10$. For the integers from 0 to 6 the following pattern of differences occurs.

x	0		1		2		3		4		5		6
$f(x) = 2x^3 + x - 10$	-10		-7		8		47		122		245		428
1st differences		3		15		39		75		123		183	
2nd differences			12		24		36		48		60		
3rd differences				12		12		12		12				

In this case, the 3rd differences are constant. Note also that 4th differences and beyond will all equal zero.

Each of the preceding examples is an instance of the following theorem. Its proof is beyond the scope of this book and is therefore omitted.

Polynomial Difference Theorem
The function $y = f(x)$ is a polynomial function of degree n if and only if, for any set of x-values that form an arithmetic sequence, the nth differences of corresponding y-values are equal and nonzero.

You might begin by relating what students know about polynomial models. Given two points not on the same vertical line, there is a unique linear function that contains them. Given three noncollinear points, no two on the same vertical line, there is a unique quadratic function that contains them. This lesson enables these ideas to be extended.

Part of the proof of the Polynomial Difference Theorem is quite symbolic. If you think your students are ready for it, you may want to explain it. Suppose there exists a polynomial function $x \rightarrow P(x)$ of degree n that fits $n + 1$ points (x_1, y_1), (x_2, y_2), . . . $(x_{n + 1}, y_{n + 1})$, with the x_i forming an arithmetic sequence with constant difference d. Then for all k, the difference in values
$$y_{k + 1} - y_k = P(x_{k + 1}) - P(x_k)$$
$$= P(x_k + d) - P(x_k)$$
$$= \sum_{i = 0}^{n} (a_i(x_k + d)^i) - \sum_{i = 0}^{n} a_i(x_k)^i.$$

Now, by the Binomial Theorem, each element of the left summation can be expanded. When the elements of the left sum are expanded, the only term of degree n will equal the corresponding term that appears in the right summation. Since they are subtracted, these terms of degree n will not appear in the difference. Thus the differences can be fit by a polynomial of degree $n - 1$.

Emphasize to students that, unlike some models of earlier chapters, the models of this lesson are exact models; they fit the given data points exactly.

Optional Activities

function if and only if the polynomial is of degree n.

Students who have studied UCSMP *Advanced Algebra* should be familiar with the content of this lesson.

Activity 1 You may wish to use this activity after discussing **Example 1**. Challenge students to make up a third degree polynomial function by "working backwards," starting with a constant difference of 2. Have them build up from that 3rd set of differences to the ordered pairs of the actual function and then use a regression feature on statistical software to determine the equation for the function. If time permits, have them experiment with starting with different constant

values, or with creating a quadratic or quartic polynomial function. [Sample: Start with a constant difference of 2 as the 3rd set of differences:

3rd			2		2		2		2
2nd		1		3		5		7		9
1st	7		8		11		16		23	
y's	5		12		20		31		47	
x's	1		2		3		4		5	

The result is the polynomial function
$y = \frac{1}{3}x^3 - \frac{3}{2}x^2 + \frac{55}{6}x - 3$.]

❶ Emphasize also that the systems formed by substituting in the manner described are always solvable by subtracting consecutive equations.

You may wish to point out that, in the solution to **Example 1,** the constants that appear in these equations are, in fact, the first 4 values of the function T in the consecutive terms, the first 3 first differences (3, 6, and 10), the first 2 second differences (3 and 4), and the first 3rd difference (1). A similar pattern always occurs.

The Polynomial Difference Theorem tells you that if a function is polynomial in degree n, it will yield constant nth differences. Also, it tells you that if values of a function produce constant nth differences for an arithmetic sequence of x-values, then there is a polynomial function containing these points. Moreover, the degree of the polynomial is the n corresponding to the nth differences that are equal.

Example 1

Consider the tetrahedral number function T described on the first page of this lesson. Is T a polynomial function? If so, what is the degree of the polynomial?

Solution 1

Construct a table of consecutive tetrahedral numbers, and take differences between consecutive terms.

n	1		2		3		4		5		6
T(n)	1		4		10		20		35		56
1st differences		3		6		10		15		21	
2nd differences			3		4		5		6		
3rd differences				1		1		1			

Since the third differences are constant use the Polynomial Difference Theorem. **The function n → T(n) is a polynomial function of degree 3.**

Solution 2

On page 570, we noted that **a recursive formula for T has T(n) = T(n − 1) + t(n), where t(n) is the nth triangular number. Subtracting T(n − 1) from both sides, we have T(n) − T(n − 1) = t(n). This indicates that the 1st differences are the triangular numbers,** which you can see in Solution 1. **But it is known from Chapter 8 that the nth triangular number is** $\frac{n(n + 1)}{2}$**, which is a quadratic polynomial. Since the 1st differences are quadratic, the 2nd differences must be linear, and so the 3rd differences are constant. Thus, T is a polynomial function of degree 3.**

❶ In order to find an explicit formula for this cubic polynomial, you can set up and solve a system of equations. You know the formula for $T(n)$ is of the form

$$T(n) = an^3 + bn^2 + cn + d.$$

You must find four coefficients a, b, c, and d to determine $T(n)$. So use any four data points in the table of tetrahedral numbers, and substitute them into the cubic form above. It is easiest if the values of n form an arithmetic sequence. Using $n = 4, 3, 2,$ and 1 gives the following four equations.

$$\begin{aligned} T(4){:} \quad & 20 = 64a + 16b + 4c + d \\ T(3){:} \quad & 10 = 27a + 9b + 3c + d \\ T(2){:} \quad & 4 = 8a + 4b + 2c + d \\ T(1){:} \quad & 1 = a + b + c + d \end{aligned}$$

Activity 2 You may wish to use this activity after students have completed **Question 11** on page 575. Have students verify the regression equation from **Question 11c** by solving a system of equations. [One system to solve is

$$\begin{cases} 350 = a \cdot 0^2 + b \cdot 0 + c \\ 340 = a + b + c \\ 320 = 4a + 2b + c \end{cases}$$

with solution $a = -5$, $b = -5$, and final equation $y = -5x^2 + -5x + 350$]

Activity 3 Technology Connection
Materials: Explorations software

Students may use *Exploration 9-3, The Polynomial Difference Theorem,* as a follow-up for Lesson 9-3. Students can enter a set of data with x-values that form an arithmetic sequence. By checking the nth differences of the y-values, students will apply the Polynomial Difference Theorem. If possible the computer will find an equation for the polynomial.

Adapting to Individual Needs

Extra Help
Be sure students realize that the process of finding finite differences is meaningful only if the x-values form an arithmetic sequence. Emphasize, however that the values we test to find the differences are the y-values.

Solve this system. To eliminate d, subtract each successive pair of sentences above. This gives the following equivalent system.

$$10 = 37a + 7b + c$$
$$6 = 19a + 5b + c$$
$$3 = 7a + 3b + c$$

Repeating the same procedure with the sentences above eliminates c.

$$4 = 18a + 2b$$
$$3 = 12a + 2b$$

Subtracting these two equations gives $1 = 6a$; so $a = \frac{1}{6}$.

To find the other coefficients, substitute back.

$3 = 12a + 2b$, so when $a = \frac{1}{6}$,

$3 = 12\left(\frac{1}{6}\right) + 2b$. Thus, $b = \frac{1}{2}$.

Similarly, $3 = 7a + 3b + c$, so when $a = \frac{1}{6}$ and $b = \frac{1}{2}$,

$3 = 7\left(\frac{1}{6}\right) + 3\left(\frac{1}{2}\right) + c$. Thus, $c = \frac{1}{3}$.

Finally, $1 = a + b + c + d$, so when $a = \frac{1}{6}$, $b = \frac{1}{2}$, and $c = \frac{1}{3}$, $d = 0$.

The resulting polynomial formula for the nth tetrahedral number is

$$T(n) = \frac{1}{6}n^3 + \frac{1}{2}n^2 + \frac{1}{3}n.$$

Hence, to find the number of apples needed in a display 25 rows high, let $n = 25$. Then $T(n) = T(25) = 2925$. So almost 3000 apples are needed for the anniversary display.

As an alternative to finding the cubic model using a system of equations, it is possible to use the regression techniques learned in Chapter 2. Some statistical utilities include a quadratic, cubic, and quartic regression feature. Because the third differences were constant, we know that a cubic model is a good model. In fact, by examining the residuals we can verify that a cubic model is an exact model in this case.

Example 2

a. Use cubic regression to find a cubic model for the tetrahedral numbers.
b. Verify that the model is an exact model by examining the residuals.

Solution

a. Enter the table at the right in a statistics utility.

x	1	2	3	4
y	1	4	10	20

Our statistics utility gives the cubic regression model

$y = 0.1666666667x^3 + 0.5x^2 + 0.3333333333x + (-3.7E12)$

A cubic model is $y = \frac{1}{6}x^3 + \frac{1}{2}x^2 + \frac{1}{3}x$.

▶

Lesson 9-3 *Finding Polynomial Models* **573**

Additional Examples

There exists a polynomial formula of degree 4 for the sum of the cubes of the integers from 1 to n. Find that formula. Let $P(n) = an^4 + bn^3 + cn^2 + dn + e$ be the polynomial. Use $P(1) = 1$, $P(2) = 9$, $P(3) = 36$, $P(4) = 100$, and $P(5) = 225$ as the points to fit. The system to be solved is
$225 = 625a + 125b + 25c + 5d + e$;
$100 = 256a + 64b + 16c + 4d + e$;
$36 = 81a + 27b + 9c + 3d + e$;
$9 = 16a + 8b + 4c + 2d + e$;
$1 = a + b + c + d + e$.
$P(n) = \frac{1}{4}n^4 + \frac{1}{2}n^3 + \frac{1}{4}n^2$.

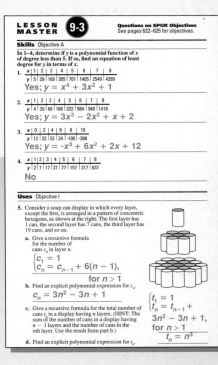

LESSON 9-3
MASTER

Questions on SPUR Objectives
See pages 622–625 for objectives.

Skills Objective A

In 1–4, determine if y is a polynomial function of x of degree less than 5. If so, find an equation of least degree for y in terms of x.

1.
x	1	2	3	4	5	6	7	8
y	5	29	109	305	701	1405	2549	4289

Yes; $y = x^4 + 3x^2 + 1$

2.
x	1	2	3	4	5	6	7	8
y	4	20	68	166	332	584	940	1418

Yes; $y = 3x^3 - 2x^2 + x + 2$

3.
x	0	2	4	6	8	10
y	12	32	52	24	-100	-368

Yes; $y = -x^3 + 6x^2 + 2x + 12$

4.
x	1	2	3	4	5	6	7	8
y	2	7	17	37	77	157	317	637

No

Uses Objective I

5. Consider a soup can display in which every layer, except the first, is arranged in a pattern of concentric hexagons, as shown at the right. The first layer has 1 can, the second layer has 7 cans, the third layer has 19 cans, and so on.

a. Give a recursive formula for the number of cans c_n in layer n.

$\begin{cases} c_1 = 1 \\ c_n = c_{n-1} + 6(n-1), \\ \quad \text{for } n > 1 \end{cases}$

b. Find an explicit polynomial expression for c_n.

$c_n = 3n^2 - 3n + 1$

c. Give a recursive formula for the total number of cans t_n in a display having n layers. (HINT: The sum of the number of cans in a display having $n - 1$ layers and the number of cans in the nth layer. Use the result from part b.)

$\begin{cases} t_1 = 1 \\ t_n = t_{n-1} + 3n^2 - 3n + 1, \\ \quad \text{for } n > 1 \end{cases}$

d. Find an explicit polynomial expression for t_n.

$t_n = n^3$

Adapting to Individual Needs

Challenge

Remind students that given $n + 1$ points, there is a polynomial of degree n (or less) that goes through those points. Have students use the linear, quadratic, cubic and quartic regressions on a calculator to find a polynomial of degree n for each of the following sets of $n + 1$ points.

1.
x	1	2
y	-5	-8

$[y = -3x - 2]$

2.
x	1	2	3
y	-5	-8	7

$[y = 9x^2 - 30x + 16]$

3.
x	1	2	3	4
y	-5	-8	7	82

$[y = 7x^3 - 33x^2 + 47x - 26]$

Notes on Questions

Question 7 Error Alert Point out that although a polynomial function does not fit the data, the exponential function $y = 2^x$ does. For exponential functions, each row of consecutive differences is a multiple of the first row. (The continuous analog is that the derivative of an exponential function is a multiple of that function.)

Question 14 This question points out the danger of trying to model with a polynomial whose degree is too low.

(Notes on Questions continue on page 576.)

---

b.

x	1	2	3	4
Observed y	1	4	10	20
Predicted y	1	4	10	20
Residuals	0	0	0	0

All of the residuals are 0, which verifies that a cubic model is an exact model.

To find the cubic model for the tetrahedral numbers, four noncollinear data points were used. Five noncollinear points are needed to determine a quartic (4th degree) model. In general, to find the equation for a polynomial of degree n you need $n + 1$ points, no three of which are collinear, no four of which are on the same parabola, and so on, which lead to a system of $n + 1$ equations in $n + 1$ unknowns.

QUESTIONS

Covering the Reading

In 1 and 2, a formula for a function f is given. **a.** Evaluate f for all integers from -1 to 7. **b.** Take differences between consecutive values until a nonzero constant is found. **See margin.**

1. $f(x) = -2x^2 + 5$ **2.** $f(x) = x^3 - x^2 + x + 1$

In 3 and 4, refer to the Polynomial Difference Theorem.

3. If the y-values are all equal to 7 for the 4th differences of consecutive integral x-values, what is the degree of the polynomial? **4**

4. The theorem applies to differences of y-values taken from what sort of x-values? **those that form an arithmetic sequence**

In 5–7, use the data listed in each table. **a.** Determine if y is a polynomial function of x of degree less than 6. **b.** If so, find its degree.

5.

x	1	2	3	4	5	6	7	8	9
y	2	12	36	80	150	252	392	576	810

a) Yes   b) 3

6.

x	1	2	3	4	5	6	7	8
y	9	26	47	66	77	74	51	2

a) Yes   b) 3; $y = -x^3 + 8x^2 + 2$

7.

x	1	3	5	7	9	11	13
y	2	8	32	128	512	2048	8192

a) No

8. Show how to find the 7th tetrahedral number using each of the following.
   a. Add the 7th triangular number to the 6th tetrahedral number.
   b. Use the explicit formula for $T(n)$ developed in the lesson.
   a) $T(7) = T(6) + t(7) = 56 + 28 = 84$
   b) $T(7) = \frac{1}{6}(7)^3 + \frac{1}{2}(7)^2 + \frac{1}{3}(7) = 84$

Additional Answers

1. **a.**

$x \rightarrow$	-1	0	1	2	3	4	5	6	7
$f(x) = -2x^2 + 5 \rightarrow$	3	5	3	-3	-13	-27	-45	-67	-93

b. 1st differences → 2 -2 -6 -10 -14 -18 -22 -26
2nd differences → -4 -4 -4 -4 -4 -4 -4

2. **a.**

$x \rightarrow$	-1	0	1	2	3	4	5	6	7
$f(x) = x^3 - x^2 + x + 1 \rightarrow$	-2	1	2	7	22	53	106	187	302

b. 1st differences → 3 1 5 15 31 53 81 115
2nd differences → -2 4 10 16 22 28 34
3rd differences → 6 6 6 6 6 6

9. Consider a function f described by the data points below.

x	0	1	2	3	4	5	6
$f(x)$	0	5	14	33	68	125	210

  a. Show that f may be a polynomial of degree less than 5, and find its degree. **See margin.**
  b. Determine an equation for f. $f(x) = x^3 - x^2 + 5x$
  c. Find $f(7)$. **329**

Applying the Mathematics

10. Consider the sequence determined by the following:

$$\begin{cases} t_1 = 17; \\ t_n = t_{n-1} - 5, \text{ for integers } n > 1. \end{cases}$$

  a. List the first six terms of the sequence. **17, 12, 7, 2, -3, -8**
  b. Tell whether the sequence can be described explicitly by a polynomial.
  c. If the answer to part **b** is yes, find the polynomial. $t(n) = -5n + 22$
  b) Yes

11. In Example 3 in Lesson 2-6, a store put an air conditioner normally selling for \$350 on sale. On the first day of the sale they reduced the price by \$10, the second day they took off an additional \$20, the third day took off an additional \$30, and so on. **See margin.**
  a. Make a table of day vs. sale price for the first 6 days of the sale.
  b. Use the polynomial difference theorem to find the degree of a polynomial function that maps day of sale to sale price. **2**
  c. Use regression to find a polynomial function to fit the data. **See left.**
  d. Find a recursive formula for the polynomial function in part **c**. **See left.**

12. Suppose $f(x) = mx + b$.
  a. Calculate $f(5) - f(4)$. m
  b. Evaluate $f(x + 1) - f(x)$. m
  c. Describe in words what the difference in part **b** represents. **The change per unit in a linear function is a constant, the slope of the function.**

13. a. If $f(x) = ax^3 + bx^2 + cx + d$, find $f(1), f(2), f(3), f(4), f(5)$, and $f(6)$.
  b. Prove that the third differences of these values are constant.
  a, b, see left.

14. Refer again to the tetrahedral numbers in the lesson. Suppose you try to model the data with a quadratic function.
  a. Use $T(1)$, $T(2)$, and $T(3)$ to find a quadratic model for the data, and verify that this formula works for the first three numbers in the sequence.
  b. Verify that this quadratic model does not predict the 4th tetrahedral number in the sequence.

  a) $Q(x) = \frac{3}{2}x^2 - \frac{3}{2}x + 1$; $Q(1) = \frac{3}{2}(1)^2 - \frac{3}{2}(1) + 1 = 1$;
  $Q(2) = \frac{3}{2}(2)^2 - \frac{3}{2}(2) + 1 = 4$; $Q(3) = \frac{3}{2}(3)^2 - \frac{3}{2}(3) + 1 = 10$
  b) $Q(4) = \frac{3}{2}(4)^2 - \frac{3}{2}(4) + 1 = 19 \neq T(4) = 20$

Margin left answers:

11c) $y = -5x^2 - 5x + 350$

d) $\begin{cases} t_0 = 350 \\ t_n = t_{n-1} - 10n, \end{cases}$
  for integers $n > 0$.

13a) $f(1) = a + b + c + d$
  $f(2) = 8a + 4b + 2c + d$
  $f(3) = 27a + 9b + 3c + d$
  $f(4) = 64a + 16b + 4c + d$
  $f(5) = 125a + 25b + 5c + d$
  $f(6) = 216a + 36b + 6c + d$

b) 1st differences:
  $7a + 3b + c, 19a + 5b + c, 37a + 7b + c, 61a + 9b + c, 91a + 11b + c$
  2nd differences:
  $12a + 2b, 18a + 2b, 24a + 2b, 30a + 2b$
  3rd differences: $6a, 6a, 6a$

Follow-up for Lesson 9-3

Practice
For more questions on SPUR Objectives, use **Lesson Master 9-3** (shown on page 573).

Assessment
Quiz A quiz covering Lessons 9-1 through 9-3 is provided in the *Assessment Sourcebook*.

Extension
The sum of the integers from 1 to n is an arithmetic series with the value $\frac{n(n + 1)}{2}$, a polynomial of degree 2. The sum of the squares of the integers from 1 to n has a polynomial formula $f(a) = \frac{1}{3}a^3 + \frac{1}{2}a^2 + \frac{1}{6}a$. The sum of the cubes of the integers is found in the *Additional Example*. Pair up students and give each pair the task of finding the formula for the sums of the 4th powers of the integers from 1 to n (a 5th degree polynomial) and the sum of the 5th powers of integers from 1 to n (a 6th degree polynomial). The systems are large, so one person should do the work while the other checks. Switch the roles for the other example. [sum of 4th powers of integers from 1 to n is $\frac{1}{5}a^5 + \frac{1}{2}a^4 + \frac{1}{3}a^3 - \frac{1}{30}a$; sum of 5th powers of integers from 1 to n is $\frac{1}{6}a^6 + \frac{1}{2}a^5 + \frac{5}{12}a^4 - \frac{1}{12}a^2$]

Project Update Project 1, *Completing the Pattern*, Project 2, *Pascal's Triangle Revisited*, and Project 4, *Properties of Cubics*, on pages 617–618, relate to the content of this lesson.

Additional Answers

9. a. 1st differences → 5   9   19   35   57   85
  2nd differences →   4   10   16   22   28
  3rd differences →   6   6   6   6
  $f(x)$ is of degree 3

11. a.

1	2	3	4	5	6
340	320	290	250	200	140

575

Notes on Questions

Questions 18–19 Students are expected to use the Binomial Theorem to find the cube of the binomial.

Questions 20–21 These questions continue the review of factoring in anticipation of later lessons in this chapter.

Question 22 This question could be saved for an assessment, albeit a difficult one.

16)
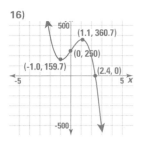

(1.1, 360.7)
(0, 250)
(-1.0, 159.7)
(2.4, 0)

18b) There are n ways to choose $n - 1$ objects from a collection of n objects. Proof: Choosing $n - 1$ objects is the same as selecting 1 object which will not be chosen. There are n ways of doing this.

Istanbul, Turkey

19a) $P = 62.5e^{0.017n}$

576

Review

15. Does $f(x) = x^3 + 2$ have any relative extrema? If so, state the coordinates of each one. *(Lesson 9-2)* **No**

16. Let h be the function defined by $h(x) = -50x^3 + 10x^2 + 150x + 250$. Draw a graph of the function. Label all intercepts and relative extrema. Give coordinates correct to the nearest tenth of the interval(s) on which h satisfies the following conditions. *(Lesson 9-2)* **See left for graph.**
    a. h is positive. **$x < 2.4$**
    b. h is negative. **$x > 2.4$**
    c. h is increasing. **$-0.9 < x < -1.0$**
    d. h is decreasing. **$x < -0.9$ or $x > 1.1$**

17. You invest \$750 at the ends of three consecutive years in an account whose annual yield is r. Your money is compounded annually and none is added or withdrawn.
    a. Write a polynomial function describing the amount in the account at the end of the third year. **$750(1 + r)^2 + 750(1 + r) + 750$**
    b. Determine the amount in part **a**, if $r = 4.8$. *(Lesson 9-1)* **\$2359.73**

18. a. In how many ways can you choose
    i. 5 objects out of 6? **6**
    ii. 99 objects out of 100? **100**
    iii. 364 objects out of 365? **365**
    b. Generalize the results of part **a** and prove your answer. *(Lesson 8-6)* **See left.**

19. The population of Turkey in 1996 was about 62.5 million, with an annual growth rate of about 1.7%. Assume the population changes continuously.
    a. Give a model for the population n years after 1996. **See left.**
    b. Predict the population in 2000. **≈ 66.9 million**
    c. Predict when the population will reach 100 million. *(Lesson 6-4)* **in the year 2024**

20. *Skill sequence.* Multiply and simplify.
    a. $(x + 3)(4x)$ **$4x^2 + 12x$**
    b. $(x + 3)(4x - 5)$ **$4x^2 + 7x - 15$**
    c. $(x + 3)(2x^2 + 4x - 5)$ *(Previous course)* **$2x^3 + 10x^2 + 7x - 15$**

21. *Skill sequence.* Solve.
    a. $x(x - 7) = 0$ **$x = 0$ or $x = 7$**
    b. $(y + 9)(3y - 7) = 0$ **$y = -9$, or $y = \frac{7}{3}$**
    c. $(z - 5)(z + 8)(z + 15) = 0$ *(Previous course)* **$z = -15$, $z = -8$, or $z = 5$**

Exploration

22. A complete set of dominoes of order n consists of t tiles with two halves each containing a number of dots according to the following criterion:

    > Each whole number less than or equal to n (including the blank, representing 0) is paired with each other number exactly once.

    Note that this means that each number is paired with itself exactly once.
    a. Draw a complete set of dominoes of order 3. **See margin.**
    b. Make a table of the number of dominoes in a complete set for orders 1, 2, 3, 4, 5, and 6. **See margin.**
    c. Determine a formula for t in terms of n. **$t(n) = \frac{1}{2}n^2 + \frac{3}{2}n + 1$**

Divide and Conquer. *The first long division problem ever printed was in an arithmetic book by Philippi Calandri in 1491. It shows that* $53497 \div 83 = 644\frac{45}{83}$.

In earlier courses you learned how to add, subtract, and multiply polynomials. Now you will learn how to divide them. The procedure is similar to dividing integers and relies on the same inverse relationship between multiplication and division.

For instance, because $5 \cdot 13 = 65$, from the definition of division you may conclude that $\frac{65}{13} = 5$. Recall that 65 is called the *dividend*, 13 is called the *divisor* and 5 is the *quotient*. Similarly for polynomials, because $(x + 3)(x + 5) = x^2 + 8x + 15$, you may conclude that $\frac{x^2 + 8x + 15}{x + 5} = x + 3$, provided $x \neq -5$.

If you do not recognize the factorization, then you can use long division. The procedure for long division of polynomials is illustrated in Example 1.

Example 1

Divide $6x^2 + 13x - 5$ by $3x - 1$.

Solution

Look at the first terms of both the dividend and divisor.

$$
\begin{array}{r}
2x \\
3x - 1 \overline{\smash{)}\ 6x^2 + 13x - 5} \\
\underline{6x^2 - 2x} \\
15x - 5
\end{array}
$$

Think: $3x\overline{\smash{)}6x^2} = 2x$. This is the first term in the quotient; write it above the dividend. Now multiply $3x - 1$ by $2x$ and subtract the product from $6x^2 + 13x - 5$.

▶

Lesson 9-4 *Division and the Remainder Theorem* **577**

Lesson 9-4

Objectives
C Divide polynomials.
G Apply the Remainder Theorem.

Resources
From the *Teacher's Resource File*
■ Lesson Master 9-4
■ Answer Master 9-4
■ Teaching Aid 80: Warm-up

Additional Resources
■ Visual for Teaching Aid 80
■ Exploration 9-4

Teaching 9-4
Lesson

Warm-up

1. Divide $12x^4$ by $3x^3$. Check your answer by substituting 5 for x.
$4x$; $12 \cdot 5^4 = 7500$; $3 \cdot 5^3 = 375$; 7500 divided by 375 equals 20, which is $4 \cdot 5$.

2. Divide $12x^4 - 6x^3$ by $3x^3$. Check your answer by substituting 2 for x.
$4x - 2$; $12 \cdot 2^4 - 6 \cdot 2^3 = 144$; $3 \cdot 2^3 = 24$; 144 divided by 24 equals 6, which is $4 \cdot 2 - 2$.

3. If $a^3 - 8a^2 + 19a - 12 = (a - 3)f(a)$, what is $f(a)$?
$a^2 - 5a + 4$

Lesson 9-4 Overview

Broad Goals This lesson covers polynomial long division, which will be new to UCSMP students, and proves the Remainder Theorem.

Perspective UCSMP texts delay and spread out the division of polynomials over two years. Prior to this course, although UCSMP students have factored quadratics and certain other special factors, they have not studied the long division of polynomials. Thus, if your students have studied algebra

from UCSMP texts, this will be their first encounter with polynomial long division. The reason for this is simple: it was not needed before and there was more important content to be covered.

However, in this course, because we are going to study the zeros of polynomials in some detail, the ability to find quotients is quite useful. If the dividend is $p(x)$ and the divisor is of the form $x - c$, the Remainder

Theorem provides students with a relatively quick way to check their work; the remainder should be $p(c)$.

In *Precalculus and Discrete Mathematics*, division of polynomials is again covered, in even more detail, because that course studies the analogies between integer and polynomial division, and because in that course

(Overview continues on page 578.)

Notes on Reading

It is useful to point out the similarities between division of polynomials and division of integers. There are two types of division of integers. Consider 25 divided by 3. As *integer division*, the quotient is 8 and the remainder is 1. As *rational number division*, the quotient is $8\frac{1}{3}$. Similarly, there are two types of division of polynomials. Consider **Example 3,** in which $2x^4 - 8x^3 + 12$ is divided by $x^2 - 2$. As *polynomial division,* the quotient is $2x^2 - 8x + 4$ and the remainder is $-16x + 20$. As *rational expression division,* the quotient is $2x^2 - 8x + 4 + \frac{-16x + 20}{x^2 - 2}$.

With integers, the quotient "may come out even." Then integer division and rational number division yield the same quotient. For instance, $\frac{54}{9} = 6$, so $54 = 9 \cdot 6$. In general, $\frac{\text{dividend}}{\text{divisor}} = $ quotient, or dividend $= $ divisor $\cdot$ quotient. Similarly, in **Examples 1–2,** polynomial and rational expression division give the same answer.

The other possibility is that there is a remainder, as in **Examples 3–4.** Then, $\frac{\text{dividend}}{\text{divisor}} = $ quotient $+ \frac{\text{remainder}}{\text{divisor}}$. The remainder is of smaller degree than the divisor; otherwise it could be divided further. When this form is written with multiplication, dividend $= $ divisor $\cdot$ quotient $+$ remainder. This latter form is used in the Remainder Theorem. For integers, $\frac{55}{9} = 6 + \frac{1}{9}$, so $55 = 9 \cdot 6 + 1$.

Now look at the first term of the divisor and the new dividend.

$$
\begin{array}{r}
2x + 5 \\
3x - 1 \overline{\smash{\big)}\, 6x^2 + 13x - 5} \\
\underline{6x^2 - 2x} \\
15x - 5 \\
\underline{15x - 5} \\
0
\end{array}
$$

Think: $3x\overline{\smash{\big)}15x} = 5$. Thus 5 is the second term in the quotient; write it above the dividend adding it to $2x$. Multiply $3x - 1$ by 5 and subtract the product from $15x - 5$. Since 0 is left, the division is finished, and there is no remainder.

Check

Does $(2x + 5)(3x - 1) = 6x^2 + 13x - 5$? Yes. It checks.

If some of the coefficients in the dividend polynomial are zero, you need to fill in all the missing powers of the variable in the dividend, using zero coefficients. Example 2 demonstrates this and also shows two ways to check a long division solution.

Example 2

Divide $5x^3 - 2x - 36$ by $x - 2$.

Solution

The coefficient of x^2 in the polynomial is zero. Insert $0x^2$ so that all powers of x appear in the dividend.

$$
\begin{array}{r}
5x^2 + 10x + 18 \\
x - 2 \overline{\smash{\big)}\, 5x^3 + 0x^2 - 2x - 36} \\
\underline{5x^3 - 10x^2} \\
10x^2 - 2x \\
\underline{10x^2 - 20x} \\
18x - 36 \\
\underline{18x - 36} \\
0
\end{array}
$$

Think: $x\overline{\smash{\big)}5x^3} = 5x^2$. Multiply $x - 2$ by $5x^2$ and subtract. Think: $x\overline{\smash{\big)}10x^2} = 10x$. Multiply $x - 2$ by $10x$ and subtract. Think: $x\overline{\smash{\big)}18x} = 18$. Multiply $x - 2$ by 18; subtract to get 0.

Check 1

Multiply quotient by divisor and use the distributive property to simplify.
$$
\begin{aligned}
(x - 2)(5x^2 + 10x + 18) &= x(5x^2 + 10x + 18) - 2(5x^2 + 10x + 18) \\
&= 5x^3 + 10x^2 + 18x - 10x^2 - 20x - 36 \\
&= 5x^3 - 2x - 36
\end{aligned}
$$

Check 2

Let $Y_1 = \frac{5x^3 - 2x - 36}{x - 2}$ and $Y_2 = 5x^2 + 10x + 18$. Make a table of values for $-3 \le x \le 3$. The output of a table utility is shown at the right. The Y-values of the table are identical except when $x = 2$. When $x = 2$, the denominator of Y_1 is zero and a division by zero "error" occurs. Mathematically we say Y_1 is undefined when $x = 2$. This confirms that $\frac{5x^3 - 2x - 36}{x - 2} = 5x^2 + 10x + 18$ except when $x = 2$.

x	Y_1	Y_2
-3	33	33
-2	18	18
-1	13	13
0	18	18
1	33	33
2	Error	58
3	93	93

Lesson 9-4 Overview, continued

rational functions, the quotients of polynomial functions, are given strong attention.

Although some books give great attention to developing a high level of proficiency in the paper-and-pencil long division of polynomials, symbol manipulators do this well, and we encourage students to learn to divide polynomials with them.

Division of Polynomials Using a Symbol Manipulator

Most symbol manipulators can divide polynomials. The input and output from two different symbol manipulators are shown below.

INPUT	OUTPUT
$\dfrac{5x^3 - 2x - 36}{x - 2}$	$5 \cdot x^2 + 10 \cdot x + 18$
Simplify $[(5x\wedge3 - 2x - 36)/(x - 2)]$	$18 + 10x + 5x^2$

The quotient polynomial is the same for both symbolic manipulators except that the first writes it in descending order of exponents; the second uses ascending order.

As in division of integers, not all polynomial division problems "come out even." In general, when a polynomial $f(x)$ is divided by a polynomial $d(x)$, it produces a quotient $q(x)$ and *remainder* $r(x)$. Either $r(x) = 0$ or $r(x)$ has degree less than the degree of the divisor, $d(x)$. In symbols,

$$f(x) = q(x) \cdot d(x) + r(x)$$

dividend = quotient · divisor + remainder

or $\dfrac{\text{dividend}}{\text{divisor}} = \text{quotient} + \dfrac{\text{remainder}}{\text{divisor}}$.

Example 3

Divide $2x^4 - 8x^3 + 12$ by $x^2 - 2$.

Solution

$$
\begin{array}{r}
2x^2 - 8x + 4 \\
x^2 - 2 \overline{)\,2x^4 - 8x^3 - 0x^2 + 0x + 12} \\
\underline{2x^4 \qquad\quad - 4x^2} \\
-8x^3 + 4x^2 + 0x \\
\underline{-8x^3 \qquad\quad + 16x} \\
4x^2 - 16x + 12 \\
\underline{4x^2 \qquad\quad - 8} \\
-16x + 20
\end{array}
$$

Because the degree of $-16x + 20$ is less than that of $x^2 - 2$, the division is complete. You may write:

The quotient is $2x^2 - 8x + 4$ with remainder $-16x + 20$,

or $\dfrac{2x^4 - 8x^3 + 12}{x^2 - 2} = 2x^2 - 8x + 4 + \dfrac{-16x + 20}{x^2 - 2}$.

Check 1

Substitute a value for x and verify the last equation.

Check 2

Does   dividend = quotient · divisor   + remainder?

Does $2x^4 - 8x^3 + 12 = (2x^2 - 8x + 4)(x^2 - 2) + (-16x + 20)$?

Does $2x^4 - 8x^3 + 12 = (2x^4 - 8x^3 + 16x - 8) + (-16x + 20)$? Yes.

Lesson 9-4   *Division and the Remainder Theorem*   **579**

Optional Activities

Activity 1 Technology Connection
Materials: Explorations software

You may wish to use *Exploration 9-4, Dividing Polynomials*, as an alternative to **Example 3** in Lesson 9-4. Students can see the step-by-step process of polynomial long division. To divide a polynomial (of degree ≤ 4) by another polynomial (of degree ≤ 3), students enter the coefficients for each term of the polynomials.

✎ Activity 2 Writing
After discussing the Remainder Theorem and its proof on page 580, have students write a paragraph to explain the theorem in their own words. Specifically, students should explain *why* the remainder is $f(c)$ if a polynomial $f(x)$ is divided by a linear factor $x - c$.

LESSON MASTER 9-4

Questions on SPUR Objectives
See pages 622–625 for objectives.

Skills Objective C

In 1–4, determine the quotient and the remainder when the first polynomial is divided by the second.

1. $x^3 - 14x^2 + 51x - 54, x - 9$ $x^2 - 5x + 6; 0$

2. $y^6 - 8y^4 - 80, y - 2$ $y^5 + 2y^4 - 4y^3 - 8y^2 - 16y - 32; -144$

3. $z^4 - z^3 - 9z^2 + 3z + 18, 2z^2 - 3$ $\frac{1}{2}z^2 - \frac{1}{2}z - \frac{15}{4}; \frac{3}{2}z + \frac{27}{4}$

4. $a^6 + 5a^4 - 21a^3 + 20a - 100, a^3 + 4$ $a^3 + 5a - 25; 0$

Properties Objective G

In 5–8, use the Remainder Theorem to find the remainder when the first polynomial is divided by the second.

5. $c^5 - c^4 + c^3 - c^2 + c - 1, c - 1$ 0

6. $x^5 - x^4 + x^3 - x^2 + x - 1, x + 1$ -6

7. $8t^6 + 8t^5 + 8t^4 + 8t^3 + 8t^2 + 8t + 8, t - \frac{1}{2}$ $\frac{127}{8}$

8. $5y^4 + 3y^2 - 1, y - \sqrt{2}$ 25

9. When $2x^2 + x - 5$ is divided by $x - c$, the remainder is -2. Find c. $c = 1$ or $c = -\frac{3}{2}$

10. When $x^3 + bx^2 - x + 4$ is divided by $x + 3$, the remainder is 7. Find b. $b = 3$

In 11 and 12, *true or false*. Use the Remainder Theorem to justify your answer.

11. $z^{79} - z$ is divisible by $z + 1$.   True; the remainder is $(-1)^{79} - (-1) = 0$.

12. There exists some polynomial $q(x)$ such that $q(x)(x - 2) = 4x^4 - 2x^2 + 2$.   False; $4(2)^4 - 2(2)^2 + 2 = 58 \neq 0$

1. Divide $-2x^3 - 7x^2 + 10x - 25$ by $x + 5$ and check your answer.
$-2x^2 + 3x - 5$; check:
$(x + 5)(-2x^2 + 3x - 5)$
$= -2x^3 - 7x^2 + 10x - 25$

2. Divide $10y^4 + 7y^2 - 2y + 3$ by $2y^2 + 3y$ and check your answer.
Quotient $5y^2 - 7.5y + 14.75$ and remainder $-46.25y + 3$;
check: $(2y^2 + 3y)(5y^2 - 7.5y + 14.75) - 46.25y + 3 = 10y^4 + 7y^2 - 2y + 3$.

3. Divide $6x^3 + 3x^2 + 14$ by $x + 4$ and check your answer using the Remainder Theorem.
Quotient $6x^2 - 21x + 84$ and remainder -322; Let $p(x) = 6x^3 + 3x^2 + 14$. Since $p(-4) = -322$, the answer checks.

Consider the special case when the divisor $d(x)$ is linear and of the form $x - c$. For the remainder to be of a lower degree than the divisor, it must be a constant, possibly zero. Then

$$\text{dividend} = \text{quotient} \cdot \text{divisor} + \text{remainder}.$$
$$f(x) = q(x) \cdot (x - c) \quad + r(x), \text{ where } r(x) \text{ is a constant}$$

This equation is true for all x. In particular, it is true when $x = c$. Then

$$f(c) = (c - c) \cdot q(c) + r(c).$$

This can be simplified.

$$f(c) = 0 \cdot q(c) + r(c)$$
$$f(c) = r(c)$$

This says that the value of the polynomial at $x = c$ is precisely the remainder when f is divided by $x - c$. These steps prove the Remainder Theorem.

Remainder Theorem
If a polynomial $f(x)$ is divided by $x - c$, then the remainder is $f(c)$.

Example 4

Find the remainder when $7x^5 - x^3 + 1$ is divided by $x - 2$.

Solution 1

Use the Remainder Theorem. Let $f(x) = 7x^5 - x^3 + 1$ and find $f(2)$.
$$f(2) = 7(2)^5 - (2)^3 + 1 = 217$$
So the remainder when $7x^5 - x^3 + 1$ is divided by $x - 2$ is 217.

Solution 2

Use polynomial long division.

$$
\begin{array}{r}
7x^4 + 14x^3 + 27x^2 + 54x + 108 \\
x - 2 \overline{) 7x^5 + 0x^4 - x^3 + 0x^2 + 0x + 1} \\
\underline{7x^5 - 14x^4} \\
14x^4 - x^3 \\
\underline{14x^4 - 28x^3} \\
27x^3 + 0x^2 \\
\underline{27x^3 - 54x^2} \\
54x^2 + 0x \\
\underline{54x^2 - 108x} \\
108x + 1 \\
\underline{108x - 216} \\
217
\end{array}
$$

Optional Activities

Activity 3 Technology Connection
After students have completed **Question 1** on page 581, have them use an automatic grapher to graph the dividend/divisor and the quotient from this question. Ask them to trace the graph of the dividend/divisor to $x \approx 7$. [Often graphing calculators will not reach exactly $x = 7$ due to pixel constraints, so students will assume that the graph is continuous at $x = 7$, and that the y-value there is about 26.] Have students look at a table of the two functions on an automatic grapher and explain the results. [Tables often display ERROR for undefined values, and students should see that there is no function value at $x = 7$ for the dividend/divisor, while the function value of the quotient for $x = 7$ is 26.] Point out to students that on an accurate graph of the dividend/divisor, there is a "hole" at $x = 7$, and that hole would be represented by an open circle at the coordinates (7, 26).

Solution 3

Use a symbol manipulator. The first time we tried this, we were surprised. Nothing happened!

INPUT	OUTPUT
$\dfrac{7x^5 - x^3 + 1}{x - 2}$	$\dfrac{7x^5 - x^3 + 1}{x - 2}$

Instruct the symbol manipulator to rewrite the input as a proper fraction.

$$\text{propFrac}\left(\frac{7x^5 - x^3 + 1}{x - 2}\right) \qquad \frac{217}{x - 2} + 7 \cdot x^4 + 14 \cdot x^3 + 27 \cdot x^2 + 54 \cdot x + 108$$

Now the output is in the form $\frac{dividend}{divisor} = \frac{remainder}{divisor} + quotient$. **So the remainder is 217.**

Notice that the Remainder Theorem has limitations:
    It only applies when dividing by a linear factor.
    It does not produce a quotient.

But it provides a quick way to find the remainder. And the Remainder Theorem has a very useful consequence, the Factor Theorem, which you will study in Lesson 9-5.

QUESTIONS

Covering the Reading

In 1 and 2, find the quotient when the first polynomial is divided by the second.

1. $3x^2 - 16x - 35,\ x - 7$
$3x + 5$

2. $6z^4 - 3z^3 - 3z - 6,\ 2z^2 + 2$
See left.

3. Given that $(x - 3)(x^2 + 5x + 1) = x^3 + 2x^2 - 14x - 3$, write each quotient as a polynomial.

  a. $\dfrac{x^3 + 2x^2 - 14x - 3}{x - 3}$
    $x^2 + 5x + 1$

  b. $\dfrac{x^3 + 2x^2 - 14x - 3}{x^2 + 5x + 1}$
    $x - 3$

4. In a division problem, state two relationships between the dividend, divisor, quotient, and remainder. See left.

5. Suppose $f(x) = d(x) \cdot q(x) + r(x), f(x) = x^2 + 3x + 7$, and $d(x) = x + 2$. Find possible polynomials for $q(x)$ and $r(x)$. $q(x) = x + 1, r(x) = 5$

6. The input and output of a symbol manipulator are given below. Identify the dividend, divisor, quotient, and remainder. See left.

INPUT	OUTPUT
Prop Frac $\dfrac{3b^5 + 16b^3 - 27b - 50}{b^3 - 7}$	$\dfrac{21 \cdot b^2 - 27 \cdot b + 62}{b^3 - 7} + 3 \cdot b^2 + 16$

In 7 and 8, two polynomials are given. **a.** Use the Remainder Theorem to find the remainder when the first polynomial is divided by the second. **b.** Check by dividing.

7. $y^3 + 4y^2 - 9y - 40,\ y - 3$ a) -4 b) See left.

8. $2x^3 - 11x^2 - 2x + 5,\ x - 5$ a) -30 b) See left.

Lesson 9-4 Division and the Remainder Theorem **581**

Side notes (left margin)

2) $3z^2 - \frac{3}{2}z - 3$

4) dividend = quotient · divisor + remainder; $\frac{dividend}{divisor}$ = quotient + $\frac{remainder}{divisor}$

6) dividend = $3b^5 + 16b^3 - 27b - 50$; divisor = $b^3 - 7$; quotient = $3b^2 + 16$; remainder = $21b^2 - 27b + 62$

7b) $y^3 + 4y^2 - 9y - 40 = (y^2 + 7y + 12) \cdot (y - 3) - 4$

8b) $2x^3 - 11x^2 - 2x + 5 = (2x^2 - x - 7) \cdot (x - 5) - 30$

Notes on Questions

Question 2 Error Alert Some students may stop when a fraction appears in the quotient. You may have to tell them to continue. Additional Example 2 is another quotient of this type.

Question 3 Part a should be applied to make **part b** easier.

Adapting to Individual Needs

Extra Help
Students may benefit from an elaboration of some of the steps of division of polynomials developed in the lesson. You may wish to point out that some books write the quotient as far to the left as possible above the dividend. In this book, the terms of the quotient are put above the corresponding terms of the dividend to parallel the way it is done with integer long division. Emphasize this format to help students make the connection.

Challenge
Have students determine whether the following statement is *true* or *false* and justify their response:
  Suppose r is the remainder when the polynomial $f(x)$ is divided by $x - a$ and k is any real number. Then kr is the remainder when $f(x)$ is divided by $x - ka$. [False; sample counterexample: dividing $x^2 + 2x + 1$ by $x - 2$ gives a remainder of 9, but dividing by $x - 3(2)$ gives a remainder of 49, not 3(9).]

Notes on Questions

Question 9 Since the remainder is zero, $x - 85$ is a factor of $f(x)$, a result generalized by the Factor Theorem of the next lesson.

Question 14 The graph of the function g is identical to the graph of $f(x) = x - 4$ except at the single point $(4, 0)$, which is on the graph of f but not on the graph of g.

Question 18 Multicultural Connection The American hot dog is a descendant of the German frankfurter, a highly seasoned mixture of pork and beef sausage.

Question 20 This question can be used as a lead-in to the next lesson. (We expect UCSMP students to have seen the Factor Theorem in a previous course.)

Question 21 This question anticipates work in Lesson 9-8.

11a) $q(a) = a + 5,$
$r(a) = 5a + 15$
b) degree of remainder = 1, degree of divisor = 2
c) $(a^2 - 5)(a + 5) + (5a + 15) = (a^3 + 5a^2 - 5a - 25) + (5a + 15) = a^3 + 5a^2 - 10$

12a) $q(x) = x^3 - 6x^2 + x + 1, r(x) = 0$
b) degree of remainder = 0, degree of divisor = 1
c) $(x^3 - 6x^2 + x + 1) \cdot (x - 3) + 0 = x^4 - 9x^3 + 19x^2 - 2x - 3$

14b) $x^3 - 12x^2 + 48x - 64 = (x - 4) \cdot (x^2 - 8x + 16)$. So, $\dfrac{x^3 - 12x^2 + 48x - 64}{x^2 - 8x + 16} = x - 4$ for all $x \neq 4$.

15a)

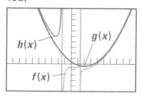

$-10 \le x \le 10,$ x-scale = 1
$-50 \le y \le 100,$ y-scale = 10

17a)

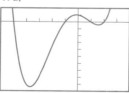

$-6 \le x \le 4,$ x-scale = 1
$-100 \le y \le 20,$ y-scale = 10

b) increasing:
$-3.7 < x < -0.1$
on $x > 1.6$
decreasing:
$x < -3.7$ or
$-0.1 < x < 1.6$
c) positive: $x < -5$ or
$-1 < x < 1$ or $x > 2$
negative: $-5 < x < -1$
or $1 < x < 2$

9. Suppose you know that when $f(x)$ is divided by $x - 85$, the remainder is zero. What is $f(85)$? $f(85) = 0$

Applying the Mathematics

10. Let $f(x) = x^5 - 32$ and $g(x) = x - 2$.
  a. Express $\dfrac{f(x)}{g(x)}$ as a polynomial in simplest terms. $x^4 + 2x^3 + 4x^2 + 8x + 16$
  b. The expression in part **a** is a finite geometric series. Identify the first term and the common ratio of the series. $t_1 = x^4, r = \dfrac{2}{x}$

In 11 and 12, two polynomials are given. **a.** Find the quotient and remainder when the first polynomial is divided by the second. **b.** Show that the degree of the remainder is less than the degree of the divisor. **c.** Check by multiplying the divisor by the quotient and then adding the remainder. **See left.**

11. $a^3 + 5a^2 - 10, a^2 - 5$ **12.** $x^4 - 9x^3 + 19x^2 - 2x - 3, x - 3$

13. What is the quotient if $x^3 + 2x^2y - 2xy^2 - y^3$ is divided by $x - y$?
$x^2 + 3xy + y^2$

14. Consider $g(x) = \dfrac{x^3 - 12x^2 + 48x - 64}{x^2 - 8x + 16}$.
  a. *True or false.* For all $x \neq 4$, g is a linear function. **True**
  b. Justify your answer to part **a**. **See left.**

15. a. Refer to Example 3. Use an automatic grapher to plot on the same set of axes
$$f(x) = \frac{2x^4 - 8x^3 + 12}{x^2 - 2}$$
$$g(x) = 2x^2 - 8x + 4$$
and
$$h(x) = 2x^2 - 8x + 4 + \frac{-16x + 20}{x^2 - 2}.$$ See left.
  b. Write several sentences comparing and contrasting the graphs.
  See margin.

Review

16. Consider the table of values below.

x	-1	0	1	2	3	4
y	3	2	3	12	35	78

  a. Find a polynomial function to fit these data. $y = x^3 + x^2 - x + 2$
  b. Find, to the nearest tenth, all zeros of the function in part **a**. -2.0
  c. Find, to the nearest tenth, all relative extrema of the function.
  (Lessons 9-2, 9-3) 3.0, 1.8

17. Let $h(x) = x^4 + 3x^3 - 11x^2 - 3x + 10$. **See left.**
  a. Graph $y = h(x)$ on a window that shows all zeros and relative extrema.
  b. Identify the intervals where h is increasing, and the intervals where h is decreasing.
  c. Identify the intervals where h is positive, and the intervals where it is negative. *(Lesson 9-2)*

Additional Answers

15. b. The graphs of f and h are the same because $\dfrac{2x^4 - 8x^3 + 12}{x^2 - 2} = 2x^2 - 8x + 4 + \dfrac{-16x + 20}{x^2 - 2}$.
g is very close to h for sufficiently large values of x because the remainder will become negligible (as x approaches positive or negative infinity, the denominator will become much larger than the numerator so the fraction will approach zero).

f and h have asymptotes because both functions are undefined at $x = \sqrt{2}$ and $x = -\sqrt{2}$. g does not have these discontinuities.

18. The total daily revenue from a hot dog stand at a ball park is given by the equation $R(x) = x \cdot p(x)$, where x is the number of hot dogs sold and $p(x)$ is the price in cents of one hot dog. The price of a hot dog also depends on x, as given by the equation

$$p(x) = 250 + .002x - .00001x^2.$$

 a. Find a polynomial expression equal to $R(x)$. $250x + 0.002x^2 - 0.00001x^3$
 b. Draw a graph of R on a window that shows all relative extrema and x-intercepts for $x \geq 0$. (Hint: You will need values of x and y larger than 1000.) **See left.**
 c. Determine the number of hot dogs to be sold to produce the maximum daily revenue. ≈ 3000 hot dogs
 d. What is the maximum daily revenue possible? **$500,000**
 e. What is the largest domain on which this model could hold?
 (Lesson 9-2) $\{x: 0 \leq x \leq 5100\}$

18b)

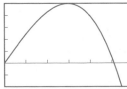

$0 \leq x \leq 6000$, x-scale = 1000
$-200000 \leq y \leq 500000$, y-scale = 100000

19. Let $g(x) = (2ax - 3b)^7$, where a and b are constants.
 (Previous course, Lesson 9-1)
 a. What is the degree of $g(x)$? **7**
 b. What is the leading coefficient of $g(x)$? **$128a^7$**
 c. What is the constant term of $g(x)$? **$-2187b^7$**

20. Consider $f(x) = 6x^2 + 13x - 5$.
 a. Solve $f(x) = 0$. $x = 0.\overline{3}$ or $x = -2.5$
 b. Factor $f(x)$. $f(x) = (3x - 1)(2x + 5)$
 c. State a relationship between the results of parts **a** and **b**.
 (Previous course)
 $(x - a)$ is a factor of $f(x)$ if and only if $f(a) = 0$

Exploration

21. a. Divide each polynomial by $x - y$.
 i. $x^3 - y^3$ $x^2 + xy + y^2$
 ii. $x^5 - y^5$ $x^4 + x^3y + x^2y^2 + xy^3 + y^4$
 iii. $x^7 - y^7$ $x^6 + x^5y + x^4y^2 + x^3y^3 + x^2y^4 + xy^5 + y^6$
 iv. $x^9 - y^9$ $x^8 + x^7y + x^6y^2 + x^5y^3 + x^4y^4 + x^3y^5 + x^2y^6 + xy^7 + y^8$
 b. Generalize the pattern above.
 $$\frac{x^n - y^n}{x - y} = \sum_{i=0}^{n-1} x^{n-1-i} y^i$$

Follow-up 9-4 for Lesson

Practice

For more questions on SPUR Objectives, use **Lesson Master 9-4** (shown on page 579).

Assessment

Written/Oral Communication
Have students **work in pairs**. Have one student use the Remainder Theorem to find the remainder when $x^3 + 2x^2 - x - 7$ is divided by $x + 1$ while the other student finds the remainder by using long division. [-5] Encourage students to discuss their results and resolve any discrepancies. Have students switch roles and repeat the above steps for $4x^5 - 4x^3 - 3x^2 + 22$ divided by $x - 1$. [19]

Extension

You may wish to extend **Question 21** by asking students to divide each of the following polynomials by $(x + y)$. These division problems also preview Lesson 9-8.
1. $x^3 + y^3 \, [x^2 - xy + y^2]$
2. $x^5 + y^5 \, [x^4 - x^3y + x^2y^2 - xy^3 + y^4]$
3. $x^7 + y^7 \, [x^6 - x^5y + x^4y^2 - x^3y^3 + x^2y^4 - xy^5 + y^6]$

Ask students to identify any patterns. [In the quotients, the powers of x decrease while the powers of y increase.] Then ask students if the patterns are similar to the patterns they discovered in **Question 21**. [The pattern of the terms is similar, except the quotients above alternate signs between terms.]

Project Update Project 3, *Synthetic Division*, on page 618, relates to the content of this lesson.

Setting Up Lesson 9-5

Questions 9 and 19 on pages 582–583 can be used as bridges to the next lesson. In each case, the remainder is 0 and so the divisor is found to be a factor of the polynomial.

Objectives

D Factor polynomials and solve polynomial equations using the Factor Theorem.

G Apply the Factor Theorem and the Factor-Solution-Intercept Equivalence Theorem.

K Relate properties of polynomial functions and their graphs.

Resources

From the *Teacher's Resource File*
- Lesson Master 9-5
- Answer Master 9-5
- Teaching Aid 80: Warm-up

Additional Resources
- Visual for Teaching Aid 80

Teaching Lesson 9-5

Warm-up

Let $f(x) = 3x^2 - 40x + 48$.

1. Which of the given polynomials is a factor of $f(x)$? **(e)**
   (a) $x - 2$ (b) $x - 3$
   (c) $x - 4$ (d) $x - 6$
   (e) $x - 12$ (f) $x - 24$

2. Which of the given values equals 0? **(e)**
   (a) $f(2)$ (b) $f(3)$
   (c) $f(4)$ (d) $f(6)$
   (e) $f(12)$ (f) $f(24)$

How Are the Zeros of a Polynomial Function Related to the Factors of the Polynomial?

Consider the following polynomial functions in standard form. A symbol manipulator was used to find the factors of the polynomial and the zeros of the function.

INPUT	OUTPUT
Define $q(x) = x^2 - 3x - 10$	Done
factor($q(x), x$)	$(x - 5) \cdot (x + 2)$
zeros($q(x), x$)	$\{-2 \quad 5\}$

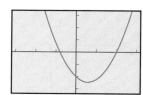

$-8 \le x \le 8$, x-scale $= 2.5$
$-17 \le y \le 17$, y-scale $= 5$

Define $r(x) = x^3 + x^2 - 12x$	Done
factor($r(x), x$)	$x \cdot (x - 3) \cdot (x + 4)$
zeros($r(x), x$)	$\{-4 \quad 0 \quad 3\}$

$-8 \le x \le 8$, x-scale $= 2.5$
$-75 \le y \le 75$, y-scale $= 25$

Define $s(x) = 2x^4 - 5x^3 - 57x^2 + 90x$	Done
factor($s(x), x$)	$x \cdot (x - 6) \cdot (x + 5) \cdot (2 \cdot x - 3)$
zeros($s(x), x$)	$\{-5 \quad 0 \quad \frac{3}{2} \quad 6\}$

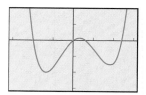

$-8 \le x \le 8$, x-scale $= 2.5$
$-800 \le y \le 500$, y-scale $= 250$

The relations between the standard forms of the polynomials and the zeros are subtle. However, when looking at the *factored* forms and the zeros a pattern emerges: each zero c of the polynomial appears to correspond with a linear factor $(x - c)$.

This result holds for all polynomials and can be proved using the Remainder Theorem from Lesson 9-4.

Lesson 9-5 Overview

Broad Goals In this lesson, the Factor Theorem is proven and applied.

Perspective A number c is a solution to a polynomial equation $p(x) = 0$ if and only if $x - c$ is a factor of $p(x)$. This statement, known as the Factor Theorem, enables a factor $x - c$ to be found from a zero of a polynomial $p(x)$. By division, a polynomial function $q(x) = \frac{p(x)}{x - c}$, whose degree is one

less, can be examined for its zeros. Thus the Factor Theorem is a powerful tool for finding more zeros of a polynomial, given that you can find one zero.

In contrast to the delay of polynomial long division, UCSMP texts cover the Factor Theorem early. A Factor Theorem for Quadratics (if r is a solution to $ax^2 + bx + c = 0$, then $x - r$ is a factor of $ax^2 + bx + c$) is given in UCSMP *Algebra* as a powerful

way to factor any quadratic. In UCSMP *Advanced Algebra*, the Factor Theorem is proved using the Graph Translation Theorem.

Students may be surprised that there are many polynomials with particular zeros, as shown in **Example 2**. Point out the analogy with whole numbers: there are many whole numbers with given factors. For instance, some whole numbers with all the factors 3, 7, and 11 are 231, 6930, and 825,132, and

Factor Theorem
For a polynomial $f(x)$, a number c is a solution to $f(x) = 0$ if and only if $(x - c)$ is a factor of f.

Proof
The theorem says "if and only if," so two statements must be proved:
(1) If $(x - c)$ is a factor of f, then c is a solution to $f(x) = 0$.
(2) If c is a solution to $f(x) = 0$, then $(x - c)$ is a factor of f.
In (1), $(x - c)$ is given to be a factor of f. So $f(x) = (x - c)\,q(x)$, where $q(x)$ is a polynomial. In particular, when $x = c$, $f(x) = f(c) = (c - c)q(c) = 0$. So $f(c) = 0$; that is, c is a solution to $f(x) = 0$.

In (2), c is given to be a solution to $f(x) = 0$. Then, by the definition of a solution, $f(c) = 0$. From the Remainder Theorem, $f(x) = (x - c)q(x) + f(c)$, so here $f(x) = (x - c)q(x)$, thus making $(x - c)$ a factor of f.

Graphically, a solution to $f(x) = 0$ is an x-intercept of the graph. Putting this fact together with the Remainder and Factor Theorems produces the following result.

Factor-Solution-Intercept Equivalence Theorem
For any polynomial f, the following are logically equivalent statements.
(1) $(x - c)$ is a factor of f.
(2) $f(c) = 0$.
(3) c is an x-intercept of the graph of $y = f(x)$.
(4) c is a zero of f.
(5) The remainder when $f(x)$ is divided by $(x - c)$ is 0.

Using the Factor Theorem to Factor Polynomials

Example 1

Factor $g(x) = 6x^3 - 25x^2 - 31x + 30$.

Solution

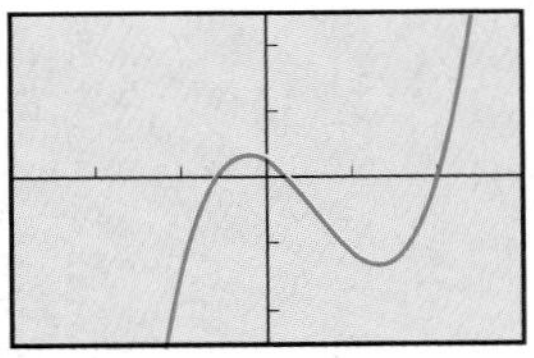

$-7.5 \le x \le 7.5$, x-scale = 2.5
$-250 \le y \le 250$, y-scale = 100

Begin with a graph to see if any zeros are obvious. On the graph at the left, there appears to be a zero at $x = 5$. Verify by substitution:

$$g(5) = 6(5)^3 - 25(5)^2 - 31(5) + 30 = 0.$$

Thus one linear factor is $(x - 5)$. Divide $6x^3 - 25x^2 - 31x + 30$ by this factor to find another factor.

$$\begin{array}{r}
6x^2 + 5x - 6 \\
x - 5\,\overline{)\,6x^3 - 25x^2 - 31x + 30} \\
\underline{6x^3 - 30x^2} \qquad\qquad \\
5x^2 - 31x + 30 \\
\underline{5x^2 - 25x} \quad\; \\
-6x + 30 \\
\underline{-6x + 30} \\
0
\end{array}$$

▸

Notes on Reading

When used with reference to an equation, the words *solution* and *root* are synonyms. A solution to a polynomial equation $p(x) = 0$ is called a *zero* of the polynomial, a *zero* of the polynomial function p, and is an *x-intercept* of its graph. For this reason, when $p(c) = 0$ for some number c, that number may be called a solution to the equation, a root of the equation, a zero of the polynomial, a zero of the polynomial function, or an x-intercept of the graph.

The Factor-Solution-Intercept Equivalence Theorem includes five equivalent statements. The middle three are simply the same statement in different language and thus a consequence of definitions. The first is equivalent to these three due to the Factor Theorem. The last is equivalent to these three because of the Remainder Theorem.

The pattern of the Factor Theorem is quite simple and easily learned when the zero is an integer. Both **Examples 1–2** involve rational zeros, and students should realize that if $\frac{a}{b}$ is a zero to a polynomial equation with integer coefficients, not only is $(x - \frac{a}{b})$ a factor of the polynomial, but so is $(bx - a)$. Still, students may not realize the generality of the theorem, so you may wish to mention zeros that are not rational. (See the Extension for this lesson.) In the next lesson, the Factor Theorem will be applied to zeros that are not real numbers.

in general any such whole number is of the form $231k$, when k is a whole number.

Optional Activities

If you use this activity, do not assign **Question 9** on page 588. Have students **work in groups** to describe different methods for answering **Question 9**. Then have the groups share their conclusions with the class. [Graph the polynomial to identify zeros, or substitute values ±2, ±1 into the polynomial to see which produce zeros.] Promote a generalized discussion by asking students how to factor any polynomial. [Graph the polynomial to identify zeros and then factors, or substitute values into the polynomial to find zeros and then factors, or use a combination of these two methods. The quadratic formula can also be used on quadratic factors.]

▶

The quotient $6x^2 + 5x - 6$ is a second factor. This polynomial can be factored into a product of binomials.

$$6x^2 + 5x - 6 = (2x + 3)(3x - 2)$$

So
$$g(x) = (x - 5)(6x^2 + 5x - 6)$$
$$= (x - 5)(2x + 3)(3x - 2).$$

Check 1

Multiply the factors.

$$(x - 5)(2x + 3)(3x - 2) = (2x^2 - 7x - 15)(3x - 2)$$
$$= 6x^3 - 21x^2 - 45x - 4x^2 + 14x + 30$$
$$= 6x^3 - 25x^2 - 31x + 30$$
$$= g(x)$$

Check 2

Check the zeros of g. In the solution above, $g(5)$ was shown to equal 0. By the Factor Theorem, the factor $(2x + 3)$ corresponds to a zero of $-\frac{3}{2}$, and the factor $(3x - 2)$ corresponds to a zero of $\frac{2}{3}$. These appear to be x-intercepts on the graph. Substitute to show that $g\left(\frac{2}{3}\right) = 0$ and $g\left(-\frac{3}{2}\right) = 0$.

Finding Polynomials When Their Zeros Are Known

The Factor Theorem can also be used to find equations of polynomials, given their zeros.

Example 2

Find an equation for a polynomial function with zeros -1, $\frac{4}{5}$, and $-\frac{8}{3}$.

Solution

Each zero indicates a factor of the polynomial. Call the polynomial $p(x)$. Then $p(x)$ has factors $(x + 1)$, $\left(x - \frac{4}{5}\right)$, and $\left(x + \frac{8}{3}\right)$. It may have other factors as well. Then $p(x) = k(x + 1)\left(x - \frac{4}{5}\right)\left(x + \frac{8}{3}\right)$ where k may be any nonzero constant or polynomial in x.

Check

Substitute -1 for x. Is $p(-1) = 0$?

$$p(-1) = k(-1 + 1)\left(-1 - \frac{4}{5}\right)\left(-1 + \frac{8}{3}\right)$$

The second factor is zero, so the product is zero.
Similarly, $p\left(\frac{4}{5}\right) = 0$ and $p\left(-\frac{8}{3}\right) = 0$.

Notice that the degree of $p(x)$ in Example 2 is at least 3. However, the degree of k is not known, so the degree of $p(x)$ cannot be determined, nor can the coefficients of its terms. Graphs of many polynomials go through

Notes on Reading

If you discuss **Example 1**, point out that it is possible that one of the other zeros, $\frac{-3}{2}$ or $\frac{2}{3}$, might have been seen first from the graph. If so, the division would have resulted in a quadratic whose solutions are the other two zeros. There is an analogy with the factorization of integers into primes; regardless of which factor is found first, the ultimate factorization has the same factors.

Additional Examples

1. Factor $12x^3 - 41x^2 + 13x + 6$ by first finding one zero of the polynomial by graphing and then dividing to find the others. $(x - 3)(4x + 1)(3x - 2)$; it is easiest to find the zero 3 by graphing.

2. Find an equation for a polynomial function p with zeros 2, -4, and $\frac{4}{7}$. $p(x) = k(x - 2)(x + 4)\left(x - \frac{4}{7}\right)$ or $p(x) = k(x - 2)(x + 4)(7x - 4)$, where k is any nonzero polynomial.

Adapting to Individual Needs

Extra Help

Some students may be confused by the case when r is negative when they apply the Factor Theorem. Remind students that if $r = -2$, then $x - r = x - (-2) = x + 2$. So, if $(x + 2)$ is a factor, then -2 is a root.

the points $(-1, 0)$, $\left(\frac{4}{5}, 0\right)$, and $\left(-\frac{8}{3}, 0\right)$. Below are graphs of three different polynomials, two of degree 3 and one of degree 4, all with zeros of -1, $\frac{4}{5}$, and $-\frac{8}{3}$.

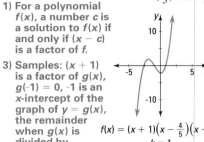

$f(x) = (x + 1)\left(x - \frac{4}{5}\right)\left(x + \frac{8}{3}\right)$
$k = 1$

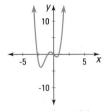

$g(x) = -3(x + 1)\left(x - \frac{4}{5}\right)\left(x + \frac{8}{3}\right)$
$k = -3$

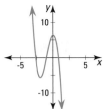

$h(x) = x(x + 1)\left(x - \frac{4}{5}\right)\left(x + \frac{8}{3}\right)$
$k = x$

1) For a polynomial $f(x)$, a number c is a solution to $f(x)$ if and only if $(x - c)$ is a factor of f.

3) Samples: $(x + 1)$ is a factor of $g(x)$, $g(-1) = 0$, -1 is an x-intercept of the graph of $y = g(x)$, the remainder when $g(x)$ is divided by $(x + 1)$ is 0.

4) Samples: $(x + 2)$ is a factor of $h(x)$, $h(-2) = 0$, -2 is a zero of $h(x)$, the remainder when $h(x)$ is divided by $(x + 2)$ is 0.

5)

-10 ≤ x ≤ 10, x-scale = 1
-200 ≤ y ≤ 50, y-scale = 25

6)

-14 ≤ x ≤ 10, x-scale = 2
-200 ≤ y ≤ 700, y-scale = 100

7a)

QUESTIONS

Covering the Reading

1. State the Factor Theorem. **See left.**

2. If $f(x) = x^3 - 3x^2 + 6x - 18$ has a factor of $(x - 3)$, what must be true about $f(3)$? **f(3) = 0**

In 3 and 4, one fact is stated about a polynomial. State at least two other conclusions you can draw. **See left.**

3. -1 is a solution to $g(x) = x^4 - x^3 + 3x^2 + 3x - 2 = 0$.

4. The graph of $h(x) = x^6 + x^5 - 2x^4$ crosses the x-axis at $x = -2$.

In 5 and 6, find the zeros of the polynomial function by graphing. Use this information to factor the polynomial into linear factors. **See left for graphs.**

5. $r(x) = 7x^3 - 22x^2 - 67x + 10$ **See below.**

6. $t(x) = 3x^3 + 20x^2 - 108x - 80$ **See below.**

7. Corina used a symbol manipulator to factor $g(x) = 3x^3 + 4x^2 - 17x - 6$ as shown below.

INPUT	OUTPUT
factor $(3x^3 + 4x^2 - 17x - 6)$	$(x - 2) \cdot (x + 3) \cdot (3x + 1)$

  a. Graph $y = g(x)$ and $f(x) = (x + 3)(x - 2)(3x + 1)$ on the same set of axes. **See left.**
  b. Is Corina's factorization correct? **Yes**

8. Find an equation for a polynomial function with zeros equal to -5, $\frac{9}{2}$, and $\frac{7}{3}$.
   Sample: $y = (x + 5)\left(x - \frac{9}{2}\right)\left(x - \frac{7}{3}\right)$ or $y = (x + 5)(2x - 9)(3x - 7) = 6x^3 - 11x^2 - 142x + 315$

5) zeros at $x = -2$, $x = \frac{1}{7}$, $x = 5$; $r(x) = (x + 2)(7x - 1)(x - 5)$

6) zeros at $x = -10$, $x = -\frac{2}{3}$, $x = 4$; $t(x) = (x + 10)(3x + 2)(x - 4)$

Lesson 9-5 *The Factor Theorem* **587**

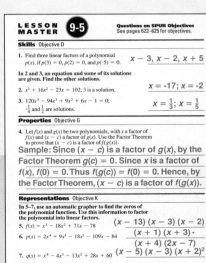

Questions 11 and 18 Error Alert
These may cause more difficulty simply because the letter *x* is not used. Stress that students need to be flexible enough to handle the manipulations regardless of the name of the variable.

Question 19 There are hexagonal numbers, heptagonal numbers, and so on..., found by considering points on the sides of the corresponding regular polygons in the same manner as is done here.

Question 21 Sports Connection
Pete Sampras did even better at Wimbledon in 1997. In winning his fourth All England Club men's singles title he won on 66% of his first serves, and double-faulted only twice in 118 service games.

Applying the Mathematics

9. Consider the polynomial $x^3 + 6x^2 + 3x - 10$. Without dividing, which two of $(x + 2)$, $(x - 2)$, $(x + 1)$, and $(x - 1)$ must be factors of the polynomial? **$(x + 2)$ and $(x - 1)$**

In 10 and 11, an equation and some of its solutions are given. Find the other solutions.

10. $4x^3 + 20x^2 - 68x - 84 = 0$; -1 is one solution. **$x = 3$ or $x = -7$**

11. $2p^4 + 13p^3 + 12p^2 - 17p - 10 = 0$; 1 and $-\frac{1}{2}$ are solutions. **$p = -2$ or $p = -5$**

In 12 and 13, a graph of a polynomial function with integer zeros is given. Find an equation of the given degree for the graph.

12. degree 3

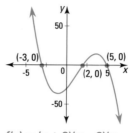

$f(x) = (x + 3)(x - 2)(x - 5)$
$= x^3 - 4x^2 - 11x + 30$

13. degree 4

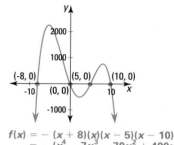

$f(x) = -(x + 8)(x)(x - 5)(x - 10)$
$= -(x^4 - 7x^3 - 70x^2 + 400x)$

Review

14. If a polynomial $g(x)$ is divided by ___?___, then the remainder is $g(a)$. *(Lesson 9-4)* **$(x - a)$**

15. Suppose $m(x) = x^5 - x^3 + 3x$. Without dividing, find the remainder when $m(x)$ is divided by $x + 4$. *(Lesson 9-4)* **-972**

16. *Multiple choice.* A polynomial $q(x)$ is divided by $x + 3$ and the remainder is 7. Which of the following points must be on the graph of $q(x)$? *(Lesson 9-4)* **a**
(a) $(-3, 7)$
(b) $(7, -3)$
(c) $(-3, 0)$
(d) $(7, 0)$
(e) none of these

In 17 and 18, find the quotient when the first polynomial is divided by the second. *(Lesson 9-4)*

17. $x^5 + 243$; $x + 3$ **$x^4 - 3x^3 + 9x^2 - 27x + 81$**

18. $y^5 + 2y^4 - 7y^3 - 14y^2$; $y^2 - 7$ **$y^3 + 2y^2$**

Adapting to Individual Needs

Challenge
For each of the following polynomials, have students: find $q(x)$ so that $f(x) = (x - 3)(q(x)) + r$; indicate whether any coefficients of $q(x)$ are negative and whether r is negative; and use a graphing calculator to conjecture whether $f(x)$ has any zeros greater than 3.

1. $f(x) = 2x^3 + 3x^2 - 5x + 3$
   $[q(x) = 2x^2 + 9x + 22$; all nonnegative; no]

2. $f(x) = x^4 + 2x^3 - 2x^2 + 3x - 9$
   $[q(x) = x^3 + 5x^2 + 13x + 42$; all nonnegative; no]

3. $f(x) = x^5 + 2x^2 - 2x + 6$
   $[q(x) = x^4 + 3x^3 + 9x^2 + 29x + 85$; all nonnegative; no]

4. Prove the following: If $f(x)$ is a polynomial with only real coefficients and $q(x)$ is the quotient polynomial when $f(x)$ is divided by $x - a$ for the positive number a, then $f(x)$ has no zeros greater than a

if the remainder is nonnegative and $q(x)$ has all nonnegative coefficients.
$[f(x) = (x - a)q(x) + r$. If $q(x)$ has all nonnegative terms and r is nonnegative, then $(x - a)q(x) + r$ is positive for all values of x greater than a. So $f(x)$ has no zeros greater than a.]

19a) 1st differences: 4, 7, 10; 2nd differences: 3, 3

c)

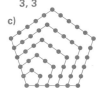

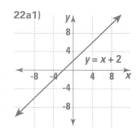

19. Pentagonal numbers $p(n)$ are the numbers of dots in the sequence of figures beginning with those pictured below. *(Lessons 2-6, 9-3)*

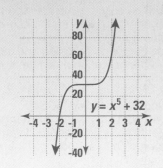

$p(1) = 1$ $p(2) = 5$ $p(3) = 12$ $p(4) = 22$

a. Show that there is a polynomial of degree 2 which generates these pentagonal numbers. **See left.**
b. Determine the quadratic polynomial $p(n)$. $p(n) = \frac{3}{2}n^2 - \frac{1}{2}n$
c. Use the polynomial of part **b** to calculate $p(5)$ and $p(6)$, and verify your answer geometrically. $p(5) = 35$, $p(6) = 51$
See left for diagram.

22a1)

$y = x + 2$

20. At the right is a graph of a polynomial $y = f(x)$.
a. Identify the zeros of f. m, p, r
b. Identify the relative extrema. $f(n), f(q)$
c. In what interval(s) is f increasing? $x < n, x > q$
d. In what interval(s) is f decreasing? $n < x < q$
e. In what interval(s) is f positive?
f. In what interval(s) is f negative?
(Lesson 9-2)
e) $m < x < p, x > r$ **f)** $x < m, p < x < r$

21. At some point during the men's final match in the 1996 U.S. Open tennis tournament, Pete Sampras had the following statistics.
   First serve in: 54%
   First serve points won: 84%
   Second serve points won: 58%
Assuming that he had not double faulted (missed both serves) up to that point, what was the probability that, next time he served, Sampras did the following?
a. got his first serve in **0.54**
b. got his first serve in and won the point $\approx$ **0.45**
c. got his second serve in **0.46**
d. got his second serve in and lost the point $\approx$ **0.19**
e. lost the point   *(Lesson 7-1)* $\approx$ **0.28**

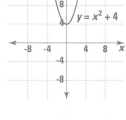

$y = x^2 + 4$

Exploration

22. a. Graph $y = x + 2$ **See left.**
           $y = x^2 + 4$ **See left.**
           $y = x^3 + 8$ **See left.**
           $y = x^4 + 16$ **See margin.**   **See margin.**
and $y = x^n + 2^n$ for two integer values of $n \geq 5$ of your choice.
b. For what values of n does $y = x^n + 2^n$ seem to have zeros? For these values of n, what binomial is a factor of $x^n + 2^n$?
odd values of n; $(x + 2)$

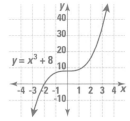

$y = x^3 + 8$

Additional Answers
22. a4

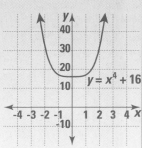

$y = x^4 + 16$

22. a5 Sample: $n = 5$

$y = x^5 + 32$

Follow-up for Lesson **9-5**

Practice
For more questions on SPUR Objectives, use **Lesson Master 9-5** (shown on page 587).

Assessment
Oral Communication Write three different zeros on the chalk board. Choose two or three students to come to the board and write a polynomial function with those zeros. Have the other students in the class use an automatic grapher to check their classmates' work. Have all students discuss and recommend necessary corrections. If any of the functions are the same, have the class work together to write different functions. [Students find polynomials given their zeros and determine zeros from the graphs of polynomial functions.]

Extension
The quadratic equation $x^2 + x - 1 = 0$ has solutions $x = \frac{-1 \pm \sqrt{5}}{2}$. Thus, by the Factor Theorem, $x^2 + x - 1 =$
$\left(x - \frac{-1 + \sqrt{5}}{2}\right)\left(x - \frac{-1 - \sqrt{5}}{2}\right) =$
$\left(x + \frac{1}{2} - \frac{\sqrt{5}}{2}\right) \cdot \left(x + \frac{1}{2} + \frac{\sqrt{5}}{2}\right)$. Have students use this idea to make up and factor other quadratics whose solutions are not rational.

Project Update Project 3, *Synthetic Division*, and Project 5, *Algebraic and Transcendental Numbers*, on page 618, relate to the content of this lesson.

Setting Up Lesson 9-6
The number i is a solution to $x^2 + 1 = 0$. Ask students: Then, according to the Factor Theorem, what polynomial is a factor of $x^2 + 1$? [$x - i$]. What is the other factor? [$x + i$].What root to the original equation is determined by this other factor? [$-i$]

589

D Factor polynomials and solve polynomial equations using the Factor Theorem.
E Perform operations with complex numbers.

Resources

From the *Teacher's Resource File*
- Lesson Master 9-6
- Answer Master 9-6
- Teaching Aids
  80 Warm-up
  83 The Complex Number System

Additional Resources
- Visuals for Teaching Aids 80, 83

Teaching **9-6**
Lesson

Warm-up
Use the binomial theorem to calculate $(2 + 2i)^4$. **-64**

The Number i

Consider the polynomial $f(x) = x^2 + 1$. Its zeros are the solutions to $x^2 + 1 = 0$ or, more simply, $x^2 = -1$. Does this sentence have any solutions?

That depends on the domain of available numbers. If x is a real number, $x^2 = -1$ has no solution, since the square of any real number is either positive or zero. The graph at the right verifies that $f(x) = x^2 + 1$ has no real zeros, because its graph does not cross the x-axis.

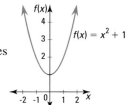

However, it is possible to define solutions to $x^2 + 1 = 0$ that are not real numbers. Because $x^2 = -1$, these solutions are called *the square roots of negative 1*. One of these solutions is denoted as $\sqrt{-1}$. It is customary also to call this number i.

Definition

$$i = \sqrt{-1}$$

The number i and its nonzero real number multiples bi are called **imaginary numbers** because when they were first used, mathematicians had no concrete way of representing them. They are, nevertheless, a reality in mathematics, and many important applications have been found for them.

❶ Clearly, $i^2 = -1$. Note that if we assume that properties of real numbers can be extended to i, then it is also true that

$$(-i)^2 = (-i) \cdot (-i) = -1 \cdot i \cdot -1 \cdot i = -1 \cdot -1 \cdot i \cdot i = 1 \cdot i^2 = 1 \cdot -1 = -1.$$

Thus, in the domain of imaginary numbers, the polynomial $f(x) = x^2 + 1$ has two zeros, i and $-i$. You can verify this by applying the Quadratic Formula to the equation $x^2 + 1 = 0$.

Square Roots of Negative Numbers

If operations with imaginary numbers are assumed to satisfy the commutative and associative properties of multiplication, the square root of any negative number can be expressed as a multiple of i. Example 1 gives an instance.

Lesson 9-6 Overview

Broad Goals This lesson reviews the four fundamental operations with complex numbers and shows students how to rewrite the nonreal solutions to quadratic equations in $a + bi$ form.

Perspective A complex number is defined here to be a number of the form $a + bi$, where a and b are real and $i^2 = -1$. We assume that complex numbers satisfy the field properties; this enables them to be

operated with as polynomials are, and so the rules for operating with them become theorems rather than definitions. The geometry of these numbers (graphing and interpretations of the operations) can be found in Lesson 13-6.

Students who have studied UCSMP *Advanced Algebra* have seen this content. If your students have never studied complex numbers, then plan to spend more than one

day on this lesson— perhaps three days on this and Lesson 9-7 together.

Example 1

Show that a square root of -5 is $i\sqrt{5}$.

Solution

Multiply $i\sqrt{5}$ by itself.

$i\sqrt{5} \cdot i\sqrt{5} = i \cdot i \cdot \sqrt{5}\sqrt{5} = i^2 \cdot 5 = -1 \cdot 5 = -5$

In general, if k is a positive real number, then $\sqrt{-k} = i\sqrt{k}$, so the square root of any negative number is the product of i and a real number. This means that all equations of the form $x^2 + k = 0$, with $k > 0$, have two solutions, $i\sqrt{k}$ and $-i\sqrt{k}$.

Operations with Complex Numbers

When an imaginary number is added to a real number, the sum is a *complex number*.

> **Definitions**
> A **complex number** is a number of the form $a + bi$, where a and b are real numbers and $i = \sqrt{-1}$. The number a is the **real part** and b is the **imaginary part** of $a + bi$.

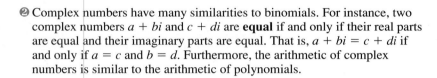

② Complex numbers have many similarities to binomials. For instance, two complex numbers $a + bi$ and $c + di$ are **equal** if and only if their real parts are equal and their imaginary parts are equal. That is, $a + bi = c + di$ if and only if $a = c$ and $b = d$. Furthermore, the arithmetic of complex numbers is similar to the arithmetic of polynomials.

Example 2

Let $z = 4 + 5i$ and $w = 2 - 3i$. Express each of the following in $a + bi$ form.

a. $z + w$ **b.** $z - w$ **c.** zw **d.** $\frac{z}{2}$

Solution

a. $z + w = (4 + 5i) + (2 - 3i)$
$= (4 + 2) + (5i - 3i)$
$= 6 + 2i$

b. $z - w = (4 + 5i) - (2 - 3i)$
$= 4 + 5i - 2 + 3i$
$= (4 - 2) + (5i + 3i)$
$= 2 + 8i$

c. $zw = (4 + 5i)(2 - 3i)$
$= (4)(2) - (4)(3i) + (5i)(2) - (5i)(3i)$
$= 8 - 12i + 10i - 15i^2$
$= 8 - 2i - 15\,(i^2)$ Use $i^2 = -1$.
$= 8 - 2i - 15(-1)$
$= 23 - 2i$

d. $\frac{z}{2} = \frac{4 + 5i}{2} = \frac{4}{2} + \frac{5}{2}i = 2 + \frac{5}{2}i$

Some books define the imaginary part of $a + bi$ to be bi, and not b. We view that as an inappropriate definition; as ordered pairs in rectangular coordinates, $a + bi = (a, b)$ and no i is needed in the description of the complex number.

Some books label *all* complex numbers as imaginary numbers.

❶ Mathematics Connection
Quaternions are an extension of complex numbers, and are of the form $a + bi + cj + dk$ where $a, b, c,$ and d are real and $i^2 = j^2 = k^2 = ijk = -1$. They cannot be ordered, and multiplication is not commutative ($ij = -ji = k$) but any polynomial equation with quaternion coefficients has a quaternion root. For many years they were widely used to solve physical problems. You may wish to have students do the *Extension* on page 595 to further explore this topic.

Examples 1 and 4 stress the definition of i as $\sqrt{-1}$. However, **Examples 2–3** give straightforward computations with complex numbers. The theorem preceding **Example 3** shows that polynomials that cannot be factored into polynomials with real coefficients can be factored into polynomials with nonreal coefficients.

❷ Emphasize the comment before **Example 2.** Students can and should rely on their knowledge of manipulating binomials to do the operations—they do not need to memorize new formulas. In a sense the only new mathematics in this lesson is the definition of i.

Optional Activities

After discussing the complex number system, have students give several examples of each type of number listed in the chart on the bottom of page 593. You may wish to take this opportunity to review the definitions of rational and irrational numbers. [Rational numbers can be expressed as a quotient of two integers; irrational numbers cannot. Many students, even advanced ones, tend to gloss over this definition and define rational numbers as "decimals."]

Notes on Reading
Teaching Aid 83 contains the complex number system.

③ Students know many types of numbers, and some of these can be easily added to the chart at the bottom of page 593. A box for "prime numbers" could be added below the box for natural numbers. A box for "nonreal numbers" may be inserted between the boxes for complex numbers and imaginary numbers. Project 5, *Algebraic and Transcendental Numbers,* on page 618, discusses two types of irritional numbers; these could be aded to the chart underneath the box for irrational numbers. Whole numbers could branch off of integers; positive numbers and negative numbers could branch off of real numbers.

The example illustrates the following theorem:

> **Theorem**
> Given two complex numbers $a + bi$ and $c + di$ and real number r, then:
>
> $$(a + bi) + (c + di) = (a + c) + (b + d)i \qquad \text{complex addition}$$
> $$(a + bi)(c + di) = (ac - bd) + (ad + bc)i \qquad \text{complex multiplication}$$
> $$\frac{a + bi}{r} = \frac{a}{r} + \frac{b}{r}i. \qquad \text{complex division by any real number } r$$

It is not necessary to memorize this theorem. Simply remember to operate as you do with binomials: combine like terms when adding and use the distributive property when multiplying.

Conjugate Factors

Just as finding solutions to equations depends on the domain of allowable numbers, so does factoring. The binomial $x^2 - 9$ can be factored over the set of polynomials with integer coefficients: $x^2 - 9 = (x + 3)(x - 3)$. In contrast, $x^2 - 5$ cannot be factored over the set of polynomials with integer coefficients. But it can be factored over the set of polynomials with real coefficients into $(x - \sqrt{5})(x + \sqrt{5})$. Finally, $x^2 + 14$ cannot be factored over either of these sets; it is factorable over the set of polynomials with complex number coefficients, into $(x - i\sqrt{14})(x + i\sqrt{14})$. The factorization of $x^2 + 14$ suggests that with the introduction of complex numbers, the sum of two squares can be factored.

> **Theorem**
> If a and b are real numbers, then
> $$a^2 + b^2 = (a + bi)(a - bi).$$

> **Proof**
> Multiply the factors, using the distributive property.
> $$(a + bi)(a - bi) = a^2 - abi + abi - (b^2 i^2)$$
> $$= a^2 - b^2(-1)$$
> $$= a^2 + b^2$$

If a and b are real numbers, the complex numbers $a + bi$ and $a - bi$ are called **complex conjugates** of each other. As the preceding proof confirms, the product of complex conjugates is a real number.

Complex conjugates are useful in performing division of complex numbers.

> ### Example 3
> Express $\frac{3 - 4i}{6 + i}$ in $a + bi$ form.

▶

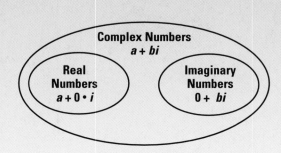

Solution

When the denominator is multiplied by its complex conjugate, the result is a real number. So multiply numerator and denominator by the complex conjugate of the denominator.

$$\frac{3-4i}{6+i} = \frac{3-4i}{6+i} \cdot \frac{6-i}{6-i} = \frac{14-27i}{36+1} = \frac{14}{37} - \frac{27}{37}i$$

Check

Multiply the quotient by the divisor.

$$\left(\frac{14}{37} - \frac{27}{37}i\right)(6+i) = \frac{1}{37}(14-27i)(6+i)$$

$$= \frac{1}{37}(84 + 14i - 162i - 27i^2)$$

$$= \frac{1}{37}(111 - 148i) = 3 - 4i$$

Complex numbers make possible the solution of all quadratic equations.

Example 4

Solve $x^2 - 4x + 13 = 0$.

Solution

Use the quadratic formula.

$$x = \frac{4 \pm \sqrt{16 - 4(1)(13)}}{2(1)} = \frac{4 \pm \sqrt{-36}}{2}$$

$$= \frac{4 \pm 6i}{2} = 2 \pm 3i$$

Note that the two solutions are complex conjugates. Recall that $b^2 - 4ac$ is the *discriminant* of the quadratic $ax^2 + bx + c = 0$. In general, if a quadratic equation with real coefficients has a negative discriminant, then the two solutions are complex conjugates of each other.

Both the Factor and the Remainder Theorems hold for complex numbers. For instance, $-i$ is a solution to the equation $x^2 + 1 = 0$, and $x + i$ is a factor of $x^2 + 1$.

❸ How Are Various Types of Numbers Related to Each Other?

For the complex number $a + bi$, if $a = 0$, then $a + bi = 0 + bi = bi$, so every imaginary number is also complex. Similarly, for any real number a, $a = a + 0i$. Thus, every real number is also complex. The diagram below shows the way that many types of numbers are related.

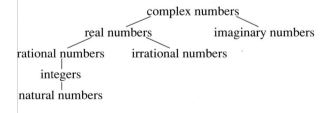

Lesson 9-6 *Complex Numbers* **593**

Adapting to Individual Needs

Challenge

Have students apply the remainder theorem to find the remainder when $2x^{93} + 3x^{52} - 5x + 3$ is divided by $x - i$. $[6 - 3i]$

---

7) $(i\sqrt{7})^2 = i^2 \cdot 7 =$ $-1 \cdot 7 = -7$; $(-i\sqrt{7})^2 =$ $(-i)^2 \cdot 7 = -1 \cdot 7 = -7$

18a) $(x + 5i)(x - 5i)$
b) $(x + 5i)(x - 5i) =$ $x^2 - 5ix + 5ix - 25i^2$ $= x^2 + 25$

19a) $9(z^2 + 2) =$ $9(z + i\sqrt{2})$ $(z - i\sqrt{2})$
b) $9(z + i\sqrt{2})$ $(z - i\sqrt{2}) =$ $9(z^2 - zi\sqrt{2} +$ $zi\sqrt{2} - 2i^2) =$ $9(z^2 + 2) = 9z^2 + 18$

20b) $x = 1 + 5i$ or $x = 1 - 5i$
c) They are complex conjugates.

21b) $x = \frac{2}{3} + 5i$ or $x = \frac{2}{3} - 5i$
c) They are complex conjugates.

22)

QUESTIONS

Covering the Reading

In 1–6, simplify.

1. $\sqrt{-25}$ *5i*

2. $\sqrt{-8}$ *2i√2*

3. $(7i)^2$ *-49*

4. i^3 *-i*

5. i^4 *1*

6. $(-i)^6$ *-1*

7. Show that $i\sqrt{7}$ and $-i\sqrt{7}$ are each square roots of -7. *See left.*

8. A complex number is a number of the form **a.** where a and b are **b.** numbers. *a) a + bi* *b) real*

9. When are two complex numbers equal? *a + bi = c + di if and only if a = c and b = d.*

10. *True or false.* Every real number is a complex number. *True*

11. Give the conjugate.
a. $2 - 3i$ *2 + 3i*
b. $6i + 5$ *-6i + 5*

12. Factor $x^2 - 3$ over each set.
a. the set of polynomials with rational coefficients *cannot be factored*
b. the set of polynomials with real coefficients $(x - \sqrt{3})(x + \sqrt{3})$

In 13–17, write in $a + bi$ form.

13. $(4 + 8i) + (-3 - 9i)$ *1 - i*

14. $5(2 - 3i)$ *10 - 15i*

15. $(2 - 3i)(4 + 7i)$ *29 + 2i*

16. $\frac{3 + i}{2 - i}$ *1 + i*

17. $\frac{5 - 3i}{1 + 2i}$ $-\frac{1}{5} - \frac{13}{5}i$

In 18 and 19, a binomial is given. **a.** Factor over the set of polynomials with complex coefficients. **b.** Check by multiplying. *See left.*

18. $x^2 + 25$

19. $9z^2 + 18$

In 20 and 21, an equation is given. **a.** Calculate its discriminant. **b.** Solve and express the solutions in $a + bi$ form. **c.** What relation do the solutions have to one another? *b, c, see left.*

20. $x^2 + -2x + 26 = 0$ *a) -100*

21. $9x^2 + 229 = 12x$ *a) -8100*

22. Refer to Example 4. Graph $f(x) = x^2 - 4x + 13$. What can you say about the graph of a quadratic polynomial if its roots are complex?
See left for graph. The graph does not cross the x-axis.

Applying the Mathematics

23. a. According to the Factor Theorem, if $g(x)$ is a polynomial, a number b is a solution to $g(x) = 0$ if and only if __?__. *(x − b) is a factor of g(x)*
b. Does part **a** hold if b is a nonreal complex number? *Yes*

24. Find the 20th term of the arithmetic sequence
$$2, 5 + i, 8 + 2i, 11 + 3i, \ldots.$$
59 + 19i

25. Let $f(x) = x^2 - 4x + 5$.
   a. Evaluate $f(2 + i)$. $f(2 + i) = 0$
   b. Evaluate $f(2 - i)$. $f(2 - i) = 0$
   c. Use the results of parts **a** and **b** to factor f over the complex numbers.
     $x^2 - 4x + 5 = (x - (2 + i))(x - (2 - i)) = (x - 2 - i)(x - 2 + i)$

26. Use the quadratic formula to factor $x^2 - 2x + 3$ over the complex numbers.
   See left.

26) $(x - (1 + i\sqrt{2})) \cdot$
  $(x - (1 - i\sqrt{2})) =$
  $(x - 1 - i\sqrt{2}) \cdot$
  $(x - 1 + i\sqrt{2})$

27. Let $z = \frac{1}{2} + \frac{\sqrt{3}}{2}i$.

   a. Calculate z^3 and write the result in $a + bi$ form. $-1 + 0i$
   b. Let w be the complex conjugate of z. Calculate w^3. See below.
   c. Both z and w are cube roots of __?__. -1
   d. Find another cube root of the answer to part **c**. -1

b) $w = \frac{1}{2} - \frac{\sqrt{3}}{2}i$; $w^3 = -1 + 0i$

28) Samples: $(x + 2)$ is a factor of $h(x)$; $h(-2) = 0$; -2 is a zero of $h(x)$; the remainder when $h(x)$ is divided by $(x + 2)$ is zero.

29) Samples: $f(x) = (x - 2)(x - 4)\left(x + \frac{6}{5}\right) = x^3 - \frac{24}{5}x^2 + \frac{4}{5}x + \frac{48}{5}$
$g(x) = 10(x - 2)$
$(x - 4)\left(x + \frac{6}{5}\right) = 10x^3 - 48x^2 + 8x + 96$
$h(x) = x^2(x - 2)$
$(x - 4)\left(x + \frac{6}{5}\right) = x^5 - \frac{24}{5}x^4 + \frac{4}{5}x^3 + \frac{48}{5}x^2$

31a) $0 \le P(x_i) \le 1$ for all x_i and $\sum_{i=1}^{8} P(x_i) = 1$.

b)
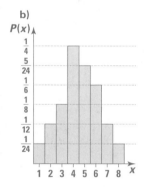

32b) To determine i^m, find the remainder, r, when m is divided by 4. If $r = 0$, $i^m = 1$. If $r = 1$, $i^m = i$. If $r = 2$, $i^m = -1$. If $r = 3$, $i^m = -i$.

Review

28. Let $h(x)$ be a polynomial function whose graph intersects the x-axis at $(-2, 0)$. State at least two conclusions you can make from this information. *(Lesson 9-5)* See left.

29. Identify three different polynomial functions with zeros at 2, 4, and $-\frac{6}{5}$. *(Lesson 9-5)* See left.

30. A wooden cube with edge of length 10 cm has a square hole with edge of length x cm bored through from top to bottom. Give the total surface area of the shape.
(Previous course, Lesson 9-1)
$6(100) + 4(10x) - 2(x^2) = 600 + 40x - 2x^2$

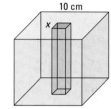
10 cm

31. The following table gives the probability of a spinner landing on each of eight numbers.

Number x_i	1	2	3	4	5	6	7	8
$P(x_i)$	$\frac{1}{24}$	$\frac{1}{12}$	$\frac{1}{8}$	$\frac{1}{4}$	$\frac{5}{24}$	$\frac{1}{6}$	$\frac{1}{12}$	$\frac{1}{24}$

a, b) See left.
   a. Verify that P satisfies the two conditions for a probability distribution.
   b. Draw a histogram of the distribution.
   c. Calculate the mean of the distribution. $\frac{109}{24} \approx 4.54$
   d. Explain what the result in part **c** indicates in terms of the spinner.
    (Lesson 7-6) Over a long period of time, the mean of the numbers the spinner lands on will approach $\frac{109}{24}$.

Exploration

32. Explore patterns in powers of i.
   a. Predict the value of each of i^{1992}, i^{1993}, and i^{2000}. 1, i, 1
   b. Describe in words or in symbols how to evaluate a large power of i.
    See left.

Practice

For more questions on SPUR Objectives, use **Lesson Master 9-6** (shown on page 593).

Assessment

Oral/Written Communication Have students **work in pairs**. Ask each student to write a problem similar to the one in **Example 3**. Then students should solve their partner's problem and check each other's work. Encourage students to discuss and clarify any discrepancies. [Students use complex conjugates to perform division of complex numbers.]

Extension

A student interested in other "numbers" that are not real (nor complex for that matter) might research *quaternions*, and write a brief report. (A quaternion has the form $a + bi + cj + dk$, where a, b, c, and d are real numbers and $i^2 = j^2 = k^2 = ijk = -1$. See Notes on Reading on page 591.) Quaternions were developed in the nineteenth century by the Irish mathematician Sir William Rowan Hamilton.

Project Update Project 5, *Algebraic and Transcendental Numbers*, on page 618, relates to the content of this lesson.

Objectives
F Apply the vocabulary of polynomials.
H Apply the Fundamental Theorem of Algebra and Conjugate Zeros Theorem.
K Relate properties of polynomial functions and their graphs.

Resources
From the **Teacher's Resource File**
■ Lesson Master 9-7
■ Answer Master 9-7
■ Assessment Sourcebook: Quiz for Lessons 9-4 through 9-7
■ Teaching Aids
  81 Warm-up
  84 Zeros of Quadratic Functions

Additional Resources
■ Visuals for Teaching Aids 81, 84

Teaching **9-7**
Lesson

Warm-up
Find a value of k so that the graph of $P(x) = 2x^4 - 5x^2 + k$ intersects the x-axis in the indicated number of points.
1. 1 **Impossible**
4. 4 **Any value of $k < 0$ or $k =$ 3.125**
3. 3 $k = 0$
4. 4 **Any value of k such that $0 < k < 3.125$**
5. 0 **Any value of $k > 3.125$**

LESSON 9-7

The Fundamental Theorem of Algebra

The Number of Zeros of a Quadratic Function

As you know, the solutions to any quadratic equation can be found using the quadratic formula. The graph of a quadratic function intersects the x-axis at two points when there are two real zeros, in exactly one point when there is a single real solution, and does not intersect the x-axis when its zeros are complex. As the table below indicates, the graph of a quadratic function, its discriminant, its zeros, and its factors are related.

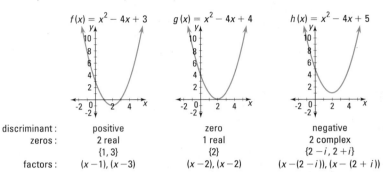

	$f(x) = x^2 - 4x + 3$	$g(x) = x^2 - 4x + 4$	$h(x) = x^2 - 4x + 5$
discriminant:	positive	zero	negative
zeros:	2 real	1 real	2 complex
	$\{1, 3\}$	$\{2\}$	$\{2 - i, 2 + i\}$
factors:	$(x-1), (x-3)$	$(x-2), (x-2)$	$(x-(2-i)), (x-(2+i))$

In general, consider the quadratic function $g(x) = ax^2 + bx + c$ with real coefficients. If the discriminant D is positive, g has two real zeros. If D is zero, g has one real zero, and if D is negative, g has two complex conjugate zeros.

The Number of Zeros of Higher-Degree Polynomial Functions

You may wonder how zeros and graphs of higher-degree polynomial functions are related. For example, are there formulas like the quadratic formula to provide zeros for all higher-degree polynomials? Can all polynomials be decomposed into linear factors as quadratics can? What is the greatest number of zeros a polynomial can have? These questions intrigued mathematicians for centuries.

The Arabian mathematician al'Khowarizmi (from whose name is derived the word "algorithm") is believed to have first discovered the quadratic formula in about 825 A.D. His use of the formula was limited to what are now called *real solutions*. Europeans first learned of his discovery in 1202 when it was translated into Latin by Fibonacci, the Italian mathematician also known for the sequence with his name.

For centuries mathematicians sought general formulas, like the quadratic formula, for finding zeros of higher-degree polynomials. Several Italian

Lesson 9-7 Overview

Broad Goals This lesson gives the history and algebraic and geometric representations of the Fundamental Theorem of Algebra, namely that every polynomial function has at least one complex zero.

Perspective Complex numbers arose as numbers that could represent solutions to quadratic equations. Then it was found that these same numbers sufficed to solve all cubic and quartic equations, even those

with nonreal coefficients. Still, the discovery by Gauss in 1797 that all polynomial equations with real or nonreal coefficients have a complex solution was an extraordinary breakthrough. After all, if you need new numbers to solve all quadratics with real coefficients, is it not natural to believe you would need still different new numbers to solve some equations of higher degree?

This lesson begins with a brief history of that theorem of Gauss, now known as the Fundamental Theorem of Algebra. From it the lesson goes on to prove that every nonzero polynomial of degree n has at most n zeros and, if multiplicities are counted, exactly n zeros. Furthermore, if the polynomial has real coefficients, the complex zeros come in conjugate pairs. These theorems enable all the zeros of many polynomial functions to be determined exactly.

Nicolo Tartaglia (woodcut, 1546)

mathematicians of the 16th century made progress with cubics. The works of Scipione dal Ferro (1465–1526) and of Nicolo Tartaglia (1500–1557) were published by Girolamo Cardano (1501–1576) in 1545 in his treatise on algebra, *Ars Magna* ("Great Art"). In that book, formulas for zeros for classes of cubics are given and complex numbers are recognized as legitimate solutions to equations. Shortly after, Ludovico Ferrari (1522–1565), a student of Cardano, found a method for finding exact zeros of any polynomial of degree 4. In all these discoveries, no new numbers were needed beyond the complex numbers. The search for a formula for zeros to all quintics and beyond continued.

In 1797, the following key result connecting previous investigations was discovered by Gauss when he was 18 years old. It made him famous among mathematicians.

Fundamental Theorem of Algebra

If $p(x)$ is any polynomial of degree $n \geq 1$ with complex coefficients, then $p(x) = 0$ has at least one complex zero.

This theorem, whose proof is beyond the scope of this book, is remarkable because:

> It refers to all polynomials.
> It tells the complex nature of at least one zero.
> It leads to another simple, yet powerful result.

Theorem

A polynomial of degree n has at most n zeros.

Proof

Let $p(x)$ be a polynomial of degree n. By the Fundamental Theorem of Algebra, $p(x)$ has at least one complex zero, call it c. Then, by the Factor and Remainder Theorems, when $p(x)$ is divided by $(x - c)$ the quotient, $q(x)$, is a polynomial of degree $n - 1$. Now begin again. $q(x)$ has at least one complex zero, so divide $q(x)$ by the factor associated with that zero to get a quotient $r(x)$ of degree $n - 2$, and so on. Each division reduces the degree of the previous polynomial by 1, so the process of repeated division can have at most n steps, each providing one zero.

Thus another important consequence of the Fundamental Theorem of Algebra is that regardless of the degree of the polynomial, each of its zeros is a complex number; no new numbers are needed!

Multiplicities of Zeros

Of course, some of the zeros at the various divisions may be the same. For example, the quadratic $g(x) = x^2 - 4x + 4$, shown at the beginning of this lesson, factors into $(x - 2)^2$. It has a *double zero*. The **multiplicity of a zero** r is the highest power of $(x - r)$ that appears as a factor of that polynomial.

Lesson 9-7 *The Fundamental Theorem of Algebra* **597**

Notes on Reading

❶ The theorem proved at the bottom of page 598 can be generalized. If p and q are different polynomial functions of degrees n and m, with $n \geq m$, then their graphs can have at most n points in common. The proof is not difficult: Consider the polynomial $p(x) - q(x)$. It has degree at most n. Thus the equation $p(x) - q(x) = 0$ has at most n solutions. Thus $p(x) = q(x)$ for at most n values of x.

You may wish to emphasize the steps in the solution to **Example 3** as follows: We know, because the polynomial is a cubic, that there are exactly 3 zeros, counting multiplicities. In **part a**, the solution $3i$ is confirmed. In **part b**, the Conjugate Zeros Theorem tells us that $-3i$ is a solution. By the Factor Theorem, we know two of the three linear factors of the polynomial. Finally, using long division, the third factor is found, from which the third zero is identified.

Example 1

Find the zeros of $p(x) = x^3 - 6x^2 + 9x$.

Solution

You can factor out an x immediately, to get
$$p(x) = x(x^2 - 6x + 9).$$
The quadratic factor is a perfect square trinomial. Thus
$$p(x) = x(x - 3)^2.$$
This means $p(x)$ has three zeros: the zero 0 has multiplicity 1; the zero 3 has multiplicity 2.

In Example 1, the polynomial p has degree 3. Notice that it has exactly 3 complex zeros. The zeros (all of which are real in this case) are indicated in the graph to the right. So there is no need to look at a larger domain to find other zeros.

In general, the idea of multiplicities of zeros and the fact that no new numbers are needed to factor polynomials of any degree implies the following result.

Number of Zeros of a Polynomial Theorem
A polynomial of degree $n \geq 1$ with complex coefficients has exactly n complex zeros, if multiplicities are counted.

Determining the Possible Degrees of a Polynomial Function from Its Graph

From the graph of a polynomial function, you can determine information about its degree. Not only does the Number of Zeros Theorem dictate the maximum number of intersections of a polynomial graph and the x-axis, it also determines the number of intersections the graph may have with any horizontal line.

---

❶ **Theorem**
Let $p(x)$ be a polynomial of degree $n \geq 1$ with real coefficients. The graph of $p(x)$ can cross any horizontal line $y = d$ at most n times.

Proof
Let $p(x)$ be a polynomial with degree $n \geq 1$ with real coefficients. The points of intersection of the graph of $y = p(x)$ and the horizontal line $y = d$ are the solutions of the equation $p(x) = d$. This equation is equivalent to $g(x) = p(x) - d = 0$. The degree of $g(x)$ is the same as the degree of $p(x)$ because the two polynomials differ only by a constant. Thus, $g(x)$ has at most n zeros. So the graph of $p(x)$ has at most n intersections with $y = d$.

Optional Activities

Activity 2 Literature Connection After completing the lesson, you might have students read and report on *Whom the Gods Love*, a highly romanticized and fictionalized account of the story of Evariste Galois, written by Leopoid Infeld (New York: Whittlesey House, 1948). This book has been reprinted by the National Council of Teachers of Mathematics and is available through NCTM. Project 6, *Tragedy Strikes*

Brilliant Young Mathematicians, on page 618 relates to this topic.

Example 2

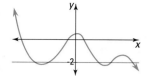

A polynomial $f(x)$ is graphed at the left. What is the lowest possible degree of $f(x)$?

Solution

The polynomial crosses the horizontal line $y = -2$ five times. So the degree of f(x) must be at least 5.

When one (or more) of the coefficients of the polynomial is nonreal, the solutions cannot be pictured on a standard graph. However, the Number of Zeros of a Polynomial Theorem can still be applied. For instance, the polynomial $g(x) = -3x^5 - ix$ has degree 5, so it has 5 zeros.

When a polynomial has real coefficients, then its nonreal zeros always come in complex conjugate pairs. The proof of this theorem is long, so we omit it.

> **Conjugate Zeros Theorem**
>
> Let $p(x) = a_nx^n + a_{n-1}x^{n-1} + \ldots + a_1x + a_0$ where $a_n, a_{n-1}, \ldots a_1, a_0$ are all real numbers, and $a_n \neq 0$. If $z = a + bi$ is a zero of $p(x)$, then the complex conjugate of z, $a - bi$, is also a zero of $p(x)$.

Example 3

Let $p(x) = 2x^3 - x^2 + 18x - 9$.
a. Verify that $3i$ is a zero of $p(x)$.
b. Find the remaining zeros of $p(x)$ and their multiplicities.

Solution

a.
$$p(3i) = 2(3i)^3 - (3i)^2 + 18(3i) - 9$$
$$= 54i^3 - 9i^2 + 54i - 9$$
$$= -54i + 9 + 54i - 9$$
$$= 0$$

b. Because 3i is a zero, then, by the Conjugate Zeros Theorem, so is its conjugate -3i. The Factor Theorem implies that (x − 3i) and (x + 3i) are factors of p(x). Thus their product (x − 3i) · (x + 3i) = x² + 9 is a factor of p(x). Divide p(x) by x² + 9 to find another factor:

$$
\begin{array}{r}
2x - 1 \\
x^2 + 9 \overline{)2x^3 - x^2 + 18x - 9} \\
\underline{2x^3 + 18x} \\
-x^2 - 9 \\
\underline{-x^2 - 9} \\
0
\end{array}
$$

Thus p(x) = (x² + 9)(2x − 1). So, the zeros of p(x) are 3i, -3i, and $\frac{1}{2}$.

Lesson 9-7 *The Fundamental Theorem of Algebra* **599**

Additional Examples

1. Find all zeros of $p(x) = 4x^{32} + x^{30}$, and give the multiplicity of each zero.
   $p(x) = x^{30}(2x + i)(2x - i)$, so $p(x)$ has 32 zeros: 0 with multiplicity 30, and $\frac{i}{2}$ and $-\frac{i}{2}$ with multiplicity 1.

2. The graph of a polynomial function $y = f(x)$ has 4 points in common with the x-axis and 6 points in common with the line $y = 5$. What can be said about the degree of $f(x)$? **The degree is at least 6.**

3. Let $p(x) = x^4 - 2x^3 + 6x^2 - 2x + 5$.
   a. Verify that i is a zero of $p(x)$.
   $i^4 - 2i^3 + 6i^2 - 2i + 5 = 1 + 2i - 6 - 2i + 5 = 0$
   b. Verify that $(1 + 2i)$ is a zero of $p(x)$. $(1 + 2i)^4 - 2(1 + 2i)^3 + 6(1 + 2i)^2 - 2(1 + 2i) + 5 = -7 - 24i - (-22 - 4i) + (-18 + 24i) - (2 + 4i) + 5 = 0$
   c. Find all other zeros of $p(x)$. **The other two zeros are $-i$ and $1 - 2i$.**

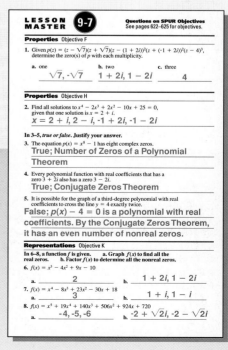

Notes on Questions

Question 1 You might ask whether students know or remember what word we get from the name of this mathematician. (Algorithm)

Question 12b There are no other real zeros, because the other ten zeros are the tenth roots of $\frac{i}{3}$.

Question 20 Note that it would be impossible for this function to have 2 or 4 real zeros; the nonreal zeros must come in pairs.

Questions 22–24 These questions help set up Lesson 9-8.

3) If $p(x)$ is any polynomial of degree $n \geq 1$ with complex coefficients, then $p(x) = 0$ has at least one complex zero.

10a) 5 with multiplicity 2 and –2 with multiplicity 3

b)

Check

In part **a**, $p(3i)$ was shown to equal 0. Similarly,
$$p(-3i) = 2(-3i)^3 - (-3i)^2 + 18(-3i) - 9$$
$$= 54i + 9 - 54i - 9 = 0$$
Also,
$$p\left(\tfrac{1}{2}\right) = 2\left(\tfrac{1}{2}\right)^3 - \left(\tfrac{1}{2}\right)^2 + 18\left(\tfrac{1}{2}\right) - 9$$
$$= \tfrac{1}{4} - \tfrac{1}{4} + 9 - 9 = 0.$$

The question of finding a formula for exact zeros to all polynomials was not settled until the early 19th century. In 1824 Niels Abel (1802–1829), a Norwegian mathematician, wrote a conclusive proof that it is impossible to construct a general formula for zeros of any polynomial beyond degree 4. Abel's work had several effects. First, the theory he developed contributed to the foundation of another advanced branch of modern mathematics, *group theory*. Second, rather than searching for exact zeros to polynomials, mathematicians knew they had to rely on approximation techniques. These techniques are studied in another branch of advanced mathematics called *numerical analysis*.

QUESTIONS

Covering the Reading

1. When and by whom was the quadratic formula first discovered?
   $\approx$ 825 A.D., by al'Khowarizmi
2. Name three mathematicians who contributed to the analysis of zeros of cubic or quartic polynomials.
   Sample: Scipione dal Ferro, Nicolo Tartaglia, Ludovico Ferrari
3. State the Fundamental Theorem of Algebra. See left.

In 4–9, *true or false*.

4. Every polynomial has at least one real zero.
   False
5. A polynomial of degree n has at most n real zeros.
   True
6. A cubic may have 4 zeros.
   False
7. A polynomial with zeros 2, 3, and –1 could be of degree greater than three.
   True
8. All polynomials with real coefficients have zeros that are complex numbers.
   True
9. Suppose $p(x)$ is a polynomial with real coefficients. If $2 + 3i$ is a zero of $p(x)$, then $2 - 3i$ is a zero of $p(x)$.
   True
10. Consider $q(x) = (x - 5)^2 (x + 2)^3$.
    a. Identify the zeros of $q(x)$ and give their multiplicities. See left.
    b. Verify your solution to part **a** by graphing $y = q(x)$. See left.

11. Find all zeros of $p(x) = x^5 - 16x$. -2, 0, 2, 2i, -2i

12. a. How many zeros does $r(x) = 3x^{11} - ix$ have? 11
    b. How many of these zeros are real? 1

Adapting to Individual Needs

✎ Challenge

Writing Have students explain why an odd degree polynomial with only real coefficients must have at least one real zero. [Since nonreal zeros come in pairs, the odd degree polynomial must have at least one real zero and, therefore, one *x*-intercept.]

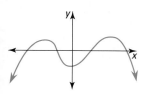

13. Consider the polynomial $p(x) = x^4 + 2x^3 + 11x^2 + 2x + 10$.
   a. Verify that i is a zero of $p(x)$. **See below.**
   b. Find the remaining zeros of $p(x)$ and their multiplicities.
      See below.
14. Suppose the graph at the left represents the polynomial function
   $y = g(x)$. What is the lowest possible degree for $g(x)$? **4**

   13a) $p(i) = i^4 + 2i^3 + 11i^2 + 2i + 10 = 1 - 2i - 11 + 2i + 10 = 0$
   b) $-i, -1 + 3i, -1 - 3i$, **all with multiplicity 1**

Applying the Mathematics

15. The zeros of $x^n - 1$ are called the **nth roots of unity**. Find the fourth
   roots of unity. **1, -1, i, -i**

16. Suppose $p(x)$ is a polynomial with real coefficients and $p(4 + 9i) = 0$.
   What is $p(4 - 9i)$? **0**

18a) $i, -\dfrac{3}{2}i$

17. Find a polynomial $p(x)$ with real coefficients, leading coefficient 1, and of
   the lowest degree possible that has the two zeros 3 and $1 - 2i$.
   $p(x) = (x - 3)(x - (1 - 2i))(x - (1 + 2i)) = x^3 - 5x^2 + 11x - 15$

19a) Yes; a horizontal
   line crosses the
   graph at most
   2 times, so the
   degree is greater
   than or equal to 2.
   b) Yes; a horizontal
   line crosses the
   graph at most
   4 times, so the
   degree is greater
   than or equal to 4.
   c) No; the graph
   crosses the x-axis
   6 times, so the
   degree is at least 6.

18. a. Find the zeros of $t(x) = 2x^2 + ix + 3$. **See left.**
   b. The zeros are not complex conjugates. Explain why this does not
      contradict the Conjugate Zeros Theorem.
      The coefficients of $t(x)$ are not all real numbers.

19. Tell whether each of the following could or could not be part of the graph
   of a fourth degree polynomial function. Explain your decision for each one.

   a. 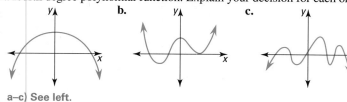   b.   c.

   a–c) See left.

20. The curve pictured at the left is the graph of a polynomial function p of
   degree 5 with real coefficients. Copy the figure and insert a horizontal axis
   so that each condition is satisfied. **Samples are given at left.**
   a. p has one real zero.   b. p has five real zeros.

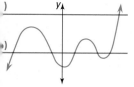

Review

21. Let $z = 3 - 8i$. Write in $a + bi$ form. *(Lesson 9-6)*
   a. w, the complex conjugate of z. **$w = 3 + 8i$**

   b. $w + z$ c. $w - z$ d. wz e. $\dfrac{w}{z}$ $-\dfrac{55}{73} + \dfrac{48}{73}i$
      6 + 0i   **0 + 16i**   **73 + 0i**

In 22–24, factor the polynomial into linear factors. *(Lesson 9-6)*

22. $3p^2 - 4$ 23. $4p^2 - 9$ 24. $4p^2 + 9$
   $(\sqrt{3}p - 2)(\sqrt{3}p + 2)$ $(2p + 3)(2p - 3)$ $(2p + 3i)(2p - 3i)$

25. How can you check a polynomial division problem when the remainder is
   not zero? *(Lesson 9-4)* **Multiply the quotient and divisor;   then add the
   remainder. The result should equal the dividend.**

26. Approximate, to the nearest tenth, all the real zeros of the polynomial
   $p(x) = x^5 - 4x^3 + 8x^2 - 12$. *(Lesson 9-2)*
   -2.5, -1.0, 1.5

Practice

For more questions on SPUR Objectives, use **Lesson Master 9-7** (shown on page 599).

Assessment

Quiz A quiz covering Lessons 9-4 through 9-7 is provided in the *Assessment Sourcebook.*

Extension

You may wish to extend **Question 15** on page 601 by asking students to find the third roots of unity. $[1, -\frac{1}{2} \pm \frac{\sqrt{3}i}{2};$ students may arrive at this solution by finding the root 1, then dividing $x^3 - 1$ by $x - 1$ and using the quadratic formula.] Then have students find the sixth roots of unity. Suggest that they use the third roots of unity to solve for the sixth roots of unity. $[1, -\frac{1}{2} \pm \frac{\sqrt{3}i}{2}, -1,$ $\frac{1}{2} \pm \frac{\sqrt{3}i}{2};$ students should recognize that $x^6 - 1 = (x^3 - 1)(x^3 + 1)$. The first factor yields the third roots of unity. The second must yield -1 as a root because $(-1)^6 - 1 = 0$, so students can divide $x^3 + 1$ by $x + 1$ and use the quadratic formula to find the other roots.]

Project Update Project 3, *Synthetic Division*, Project 5, *Algebraic and Transcendental Numbers*, and Project 6, *Tragedy Strikes Brilliant Young Mathematicians*, on page 618, relate to the content of this lesson.

27. A silo is in the shape of a cylinder with a hemispherical top. The height of the cylinder is 17 m. *(Lesson 9-1)*
   a. Write a polynomial equation $V(r)$ which expresses the volume of the silo as a function of r, its radius. $V(r) = 17\pi r^2 + \frac{2}{3}\pi r^3$
   b. What is the degree of $V(r)$? **3**
   c. What is the leading coefficient of $V(r)$? $\frac{2}{3}\pi$
   d. Suppose the radius may be anywhere from 3 m to 5 m. What are the maximum and minimum capacities of the silo, assuming the entire space can be filled? **maximum ≈ 1597 m³; minimum ≈ 537 m³**

28. Expand $(x - 5)^3$. *(Lesson 8-8)* $x^3 - 15x^2 + 75x - 125$

29. The government of a certain country decides to increase the salaries of all government employees by 5%. Disregarding all other factors (such as promotions, resignations, or new hirings), how will this raise affect each statistic?
   a. the average salary of government employees nationally
   b. the standard deviation of salaries *(Lesson 3-6)*
   a, b) **Both will increase by 5%.**

In 30 and 31, *true or false*. *(Lesson 3-4)*

30. The graph of every odd function passes through the origin. **True**

31. If z is a zero of an odd function f, then $-z$ is also a zero of $-f$. **True**

Exploration

32. Write your nine-digit social security number. (Make up one if you do not have one.) Use the digits in order as the coefficients of a polynomial of degree 8 with alternating signs. For instance, if your social security number is 369-46-4564, your polynomial is
$$y = 3x^8 - 6x^7 + 9x^6 - 4x^5 + 6x^4 - 4x^3 + 5x^2 - 6x + 4.$$
   a. Graph your social security number polynomial. Tell how many real zeros it has. **Answers will vary.**
   b. If the nine digits of a social security number may be any one of 0 through 9, and the system of alternating signs of coefficients is used to create a polynomial, what is the least number m of real zeros the polynomial can have? What is the greatest number M of real zeros it may have? Can a social security polynomial have any number of zeros between m and M? Why or why not?
   The least number m of real zeros is 0; the greatest number M of real zeros is 8; any number of real zeros between 0 and 8 is possible since each of the polynomials $-x^7, x^6, -x^5, x^4, -x^3, x^2, -x$ is a valid social security polynomial.

Setting Up Lesson 9-8

Be certain to discuss **Questions 22–24** on page 601. Point out the difference between factoring over the set of polynomials with real coefficients (whereby the polynomial of **Question 24** cannot be factored) and factoring over the set of polynomials with complex coefficients.

Factoring Sums and Differences of Powers

Finding All Cube Roots of a Real Number

We usually think of 5 as being *the* cube root of 125, but every solution to $x^3 = 125$ is a cube root of 125, and according to the Number of Zeros Theorem, $x^3 - 125 = 0$ has three complex roots. You might think 5 is the only root, with multiplicity three, but then $x^3 - 125$ would have to equal $(x - 5)^3$. The Binomial Theorem shows that these are not equal, so a different approach is needed.

Example 1

Find the cube roots of 125 other than 5.

Solution

The desired cube roots are the solutions to $P(x) = x^3 - 125 = 0$. Since $P(5) = 0$, $(x - 5)$ is a factor of $x^3 - 125$. Divide to obtain the other factor.

$$
\begin{array}{r}
x^2 + 5x + 25 \\
x - 5 \overline{\smash{\big)}\ x^3 + 0x^2 + 0x - 125} \\
\underline{x^3 - 5x^2} \\
5x^2 + 0x - 125 \\
\underline{5x^2 - 25x} \\
25x - 125 \\
\underline{25x - 125} \\
0
\end{array}
$$

Thus $x^3 - 125 = (x - 5)(x^2 + 5x + 25)$. Now use the quadratic formula to find the zeros of the quadratic factor. If $x^2 + 5x + 25 = 0$, then

$$x = \frac{-5 \pm \sqrt{5^2 - 4 \cdot 25}}{2} = \frac{-5 \pm \sqrt{-75}}{2} = \frac{-5 \pm 5\sqrt{3}\,i}{2}.$$

The other cube roots of 125 are $-\frac{5}{2} + \frac{5\sqrt{3}}{2}\,i$ and $-\frac{5}{2} - \frac{5\sqrt{3}}{2}\,i$.

Check

$$
\begin{aligned}
\left(-\frac{5}{2} + \frac{5\sqrt{3}}{2}\,i\right)^3 &= \left(-\frac{5}{2} + \frac{5\sqrt{3}}{2}\,i\right)\left(-\frac{5}{2} + \frac{5\sqrt{3}}{2}\,i\right)^2 \\
&= \left(-\frac{5}{2} + \frac{5\sqrt{3}}{2}\,i\right)\left(\frac{25}{4} - \frac{25\sqrt{3}}{2}\,i - \frac{75}{4}\right) \\
&= \left(-\frac{5}{2} + \frac{5\sqrt{3}}{2}\,i\right)\left(-\frac{25}{2} - \frac{25\sqrt{3}}{2}\,i\right) \\
&= \frac{125}{4} + \frac{125\sqrt{3}}{4}\,i - \frac{125\sqrt{3}}{4}\,i + \frac{375}{4} \\
&= \frac{500}{4} = 125
\end{aligned}
$$

A check for $\left(-\frac{5}{2} - \frac{5\sqrt{3}}{2}\,i\right)$ is asked for in Question 1.

Lesson 9-8 Overview

Broad Goals In this lesson, the Sums and Differences of Powers are factored, and students learn the particular factorizations for the sum and difference of two cubes.

Perspective If $x^n = a^n$, then $x^n - a^n = 0$, and solutions can be found by factoring $x^n - a^n$. These are the nth roots of a^n. We know that one of the nth roots of a^n is a itself, and by the Factor Theorem that means that $x - a$ is a factor of $x^n - a^n$

for all n. The other factor can be found by division.

Objectives

D Factor sums or differences of powers.

Resources

From the *Teacher's Resource File*
- Lesson Master 9-8
- Answer Master 9-8
- Teaching Aid 81: Warm-up
- Technology Sourcebook Calculator Master 9

Additional Resources
- Visual for Teaching Aid 81

Teaching 9-8
Lesson

Warm-up

Factor $x^4 - 1$ over the set of polynomials with the indicated coefficients.
1. Real coefficients
   $(x - 1)(x + 1)(x^2 + 1)$
2. Complex coefficients
   $(x - 1)(x + 1)(x - i)(x + i)$

Notes on Reading

Have students record the results of the **Activity** for use with **Question 8** on page 606.

Students who studied from UCSMP *Algebra* have seen formulas for factoring the sum and difference of cubes but have not seen the general formulas for factoring the sum and difference of nth powers. You might begin by asking how many students had seen these formulas before.

As you discuss **Example 1,** you might note that it is possible to find all the cube roots, 4th roots, and 6th roots of real numbers by factoring, but not most higher roots. However, in Chapter 13, a theorem (DeMoivre's) is proved which enables all n nth roots of any real number to be found.

603

604

Checking the result of **Example 3** in class may enable students to see the pattern well enough so that they could reproduce the factorization even if they forgot it. Point out that the polynomial $a^4 - a^3b + a^2b^2 - ab^3 + b^4$ can be factored into two quadratic polynomials with *real* coefficients. (This can be proved from the Conjugate Zeros Theorem.) However there is no factorization into polynomials with *rational* coefficients.

Factoring Sums and Differences of Cubes

In Example 1, the difference of two cubes $x^3 - 125$ was factored. More generally, consider the problem of factoring $x^3 - y^3$, the difference of any two cubes. Notice that $x = y$ is clearly a solution to $x^3 - y^3 = 0$, so $x - y$ is one factor. Divide $x^3 - y^3$ by $x - y$ to find the other factor.

$$\begin{array}{r}
x^2 \;+\; xy \;+\; y^2 \\
x - y \overline{)\, x^3 - 0x^2y - 0xy^2 - y^3} \\
\underline{x^3 - x^2y} \\
x^2y - 0xy^2 - y^3 \\
\underline{x^2y - xy^2} \\
xy^2 - y^3 \\
\underline{xy^2 - y^3}
\end{array}$$

Thus $x^3 - y^3 = (x - y)(x^2 + xy + y^2)$.

This proves the second part of the following theorem.

Sums and Differences of Cubes Theorem
For all x and y,
$$x^3 + y^3 = (x + y)(x^2 - xy + y^2)$$
$$x^3 - y^3 = (x - y)(x^2 + xy + y^2)$$

$(x + y)(x^2 - xy + y^2) = x^3 + x^2y - x^2y - xy^2 + xy^2 + y^3 = x^3 + y^3$

Activity

Prove the first part of the theorem. See left.

Neither one of the quadratic factors in the Sums and Differences of Cubes Theorem can be factored further over the set of polynomials with real coefficients.

Example 2

Factor $8a^3 + 27b^6$.

Solution

This is an instance of the sum of two cubes $x^3 + y^3$ where $x = 2a$ and $y = 3b^2$. Apply the previous theorem.

$$8a^3 + 27b^6 = (2a)^3 + (3b^2)^3$$
$$= (2a + 3b^2)((2a)^2 - (2a)(3b^2) + (3b^2)^2)$$
$$= (2a + 3b^2)(4a^2 - 6ab^2 + 9b^4)$$

Factoring Sums and Differences of Odd Powers

The method used to find factors of sums and differences of cubes generalizes to all odd powers.

Optional Activities

Activity 1 As an alternate approach to **Example 2,** you might have students first write down the general formula $x^3 + y^3 = (x + y)(x^2 - xy + y^2)$. Then students can easily substitute $2a$ for x and $3b$ for y directly underneath this formula. This has the advantage of recording the general theorem that is being used as justification.

Activity 2 Technology Connection
You may wish to assign *Technology Sourcebook, Calculator Master 9*. Students use a graphics calculator to find the zeros of polynomial functions. Then they use the zeros to factor the polynomials.

Adapting to Individual Needs

Extra Help
Some students may have more success using the patterns of factoring if they get in the habit of first rewriting constants as powers whenever possible. For example, 8 can be written as 2^3, and 27 is written as 3^3. Also, in **Example 4**, $64 = 2^6$. Students should apply this idea in **Questions 2, 3, 5–7, 9, 10, 13, 15, 17, and 18**.

You are asked in the Questions to verify the theorem for specific values of n. Example 3 applies it to a sum of fifth powers.

Example 3

Factor $a^5 + b^5$.

Solution

Since $a^5 + b^5$ is a sum, $a + b$ is a factor, and in the other factor the signs alternate.
Thus,
$$a^5 + b^5 = (a + b)(a^4 - a^3b + a^2b^2 - ab^3 + b^4).$$

A similar theorem for the factorization of sums and differences of even powers does not exist. If n is a positive even integer, then $x^n + y^n$ does not have a linear factor with real coefficients. To factor the difference of two powers, $x^n - y^n$ for n even, consider the even power as the square of some lower power, and reduce the problem to the difference of two squares. Example 4 illustrates a specific case.

Example 4

Factor $x^6 - 64$ completely over the set of polynomials with real coefficients.

Solution

$x^6 = (x^3)^2$, and $64 = 2^6 = (2^3)^2$.
So
$$x^6 - 64 = (x^3)^2 - (2^3)^2$$
$$= (x^3 - 2^3)(x^3 + 2^3).$$
Each of the factors is a sum or difference of cubes, so they can be factored further. Hence,
$$x^6 - 64 = (x - 2)(x^2 + 2x + 4)(x + 2)(x^2 - 2x + 4).$$
Since $x^2 + 2x + 4$ and $x^2 - 2x + 4$ each has discriminant -12, they cannot be factored into polynomials with real coefficients. So this factorization is complete.

QUESTIONS

Covering the Reading

1. Show that $-\frac{5}{2} - \frac{5\sqrt{3}}{2}i$ is a cube root of 125. **See left.**

In 2 and 3, a function is described. **a.** Find the zeros of the function by factoring. **b.** Verify your result by drawing a graph. **See left.**

2. $f(x) = 2x^3 - 32x$

3. $g(x) = x^3 - 64$

Lesson 9-8 *Factoring Sums and Differences of Powers* **605**

Left margin:

1) $\left(-\frac{5}{2} - \frac{5\sqrt{3}}{2}i\right)^3$

$= \left(-\frac{5}{2} - \frac{5\sqrt{3}}{2}i\right) \cdot \left(-\frac{5}{2} - \frac{5\sqrt{3}}{2}i\right)^2$

$= \left(-\frac{5}{2} - \frac{5\sqrt{3}}{2}i\right) \cdot \left(\frac{25}{4} + \frac{25\sqrt{3}}{2}i - \frac{75}{4}\right)$

$= \left(-\frac{5}{2} - \frac{5\sqrt{3}}{2}i\right) \cdot \left(-\frac{25}{2} + \frac{25\sqrt{3}}{2}i\right)$

$= \frac{125}{4} - \frac{125\sqrt{3}}{4}i + \frac{125\sqrt{3}}{4}i + \frac{375}{4}$

$= \frac{500}{4} = 125$

2a) $2x^3 - 32x = 2x(x^2 - 16) = 2x(x + 4)(x - 4)$; zeros are -4, 0, and 4.

b)

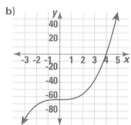

3a) $x^3 - 64 = (x - 4)(x^2 + 4x + 16)$; zeros are 4, $-2 + 2\sqrt{3}i$, and $-2 - 2\sqrt{3}i$.

b)

Additional Examples

1. Find the four fourth roots of 16.
The fourth roots of 16 are the solutions to $x^4 - 16 = 0$.
$x^4 - 16 = (x^2 + 4)(x^2 - 4) = (x + 2i)(x - 2i)(x + 2)(x - 2)$, so the fourth roots are $-2i$, $2i$, -2, and 2.

2. Factor $x^3 - 64y^{12}$ over the set of polynomials with rational coefficients.
$(x - 4y^4)(x^2 + 4xy^4 + 16y^8)$

3. Factor $m^6 + n^6$ over the set of polynomials with rational coefficients.
$(m^2 + n^2)(m^4 - m^2n^2 + n^4)$

4. Factor $x^{10} - y^{10}$ completely over the set of polynomials with rational coefficients. $(x - y)(x + y) \cdot (x^4 - x^3y + x^2y^2 - xy^3 + y^4) \cdot (x^4 + x^3y + x^2y^2 + xy^3 + y^4)$

Notes on Questions

Questions 2 and 15 Error Alert
Some students may forget to look first for the common monomial factor.

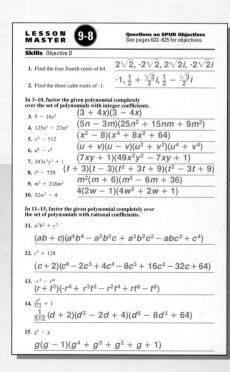

LESSON MASTER **9-8**

Questions on SPUR Objectives
See pages 622–625 for objectives.

Skills Objective D

1. Find the four fourth roots of 64. $2\sqrt{2}, -2\sqrt{2}, 2\sqrt{2}i, -2\sqrt{2}i$

2. Find the three cube roots of -1. $-1, \frac{1}{2} + \frac{\sqrt{3}}{2}i, \frac{1}{2} - \frac{\sqrt{3}}{2}i$

In 3–10, factor the given polynomial completely over the set of polynomials with integer coefficients.

3. $9 - 16x^2$ $(3 + 4x)(3 - 4x)$

4. $125n^3 - 27m^3$ $(5n - 3m)(25n^2 + 15nm + 9m^2)$

5. $x^6 - 512$ $(x^2 - 8)(x^4 + 8x^2 + 64)$

6. $u^8 - v^8$ $(u + v)(u - v)(u^2 + v^2)(u^4 + v^4)$

7. $343x^3y^3 + 1$ $(7xy + 1)(49x^2y^2 - 7xy + 1)$

8. $t^6 - 729$ $(t + 3)(t - 3)(t^2 + 3t + 9)(t^2 - 3t + 9)$

9. $m^3 + 216m^2$ $m^2(m + 6)(m^2 - 6m + 36)$

10. $32w^3 - 4$ $4(2w - 1)(4w^2 + 2w + 1)$

In 11–15, factor the given polynomial completely over the set of polynomials with rational coefficients.

11. $a^5b^5 + c^5$ $(ab + c)(a^4b^4 - a^3b^3c + a^2b^2c^2 - abc^3 + c^4)$

12. $c^7 + 128$ $(c + 2)(c^6 - 2c^5 + 4c^4 - 8c^3 + 16c^2 - 32c + 64)$

13. $-r^5 - t^{10}$ $(r + t^2)(-r^4 + r^3t^2 - r^2t^4 + rt^6 - t^8)$

14. $\frac{d^9}{512} + 1$ $\frac{1}{512}(d + 2)(d^2 - 2d + 4)(d^6 - 8d^3 + 64)$

15. $g^6 - g$ $g(g - 1)(g^4 + g^3 + g^2 + g + 1)$

Question 4 Stress the connection between the factors and the cube roots. Point out that one cube root of 27 is well-known, but by factoring, the other two cube roots can be determined. Also note that the other two cube roots must not be real because the graph of $y = x^3 - 27$ intersects the x-axis in only one point.

Questions 9–10 Some students may need to write 32 as 2^5 and 10,000,000 as 10^7 before they can do the factorization.

Question 23 Remind students that if they are stumped, they could always try to substitute a specific polynomial for $f(x)$. For instance, they could let $f(x) = (x - 3)(x + 5) = x^2 + 2x - 15$. Working with this polynomial can quickly indicate which answers are true, which false.

Question 25 Social Studies Connection In 1990, 45% of the labor force in the United States was women. This is a significant increase from 1960 when around 33% of the labor force was women.

Question 26g The generalization is sometimes called the Rational Root Theorem or Rational Zero Theorem, when applied to solving polynomial equations.

4a)

$$
\begin{array}{r}
x^2 + 3x + 9 \\
x - 3{\overline{\smash{\big)}\,x^3 \qquad\qquad - 27}} \\
\underline{x^3 - 3x^2} \\
3x^2 \\
\underline{3x^2 - 9x} \\
9x - 27 \\
\underline{9x - 27} \\
0
\end{array}
$$

b) $(x - 3)(x^2 + 3x + 9) = x^3 - 27$

c) $b^2 - 4ac = 3^2 - 4(1)(9) = -27$

d) $3, -\dfrac{3}{2} + \dfrac{3\sqrt{3}}{2}i, -\dfrac{3}{2} - \dfrac{3\sqrt{3}}{2}i$

5a) difference of squares
b) $(a - 8x)(a + 8x)$

6a) sum of cubes
b) $(5x + 1) \cdot (25x^2 - 5x + 1)$

7a) difference of cubes
b) $(3 - 4a) \cdot (9 + 12a + 16a^2)$

8) $(x + y)(x^2 - xy + y^2) = x^3 + x^2y - x^2y - xy^2 + xy^2 + y^3 = x^3 + y^3$

11) False;   Sample: If $(x + y)$ is a factor of $x^4 + y^4$, then $x = -y$ should be a solution to $x^4 + y^4 = 0$. But $(-y)^4 + y^4 = 2y^4 \ne 0$.

12) True, by the Sums and Differences of Odd Powers Theorem

15) $7x^2(2y + x)(2y - x)$

16) $(x^2 + y^2)(x + y)(x - y)$

17) $(2xy + 7z)(4x^2y^2 - 14xyz + 49z^2)$

4. a. Show that $x - 3$ is a factor of $x^3 - 27$ by using long division.
  b. Check your answer by multiplying $x - 3$ by the quotient.
  c. Show that the quotient is not factorable over the set of polynomials with real coefficients by calculating its discriminant.
  d. Determine the three cube roots of 27.
  a–d, see left.

In 5–7, a binomial is given. **a.** Describe the polynomial as a difference of squares, sum of squares, difference of cubes, or sum of cubes. **b.** Factor the given polynomial. See left.

5. $a^2 - 64x^2$ **6.** $125x^3 + 1$ **7.** $27 - 64a^3$

8. Give your answer to the Activity. See left.

In 9 and 10, a binomial is given. **a.** Factor the expression using the Sums and Differences of Odd Powers Theorem. **b.** Justify your answer using either multiplication or division, or a graph. See margin.

9. $x^5 - 32$ **10.** $x^7 + 10,000,000$

In 11 and 12, *true or false.*   Justify your answer. See left.

11. $(x + y)$ is a factor of $x^4 + y^4$.

12. $(a - b)$ is a factor of $a^n - b^n$, if n is an odd integer.

In 13 and 14, a binomial is given. **a.** Factor the given binomial over integers using the Sums and Differences of Odd Powers Theorem. **b.** Verify the factorization by multiplying. See margin.

13. $t^9 - 512$ **14.** $x^7 + y^7$

Applying the Mathematics

In 15–17, factor completely over the set of polynomials with integer coefficients. See left.

15. $28x^2y^2 - 7x^4$ **16.** $x^4 - y^4$ **17.** $8x^3y^3 + 343z^3$

18. Refer to Example 4. See margin.
  a. Factor $x^6 - 64$ as a difference of cubes.
  b. Verify that the result you get in part **a** can be factored further to get the solution shown in Example 4.

19. Let $p(x) = x^5 - 5x^3 + 4x$. See margin.
  a. Find the zeros of the polynomial function p by factoring.
  b. Verify your results to part **a** by graphing the function p.

Review

20. *True or false.*   The Fundamental Theorem of Algebra guarantees that the equation $4x^4 + 16x^3 + 5x^2 + 25 = 0$ has at least one real solution. *(Lesson 9-7)* **False**

21. *True or false.*   The polynomial $c(x) = x^3 - 1271x^2 + 1273x - 1272$ has at least one real zero.   *(Lesson 9-7)* **True**

606

Additional Answers
9. a. $x^5 - 32 = (x - 2)(x^4 + 2x^3 + 4x^2 + 8x + 16)$
   b. $(x - 2)(x^4 + 2x^3 + 4x^2 + 8x + 16) = x^5 + 2x^4 + 4x^3 + 8x^2 + 16x - 2x^4 - 4x^3 - 8x^2 - 16x - 32 = x^5 - 32$
10. a. $x^7 + 10,000,000$
    $= (x + 10)(x^6 - 10x^5 + 10^2x^4 - 10^3x^3 + 10^4x^2 - 10^5x + 10^6)$
    b. $(x + 10)(x^6 - 10x^5 + 10^2x^4 - 10^3x^3 + 10^4x^2 - 10^5x + 10^6)$
    $= x^7 - 10x^6 + 10^2x^5 - 10^3x^4 + 10^4x^3 - 10^5x^2 + 10^6x + 10x^6 - 10^2x^5 + 10^3x^4 - 10^4x^3 + 10^5x^2 - 10^6x + 10^7$
    $= x^7 + 10^7 = x^7 + 10,000,000$

22. What is the minimum degree of the polynomial function graphed at the right? *(Lesson 9-7)*
5

23. Suppose that $(x - 3)$ is a factor of the polynomial $f(x)$. *True or false.*
   a. 3 is a solution to the equation $f(x) = 0$. **True**
   b. −3 is a solution to the equation $f(x) = 0$. **False**
   c. The graph of $f(x)$ crosses the x-axis at $(3, 0)$. **True**
   d. When $f(x)$ is divided by $(x - 3)$, the remainder is zero. **True**
   e. $f(3) = 0$. *(Lesson 9-5)* **True**

24a) *x*-intercepts:
$-3\sqrt{3}$, 0, $3\sqrt{3}$;
y-intercept: 0
c) *x*-intercepts:
$-3\sqrt{3} + 2$, 2,
$3\sqrt{3} + 2$;
y-intercept: 46

24. Consider the functions f and g with $f(x) = x^3 - 27x$ and $g(x) = (x - 2)^3 - 27(x - 2)$. *(Lessons 3-3, 3-4, 9-2)*
   a. Find the x- and y-intercepts of f. **See left.**
   b. State whether f is odd, even, or neither. **odd**
   c. Find x- and y-intercepts of g. **See left.**
   d. State whether g is odd, even, or neither. **neither**

25. Suppose that 36% of the available labor force of a certain country are women. A company hires twelve new workers.
   a. Determine the probability that exactly three of the new workers are women.
   b. What is the probability that fewer than four of the new workers are women? *(Lesson 8-9)* $\approx$ **0.32**
   a) $_{12}C_3 \cdot (0.36)^3(0.64)^9 \approx 0.18$

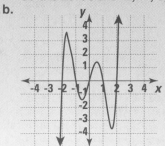

Aquaculture. *This woman is working in the hydroponics industry. Hydroponics is an alternative to growing vegetables in soil.*

Exploration

26d) **The numerators are the constant terms in the factors.**
e) **The denominators are the coefficients of *x* in the factors.**
f) **constant = *bdfh*; leading coefficient = *aceg*; the constant term is the product of the constants of the factors, and the leading coefficient is the product of the leading coefficients of the factors.**

26. Consider the polynomial which when factored is $(3x - 5)(2x + 9)(2x + 7)$.
   a. When it is expanded, what will the leading coefficient be? **12**
   b. When it is expanded, what will the constant term be? **−315**
   c. Write the zeros of the polynomial as simple fractions. $\frac{5}{3}$, $-\frac{9}{2}$, and $-\frac{7}{2}$
   d. Ignoring the sign, what is the relationship of the numerators of the zeros to the linear factors? **See left.**
   e. Ignoring the sign, what is the relationship of the denominators of the zeros to the linear factors? **See left.**
   f. Suppose a polynomial in factored form is $(ax + b)(cx + d)(ex + f)(gx + h)$.
   Tell what the constant term will be, what the leading coefficient will be, and give the relationship of these products to the coefficients in the original polynomial in expanded form. **See left.**
   g. Generalize parts **a-f**.
   If a simple fraction $\frac{a}{b}$ is a zero of a polynomial $P(x)$ with integer coefficients, then a is a factor of the constant term of $P(x)$ and b is a factor of the leading coefficient.

Lesson 9-8 *Factoring Sums and Differences of Powers*   **607**

Practice
For more questions on SPUR Objectives, use **Lesson Master 9-8** (shown on page 605).

Assessment
Written Communication Have students write a paragraph explaining which sums and differences of powers can be factored, identify the general form of the patterns, and include specific examples to support their explanations. [Students explain how to factor the difference of squares and the sum or difference of odd powers and include appropriate examples.]

Extension
Have students **work with a partner** and apply the theorems of this lesson to determine that certain numbers are not prime. For instance, consider the number $9^5 - 32$, which equals 59,017. Since this number is $9^5 - 2^5$, it is divisible by 9 − 2, or 7. As another example, 10,000,001 = $10^7 + 1^7$, so it is divisible by 10 + 1, or 11. One partner should find a number that he or she knows not to be prime due to the theorems of this lesson. It is up to the other student to find the factors.

Project Update Project 3, *Synthetic Division*, and Project 5, *Algebraic and Transcendental Numbers*, on page 618, relate to the content of this lesson.

Teaching Lesson **9-9**

Warm-up

1. Factor $2x^3 + 3x^2 + x$.
   $x(x + 1)(2x + 1)$
2. Factor $2x^3 + 2x^2 + x^2 + x$.
   $x(x + 1)(2x + 1)$; the expressions are equal but note that the second expression is in a form suitable to be factored by grouping

Notes on Reading

You might wish to summarize the various kinds of factoring that students are expected to know. Before this course, students should have become familiar with the following types of factoring:
- –common monomial
- –difference of squares
- –perfect squares
- –quadratic trinomials.

LESSON 9-9

Advanced Factoring Techniques

In previous lessons, polynomials were factored by using graphs, recognizing special patterns (sums and differences), and using the quadratic formula. In this lesson, you will utilize chunking and another factoring technique called *grouping*. Grouping is used to factor polynomials which contain groups of terms with common factors, usually monomials. It involves only the repeated application of the distributive property. Example 1 gives an instance of this technique.

Example 1

Factor $x^3 + 2x^2 - 9x - 18$.

Solution

Observe that the first two terms have a common factor of x^2 and the last two terms are each divisible by -9. Factoring these pairs of terms yields
$$x^3 + 2x^2 - 9x - 18 = x^2(x + 2) - 9(x + 2).$$
This shows that another common factor is $(x + 2)$. Now apply the Distributive Property.
$$= (x^2 - 9)(x + 2)$$
Finally, factor the difference of squares.
$$= (x - 3)(x + 3)(x + 2)$$

Check 1

Multiply the factors. You are asked to do this in the Questions.

Check 2

Draw graphs of $y = x^3 + 2x^2 - 9x - 18$, and $y = (x - 3)(x + 3)(x + 2)$. If the factorization is correct, the two graphs will coincide. At the right is the output from an automatic grapher. The two graphs are identical. Also, the graphs have zeros at -3, -2, and 3, as predicted by the factored form.

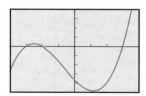

$-4 \le x \le 4$, x-scale = 1
$-25 \le y \le 20$, y-scale = 5

Grouping can be applied to factor the general trinomial $ax^2 + bx + c$. If there exist two numbers n_1 and n_2 such that $n_1n_2 = ac$ and $n_1 + n_2 = b$, then the middle term bx can be split up into $n_1x + n_2x$ (since $n_1 + n_2 = b$). This new polynomial, $ax^2 + n_1x + n_2x + c$, is always factorable by grouping. Example 2 illustrates this.

608

Lesson 9-9 Overview

Broad Goals In this lesson, students are asked to factor expressions of the form $ax + bx + ay + by$ and $ax^2 + bxy + cy^2$.

Perspective The "advanced" factoring techniques studied here are found in many first-year algebra books. We call them "advanced" because there is no need for them to be learned that early, and because they involve more than the direct application of theorems like the Factor Theorem or

learned formulas or the distributive property in its simplest form. These factorizations are difficult enough that often trial and error or a search mechanism is needed to find them. In Chapter 12, students will apply these factorizations to graph relations of the form $(ax + by + c)(dx + ey + f) = 0$, which are degenerate conic sections.

Optional Activities

Activity 1 You may wish to use this activity at the conlusion of the lesson. Have students use factoring to show that 1 greater than the product of four consecutive integers is always a perfect square.
$[1 + x(x + 1)(x + 2)(x + 3) = x^4 + 6x^3 + 11x^2 + 6x + 1 = (x^2 + 3x + 1)^2]$

Example 2

Factor $6x^2 - 13x + 5$.

Solution

Here $a = 6$, $b = -13$, and $c = 5$. Are there two numbers whose product is 30 and whose sum is -13? Mentally you realize that the numbers are -3 and -10. So rewrite the given polynomial as

$$6x^2 - 3x - 10x + 5.$$

Now group:

$$6x^2 - 3x - 10x + 5 = (6x^2 - 3x) + (-10x + 5)$$
$$= 3x(2x - 1) - 5(2x - 1)$$
$$= (3x - 5)(2x - 1).$$

Check

Multiply:
$$(3x - 5)(2x - 1) = 6x^2 - 3x - 10x + 5$$
$$= 6x^2 - 13x + 5.$$

Combining grouping and chunking can allow the factoring of polynomials with more than one variable. When a polynomial in two variables is equal to 0, as in Example 3, grouping terms may help you draw the graph of the relation.

Example 3

Draw a graph of $y^2 - xy + 5x - 5y = 0$.

Solution

The form of the equation makes it difficult to evaluate numbers and plot by hand; and many automatic graphers cannot accept an equation if it is not solved for y. Grouping with repeated applications of the Distributive Property yields the following.

$$0 = y^2 - xy + 5x - 5y$$
$$= y(y - x) + 5(x - y)$$
$$= y(y - x) - 5(y - x)$$
$$= (y - 5)(y - x)$$

So the original equation is true if and only if $y - 5 = 0$ or $y - x = 0$; that is, if $y = 5$ or $y = x$. The graphs of these equations are lines. **Thus the graph of the original equation is the union of these two lines, as shown at the right.**

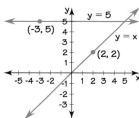

Check

Pick any point on the line $y = x$, say $(2, 2)$. Substitute these coordinates in the original equation. Does $2^2 - 2 \cdot 2 + 5 \cdot 2 - 5 \cdot 2 = 0$? Yes. They check. Similarly, the coordinates of any point on the line $y = 5$, say $(-3, 5)$, check:

$$5^2 - (-3)(5) + 5(-3) - 5 \cdot 5 = 0.$$

From earlier lessons in this chapter, students should be familiar with the use of the following theorems to factor polynomials with higher degree:
- –Factor Theorem
- –the sum of nth powers
- –the difference of nth powers.

In this lesson students will learn another technique of factoring, which is grouping.

These are not the only kinds of factoring techniques. For instance, though many students are taught that a sum of squares can never be factored over polynomials with real coefficients, it is the case that $x^4 + 4 = (x^2 - 2x + 2)(x^2 + 2x + 2)$, and more generally, $x^4 + \frac{b^4}{4} = \left(x^2 - bx + \frac{b^2}{2}\right) \cdot \left(x^2 + bx + \frac{b^2}{2}\right)$, and if b is even, only integers are involved in the factoring.

The strategy used in **Example 1** is quite powerful. Find two terms that have a common factor and factor it out; then look to see if the noncommon factor is present in the other two terms. When four terms are the product of two binomials, as in **Example 1,** there are always two ways to group. Students find the second way in **Question 1.**

Some students may have been taught to factor quadratic trinomials using the method of **Example 2.** Most students, however, are taught to use trial and error.

The set of ordered pairs in **Example 3** is an example of a quadratic relation whose graph is a degenerate hyperbola. These are discussed further in Chapter 12.

Adapting to Individual Needs

✎ **Activity 2 Writing** You may wish to use this activity after discussing **Example 2.** Have students explain why the grouping method of factoring is sometimes referred to as "splitting the middle term" when it is applied to a quadratic trinomial. Have them use examples to support their explanation. [In the procedure for grouping, the middle term is split into two terms with coefficients whose product is equal to ac and whose sum is equal to b.]

Extra Help
Suggest that students check their factoring by substituting values for the variables in the given polynomial and in the factored answer. You may wish to use **Examples 1–2** to demonstrate this procedure.

Challenge
Have students use factoring to simplify the following nonpolynomial expression which is typical of expressions found in Calculus:

$$\frac{(x + 2)^{1/2}(6x^2) - x^3(x + 2)^{-1/2}}{x + 2}.$$

$$\left[\frac{5x^3 + 12x^2}{(x + 2)^{3/2}}\right]$$

610

Additional Examples

1. Factor $6a^2b + 2ac + 3ab^2 + bc$.
   $(3ab + c)(2a + b)$

2. Factor $4x^2 + 4x - 15$ by grouping.
   $= 4x^2 + 10x - 6x - 15$
   $= (2x - 3)(2x + 5)$

3. Describe the set of ordered pairs (x, y) satisfying $x^3 + 3x^2 - yx - 3y = 0$. **The union of the sets of ordered pairs satisfying $x + 3 = 0$ and $x^2 - y = 0$. The first is the vertical line through $(-3, 0)$; the second is the parent parabola.**

Notes on Questions

Question 1 Error Alert Point out that the factored answer contains the same factors as in **Example 1**. Writing terms in a different order leads to different grouping, but the final factors are the same.

Questions 6 and 11 If an equation is desired whose graph is the union of the graphs of two relations, you can rewrite the equations for those relations so that the right sides are 0 and then multiply the nonzero sides to get an equation for the relation.

Question 24 The Rational Root Theorem (Lesson 9-8, Question 26) can be applied here.

---

1) $x(x^2 - 9) + 2(x^2 - 9)$
   $= (x + 2)(x^2 - 9)$
   $= (x + 2)(x - 3)(x + 3)$

2) $(x - 3)(x + 3)(x + 2)$
   $= (x^2 - 9)(x + 2)$
   $= x^3 + 2x^2 - 9x - 18$

3) $x^2(x + 3) - 4(x + 3)$
   $= (x^2 - 4)(x + 3)$
   $= (x + 2)(x - 2)(x + 3)$

6a)

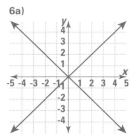

b) It is the union of the lines $y = x$ and $y = -x$.

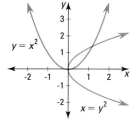

$y = x^2$

$x = y^2$

17) $\sqrt[3]{10}$,
$-\dfrac{\sqrt[3]{10}}{2} + \dfrac{\sqrt{3}\,\sqrt[3]{10}}{2}\,i$,
$-\dfrac{\sqrt[3]{10}}{2} - \dfrac{\sqrt{3}\,\sqrt[3]{10}}{2}\,i$

QUESTIONS

Covering the Reading

In 1 and 2, refer to Example 1. **See left.**

1. Factor the polynomial by rewriting it as $(x^3 - 9x) + (2x^2 - 18)$ and then applying the Distributive Property twice.

2. Verify that the product $(x - 3)(x + 3)(x + 2)$ equals $x^3 + 2x^2 - 9x - 18$.

3. Factor the polynomial $x^3 + 3x^2 - 4x - 12$ by grouping the first and second terms and the third and fourth terms and then applying the Distributive Property twice. **See left.**

In 4 and 5, use grouping to factor the following trinomials. **See margin.**

4. $12x^2 + 8x + 1$

5. $2n^2 - 9n - 5$

6. **a.** Graph the set of ordered pairs (x, y) satisfying **See left.**
   $$y^2x - x^3 - y^3 + x^2y = 0.$$
   b. Describe the graph in words. **See left.**

Applying the Mathematics

7. Find the zeros of the function $f(x) = 2x^3 - 5x^2 + 6x - 15$ using each method. **See margin.**
   a. by grouping and factoring
   b. by drawing a graph

In 8 and 9, factor.

8. $ax - bx - by + ay$
   $(x + y)(a - b)$

9. $2x^2 + xy - 2xz - yz$
   $(x - z)(2x + y)$

10. Draw a graph of $\{(x, y): -x^2 + xy + 2y^2 = 0\}$. **See margin.**

11. Find an equation describing the graph of the union of the two relations $y = x^2$ and $x = y^2$ shown at the left. **Sample: $x^3 - x^2y^2 - xy + y^3 = 0$**

12. Let $f(x) = x^2 + 6x + 8$. Simplify $\dfrac{f(x) - f(b)}{x - b}$. **$x + b + 6$**

Review

In 13–16, factor over the set of polynomials with real coefficients. *(Lesson 9-8)*

13. $x^3 - 8$ 14. $t^5 + u^5$ 15. $36x^6 - y^2z^4$ 16. $x^6y^3 - 27z^6$

13–16, See below.

17. Determine the three cube roots of 10. *(Lesson 9-8)* **See left.**

18. **a.** Find the sum of the 6th roots of unity. **0**
    b. Find the product of the 6th roots of unity. *(Lessons 9-6, 9-7, 9-8)* **–1**

13) $(x - 2)(x^2 + 2x + 4)$
14) $(t + u)(t^4 - t^3u + t^2u^2 - tu^3 + u^4)$
15) $(6x^3 - yz^2)(6x^3 + yz^2)$
16) $(x^2y - 3z^2)(x^4y^2 + 3x^2yz^2 + 9z^4)$

Additional Answers

4. $12x^2 + 6x + 2x + 1$
   $= 6x(2x + 1) + 2x + 1$
   $= (6x + 1)(2x + 1)$

5. $2n^2 + n - 10n - 5$
   $= n(2n + 1) - 5(2n + 1)$
   $= (n - 5)(2n + 1)$

7. **a.** $f(x) = x^2(2x - 5) + 3(2x - 5)$
   $= (x^2 + 3)(2x - 5)$
   $= (x + i\sqrt{3})(x - i\sqrt{3})(2x - 5)$
   The zeros of f are $\frac{5}{2}$, $i\sqrt{3}$, and $-i\sqrt{3}$.

7. b.

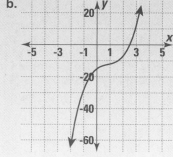

10.

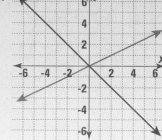

19c) $\theta = \frac{\pi}{6} + 2\pi n,$

$\frac{5\pi}{6} + 2\pi n, \frac{\pi}{2} + \pi n,$

for n an integer

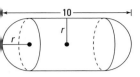

Playing in the Rain. *Some sports are played rain or shine, and rain may affect the outcome.*

20a) $V(r) = \frac{4}{3}\pi r^3 +$

$\pi r^2(10 - 2r),$

$(0 \le r \le 5)$

b)

$0 \le x \le 5, \quad x\text{-scale} = 1$
$0 \le y \le 600, \quad y\text{-scale} = 100$

22) Sample: Let the digits 0, 1, 2, 3, 4, and 5 denote rain on one day, and let the digits 6, 7, 8, and 9 denote no rain. The weather on the weekend is represented by choosing 2 random digits.

---

19. *Skill sequence.* Find all real solutions. *(Lessons 5-7, 9-6, 9-7)*

a. $2x^3 - x^2 = 0$ a) $x = 0, \frac{1}{2}$ b) $x = -1, \frac{1}{2}, 1$

b. $2x^3 - x^2 - 2x + 1 = 0$

c. $2\sin^3\theta - \sin^2\theta - 2\sin\theta = -1$ **See left.**

20. A propane gas tank is in the shape of a cylinder with hemispheres on each end as shown at the left. Suppose that the total length of the tank is 10 ft. *(Lessons 9-1, 9-2)*

    a. Find the volume $V(r)$ of the tank in terms of its radius r.   **See left.**

    b. Draw a graph of the equation $y = V(r)$ over the largest domain over which r is defined.   **See left.**

    c. What is the largest volume such a tank can have? $\approx 523.6 \text{ ft}^3$

21. Suppose a binomial probability is given by $_nC_r p^r q^{n-r} = 45p^r\left(\frac{1}{9}\right)^{10-r}$.

    a. How many trials are there?   **10**

    b. How many successes are there?   **r**

    c. What is the probability of success for each trial?   *(Lesson 8-9)* $\frac{8}{9}$

22. A meteorologist has predicted that the probability of rain in each of the two days of a weekend is 0.6. Explain how to code a set of random digits to simulate the weather on both days of the weekend. *(Lesson 7-7)* **See left.**

23. a. How many permutations consisting of four letters each can be formed from the letters of FACTORING?   **3024**

    b. How many of the permutations in part **a** end in G? *(Lesson 7-4)*   **336**

Exploration

24. Consider the function f, with $f(x) = 12x^4 - 8x^3 - 27x^2 + 18x$.

    a. Graph f on the domain $-4 \le x \le 4$. Use a range that allows you to see all four zeros and three relative extrema.   **See below.**

    b. Estimate the zeros to the nearest tenth.   **-1.5, 0, 0.7, 1.5**

    c. Use factoring to determine the zeros exactly.

      $f(x) = x(2x - 3)(2x + 3)(3x - 2)$, so the zeros are $0, \frac{3}{2}, -\frac{3}{2}$, and $\frac{2}{3}$.

a)

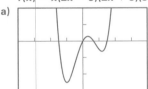

$-4 \le x \le 4, \quad x\text{-scale} = 1$
$-30 \le y \le 20, \quad y\text{-scale} = 10$

Follow-up 9-9
for Lesson

Practice
For more questions on SPUR Objectives, use **Lesson Master 9-9** (shown on page 611).

Assessment
Oral/Written Communication Have students **work in pairs**. Ask each student to find the product of any two or three binomials, and give the resulting polynomial to their partner to factor. Partners should check each other's answers and discuss the factoring methods used.

Extension
Project Update Project 3, *Synthetic Division,* and Project 5, *Algebraic and Transcendental Numbers,* on page 618, relate to the content of this lesson.

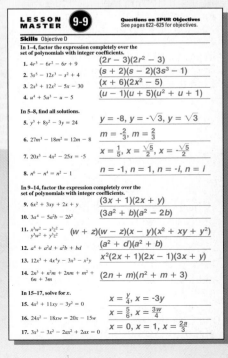

Objectives

There are no SPUR Objectives for any reading lesson.

Resources

From the *Teacher's Resource File*
- Answer Master 9-10
- Teaching Aids
  81 Warm-up
  85 Theorems for Roots and Coefficients

Additional Resources
- Visuals for Teaching Aids 81, 85

Teaching **9-10**
Lesson

Warm-up

Find the two solutions to $14x^2 + 50x - 39 = 0$. Then find the sum of the solutions and the product of the solutions.

$\frac{-50 \pm \sqrt{4684}}{28}$; sum $-\frac{25}{7}$; product $-\frac{39}{14}$

Notes on Reading

❶ You might begin by trying to solve Cardano's problem as if students had none of the mathematics of this chapter. Then we want two numbers r and s such that $r + s = 10$ and $rs = 40$. Solving the first equation for r yields $r = 10 - s$. Substituting into the second equation, we find $(10 - s)s = 40$, or $10s - s^2 = 40$, or in standard form, $s^2 - 10s + 40 = 0$. This is exactly the equation we get from the first theorem of the lesson.

9-10

Roots and Coefficients of Polynomials

In mathematics, it is common to switch the given information with what is to be found and thus invent a new problem. For instance, instead of using the lengths of two sides of a rectangle to find its area, you could be given its area and search for possible lengths of sides. Or, instead of being given x and asked to find tan x, you could know tan x and need to find x. As you saw in the previous lessons of this chapter, instead of multiplying binomials to obtain a polynomial, it is often helpful to be given the polynomial and asked to find its factors.

To reverse the process of solving equations, you could begin with the solutions and, from them, find the equation. Of course, more than one equation could have the same solution. For instance, if $x = 6$ is the only solution, any of the following could be an equation, and you could find many more.

$$\log x \approx .7782 \quad 2^x = 64 \quad 3x^2 - 6x + 8 = 80 \quad x - 6 = 0$$

However, if the equation must be a polynomial equation in standard form $a_n x^n + a_{n-1}x^{n-1} + \ldots + a_1 x + a_0 = 0$, then the choice is more restricted. Only the two rightmost equations above are polynomial equations, and only the rightmost is in standard form. If the multiplicities of solutions are to be considered as 1 unless otherwise indicated, then only the equations of the form $ax - 6a = 0$, where a is any nonzero complex number, would have the solution $x = 6$. Finally, if the leading coefficient must be 1, then only the equation $x - 6 = 0$ satisfies all these criteria and has only the solution $x = 6$. Thus, with certain constraints—standard form, multiplicities known, leading coefficient 1—the polynomial is uniquely determined.

Roots and Coefficients of Quadratic Equations

What polynomial equation in standard form, and with leading coefficient 1, has the solutions $\frac{2}{3}$ and -5? Using the Factor Theorem, the polynomial can be found by multiplying $\left(x - \frac{2}{3}\right)(x - -5)$ to obtain the left side of the desired equation $x^2 + \frac{13}{3}x - \frac{10}{3} = 0$.

In general, if a polynomial equation in standard form $P(x) = 0$ has leading coefficient 1 and two zeros or *roots* r_1 and r_2, then $P(x)$ is found by multiplying $(x - r_1)(x - r_2)$, and the equation is $x^2 - (r_1 + r_2)x + r_1 r_2 = 0$. This argument proves the following theorem.

> **Theorem**
> For the quadratic equation $x^2 + bx + c = 0$, the sum of the roots is $-b$ and the product of the roots is c.

612

Lesson 9-10 Overview

Broad Goals Many students will already be familiar with the fact that if r and s are the roots of a quadratic equation $ax^2 + bx + c = 0$, then $r + s = \frac{-b}{a}$ and $rs = \frac{c}{a}$. This lesson discusses the extension of that result to cubic equations and then further to all polynomial equations. It is a reading lesson; there are no objectives in the Chapter Review relating to this lesson and the lesson is not tested.

Perspective There are three theorems here. The proofs of the first and second use the factorization of the polynomial obtained from the Factor Theorem. The proof of the third theorem, the generalization of the first two, shows that the idea of combinations from Chapter 8 is involved. All three theorems enable polynomial equations to be formed rather easily with any given solutions.

An alternate approach to the proof of the first theorem is to use the Quadratic Formula. Add $\frac{-b + \sqrt{b^2 - 4ac}}{2a}$ to $\frac{-b - \sqrt{b^2 - 4ac}}{2a}$; the sum is $\frac{-2b}{2a}$, which equals $-\frac{b}{a}$. In this case $a = 1$, so the sum is $-b$. Multiply the two solutions; the product is $\left(\frac{-b}{2a}\right)^2 - \left(\frac{\sqrt{b^2 - 4ac}}{2a}\right)^2 = \frac{b^2 - (b^2 - 4ac)}{4a^2} = \frac{4ac}{4a^2} = \frac{c}{a}$, and again $a = 1$, so the product is c. We did not use this

*Girolamo Cardano
(woodcut, 1539)*

① For example, to find two numbers whose sum is 10 and whose product is 40, you need only solve the quadratic equation $x^2 - 10x + 40 = 0$. The solutions are the desired numbers. This exact problem was used by Girolamo Cardano in 1533 to introduce complex numbers for the first time.

Roots and Coefficients of Cubic Equations

If a polynomial equation $P(x) = 0$ has three roots (counting multiplicities), then you know $P(x)$ is of degree 3. If $a_n = 1$ and the roots are r_1, r_2, and r_3, then

$$P(x) = (x - r_1)(x - r_2)(x - r_3).$$

To write $P(x) = 0$ in standard form, multiply the three binomials. The result is the equation

$$x^3 - (r_1 + r_2 + r_3)x^2 + (r_1r_2 + r_1r_3 + r_2r_3)x - r_1r_2r_3 = 0.$$

Notice how the multiplication of the three binomials creates this polynomial. The coefficient of x^3 is 1 because there is only one way to multiply the three x's from the binomials. To explain the x^2 term, notice that there are three ways to choose two of the x's, and in each case one of the r_i must be the other factor. This creates the x^2 term. For the x term, there are three ways to choose the x, but the other two factors in each term must be pairs of r_i. And then, choosing r_i from each of the three binomials can be done in only one way. (You are asked to confirm this result in the Questions.) The alternating subtraction and addition occurs because each root is subtracted in its binomial, and so the sign of the product depends on whether there are an odd or even number of roots multiplied.

> **Theorem**
> For the cubic equation $x^3 + bx^2 + cx + d = 0$, the sum of the roots is $-b$, the sum of the products of the roots two at a time is c, and the product of the three roots is $-d$.

Roots and Coefficients of Any Polynomial Equation

The theorems for quadratic and cubic equations can be generalized to polynomial equations of any degree. If a polynomial equation $P(x) = 0$ has leading coefficient $a_n = 1$ and n roots $r_1, r_2, \ldots r_n$, then

$$P(x) = (x - r_1)(x - r_2)(x - r_3) \ldots (x - r_n).$$

The key to understanding the generalization is to see the multiplication of the binomials $(x - r_i)$ as a problem in combinations. Each term contributing to the coefficient of x^k is a result of choosing x from k of the binomial factors and the r_i from the other $n - k$ binomial factors. So there are $_nC_k$ terms with the factor x^k. The coefficient of x^k is the sum of the coefficients in all these terms—that is, the sum of the products of the roots taken $n - k$ at a time, multiplied by -1 if the number of roots chosen is odd.

You might ask how the three theorems of this lesson are related. [The third theorem is a generalization of the first two.] Then take the students through examples of increasing degree. You might ask students to provide the roots, keeping the roots as nonzero integers between -10 and 10 to hold the arithmetic to a minimum. The theorems are available on **Teaching Aid 85.**

Here are examples; we use "Σ of p" to mean "sum of the product" to save space.

Roots (given): 2, -7
  Σ of p of roots 1 at a time: -5
  Σ of p of roots 2 at a time: -14
Equation: $x^2 + 5x - 14 = 0$.

Roots: 2, -7, 3
  Σ of p of roots 1 at a time: -2
  Σ of p of roots 2 at a time: -29
  Σ of p of roots 3 at a time: -42
Equation: $x^3 + 2x^2 - 29x + 42 = 0$.

Roots: 2, -7, 3, 10
  Σ of p of roots 1 at a time: 8
  Σ of p of roots 2 at a time: -49
  Σ of p of roots 3 at a time: -332
  Σ of p of roots 4 at a time: -420
Equation: $x^4 - 8x^3 - 49x^2 + 332x - 420 = 0$.

You can extend this process for as many roots as you wish.

You can check each answer by multiplying the factors one would get by using the Factor Theorem. That multiplication will involve the same arithmetic as was used to get the equation in the first place, though not in the same order. Notice how all the combinations of the n roots are involved; there are a total of 2^n terms that have to be added.

Optional Activities

approach, even though it may be more understandable for students, because we have no explicit formula for the roots of polynomial equations of any higher degree, and so this proof does not extend even to the cubic.

Activity 1 Cooperative Learning After discussing the theorem on page 614, you may wish to have students **work in groups** to verify that the polynomial on page 614 has roots -8, 9, 2, 5. Suggest that they substitute these values for x, or graph the polynomial function $y = x^4 - 8x^3 - 55x^2 + 494x - 720$, or do both to verify the zeros . (A good window to use is $-10 \leq x \leq 10$; $-3000 \leq y \leq 1000$.) Ask students how they could come up with another different polynomial function

with these same zeros. [Sample: Multiply all coefficients by a constant.] Have students list a few different functions and describe how the graphs are similar to and different from the original function. [Sample: The graph of $y = -x^4 + 8x^3 + 55x^2 - 494x + 720$ is the reflection image of the original graph over the x-axis; $y = 0.5x^4 - 4x^3 - 27.5x^2 + 247x - 360$ is the image of the original graph under a scale change of 0.5. All the graphs have the same zeros.]

The second idea presented in this lesson is the writing of an equation for the union of two relations, motivated as an application to databases. This idea was first used in Lesson 9-9.

For instance, to find a polynomial equation with roots -8, 9, 2, and 5, you could multiply

$$(x + 8)(x - 9)(x - 2)(x - 5)$$

and set the product equal to zero. You could also determine the coefficients by taking the products of the roots one at a time, two at a time, three at a time, and four at a time. The coefficient of x^4 is 1. Products one at a time are just the terms, and the opposite of their sum is the coefficient of x^3.

$$-(-8 + 9 + 2 + 5) = -8$$

There are $_4C_2 = 6$ products two at a time. Their sum gives the coefficient of x^2.

$$-8 \cdot 9 + -8 \cdot 2 + -8 \cdot 5 + 9 \cdot 2 + 9 \cdot 5 + 2 \cdot 5 = -55$$

There are $_4C_3 = 4$ products three at a time. The opposite of their sum gives the coefficient of x.

$$-(-8 \cdot 9 \cdot 2 + -8 \cdot 9 \cdot 5 + -8 \cdot 2 \cdot 5 + 9 \cdot 2 \cdot 5) = 494$$

There is $_4C_4 = 1$ product four at a time. This is the product of the 4 roots, and it gives the constant term, the coefficient of x^0.

$$-8 \cdot 9 \cdot 2 \cdot 5 = -720$$

A polynomial equation with roots -8, 9, 2, and 5 is therefore

$$x^4 - 8x^3 - 55x^2 + 494x - 720 = 0.$$

An Application to Databases

Finding equations with given solutions sometimes arises when working with databases. In databases, people or other variables are typically categorized in various ways, and the categories are identified by numbers. For instance, in a database for students in a high school, one variable might be the section of the community in which a student lives. Name this variable SECT and suppose it has the 8 integer values 1 to 8, each identifying a particular section of the community. Suppose that a survey is to be done of how students get to school, and further suppose sections 3, 5, and 6 are very close to the school. To choose students from these sections, you could use the following instruction.

IF SECT = 3 OR SECT = 5 OR SECT = 6 THEN ...

614

Optional Activities

Activity 2 Technology Connection Have students use a graphing calculator to complete the table at the right for the three functions below:
a. $f(x) = x^3 + 2x^2 - x - 3$
b. $f(x) = x^3 - 2x^2 + x - 3$
c. $f(x) = x^3 + 2x^2 + x + 3$

f(x)	a	b	c
Number of changes in sign in the coefficients of $f(x)$	[1]	[3]	[0]
Number of positive x-intercepts	[1]	[1]	[0]
Number of changes in sign in the coefficients of $f(-x)$	[2]	[0]	[3]
Number of negative x-intercepts	[0]	[0]	[1]

Ask students to look up Descartes' Rule of Signs and see how the theorem applies to these examples. [The number of positive x-intercepts is equal to the number of changes in sign in $f(x)$ (or $2n$ less); the number negative x-intercepts is equal to the number of changes in sign in $f(-x)$ (or $2n$ less).]

The three equations and the two OR statements can be replaced by a single equation

$$\text{IF (SECT} - 3)\text{*(SECT} - 5)\text{*(SECT} - 6) = 0 \text{ THEN} \dots$$

Multiplying the three binomials does not result in a shorter form of the line of the instruction. To see this, replace SECT by x and use the results of the previous theorem to rewrite the polynomial in standard form.

$$(x - 3)(x - 5)(x - 6) = x^3 - (3 + 5 + 6)x^2 +$$
$$(3 \cdot 5 + 5 \cdot 6 + 3 \cdot 6)x - 3 \cdot 5 \cdot 6$$
$$= x^3 - 14x^2 + 63x - 90$$

Since computers are often preprogrammed to use logarithms to calculate powers, and because that arithmetic involves approximations, it may be better to put the final polynomial in nested form.

$$= ((x - 14)x + 63)x - 90$$

The replacement of x by SECT in the decision line gives the following.

$$\text{IF ((SECT} - 14)\text{*SECT} + 63)\text{*SECT} - 90 = 0 \text{ THEN} \dots$$

In our tests, the OR statements ran faster. But for large programs, there might be a savings of computer time and memory to use the other statements.

QUESTIONS

Covering the Reading

1) Samples: $x^4 - 1 = 0$; $x^4 - x^3 + 4x^2 - 3x - 1 = 0$; $5^{x-1} = 1$; $\log(2x - 1) = 0$

1. Give four equations different from those in this lesson that have the solution $x = 1$. Try to make your equations unlike each other. **See left.**

2. A quadratic equation has solutions $-\frac{3}{4}$ and 6. If the leading coefficient of the quadratic is 1, write the equation in standard form. $x^2 - \frac{21}{4}x - \frac{9}{2} = 0$

3. Solve Cardano's problem. $x = 5 + \sqrt{15}i$ or $x = 5 - \sqrt{15}i$

4. The sum of two numbers is 17 and their product is 100. What are the numbers? $\frac{17}{2} + \frac{\sqrt{111}}{2}i$ and $\frac{17}{2} - \frac{\sqrt{111}}{2}i$

5. Find a polynomial equation with the three solutions 1, 2, and 3.
   Sample: $x^3 - 6x^2 + 11x - 6 = 0$

6. A polynomial equation in x has the five solutions -10, -5, 0, 5, and 10. The leading coefficient of the polynomial is 1.
   a. Give the coefficient of x^4. **0**   b. Give the coefficient of x^3. **-125**
   c. Give a possible equation. $x^5 - 125x^3 + 2500x = 0$

7. Consider the equation $x^5 - 3x^2 + 60 = 0$.
   a. What is the sum of the roots of this equation? **0**
   b. What is the product of the roots of this equation? **-60**

8. In instructions to find a file in a database, how could the following OR statement be replaced by a statement with one equation and no OR?
   $$\text{IF SECT} = 7 \text{ OR SECT} = 2 \text{ OR SECT} = 6 \text{ THEN} \dots$$
   Sample: IF ((SECT $- 15$)* SECT $+ 68$)* SECT $- 84 = 0$ THEN $\dots$

Notes on Questions
Question 2 Stress that there are always many equations with the same solutions; for instance, here the answer $x^2 - \frac{21}{4}x - \frac{9}{2} = 0$ could be multiplied by 4 to obtain $4x^2 - 21x - 18 = 0$. Adding $21x + 18$ to both sides yields $4x^2 = 21x + 18$. We ask for answers in standard form in order to make them unique.

Question 7 Note that the sum of the roots of $x^n - a = 0$ is zero also. The solutions to that equation are the nth roots of a. So, from the Roots and Coefficients Theorem, it is easy to prove that the sum of the nth roots of any number is zero. Students can try that on some numbers and nth roots they know.

Adapting to Individual Needs

Extra Help
You may wish to point out that to apply the theorem at the top of page 614, the required multiplication involves all the combinations of the n roots and that there are a total of 2^n terms that need to be added.

Challenge
Remind students that $i^3 = -i$ so i is a cube root of $-i$. Ask students to use the Factor Theorem to find the other two cube roots of $-i$. $\left[\frac{-i \pm \sqrt{3}}{2}\right]$

Question 12a Students have to take on faith the fact that a root c of multiplicity 2 means that the graph is tangent to the x-axis at $(c, 0)$.

Follow-up 9-10
for Lesson

Extension

Have students **work in groups** to research more information about Girolamo Cardano. Suggest that students choose a creative way to present or display their research.

Additional Answers

14. $-\frac{4}{3}$ is a solution of $g(x) = 0$

15. a. $ax^3 - ax^2 - 2ax = f(x)$
   b. $\frac{1}{2}x^3 - \frac{1}{2}x^2 - x = g(x)$
   c. $\frac{1}{2}x^3 - \frac{1}{2}x^2 - x = g(x)$ is the specific case of $ax^3 - ax^2 - 2ax = f(x)$ for $a = \frac{1}{2}$.

9) $p(x) = (x + 1)^2 \cdot (x^2 - x + 1)(x - 1)$; zeros are -1 (multiplicity 2), 1, $\frac{1}{2} + \frac{\sqrt{3}}{2}i, \frac{1}{2} - \frac{\sqrt{3}}{2}i$.

10c) $(t - 1) \cdot$
$\left(t + \frac{1}{2} + \frac{\sqrt{3}}{2}i\right) \cdot$
$\left(t + \frac{1}{2} - \frac{\sqrt{3}}{2}i\right)$

12a)

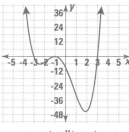

b)

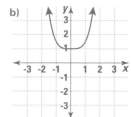

Pea or Nut? *Peanuts are not true nuts; they are legumes like peas. A peg grows from the base of the peanut plant flower and digs as far as 10 cm into the ground where the peanuts grow.*

616

9. Find the zeros of $p(x) = x^5 - x^3 + x^2 - 1$ by grouping. Describe any multiple zeros. *(Lessons 9-7, 9-9)* **See left.**

10. Factor the polynomial $t^3 - 1$ over each set of numbers.
   a. integers
   b. reals
   c. complex numbers
   (Lessons 9-6, 9-8) **a, b)** $(t - 1)(t^2 + t + 1)$ **See left.**

11. Find the exact solutions of $\sin^4\theta - \cos^4\theta = 0$ in the interval $0 \le \theta \le 2\pi$. *(Lessons 4-4, 5-7, 9-8)* $\theta = \frac{\pi}{4}, \frac{3\pi}{4}, \frac{5\pi}{4}$, and $\frac{7\pi}{4}$

12. Sketch the graph of a fourth degree polynomial satisfying the given condition. **See left for samples.**
   a. four real roots, one of multiplicity two
   b. no real roots *(Lesson 9-7)*

13. The first two terms of a geometric sequence are $6i$ and -12. Find each.
   a. the common ratio $2i$
   b. the next two terms $-24i$, 48
   c. the 100th term *(Lessons 8-1, 9-6)* $3 \cdot 2^{100}$

14. When a polynomial $g(x)$ is divided by $3x + 4$, the remainder is 0. Make a conclusion about the equation $g(x) = 0$. *(Lessons 9-4, 9-5)* **See margin.**

15. a. Find a general equation for a cubic function with zeros at -1, 0, and 2.
   b. Use the result in part **a** to find an equation for the cubic function passing through the points $(-1, 0)$, $(0, 0)$, $(1, -1)$, and $(2, 0)$.
   c. How are the answers to parts **a** and **b** related? *(Lessons 9-3, 9-5)* **See margin.**

16. When a polynomial $p(x)$ is divided by $x - 12$, the quotient is $x^3 + 5$ and the remainder is -1. Determine $p(x)$. *(Lesson 9-4)* $p(x) = x^4 - 12x^3 + 5x - 61$

17. Consider a (closed) rectangular box with dimensions x, $x + 3$, and $x - 5$.
   a. Write a polynomial in expanded form for $V(x)$, the volume of the box.
   b. Write a polynomial in expanded form for $S(x)$, the surface area of the box. $S(x) = 6x^2 - 8x - 30$
   c. If x is measured in cm, in what unit is each of $V(x)$ and $S(x)$ measured? *(Lesson 9-1)* $V(x)$: **cubic centimeters;** $S(x)$: **square centimeters**
   a) $V(x) = x^3 - 2x^2 - 15x$

18. In 1995, about 24.5% of the U.S. population was aged 40 to 60. Determine the probability that the first four people called in a national telephone survey in 1995 were all aged 40 to 60. *(Lessons 7-3, 7-5)* $(0.245)^4 \approx 0.0036 \approx 0.4\%$

19. The 12-oz packages (in glass jars) of a certain brand of peanuts are found to weigh 24.5 ounces on the average and the weights have a standard deviation of 0.45 oz. The company decides to switch to plastic jars which weigh 8 ounces less than the glass ones. Determine the mean and standard deviation of the weights of the new packages. *(Lesson 3-3)* **mean = 16.5 oz; standard deviation = 0.45 oz**

20. Explore a database program and explain how it sets up files and how it enables the user to make choices from those files. **Answers will vary.**

Possible responses, page 617

1. a. Sample: $y = x^3 - 5x^2 + 11x - 6$
   b. Sample: If the third difference is 1, we get $y = \frac{1}{6}x^3 + \frac{11}{6}x - 1$.
   c. The fourth differences must be the same, but the third differences must be different. If the 4th differences are 1 and the 3rd differences are linear 1, 2, 3, ..., then working backwards, $y = 17$ for $x = 4$ and $y = 30$ for $x = 5$.
   d. Given n data points, there is a polynomial of degree $n - 1$ that fits the data. It's possible that a polynomial of lesser degree fits. Given three data points that all lie on the same line, a polynomial of degree 1 (a linear line) is enough to fit the data. There are an infinite number of polynomials of degree greater than $n - 1$ that fit n data points.

2. Move from any diagonal of Pascal's Triangle toward the side that is parallel to that diagonal. Each diagonal contains differences of the diagonal preceding it. Since all the elements in the side of the triangle are the same, you get a constant difference when you reach the side. We can let the elements in the original diagonal be the y-values corresponding to the x-values 1, 2, 3, ..., and then find a polyno-

A project presents an opportunity for you to extend your knowledge of a topic related to the material of this chapter. You should allow more time for a project than you do for a typical homework question.

1, 4, 9, 16, ...

1 Completing the Pattern

On some tests you are asked to "complete the pattern," or to find the next term in a sequence such as

$$1, 4, 9, \ldots .$$

These are misleading questions, because there are always many justifiable answers to such problems. In fact, for any n points, if you add one more point of your own, you can find a polynomial of degree n to model the data. For example, below is a table of differences for the pattern begun above.

Only one second difference, 2, is known.

Now make up any value you like for the third difference, 6 for instance, and work backward from the third difference to the next y value.

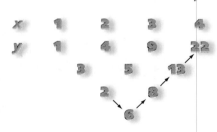

a. Use the method of finite differences to find a polynomial for these data. Check that the first four values fit the polynomial.

b. Now go back to the original data and choose a different value for the third difference, and work backwards to find the y value associated with $x = 4$. Use finite differences to find a polynomial different from that in part **a** that models the original data.

c. Find a value for y when $x = 4$ that could be justified by a quartic model.

d. If n data points are given, what is the degree of the polynomial needed to fit all of the data? What do the results of your investigation in parts **a–c** tell you about the number of polynomials of higher degree that might fit the data?

2 Pascal's Triangle Revisited

Examine each diagonal of Pascal's Triangle. These are the sequences of numbers indicated by the arrows in the figure at the right. Explain why the nth term of each diagonal can be represented by a polynomial. Find examples of diagonals in this triangle that can be described by linear, quadratic, cubic, quartic, and quintic polynomials, and find formulas for those polynomials.

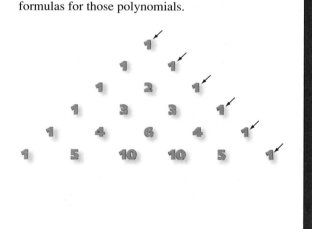

Chapter 9 Projects

The projects relate chiefly to the content of the lessons of this chapter as follows:

Project	Lesson(s)
1	9-1, 9-3
2	9-3
3	9-4, 9-5, 9-7, 9-8, 9-9
4	9-2, 9-3
5	9-5, 9-6, 9-7, 9-8, 9-9
6	9-7

1 Completing the Pattern This project allows for a great deal of freedom. Encourage students to create patterns that start simply but do not remain that way, for instance, 2, 4, 6, 13,. . . . Students might also use patterns from numbers in their life, like their telephone numbers.

2 Pascal's Triangle Revisited You might have students look for patterns in Pascal's Triangle other than those mentioned in this chapter.

---

mial to fit the data. In the first drawing at the right, the first differences are constant, and we can show that the polynomial $y = x$ fits the data. In the second triangle, the second differences are constant, so the elements on this diagonal are on a quadratic curve, namely $y = \frac{1}{2}x^2 + \frac{1}{2}x$.

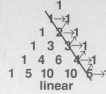

linear

quadratic

Continuing on to the next diagonal, 1, 4, 10, 20, ..., can be described by the cubic $y = \frac{1}{6}x^3 + \frac{1}{2}x^2 + \frac{1}{3}x$. The next

diagonal, 1, 5, 15, 35, 70, ..., can be described by the quartic $y = \frac{1}{24}x^4 + \frac{1}{4}x^3 + \frac{11}{24}x^2 + \frac{1}{4}x$. And the next diagonal, 1, 6, 21, 56, 126, 252, ..., can be described by the quintic $y = \frac{1}{120}x^5 + \frac{1}{12}x^4 + \frac{7}{24}x^3 + \frac{5}{12}x^2 + \frac{1}{5}x$.

(Responses continue on page 618.)

Left sidebar (project descriptions)

3 Synthetic Division Synthetic division is described in many precalculus texts.

4 Properties of Cubics This project explains why the graphs of cubic functions can be classified into two types.

5 Algebraic and Transcendental Numbers Books on the history of mathematics will give much of the information needed for this project.

6 Tragedy Strikes Brilliant Young Mathematicians E.T. Bell's volume *Men of Mathematics* is one source of information for this project.

Possible responses

3. This topic is discussed in UCSMP *Precalculus and Discrete Mathematics*.

4. **a.** A point-symmetry can be observed.

   b. If $f(x) = ax^3 + p(x)$, then
   $f(-x) = a(-x)^3 + p(-x)$
   $\quad = -ax^3 - px$
   $\quad = -(ax^3 + px) = -f(x)$,
   so f is odd. Suppose a point $(b, f(b))$ is on the curve. Since f is odd $(-b, f(-b)) = (-b, -f(b))$ is on the curve. The line connecting these two points is
   $(y - f(b)) = \frac{f(b) - (-f(b))}{(b - (-b))}(x - b)$
   or equivalently $y = \frac{f(b)}{b}x$.
   This line passes through the origin. Also the distance from the origin to $(b, f(b))$ is the same as the distance from the origin to $(-b, -f(b))$. Thus $(-b, -f(b))$ is the image of $(b, f(b))$ under a rotation of 180° about the origin. That is, $(0, 0)$ is a center of symmetry for $f(x) = ax^3 + px$.

   c. The center of symmetry is $(0, q)$.

   d. (h, q)

Center column

(continued)

3 Synthetic Division
Synthetic division is another way to perform long division of a polynomial by a linear factor. Find a book that explains this procedure. Teach yourself to do it. Prove why it works. Figure out how to use the Remainder Theorem in conjunction with it.

4 Properties of Cubics
Recall that the graph of every quadratic function $f(x) = ax^2 + bx + c$ is reflection-symmetric to the line $x = -\frac{b}{2a}$. The purpose of this project is to explore the symmetry of the graph of the general cubic function $f(x) = ax^3 + bx^2 + cx + d$.

a. Graph $y = x^3$ and four other cubic functions. Describe any line or point symmetry you observe.

b. Examine specifically several functions with equations of the form $f(x) = ax^3 + px$. Prove that each of these is an odd function, and explain how your proof shows that the origin is a center of symmetry for the graph of $f(x) = ax^3 + px$.

c. Now, examine graphs of equations of the form $y = ax^3 + px + q$. What is the center of symmetry for these curves?

d. Consider equations of the form
$$f(x) = a(x - h)^3 + p(x - h) + q.$$
What are the coordinates of the center of symmetry for these curves?

e. When an equation of the form
$$f(x) = a(x - h)^3 + p(x - h) + q$$
is expanded and like terms are combined, explain why it must be of the form
$$f(x) = ax^3 + bx^2 + cx + d.$$

618

Right column

By equating coefficients of terms of equal degree, prove that $h = -\frac{b}{3a}$. Use this result to find a center of symmetry for the graph of
$$f(x) = ax^3 + bx^2 + cx + d.$$

5 Algebraic and Transcendental Numbers
Algebraic numbers and *transcendental numbers* are two types of real numbers. Two transcendental numbers you have studied are π and e. What are the distinguishing characteristics of transcendental or algebraic numbers? How are they related to the rational and irrational numbers? Where are they used? What led to their discovery?

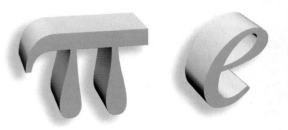

6 Tragedy Strikes Brilliant Young Mathematicians
Like Abel, Evariste Galois contributed important results to the study of polynomials at an early age. And also like Abel, Galois died at an early age. Find out more about the mathematical work of these two men and the tragic circumstances that led to their early deaths.

Bottom

4. **e.** $a(x - h)^3 + p(x - h) + q$
   $= a(x^3 - 3x^2h + 3xh^2 - h^3) + p(x - h) + q$
   $= ax^3 - 3ax^2h + 3axh^2 - ah^3 + px - ph + q$
   $= ax^3 - 3ahx^2 + (3ah^2 + p)x + (-ah^3 - ph + q)$.

   So, if $f(x)$ is of the form $ax^3 + bx^2 + cx + d$, $-3ah = b \Rightarrow h = -\frac{b}{3a}$. Also $c = 3ah^2 + p$.

   Substituting for h gives $c = 3a\left(-\frac{b}{3a}\right)^2 + p \Rightarrow p = c - \frac{b^2}{3a}$. Finally, we have

   $d = -ah^3 - ph + q$. Substituting for h and p gives $d = -a\left(-\frac{b}{3a}\right)^3 - \left(c - \frac{b^2}{3a}\right)\left(-\frac{b}{3a}\right) + q$

   $= \frac{b^3}{27a^2} + \frac{bc}{3a} - \frac{b^3}{9a^2} + q = -\frac{bc}{3a} - \frac{b^3}{9a^2} + q = -\frac{2b^3}{27a^2} + \frac{bc}{3a} + q \Rightarrow q = d + \frac{2b^3}{27a^2} - \frac{bc}{3a}$.

   So the center of symmetry for the graph is $\left(\frac{b}{3a}, d + \frac{2b^3}{27a^2} - \frac{bc}{3a}\right)$.

SUMMARY

A polynomial in x of degree n is an expression of the form $a_n x^n + a_{n-1} x^{n-1} + \ldots + a_1 x + a_0$, where $a_n \neq 0$. Polynomials model situations such as long-term loan repayment, savings accounts with periodic installments, volumes and surface areas of three-dimensional figures, and so forth.

The graphs of polynomial functions of a given degree n share certain characteristics. To approximate or determine specific values for a given polynomial (such as relative extrema, zeros, or intercepts), automatic graphers or computer programs that tabulate values of the function over specified intervals can be used.

For any nth degree polynomial, the nth differences of y-values corresponding to any arithmetic sequence of x-values are equal and nonzero. If a polynomial of degree n fits a given set of data, then $n + 1$ points give rise to $n + 1$ equations that determine its coefficients.

The algorithm for dividing polynomials is very similar to that for dividing integers. If there is a remainder, its degree is always less than the degree of the dividend. Thus, when a polynomial $f(x)$ is divided by the linear factor $(x - c)$, the remainder is $f(c)$. Consequently, a number c is a solution to $f(x) = 0$ if and only if $(x - c)$ is a factor of $f(x)$. Thus, binomial factors of polynomial functions can be used to determine x-intercepts of their graphs or solutions to polynomial equations. Conversely, equations for polynomial functions can always be constructed if their zeros are known.

Imaginary numbers are nonzero real-number multiples of $i = \sqrt{-1}$. Complex numbers are sums of imaginary and real numbers. Operations with complex numbers are similar to those with polynomials. The Fundamental Theorem of Algebra and some of its consequences guarantee that every polynomial of degree $n \geq 1$ with complex coefficients has exactly n complex zeros, if multiplicities are counted.

No general formula exists for finding exact solutions for all polynomial equations. However, some polynomial equations can be solved by factoring. All sums and differences of the same odd power can be factored as can differences of even powers. Another technique is to group terms with common factors and then use the distributive property.

Coefficients of a polynomial are directly determined by its roots. If the leading coefficient is 1, the next coefficient is the opposite of the sum of the roots, the next one is the sum of the products of the roots taken two at a time, and so on.

5. **Sample: Algebraic numbers are roots of polynomial functions with rational coefficients. π or e can never be the solution of a polynomial equation. All transcendental numbers are irrational (but not all irrationals are transcendental). Although there are infinitely many transcendental numbers, the two best known, e and π, are used in trigonometry and exponential modeling. Georg Cantor first proved the existence of transcendentals in the** early 1860s. In 1873, Charles Hermite proved that e is transcendental, and, in 1882, F. Lindemann proved that π is transcendental.

6. **Students' reports may include some of the following main points:**
Abel:
1. **Abel's birth in Norway (1802)**
2. **Proof that general quintic cannot be solved by means of radicals**

3. *Abel's integral equation, Abel's Theorems, Abel's convergence test, Abelian groups*
4. **Death in 1829 from tuberculosis**
Galois:
1. **Galois' birth in Paris (1811)**
2. **Difficulty in school**
3. **Important results submitted to the French academy at age 17**
4. **Theory of groups**
5. **Theory of equations**
6. **Death in a love-affair duel (1832)**

Vocabulary

Terms, symbols, and properties are listed by lesson to provide a checklist of concepts a student must know. Emphasize to students that they should read the vocabulary list carefully before starting the Progress Self-Test. If students do not understand the meaning of a term, they should refer back to the indicated lesson.

VOCABULARY

Below are the most important terms and phrases for this chapter. You should be able to give a general description and a specific example of each and a precise definition for those marked with an asterisk (*).

Lesson 9-1
*polynomial in x
general form, standard form
degree of a polynomial
coefficient, leading coefficient
monomial, binomial, trinomial
degree of a polynomial in more than one variable
polynomial function
square numbers, triangular numbers

Lesson 9-2
extreme values
extrema of functions, extrema
maximum/minimum value of a function
relative maximum/minimum
zeros, roots of a polynomial function p
linear/quadratic polynomial function
positive/negative on an interval
increasing/decreasing on an interval

Lesson 9-3
tetrahedral numbers
Polynomial Difference Theorem

Lesson 9-4
dividend, divisor, quotient
remainder
Remainder Theorem

Lesson 9-5
Factor Theorem
Factor-Solution-Intercept Equivalence Theorem
pentagonal numbers

Lesson 9-6
*imaginary numbers, i
*complex numbers, $a + bi$
*real part, imaginary part (of a complex number)
equal (complex numbers)
factored over a set
*complex conjugates

Lesson 9-7
Fundamental Theorem of Algebra
multiplicity of a zero
Number of Zeros of a Polynomial Theorem
Conjugate Zeros Theorem
nth roots of unity

Lesson 9-8
Sums and Differences of Cubes Theorem
Sums and Differences of Odd Powers Theorem

PROGRESS SELF-TEST

Take this test as you would take a test in class. You will need an automatic grapher. Then check the test yourself using the solutions at the back of the book.

1. In the data given below, y is a polynomial function of x. Find an equation of least degree for the polynomial. $y = 3x^2 - 8x + 1$

x	1	2	3	4	5	6	7
y	-4	-3	4	17	36	61	92

2. Approximate, to the nearest hundredth, the smallest positive x-intercept of the graph of $y = x^5 - x^3 + 3x^2 - 9$. $x \approx 1.42$

3. Determine the quotient and remainder when $3x^4 - 7x^3 + 8x^2 - 14x - 10$ is divided by $x + 2$. $3x^3 - 13x^2 + 34x - 82$; 154

4. Factor $9x^2 - 3x - 2$. $(3x - 2)(3x + 1)$

5. Factor $t^6 + 1000y^3$ over the set of polynomials with integer coefficients. **See below.**

6. *Multiple choice.* For the polynomial $f(x) = x^8 - 7x^6 + 6x^3 - 4x^2 + 12x - 8$, $f(1) = 0$. Which is a factor of $f(x)$? **a**
   (a) $x - 1$ (b) $x + 1$
   (c) $x - 2$ (d) $x + 2$

7. Let $z = 2 + 5i$ and $w = 3 - i$. Express each of the following in $a + bi$ form.
   a. $2z + w$ **7 + 9i**   **b.** $\frac{z}{w}$ $\frac{1}{10} + \frac{17}{10}i$

In 8–10, consider the polynomial function g, with $g(x) = (x - 8)^3(2x + 3)^2(5x - 1)$.

8. Which zero of g has multiplicity two? $-\frac{3}{2}$

9. What is the degree of $g(x)$? **6**

10. How many x-intercepts does the graph of g have? **3**

11. Explain why a polynomial function of degree seven with real coefficients must have at least one real zero. **See margin.**

12. Solve $x^4 + 11x^2 + 10 = 0$ completely, given that one of the solutions is i.
    $x = i, -i, \sqrt{10}i, -\sqrt{10}i$

5) $(t^2 + 10y)(t^4 - 10t^2y + 100y^2)$

13. The prices for a thin crust spinach pizza at Sophia's pizzeria are listed below. **$10.60**

10"	12"	14"
$5.95	$6.95	$8.50

If pricing is based on a quadratic function containing these three points, what should a 16" pizza cost (rounded to the nearest penny)?

14. In a right triangle the sides are as given at the right. Find x to the nearest hundredth. $x \approx 1.27$

15. Part of the graph of a polynomial function t is graphed below.

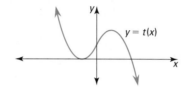
$y = t(x)$

   a. At least how many real zeros (including multiplicities) does t have? **at least 3**
   b. What is the lowest degree the polynomial $t(x)$ must have? **at least 3**

16. A 25-meter high cylindrical grain silo is to have 35 cm of insulation between two layers of sheet metal, as shown below.

35 cm

25 m

r

Express the volume V of insulation material as a polynomial function of r, the radius of the outer layer of the silo.
$V = 17.5\pi r - 3.0625\pi$ m^3

Chapter 9 Review

Resources

From the *Teacher's Resource File*
- Answer Master for Chapter 9 Review
- Assessment Sourcebook:
  Chapter 9 Test, Forms A-D
  Chapter 9 Test, Cumulative Form
  Comprehensive Test,
  Chapters 1–9

Additional Resources
- Quiz and Test Writer

The main objectives for the chapter are organized in the Chapter Review under the four types of understanding this book promotes—Skills, Properties, Uses, and Representations.

Whereas end-of chapter material may be considered optional in some texts, in UCSMP *Functions, Statistics, and Trigonometry* we have selected these objectives and questions with the expectation that they will be covered. Students should be able to answer these questions with about 85% accuracy after studying the chapter.

CHAPTER REVIEW

Questions on SPUR Objectives

SPUR stands for **S**kills, **P**roperties, **U**ses, and **R**epresentations. The Chapter Review questions are grouped according to the SPUR Objectives for this chapter.

SKILLS DEAL WITH THE PROCEDURES USED TO GET ANSWERS.

Objective A: *Use finite differences and systems of equations to determine an equation for a polynomial function from data points.*   *(Lesson 9-3)*

1. In a set of data points, the x values form an arithmetic sequence, and the 5th differences of y-values for the consecutive x-values are the first set of differences equal to 0.
   a. What is the degree of the polynomial function for y in terms of x? **4**
   b. How many data points are necessary to determine an equation for this polynomial? **5**

2) See margin.

In 2 and 3, use the data listed in the table.
a. Determine if y is a polynomial function of x of degree less than 5. b. If so, find an equation for it.

2.

x	1	2	3	4	5	6	7
y	6	13	26	45	70	101	138

3.

x	2	4	6	8	10	12	14
y	4	16	64	256	1024	4096	16384

No

4. The following are the first six triangular numbers, t_n.
   $t_1 = 1, t_2 = 3, t_3 = 6, t_4 = 10, t_5 = 15, t_6 = 21$
   a. Determine a polynomial formula for t_n.
   b. Calculate t_{100}. $t_{100} = 5050$
   a) $t_n = \frac{1}{2}n^2 + \frac{1}{2}n$

Objective B: *Calculate or approximate zeros and relative extrema of polynomial functions.*
(Lesson 9-2)

In 5–7, consider the function g, with
$g(t) = t^3 - 2t^2 - 4t + 3$.

5. Determine, to the nearest hundredth, a negative zero of g. **-1.62**

6. Determine, to the nearest tenth, a relative maximum of g by graphing. **(-0.7, 4.5)**

7. Explain why 3 must be a t-intercept of the graph of g. **See margin.**

8. Approximate, to the nearest hundredth, the largest x-intercept of the graph of $y = x^3 - x^2 - 10x + 10$. **3.16**

Objective C: *Divide polynomials.*   *(Lesson 9-4)*
In 9–12, determine the quotient and remainder when the first polynomial is divided by the second.

9. $2t^5 - 3t^3 + t^2 + 11, t^2 + 3$

10. $t^6, t^3 - 1$

11. $x^6 - 2x^5 + x^4 - 2x^3 + 2x^2 - x + 1, x^3 - 1$

12. $x^3 + 2x^2y - 2xy^2 - y^3, x - y$
9–12) See margin.

Objective D: *Factor polynomials and solve polynomial equations using the Factor Theorem, sums or differences of powers, grouping terms, or trial and error.*   *(Lessons 9-5, 9-6, 9-8, 9-9)*

13. True or false. Since $\left(x - \sqrt{5}\right)$ is a factor of $x^4 - 2x^2 - 15$, then $\sqrt{5}$ is a solution to $x^4 - 2x^2 - 15 = 0$. **True**

14. Solve $x^3 - x^2 - 4x + 4 = 0$. $x = -2, 1, 2$
15–17) See margin.
In 15–20, factor over the set of polynomials with coefficients in the indicated domain.

15. $243t^5 - u^5$; integers

16. $x^5 + x^2 - 2x^3 - 2$; reals

17. $z^3 - 8$; complex numbers

18. $8x^2 + 10x + 3$; integers **$(2x + 1)(4x + 3)$**

19. $20x^2 - 8x - 1$; integers **$(2x - 1)(10x + 1)$**

20. $t^5 - t^4 - 16t + 16$; integers
   $(t - 1)(t - 2)(t + 2)(t^2 + 4)$

622

Additional Answers
2. a. **Yes**
   b. $y = 3x^2 - 2x + 5$
7. **Because $g(3) = 0$, by the Factor-Solution-Intercept Equivalence Theorem, 3 must be a t-intercept of the graph of g.**
9. $q(t) = 2t^3 - 9t + 1; r(t) = 27t + 8$
10. $q(t) = t^3 + 1; r(t) = 1$
11. $q(x) = x^3 - 2x^2 + x - 1; r(x) = 0$
12. $q(x) = x^2 + 3xy + y^2; r(x) = 0$
15. $(3t - u)(81t^4 + 27t^3u + 9t^2u^2 + 3tu^3 + u^4)$

16. $(x + \sqrt{2})(x - \sqrt{2})(x + 1)(x^2 - x + 1)$
17. $(z - 2)(z + 1 - \sqrt{3}i)(z + 1 + \sqrt{3}i)$

Objective E: *Perform operations with complex numbers.* (*Lesson 9-6*)

21. Let $z = 3 + 2i$ and $w = 5 - 4i$. Express each of the following in $a + bi$ form.

   a. $5z + w$ **20 + 6i**   **b.** $z - w$ **-2 + 6i**

   c. zw^2 **107 − 102i**   **d.** $\frac{z}{w}$ **$\frac{3}{4} + \frac{1}{2}i$**

22. Repeat Question 21 if $z = 1 + 6i$ and $w = -2 - 3i$. **See below.**

23. Express $\frac{6 + i}{3 - 4i}$ in $a + bi$ form. **$\frac{14}{25} + \frac{27}{25}i$**

24. Express $\frac{2 + 2i}{-8 + 3i}$ in $a + bi$ form. **$-\frac{10}{73} - \frac{22}{73}i$**

22a) 3 + 27i   **b)** 3 + 9i   **c)** -77 − 18i   **d)** $\frac{1}{4} + \frac{3}{2}i$

25. Determine the sum $\sum\limits_{k=1}^{100} i^k$, where $i = \sqrt{-1}$. **0**

26. Show that $-2 + 2\sqrt{3}\,i$ is a cube root of 64.
See margin.

PROPERTIES DEAL WITH THE PRINCIPLES BEHIND THE MATHEMATICS.

Objective F: *Apply the vocabulary of polynomials.* (*Lessons 9-1, 9-2, 9-7*)

27. Given the polynomial function
$P(x) = 3x^7 + x^5 - 2x^3 + 6x^2 - 127$,
indicate each.

   a. the degree of the polynomial **7**

   b. the leading coefficient **3**

   c. the coefficient of x^4 **0**

   d. the constant term **-127**

   e. the number of zeros P must have **7**

28. Write a cubic polynomial with two terms and a leading coefficient of 4. **Sample: $p(x) = 4x^3 + 17$**

29. *True or false.* If a polynomial function p has a relative minimum at $(5, 1)$, then the graph of $y = p(x)$ never crosses the x-axis. **False**

30. Consider the polynomial function m with $m(z) = (z - 3)(z + 2)^2(z - 1)^3$. Determine the zero(s) of m with each multiplicity.

   a. one **3**   **b.** two **-2**   **c.** three **1**

Objective G: *Apply the Remainder Theorem, Factor Theorem, and Factor-Solution-Intercept Equivalence Theorem.* (*Lessons 9-4, 9-5*)

In 31–33, $f(x)$ is a polynomial. *True or false.*

31. If the remainder is 6 when $f(x)$ is divided by $(x - 1)$, then $f(6) = 1$. **False**

37) All four zeros must not be real.

32. If the remainder is 0 when $f(x)$ is divided by $(x^2 - 9)$, then $f(3) = 0$. **True**

33. If the remainder is 0 when $f(x)$ is divided by $(x^2 - 5)$, then $f(x) = (x^2 - 5)p(x)$, where $p(x)$ is another polynomial. **True**

34. Given that $g(x) = (x + 2)^2(3x - 4)(5x + 1)$, how many x-intercepts does the graph of $y = g(x)$ have? **3**

Objective H: *Apply the Fundamental Theorem of Algebra and Conjugate Zeros Theorem.* (*Lesson 9-7*)

35. Explain why every real number is equal to its complex conjugate. **See below.**

36. *True or false.* Every odd-degree polynomial with real coefficients must have at least one real zero. Explain your answer. **See margin.**

37. If the graph of a fourth degree polynomial does not cross the horizontal axis, what conclusions can be made about its zeros? **See below left.**

38. Solve $x^4 + 5x^2 - 36 = 0$ completely, given that one of the solutions is $3i$. **$x = 2, -2, 3i, -3i$**

39. *True or false.* If $2 + i$ is a zero of $z^3 + 3z^2 - 23z + 35$, then $1 + i$ cannot be another zero of it. Explain your answer. **See margin.**

35) For all real a, $a = a + 0i$. The complex conjugate of $a + 0i$ is $a - 0i = a$. Thus every real number is equal to its complex conjugate.

Additional Answers

26. $(-2 + 2\sqrt{3}\,i)^3 = (-2 + 2\sqrt{3}\,i)$
$(-2 + 2\sqrt{3}\,i)(-2 + 2\sqrt{3}\,i)$
$= (-2 + 2\sqrt{3}\,i)(4 - 8\sqrt{3}\,i - 12)$
$= (-2 + 2\sqrt{3}\,i)(-8 - 8\sqrt{3}\,i)$
$= 16 + 16\sqrt{3}\,i - 16\sqrt{3}\,i + 48 = 64$

36. True. An odd degree polynomial has an odd number of zeros, counting multiplicities. Since complex zeros occur in conjugate pairs, the total number of non-real zeros must be even. Therefore, there must be at least one real zero.

39. True. If $2 + i$ is a zero, then $2 - i$ must also be a zero because non-real zeros occur as conjugate pairs. If $1 + i$ were a zero, then $1 - i$ would also have to be a zero. But, since the polynomial is a cubic polynomial, it only has three zeros. The zeros must be $2 + i$, $2 - i$, and another zero which must be real.

You may assign these questions over a single night to help students prepare for a test the next day, or you may assign the questions over a two-day period. If you work the questions over two days, then we recommend assigning the *evens* for homework the first night so that students get feedback in class the next day, then assigning the *odds* the night before the test, because answers are provided to the odd-numbered questions.

It is effective to ask students which questions they still do not understand and use the day or days as a total class discussion of the material which the class finds most difficult.

Assessment

Evaluation The *Assessment Sourcebook* provides six forms of the Chapter 9 Test. Forms A and B present parallel versions in a short-answer format. Forms C and D offer performance assessment. The fifth test is Chapter 9 Test, Cumulative Form. About 50% of this test covers Chapter 9, 25% of it covers Chapter 8, and 25% of it covers earlier chapters. In addition to these tests, Comprehensive Test Chapters 1–9 gives roughly equal attention to all chapters covered thus far.

For information on grading, see *General Teaching Suggestions; Grading* in the *Professional Sourcebook*, which begins on page T20 in the Teacher's Edition.

Feedback After students have taken the test for Chapter 9 and you have scored the results, return the tests to students for discussion. Class discussion of the questions that caused trouble for the most students can be very effective in identifying and clarifying misunderstandings. You might want to have them write down the items they missed and work, either in groups or at home, to correct them. It is important for students to receive feedback on every chapter test, and we recommend that students see and correct their mistakes before proceeding too far into the next chapter.

USES DEAL WITH APPLICATIONS OF MATHEMATICS IN REAL SITUATIONS.

Objective I: *Construct and interpret polynomials that model real situations.*   *(Lessons 9-1, 9-3)*

40. Each month Mehmet deposits $40 from his salary directly into a bank account where interest is calculated monthly. He keeps this account (and his job) for a whole year without any other transactions. Assume that he opened the account with an initial amount of $100, and deposits take effect on the last business day of each month. Let $x = 1 + r$, where r is the monthly interest rate for this account.

  a. Write a polynomial $M(x)$ which gives the balance in Mehmet's account at the end of the year. **See below.**

  b. Calculate how much Mehmet's account would have at the end of the year if the monthly interest rate is .5625%. **$602.09**

41. A rectangular horse-training area is to be enclosed with 1000 ft of fencing, leaving a 20-ft opening for a gate, as shown below.

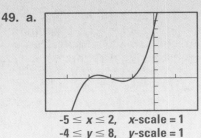

The area of the enclosed region is given by $w\ell$, and the amount of available fencing indicates that $2\ell + 2w - 20 = 1000$.

  a. Express ℓ in terms of w and use this to write a polynomial $A(w)$ which gives the area of the training pen.

  b. Use the polynomial $A(w)$ in part **a** to determine the area of the training pen when its width is each of the following.

    i. 100 feet   **ii.** 250 feet   **iii.** 300 feet

  c. Find the dimensions of the pen with the largest possible area. $\ell = 255$ ft, $w = 255$ ft

  a) $\ell = 510 - w$; $A(w) = w(510 - w)$
  bi) 41,000 ft²   ii) 65,000 ft²
  iii) 63,000 ft²

40a) $M(x) = 100x^{12} + 40x^{11} + 40x^{10} + 40x^9 + 40x^8 + 40x^7 + 40x^6 + 40x^5 + 40x^4 + 40x^3 + 40x^2 + 40x + 40$

42. The total daily revenue from a yogurt stand is given by the equation $R(c) = c \cdot p(c)$, where c is the number of cups of yogurt sold and $p(c)$ is the price of one cup of yogurt. The price of one cup is given by the equation $p(c) = 2.50 + .001c - .00002c^2$.

  a. Find a polynomial in standard form equal to $R(c)$. $R(c) = -0.00002c^3 + 0.001c^2 + 2.50c$

  b. Use an automatic grapher to approximate the number of cups of yogurt that would produce the maximum daily revenue. $\approx$ **221 c**

  c. What is the maximum daily revenue possible? $\approx$ **$385**

In 43 and 44, a confectioner is designing a new fruit-bit-and-nut treat that looks like an ice cream cone with a hemisphere of goodies on top.

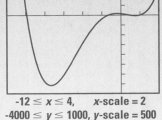

The height of the cone is h cm, and the radius is r cm. The entire shape is to be filled with bits of fruit and nuts. $V = \frac{1}{3}\pi r^2 h + \frac{2}{3}\pi r^3$

43. Write a formula for the volume of the treat in terms of r and h.

44. a. If the height of the cone is fixed at 6 cm, write a polynomial in r for the volume of the bits of fruit and nuts needed. $V = 2\pi r^2 + \frac{2}{3}\pi r^3$

  b. Identify the degree of the polynomial and tell why it is a reasonable degree for the situation.

  c. What is the leading coefficient of the polynomial? $\frac{2}{3}\pi$

  b) 3; **volume is a 3-dimensional quantity.**

Additional Answers, page 625

48. a.

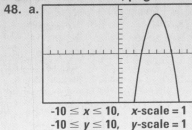

  $-10 \le x \le 10$, x-scale = 1
  $-10 \le y \le 10$, y-scale = 1

  b. maximum: (5, 8)

  c. 3, 7

49. a.

  $-5 \le x \le 2$, x-scale = 1
  $-4 \le y \le 8$, y-scale = 1

  b. relative maximum: (-2.6, 0.4);
    relative minimum: (-1.4, -0.4)

  c. -3, -2, -1

50. a.

  $-12 \le x \le 4$, x-scale = 2
  $-4000 \le y \le 1000$, y-scale = 500

REPRESENTATIONS DEAL WITH PICTURES, GRAPHS, OR OBJECTS THAT ILLUSTRATE CONCEPTS.

Objective J: *Represent two- or three-dimensional figures with polynomials.* *(Lesson 9-1)*

45. A cone is inscribed in a sphere of radius 5 inches, as shown below. Let x be the distance from the center of the sphere to the base of the cone.

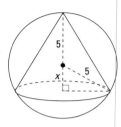

a. Express the volume of the cone as a polynomial function of x. **See below right.**

b. What is the degree of this polynomial? **3**

c. Find the value of x which makes the volume of the cone 27π. **4 inches**

46. A cube with side s is expanded by adding h cm to each edge as shown.

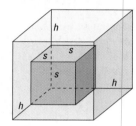

Write the volume of the new figure as a polynomial in expanded form. **See right.**

47. The lengths of the sides (measured in cm) of a right triangle, shown below, form an arithmetic sequence. Determine the area of the triangle in cm^2. **24 cm^2**

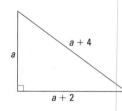

Objective K: *Relate properties of polynomial functions and their graphs.* *(Lesson 9-2, 9-5, 9-7)*

In 48–51, an equation for a polynomial function is given. **a.** Graph the function using an automatic grapher. **b.** Estimate any relative extrema. **c.** Estimate all real zeros. **48–51, see margin.**

48. $y = -2x^2 + 20x - 42$

49. $y = x^3 + 6x^2 + 11x + 6$

50. $y = 3x^4 + 25x^3 - 53x^2 - 54x + 72$

51. $y = x^5 - x^3 + x^2 - 1$

In 52–54, consider the part of the graph of $f(x) = 0.1x^5 - 2x^3 + x^2 - 27$ shown below.

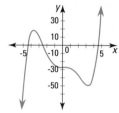

52b, 53, 54, see below.

52. a. How many real zeros does f seem to have? **3**

   b. The number of real zeros and the degree of f do not match. Give a possible explanation.

53. *True or false.* The equation $0.1x^5 - 2x^3 + x^2 - 27 = 0$ has exactly three solutions. Explain your answer. If the statement is false, suggest a change to make it true.

54. Explain why the graph of f above probably contains all the essential information about the function.

45a) $V = \frac{1}{3}\pi(25 - x^2)(x + 5) = -\frac{1}{3}\pi x^3 - \frac{5}{3}\pi x^2 + \frac{25}{3}\pi x + \frac{125}{3}\pi$

46) $V = s^3 + 3s^2h + 3sh^2 + h^3$

52b) f has 2 nonreal zeros which cannot be seen on the coordinate plane.

53) False; the equation $0.1x^5 - 2x^3 + x^2 - 27 = 0$ has exactly three real solutions.

54) Since f has only three real zeros, it does not cross the x-axis again. Thus there are no more maxima, minima, or intercepts.

50. b. minimum: (-7.4, -3566); relative maximum: (-0.4, 84); relative minimum: (1.5, -29)
   c. 2, 0.9, -1.3, -9.9

51. a.

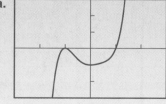

$-3 \le x \le 3$, x-scale = 1
$-3 \le y \le 3$, y-scale = 1

51. b. relative maximum:(-1, 0); relative minimum: (0, -1)
   c. -1 (multiplicity 2); 1

Adapting to Individual Needs

The student text is written for the vast majority of students. The chart at the right suggests two pacing plans to accommodate the needs of your students. Students in the Full Course should complete the entire text by the end of the year. Students in the Minimal Course will spend more time when there are quizzes and more time on the Chapter Review. Therefore, these students may not complete all of the chapters in the text.

Options are also presented to meet the needs of a variety of teaching and learning styles. For each lesson, the Teacher's Edition provides a section entitled *Adapting to Individual Needs.* This section regularly includes **Optional Activities, Challenge** problems, **English Language Development** suggestions, and suggestions for providing **Extra Help.** The Teacher's Edition also frequently includes an **Error Alert,** an **Extension,** and an **Assessment** alternative. The options available in Chapter 10 are summarized in the chart below.

Chapter 10 Pacing Chart

Day	Full Course	Minimal Course
1	10-1	10-1
2	10-2	10-2
3	10-3	10-3
4	Quiz*; 10-4	Quiz*; begin 10-4.
5	10-5	Finish 10-4.
6	10-6	10-5
7	Quiz*; 10-7	10-6
8	10-8	Quiz*; begin 10-7.
9	Self-Test	Finish 10-7.
10	Review	10-8
11	Test*	Self-Test
12		Review
13		Review
14		Test*

*in the Teacher's Resource File

In the Teacher's Edition...

Lesson	Optional Activities	Extra Help	Challenge	English Language Development	Error Alert	Extension	Cooperative Learning	Ongoing Assessment
10-1	●	●	●		●	●		Oral
10-2	●	●	●			●	●	Written
10-3	●	●	●		●	●	●	Quiz
10-4	●	●	●	●		●		Written
10-5	●	●	●			●	●	Written
10-6	●	●	●			●		Quiz
10-7	●	●	●		●	●		Oral
10-8	●	●	●		●	●		Written

Chapter 10 Block Schedule

Day	Recommended Pacing
1	Lesson 10-1, 10-2
2	Lessons 10-3
3	Lesson 10-4
4	Lessons 10-5, 10-6
5	Lesson 10-7
6	Lesson 10-8, Self-Test, Chapter Review
7	Chapter Review, Chapter Test

In the Additional Resources...

Lesson	In the Teacher's Resource File							Explorations Software
	Lesson Masters	Teaching Aids*	Answer Masters	Technology Sourcebook	Assessment Sourcebook	Visual Aids**	Technology	
10-1	10-1	86, 89, 90	10-1			86, 89, 90, AM		
10-2	10-2	86	10-2	Comp 10		86, AM	StatExplorer	
10-3	10-3	87	10-3		Quiz	87, AM		
In-class Activity			10-4			AM		
10-4	10-4	87, 91	10-4			87, 91, AM		
10-5	10-5	87	10-5			87, AM		
10-6	10-6	88, 92	10-6	Comp 11	Quiz	88, 92, AM	StatExplorer	10-6
In-class Activity			10-7			AM		10-7
10-7	10-7	88, 93, 94	10-7			88, 93, 94, AM		
10-8	10-8	88	10-8			88, AM		
End of chapter					Tests			

*Teaching Aids, except Warm-ups, are pictured on pages 626C and 626D.

**Visual Aids provide transparencies for all Teaching Aids and all Answer Masters.

Also available is the Study Skills Handbook which includes study-skill tips related to reading, note-taking, and comprehension.

Integrating Strands and Applications

	10-1	10-2	10-3	10-4	10-5	10-6	10-7	10-8
Mathematical Connections								
Number Sense							●	
Algebra	●	●	●	●	●	●	●	●
Geometry	●	●	●	●	●	●		
Logic and Reasoning	●	●	●	●	●	●	●	●
Probability	●	●	●	●	●	●	●	●
Statistics/Data Analysis		●	●	●	●	●	●	●
Patterns and Functions	●	●	●	●	●	●	●	
Discrete Mathematics	●	●	●	●	●	●	●	●
Interdisciplinary and Other Connections								
Science		●	●		●	●	●	●
Social Studies		●	●	●			●	●
Technology	●	●		●	●	●		
Consumer			●			●	●	●
Sports	●	●	●			●	●	

Teaching and Assessing the Chapter Objectives

Chapter 10 Objectives (Organized into the SPUR categories—Skills, Properties, Uses, and Representations)	Lessons	Progress Self-Test Questions	Chapter Review Questions	Chapter Test, Forms A and B	Chapter Test, Forms C	Chapter Test, Forms D
In the Teacher's Resource File						
Skills						
A: Calculate the mean and standard deviation of a binomial probability distribution.	10-2	3	1-6	3	1	
B: Use the Standard Normal Distribution to find probabilities.	10-5	7, 8	7-12	5, 6	3	
Properties						
C: Compare and contrast characteristics of different binomial probability distribution graphs.	10-1	2	13-16	2	3	
D: Use properties of normal distributions and their parent function.	10-4, 10-5, 10-6	5, 6, 11, 12	17-20	4, 11	3	✓
Uses						
E: Solve probability problems using binomial or normal distributions.	10-1, 10-2, 10-6	13	21-24	7	1	
F: Use binomial and normal distributions to test hypotheses.	10-3, 10-7	9	25-28	10	2	
G: Apply the Central Limit Theorem.	10-7	10	29-32	8	4	
H: Apply confidence intervals to real-world problems.	10-8	4	33-35	12, 13	5	✓
Representations						
I: Graph and interpret a binomial probability distribution.	10-1	1	36-41	1	1	
J: Graph and interpret normal distributions.	10-5, 10-6	14	42-48	9	3	✓

Multidimensional Assessment
Quiz for Lessons 10-1 through 10-3   Chapter 10 Test, Forms A–D
Quiz for Lessons 10-4 through 10-6   Chapter 10 Test, Cumulative Form

Quiz and Test Writer

Teaching Aids

Warm-up
Lesson 10-1

Suppose a basketball player makes 25% of free throw attempts and that the attempts are independent of each other. To the nearest percent, determine the probability that the player makes x free throws in 8 attempts, when x ranges from 0 to 8.

Warm-up
Lesson 10-2

Suppose a spinner has 5 sectors, with the following point values and probabilities of landing in them.

Sector	Point Value	Probability
1	10	0.20
2	20	0.25
3	30	0.30
4	0	0.20
5	50	0.05

What is the expected value of the number of points a person will get in one toss?

Warm-up
Lesson 10-3

Write a brief paragraph explaining why you can never tell for sure that a coin is a fair coin.

Warm-up
Lesson 10-4

State the domain, range, and any maxima, minima, or asymptotes of each function.

1. $y = 5 - x^2$ **2.** $y = 2^x$ **3.** $y = \sin x$

Warm-up
Lesson 10-5

Consider the triangle with vertices $(-1,0)$, $(0,1)$, and $(1,0)$. (This is a right isosceles triangle whose right angle is the graph of $y = -|x| + 1$.)

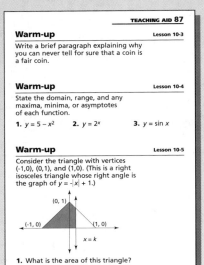

1. What is the area of this triangle?

2. Find the value of k so that 75% of the area of the triangle is to the left of the line $x = k$, and 25% to the right.

Warm-up
Lesson 10-6

For each equation below, describe the transformation from the parent graph $y = -x^2$.

1. $y = -(x - 5)^2$ **2.** $y = -\left(\frac{x-5}{2}\right)^2$ **3.** $y = -\left(\frac{x-5}{2}\right)^2 + 3$

Warm-up
Lesson 10-7

Share what you wrote for the answer to Question 4 of the In-class Activity on page 670 in the Student Edition with three other students.

Warm-up
Lesson 10-8

If a set of data is normally distributed, what percent of data would be expected to lie within

1. 1 standard deviation of the mean?

2. 2 standard deviations of the mean?

3. 3 standard deviations of the mean?

4. Justify your answers to Questions 1–3.

Lesson 10-1

Graphs of Binomial Distribution for a Fixed Number of Trials

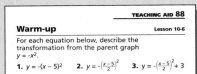

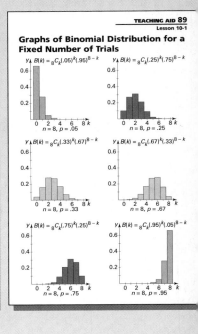

Lesson 10-1

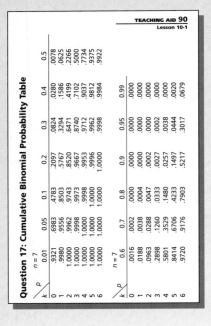

Question 17: Cumulative Binomial Probability Table

$n = 7$

p \ k	0.01	0.05	0.1	0.2	0.3	0.4	0.5
0	.9321	.6983	.4783	.2097	.0824	.0280	.0078
1	.9980	.9556	.8503	.5767	.3294	.1586	.0625
2	1.0000	.9962	.9743	.8520	.6471	.4199	.2266
3	1.0000	.9998	.9973	.9667	.8740	.7102	.5000
4	1.0000	1.0000	.9998	.9953	.9712	.9037	.7734
5	1.0000	1.0000	1.0000	.9996	.9962	.9812	.9375
6	1.0000	1.0000	1.0000	1.0000	.9998	.9984	.9922

$n = 7$

p \ k	0.6	0.7	0.8	0.9	0.95	0.99
0	.0016	.0002	.0000	.0000	.0000	.0000
1	.0188	.0038	.0004	.0000	.0000	.0000
2	.0963	.0288	.0047	.0002	.0002	.0000
3	.2898	.1260	.0333	.0027	.0038	.0020
4	.5801	.3529	.1480	.0257	.0444	.0679
5	.8414	.6706	.4233	.1497	.3017	.3017
6	.9720	.9176	.7903	.5217		

Lesson 10-4

Standard Normal Distribution and its Properties

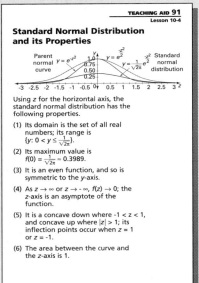

Using z for the horizontal axis, the standard normal distribution has the following properties.

(1) Its domain is the set of all real numbers; its range is $\{y: 0 < y \le \frac{1}{\sqrt{2\pi}}\}$.

(2) Its maximum value is $f(0) = \frac{1}{\sqrt{2\pi}} = 0.3989$.

(3) It is an even function, and so is symmetric to the y-axis.

(4) As $z \to \infty$ or $z \to -\infty$, $f(z) \to 0$; the z-axis is an asymptote of the function.

(5) It is a concave down where $-1 < z < 1$, and concave up where $|z| > 1$; its inflection points occur when $z = 1$ or $z = -1$.

(6) The area between the curve and the z-axis is 1.

Lesson 10-6

Example 1 Graphs

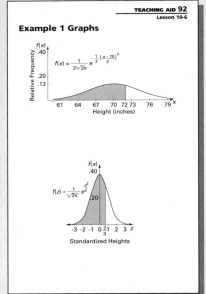

Lesson 10-7

Example 1 Graphs

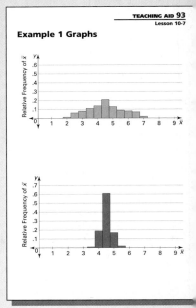

Central Limit Theorem (CLT)

Suppose random samples of size n are selected from a population with mean μ and standard deviation σ. Then, as n increases, the following occur.

1. The mean $\mu_{\bar{x}}$ of the distribution of sample means approaches μ.

2. The standard deviation $\sigma_{\bar{x}}$ of the distribution of sample means approaches $\frac{\sigma}{\sqrt{n}}$.

3. The distribution of sample means approaches a normal distribution with mean μ and standard deviation $\frac{\sigma}{\sqrt{n}}$.

Corollary

Consider a population with mean μ and standard deviation σ from which random samples of size n are taken. Then the distribution of sample means is approximately normal with mean $\mu_{\bar{x}} = \mu$ and standard deviation $\sigma_{\bar{x}}$ approximately equal to $\frac{\sigma}{\sqrt{n}}$ whenever one of t he following occurs:

a. the population itself is normally distributed, or

b. the sample size $n \geq 30$.

Chapter Opener

Chapter 10

Pacing

All lessons in this chapter are designed to be covered in one day. At the end of the chapter, you should plan to spend 1 day to review the Progress Self-Test, 1–2 days for the Chapter Review, and 1 day for a test. You may wish to spend a day on projects, and possibly a day is needed for quizzes and the In-class Activities. This chapter should therefore take 11–14 days. Spending more than 15 days on this chapter is not recommended; there is ample opportunity to review ideas in later chapters.

Using Pages 626–627

You might have your students measure their heights, rounding to the nearest 2 inches. Then get a distribution for the class. Discuss how the distribution might change if all other students from the same grade level in the school were measured. This will help to reintroduce distributions and the representativeness of samples, two ideas that run through the chapter.

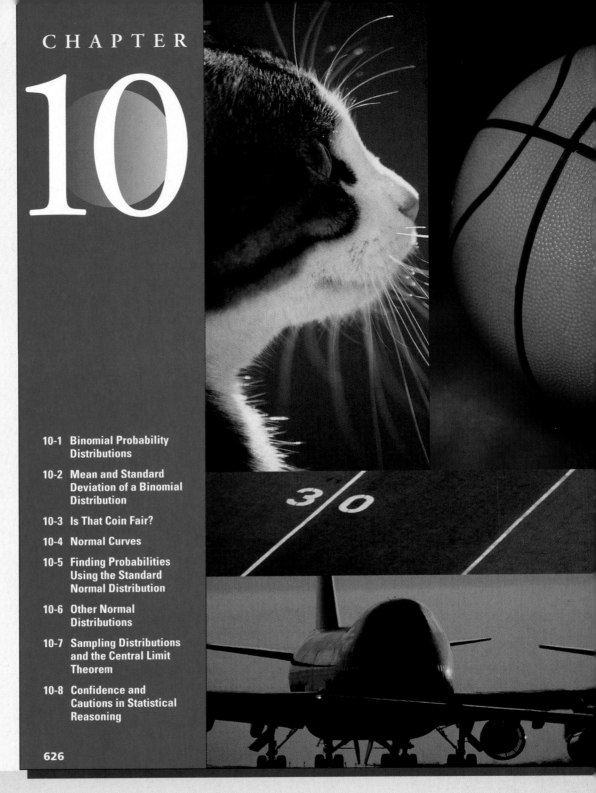

626

Chapter 10 Overview

This chapter constitutes the last extended discussion of statistics in this book. The goal of the chapter is to discuss the binomial and normal distributions and the use of statistics in hypothesis testing. The shape of histograms of binomial distributions with large numbers of trials leads into the study of the normal curve and its properties. Students use a table of probabilities to estimate the area of regions under the normal curve.

These probabilities are then used in conjunction with the Central Limit Theorem and the Law of Large Numbers to calculate confidence intervals for particular occurrences of events in continuous data sets.

Lesson 10-1 presents an analysis of one experiment having a variable probability and a fixed number of trials, and a second with a fixed probability and a variable number of trials. In Lesson 10-2, the formulas for the

mean and standard deviation of such distributions are discussed.

In Lesson 10-3, binomial probabilities are employed in direct hypothesis testing. The next three lessons provide an extended introduction to the normal distribution. In the In-class Activity preceding Lesson 10-4, the function $f(x) = e^{-x^2}$, the parent of the normal curves, is introduced, and other normal curve offspring are derived. In Lesson 10-5,

BINOMIAL AND NORMAL DISTRIBUTIONS

Below are two distributions of heights of people. The histogram on the left shows the distribution of heights (in inches) of the players in the National Basketball Association during the 1995–1996 season. It approximates the graph of a *binomial probability distribution*. Each bar indicates the number of players with heights in a 2" interval. The graphs on the right model distributions of heights of American adults. Each model is a bell-shaped curve called a *normal curve*, picturing a probability distribution called a *normal distribution*.

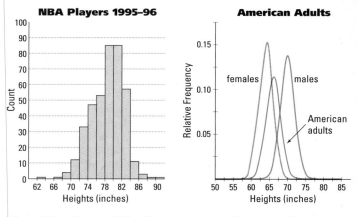

Binomial and normal distributions are very important functions in mathematics, and are often employed to make or to support decisions in situations involving uncertainty. In this chapter, you will see how these distributions are related to the testing of hypotheses, to standardized tests, and to the degree of confidence one can have in the results of random sampling.

the parent normal function is scaled so that the area between the image and the *x*-axis is 1, yielding the standard normal distribution. Students are asked to use a table of probabilities to estimate areas of specific regions under the curve. In Lesson 10-6, the skills of Lesson 10-5 are put to use to find probabilities of events happening in any normally distributed data set. Also included here is the use of the normal distribution to approximate a binomial distribution.

The last two lessons discuss hypothesis testing using the normal distribution. In Lesson 10-7, the Central Limit Theorem, the main mathematical tool in the use of the normal distribution in testing hypotheses, is discussed. The chapter closes with a discussion of confidence intervals for hypothesis testing and the potential hazards facing the user of such testing.

Objectives

C Compare and contrast character-istics of different binomial proba-bility distribution graphs.
E Solve probability problems using binomial distributions.
I Graph and interpret a binomial probability distribution.

Resources

From the *Teacher's Resource File*
■ Lesson Master 10-1
■ Answer Master 10-1
■ Teaching Aids
   86 Warm-up
   89 Graphs of Binomial Distributions for a Fixed Number of Trials
   90 Question 17: Cumulative Binomial Probability Table

Additional Resources
■ Visuals for Teaching Aids 86, 89, 90

Teaching Lesson 10-1

Warm-up

Suppose a basketball player makes 25% of free throw attempts and that the attempts are independent of each other. To the nearest percent, deter-mine the probability that the player makes x free throws in 8 attempts, when x ranges from 0 to 8. **The results are the same as those in Example 1 in Lesson 10-1, but reversed. The graph of this distri-bution would be the image of the graph shown in Example 1 when reflected over the line $x = 4$.**

Notes on Reading

Have students record the results of **Activities 1–2** on pages 629–630 for use with **Questions 3–4** on page 631 respectively.

This lesson generalizes the method-ology and theorem of Lesson 8-9 to binomial experiments with n trials, so you might wish to begin by referring students to that earlier lesson.

LESSON

10-1

Binomial Probability Distributions

Recall that a binomial probability experiment is one in which there are a fixed number of independent trials, each with only two possible outcomes (with fixed probabilities), usually called *success* and *failure*. In Lesson 8-9, you studied the Binomial Probability Theorem, that in a binomial experiment with n trials in which the probability of success is p, the probability of exactly k successes is

$$_nC_k \cdot p^k(1 - p)^{n-k}.$$

An Example of a Binomial Probability Distribution

Studies of long sequences of free throws by basketball players have found no evidence that successive shots are dependent. Thus, it is reasonable to consider successive free throw attempts as independent trials of a binomial experiment in which making a free throw is considered a success, and missing a free throw is considered a failure. Then, the distribution of the numbers k of free throws made in n attempts by a player with a known free throw success percentage p yields a binomial probability distribution.

Example 1

Assume a basketball player makes 75% of free throw attempts and that the attempts are independent of each other. Determine and graph the probability distribution for the number of free throws made in 8 attempts.

Solution

Let x be the number of successes in 8 trials. Then x can be any whole number from 0 to 8. The probability p of success is given here as 0.75. By the Binomial Probability Theorem, $P(x) = {_8C_x} \cdot (.75)^x(.25)^{8-x}$. Evaluating this expression for each possible value of x generates the numbers in the table below at the left. The data are graphed in the histogram below at the right. Notice that the bars of the histogram are centered on the value of the random variable.

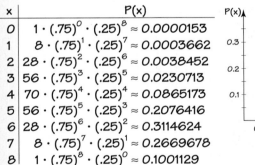
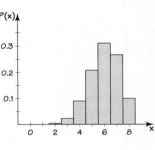

x	$P(x)$
0	$1 \cdot (.75)^0 \cdot (.25)^8 \approx 0.0000153$
1	$8 \cdot (.75)^1 \cdot (.25)^7 \approx 0.0003662$
2	$28 \cdot (.75)^2 \cdot (.25)^6 \approx 0.0038452$
3	$56 \cdot (.75)^3 \cdot (.25)^5 \approx 0.0230713$
4	$70 \cdot (.75)^4 \cdot (.25)^4 \approx 0.0865173$
5	$56 \cdot (.75)^5 \cdot (.25)^3 \approx 0.2076416$
6	$28 \cdot (.75)^6 \cdot (.25)^2 \approx 0.3114624$
7	$8 \cdot (.75)^7 \cdot (.25)^1 \approx 0.2669678$
8	$1 \cdot (.75)^8 \cdot (.25)^0 \approx 0.1001129$

Check

The nine probabilities in the table should add to 1, which is the case.

Lesson 10-1 Overview

Broad Goals We call the function that maps x onto $_nC_xp^{x}(1 - p)^{n-x}$ the *binomial probability distribution with probability p and n trials*. In this lesson students explore the values and graphs of binomial probability distributions for various values of p and n.

Perspective In Chapter 8, students calcu-lated the probability $_nC_kp^{k}(1 - p)^{n-k}$ that an event with probability p of occurring will occur k times in n repeated trials. In this

lesson, we discuss functions that arise from the calculation of these probabilities. In the first edition of this book, we identified the function that maps the ordered triple (k, n, p) onto $_nC_kp^k(1 - p)^{n-k}$ as $B(k, n, p)$; this is done in many statistics books. In this edition, we have adopted the simpler nota-tion B to name such a function and $B(k)$ for its values. This forces us to keep the values of n and p in mind because they are not always written.

The expression $_nC_k\,p^k(1-p)^{n-k}$ has three variables: k, n, and p. For given values of n and p, the function B with $B(k) = {}_nC_k\,p^k(1-p)^{n-k}$ is called a **binomial distribution function**. $B(k)$ is the probability of getting exactly k successes in n binomial trials, each of which has probability p of success. The numbers n and p are *parameters* of the binomial distribution.

Some calculators and statistical packages have built-in features to generate all values of a binomial probability distribution at once.

a) **Sample:** Microsoft Excel uses the variables k, n, and p as does the text.
b) **Sample:** In Excel, the formula needs to be entered for each cell. Then the cells can be highlighted and graphed if one uses the graphing function.

Activity 1

a. Determine if your technology has a binomial probability distribution generator. If it does, what variables does it use for what we call k, n, and p? Use your technology to check the values in the table in Example 1.
b. Will your technology draw graphs of binomial distributions? If yes, explain how to do this. Then draw the graph to check the histogram in Example 1.

Graphs of Binomial Distributions for a Fixed Number of Trials

Suppose that the number of trials in a binomial experiment is fixed at 8, and a particular value of p is chosen. The graph of B can be determined for the nine possible values of k. Below are graphs showing the distributions for the probability of success on six such binomial experiments with probabilities of success ranging from $p = 0.05$ to $p = 0.95$. For instance, the graph with $p = 0.75$ represents the situation in Example 1, showing the probability of k successes in 8 free throws from a player with a free throw success rate of 75%. The other graphs could represent similar situations with other success rates.

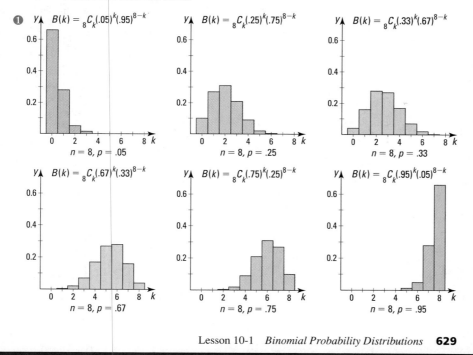

Lesson 10-1 *Binomial Probability Distributions* **629**

Since the domain of B has three variables, it cannot be graphed on a two-dimensional graph unless two of the variables are fixed. But this does not cause problems because typically p and n are given and only k varies. For instance, if we imagine a fair coin being tossed 10 times, then $p = \frac{1}{2}$ and $n = 10$ are known and only k can vary. In this case $B(k) = \frac{{}_{10}C_k}{2^{10}}$ for $k = 0, 1, 2, \ldots, 10$, proportional to the numbers in row 10 of Pascal's triangle, as in the third graph in **Example 2**. If $p \neq \frac{1}{2}$, then the values of the distribution are a little more complicated to compute and the distribution is no longer symmetric to its mean. That is what occurs in **Example 1**.

We are interested in two aspects of binomial probability functions. First, what happens when n (the number of trials) is fixed and different values of p (the probability of success) are chosen. For example, what would the basketball player's probability distribution for **Example 1** look like if the player had a different probability of making each shot? This begins in **Example 1** and runs through **Activity 2**. Second, we are interested in what happens as n gets larger, because the distribution approaches a normal distribution. This is the motivation behind **Example 2**.

In **Example 1**, you might ask students what they think would constitute an unusual event. Is it an event with a probability of 0.25? 0.1? 1 in a million? This will help prepare students for Lesson 10-3. Point out that if a player has many opportunities to shoot sets of 8 free throws, then what might be unusual if the player had only one chance would not be unusual if the player had many chances.

❶ These graphs are on **Teaching Aid 89**.

If you choose to do **Question 17**, plan to add a half day to the lesson. It is time-consuming, though not especially difficult.

Additional Examples

1. Suppose a baseball player has a .300 batting average.
   a. If, in fact, the player has a .300 probability of getting a hit each time at bat, determine the probability distribution for the number of hits in 5 at-bats in a game.

x	P(x)
0	0.168
1	0.360
2	0.309
3	0.132
4	0.028
5	0.002

   b. How unusual is it for this batter to get 3 or more hits in a game with 5 at bats? **The probability is about 0.162, about 1 in 6, not particularly unusual.**

(Additional Examples continue on page 630.)

2. A coin that is biased so that heads occurs 60% of the time is tossed 50 times by someone who does not know it is biased. What is the probability that between 23 and 27 heads occurs, so that the person is, by mistake, rather sure the coin is fair? ≈ .0153 + .0259 + .0405 + .0584 + .0778 = 0.2179, or about 22%; this points out the need for a larger sample of tosses

3. a. Draw graphs of the binomial probability distributions with $p = 0.6$, when $n = 2, 5, 10,$ and 50.

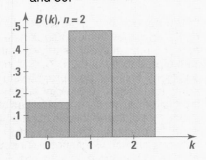
$B(k)$, $n = 2$

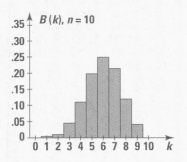
$B(k)$, $n = 5$

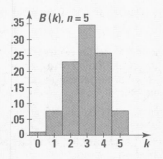
$B(k)$, $n = 10$

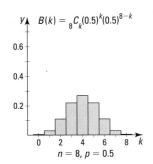
$$B(k) = {}_8C_k(0.5)^k(0.5)^{8-k}$$
$n = 8$, $p = 0.5$

Sample:
a) A player has a free throw success rate of 0.67. The player is attempting 8 free throws, and making a basket is called a success.
b) The graphs are reflection images of each other over the line $k = 4$. This is because $B(k)$ when $p = 0.05$ equals $B(8 - k)$ when $p = 0.95$.
c) The mode increases.

630

Examine the graphs on page 629. **See left.**
a. Describe a free throw situation that would lead to the distribution in which $B(k) = {}_8C_k(.67)^k(.33)^{8-k}$.
b. When two values of p total 1, for instance $p = 0.05$ and $p = 0.95$, how are the two graphs related to each other? Explain why this happens.
c. As the value of p increases, what happens to the **mode** of the distribution (the domain value for which the probability function has its maximum value)?

From the preceding graphs, you might expect that when $n = 8$ and $p = 0.5$, the binomial distribution is symmetric to the line $k = 4$, the mode of the distribution. As shown in the graph at the left, this is indeed the case.

The Graphs of Binomial Distributions for a Fixed Probability

It is also useful to study the graphs of binomial distributions for a fixed probability p and various values of n, the number of trials.

Example 2

a. Let $p = 0.5$. Draw graphs of the binomial probability distributions when $n = 2, 6, 10,$ and 50.
b. Describe the effect of increasing n on the probability distribution B when $p = 0.5$.

Solution

a. The data for the graphs determined by $n = 2, 6,$ and 10 can be generated by hand. But for the case of $n = 50$, we use a calculator or statistics utility with a built-in feature for generating binomial distributions.

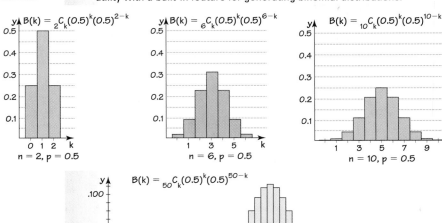
$B(k) = {}_2C_k(0.5)^k(0.5)^{2-k}$ — $n = 2$, $p = 0.5$
$B(k) = {}_6C_k(0.5)^k(0.5)^{6-k}$ — $n = 6$, $p = 0.5$
$B(k) = {}_{10}C_k(0.5)^k(0.5)^{10-k}$ — $n = 10$, $p = 0.5$

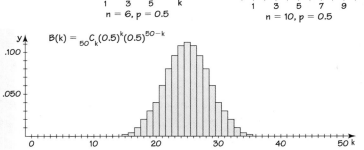
$B(k) = {}_{50}C_k(0.5)^k(0.5)^{50-k}$
$n = 50$, $p = 0.5$

Additional Answers
7. a.
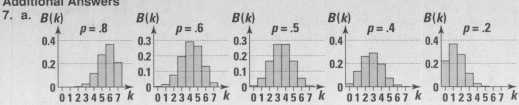
$B(k)$ $p = .8$ — $B(k)$ $p = .6$ — $B(k)$ $p = .5$ — $B(k)$ $p = .4$ — $B(k)$ $p = .2$

b. The graph for $p = 0.8$ is a reflection image of the graph for $p = 0.2$ and the graph for $p = 0.6$ is a reflection image of the graph for $p = 0.4$.
c. Sample: As p decreases, the mode decreases; the graph bunches up nearer the y-axis.

1a)

x	P(x)
0	.01680
1	.08958
2	.20902
3	.27869
4	.23224
5	.12386
6	.04129
7	.00786
8	.00066

b. When $p = 0.5$, as n increases, the following patterns can be observed.
1. *The mode of the distribution increases along the k-axis. That is, the more trials, the greater the most likely value.*
2. *The graph is symmetric to the bar at $\frac{n}{2}$.*
3. *The graph "spreads out."*
4. *The maximum value of the range, which is the maximum probability, decreases. That is, the distribution "flattens."*

In the next lesson you will see theorems that justify the patterns observed in this lesson.

QUESTIONS

Covering the Reading

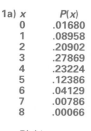

1. Assume a basketball player makes 40% of shots taken and that the attempts are independent.
   a. Determine and graph the probability distribution for the number of free throws made in 8 attempts. **See left.**
   b. What is the probability that the player will make at least 6 of the next 8 shots? ≈ .0498
   c. Compare and contrast the graph in part **a** to the one drawn in Example 1. **Sample: The distribution in part a is shifted downward and is a little more spread out.**

2. The expression $_nC_k\, p^k(1 - p)^{n-k}$ gives the probability of getting exactly **a.** successes in **b.** trials of a **c.** experiment in which the probability of success on each trial is **d.** .
   a) k   b) n   c) binomial   d) p

3. If your calculator or statistics utility has a built-in feature for generating values of a binomial distribution, show what you found for Activity 1. **See page 629.**

4. Indicate your answers to Activity 2. **See page 630.**

Sheryl Swoopes at the 1996 Olympic Games.

In 5 and 6, consider a binomial probability distribution. *True or false.*

5. When $p = 0.5$, the graph is symmetric to the line $k = \frac{n}{p}$. **False**

6. When $p = 0.5$, as n increases, the probability of getting the modal number of successes increases. **False**

7. **a.** Graph the five probability distributions B with $n = 7$, and $p = 0.8, 0.6, 0.5, 0.4,$ and 0.2.
   b. Which of the graphs are reflection images of each other?
   c. As p decreases, what is the effect on the graph of B?
   a–c) **See margin.**

8. **a.** Graph the probability distributions B when $p = 0.3$ and $n = 5, 10, 25,$ and 100. **See margin.**
   b. Describe the effect on this distribution of fixing p and increasing n.
   The mode increases; the graph approximates a bell-shaped curve; the distribution "spreads out" and "flattens."

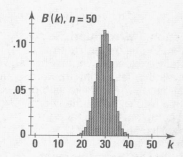

b. Describe the effect of increasing n on the graph. **As n increases, the graph increasingly resembles a bell-shaped curve, the distribution spreads out and flattens, and near the mode it looks more and more symmetric.**

Notes on Questions

Question 7b You might ask students to explain why the graphs are reflection images.

Additional Answers

8. a. $p = 0.3$

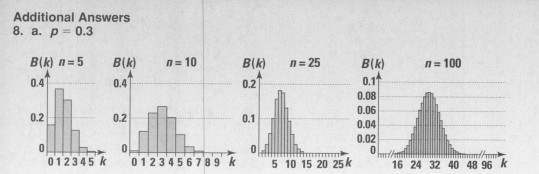

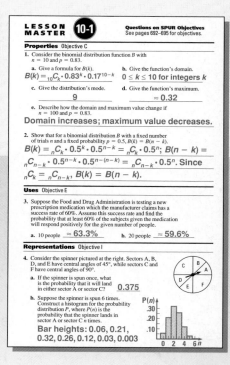

Question 9 Error Alert Be sure students realize these are not all mutually exclusive events. **Part a** involves 5 or less right answers, so it is not mutually exclusive with **part b. Parts a and c** are mutually exclusive (and complementary), and their probabilities add up to 1.

Question 10 Entertainment Connection During part of the game on the television show *Wheel of Fortune,* the spinning wheel has 24 sections, 21 with prizes, 1 "lose a turn," 1 "bankrupt," and 1 "free spin." You might ask: If each section is equally likely, what is the probability of spinning 10 times without going bankrupt? $\left[\left(\frac{23}{24}\right)^{10} \approx 0.65\right]$

Question 12 The distribution here is an example of a multinomial probability distribution.

Question 17 This table is on **Teaching Aid 90.**

13) Sample: Use the command rand on a TI-83 to generate 20 random numbers *x* between 0 and 1. If $0 \le x \le 0.15$, the watermelon is large, if $0.15 < x \le 0.5$, then the watermelon is small, and if $0.5 < x \le 1$, then the watermelon is medium. In our simulation, we obtained 3 large, 7 small, and 10 medium watermelons.

Applying the Mathematics

9. A multiple-choice test has 15 questions each with 5 alternatives. Assume that a student answers all questions by random guessing. Determine the following probabilities.
   a. *P*(no more than 5 right answers) **0.939**
   b. *P*(exactly 5 right answers)   c. *P*(more than 5 right answers)
      0.103   **0.061**

10. The wheel used on a certain TV game show has 19 sections. Nine sections have big prizes, nine sections have small prizes, and one section throws the player out of the game. The scatterplot below shows the probability of winning *k* big prizes in 50 spins of this wheel.

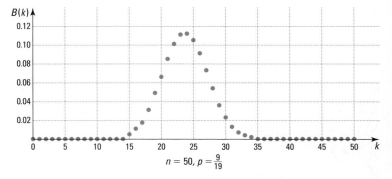

$n = 50, p = \frac{9}{19}$

   a. From the graph, estimate the probability of winning 30 or more big prizes. **≈ 0.02**
   b. The graph is nearly reflection-symmetric. Why? **p is nearly 0.5.**
   c. If the wheel were spun more than 50 times, how would you expect the graph to change? **Sample: The graph would "flatten out" more and the mode would increase.**

Review

In 11 and 12, determine whether the given situation is a binomial experiment. *(Lesson 8-9)*

11. At a highway weigh station, all trucks are stopped and weighed. Trucks over 40 tons are not allowed to continue traveling on that highway. Statistics at this weigh station show that about 2% of trucks are rerouted. It is desired to determine the probability that exactly 3 of the first 50 trucks weighed on a particular day will be rerouted. **binomial**

12. Suppose that 100 watermelons are being emptied from a truck at a farmer's market. Each one is weighed and put into one of three piles (small, medium, and large). In the past years, this farm has produced about 35% small, 50% medium, and 15% large watermelons. It is desired to determine the probability that this will again be the distribution today. **not a binomial**

13. Design a simulation using the RND function to model the situation in Question 12 for a selection of 20 watermelons. How many small, medium, and large watermelons do you end up with? *(Lesson 7-8)* **See left.**

Optional Activities

Have students use this BASIC program to calculate binomial probabilities.

```
5    REM CALCULATING BINOMIAL
     PROBABILITIES
10   INPUT "NUMBER OF TRIALS"; N
20   INPUT "PROBABILITY OF
     SUCCESS"; P
30   X = N
40   INPUT "NUMBER OF SUCCESSES"; K
50   C = 1
60   FOR I = 1 TO K
70   C = C * X/I
80   X = X – 1
90   NEXT I
100  PROB = C * P^K * (1–P)^(N–K)
110  PRINT "PROBABILITY OF EXACTLY
     ";K; " SUCCESSES"
120  PRINT "IN ";N; " TRIALS IS ";PROB
130  INPUT 'TYPE 1 TO CONTINUE, 0
     TO STOP'; AGAIN
140  IF AGAIN = 1 THEN GO TO 30
150  END
```

Adapting to Individual Needs

Extra Help
Some students may be misled by their intuition. For instance, in **Example 1**, while intuition correctly suggests that getting exactly 6 free throws out of 8 attempts is the most likely event in the sample space (since 6 is 75% of 8), students may incorrectly surmise that the probability of getting *exactly* 6 free throws is quite high, perhaps greater than 0.5. Similarly, in **Example 2**, intuition tells us correctly that getting exactly 25 heads in

m	P(m)
1	0.125
2	0.375
4	0.375
8	0.125

14. Three fair coins are tossed. Each head is assigned a value of 2, and each tail a value of 1. Let m be the product of the values of the three tossed coins.
  a. Find the probability distribution for m. **See left.**
  b. What is the mean of the distribution? *(Lesson 7-6)* **3.375**

In 15 and 16, find θ. *(Lessons 5-2, 5-4)*

15.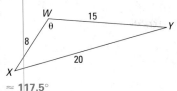

$\approx 117.5°$

16.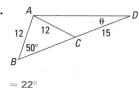

$\approx 22°$

Exploration

17. A *cumulative binomial probability table* gives, for fixed n and p, the probabilities for k or fewer successes. Below is a table of cumulative binomial probabilities when $n = 7$. The number in row k and column p represents the probability of k or fewer successes in 7 binomial trials, each of which has probability p. For instance, the probability of no more than 2 successes in 7 binomial trials, each of which has probability of success equal to 0.8, is about 0.0047.

p \ k	n = 7 0.01	0.05	0.1	0.2	0.3	0.4	0.5	0.6	0.7	0.8	0.9	0.95	0.99
0	.9321	.6983	.4783	.2097	.0824	.0280	.0078	.0016	.0002	.0000	.0000	.0000	.0000
1	.9980	.9556	.8503	.5767	.3294	.1586	.0625	.0188	.0038	.0004	.0000	.0000	.0000
2	1.0000	.9962	.9743	.8520	.6471	.4199	.2266	.0963	.0288	.0047	.0002	.0000	.0000
3	1.0000	.9998	.9973	.9667	.8740	.7102	.5000	.2898	.1260	.0333	.0027	.0002	.0000
4	1.0000	1.0000	.9998	.9953	.9712	.9037	.7734	.5801	.3529	.1480	.0257	.0038	.0000
5	1.0000	1.0000	1.0000	.9996	.9962	.9812	.9375	.8414	.6706	.4233	.1497	.0444	.0020
6	1.0000	1.0000	1.0000	1.0000	.9998	.9984	.9922	.9720	.9176	.7903	.5217	.3017	.0679

  a. Use the table to determine the probability of five or fewer successes in a binomial experiment with 7 trials, if in each trial the probability of success is 0.8. Compare this answer to the one you get by applying the method learned in Chapter 8 directly. **0.4233**
  b. Cumulative binomial probability tables can also be used to calculate probabilities for single events. Figure out how to use a cumulative binomial table to determine the probability of exactly two successes in seven trials, each with 0.4 probability of success. Verify your answer by direct calculation using the Binomial Probability Theorem.
  c. Some statistics utilities have built-in features for generating cumulative binomial probabilities. Find out whether your calculator has such a feature. If it does, use it to check your work in part **a**.
  Answers will vary.
  b) **0.2613**

Practice

For more questions on SPUR Objectives, use **Lesson Master 10-1** (shown on page 631).

Assessment

Oral Communication Have students explain (1) how changes in the probability p affect the graphs of the probability distribution for a fixed number of trials and (2) how changes in the number of trials affect the probability distribution for a fixed probability p. [Students interpret various characteristics of binomial probability distribution graphs.]

Extension

Use 60% as the passing grade on the multiple choice test described in **Question 9**. Ask students to determine the probability of passing the test by random guessing (i.e., without studying.) [Students must answer 9 or more out of 15 questions correctly; $P(x \geq 9) = 0.000722$, which is less than 0.1%.]

Project Update Project 1, *The Quincunx,* and Project 2, *Cumulative Percentile Curves,* on page 687, relate to the content of this lesson.

---

50 tosses is the most likely outcome. However, here too, it is incorrect to conclude a great likelihood for getting *exactly* 25 heads. Point out that the probability of getting *about* 6 free throws in **Example 1** is quite high. (The probability of 5, 6, or 7 successes is about 0.79.) Similarly, the probability of getting *about* 25 heads in **Example 2** is also quite high. (The probability of getting 22 to 28 heads is about 0.68.)

Challenge
Have students answer the following questions. Six ordered pairs are picked at random from the rectangle: $\{(x, y) \mid -4 \leq x \leq 4; -5 \leq y \leq 5\}$. The number n of pairs that lie within the circle $\{(x, y) \mid x^2 + y^2 \leq 16\}$ is noted.
1. Is this experiment a binomial probability situation? If so, what is p?
  [Yes; $\frac{16\pi}{80} \approx .628$]

2. Give the probability distribution for this experiment.

x	$p(x)$
0	.00264
1	.02674
2	.11301
3	.25473
4	.32296
5	.21838
6	.06153

Objectives

A Calculate the mean and standard deviation of a binomial probability distribution.

E Solve probability problems using binomial distributions.

Resources

From the *Teacher's Resource File*
- Lesson Master 10-2
- Answer Master 10-2
- Teaching Aid 86: Warm-up
- Technology Sourcebook
  Computer Master 10

Additional Resources
- Visual for Teaching Aid 86
- StatExplorer

Warm-up

Suppose a spinner has 5 sectors, with the following point values and probabilities of landing in them.

Sector	Point Value	Probability
1	10	0.20
2	20	0.25
3	30	0.30
4	0	0.20
5	50	0.05

What is the expected value of the number of points a person will get in one toss? **10·0.2 + 20·0.25 + 30·0.3 + 0·0.2 + 50·0.05 = 18.5**

LESSON

10-2

Mean and Standard Deviation of a Binomial Distribution

Conventional way. *President Clinton and Vice-President Gore greet attendees at the 1996 Democratic National Convention. On election day, they received 50% of the popular vote while the Republicans received 41% and others 9%.*

In the previous lesson, you studied the shapes of the graphs of binomial probability distributions produced under two conditions: (1) fixing the number *n* of trials, and allowing *p*, the probability of success on an individual trial, to vary; or (2) fixing the value of *p*, and allowing *n* to vary. In particular, you saw that if *p* is fixed, then as *n* increases, the mode of the distribution increases, and the distribution spreads out. In this lesson we examine the effect of *n* and *p* on two other measures of center and spread, the mean and standard deviation. You will see that despite the variety of shapes binomial distributions can have, each of these statistics can be calculated using a surprisingly simple formula.

The Mean of a Binomial Probability Distribution

Consider the binomial distribution *P* from Example 1 of Lesson 10-1. *P* gives the probability of *x* successes in 8 trials, when the probability of success in any one trial is .75. The graph of *P* is repeated at the right.

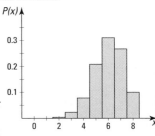

In Example 1 of Lesson 10-1, *P* referred to a situation in basketball. *P* is also the model for other situations with the same characteristics. Suppose candidate *C* for an election is thought to be preferred by 75% of the voters. When a sample poll is taken of 8 people from the population of voters, it is not always the case that 6 people will say they prefer *C*, even though 6 is 75% of 8. But the *mean* of the binomial probability distribution is 6. This can be verified by substituting the values from Example 1 into the formula for the mean of a general probability distribution, which you saw in Lesson 7-6.

Lesson 10-2 Overview

Broad Goals The two theorems of this lesson provide a way to quickly calculate the mean μ and standard deviation σ of a binomial probability distribution.

Perspective The mean of a distribution is the mean value you would expect to get as the number of trials gets larger and larger; for this reason it is also the expected value of the distribution. For instance, in tossing a fair die with possible values 1, 2, 3, 4, 5, 6,

the mean value is 3.5. But if the die is not fair, let's say with $P(2) = \frac{1}{3}$ while $P(6) = 0$ and all other probabilities are $\frac{1}{6}$, then the number 2 will come up $\frac{1}{3}$ of the time and the number 6 not at all, so the mean value is $\frac{1}{6} \cdot 1 + \frac{1}{3} \cdot 2 + \frac{1}{6} \cdot 3 + \frac{1}{6} \cdot 4 + \frac{1}{6} \cdot 5$, or $\frac{17}{6}$. The values are weighted by the probabilities. The general formula is that, if the random variable can take on the values x_i with

corresponding probabilities $P(x_i)$, then the mean $\mu = \sum_{i=1}^{n} x_i P(x_i)$. The letter μ is used to indicate that this is a theoretical mean and not a sample mean. Similarly, in the general formula for the variance:

$$\sigma^2 = \sum_{i=1}^{n} x_i^2 P(x_i) - \mu^2,$$ the Greek letter σ is used rather than *s*, which would be used for a sample variance.

$$\mu = \sum_{x=0}^{8} x \cdot P(x)$$
$$= 0 \cdot P(0) + 1 \cdot P(1) + 2 \cdot P(2) + 3 \cdot P(3) + 4 \cdot P(4) + 5 \cdot P(5) + 6 \cdot P(6) + 7 \cdot P(7) + 8 \cdot P(8)$$
$$\approx 0 \cdot 0.0000153 + 1 \cdot 0.0003662 + \ldots + 8 \cdot 0.1001129$$
$$= 6$$

Activity 1

Using the other values found in Example 1 of Lesson 10-1, check the arithmetic above. **Check students' work.**

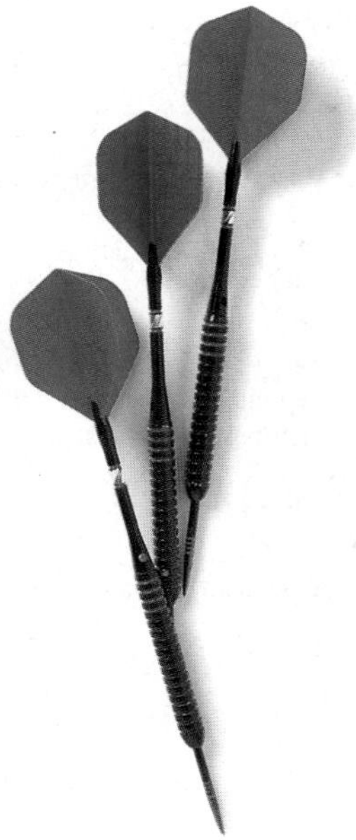

This confirms that our intuition is correct.

The following example shows how the mean of a binomial distribution varies with the probability of success of a single event.

Example 1

Suppose a darts player has probability p of hitting the bull's-eye with a single dart, and all attempts are independent. Find the expected number of bull's-eyes the player will hit in three attempts.

Solution

This is a binomial experiment with $n = 3$ and probability of success p, and probability $q = 1 - p$ of failure. The probability distribution for the random variable, number of bull's-eyes, is shown below.

x = number of bull's-eyes	3	2	1	0
B(x) = probability	p^3	$3p^2q$	$3pq^2$	q^3

Let μ be the mean of this distribution. Then by the definition

$$\mu = \sum_{x=0}^{3} x\,B(x)$$
$$\mu = 3(p^3) + 2(3p^2q) + 1(3pq^2) + 0(q^3)$$
$$= 3p^3 + 6p^2q + 3pq^2$$
$$= 3p(p^2 + 2pq + q^2)$$
$$= 3p(p + q)^2.$$

Because $p + q = 1$,

$$\mu = 3p.$$

So the player can expect to hit $3p$ bull's-eyes with three shots.

Check

Substitute a value for p. If the probability of getting a bull's-eye is $\frac{2}{3}$, then in 3 shots the player will get, on average, 2 bull's-eyes. This agrees with intuition.

Notes on Reading

The formulas $\mu = np$ and $\sigma = \sqrt{npq}$ are so simple to use students may not care to see how they are derived. Still, we believe it is instructive to go through the proof of the Mean of a Binomial Distribution Theorem, so that students realize that properties of summations and factorials help to deduce other properties.

The formula for the variance of a set of n numbers $x_1, x_2, \ldots, x_n$ is written in two ways. Here are the missing steps, with the index of the summation always from $i = 1$ to $i = n$.

$$\frac{\sum(x_i - \bar{x})^2}{n}$$
$$= \frac{\sum x_i^2 - 2\bar{x}\sum x_i + \sum(\bar{x})^2}{n}$$
$$= \frac{\sum x_i^2 - 2\frac{\sum x_i}{n}\sum x_i + n(\bar{x})^2}{n}$$
$$= \frac{\sum x_i^2}{n} - 2\bar{x}^2 + \bar{x}^2$$
$$= \frac{\sum x_i^2}{n} - \bar{x}^2.$$

Optional Activities

Activity 1 Refer students to **Question 12.** Ask students how **part a**, the probability that at least one person out of 20 would be labeled deceptive, would change if the polygraph detector mislabeled a truthful person as deceptive in 10% of the cases. [$1 - (.9)^{20} \approx 87.8\%$; the percentage drops by 11%] Ask them to find "how correct" the polygraph detector needs to be in order that less than 50% of the time at least one person out of 20 would be mislabeled deceptive.

[Solve $1 - x^{20} < \frac{1}{2}$ to find $x > \sqrt[20]{.5} \approx .967$]

LESSON MASTER 10-2

Questions on SPUR Objectives
See pages 692–695 for objectives.

Skills Objective A

In 1–4, a binomial experiment is described.
a. Find the mean number of successes.
b. Find the standard deviation for the number of successes.

1. The number of trials is 30 and the probability of success on each trial is 0.7. a. 21 b. ≈ 2.5
2. The number of trials is 100 and the probability of failure on each trial is 0.85. a. 15 b. ≈ 3.57
3. A student guesses randomly on a test with 50 true-false questions. a. 25 b. ≈ 3.54
4. Two fair dice are tossed 180 times. A success is tossing a 7. a. 30 b. 5

Uses Objective E

5. A manufacturer of spark plugs has estimated that the probability that a spark plug will be defective is 0.0125. A trucking company recently bought ten gross (1440) of these spark plugs for their fleet.
   a. About how many spark plugs should the trucking company expect to be defective? 18 spark plugs
   b. What is the probability that the trucking company will find exactly the expected number of defective spark plugs? ≈ 0.094
6. Suppose you flip a quarter 16 times and count the times it lands heads up.
   a. What is the expected number of heads? 8 heads
   b. What is the probability that the number of heads is no more than one standard deviation from the expected number? ≈ 0.79
7. Suppose the following experiment is conducted: A die with s sides marked 1 through s is tossed n times and the number of times a 1 is tossed is recorded. After many repetitions of the experiment, it is found that the number of 1s tossed has a mean of 33 and a standard deviation of 5.5.
   a. If the die is assumed to be fair, what is the most likely number of sides it has? 12 sides
   b. If the die is assumed to be fair, how many times n was it tossed in each experiment? 396 times

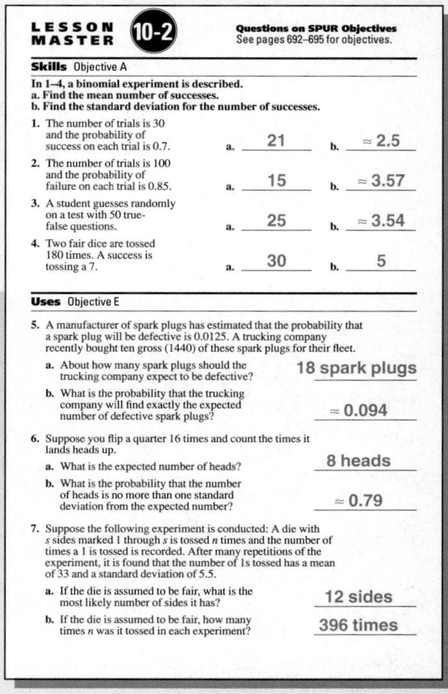

The results about the basketball player and the darts player generalize to a simple formula for the mean of any binomial distribution. Its proof is not so simple, but uses only properties you have studied.

Theorem (Mean of a Binomial Distribution)
The mean μ of a binomial distribution B with n trials and probability p of success on each trial is given by $\mu = np$.

Proof

$$\mu = \sum_{x=0}^{n} xB(x) = \sum_{x=0}^{n} x\binom{n}{x}p^x(1-p)^{n-x}$$
B is a binomial distribution.

$$= \sum_{x=1}^{n} x\frac{n!}{x!(n-x)!}p^x(1-p)^{n-x}$$
Formula for $\binom{n}{x}$
When $x = 0$, the term is 0.

$$= \sum_{x=1}^{n} \frac{n \cdot (n-1)!}{(x-1)!(n-x)!} p \cdot p^{x-1}(1-p)^{n-x}$$
Rewriting factorials and powers

$$= np \sum_{x=1}^{n} \frac{(n-1)!}{(x-1)!(n-x)!} p^{x-1}(1-p)^{n-x}$$
Since n and p do not depend on x, they distribute over the sum.

$$= np \sum_{x=1}^{n} \binom{n-1}{x-1}p^{x-1}(1-p)^{n-x}$$
Formula for $\binom{n-1}{x-1}$

$$= np(p + (1-p))^{n-1}$$
Binomial Theorem

$$= np \cdot 1^{n-1}$$
$p + (1-p) = 1$

$$= np$$

The Variance and Standard Deviation of a Binomial Distribution

The variance and standard deviation of a binomial probability distribution can also be calculated directly from n and p. Recall that the variance σ^2 of a population with n values $x_1, x_2, \ldots, x_n$ equals $\dfrac{\sum_{i=1}^{n}(x_i - \bar{x})^2}{n}$, where $\bar{x}$ is the mean of the numbers $x_1, x_2, \ldots, x_n$. This can be rewritten as

$$\sigma^2 = \frac{\sum_{i=1}^{n} x_i^2}{n} - \bar{x}^2.$$

The analogous formula for the **variance σ^2 of a probability distribution** P with n outcomes and mean μ is

$$\sigma^2 = \sum_{i=1}^{n} (x_i^2 \cdot P(x_i)) - \mu^2.$$

Optional Activities

Activity 2 Here is a derivation of the formula for the Variance of a Binomial Distribution, which you may want to show your students. Ask students to tell what was done to get from each step to the next.

$$\sigma^2 = \sum x^2 \frac{n!}{x!(n-x)!} p^x(1-p)^{n-x} - n^2p^2 \qquad \text{[definition of variance]}$$

$$\sigma^2 = \sum x \frac{n!}{(x-1)!(n-x)!} p^x(1-p)^{n-x} - n^2p^2 \qquad \text{[rewriting the factorial]}$$

$$\sigma^2 = np\sum x \frac{(n-1)!}{(x-1)!(n-x)!} p^{x-1}(1-p)^{n-x} - n^2p^2 \qquad \text{[factoring out } np \text{ as in proof of the formula for the Mean]}$$

$$\sigma^2 = np\left(\sum x \frac{(n-1)!}{(x-1)!(n-x)!} p^{x-1}(1-p)^{n-x} - np\right) \qquad \text{[}np \text{ is common factor]}$$

Example 2

Find the variance and standard deviation for the distribution generated by the darts player in Example 1.

Solution

Use the table of values of the probability distribution given in the solution of Example 1, and the result that $\mu = 3p$.

By definition,

$$\sigma^2 = \sum_{x=0}^{3} x^2 B(x) - \mu^2$$

$$\sigma^2 = (3^2 p^3 + 2^2(3p^2 q) + 1^2(3pq^2) + 0^2 q^3) - (3p)^2.$$

Expand and rearrange terms to simplify.

$$\sigma^2 = 9p^3 + 12p^2 q + 3pq^2 - 9p^2$$

Rewrite $12p^2 q$ as $9p^2 q + 3p^2 q$.

$$\sigma^2 = 9p^3 + 9p^2 q + 3p^2 q + 3pq^2 - 9p^2$$
$$= 9p^2(p + q) + 3pq(p + q) - 9p^2$$
$$= 9p^2 + 3pq - 9p^2 \qquad \text{since } p + q = 1$$

Thus $\sigma^2 = 3pq$.

The standard deviation is the square root of the variance.

$$\sigma = \sqrt{3pq}$$

The result in Example 2 also generalizes. The proof is quite lengthy and is omitted here.

❶ **Theorem (Variance and Standard Deviation of a Binomial Distribution)**
In a binomial distribution with n trials, probability p of success and probability q of failure on each trial, the variance $\sigma^2 = npq$, and the standard deviation $\sigma = \sqrt{npq}$.

Applying the Theorems about Means and Standard Deviations

Example 3

In the United States, the probability that a newborn child will be female is about $p = 0.48$. Suppose a large hospital has 2500 live births in a given year. Let $B(x) =$ the probability that x females are born.
a. What is the mean of the distribution B?
b. What is the standard deviation of the distribution B?

Solution

Let x be the number of female children in 2500 live births. If births are independent, then the probability distribution B is binomial with n = 2500 and p = 0.48. By the previous theorems,
a. the mean $\mu = 2500(0.48) = 1200$;
b. the standard deviation $\sigma = \sqrt{2500(0.48)(0.52)} = \sqrt{624} \approx 25$.

▶

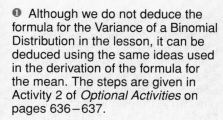

❶ Although we do not deduce the formula for the Variance of a Binomial Distribution in the lesson, it can be deduced using the same ideas used in the derivation of the formula for the mean. The steps are given in Activity 2 of *Optional Activities* on pages 636–637.

Additional Examples

1. Suppose a dart player has probability p of hitting the bull's-eye with a single dart, and all attempts are independent. Prove that the expected number of bull's-eyes the player will hit in two attempts is $2p$.
   Let $q = 1 - p$. By the definition of the mean of a probability distribution,
   $\mu = 2(p^2) + 1(2pq) + 0(q^2) = 2p^2 + 2pq = 2p(p + q) = 2p$.

2. Prove that the variance and standard deviation for the distribution generated by the dart player in Additional Example 1 are $2pq$ and $\sqrt{2pq}$. By the definition of the variance of a probability distribution,
   $\sigma^2 = 2^2(p^2) + 1^2(2pq) + 0^2(q^2) - \mu^2 = 4p^2 + 2pq - (2p)^2 = 2pq$. From this, $\sigma = \sqrt{2pq}$.

3. In the binomial distribution of tossing a fair coin 250 times and counting the number of heads, what is the mean and standard deviation? mean = 125; standard deviation = $\sqrt{62.5} \approx 7.9$

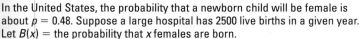

$$\sigma^2 = np\left(\sum(x-1)\frac{(n-1)!}{(x-1)!(n-x)!} p^{x-1}(1-p)^{n-x} + \sum \frac{(n-1)!}{(x-1)!(n-x)!} p^{x-1}(1-p)^{n-x} - np\right) \qquad [x = (x-1) + 1]$$

$$\sigma^2 = np\left((n-1)p\sum \frac{(n-2)!}{(x-2)!(n-x)!} p^{x-2}(1-p)^{n-x} + \sum \frac{(n-1)!}{(x-1)!(n-x)!} p^{x-1}(1-p)^{n-x} - np\right) \qquad \text{[factoring out } (n-1)p \text{ in a manner similar to that in the proof of the Mean]}$$

$$\sigma^2 = np((n-1)p + 1 - np) \qquad \text{[both summations equal 1]}$$

$$= np(1-p)$$

$$= npq$$

Question 3 Sports Connection
Darts, a traditional English pub game, is becoming a tournament sport in the United States. An annual Spring Dart Tournament is held at the Blueberry Hill restaurant in St. Louis, Missouri. The tournament started in 1973 with $150 in prize money. In 1998, there will be $20,000 in prizes.

Question 7 You might ask how many students know their blood type. It is a useful bit of information to know.

Question 8 Try some values to see if the answers are reasonable. For instance, when the batting average $a = .250$, the mean is $25(.250) = 6.25$, so the player should expect 6 to 7 hits, with a standard deviation of $\sqrt{25(.250)(.750)} \approx 2.2$.

Question 12 For the reason given in this question, many people do not believe in the validity of lie-detector tests.

▶ **Check**

It is very tedious to calculate by hand a table of values of the probability distribution. Below is the output generated by a statistics package.

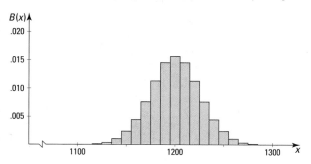

From the graph you can see that the mean appears to be about 1200, and that most of the other values are within 50 units, or two standard deviations, of the mean.

QUESTIONS

Covering the Reading

In 1 and 2, consider a basketball player with a 60% free throw average who attempts five consecutive free throws.

1a) $\mu = \sum\limits_{x=0}^{5} x\, p(x) =$
$0 + 1 \cdot 5(0.6)(0.4)^4 +$
$2 \cdot 10(0.6)^2(0.4)^3 +$
$3 \cdot 10(0.6)^3(0.4)^2 +$
$4 \cdot 5(0.6)^4(0.4)^1 +$
$5(0.6)^5 = 3$

1. Let μ be the expected number of made free throws.
   a. Find μ by calculating a sum using the definition of the mean of a probability distribution. **See left.**
   b. Find μ by using the theorem in this lesson. $\mu = np = 3$

2. a. Find the variance for the distribution of made free throws. **1.2**
   b. Find the standard deviation for the distribution of made free throws.
   $\sqrt{1.2} \approx 1.095$

3. Suppose a darts player has probability $p = \frac{2}{3}$ of hitting a bull's-eye on any toss of a single dart.
   a. Suppose the player throws 100 darts. Find the expected number of bull's-eyes. **66.6**
   b. Let $P(x)$ be the probability of x bull's-eyes. Find the standard deviation for the distribution P. $\sqrt{\dfrac{200}{9}} \approx 4.7$

In 4 and 5, characteristics of a binomial probability experiment are given.
a. Find the mean of the probability distribution. **b.** Find the variance of the probability distribution. **c.** Find the standard deviation of the probability distribution.

4. $n = 10$, $p = .3$ a) 3   b) 2.1   c) $\sqrt{2.1} \approx 1.45$

5. $n = 50$, $p = 0.75$ a) 37.5   b) 9.375   c) $\sqrt{9.375} \approx 3.06$

Optional Activities

Activity 3 Technology Connection
In *Technology Sourcebook, Computer Master 10*, students use *StatExplorer* or similar software to simulate and interpret binomial experiments. Then students compare the results to the related binomial probability distribution.

Adapting to Individual Needs

Extra Help
Some students may be confused by the Greek variables used in this lesson. You might want to discuss the table at the right with your students.

Symbol	What it represents
Σ (capital sigma)	summation
μ (mu)	mean of a probability distribution
σ (lower case sigma)	standard deviation of a probability distribution
σ^2	variance of a probability distribution

7a)

x	P(x)
0	0.316
1	0.422
2	0.211
3	0.047
4	0.004

b)

6. Consider the same hospital and year referred to in Example 3. Let
$P(x)$ = the probability that x males are born.
a. What is the mean of the distribution? **1300**
b. What is the standard deviation of P? $\sqrt{624} \approx 25$

Applying the Mathematics

7. Suppose that both parents in a family with four children carry genes
for blood types A and B. Then the blood types of their children are
independent, and each child has probability $\frac{1}{4}$ of having blood type A.
Let $P(x)$ = the probability that x of the four children in the family have
type A blood.
a. Construct a table for the probability distribution P. **See left.**
b. Draw a histogram of the distribution in part **a**. **See left.**
c. Find the mean number of children with type A blood, and mark the
location of the mean on the histogram. **1**
d. Find the standard deviation of the distribution. $\sqrt{3}/2 \approx .866$

8. A baseball player has a batting average a, where $0 \le a \le 1$. Let
x = the number of hits made in the next 25 times at bat, and consider
the probability distribution $P(x)$. For this distribution, find each statistic.
a. the mean **25a**
b. the variance **25a(1 − a)**

9. How many six-sided dice must be tossed if the expected number of 1's
showing is to be 4? **24**

10. If for some binomial probability distribution, $\mu = 45$ and $\sigma = 6$, find
n and p. **n = 225; p = .2**

11. *True or false.*
a. The mean of a binomial distribution is directly proportional to n, the
number of trials. **True**
b. The standard deviation of a binomial distribution is directly
proportional to n, the number of trials. **False**

12. According to a study by a federal agency, the probability is about 0.2 that
a polygraph (lie detector) test given to a truthful person suggests that the
person is deceptive. (That is, in about 20% of cases a truthful person will
be labeled deceptive.) Suppose that a firm asks 20 job applicants about
thefts from previous employers, and uses a polygraph to judge their
truthfulness. Suppose also that all 20 answer truthfully.
a. What is the probability that the polygraph tests show that at least one
person is deceptive? $\approx .988$
b. What is the mean number among 20 truthful persons who will be
classified as deceptive? What is the standard deviation of the number
expected to be classified as deceptive? $\mu = 4; \sigma = \sqrt{3.2} \approx 1.8$
c. What is the probability that the number classified as deceptive is less
than the mean? $\approx .41$

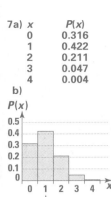

Cal Ripken, Jr.

Lesson 10-2 *Mean and Standard Deviation of a Binomial Distribution* **639**

Follow-up
for Lesson **10-2**

Practice
For more questions on SPUR
Objectives, use **Lesson Master 10-2**
(shown on page 635).

Assessment
Written Communication Have
students **work in pairs.** Refer to
Question 1 and ask one student to
complete **part a** and the other **part b**
for a free throw average of 80%.
Have students compare answers.
Then have them reverse roles and
repeat for a free throw average of
65%. [Students use two different
methods to calculate the mean of a
binomial probability distribution.]

Extension
Refer students to **Question 10.**
Have them derive a formula for σ in
terms of μ and p. [$\sigma = \sqrt{\mu(1 - p)}$]

Project Update Project 1, *The
Quincunx,* on page 687, relates
to the content of this lesson.

Adapting to Individual Needs

Challenge
Have students determine the probability of
success and the standard deviation in each
of the following binomial distributions. In
each case, x = number of successes.

1.

x	p(x)
0	$\frac{3125}{7776}$
1	$\frac{3125}{7776}$
2	$\frac{625}{3888}$
3	$\frac{125}{3888}$
4	$\frac{25}{7776}$
5	$\frac{1}{7776}$

1. $[p = \frac{1}{6};$
$\sigma = \frac{5}{6}]$

2.

x	p(x)
0	0.0625
1	0.25
2	0.375
3	0.25
4	0.0625

2. $[p = \frac{1}{2}; \sigma = 1]$

639

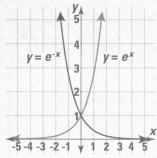
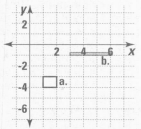
13a)

x	$P(x) \approx$
0	0.555
1	0.337
2	0.092
3	0.015
4	0.002
5	0
6	0
7	0
8	0
9	0
10	0

$P(x)$

c) Sample: The mode would increase, the standard deviation decrease, and the graph become closer to bell-shaped.

d) Sample: The mode would increase, the standard deviation increase, and the graph become closer to bell-shaped.

14c) P(living near the plant and having polluted water) = 0.0075. P(living near the plant) · P(having polluted water) = (0.048)(0.03) = 0.0014. Since 0.0075 ≠ 0.0014, the events are not independent.

Review

13. Customs officers have the following policy for accepting shipments of packaged dried fruit from another country: Select a sample of 8 boxes and check. If two or more are found substandard, reject the entire shipment. *(Lesson 10-1)*
  a. Determine and graph the probability distribution of the number of shipments rejected out of the next 10 if 5% of the boxes of dried fruit produced by this country are defective. **See left.**
  b. What is the probability that at least 8 of the next 10 shipments of dried fruit will be accepted? **about 0.984**
  c. How would the graph of the probability distribution change if, instead of 5%, 10% of the boxes of dried fruit were defective?
  d. How would the graph of the probability distribution change if, instead of sampling 8 boxes, customs officers sampled 20 boxes?
  c, d) See left.

14. About 3% of a city's 327,000 water patrons have complaints about polluted water. Of these, 25% are from the residential area next to the chemical plant in town. There are 15,840 water patrons in this area.
  a. Determine the probability that a water patron is from the area near the chemical plant. **0.048**
  b. Determine the probability that a water patron is from the area near the plant and has polluted water. **0.0075**
  c. Show that living near the chemical plant and having polluted water are *not* independent events. *(Lessons 7-1, 7-5)* **See left.**

15. a. Graph $f(x) = e^x$ and $g(x) = e^{-x}$ on the same set of axes. **See margin.**
  b. What transformation maps *f* to *g*? $T(x, y) \rightarrow (-x, y)$
  c. What is $\lim_{x \to \infty} g(x)$? **0**
  d. What is $\lim_{x \to -\infty} f(x)$? *(Lessons 2-4, 3-5, 6-4, 8-2)* **0**

In 16 and 17, solve exactly. *(Lessons 6-5, 6-6)*

16. $e^y = 198$ ln(198)   **17.** $\log(m^2 + 10) = 3$ $\pm 3\sqrt{110}$

18. a. Draw a square whose sides are parallel to the *x*- and *y*-axes.
  b. Apply the transformation $S: (x, y) \rightarrow \left(3x, \frac{y}{4}\right)$.
  c. Describe the effect of this transformation on the shape, and on the area of the preimage. *(Lesson 3-5)*
  a–c) See margin.

19. a. What is the sum of the measures of the interior angles of a convex pentagon? **540°**
  b. Use an indirect proof to explain why a convex pentagon cannot contain four acute angles. *(Previous course)* **See margin.**

Exploration

20. a. Find a dartboard, and, using area, compute the probability *p* that a dart that hits the target at random is a bull's-eye. **See margin.**
  b. Compute answers for Examples 1 and 2 of this lesson using the value of *p* found in part **a.** $\mu = 0.00231$; $\sigma^2 \approx 0.002313$, $\sigma = 0.048$.

Setting Up Lesson 10-3

In **Example 3**, note that if the probability were 0.5, then the hospital would have been expected to have 1250 births of girls. With a probability of 0.48, having 1250 girls in 2500 births is two standard deviations away from the mean. Would it be unusual for a hospital of this size to have as many girls as boys born in a year? Questions like this are examined in Lesson 10-3.

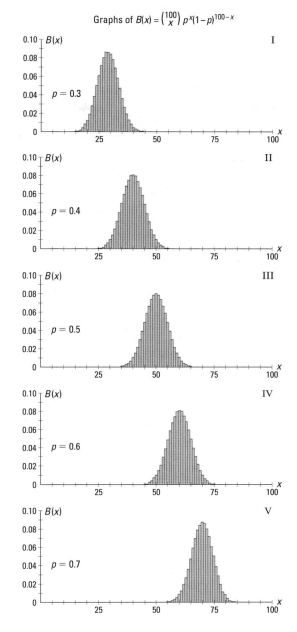

Graphs of $B(x) = \binom{100}{x} p^x (1-p)^{100-x}$

Can You Tell Whether a Coin Is Fair?

In questions involving probability, it is common to assume that a coin is fair. The question we consider in this lesson is: Is it possible to tell *for certain* whether an actual coin is fair? To answer this question, consider the five binomial probability distributions graphed above. They show the

Lesson 10-3

Objectives
F Use binomial distributions to test hypotheses.

Resources
From the *Teacher's Resource File*
■ Lesson Master 10-3
■ Answer Master 10-3
■ Assessment Sourcebook: Quiz for Lessons 10-1 through 10-3
■ Teaching Aid 87: Warm-up

Additional Resources
■ Visual for Teaching Aid 87

Teaching Lesson 10-3

Warm-up

✎ **Writing** Write a brief paragraph explaining why you can never tell for sure that a coin is a fair coin.

Notes on Reading

To set the lesson up, we begin by showing various binomial distributions with different values of *p* when a coin is tossed 100 times. Emphasize that these are theoretical models. When an actual coin is tossed, we do not know the probability of heads, and even when the tossing is simulated, say with a table of random numbers, we would not get exactly these distributions. Events in the real world must be weighed in the light of these theoretical models.

Lesson 10-3 Overview

Broad Goals This lesson introduces the notion of hypothesis testing in situations that are modeled by binomial distributions.

Perspective Probabilities indicate only the likelihood that an event may occur. When a probability is low, but not zero, we consider the event unlikely, but not impossible.

This lesson is devoted to inferential statistics, the use of statistics to make judgments.

With actual data, if the probability of the results we find is very low, we may decide that our assumptions are wrong. These ideas, along with those of the *null hypothesis, alternative hypothesis,* and *significance level,* form the basis of hypothesis testing. We never know the exact probability that an event will occur. With data from repeated trials, we can calculate how likely the *relative frequency* we obtained is, under some hypothesis H_0 about the exact probability. If

the relative frequency we obtained is quite unlikely under that hypothesis, then we reject the hypothesis. For example, if a coin lands heads up 8 times out of 10, as in **Example 2**, we could hypothesize that the coin is biased to land on heads with a probability of 0.75. Then this event would be quite reasonable and we would not reject the hypothesis.

(Overview continues on page 642.)

Suppose a coin is tossed 100 times and 39 heads occur, as in **Example 1**. We see that there are many possible reasonable probabilities for heads with this coin. The most reasonable probability, if we only had this result, is that the coin has a probability of .39 of landing on heads. But we have a strong belief that coins are closer to fair, so we ask in **Example 1** whether a fair coin could reasonably be expected to land heads up 39 times out of 100. Calculation shows that this event is not particularly rare.

With more tosses, we have more evidence. If we got 390 heads in 1000 tosses, then we would have an event that is quite rare *if the coin is fair*, so we would tend to reject the hypothesis that the coin is fair. But what probability would we pick? We might then pick 0.39, or perhaps 0.40, because it is simpler.

Returning to **Example 3** in Lesson 10-2, it was only after a great deal of data was collected that people realized that more boys than girls are born. There is a very strong tendency for people to want to assume that the same number of boys and girls are born. For most situations, the difference of 2% does not have much significance, but statistically the data compel us to reject the hypothesis that the births of boys and girls are, in theory, equal. Something causes more boys to be born.

probabilities of getting x heads in 100 tosses when the probability of heads is .3, .4, .5, .6, and .7.

Suppose that you actually toss a coin 100 times in an attempt to determine whether it is fair. And suppose you get 50 heads and 50 tails. You might immediately think that the coin must be fair, but from examination of the binomial probability distributions above, you can see that many situations are possible. We call each possible situation a **hypothesis**.

One possible hypothesis is that the coin *is* fair. This certainly is reasonable; Distribution III shows that 50 heads and 50 tails can happen when the coin is fair. However, Distribution II shows that if the probability of heads is .4, it is also possible to obtain 50 heads in 100 tosses, though this is less likely. Distribution IV shows the same result if the probability of heads is .6. Even if the coin were so weighted that the probability of heads was .7 or .3, there is a possibility, though a remote one, that there could be 50 heads in 100 tosses. This argument holds regardless of how many times you toss the coin. It shows that you can never tell for certain if a coin is fair.

Can You Tell Whether a Coin Is Unfair?

Can a person tell for certain that a coin is *not* fair? Consider this example.

Example 1

A coin is tossed 100 times and 39 heads occur. Find the probability that outcomes as unusual as 39 or fewer heads occur in 100 tosses of a fair coin. Should the hypothesis that the coin is fair be rejected?

Solution

When tossing a coin 100 times, the probability of any particular outcome is quite small. So consider all the possible outcomes that are at least as far from the mean as 39 heads. Because the hypothesis is that the coin is fair, suppose the probability of heads were 0.5. Then, if x is the number of heads, using a calculator or statistics utility,

$$P(x \le 39) = \sum_{x=0}^{39} \binom{100}{x}(0.5)^x(1 - 0.5)^{100-x} \approx 0.0176.$$

So 39 or fewer heads would occur about 2% of the time if the coin were fair. Also, 39 or more tails would occur about 2% of the time. Thus an outcome at least as unusual as 39 heads in 100 tosses would occur about 4% of the time even if the coin were fair. For us, this is not rare enough to reject the hypothesis that the coin is fair.

A probability distribution is a model for a situation of chance. Every situation of chance may be explained by more than one model. The word "hypothesis" is often used by researchers when they are considering various models. Example 1 demonstrates that as long as an outcome has a positive probability under a particular hypothesis, you cannot reject that hypothesis for certain. A rare event might have occurred. Thus you never can say for sure whether a coin is fair or not fair.

642

Lesson 10-3 Overview, continued

If we hypothesize that the coin is fair, we find that an event like this one could occur over 10% of the time. That still is not rare enough for most people to reject the hypothesis, because fairness is something we believe strongly in about coins. However, if we hypothesized that the coin was biased to land heads up only 30% of the time, then this would be a very unlikely event, and we would probably reject that hypothesis.

Optional Activities

Refer students to **Question 6**. Ask them to test the hypothesis at the 0.01 significance level that this precinct went for Candidate B if seven voters were polled, all of whom voted for Candidate A. [The probability is 0.01564 that the precinct still went for Candidate B.] Then tell them to assume that the number of voters polled increases. Ask students to find the number of voters polled, all of whom voted for Candidate A that would allow them to reject the hypothesis at the

0.01 significance level that the precinct went for Candidate B. [8] At the .001 significance level? [11; The results are as follows:

# voters polled	P(all or none vote for A)
6	0.03218
7	0.01564
8	0.00782
9	0.0039
10	0.00196
11	0.00098]

What Can You Say in a Situation of Uncertainty?

If you tossed a coin 100 times and only 10 heads occurred, then there is a great deal of evidence that the coin is not fair, *because the probability of an event as extreme as this is so low*. But how small must the probability of an event be before you reject the hypothesis that led to it? That depends on the situation. If the hypothesis is that a coin is fair, then you might choose 0.05 or 0.01 as the level below which you would reject it. If the hypothesis is that a person is innocent of a serious crime, you might choose 0.000001, or $\frac{1}{1,000,000}$, as the level that would cause a belief that the person is guilty.

The level chosen is called a **significance level** for a hypothesis. The most common significance levels are 0.05, 0.01, and 0.001. To reject a hypothesis for an experiment at the 0.05 significance level means that the event consisting of the experiment's outcome and all more extreme ones has a theoretical probability that is less than 0.05.

Significance levels are often set before an experiment to avoid debate after the fact. For instance, in Example 1, if the significance level 0.05 had been agreed to before testing the coin, and 39 heads appeared in 100 tosses, you would be obliged to reject the hypothesis that the coin is fair.

❶ Hypothesis Testing

The logic of reasoning in Example 1 is an instance of statistical *hypothesis testing*. In this example, we hypothesized that the coin is unbiased. Such an assumption is called a *null hypothesis*, abbreviated H_0 and pronounced "*H*-naught." The word "null" suggests that the coin is not out of the ordinary. Usually, a **null hypothesis** is a statement of "no effect" or "no difference." A null hypothesis is usually contrasted with an **alternative hypothesis** H_1 which identifies an alternative conclusion from the same experiment. An alternative hypothesis is often the complement of the null hypothesis. For the coin flip, compare the null hypothesis and an alternative hypothesis.

Null H_0: The probability that the coin lands heads is 0.5.
Alternative H_1: The probability that the coin lands heads is not 0.5.

The choice of null and alternative hypotheses is subjective. Another alternative hypothesis is H_2: The probability that the coin lands heads is greater than 0.5. Once hypotheses are made, probability theory and statistical inference are used to determine whether a hypothesis should be accepted. The logic of hypothesis testing is similar in structure to that of indirect proof. In an indirect proof, there is a statement *S* you wish to prove.

> Assume not-*S*.
> Reason from not-*S*.

If you arrive at a false statement, or contradiction, reject not-*S*, which means accepting *S*.

---

❶ The traditional notation of stating null and alternative hypotheses is included here not just for formality, but because students who continue studying statistics are likely to see it. In practice, however, more and more statistical analyses are being written with more prose and less technical symbolism.

It will be helpful to go through the logic of **Example 2** on page 644 with students. An event occurs. We make an assumption such as randomness about the situation. We assign a significance level below which we consider the event to be unusual. If the probability for the event, *given our assumptions*, is below the significance level, then we reject the hypothesis that our assumptions were correct.

Adapting to Individual Needs

Extra Help

Students might confuse the meaning of *hypothesis* as used here and *hypothesis* as they may have used it in geometry classes. Here, a hypothesis represents a possible situation, similar to what is called a theory in science. In hypothesis testing, you can never conclude with certainty whether the hypothesis is true. You can only judge its likelihood. It is because of this dual meaning that UCSMP uses *antecedent* instead of *hypothesis*.

Additional Examples

1. If a coin is tossed 50 times and less than 20 heads or greater than 30 heads occur, is a person justified in thinking the coin is unfair? **Generally not, with a fair coin the probability is about 12% that this event would happen.**

2. A coin is tossed 5 times and 5 heads occur. At the .05 level, test the hypothesis that the coin is fair. **Null hypothesis: The probability of heads is $\frac{1}{2}$.**
   $P(\text{5 heads in 5 tosses}) = \frac{1}{32}$.
   $P(\text{5 tails in 5 tosses}) = \frac{1}{32}$.
   Together, these two events have a probability of about 0.06. At a significance level of .05, there is not enough evidence to conclude that the coin is biased.

3. Tickets for two concerts went on sale at the same time. Of the first 30 tickets sold, 12 were for the first concert and 18 for the second. Is the concert hall manager justified in thinking that many more tickets will be sold for the second concert? **Null hypothesis: There is an equal probability that a person will purchase a ticket to each concert. $P(\text{12 or fewer tickets of 30 for one of the concerts}) \approx .28$. It is not justified.**

(Notes on Questions begin on page 646.)

In testing a hypothesis, the logic is quite similar.

> Assume a null hypothesis H_0.
> Reason from H_0.
> If you arrive at a situation whose probability is less than your significance level, reject H_0, which means accepting an alternative hypothesis.

Here is another example of how statisticians use probability to test a hypothesis.

Example 2

A coin was tossed 10 times and 8 heads occurred.
a. At the .05 level, test the hypothesis that the coin is fair.
b. At the .05 level, test the hypothesis that the coin is weighted towards heads.

Solution

a. First state the null hypothesis H_0: **The coin is fair.**
   Then state an alternative hypothesis H_1: **The coin is not fair.** Notice that H_1 is the opposite of H_0, so if H_0 is rejected, then H_1 must be accepted. Now determine the probability of the outcome that occurred or that outcomes like it occurred. In this case, we wish to include the possibility that 9 or more heads occurred, or that 8 or more tails occurred, because they are the same kind of event as what occurred. So we ask: **What is the probability that when a fair coin is tossed 10 times, 8 or more heads or 8 or more tails occur?** Pascal's triangle helps in determining the probabilities. In **10 tosses of a fair coin**

   $$P(\text{exactly 8 heads}) = \frac{45}{1024} = P(\text{exactly 8 tails}),$$

   $$P(\text{exactly 9 heads}) = \frac{10}{1024} = P(\text{exactly 9 tails}), \text{ and}$$

   $$P(\text{10 heads}) = \frac{1}{1024} = P(\text{10 tails}).$$

   Since these six outcomes are mutually exclusive, the total probability is $\frac{112}{1024}$. Since the probability of the event is greater than .05, we cannot reject the hypothesis H_0. So we cannot accept the hypothesis H_1.

b. Although one might take as a null hypothesis that the coin is not weighted towards heads, this does not make it easy to calculate probabilities. So we again take as the null hypothesis H_0: **The coin is fair.** But the alternate hypothesis now is H_2: **the coin is weighted towards heads.** So we calculate only the probability that 8 or more heads might occur in the tossing of a coin 10 times. This probability is half that found in part **a**.

   $$P(\text{8 or more heads in 10 tosses of a fair coin}) = \frac{56}{1024}$$

   Again the probability is greater than .05, so we cannot reject the hypothesis that the coin is fair. **Thus the data do not lead us to accept the hypothesis that the coin is weighted towards heads.**

Adapting to Individual Needs

Challenge

Have students perform the following experiment.

1. Flip a coin 50 times and record the number of heads. Is your coin fair
   a. at the .05 significance level?
   b. at the .01 significance level?
      [Answers will vary.]

2. What range of the number of heads would require you to accept the hypothesis that the coin is fair

a. at the .05 significance level?
   [From 18 to 32]
b. at the .01 significance level?
   [From 16 to 34]

In Example 2, notice that the probability of the outcome "8 heads in 10 tosses" is less than .05. That particular outcome is unusual. But we are testing whether the coin is fair or weighted, not whether the outcome is unusual. So we must consider all possible similarly unusual outcomes. It is not always easy to determine what outcomes are similar to a given outcome.

The use of probability to test hypotheses has applications well beyond coins and games of chance. In medicine it is very unusual for all patients to react the same way to a new treatment. For some the treatment may be helpful, while for others it is not. We can never be certain that a new treatment is better than an old one, so we are forced into hypothesis testing. In elections, seldom do all people favor the same candidate. So a sample poll can never tell for certain whether one candidate will win. Instead, hypothesis testing is used. A typical null hypothesis is that the candidates are equally popular. Then, when the poll's results are found, pollsters ask: If the candidates were equally popular, how unusual would it be to get poll results like these?

In medicine, polling, and coin flips, and almost all other places where this type of testing is done, the samples are larger than the ones we have used here. Calculations of individual probabilities, as in Example 2, are tedious. Fortunately, when the number of trials increases, binomial distributions become closer and closer to a distribution whose characteristics are given in statistical tables. That distribution is the subject of the next lesson.

QUESTIONS

Covering the Reading

2) If the event consisting of the experiment's outcome and all more extreme ones has a probability of less than 0.01, then the null hypothesis is rejected.

3) H_1: The average miles per gallon is increased with the new oil. Sample H_0: The average miles per gallon is not increased by the new oil.

1. Suppose a coin is tossed 100 times, and 30 heads occur.
   a. Under the hypothesis that the coin is fair, use a calculator to estimate the following probabilities.
   i. $P(H = 30)$ **2.3171×10^{-5}**   ii. $P(H \leq 30)$ **3.9251×10^{-5}**
   b. If a 0.05 significance level is used to test the hypothesis that the coin is fair, should the hypothesis be accepted? **No**

2. What does it mean to test a hypothesis for an experiment at the 0.01 level? **See left.**

In 3 and 4, state an appropriate null hypothesis H_0, and an alternative hypothesis H_1.

3. A new car averages 30 miles per gallon on the highway. The owner switches to a new motor oil that claims to increase gas mileage. After driving 2000 miles with the new oil, the owner wants to determine if gas mileage has actually increased. **See left.**

4. A bag of kitty litter is supposed to contain 10 lb. A consumer group thinks that the manufacturer is consistently filling the bags with less than the labeled amount. They weigh some bags.
   H_0: **The weight of a bag of kitty litter is 10 lb. Sample H_1: The weight of a bag of kitty litter is less than 10 lb.**

Lesson 10-3 *Is That Coin Fair?* **645**

Practice
For more questions on SPUR Objectives, use **Lesson Master 10-3** (shown on page 643).

Assessment
Quiz A quiz covering Lessons 10-1 through 10-3 is provided in the *Assessment Sourcebook*.

Extension
Cooperative Learning Have students **work in groups** to write problems from their own experience that are similar to **Questions 7–10**.

Project Update Project 1, *The Quincunx*, and Project 6, *Design a Study*, on pages 687–688, relate to the content of this lesson.

Questions 5–7 Any of these questions can be used to guide class discussion about the steps in hypothesis testing.

Question 5 Because the hypothesis being tested is that the coin is fair, Pascal's Triangle can be used to quickly obtain probabilities. Look at the 12th row and divide by 2^{12} to obtain the probabilities.

Question 6 Of course if there are less than 12 people who voted in this precinct, then the precinct had to go for candidate A. This points out that the probabilities are always "in the long run" and in practice the statistics only applies if we think of there being more than a small number of possible repeated trials. In this case, suppose there were only 30 voters in the precinct. Then, in order for the precinct to go for candidate A, more than 15 of the remaining 24 voters would have to vote for A. If the precinct were equally divided among A and B, we can calculate the probability that 15 or more of the other 24 voters would vote for B. This would happen about 11% of the time. We find the easiest way to calculate this is to approximate the binomial by a normal distribution with mean $np = 24 \cdot \frac{1}{2} = 12$ and standard deviation $\sqrt{npq} = \sqrt{24 \cdot \frac{1}{2} \cdot \frac{1}{2}} = \sqrt{6} \approx 2.236$. Normalizing the data, 15 is 1.22 standard deviations from the mean, and Appendix D shows that about 11% of the time an event at least this far from the mean would occur.

5a) 10 tails, 11 tails, 12 tails, 0 tails, 1 tail, and 2 tails

b) Since $0.03857 < 0.05$, reject H_0 and accept H_1.

Scott Blanton (16) and Gus Frerotte (12) of the Washington Redskins

6) Significance level = 0.01. H_0: Candidate B received 50% or more of the vote in the precinct. H_1: Candidate B received less than 50% of the vote. P(B receives no votes from 6 voters if half of the precinct goes for B) = $0.0156 > 0.01$. Thus, we cannot reject the null hypothesis.

5. A coin is tossed 12 times and 10 tails occur.
   a. To test H_0: the coin is fair, against H_1: $P(\text{heads}) \neq .5$, what outcomes should be considered along with this outcome? **See left.**
   b. At the .05 level, test the hypothesis that the coin is fair. **See left.**
   c. At the .01 level, test the hypothesis that the coin is fair. **See below.**
   d. At the .01 level, test the hypothesis that the coin is weighted in favor of tails. **Since $0.019287 > 0.01$, cannot reject H_0.**

c) Since $0.03857 > 0.01$, cannot reject H_0.

Applying the Mathematics

6. A pollster taking an exit poll in a particular precinct after an election polls 6 voters and finds that all of them voted for candidate A. At the .01 significance level, test the hypothesis that this precinct went for candidate B. **See left.**

7. A coin is tossed 10 times and 5 heads occur. At the .05 significance level, test the hypothesis that the probability of heads is $\frac{1}{3}$. **See margin.**

8. A field-goal kicker in football is thought to be able to make 90% of field-goal attempts from within 20 yards. On the first 5 attempts of the season from within 20 yards, the kicker makes only 2 field goals. Is the coach justified in saying that the kicker seems no longer able to make 90% of field-goal attempts from within 20 yards? Answer the question by using hypothesis testing. **See margin.**

9. Determine the mean and standard deviation of the binomial distribution of the null hypothesis in Question 7.

   mean $= 3\frac{1}{3}$; $\sigma = \dfrac{\sqrt{20}}{3}$

Review

10. Consider a multiple-choice test of 20 questions, each of which has four choices.
    a. Find the expected number of questions a student guessing on all answers will get right. **5**
    b. Find the standard deviation for the corresponding binomial distribution. *(Lessons 10-1, 10-2)* $\sqrt{3.75} \approx 1.936$

11. *True or false.* The graph of a binomial distribution with a fixed probability of success "spreads out" as the number of trials is increased. *(Lessons 10-1, 10-2)* **True**

12. Suppose that a certain disease has a 50% recovery rate.
    a. What is the probability that in a study of five people all five will recover? **0.03125**
    b. In one experiment, a drug is tested on five people and all five recover. Consider your answer to part **a**; comment on the drug's effectiveness.
    c. In a second experiment, 25 people get the drug. Find the probability that 18 or more people recover even if the drug has no effect on the illness. $P(x \geq 18) \approx 0.0216$
    d. Consider your answers to parts **b** and **c**. Does the drug appear to be effective? Which experiment might be considered more conclusive and why? *(Lesson 10-1)*
    b, d) See margin.

Additional Answers

7. P(5 or more heads given the probability of heads is $\frac{1}{3}$) $\approx 0.213 > 0.05$. Thus, we cannot reject the null-hypothesis at the 0.05 level.

8. Sample: Set the significance level at 0.05. H_0: The kicker's probability of making a field goal within 20 yards is .90. H_1: The probability of a made field goal is less than .90. $P(x \leq 2) = 0.00856 < 0.05$. Thus, we should reject the null hypothesis in favor of the alternative.

12. b. At the 0.05 level the results suggest the drug is effective.
    d. Sample: The drug seems effective at the 0.05 significance level. The second test is more conclusive than the first, because the sample is larger in the second.

13. Factor $2a^5 + 486a^5b^5c^{10}$ over the set of polynomials with integer coefficients. *(Lesson 9-8)*
$2a^5(1 + 3bc^2)(1 - 3bc^2 + 9b^2c^4 - 27b^3c^6 + 81b^4c^8)$

14. There are eleven girls in Carla's Girl Scout troop and thirteen in her second grade class. Altogether, there are twenty girls in the two groups. How many girls are in both the Girl Scout troop and the class? *(Lesson 7-2)* **4**

grade equivalent	percent
2.0 − 2.9	0.5
3.0 − 3.9	3.5
4.0 − 4.9	5.2
5.0 − 5.9	18.4
6.0 − 6.9	23.8
7.0 − 7.9	22.8
8.0 − 8.9	16.4
9.0 − 9.9	7.3
10.0 − 10.9	1.5
11.0 − 11.9	0.5
12.0 − 12.9	0.1

15. The table at the left summarizes the mathematics achievement scores (as grade equivalents) of a large group of seventh graders.
a. Draw a histogram of these data. **See margin.**
b. If a student is selected at random from this group of seventh graders, what is the probability that the student's mathematics achievement is at least one year above grade level? **0.258**
c. Shade the region of the histogram corresponding to part **b**.
(Lessons 1-5, 7-2) **See margin.**

16. The graph below represents an EKG reading of the electrical impulses from the heart, abnormal in this case. Each large square represents 0.2 seconds. Find the period of this heartbeat pattern. *(Lesson 4-6)*
≈ 0.32 seconds

17. A circular archery target is 122 cm in diameter and consists of a bull's-eye of diameter 12.2 cm, surrounded by nine evenly spaced concentric circles. Assume that an arrow that hits a target from 90 meters away is equally likely to land anywhere on the target. Find the probability that the arrow hits within the given region.
a. the bull's-eye **0.01**
b. somewhere in the outermost 4 circles **0.64**
c. within the fifth ring counting from the outer edge *(Lesson 7-1)* **0.11**

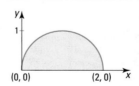

Exploration

18. What combinations of horizontal and vertical scale changes can be applied to the semicircular region at the right so that the area of the image is 1? **Sample: Let S be the scale change with $S(x, y) = \left(\frac{x}{\pi}, 2y\right)$. The area of the image is $\frac{1}{\pi} \cdot 2$ times the original area, or $\frac{1}{\pi} \cdot 2 \cdot \frac{1}{2}\pi \cdot 1^2 = 1$.**

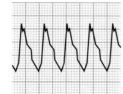
y axis, height 1, points (0, 0) and (2, 0)

Additional Answers
15. a., c.

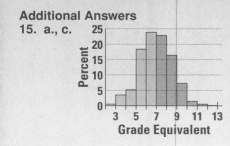
Histogram: Percent vs. Grade Equivalent

In-class Activity

Resources

From the *Teacher's Resource File*
■ Answer Master 10-4

This very brief activity is designed to ease the introduction of a new family of functions, those with parent $y = e^{-x^2}$.

Powering is not an associative operation, so $e^{(-x^2)}$ is not equal to $(e^{-x})^2$. When no parentheses are written, as is the custom, it is the first of these that is meant. Specifically, operations are done within the exponent first before the power is taken. (There is assumed parentheses around the exponent.)

IN-CLASS ACTIVITY

The Graph of $y = e^{-x^2}$

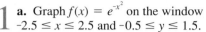

The function with equation $y = e^{-x^2}$ is the parent of many probability distributions. Its graph is sometimes called the **parent normal curve**.

1   **a.** Graph $f(x) = e^{-x^2}$ on the window $-2.5 \le x \le 2.5$ and $-0.5 \le y \le 1.5$.
b. Describe the shape of the curve. **See below.**

2   What kind of symmetry does f have? Justify your response with an algebraic argument. **See below.**

3   **a.** Evaluate $\lim_{x \to \infty} f(x)$. **0**
b. Describe what happens to the values of $f(x)$ as $x \to -\infty$. **They converge to 0.**

4   Does the graph of $y = f(x)$ have any asymptotes? If yes, give equations for all asymptotes. If no, explain why not. **Yes; $y = 0$**

5   Notice that near the y-intercept the graph is curved downward, called **concave down**. Farther away from the y-axis, the graph is curved upward, called **concave up**.

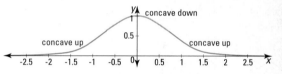

At two points, the graph changes concavity. These points are called **inflection points**. Estimate the coordinates of the inflection points as closely as you can. **Sample: (0.7, 0.6); (−0.7, 0.6)**

1a)

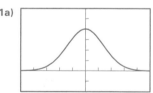

$-2.5 \le x \le 2.5$, x-scale = 0.5
$-0.5 \le y \le 1.5$, y-scale = 0.25

b) Sample: It is a bell-shaped curve.

2) reflection over the y-axis;
$f(-x) = e^{-(-x)^2} = e^{-x^2} = f(x)$

This mirror is both concave and convex, which stretches and shrinks the image.

You have seen that when the probability p of success is fixed, then as the number n of trials increases, the graph of a binomial probability distribution approaches a bell-shaped curve. For instance, below is a set of binomial probability distributions for $p = .8$ showing the change in the shape of the distribution as n takes on the values of 5, 20, 50, and 100.

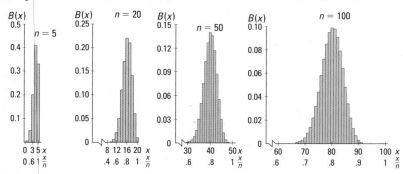

As n increases, the values of the binomial distribution approach those of a continuous function called a *normal distribution*.

The Parent Normal Curve

The graph of a normal distribution is called a **normal curve**. Normal curves were first studied by Gauss and Pierre Simon de Laplace in the early part of the 19th century. The **parent normal curve** is the graph of $f(x) = e^{-x^2}$, which you studied in the preceding In-class Activity.

Many everyday data sets or natural phenomena have approximately normal distributions. For instance, the heights of people from the same population can usually be modeled closely by an image of the parent normal curve under a rubberband transformation. Other data which have approximately normal distributions are the amounts of annual rainfall in a city over a long period of time, and the weights of individual fruits from a particular orchard in a year.

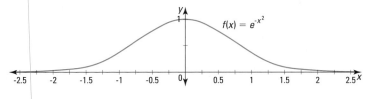

$f(x) = e^{-x^2}$

Objectives

D Use properties of normal distributions and their parent function.

Resources

From the **Teacher's Resource File**
- Lesson Master 10-4
- Answer Master 10-4
- Teaching Aids
  87 Warm-up
  91 Standard Normal Distribution and its Properties

Additional Resources
- Visuals for Teaching Aids 87, 91

Teaching **10-4**
Lesson

Warm-up

State the domain, range, and any maxima, minima, or asymptotes of each function.

1. $y = 5 - x^2$ **Domain is the set of all reals; range is {$y: y \leq 5$}; maximum at (0, 5)**

2. $y = 2^x$ **Domain is the set of all reals; range is {$y: y \geq 0$}; asymptote at $y = 0$**

3. $y = \sin x$ **Domain is the set of all reals; range is {$y: -1 \leq y \leq 1$}; maxima at ($\frac{\pi}{2} + 2n\pi$, 1), minima at ($\frac{3\pi}{2} + 2n\pi$, -1), for all integers n**

Lesson 10-4 Overview

Broad Goals Students are expected to be able to identify the critical points of normal curves, including the maximum and inflection points, and to describe its curvature and asymptotic behavior.

Perspective This lesson applies many of the ideas about functions students have seen with other functions: scale changes, asymptotes, maximum values, even (as opposed to odd) functions.

The parent of the normal curve, the function with equation $f(x) = e^{-x^2}$, has a bell shape but the area between it and the x-axis is not 1. Students are expected to be able to identify the critical points of the curve, including the maximum and inflection points, and to describe its curvature and asymptotic behavior. From the behavior of this function, which is easily seen to be an even function with asymptotes in both directions of the x-axis, and with maximum 1, it

is easy to determine the behavior of its offspring.

There is one particular offspring in which we are interested, the *standard normal distribution*. It is notable for two reasons: first, the area between the curve and the x-axis is 1, making it suitable to be a probability distribution; second, the points of inflection (points

(Overview continues on page 650.)

The graphs of binomial distributions are used to motivate this lesson, but of course the normal curve itself is continuous. Since $B(x)$ has as its domain the set of integers, it is not a continuous function. Such a function is said to be *discrete*. The variable x is a discrete variable. Just as we graph a binomial distribution as a histogram in order that the area above a point represents a probability, so an individual point on a normal distribution curve does not represent a probability because the area under that point is 0. Parts of the graph above intervals on the x-axis are what represent probabilities.

❶ These properties should agree with what students found in the In-class Activity on page 648.

A main idea in this lesson is the reasoning that leads to the scale changes of the parent normal distribution to make it the standard normal distribution with the special properties that distribution has. Of the six properties listed on page 652, students will have to accept properties (1), (2), and (4), though they can verify (2) and (4) with an automatic grapher. Furthermore, they need to accept that one standard deviation from the mean are the points of inflection.

You may wish to use **Teaching Aid 91** or an automatic grapher for demonstration purposes. The asymptotic behavior of the graph can be investigated by zooming in on the graph for large positive and negative values of x. Have students verify that the maximum point of the parent normal curve is (0, 1), and that the inflection points of the curve are near ($\pm$ 0.71, 0.61).

❶ The following are some properties of the function f with $f(x) = e^{-x^2}$.

1. Its domain is the set of real numbers; the range is $\{y: 0 < y \leq 1\}$.

2. The maximum value of the function is 1. This value occurs when $x = 0$.

3. f is an even function, so the y-axis is an axis of symmetry.

4. $\lim_{x \to \infty} f(x) = 0$ and $\lim_{x \to -\infty} f(x) = 0$, so the x-axis is an asymptote of the function.

5. The graph changes concavity when $x = \pm\frac{1}{\sqrt{2}} = \pm\frac{\sqrt{2}}{2}$.

Even though the graph of $f(x) = e^{-x^2}$ never touches the x-axis, it can be shown that the area under the parent of the normal curve is finite. Finding the area exactly requires calculus, but it can be approximated using Monte Carlo methods.

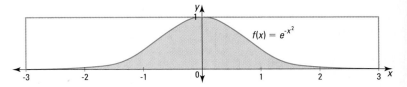

Imagine a rectangle containing the part of $f(x) = e^{-x^2}$ between $x = -3$ and $x = 3$ and between $y = 0$ and $y = 1$, as shown above. Randomly pick n points in the rectangle and count the number m which are under the curve. Then an approximation to the area under the curve is $\frac{m}{n}$ times the area of the rectangle. We used the technique described in Lesson 7-8 ten times, each time picking $n = 3000$ points from the rectangle with $-3 \leq x \leq 3$ and $0 \leq y \leq 1$. The number of points under f generated by a computer in the ten runs were 908, 928, 914, 843, 891, 879, 885, 897, 900, and 842. The mean of these ten numbers is 888.7. So $\frac{m}{n} = \frac{888.7}{3000} \approx 0.296$, giving an area under the curve of about $6 \cdot 0.296 = 1.776$. This value is very close to 1.772, the approximate value for the area under $f(x) = e^{-x^2}$ from $x = -3$ to $x = 3$ that can be found using calculus.

Using calculus, it can be shown that the area between the complete graph of $f(x) = e^{-x^2}$ and the x-axis is $\sqrt{\pi} \approx 1.7725$. Clearly, not much area is added to the region under $f(x) = e^{-x^2}$ when $|x| > 3$. In fact, because $\frac{1.772}{\sqrt{\pi}} \approx 0.9997$, about 99.97% of the area under $f(x) = e^{-x^2}$ is between $x = -3$ and $x = 3$.

Lesson 10-4 Overview, continued

where the curvature changes from concave up to concave down or vice-versa) are 1 unit from the mean. There is another kind of offspring—the normal curves used as models for frequency distributions. These are rubberband transformation images of the standard normal and are discussed in Lesson 10-6.

Optional Activities

After discussing **Question 15**, have students approximate the area under the standard normal curve from $x = -1$ to $x = 1$. They can use Monte Carlo methods as used on page 650. They may want to use a spreadsheet to generate the random numbers. [68% or 0.68]

The Standard Normal Curve

An important offspring of the function $y = e^{-x^2}$ is $y = f(z)$, the bell-shaped curve shown below. This curve has two important properties. The inflection points are when $x = 1$ and $x = -1$. And the area between the curve and the x-axis is 1. Now we find its equation.

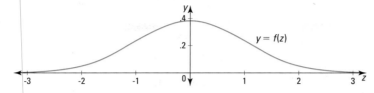

Since the inflection points of $y = e^{-x^2}$ are where $x = \pm\frac{1}{\sqrt{2}}$, to make the points of inflection of the image curve occur at $x = \pm 1$, apply the scale change $S_1 \colon (x, y) \to (\sqrt{2}\,x, y)$. The image is $y = e^{-(x/\sqrt{2})^2}$, which simplifies to $y = e^{-x^2/2}$.

❷ The parent (blue) and image (orange) under S_1 are graphed below. Notice that under the transformation $S_1 \colon (x, y) \to (\sqrt{2}\,x, y)$, the maximum point stays at $(0, 1)$.

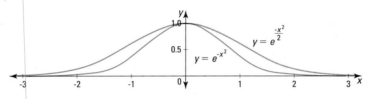

The area between the graph of $y = e^{-x^2}$ and the x-axis is $\sqrt{\pi}$. The scale change S_1 multiplies area by $\sqrt{2}$, so the area between the graph of $y = e^{-x^2/2}$ and the x-axis is $\sqrt{\pi} \cdot \sqrt{2} = \sqrt{2\pi}$. When a second scale change $S_2 \colon (x, y) \to \left(x, \frac{y}{\sqrt{2\pi}}\right)$ is applied to $y = e^{-x^2/2}$, the area under the image is 1.

Specifically, an equation of the image of $y = e^{-x^2/2}$ under S_2 is
$$\sqrt{2\pi}\, y = e^{-x^2/2}.$$

Solving for y gives an equation of this curve.
$$y = \frac{1}{\sqrt{2\pi}}\, e^{-x^2/2}$$

This graph is known as the **standard normal curve**. It represents a probability distribution called the **standard normal distribution**. It is the most important of all probability distributions.

Shown on page 652 is a graph of the standard normal distribution and its relation to the parent curve. We have labeled the horizontal axis as the z-axis. This is customary for the standard normal curve because of the relation between the standard normal curve and z-scores.

Lesson 10-4 *Normal Curves* **651**

---

❷ One important thing for students to know regarding the area under the parent normal curve is that almost all of it is in the region where $|x| < 3$. This provides a background for understanding why virtually all points under the *standard* normal curve are within 3 standard deviations of the mean.

Additional Examples

Explain why, if t is a positive real number, the value of e^{-t} can never be greater than 1. $e^{-t} = \frac{1}{e^t}$.
Since e^t is the positive power of a number greater than 1, it must be larger than 1. So the fraction must have a value less than 1.

Adapting to Individual Needs

Extra Help
When discussing **Question 1**, stress that for *any* fixed value of p, as the number of trials increases the graph of the distribution approaches a bell-shaped curve. Point out that the probability of success, $p = 0.8$, given in **Question 1** is just one example.

English Language Development
Be certain that students realize that the word "normal" as used here is a technical word. Its use here is derived from its meaning as "standard," and not from its meaning as "free from mental disorder."

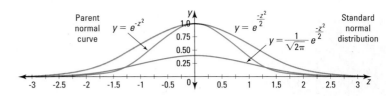

Using z for the horizontal axis, the standard normal distribution has the following properties.

(1) Its domain is the set of all real numbers; its range is $\{y: 0 < y \leq \frac{1}{\sqrt{2\pi}}\}$.

(2) Its maximum value is $f(0) = \frac{1}{\sqrt{2\pi}} \approx 0.3989$.

(3) It is an even function, and so is symmetric to the y-axis.

(4) As $z \to \infty$ or $z \to -\infty$, $f(z) \to 0$; the z-axis is an asymptote of the function.

(5) It is concave down where $-1 < z < 1$, and concave up where $|z| > 1$; its inflection points occur when $z = 1$ or $z = -1$.

(6) The area between the curve and the z-axis is 1.

QUESTIONS

Covering the Reading

1. *True or false.* Given a binomial probability distribution where the probability of success on a single trial is 0.8, then as the number of trials increases, the graph of the distribution approaches a bell-shaped curve. **True**

In 2 and 3, give an equation of the indicated feature of the graph of $y = e^{-x^2}$.

2. line of symmetry $x = 0$ **3.** asymptote(s) $y = 0$

In 4 and 5, for the graph of $y = e^{-x^2}$, give the coordinates of the indicated points.

4. all inflection points **See left.**   **5.** all relative extrema **(0, 1)**

In 6 and 7, give an equation for the curve.

6. parent normal curve $y = e^{-x^2}$ **7.** standard normal curve **See left.**

8. What type of transformation maps the parent normal curve to the standard normal curve? **scale change; $T(x, y) = \left(\sqrt{2}x, y/\sqrt{2\pi}\right)$**

9. a. Use an automatic grapher to graph the parent normal curve and the standard normal curve on the same set of axes.
   b. Describe two ways the graphs are alike, and two ways the graphs are different.
   a, b) See left.

In 10 and 11, give an equation of the indicated feature of the standard normal curve.

10. line of symmetry $z = 0$ **11.** asymptotes $y = 0$

Side notes (left margin)

4) $\left(\frac{\sqrt{2}}{2}, \frac{1}{\sqrt{e}}\right), \left(\frac{-\sqrt{2}}{2}, \frac{1}{\sqrt{e}}\right)$
$\approx (0.707, 0.607),$
$(-0.707, 0.607)$

7) $y = \frac{1}{\sqrt{2\pi}} e^{-\frac{x^2}{2}}$

9a)

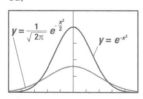

$-2.5 \leq x \leq 2.5$, x-scale = 0.5
$0 \leq y \leq 1.25$, y-scale = 0.25

b) Sample: The graphs both have asymptotes at $y = 0$, and the same mode. The two graphs do not have the same inflection points or maximums.

12) $\left(1, \frac{1}{\sqrt{2\pi e}}\right)$,

$\left(-1, \frac{1}{\sqrt{2\pi e}}\right) \approx$

(1, 0.242), (-1, 0.242)

In 12 and 13, for the standard normal curve, give coordinates of the indicated points.

12. all inflection points

See left.

13. all relative extrema

$\left(0, \frac{1}{\sqrt{2\pi}}\right) \approx$ (0, 0.3989)

Applying the Mathematics

14. The distribution of heights of junior girls is nearly normal. It has been found that the median height of junior girls is 163 cm, and 22% of them have a height greater than 169 cm. Estimate the probability that a randomly chosen junior girl will have height h in cm as follows.
   a. $h > 163$ **b.** $h < 169$ **c.** $163 < h < 169$
     0.5   0.78   0.28

15. Use a Monte Carlo technique to approximate the area under the standard normal curve from $x = -2$ to $x = 2$. $\approx$ 0.96

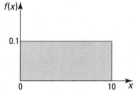

f(x)

0.1

0   10 x

16. The figure at the left represents a uniform (constant) probability distribution in which $f(x) = 0.1$ for $0 \leq x \leq 10$ and $f(x) = 0$, elsewhere.
   a. Suppose a point is selected randomly from the rectangular region. What is the probability that its x-coordinate is between 1.5 and 8.5?
   b. If five points are selected randomly from the rectangular region, what is the probability that all five will have x-coordinates between 1.5 and 8.5? **0.16807**

a) 0.7

17) Let x = number of tails. $P(x \geq 8$ or $x \leq 3) \approx .2266$, which is greater than 0.01, so the hypothesis cannot be rejected.

18) Yes. P(spinner lands 4 times out of 4 on the same section) = .0016, which is less than 0.01, so we would reject the hypothesis that the spinner is fair.

REPUBLIQUE FRANÇAISE

30^F $^{+}9^F$

POSTES

LAPLACE

1749-1827

Review

17. A coin is tossed 11 times and 8 tails appear. Is this ample evidence to reject the hypothesis that the coin is fair at the .01 level?   *(Lesson 10-3)*
See left.

18. A spinner with 5 equal sections lands on the same section 4 times in a row at the beginning of the game. Would you replace the spinner? Why or why not? *(Lesson 10-3)* See left.

19. Express the quotient $\frac{x^5 - 32}{x - 2}$ as a polynomial.   *(Lesson 9-4)*
$x^4 + 2x^3 + 4x^2 + 8x + 16$

20. Expand $(3x - 5)^4$ using the Binomial Theorem.   *(Lesson 8-8)*
$81x^4 - 540x^3 + 1350x^2 - 1500x + 625$

21. Consider two events, A and B. *True or false.*   Justify your answer.
   a. If $P(A) + P(B) = 1$, then A and B must be complementary events.
   b. If A and B are complementary events, then $P(A) + P(B) = 1$.
   (Lesson 7-2)
a, b) See margin.

22. A school compares its students' performance on a college-entrance examination to the performance of students in the nation.
   a. What is the population? See below.
   b. What is the sample?   *(Lesson 1-1)*
   The students in the school taking the exam.
a) all students in the nation taking college entrance exams

Exploration

23. Find out some things about the mathematician Pierre Simon de Laplace.
See margin.

Lesson 10-4 *Normal Curves* **653**

Additional Answers
21. a. False; A and B might not be mutually exclusive.
   b. True, by the definition of complementary

23. Sample: Laplace furthered the study of mathematics with contributions in analysis and other areas. The Laplace distribution is named for him.

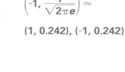

Practice
For more questions on SPUR Objectives, use **Lesson Master 10-4** (shown on page 651).

Assessment
Written Communication Have students write a paragraph explaining which transformations change the parent normal curve to the standard normal curve and how these transformations affect key points. [Students explain how to transform the parent normal curve to the standard normal curve and interpret key points.]

Extension
As mentioned on page 649, normal curves were first studied extensively by Gauss and Laplace. In honor of Gauss, these distributions are sometimes called *Gaussian distributions*. But normal distributions were probably first found by Abraham DeMoivre in 1733 and only later discovered by Gauss and Laplace. Interested students can research why Gauss was interested in the normal distribution. [It came from his interest in errors of observations of orbits of asteroids. Distributions of observations, under certain assumptions about errors, are normally distributed.]

Project Update Project 2, *Cumulative Percentile Curves*, on page 687, relates to the content of this lesson.

Setting Up Lesson 10-5
Be certain to discuss **Question 14**.

Objectives

B Use the Standard Normal Ddistribution to find probabilities.
D Use properties of normal distributions and their parent function.
J Graph and interpret normal distributions.

Resources

From the *Teacher's Resource File*
- Lesson Master 10-5
- Answer Master 10-5
- Teaching Aid 87: Warm-up

Additional Resources
- Visual for Teaching Aid 87

Teaching **10-5**
Lesson

Warm-up

Consider the triangle with vertices (-1,0), (0,1), and (1,0). (This is a right isosceles triangle whose right angle is the graph of $y = -|x| + 1$.)

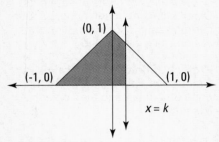

(0, 1)

(-1, 0)   (1, 0)

$x = k$

1. What is the area of this triangle? **1**
2. Find the value of *k* so that 75% of the area of the triangle is to the left of the line $x = k$, and 25% to the right. **The area of the triangle to the right of $x = k$ is $\frac{1}{2} \cdot (1-k) \cdot (1-k)$, which must equal $\frac{1}{4}$, from which $k = 1 - \frac{\sqrt{2}}{2} \approx .2928$.**

Finding Probabilities Using the Standard Normal Distribution

Below is the standard normal curve, the graph of $f(z) = \frac{1}{\sqrt{2\pi}} e^{-z^2/2}$.

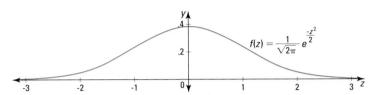

$$f(z) = \frac{1}{\sqrt{2\pi}} e^{\frac{-z^2}{2}}$$

In the last lesson, the standard normal distribution was called the most important probability distribution of all. It is important among all normal distributions because any other normal distribution can be transformed into it by the use of *z*-scores. In Lesson 10-6, you will see how this transformation is accomplished. Here we work with the standard normal distribution to prepare for that lesson.

This curve can represent a probability distribution because the area between it and the *z*-axis is 1. It is called the standard normal distribution because its mean and standard deviation are 0 and 1, respectively. Recall from Lesson 3-9 that these are exactly the mean and standard deviation of a set of data that has been transformed into *z*-scores. *The standard normal probability distribution is a distribution of z-scores.*

❶ From Area to Probability

The calculation of probabilities using the standard normal distribution is different in a major way from the calculation of binomial probabilities. With a binomial distribution, we can calculate the probability that there are 12 heads in 20 tosses of a fair coin. The probability is the area of the histogram bar above 12 in the graph at the right.

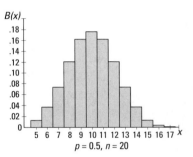

$p = 0.5, n = 20$

However, a normal distribution is continuous. The area above 12 in its graph on page 655 is 0. So when we approximate the binomial distribution by a normal distribution, we calculate the probability that there are between 11.5 heads and 12.5 heads (even though exactly 12 heads is the only possibility). The answer is given by the area between the vertical lines for the *z*-scores corresponding to $x = 11.5$ and $x = 12.5$. That is, using a normal distribution, we can only calculate the probability that *x* (or its corresponding *z*-score) lies in a particular interval.

Lesson 10-5 Overview

Broad Goals The goal of this lesson is to become familiar with the standard normal distribution and the use of tables to determine probabilities with it.

Perspective The parent normal curve function cannot be a probability distribution because the area under it is not 1. By doing an appropriate vertical and horizontal scale change, the area under the curve can be made equal to 1 and the *x*-coordinates of

the points of inflection can be at ±1. The significance of this is that the function becomes a probability distribution with mean 0 and standard deviation 1.

The normal distribution is important because so many natural phenomena seem to be normally distributed, because normal distributions are fine approximations to binomial distributions, and the distributions of sample means are normal. The last of these is

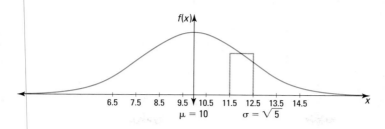

Calculating Specific Probabilities

Consider first the probability that a normally distributed value is less than the mean. That means the corresponding z-score is less than 0. This is represented by the shaded area below. Because of the symmetry of the standard normal curve and the fact that the area between the curve and the z-axis is 1, $P(z < 0) = 0.5$. This is what you would expect. Also $P(z > 0)$ is $1 - 0.5$, which is also 0.5.

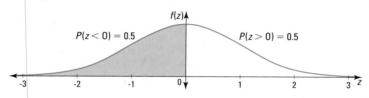

The standard normal distribution is so important that probabilities derived from it have been calculated and recorded in tables. Below is part of the **Standard Normal Distribution Table** given in Appendix D. It gives the area under the standard normal curve to the left of a given positive number a. The table does not give values for $a > 3.09$ because there is very little area under the standard normal curve to the right of $z = 3.09$.

Standard Normal Distribution Table $P(z < a)$ for $a \geq 0$										
a	0	1	2	3	4	5	6	7	8	9
0.0	.5000	.5040	.5080	.5120	.5160	.5199	.5239	.5279	.5319	.5359
⋮										
0.6	.7257	.7291	.7324	.7357	.7389	.7422	.7454	.7486	.7517	.7549
0.7	.7580	.7611	.7642	.7673	.7704	.7734	.7764	.7794	.7823	.7852
0.8	.7881	.7910	.7939	.7967	.7995	.8023	.8051	.8078	.8106	.8133
0.9	.8159	.8186	.8212	.8238	.8264	.8289	.8315	.8340	.8365	.8389
1.0	.8413	.8438	.8461	.8485	.8508	.8531	.8554	.8577	.8599	.8621
⋮										
1.7	.9554	.9564	.9573	.9582	.9591	.9599	.9608	.9616	.9625	.9633
⋮										
2.9	.9981	.9982	.9982	.9983	.9984	.9984	.9985	.9985	.9986	.9986
3.0	.9987	.9987	.9987	.9988	.9988	.9989	.9989	.9989	.9990	.9990

Example 1 considers the probability that a value in a normal distribution is less than 0.85 standard deviations above the mean. Since all values below the mean are included, you should expect a probability greater than 0.5.

Notes on Reading
❶ Emphasize a point made in the notes to the last lesson and at the beginning of this lesson: just as we graph a binomial distribution as a histogram in order that the area above a point represents a probability, so an individual point on a normal distribution curve does not represent a probability because the area under that point is 0. Parts of the graph above intervals on the x-axis are what represent probabilities. Students should be able to calculate probabilities of the form $P(z < a)$, $P(z > b)$, and $P(a < z < b)$ for any a and b between -3.09 and 3.09. The application of these skills in realistic contexts begins in Lesson 10-6.

❷ Page 655 and Appendix D on page 875 contain the Standard Normal Distribution Table.

Technology If students have a calculator which gives normal distribution values, we suggest that they check how the machine works. You may wish to make a note of students having this capability and to familiarize yourself with the mechanics so that you can assist those students.

discussed in Lesson 10-7. The normal distribution is so important that tables listing areas under this curve have been compiled to indicate the probability that an event can happen.

Optional Activities
When assigning **Questions 3, 4, 5, 6, 13, and 14**, you may want to have students draw standard normal curves and shade the desired areas. Then have them describe how they will use the values in the Standard Normal Distribution Table to get the desired probability.

1. Find the probability that a randomly chosen observation from a standard normal distribution is less than 0.96. $.8315 \approx .83$
2. Find the probability that an observation from a normally distributed random variable falls within the given range.
   a. Between 0 and 0.96 $\approx .3315$
   b. Greater than 0.96 $\approx .1685$
   c. Less than -0.96 $\approx .1685$
   d. Between -0.96 and 0.96 $\approx .6630$
3. If a set of data is normally distributed, what percent of the data is within 1.5 standard deviations of the mean? (Use Appendix D.) $\approx 87\%$

Example 1

Find the probability that a randomly chosen observation from a standard normal distribution is less than 0.85.

Solution

Imagine or sketch a standard normal curve. The desired probability is the area under the curve to the left of the line $z = 0.85$.

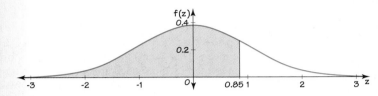

Use the table directly. Read down the a-column until you get to 0.8. Go across this row until you get to the column headed by 5. The entry there is .8023. So
$$P(z < 0.85) \approx 0.8023.$$

By adding and subtracting areas and using symmetry properties of the standard normal curve, the Standard Normal Distribution Table can be used to calculate probabilities that are not of the form $P(z < a)$ with $a \geq 0$.

Example 2

Find the probability that a randomly chosen observation from a standard normal distribution is in the given interval.
a. between 0 and 0.85   b. greater than 0.85
c. less than -1.73   d. greater than -1.73

Solution

a. We wish $P(0 < z < 0.85)$. This is the area under the normal curve between $z = 0$ and $z = 0.85$. It can be found by subtracting $P(z \leq 0)$ from $P(z < 0.85)$.
$$P(0 < z < 0.85) = P(z < 0.85) - P(z \leq 0).$$

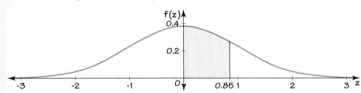

From Example 1, $P(z < 0.85) \approx 0.8023$. From the symmetry of f, $P(z \leq 0) = 0.5$. So
$$P(0 < z < 0.85) \approx 0.8023 - 0.5000$$
$$= 0.3023.$$

▶

Extra Help
Some students might be confused about how to locate values of a in the Standard Normal Distribution Table. Explain that the numbers given in the column under a are values only to tenths. The hundredths digit is given in the row to the right of a. Suggest to students that to locate entries such as 0.8, or 1.7, they should think of these numbers in hundredths: 0.80 and 1.70.

Challenge
Simpson's Rule from Calculus can be used to approximate area under a curve. Let $f(z)$ be the standard normal probability function. The area under the curve from 0 to a can be approximated with the formula:
$$\frac{a}{12}\left(f(0) + 4f(\tfrac{a}{4}) + 2f(\tfrac{a}{2}) + 4f(\tfrac{3a}{4}) + f(a) \right).$$
For each value of a, have students find $P(0 < z < a)$ using the table in Appendix D and the approximation formula.

1. $a = 0.23$ [0.0910; 0.0910]
2. $a = 1.35$ [0.4115; 0.4115]
3. $a = 2.91$ [0.4982; 0.4980]

b. We wish $P(z > 0.85)$. It is the area of the shaded region below.

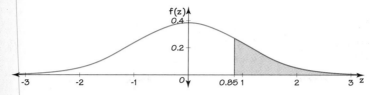

To find the area under the standard normal curve to the *right* of a given value, subtract the area to its *left* from the total area under the curve, which is 1.

$$P(z > 0.85) = 1 - P(z < 0.85)$$
$$\approx 1 - 0.8023$$
$$= 0.1977$$

c. The table does not show values of $P(z < a)$ when a is negative. To find $P(z < -1.73)$, the user is expected to apply the symmetry of the graph.
$$P(z < -1.73) = P(z > 1.73)$$

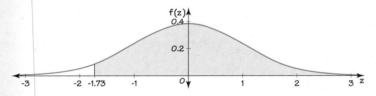

Now find $P(z > 1.73)$ as in part **b**.
$$P(z > 1.73) = 1 - P(z < 1.73)$$
$$\approx 1 - .9582$$
$$= 0.0418$$
So $P(z < -1.73) \approx 0.0418$.

d. Here we wish to find $P(z > -1.73)$. It is the area of the shaded region below.

You can subtract the area found in part **c** from the total area.
$$P(z > -1.73) = 1 - P(z < -1.73)$$
$$\approx 1 - 0.0418$$
$$= 0.9582$$
Or you can use symmetry.
$$P(z > -1.73) = P(z < 1.73)$$
$$\approx 0.9582$$

Lesson 10-5   *Finding Probabilities Using the Standard Normal Distribution*   **657**

Notes on Questions

Notes on Questions

Question 9 A more formal way of putting this is: About two-thirds of the time, a normally distributed random variable will have a value within one standard deviation from the mean.

Questions 9–10 These two facts are important to remember.

Questions 11, 13-16 These questions require the table in Appendix D on page 875.

Note that the probability for any particular value, such as $P(z = a)$, is zero by the area interpretation. For this reason, if z is normally distributed, it is always the case that $P(z < a) = P(z \le a)$.

Many calculators or statistics utilities provide values from the normal distribution table. Some provide values for $P(z < a)$ as we do in the table in Appendix D. However, others give $P(0 < z < a)$, that is, the area under the curve from 0 to a. And still others give the area to the right of a. Check that you know how to use the technology available to you.

Example 3 derives another important property of the standard normal distribution.

Example 3

About what percent of the data in a standard normal distribution are within one standard deviation of the mean?

Solution

Sketch the standard normal curve.

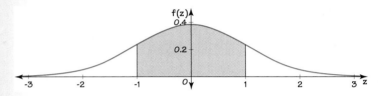

Being within one standard deviation of the mean means that $-1 < z < 1$. From the symmetry of the standard normal curve,

$$P(-1 < z < 1) = 2 \cdot P(0 < z < 1)$$
$$= 2(P(z < 1) - P(z < 0))$$
$$\approx 2(0.8413 - 0.5)$$
$$= 0.6826.$$

Thus, about 68% of normally distributed data are within one standard deviation of the mean.

Check

The shaded area seems to be about $\frac{2}{3}$ of the area under the curve.

In the Questions you are asked to estimate what percent of the data in a standard normal distribution are within two (or three) standard deviations of the mean. These are important estimates to know.

Covering the Reading

In 1 and 2, use the fact that in a standard normal distribution, $P(z < 1.6) \approx .9452$.

1. The graph below shows a standard normal curve.

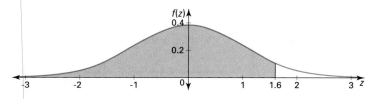

   a. What is the area of the shaded region? $\approx$ **0.9452**
   b. What is the area of the unshaded region between the curve and the z-axis? $\approx$ **0.0548**

2. Calculate the following probabilities.
   a. $P(0 < z < 1.6)$ b. $P(|z| < 1.6)$ c. $P(z > \text{-}1.6)$
   $\approx$ **0.4452** $\approx$ **0.8904** $\approx$ **0.9452**

In 3–6, evaluate using the Normal Distribution Table in Appendix D.

3. $P(z < 1.88)$ **0.9699**   4. $P(z > 0.07)$ **0.4721**

5. $P(\text{-}1.5 < z < 1.3)$ **0.8364**   6. $P(z > \text{-}2)$ **0.9772**

7. Find the area of the shaded region shown under the standard normal distribution curve below. **0.3830**

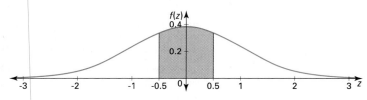

8. State each for the standard normal distribution.
   a. the mean **0**   b. the standard deviation **1**

9. *True or false.* About two-thirds of the observations from a standard normal distribution are within one standard deviation of the mean. **True**

10. Explain why about 95% of the values in the standard normal distribution are within two standard deviations of the mean.
   $P(\text{-}2 < z < 2) = 2P(0 < z < 2) \approx 2(0.9772 - .5) = 2(0.4772) = 0.9544$

11. About what percent of the data in a standard normal distribution are within three standard deviations of the mean? $\approx$ **99.7%**

12. Give a reason why the Normal Distribution Table does not list probabilities for z larger than 3.09.
   Sample: Only a tiny percent of scores are beyond 3.09 standard deviations from the mean.

Lesson 10-5 *Finding Probabilities Using the Standard Normal Distribution* **659**

Notes on Questions

Question 18, 24, and 26 These are important review for the next lesson.

Question 26 Science Connection Calories measure heat energy. One calorie raises the temperature of one gram of water by one degree Celsius. Among fruits and vegetables, the cucumber is the least calorific with only 73 calories per pound; and the avocado is the most, with 741 calories per pound.

17) The area under $y = e^{-x^2}$ is $\sqrt{\pi}$, while the area under the standard normal curve is 1.

20b)

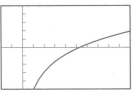

$-2 \le x \le 10$, x-scale = 1
$-5 \le y \le 5$, y-scale = 1

Reading the graph, we see that the zero is about 5.3.

21b)

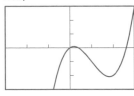

$-3 \le x \le 3$, x-scale = 1
$-3 \le y \le 3$, y-scale = 1

From the graph, the zeros are 0, ≈ 2.62, ≈ 0.38.

score	percent
750–800	8
700–740	22
650–690	21
600–640	17
550–590	8
500–540	13
450–490	5
400–440	4
350–390	2

Applying the Mathematics

In 13 and 14, find the value of c satisfying the equation.

13. $P(z < c) = 0.975 \approx 1.96$

14. $P(z \ge c) = 0.4522 \approx 0.12$

15. Which value of the random variable in a standard normal distribution is exceeded by about 75% of the distribution? ≈ -0.67

16. Complete: 90% of the observations of a standard normal distribution fall within __?__ standard deviations of the mean. ≈ 1.65

Review

17. How do the areas under the parent $y = e^{-x^2}$ and the standard normal curve compare? *(Lesson 10-4)* **See left.**

18. If for some binomial probability distribution $\mu = 20$ and $\sigma = 2.3$, find n and p. *(Lesson 10-2)* **$p = 0.7355$, $n \approx 27$**

19. Let $f(x) = 2x^2 + 3x + 4$. Evaluate $\frac{f(x) - f(h)}{x - h}$. *(Lesson 9-9)* **$2x + 3 + 2h$**

In 20 and 21, an equation for a function is given. **a.** Find the exact zeros of the function. **b.** Check your answer by graphing the function and locating zeros correct to the nearest hundredth. *(Lessons 6-4, 9-5)*

20. $s(x) = 3 \ln x - 5$ a) $e^{\frac{5}{3}}$ b) See left.

21. $p(x) = x^3 - 3x^2 + x$ a) $0, \dfrac{3 \pm \sqrt{5}}{2}$ b) See left.

22. A box has length 4 inches, width 3 inches, and height 2 inches. Another box with twice the volume has dimensions $4 + x$, $3 + x$, and $2 + x$ inches. Approximate the value of x to the nearest 0.1 inch. *(Lessons 9-1, 9-2)* **$x \approx 0.7$ inch**

23. In a certain city, 60% of the citizens are in favor of a school bond rate increase. A sample of ten citizens is taken at random. What is the probability that fewer than half of them will be in favor of the increase? *(Lesson 8-9)* ≈ 0.166

24. The table at the left summarizes the SAT-Math scores of a large group of students.
   a. Construct a histogram of these data. **See margin.**
   b. Find a scale change that can be applied to the histogram in part **a** so that the area of the histogram is 1. **See margin.**
   c. If a student is selected at random from this group, what is the probability that the student's SAT-Math score is over 600? ≈ 0.68
   d. Shade the region of the histogram corresponding to part **c**.
   (Lessons 1-5, 7-2) **See margin.**

660

Additional Answers

24. a, d.

Intervals include left endpoint only.

b. The transformation
S: (score, percent) $\to \left(\dfrac{\text{score}}{50}, \dfrac{\text{percent}}{100}\right)$
will give bar widths of 1 unit and bar heights in hundredths.

25. Consider $f(x) = -x^2 + 9$.
   a. Find an equation for g, the image of f under the transformation
      $T: x \rightarrow \frac{x-2}{3}$. $g(x) = -9x^2 - 12x + 5$
   b. Predict how the axes of symmetry of $y = f(x)$ and $y = g(x)$ are related.
   c. Check your prediction in part **b** by graphing the two functions.
      (Lesson 4-9)
      b, c) See left.
26. The number of calories in one ounce of each of five different kinds of cereal is: 145, 90, 110, 110, 100.
   a. Find the mean and standard deviation of these data.
   b. Let x_i = the number of calories in the ith cereal. Let $z_i = \frac{x_i - m}{s}$,
      where m is the mean and s the standard deviation found in part **a**. Find the mean and standard deviation of the transformed data.   *(Lesson 3-9)*
      a) **$m = 111$ calories, $s \approx 20.736$ calories**   b) $\mu_{z_i} = 0$, $\sigma_z = 1$

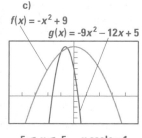

25b) The axis of symmetry for the graph of g is $\frac{2}{3}$ units to the left of the axis of symmetry for the graph of f

c)
$f(x) = -x^2 + 9$
$g(x) = -9x^2 - 12x + 5$

$-5 \leq x \leq 5$, x-scale = 1
$-5 \leq y \leq 10$, y-scale = 1

Exploration

27. **a.** Examine the differences between successive values in the first row of the Standard Normal Distribution Table. Estimate the following values.
   i. $P(z < 0.035)$ **0.5140**   **ii.** $P(z < 0.068)$ **0.5271**
   b. Why are the differences referred to in part **a** almost constant?
   c. Why are differences between successive values in other rows of the table not constant?
      The graph is not close to linear in these areas.
   b) The graph is nearly a straight line for the interval $0 < z < 0.09$.

Lesson 10-5   *Finding Probabilities Using the Standard Normal Distribution*   **661**

Practice

For more questions on SPUR Objectives, use **Lesson Master 10-5** (shown on page 657).

Assessment

Written Communication Have students **work in pairs**. Have each student make up a problem like **Example 2** for his or her partner. Students should provide appropriate sketches and solve their partner's problem. Ask students to check each other's work. [Students use the Standard Normal Distribution to find probabilities.]

Extension

As an extension to **Question 16**, ask students to complete the statement "80% of the observations of a standard normal distribution fall within _____ standard deviations of the mean." [1.29] Then repeat the statement for 70%, 60%, 50%, 40%, 30%, 20%, and 10%. [1.04, 0.84, 0.68, 0.53, 0.39, 0.26, 0.13]

Project Update Project 2, *Cumulative Percentile Curves*, Project 3, *Is Your Class Typical?*, Project 5, *Sums of Random Digits*, and Project 6, *Design a Study*, on pages 687–688, relate to the content of this lesson.

Setting Up Lesson 10-6
Discuss **Questions 18, 24, and 26**.

Objectives

D Use properties of normal distributions and their parent function.
E Solve probability problems using normal distributions.
J Graph and interpret normal distributions.

Resources

From the Teacher's Resource File
- Lesson Master 10-6
- Answer Master 10-6
- Assessment Sourcebook: Quiz for Lessons 10-4 through 10-6
- Teaching Aids
  88 Warm-up
  92 Example 1 Graphs
- Technology Sourcebook
  Computer Master 11

Additional Resources
- Visuals for Teaching Aids 88, 92
- StatExplorer
- Exploration 10-6

Warm-up

For each equation below, describe the transformation from the parent graph $y = -x^2$.

1. $y = -(x - 5)^2$ **The graph has been translated 5 units to the right.**

2. $y = -(\frac{x-5}{2})^2$ **The graph has been translated 5 units to the right and then stretched horizontally by a scale factor of 2.**

3. $y = -(\frac{x-5}{2})^2 + 3$ **The graph has been translated 5 units to the right, stretched horizontally by a scale factor of 2, and then translated three units up.**

LESSON

10-6

Other Normal Distributions

Transforming Any Normal Curve into the Standard Normal Curve

Recall that if each number in a data set is translated by a constant, the mean of the distribution is also translated by that constant, but the standard deviation remains unchanged. For instance, consider the fact that the heights of adult men in the United States are approximately normally distributed with a mean of 70 inches and a standard deviation of 3 inches. If $m = 70$ is subtracted from each height, the mean of the resulting distribution is $70 - 70 = 0$. This translation has no effect on the standard deviation of the resulting distribution.

If each translated height is multiplied by $\frac{1}{3}$, the standard deviation of the resulting distribution is $\frac{1}{3} \cdot 3 = 1$. Thus, the rubberband transformation $x \rightarrow \frac{x - 70}{3}$ maps the distribution of heights with $m = 70$ and $s = 3$, shown below at the left, onto a distribution with mean 0 and standard deviation 1. With the Graph-Standardization Theorem you can show that this distribution can be transformed into the standard normal curve shown below at the right.

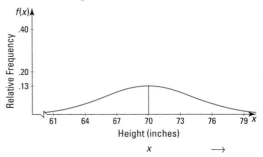

Height (inches)
x

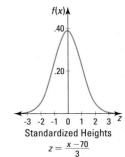

Standardized Heights
$z = \frac{x - 70}{3}$

The preceding analysis generalizes to the following theorem.

> **Theorem**
> If a variable x has a normal distribution with mean m and standard deviation s, then the transformed variable
>
> $$z = \frac{x - m}{s}$$
>
> has the standard normal distribution.

662

Lesson 10-6 Overview

Broad Goals This lesson considers some distributions that are assumed to be normal, or that are theoretically very close to normal, and uses tables to find probabilities that the random variable lies in a particular interval.

Perspective This lesson applies many of the ideas found in the preceding five lessons. The distributions that are assumed to be normal in this lesson are heights of people, diameters of lead in pencils, and people

who show up for an airline flight. They are found in **Examples 1–3**. The distribution that theoretically is very close to normal is the binomial distribution with a large number of trials. This is found in **Example 4**.

Even when a random variable is normally distributed, it is rather unlikely that its mean is 0 and its standard deviation is 1. However, if its mean is m and its standard deviation s, then the transformation $x \rightarrow \frac{x - m}{s}$ will trans-

form it into a random variable whose distribution is standard normal. Then tables can be used to find probabilities, and the results can be applied to the given distribution.

As is the case with finite data sets, the value of the transformed variable z is called the **standard score** or **z-score** for the value x. The process of getting z-values from an original data set by applying the transformation

$$x \rightarrow \frac{x - m}{s}$$

is often referred to as **standardizing** the variable. By standardizing the values of normal distributions, you can determine many probabilities.

Standardizing Variables to Find Probabilities

Example 1

An adult American male is selected randomly. What is the probability that the man is less than 6 feet tall?

Solution

Because the height x of adult American males has approximately a normal distribution with a mean of 70 inches and standard deviation of 3 inches, the variable $z = \frac{x - 70}{3}$ has a **standard normal distribution**. The z-score associated with $x = 72$ is $z = \frac{72 - 70}{3} = \frac{2}{3} \approx 0.67$. This means that a height of 72 inches is $\frac{2}{3}$ of a standard deviation above the mean of 70 inches. As illustrated by the graphs of the normal distribution and standard normal distribution below, the two shaded areas are equal. Because each area represents a probability, the two probabilities are equal.

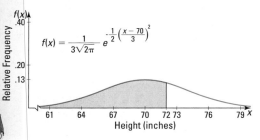
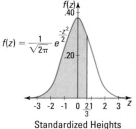

From the table of values for the standard normal distribution,
$$P(x < 72) \approx P(z < 0.67)$$
$$\approx 0.7486.$$
The probability of a randomly selected adult American male being less than 6 feet tall is about 0.75. In other words, about $\frac{3}{4}$ of all adult males in the United States are less than 6 feet tall.

Optional Activities

Activity 1 Technology Connection
Materials: Explorations software

You may use *Exploration 10-6, Normal Distributions,* to introduce Lesson 10-6. Students will be able to find the probability that a variable with a normal distribution is within a given interval. The computer displays the related z-score for the set boundaries, a and b, as well as the calculated probability that x is between z_a and z_b.

Activity 2 As an extension of **Question 14,** you might have students find the probability that a randomly selected student in 1996 had an SAT verbal score
a. of 800. [0.38%]
b. over 700. [3.84%]
c. over 600. [19.5%]
d. less than 300. [3.14%]

Activity 3 Technology Connection
You may want to assign *Technology Sourcebook, Computer Master 11.* Students use *StatExplorer* or similar software to simulate the heights of randomly chosen men and women. Then students compare the simulated data to the theoretical normal distribution.

The solution to **Example 2** points out the use of the theorem which precedes these examples. **Question 3** is similar to **Example 1,** so you may choose to do this question as part of your class discussion.

The normal approximation to a binomial distribution allows students to estimate probabilities in binomial situations with comparative ease. The steps are shown in **Example 4:** Determine n, p, and q from the given information; then calculate np and $\sqrt{npq}$ to obtain the mean and standard deviation you want for the normal distribution. Next, calculate z-scores for the data under consideration using $\frac{x - np}{\sqrt{npq}}$, and find the corresponding probabilities from tables for the z-scores.

Emphasize the power of the normal distribution. If you know (or assume) that a variable is normally distributed, the tables of the normal distribution enable a determination of the probability that the variable lies in any interval.

In Example 2, we want the probability that the width of a pencil lead lies in a particular interval.

Example 2

The refills for a particular mechanical pencil are supposed to be 0.5 mm in diameter. Refills of 0.485 mm or less in diameter do not stay in the pencil, while those of 0.520 mm or more do not fit in the pencil at all. If a firm makes refills with diameters whose differences from the correct size are normally distributed with a standard deviation of .01 mm, find the probability that a randomly chosen refill will fit.

Solution

Let x = the diameter of the refill in mm. The task is to find $P(0.485 < x < 0.520)$, where x is normally distributed with $m = 0.5$ and $s = 0.01$. Change to standard scores using
$$z = \frac{x - 0.5}{0.01}.$$
The z-score z_1 associated with $x = 0.485$ is
$$z_1 = \frac{0.485 - 0.5}{0.01}$$
$$= -1.5.$$
The z-score z_2 associated with $x = 0.520$ is
$$z_2 = \frac{0.520 - 0.5}{0.01}$$
$$= 2.$$
According to the preceding theorem, z_1 and z_2 are on the standard normal distribution. Thus, the probability of a diameter between 0.485 mm and 0.52 mm equals the probability of having a z-score between $z_1 = -1.5$ and $z_2 = 2$.

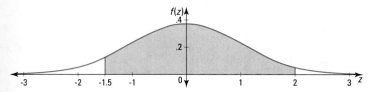

Use the table of values for the standard normal distribution.
$$P(0.485 < x < 0.520) = P(-1.5 < z < 2.0) = P(z < 2.0) - P(z < -1.5)$$
$$= P(z < 2.0) - (1 - P(z < 1.5))$$
$$\approx 0.9772 - (1 - 0.9332)$$
$$= 0.9104$$
The probability that a refill will fit is about 0.91. That is, about 91% of the refills will fit the pencil, 9% will not.

The answer to Example 2 is too far from 100%; the manufacturer should probably adjust the machinery and the procedures used in order to get more accurate thicknesses.

Adapting to Individual Needs

Extra Help
Some students might not understand how the distribution of heights is mapped onto the standardized distribution of heights. You may want to show equations for the transformations that accomplish this by working backwards. We know an equation for the standard normal curve is $y = \frac{1}{\sqrt{2\pi}} e^{\frac{-z^2}{2}}$.
The substitution of $x - 70$ for z moves the

mean from 0 to 70. The substitution of $\frac{x - 70}{3}$ for $x - 70$ changes the standard deviation from 1 to 3. But it also multiplies the area by 3. Since we need the area to be 1, we have to shrink the y-axis to $\frac{1}{3}$ of what it was.

This is done by substituting $\frac{y}{\frac{1}{3}}$ for y, or equivalently, $3y$ for y, which, when solved for y, results in the 3 in the denominator

on the right side: $y = \frac{1}{3\sqrt{2\pi}} e^{-\frac{1}{2}\left(\frac{x - 70}{3}\right)^2}$

Approximating a Binomial Distribution with a Normal Distribution

The normal distribution is related to many other probability distributions. In particular, as you have seen earlier in this chapter, some binomial distributions are approximately bell-shaped.

For instance, the binomial probability distribution B with $n = 100$ and $p = 0.2$ has mean $\mu = 100(0.2) = 20$ and standard deviation $\sigma = \sqrt{npq} = \sqrt{100(0.2)(0.8)} = \sqrt{16} = 4$. Below is the probability histogram for this binomial distribution with the curve for the normal distribution with mean 20 and standard deviation 4 superimposed.

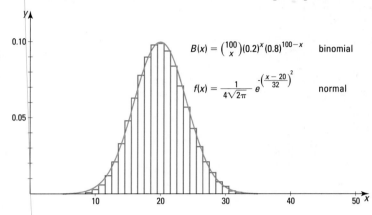

$$B(x) = \binom{100}{x}(0.2)^x (0.8)^{100-x} \quad \text{binomial}$$

$$f(x) = \frac{1}{4\sqrt{2\pi}}\, e^{-\left(\frac{x-20}{32}\right)^2} \quad \text{normal}$$

For these values of n and p, the normal distribution appears to approximate the binomial distribution quite well.

In general, if n is quite large, or when p is close to 0.5, a normal curve approximates a binomial distribution quite well. If n is small and p is near 0 or 1, the binomial distribution is not well approximated by a normal distribution. With $q = 1 - p$, a rule of thumb is that a binomial distribution can be approximated by a normal distribution with mean np and standard deviation $\sqrt{npq}$ provided np and nq are each ≥ 5.

The graphs of binomial distributions in Lessons 10-1 and 10-2 provide evidence for this approximation. Example 3 shows how to apply it.

Additional Examples

Additional Examples

1. An adult American male is selected randomly. Estimate the probability that the man is shorter than 5 feet 6 inches tall.
$z < $ -1.33; about 9.2%

2. A batch of light bulbs is tested and found to have lifetimes that are normally distributed with a mean of 1067 hours and a standard deviation of 92 hours. If the manufacturer guarantees that the light bulbs will last for 800 hours, about what percent of light bulbs would be expected not to perform as guaranteed?
$\frac{800 - 1067}{92} \approx$ -2.90; 99.81% of area lies to the right of -2.90, so 0.19% of bulbs would be expected not to perform as guaranteed.

3. You are the operator of a hotel with 100 rooms. From past experience, you know that 80% of people who make reservations with you show up. If you take reservations for 105 rooms, estimate the probability that more than 100 people will show up.
Near zero; 100 is about 4 standard deviations from the expected value of 84.

(Additional Examples continue on page 666.)

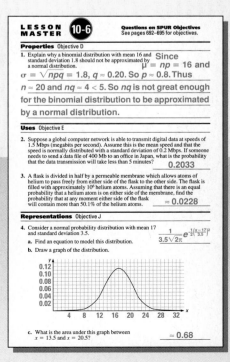

Adapting to Individual Needs

Challenge
Give students a distribution of grades for some of your tests. Include the raw scores and the letter grades assigned. Have them answer the following questions.

1. Calculate μ and σ for the test scores and the distribution of grades based on the grading scale used.

2. Adjust the raw test scores to z-scores. (See Challenge for Lesson 3–9.)

3. How would your grades be affected if grades were assigned as follows:
A: $z \geq 1.29$
B: $.85 \leq z < 1.29$
C: $-.85 \leq z < .85$;
D: $-1.29 \leq z < -.85$;
F: $z < -1.29$?
[Answers will vary.]
Discuss the advantages and disadvantages of assigning grades on the basis of this "curve."

4. Use a normal approximation to a binomial distribution to estimate the probability of getting fewer than 20 or more than 30 heads in 50 tosses of a fair coin. **The normal distribution has mean 25 and standard deviation $\sqrt{12.5} \approx 3.54$. 19 or 31 heads is about 1.70 standard deviations from the mean; $z \leq -1.70$ or $z > 1.70$ appears with probability about 8.9%.**

O'Hare International Airport, Chicago

Example 3

In the past, about 85% of ticketed passengers have shown up for the regularly scheduled Chicago-New York flights with a capacity of 240. The airline company proposes to accept 270 reservations. What is the probability that with this policy, the Chicago-New York flight will be overbooked?

Solution

Because each passenger either arrives or doesn't arrive, and all passengers are assumed to act independently, **the number of passengers arriving is binomially distributed. The distribution has n = 270, p = 0.85, and q = 0.15. Because each of np = 229.5 and nq = 40.5 is greater than 5, the normal approximation to the binomial distribution can be used. The appropriate normal distribution has mean np = 229.5 and standard deviation $\sqrt{npq} \approx 5.87$. The flight is overbooked when the number n of passengers is greater than 240.** The binomial distribution interval is (239.5, 240.5). Since the number of passengers cannot exceed 240, you should calculate $p(n > 240.5)$, which is represented by the area shaded below.

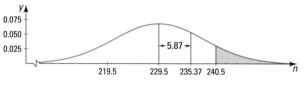

$$P(n > 240.5) = P\left(z > \frac{240.5 - 229.5}{5.87}\right)$$
$$\approx P(z > 1.87)$$
$$\approx 1 - 0.9693$$
$$= 0.0307$$

So the flight will be overbooked about 3.1% of the times it departs. If the flight operates once a day except on Sundays, company officials should expect it to be overbooked about once a month.

Note how much simpler the calculation is for the normal approximation than is the calculation for the exact answer using the binomial distribution. The exact answer would require calculating a sum of 30 terms:

$$_{270}C_{241}(.85)^{241}(.15)^{29} + {}_{270}C_{242}(.85)^{242}(.15)^{28} + \ldots + {}_{270}C_{270}(.85)^{270}(.15)^{0}.$$

As a final example, we return to the situation of testing whether a coin is fair or not. Notice how the use of the normal approximation to the binomial allows us to deal with the large numbers that are more realistic in real tests.

Example 4

A coin is tossed 1000 times and 530 heads result. Using the .01 significance level, test the hypothesis that the coin is fair.

Solution

The number of heads is binomially distributed. Assuming the coin is fair, $p = 0.5$, and in this case $n = 1000$. So the binomial distribution and the approximating normal distribution have mean $np = 500$ and standard deviation

$$\sqrt{npq} = \sqrt{1000 \cdot 0.5 \cdot 0.5} = \sqrt{250} \approx 15.81.$$

The z-score equivalent of 530 is thus $\frac{530 - 500}{15.81}$, which is about 1.898. (That is, 530 is about 1.898 standard deviations away from the mean.) Consequently, you must find the probability of an outcome at least as far from the mean as 530. That is, find $P(z \geq 1.898$ or $z < -1.898)$. To use the Standard Normal Distribution Table, you must round these values to the nearest hundredth, to 1.90 and -1.90.

The table indicates that $\qquad P(z < 1.90) \approx 0.9713.$
So $\qquad\qquad\qquad\qquad\qquad P(z \geq 1.90) \approx 1 - 0.9713$
$$= 0.0287.$$
Thus $\qquad\qquad P(z \geq 1.898 \text{ or } z < -1.898) \approx 2(.0287)$
$$= 0.0574.$$

This probability is higher than 0.01, so the hypothesis cannot be rejected. Even a fair coin would result in 530 or more heads or 530 or more tails in 1000 tosses over 5% of the time.

QUESTIONS

Covering the Reading

In 1–4, use the fact that the heights of adult men in the United States are normally distributed with mean 70" and standard deviation 3".

1. Suppose a variable x is normally distributed with mean 70 and standard deviation 3. If the transformation $x \to \frac{x - 70}{3}$ is applied to each data point, what type of distribution results?
   a standard normal distribution
2. What is the median height? **70"**

3. What proportion of men are less than five feet, nine inches tall?
   0.3707
4. How many of a group of 1200 male employees of a company can the basketball coach of the company team expect to be taller than six feet, six inches? $P(x > 78) = P(1 - P(z \leq 2.67) = .0038$, so 4 or 5 men may be taller than 6'6".
5. Refer to the distribution of mechanical pencil refill sizes in Example 2.
   a. What is the probability a randomly chosen refill will be too large?
   b. What is the probability a randomly chosen refill will be too small?
   a) 0.0228   b) 0.0668

Questions 1–4 These questions and **Example 1** assume that no other information is known about the men. There are different distributions for various racial and ethnic groups.

(Notes on Questions continue on page 668.)

Follow-up for Lesson 10-6

Practice

For more questions on SPUR Objectives, use **Lesson Master 10-6** (shown on page 665).

Assessment

Quiz A quiz covering Lessons 10-4 through 10-6 is provided in the *Assessment Sourcebook*.

Extension

Three extremely talented hitters in baseball were Ty Cobb with a batting average of .420 in 1911, Ted Williams with an average of .406 in 1941, and George Brett with an average of .390 in 1981. These averages cannot be compared directly because the distribution of batting averages has changed over the decades, with the mean remaining fairly constant but the standard deviation dropping over time. Below is a table of the mean and standard deviation for different decades. Have students standardize the batting averages for Cobb, Williams, and Brett to see how outstanding they really were.

Decade	Mean	Std dev
1910s	.266	.0371
1940s	.267	.0326
1970s	.261	.0317

[Cobb: 4.15; Williams: 4.26; Brett: 4.07; Williams is the highest when standardized, though not the highest numerically; note that all are over 4 standard deviations above the mean—extremely rare!]

Project Update Project 3, *Is Your Class Typical?*, Project 5, *Sums of Random Digits*, and Project 6, *Design a Study*, on page 688, relate to the content of this lesson.

Notes on Questions

Question 7 Emphasize that, based on the probabilities for various numbers of reservations, the airline can deduce how many reservations it should accept. This is an easier process than the Monte Carlo method used in Chapter 7, but each method can be used to check the other.

Question 9 Students may ask what significance level is best. There is no rule. The choice of significance level depends on the importance of the decision. To avoid the choice of significance level, some people indicate the probability of getting 273 or more heads or 273 or more tails, rather than indicating a significance level. In this case, the probability is about 4.0%.

Question 11 Science Connection The first dry-cell batteries were made in New York City in 1898, following the work of Georges Leclanche in the 1860s. The batteries are called dry because they contain a nonspillable, jelly-like electrolyte.

Questions 12–13 Error Alert This may be a good time to caution students not to assume that every distribution is normal. In this case, it is very possible that the distribution is not normal. There are other distributions studied in statistics that might apply here. Statisticians would take the data and see what kind of distribution gives a good fit before making an assumption like the one used here.

Question 14 In contrast to **Questions 12–13,** SAT test scores are scaled so that a normal distribution fits the test scores distribution well.

Question 15 This is a true story, but we do not know whether the coin was tested before it was tossed.

Questions 20–21 The answers show that the connection of **Question 21** is more reliable.

9a) **We can reject the hypothesis that the coin is fair.**
b) **We cannot reject the hypothesis that the coin is fair.**
c) **We cannot reject the hypothesis that the coin is fair.**

11a) $z = \dfrac{t - 100}{4}$

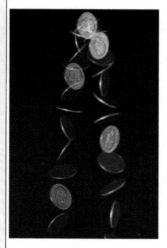

6. Under what conditions may a binomial distribution be approximated by a normal distribution? **if np and nq are each ≥ 5**

7. Refer to Example 3. Find the probability that the flight will be overbooked if 280 bookings are accepted. **≈ 0.34**

8. A binomial distribution with $p = 0.15$ and $n = 80$ can be approximated by the normal distribution with mean **a.** and standard deviation **b.** .
   a) **12**   b) **$\sqrt{10.2} \approx 3.19$**

9. A coin is tossed 500 times, resulting in 273 heads and 227 tails. Test the hypothesis that the coin is fair using each significance level.
   a. .05   b. .01   c. .001
   a–c) See left.

10. State one advantage of using a normal approximation for a binomial distribution. **Sample: Calculations are simpler.**

Applying the Mathematics

11. Suppose that the lifetime t of a flashlight battery is normally distributed with mean 100 hours and standard deviation 4 hours.
    a. Identify a transformation that can be used to transform t to z, the argument in the standard normal distribution. **See left.**
    b. What are the mean and standard deviation of the distribution of z-scores? **$\mu = 0$, $\sigma = 1$**

In 12 and 13, assume that the time for a certain surgical incision to heal is normally distributed with a mean of 150 hours and a standard deviation of 20 hours.

12. What proportion of incisions should heal within a week? **≈ 0.8159**

13. If a patient must stay in the hospital until his or her wound heals, what is the probability that a randomly chosen patient will stay ten days or more? **almost 0**

14. In 1996, the scaled scores on the SAT verbal section had mean 505 and standard deviation 110. Assume that the scaled scores are normally distributed. What is the probability that a randomly selected student in 1996 had an SAT verbal score between 500 and 600? **≈ 0.325**

15. Officials in Lawrence, Pennsylvania, needed to select a bank that would lend the town $450,000 at the lowest rate. When they opened the sealed bids from the banks, they found that National City Bank and National Bank of the Commonwealth had submitted identical bids. They decided the bid by a coin toss. Suppose that you were entrusted with the job of ensuring that the coin used was a fair coin. **A sample is given.**
    a. How many times would you flip the coin to test it? **500**
    b. What significance level would you use? **0.05**
    c. For your number of tosses, how many heads could appear and still not cause you to think the coin was unfair? **between 228 and 272**

668

Review

In 16 and 17, suppose the variable z has a standard normal distribution.

16. Find the area of the shaded region below. ≈ **0.9505**

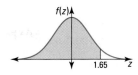

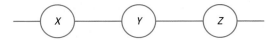

17. Determine $P(z \geq 2.67)$. *(Lesson 10-5)* ≈ **0.0038**

18. Complete: In a standard normal distribution 99% of the observations are within __?__ standard deviations of the mean. *(Lesson 10-5)* ≈ **2.58**

19. How many ways are there of selecting a committee of five faculty and two students from a group of 20 faculty and 300 students? *(Lesson 8-6)*
$_{20}C_5 \cdot {}_{300}C_2 = \mathbf{695,354,400}$

In 20 and 21, suppose that a system on a spacecraft is composed of three independent subsystems, X, Y, and Z. The probability that these will fail during a mission is 0.002, 0.006, and 0.003, respectively. *(Lessons 7-2, 7-3, 7-4)*

20. If the three are connected in series, as below, a failure in any one of the three will lead to a failure in the whole system.

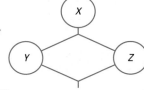

What is the probability that the system will be reliable—that is, it will *not* fail? ≈ **0.989**

21. Suppose the subsystems are connected as shown at the right. In this case, both X and either Y or Z must be reliable for the whole system to be reliable. What is the probability that this whole system will not fail?
≈ **0.998**

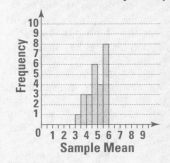

22. Consider the set {0, 1, 2, 3, 4, 5, 6, 7, 8, 9}.
  a. Find the mean of the numbers in the set.
  b. Find the standard deviation of the numbers in the set. *(Lessons 1-3, 1-7)* ≈ **3.03**
  a) **4.5**

23) **Sample: This rule works because for a normally distributed variable, the largest and the smallest data values fall about 3 standard deviations from the mean. Therefore, the complete range is equal to about 6 standard deviations, from 3 above the mean to 3 below.**

Exploration

23. Some books give the following rule of thumb for finding the standard deviation of a normally distributed variable:

$$s \approx \frac{\text{range}}{6}.$$

Explain why this rule of thumb works. **See left.**

Additonal Answers, page 670
1. Mean = 4.5;
   Standard deviation ≈ 2.872
2. a, b Answers will vary.
   c. Sample:

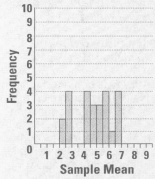

   d. Sample:
   Distribution mean = 4.39;
   Distribution standard deviation ≈ 1.46
3. a–c. Answers will vary. Sample:

   d. Sample:
   Distribution mean ≈ 4.40;
   Distribution standard deviation ≈ 0.734
4. Sample: As the sample size gets larger, the mean of the distribution of sample means approaches the mean of the uniform distribution, and the standard deviation of the sample means approaches 0.

Setting Up Lesson 10-7
Do the In-class Activity on page 670.

In-class Activity

Resources

From the *Teacher's Resource File*
■ Answer Master 10-7

Additional Resources
■ Exploration 10-7

This Activity is designed to introduce the idea of the distribution of sample means. This can be confusing because each element of the distribution of sample means comes itself from a distribution. Be careful that students distinguish the various distributions in this activity.

1. The uniform distribution of digits This is the distribution graphed. In this distribution, *x* takes on integer values 0 through 9, and for all *x*, $P(x) = .1$.
2. The distribution of means of 25 random samples of size 4 taken from the uniform distribution. This is obtained in step 2 of the Activity. Students graph this distribution in part **c**.
3. The distribution of means of 25 random samples of size 15 taken from the uniform distribution. This is obtained in step 3 of the Activity.
4. The distribution of means of 1000 random samples of size 4 taken from the uniform distribution. Students are asked to conjecture about this distribution in step 4 of the activity. You could ask them also to conjecture about what might happen if 1000 random samples of size 15 were taken. That is considered in Example 1 of Lesson 10-7.

The key idea is that as *n* increases, the distributions of *n* sample means (from samples of sufficient size) approach a normal distribution even though the original distribution was not normal.

The Sampling Distribution of the Mean

You will need something to generate random digits—a calculator or a table of random digits. Work with a partner.

To understand how measures of a sample are related to the corresponding measures of the population from which it was taken, it is helpful to study how various samples drawn from the same population vary. In this activity, you will investigate how random samples from a uniform distribution vary.
1–4) See margin.

1 Consider the uniform distribution of random digits from 0 through 9. A histogram of this probability distribution is shown at the right. Use the formulas from Lesson 10-2 to determine the mean and standard deviation of this distribution.

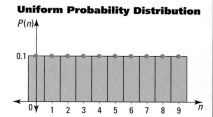

Uniform Probability Distribution

2 a. Design a simulation to choose a random sample of size four from the uniform distribution of digits from 0 to 9. Run the simulation and calculate the mean of the four numbers that occur.
b. Run the simulation in part **a** 24 more times. After each run, record the mean of the sample of size four.
c. Draw a histogram to illustrate the distribution of your 25 sample means.
d. Calculate the mean and standard deviation of the distribution of sample means in part **c**.

3 a. Choose a random sample of size 15 from the uniform distribution of digits from 0 to 9. Run the simulation and calculate the mean of the 15 numbers.
b. Repeat part **a** 4 more times.
c. Combine your data from part **b** with that of four other people to obtain 25 sample means.
d. Calculate the mean and standard deviation of the distribution in part **c**.

4 Make a conjecture about the mean and standard deviation of the distribution of sample means, if 1000 random samples, each of size four, were taken from the uniform distribution of digits from 0 to 9.

Additional Answers
See page 669.

Technology Connection
Materials: Explorations software

Students may use *Exploration 10-7, A Sampling Distribution of the Mean,* to do this In-Class Activity. By investigating random samples of a chosen size, students will discover how statistical measures for a sample vary. The random numbers and the sampling distribution of the mean are shown in a table and as a histogram.

As you know, it is often too costly, too difficult, or impossible to study an entire population. Usually a sample is taken. Then inferences about the population are made from the sample data. However, even if a random sample is taken, the characteristics of the sample are not likely to be identical to the corresponding characteristics of the population. For instance, the means of various samples from the same population are likely to differ somewhat from each other, and from the population mean.

What Is a Sampling Distribution?

In the preceding In-class Activity, three types of means were calculated—the mean of the probability distribution, the means of individual samples, and the mean of a set of sample means. We will assume that the digits you generated from a table or calculator are indeed random. With this assumption, the statistics of the population (all possible random digits that could be generated) are the same as the statistics for the model (the uniform distribution). It is customary to use $\bar{x}$ to stand for the mean of a sample, and μ to indicate the population mean. We shall use $\mu_{\bar{x}}$ to stand for the mean of a set of sample means. Similarly, we use s for the sample standard deviation, σ for the population standard deviation, and $\sigma_{\bar{x}}$ for the standard deviation of the set of sample means.

Activity 1

Refer to your data from the preceding In-class Activity. **See margin on page 676.**
   a. What are the values of μ and σ for the population studied?
   b. What is the first value of $\bar{x}$ you calculated?
   c. For the means of the samples of size 4, give the values for $\mu_{\bar{x}}$ and $\sigma_{\bar{x}}$.
   d. For the means of the samples of size 15, give the values of $\mu_{\bar{x}}$ and $\sigma_{\bar{x}}$.

When the samples are all the same size, as they were in the In-class Activity, a distribution of their means is called a **sample distribution** or a **sampling distribution**. Note that although the distribution of the original population (the digits) used in the In-class Activity is a uniform distribution, the distribution of sample means is not. However, you should have found that the mean of the distribution of sample means is almost equal to the population mean.

You should have also found that the standard deviation of the distribution of sample means is much less than the standard deviation σ of the population. That is, averages are less variable than individual observations.

Finally, you may have noted that as the number of samples increases, say from 25 to 1000, that the distribution of $\bar{x}$, the sampling distribution, becomes nearly bell-shaped.

Lesson 10-7 *Sampling Distributions and the Central Limit Theorem* **671**

Objectives
F Use binomial and normal distributions to test hypotheses.
G Apply the Central Limit Theorem.

Resources
From the *Teacher's Resource File*
■ Lesson Master 10-7
■ Answer Master 10-7
■ Teaching Aids
   88 Warm-up
   93 Example 1 Graphs
   94 Central Limit Theorem (CLT) and Corollary

Additional Resources
■ Visuals for Teaching Aids 88, 93, 94

Teaching Lesson **10-7**

Warm-up
Share what you wrote for the answer to Question 4 of the In-class Activity on page 670 with three other students.

Notes on Reading
In lieu of sophisticated proofs, we use simulations to support the conclusions in this lesson, as we did in Lesson 10-5. **Teaching Aid 93** is provided to help you discuss the graphs of **Example 1.** Point out that these examples do not constitute proof. The proofs are studied in some college-level statistics courses.

Lesson 10-7 Overview

Broad Goals This lesson covers the Central Limit Theorem: If samples of size n are taken from a population with mean μ and standard deviation σ, then as n increases, the sample means approach a normal distribution with mean μ and standard deviation $\frac{\sigma}{\sqrt{n}}$. The power of this theorem is that it applies to means of samples of any size over 30. The proof of this theorem is beyond the scope of this course, so computer

simulations are exhibited to give credibility to the theorem.

Perspective In Lesson 10-6, students saw that the normal distribution crops up in two places: as the limit of binomial distributions as the number of trials increases, and in many real situations (such as heights of people from the same population). In this lesson, normal distributions arise as distributions of sample means.

672

We did this experiment, taking 1000 random samples of size four from the digits from 0 to 9. Pictured below is the sampling distribution, that is, the distribution of sample means. Note that this sampling distribution is clearly not uniform. It can be modeled by a normal distribution with mean 4.5.

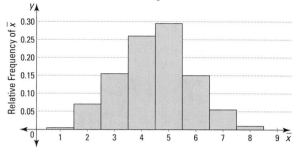

Sampling Distribution of $\bar{x}$ from a Uniform Distribution Based on 1000 Samples Each of Size 4

The Effect of Sample Size on the Sampling Distribution

The work with samples drawn from a uniform distribution can be generalized to populations with other distributions. If a large number of random samples of sufficient and equal size are drawn from *any* population, the distribution of sample means approaches a normal distribution, and the mean $\mu_{\bar{x}}$ of the sample means approaches the mean μ of the population.

As the size n of the individual samples increases, another pattern emerges.

Is This Batch Tasty? *A sample of size 30, as shown here, is about the smallest size for which means are normally distributed.*

Example 1

Simulate drawing the following samples from the uniform distribution of digits from 0 to 9. Find the mean of each sample, and the mean and standard deviation of each distribution of sample means.
a. 1000 samples of size 15   **b.** 1000 samples of size 100

Solution

Simulations of this size are best done by computer or calculator, not by using a table of random digits. Below is output we obtained from a statistics utility.
a. *1000 sample means, each the mean of a sample of 15 random digits, gave $\mu_{\bar{x}} = 4.494$ and $\sigma_{\bar{x}} = 0.758$.*

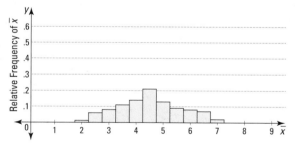

Optional Activities

Have students find the heights of the members of your school's girls' basketball teams and the heights of the members of the teams that your school competes against. Have them compute the mean of the sample and use the information in **Question 11** to compute the standard deviation of the sample. Have them determine whether or not the girls on the teams are unusually tall. [For example, assume there are 50 girls on all the basketball teams. Assume the mean height is 65 inches, which is not much more than the mean of the population. The standard deviation of the sample is then 0.368. Students may be surprised that the *z*-score is 3.53, over three standard deviations above the mean!]

b. 1000 sample means, each the mean of a sample of 100 random digits, gave $\mu_{\bar{x}} = 4.5031$ and $\sigma_{\bar{x}} = 0.286$.

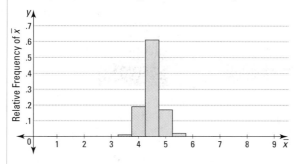

Note that as the size of the sample n increases, the mean $\mu_{\bar{x}}$ of the sampling distribution does not vary very much, but the standard deviation $\sigma_{\bar{x}}$ decreases. Surprisingly, the relations between the sample size n, the means of the population and of the sampling distribution, and the standard deviations of the population and the sampling distribution are quite simple. They were first proved by Pierre Simon Laplace (1749–1827), and are summarized in the *Central Limit Theorem*. The proof of this theorem is well beyond the scope of this course.

---

❶   The Central Limit Theorem (CLT)

Suppose random samples of size n are selected from a population with mean μ and standard deviation σ. Then, as n increases, the following occur.

1. The mean $\mu_{\bar{x}}$ of the distribution of sample means approaches μ.

2. The standard deviation $\sigma_{\bar{x}}$ of the distribution of sample means approaches $\frac{\sigma}{\sqrt{n}}$.

3. The distribution of sample means approaches a normal distribution with mean μ and standard deviation $\frac{\sigma}{\sqrt{n}}$.

Activity 2

In the In-class Activity, you used samples of size $n = 4$. For the population consisting of the digits from 0 to 9, calculate the value of $\frac{\sigma}{\sqrt{n}}$. This should be approximately equal to the value you found for $\sigma_{\bar{x}}$ in Activity 1.

$\frac{\sigma}{\sqrt{n}} \approx \frac{2.872}{2} \approx 1.44$

Making Inferences Using the Central Limit Theorem

The Central Limit Theorem allows you to make predictions about samples if characteristics of the population are known.

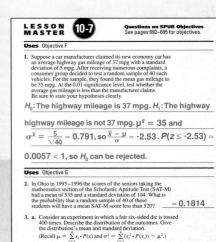

Adapting to Individual Needs
Extra Help

Some students might have difficulty understanding the distinction between the Central Limit Theorem and its Corollary. Explain that the theorem itself concerns the limit $n \to \infty$ of the distribution of sample means of size n from any distribution. It says the limit is a normal distribution. The corollary indicates the size n that is sufficient to be "close enough" so that the normal approximation can be utilized without much worry.

4. At a particular large bingo parlor, it is advertised that a player should win a large prize about once in every 10 nights. Thirty regular players are interviewed and it is found that in the last 50 nights, they won a total of 100 large prizes. Is the advertisement to be believed? **The null hypothesis is that the probability of winning a large prize in a night is $\frac{1}{10}$, or 0.1. In 50 nights, with a binomial distribution, one would expect a mean of 5 wins and a standard deviation of $\sqrt{50 \cdot .1 \cdot .9} = \sqrt{4.5} \approx 2.12$. For the sampling distribution of 30 samples, a mean of 5 and a standard deviation of $\frac{\sqrt{4.5}}{\sqrt{30}} \approx .388$ is expected. But the mean number of winnings here is $\frac{100}{30} \approx 3.33$, which is about 4.30 standard deviations from the mean. This would occur with far less than .001 probability and suggests that the advertisement is not to be believed; a typical person does not win a prize about once in every ten nights.**

Example 2

In a certain country, the mean family income (when converted to U.S. dollars) is known to be \$13,500 with a standard deviation of \$2000. Suppose random samples of 100 families are to be chosen. Determine each of the following.
a. the mean of $\bar{x}$
b. the standard deviation of $\bar{x}$
c. the distribution of $\bar{x}$

Solution

Use the Central Limit Theorem. For a large number of samples,

a. $\mu_{\bar{x}} \approx \mu = \$13,500$;

b. $\sigma_{\bar{x}} \approx \frac{\sigma}{\sqrt{n}} = \frac{\$2000}{\sqrt{100}} = \frac{\$2000}{10} = 200$;

c. The distribution of sample means will approach a normal distribution with mean \$13,500 and standard deviation \$200.

The Central Limit Theorem is *central* because it deals with a mean of a population, a measure of its *center*. It is a *limit* theorem because it deals with what can be expected as samples of larger and larger size are involved.

Note that the Central Limit Theorem states that even if the underlying population distribution is not normal, the means of samples of sufficient size will be normally distributed. However, the Central Limit Theorem does not specify exactly what that sufficient size is. Fortunately, a corollary to the Central Limit Theorem provides a rule of thumb for determining how large the samples should be so that the distribution of sample means is close enough to normal. The proof of this corollary is also beyond the scope of this course.

Corollary
Consider a population with mean μ and standard deviation σ from which random samples of size n are taken. Then the distribution of sample means is approximately normal with mean $\mu_{\bar{x}} \approx \mu$ and standard deviation $\sigma_{\bar{x}}$ approximately equal to $\frac{\sigma}{\sqrt{n}}$ whenever one of the following occurs:

a. the population itself is normally distributed, or
b. the sample size $n \geq 30$.

Calculating Probabilities Using the Central Limit Theorem

The Central Limit Theorem and its corollary allow you to test hypotheses about the sample means for "large" samples, whether or not the population is normal.

Adapting to Individual Needs

Challenge
Have students research the Law of Large Numbers, and its history. [The Law of Large Numbers was first proved by the Swiss mathematician Jacob Bernoulli (1654–1705). Popularly it is sometimes known as the "law of averages" because the central idea is that in the "long run," that is over many trials, the relative frequency of outcomes approaches the probability distribution and the average outcome approaches the mean of the distribution, with the important stipulation that successive trials be independent. Gambling casinos stay in business largely based on this principle.]

Example 3

A manufacturer of copy machines claims that the relative frequency distribution of x, the amount of time needed by a technician to perform routine maintenance on a copy machine, is modeled by the distribution graphed at the right, with $\mu = 1$ hour and $\sigma = 1$ hour. A local supplier finds that the average maintenance time for a random sample of 50 machines is 75 minutes, and believes that the manufacturer is underestimating the maintenance time for the machines. Test the manufacturer's hypothesis at the 0.01 level.

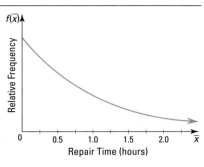

Solution

First, state the hypothesis to be tested. **The null hypothesis H_0 is: The mean maintenance time for this brand of copy machine is 1 hour.** Now, using the manufacturer's model, compute the probability that the average maintenance time for a sample of 50 machines is greater than 75 minutes. **Since the sample size $n \geq 30$, use the Central Limit Theorem and its corollary on the manufacturer's model. They imply that $\bar{x}$, the mean maintenance time for a sample of 50 machines, is approximately normally distributed, with mean $\mu_{\bar{x}} \approx \mu = 1$ hour and standard deviation $\sigma_{\bar{x}} \approx \dfrac{\sigma}{\sqrt{50}} = \dfrac{1}{\sqrt{50}} \approx 0.14$ hours. Thus, the variable $z = \dfrac{\bar{x} - 1}{0.14}$ has a standard normal distribution.** Because 75 minutes is 1.25 hours, the probability that the average maintenance time is greater than 75 minutes is

$$P(\bar{x} > 1.25) \approx P\left(\frac{\bar{x} - 1}{0.14} > \frac{1.25 - 1}{0.14}\right)$$
$$\approx P(z > 1.79).$$
$$P(z > 1.79) = 1 - P(z < 1.79)$$
$$\approx 0.0367$$

Thus, assuming the manufacturer's model, in 3.67% of all samples of 50 machines, the mean maintenance time would be greater than 75 minutes. Because 0.0367 is not less than 0.01, the null hypothesis cannot be rejected. The supplier is not justified in claiming that the manufacturer is underestimating the maintenance time for the machines.

Check

The standard deviation $\sigma_{\bar{x}}$ is about 0.14 hours, or 8.4 minutes. The local supplier's mean was 75 minutes. So the supplier's mean was within 2 standard deviations of the manufacturer's claim. In a standard normal distribution about 95% of the area under the curve is within 2 standard deviations of the mean 0. Thus it seems reasonable that over 2.5% of the time this could happen.

Notes on Questions

Questions 6–8 Error Alert
Students who miss these questions need better understanding of the three parts of the Central Limit Theorem.

Notice that in Examples 2 and 3 the mean μ and standard deviation σ of the population were known, and from them questions about the sample mean $\bar{x}$ and its probability distribution were answered. In Lesson 10-8 we consider the converse problem, that of predicting population statistics μ and σ when the sample statistics $\bar{x}$ and s are known.

QUESTIONS

Covering the Reading

1) Sample: A sample is a subset of the population. A sampling distribution is a set of sampling means from samples of the same size.

3) $\frac{\sigma}{\sqrt{n}} \approx \frac{2.872}{2} \approx 1.44$

1. Explain the difference between a sample and a sampling distribution. **See left.**

2. Write your answers to Activity 1. **See margin.**　**3.** Write your answer to Activity 2. **See left.**

In 4 and 5, consider the uniform distribution of integers from 0 to 9. Suppose two simulations A and B are conducted where A has 100 random samples each of size 50, and B has 10 random samples each of size 500.

4. *True or false.* The means of the sample means from the two experiments will be approximately equal. **True**

5. Which experiment is likely to yield the sampling distribution with the larger standard deviation? **A**

In 6–8, consider a population from which a very large number of random samples of equal size are taken. *True or false.*

6. The mean of the sample means approximates the population mean. **True**

7. The standard deviation of the sample means approximates the standard deviation of the population. **False**

8. The shape of the distribution of the sample means approximates the shape of the population. **False**

9. To what populations does the Central Limit Theorem apply? **Any populations**

10. To what kinds of samples do the Central Limit Theorem and its corollary apply? **random samples of size ≥ 30**

11a) $\mu_{\bar{x}} \approx 63.7$ inches, $\sigma_{\bar{x}} \approx .26$ inch
b) Sample: It is approximately normal with mean 63.7 inches and standard deviation of .26 inch.

11. The distribution of heights of young adult women in the United States can be modeled by a normal distribution with $\mu = 63.7$ inches and $\sigma = 2.6$ inches. A medical study is conducted in which women are randomly selected from this population in sample sizes of 100 and the mean height of the women in each sample is recorded.
   a. Estimate the mean and standard deviation of the numbers recorded.
   b. Describe the distribution of sample means.
   a, b) See left.

In 12 and 13, refer to Example 3. Assume the manufacturer's claim is correct.

12. Consider the distribution of the average amount of time needed by a technician to perform maintenance on a random sample of 50 copy machines.
   a. Give the mean. **1 hour**
   b. Give the standard deviation. **.14 hour or 8.4 minutes**
   c. Describe the distribution. **The distribution is approximately normal with a mean of 1 hour and a standard deviation of .14 hour.**

676

13. Suppose another supplier maintains a random sample of 100 such machines. Find the probability that the average maintenance time for these machines exceeds 45 minutes. .9938

Applying the Mathematics

In 14 and 15, use the graphs below, showing the relative frequency distributions of 100 sample means from the same population. The scales on the *y*-axes are not the same.

a.
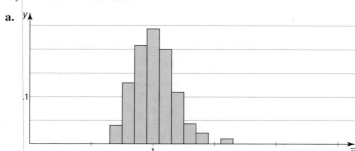

b.
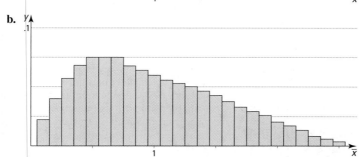

c.
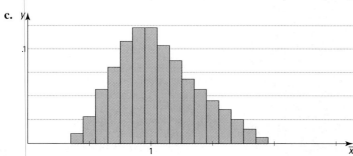

14. Match each graph to the most likely sample size.

(i) 2 b   (ii) 15 c   (iii) 40 a

15. Was the population from which the samples were drawn normal? How can you tell? No; the distribution for the small samples is skewed.

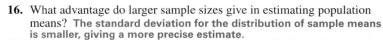

Notes on Questions

Question 17 This question deals with the common sense nature of the Central Limit Theorem. The larger the number of bowling games that contribute to the scores, the smaller will be the variance in the mean.

Sports Connection In 1994, 37,356,000 Americans participated in bowling and $157 million was spent on bowling accessories. (*Statistical Abstract of the United States 1996*)

Question 19 Without much calculation, we see that the mean of 22.9 is over 3 standard deviations above what would be expected for the mean of a sample of this size taken from the entire ACT population. The probability of this occurring is less than .01. Thus we might infer that the students from Acme High were better-scoring students than a similar group chosen randomly from the national population.

17b) The scores of the 45 games; these scores are the population with a standard deviation σ, while the 15 weekly averages are a subset consisting of 15 samples of size 3 with a smaller standard deviation:

$$\sigma_{\bar{x}} = \frac{\sigma}{\sqrt{3}}.$$

16. What advantage do larger sample sizes give in estimating population means? **The standard deviation for the distribution of sample means is smaller, giving a more precise estimate.**

17. Consider a bowler in a league who keeps track of individual games, as well as average scores for three games played each time the league meets. The league meets once a week for 15 weeks during a season.
    a. How is the mean of the 45 games bowled related to the mean of the 15 weekly averages? **They are the same**.
    b. Which will have the larger spread, the scores of the 45 games or the 15 weekly averages? Explain why. **See left.**

In 18 and 19, in a recent year the scores of students on the ACT college entrance exam were modeled by a normal distribution with $\mu = 20.9$ and $\sigma = 4.7$.

18. What is the probability that a randomly chosen student from the population who took the exam has a score of 24 or higher? **.2546**

19. The mean score of the 84 students at Acme High who took the ACT that year was 22.9. **a) ≈ 0**
    a. What is the probability that the mean score for 84 students selected randomly from all who took the test nationally is 22.9 or higher?
    b. The people at Acme believe they scored significantly higher than the nation as a whole. Test this hypothesis at the .01 level. **See margin.**

Review

20. An electrical company estimates the maintenance-free life of a dishwasher to be approximately normally distributed with mean ten years and standard deviation ten months and guarantees to make spare parts available to the original purchaser within twelve years of the purchase date. If the company's estimates are correct, what proportion of dishwashers will need repairs before the guarantee expires? *(Lesson 10-6)* **.9918**

21. Consider the standard normal curve for variable z. Determine the probability that z is between -1.65 and 1.65. *(Lesson 10-5)* **$\approx .901$**

22. *True or false.* Given any normally distributed variable, its mean, median, and mode are equal. *(Lesson 10-4)* **True**

23. A researcher is testing for color preference of babies. There are ten balls of identical size in a box; five are red, five are green. A baby is observed picking up four balls from the box. She chooses three red balls and a green one. **See margin.**
    a. State a null hypothesis H_0 and an alternative hypothesis H_1 for this experiment.
    b. What outcomes should be considered in deciding whether the null hypothesis should be rejected?
    c. Determine which hypothesis should be accepted at the .05 significance level. *(Lessons 8-6, 10-3)*

24. Factor $6a^2 - 10a + 3ab - 5b$, if possible. *(Lesson 9-9)*
    $(b + 2a)(3a - 5)$

B.C.   by johnny hart

ID LIKE TO SELL MY SHADOW.

WHAT'S YOUR ASKING PRICE?

5 CLAMS A FOOT.

TELL YOU WHAT, COME BACK TOMORROW AROUND NOON.

WE BUY OR SELL ANYTHING

Practice

For more questions on SPUR Objectives, use **Lesson Master 10-7** (shown on page 673).

Assessment

Oral Communication Have students explain the Central Limit Theorem in his or her own words. Be sure students describe any variables given in the explanation. [Students explain the meaning of the Central Limit Theorem.]

Extension

Project Update Project 3, *Is Your Class Typical?*, Project 5, *Sums of Random Digits,* and Project 6, *Design a Study,* on page 688, relate to the content of this lesson.

26a, c)

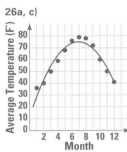

Average Temperature (F°) vs. Month

b) Sample: $(-1.32)x^2 + 18.27x + 11.89$
d) Sample: Over more than a year's duration, the data are likely to be periodic, not quadratic. A sine curve is more appropriate.

25. Refer to the cartoon above.
   a. If the person on the left is 5'6" tall and has a shadow 15' long, what is the angle of elevation of the sun? ≈ 20° 8′
   b. Why does the person on the right want the person on the left to come back around noon? **At that time the shadow will be near its shortest length and thus its lowest price.**

26. The following are the average monthly temperatures in °F for Nashville, Tennessee. **See left.**

Jan.	Feb.	Mar.	Apr.	May	June	July	Aug.	Sept.	Oct.	Nov.	Dec.
36	40	50	59	68	76	79	78	72	60	50	41

   a. Draw a scatterplot of these data, using x = number of the month of the year.
   b. Pick three points and determine a quadratic function to model the data.
   c. Graph the function you found in part **b** on the same axes with the scatterplot.
   d. Explain why a quadratic function is probably not the best choice for modeling data on weather. *(Lessons 1-1, 2-6, 4-10)*

27. Solve for x: $z = \frac{x - m}{s}$. *(Previous course)* $x = zs + m$

Exploration

28) Sample: $\bar{x}$'s = 10.4, 12.5, 20.5, 16.5, 9, 12, 11.2, 11.5, 9.7, 6.4
a) $\mu_{\bar{x}} \approx 11.97$;
$\sigma_{\bar{x}} \approx 3.97$
b) Sample: There are approximately 12 words per sentence on average with a standard deviation of 4 words.

28. Begin on a randomly chosen page of text in this book. Choose 30 consecutive sentences (continue to successive page(s) of text if necessary). Count the number of words in each sentence. Then calculate the mean of these counts. Repeat this process with different pages ten times.
   a. Determine the mean $\mu_{\bar{x}}$ and standard deviation $\sigma_{\bar{x}}$ of the ten means.
   b. Based on the Central Limit Theorem, what can you predict about the mean and standard deviation of the distribution of the number of words in all the sentences in this book? **a, b) See left.**
   c. State one assumption which allows the use of the Central Limit Theorem in making the prediction in part **b**. **See margin.**
   d. Discuss how different (if at all) the results would be for parts **a** and **b** if you used each of the following. **See margin.**
      i. a physics textbook
      ii. a novel
      iii. a computer software manual

Lesson 10-7 *Sampling Distributions and the Central Limit Theorem* **679**

Additional Answers
28. c. The number of words per sentence is normally distributed.
   d. Sample:
      i. A physics textbook may have fewer but more complicated explanations, yielding a higher mean.
      ii. A novel might have some very long sentences (depending on the author) and some very short sentences because of dialog. Thus, the mean would be about the same but the standard deviation would be higher.
      iii. A computer software manual might have short, concise sentences leading to a lower mean and a smaller standard deviation.

Teaching **10-8**
Lesson

Warm-up

If a set of data is normally distributed, what percent of data would be expected to lie within
1. 1 standard deviation of the mean? **68%**
2. 2 standard deviations of the mean? **95%**
3. 3 standard deviations of the mean? **99%**
4. Justify your answers to Questions 1–3. **Use the Standard Normal Distribution Table to find** $P(-1 \leq z \leq 1)$, $P(-2 \leq z \leq 2)$, $P(-3 \leq z \leq 3)$

LESSON

10-8

Confidence and Cautions in Statistical Reasoning

Estimating the Population Mean from a Sample Mean

Consider the following situation. In Ohio in 1995–1996 the scores of the seniors taking the mathematics section of the Scholastic Aptitude Test (the SAT-M) had a mean of 535 and a standard deviation of 104. This group is clearly not a random sample of all seniors. Students choose to take the test, and virtually all are college-bound. In fact, only about 24% of seniors in Ohio took the SAT-M in 1995–1996.

Suppose that you want to know how *all* high school seniors in Ohio might do on the SAT-M. After considerable effort and expense, you give the SAT-M to a random sample of 400 high school seniors and find that the mean of this sample is 440 and the standard deviation is 119. What can you say about the mean on the SAT-M if all seniors in Ohio took this test? That is, what does your sample mean predict about the population mean?

Clearly, another sample of 400 students would be likely not to yield a mean of 440 again. By the Central Limit Theorem, in repeated samples of size 400, the sample means are normally distributed with mean $\mu_{\bar{x}} = \mu$ and standard deviation $\sigma_{\bar{x}} \approx \frac{\sigma}{\sqrt{n}}$, where μ and σ are the mean and standard deviation of the population you are trying to describe.

With no other information available, it is natural to assume that the population mean is the sample mean and that the variation among the SAT-M scores of the entire population of seniors in the state of Ohio is equal to the variation among the SAT-M scores of the seniors who took the test in 1995–1996 (an unrealistic assumption, but one that you make, because without some value for σ the mathematics is a bit more complicated). That is, assume $\sigma = 119$. Thus, in repeated samples of 400 randomly chosen students, the distribution should be approximately normal with $\mu_{\bar{x}} \approx \mu \approx 440$ and $\sigma_{\bar{x}} \approx \frac{\sigma}{\sqrt{n}} = \frac{119}{\sqrt{400}} = \frac{119}{20} \approx 6$.

With this information and these assumptions, you can make inferences about μ, the mean of the population. The reasoning goes as follows. You know that in a normal distribution, about 68% of the data fall within one standard deviation of the mean. Thus, the probability is about 0.68 that a sample mean $\bar{x}$ will be within 6 points of the population mean 440. So you can say that in about 68% of random samples of size 400 from the population of seniors the mean will fall between $440 - 6$ and $440 + 6$, that is, between 434 and 446.

Lesson 10-8 Overview

Broad Goals The ideas from the previous two lessons are applied here to discuss the fundamental question of how large a sample needs to be in order to have a particular level of confidence in the results.

Perspective The Central Limit Theorem indicates what will happen with samples of a particular size; the notion of a particular likelihood being a test value is extended here to the idea of confidence interval. The

surprise is that the accuracy of a random sample is dependent on the size of the sample, and has nothing to do with the size of the population (unless the sample is very close to the size of the population). A random sample of 1200 taken from a population of 240,000,000 can be treated with the same confidence as one of 1200 from a population of 2400.

Confidence Intervals

The interval $434 \leq \mu \leq 446$ is called the *68% confidence interval* for the population mean μ. The quantity ± 6 is called the *margin of error* for the confidence interval.

Confidence intervals were invented in 1937 by Jerzy Neyman (1884–1981), a Polish mathematician who moved to the United States where he was professor of mathematics for many years at the University of California at Berkeley. Statisticians have invented techniques for finding confidence intervals for many different parameters based on various assumptions. But all confidence intervals share two properties: There is an interval of possible values constructed from the sample data, and a confidence level which gives the probability that the method produces an interval which contains the true value of the parameter.

The user chooses the confidence level, a percent near 1. Usually it is at least 90%, and 95% and 99% are commonly used. A 95% level for μ indicates that 95% of the sample means fall within about two standard deviations of the population mean; for this situation, between $440 - 2(6) = 428$ and $440 + 2(6) = 452$. You can report with 95% confidence that the mean score of the population of seniors in Ohio on the SAT-M is between 428 and 452.

Jerzy Neyman

Compare this result with the one found earlier: a 68% confidence interval for the mean is $434 \leq \mu \leq 446$. Notice that, except for rounding, each interval is centered on $\bar{x} = 440$, the sample mean.

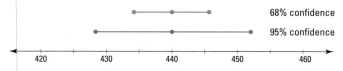

Also, as the level of confidence increases, so does the width of the confidence interval. This is because, if you want to place a higher probability on your estimate, you need a wider estimate to "cover your bases."

What does this mean if you would like a "finer tuning" or closer estimate of the mean? You have two choices: choose a lower confidence level or use a larger sample. Generally, people who use statistics do not want to use a confidence level below 90%, so in order to get within a desired margin of error, they must increase the sample size.

How Large a Sample Is Necessary?

Surprisingly, it is relatively simple to figure out how large a sample size is needed to ensure a certain margin of error at a desired confidence level.

The Ohio SAT-M example deals with the question of whether a sample is representative of a population. The major point is that we can determine the distribution of the sample means from the population mean and standard deviation (from the Central Limit Theorem) and thus we can tell whether a sample mean is unusual or not.

To convert this idea to the idea of polling, as in **Questions 9–10,** think of the people polled as a random sample and the percentage of people who say that they will vote for a particular candidate as the mean for that sample. If we know the sample size, then we can determine the accuracy of the sample means.

Throughout this book we have tried to keep students aware that statistics is an inexact science, and to be wary of accepting statistical evidence as statement of fact. Samples must be random for these theorems to hold, but few real samples are totally random. Even with the best of intentions, it is possible for researchers to make errors in methodology, analysis, and interpretation of results. And even without errors, there is always the potential that a sample does not accurately represent a population.

Optional Activities

As an extension of **Question 10,** have students determine the confidence level if the pollster can poll only 1000 people. [≈ 80%] Then have students determine how accurate the pollster can be if only 1000 people can be polled but a 95% confidence interval is still wanted. [The pollster can be accurate to within 3.1%.] Finally, ask students to determine how many people must be polled if the pollster wants accuracy to within 1% and a 95% confidence interval. [10,000]

There have been books written on the misuse of statistics; perhaps the most famous is Darrell Huff's *How to Lie with Statistics*. We have purposefully not gone into great detail on this subject because we believe that if students understand the proper use of statistics, then they will tend to notice the misuses without instruction.

Additional Examples

You are working for a political candidate who has asked you to do a poll of potential voters that would be accurate to within 3% with 98% confidence. How many voters should you poll? (Use the fact that the largest possible standard deviation for the population is $\frac{1}{2}$, when the election is even.) **The maximum standard deviation that can occur with 98% confidence means that $|z| < 2.33$, so $2.33 = \frac{3\%}{\frac{.5}{\sqrt{n}}}$ from which $n \approx 1508$.**

Example

Suppose you want to estimate the mean score of all seniors in Ohio on the SAT-M with 99% confidence to within 10 points. How large a sample size is necessary?

Solution

You know that the standard score for the sample mean is

$$z = \frac{\bar{x} - \mu_{\bar{x}}}{\sigma_{\bar{x}}} = \frac{\bar{x} - \mu}{\frac{\sigma}{\sqrt{n}}}.$$

From the table of the Standard Normal Distribution, in order for the confidence level to be 99%, z must equal 2.57. Suppose you want $|\bar{x} - \mu| = 10$. If you assume as we did earlier that $\sigma = 119$, you must find n so that

$$2.57 = \frac{10}{\frac{119}{\sqrt{n}}}.$$

$$2.57 = \frac{10\sqrt{n}}{119} \qquad \text{Rewrite the right side.}$$

$$\frac{(2.57)(119)}{10} = \sqrt{n} \qquad \text{Multiply each side by 119, and divide each side by 10.}$$

$$935.32 \approx n \qquad \text{Square each side.}$$

or $\qquad n \approx 935$.

That is, to estimate the population mean to within 10 points at the 99% confidence level, you would have to select a random sample of nearly 1000 students. You would have to decide whether the increase in precision of measurement is worth the increased cost of selecting and testing this much larger sample.

In general, to find the sample size needed so that you can estimate a mean μ for a population with known standard deviation σ at a given confidence level and accuracy A, where $A = |\bar{x} - \mu|$, you must first find the z-score corresponding to that confidence level. Then you must solve the following equation for n:

$$z = \frac{A}{\frac{\sigma}{\sqrt{n}}}.$$

Repeating the steps used in the Example gives

$$n = \left(\frac{z\sigma}{A}\right)^2.$$

Notice that n varies directly with the square of z and inversely with the square of A. Thus, as the desired accuracy gets smaller, the needed sample size increases quite rapidly. Consequently, getting a high level of confidence and small margin of error simultaneously can result in the need for very large sample sizes, and these, in turn, can be very costly. Even in statistics, there is no such thing as a free lunch!

Adapting to Individual Needs

Extra Help

Point out to students that one usually tries to keep the confidence interval as small as possible, but to make it smaller requires a larger sample size. Because the sample size n varies inversely with the square of the width A of the confidence interval (see page 682), to halve the width requires four times the sample size. Thus, while a sample of 1200 people gives an accuracy of about 3% with a confidence level of 95%, a sample of 4800 would be required to give an accuracy of 1.5% with the same confidence level.

Cautions about Statistical Inferences

You should note that just as medications carry warnings about their potential harmful effects, the techniques described in this lesson to make inferences about populations must be applied with caution. First, the data collected must be from a random sample of the population. The methods used here to determine a confidence interval for μ do not apply to other types of samples such as volunteers or similar "convenient" samples. Second, as a practical matter, if the sample size is relatively small, outliers can have a large effect on the confidence interval. You should always look for outliers in a sample, and try to correct them or justify their removal before computing a sample mean.

Third, the techniques developed here require that you know the standard deviation σ of the population. In most surveys this is unrealistic. There are ways to estimate σ from the sample standard deviation s, and to construct confidence intervals based on s, but they require distributions other than the binomial or normal. Fourth, the margin of error in a confidence interval covers only random sampling errors. That is, the margin of error describes typical error expected because of chance variation in random selection. It does not describe errors arising from sloppy data collection or data entry. Fancy formulas can never compensate for sloppy data.

Covering the Reading

In 1 and 2, refer to the SAT-M data in the text with samples of size 400. A confidence level is given. **a.** Find the confidence interval. **b.** Find the margin of error.

1. 68% level **a)** $434 \le \mu \le 446$
   b) ± 6

2. 95% level **a)** $428 \le \mu \le 452$
   b) ± 12

3. Find a 90% confidence interval for the SAT-M scores of the seniors in the state of Ohio. Assume, as in the lesson, that $\bar{x} = 440$, $\sigma = 119$, and $n = 400$. $430 \le \mu \le 450$

In 4 and 5, *true or false*.

4. In most statistical applications a confidence level of at least 90% is used. **True**

5. As the confidence level increases, the width of the confidence interval increases. **True**

6. Below are shown 90% and 95% confidence intervals for a population with mean μ.
   a. Estimate μ. ≈ 20
   b. Which is the 95% confidence interval? How can you tell?
      ii; **because it contains more values**

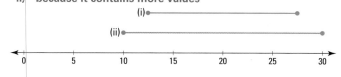

Lesson 10-8 *Confidence and Cautions in Statistical Reasoning* **683**

683

Notes on Questions

Questions 9–10 Error Alert
Before an election, it is not uncommon for newspapers or TV stations to conduct polls using 500 or 800 people. These results are then generalized to apply to an election which may involve more than 100 times as many people. It is natural that people are skeptical that this can be done; they do not know enough about statistics to see why it can work. They often, however, do know the possible pitfalls, such as a nonrandom sample, a biased interviewer, and so on.

Question 10 The 95% confidence interval with a margin of error of 2% describes the distribution of sample means. The population standard deviation of $\frac{1}{2}$ is approximated by the sample standard deviation. Assuming a normal approximation to the binomial distribution, $\sigma_{\bar{x}} = \frac{\sigma}{\sqrt{n}} = \frac{\sqrt{npq}}{\sqrt{n}} = \sqrt{pq} = \sqrt{.5^2} = \frac{1}{2}$ or 50%.

Question 17 Science Connection
There are often outliers in any data about plant life. You may wish to share the following examples with your students.
1. There is an orchid species, Grammatophyllum speciosum, from Malaysia that has reached heights of 25 feet.
2. A creosote plant, Larrea tridentata, in southwest California is estimated to be 11,700 years old.
3. Flowering plants were found at 21,000 feet on Mount Kamet in the Himalayas.
4. A maroon algae was found at a depth of 884 feet where 99.9995% of sunlight is filtered out.
5. The fastest growing flowering plant, Hesperoyucca whipplei, has been observed to grow 12 feet in 14 days.

7. Identify two ways to decrease the range of a confidence interval.
   lower the confidence level; increase the sample size
8. Refer again to the SAT-M data in the lesson. Suppose you wanted to estimate μ with 95% confidence to within 10 points. How large a sample would be needed? **544**

Applying the Mathematics

9. When opinion polls are conducted, the results are often reported as a percent in favor of something $\pm$ a margin of error as a percent. In most polls it is standard practice to report the margin of error for a 95% confidence interval unless stated otherwise.
   a. Suppose you read that 28% of Americans surveyed recently felt that homelessness was the most serious problem in the United States, and that the poll has a margin of error of $\pm 3\%$. What is the 95% confidence interval for the percent of adults who think that homelessness is the most serious problem in the United States?
   b. Can you be certain that the true population percent falls within the interval in part **a**? **No**
   a) $25\% \leq \mu \leq 31\%$

10. A pollster wants accuracy to within 2% in a close election between candidates A and B, with a 95% confidence interval. Assuming a 50% probability of a person preferring candidate A, then $\sigma = \frac{1}{2}$. How many people need to be polled? **about 2400**

11. The test for cholesterol level is not perfectly precise. Moreover, level of blood cholesterol varies from day to day. Suppose that repeated measurements for an individual on different days vary normally with $\sigma = 5$ mg/dl. On a single test Alisa's cholesterol level is reported to be 180 mg/dl.
   a. Find a 95% confidence level for her mean cholesterol level.
   b. A person with a cholesterol level of about 200 mg/dl is considered moderately at risk for a stroke or heart attack, and if the person is either overweight or smokes the risks are even higher. Should Alisa be concerned about the results of her cholesterol test? **No**
   a) $170 \leq \mu \leq 190$

Review

In 12 and 13, refer to the Central Limit Theorem. *True or false.* *(Lesson 10-7)*

12. As more and more samples are selected, the mean of the sample means approaches the population mean. **True**

13. As more and more samples are selected, the standard deviation of the sample means approaches the standard deviation of the population. **False**

14b) H_0: The average
monthly cost has
not increased.
H_1: The average
monthly cost
has increased.
$P(x \geq 29.90) =$
$0.011 > 0.01$, so
we cannot reject
the null hypothesis.

14. Suppose that in the past year the monthly cost of residential customers' long-distance phone calls in a particular city had a mean of $28.25 and a standard deviation of $7.20.
   a. If 100 telephone bills from the past year are randomly selected, what is the probability that the mean charge for long-distance calls on these bills is greater than $29.00? ≈ **15%**
   b. Suppose that in the past few months random samples of 100 bills have shown a mean charge of $29.90 for long-distance charges. Test at the 0.01 level the hypothesis that the average monthly cost has not increased. *(Lesson 10-7)* **See left.**

In 15 and 16, consider the set of two-digit numbers from 10 to 99. *(Lessons 7-6, 10-7)*

15. Suppose one number is chosen at random.
   a. Name the type of probability distribution that best models this situation. **uniform distribution**
   b. Find the mean of this distribution. **54.5**

16. Suppose random samples of size 40 are selected, and their means calculated.
   a. What type of distribution models the distribution of sample means?
   b. How does the mean of the distribution in part **a** compare to the mean of the distribution in Question 15?
   a) **a normal distribution**   b) **They are approximately equal.**

17. The height of a certain species of plant is known to be normally distributed with mean 61 cm and standard deviation 5 cm. If a nursery grows 3000 plants of this species in preparation for Mother's Day, how many should they expect to be less than 48 cm tall (and consequently, too short to sell as top-quality)? *(Lesson 10-6)* **about 14**

18. Consider a standard normal distribution of a variable z. Suppose it is known that the probability that z is less than a is p. Express each of the following probabilities in terms of p. *(Lesson 10-5)*

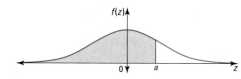

a. $P(z \geq a)$ b. $P(-a \leq z \leq a)$ c. $P(z < -a)$
   1 − p   **2p − 1**   **1 − p**

19. *Multiple choice.*   Which of the following questions does a hypothesis test answer? **b**
   (a) Is the sample random?
   (b) Is the experiment properly designed?
   (c) Is the result due to chance?
   (d) Is the result important? *(Lesson 10-3)*

Practice

For more questions on SPUR Objectives, use **Lesson Master 10-8** (shown on page 683).

Assessment

Written Communication Have students write a paragraph explaining how the original answer to **Question 10** would be affected if the pollster wanted accuracy to within 3% with a 95% confidence level and if the pollster wanted accuracy to within 2% with a 98% confidence interval. [Students apply confidence intervals to real-world problems.]

Extension

In the early part of this century, William S. Gasset, who was an Irish statistician, published many papers on interpreting data obtained by sampling. Gasset wrote under the pen name "Student." He developed procedures for determining probabilities from small samples when the standard deviation of the population is not known. The probability distribution is not a normal distribution and, in honor of Gasset's pen name, is called Student's *t*-distribution. Students may be interested in finding out more about who Student was and what Student's *t*-distribution is.

Project Update Project 3, *Is Your Class Typical?*, Project 4, *How Common Is the Letter e?* and Project 6, *Design a Study,* on page 688, relate to the content of this lesson.

Engineer Mountain, Durango, Colorado

In 20–23, *multiple choice.* What equation corresponds to the graph?
(Lessons 6-4, 10-4, 10-5, 10-6)

(a) $y = e^{-x}, x > 0$

(b) $y = e^{-x^2}$

(c) $y = \frac{1}{\sqrt{2\pi}} e^{-x^2/2}$

(d) $y = \frac{1}{\sqrt{2\pi}} e^{-\frac{1}{2}(x-1)^2}$

20.
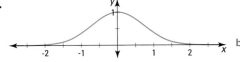
b

21.

a

22.
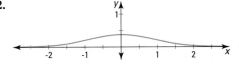
c

23.
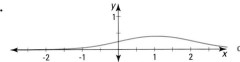
d

In 24 and 25, a series is given. **a.** Evaluate. **b.** Identify the series as arithmetic, geometric, or neither. *(Lessons 8-3, 8-4)*

24. $\sum_{i=1}^{7} (2i - 1)$ a) 49
b) arithmetic

25. $\sum_{k=4}^{6} 2^k$ a) 112
b) geometric

26. a. How many permutations consisting of four letters each can be formed from the letters of the word CONFIDE? 840

b. How many of the permutations in part **a** begin with a vowel?
(Lesson 7-4) 360

27. The land area of the United States is about 3,717,796 square miles. The area of Colorado is about 104,100 square miles. What is the probability that a randomly chosen point of land in the United States is in each area?

a. in Colorado
≈ 0.028

b. not in Colorado *(Lesson 7-1)*
≈ 0.972

Exploration

28. What size sample is used to determine the number of viewers of TV programs? What is the accuracy of these ratings? What is the confidence level? **Answers may vary.**

Possible responses, pages 687–688
1. **a.** Observe a pattern of increasing and then decreasing columns of balls.
   b. If there are *n* rows of pins, the binomial distribution has 2*n* trials and 0.5 probability of success in each trial. Success can be defined as a fall to the right of a pin and failure as a fall to the left.
2. **Sample:**
   a. Both graphs have an "S" shape.

However, the Poisson cumulative distribution function with mean equal to 15 is not as "steep" as the Binomial with *p* = .5 and *n* = 24.

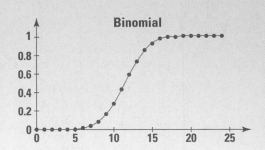

Binomial

A project presents an opportunity for you to extend your knowledge of a topic related to the material of this chapter. You should allow more time for a project than you do for a typical homework question.

PROJECTS 10
CHAPTER TEN

b. What binomial probability distribution does your quincunx represent? Discuss the relation between your observations in part **a** and this probability distribution.

1 The Quincunx

In the early 1870s the English physician, explorer, and scientist, Sir Francis Galton, designed an apparatus he called a *quincunx* to illustrate binomial experiments. Sometimes the quincunx is called a Galton board. The original quincunx had a glass face and a funnel at the top. Small balls were poured through the funnel and cascaded through an array of pins. Each ball struck on a pin at each level; theoretically, it had an equal probability of falling to the right or left. The balls collected in compartments at the bottom. Turning the quincunx upside down sent all the balls back to their original position. Galton's original quincunx still survives in England (see photo below); large replicas exist in many science museums, and smaller ones can be purchased from science suppliers.

a. Obtain an example, or build your own Galton board with at least ten rows of pins. Release the balls and observe the distribution. Repeat this experiment 20–30 times and describe any trends.

2 Cumulative Percentile Curves

The curves in the graph below are called *percentile curves* or *cumulative percentage curves*. Each ordered pair (x, y) represents the percent y of the data in the set that are less than x. For instance, in the data set pictured by these curves, about 60% of the girls and about 18% of the boys had scores less than 35 on a test of coordination.

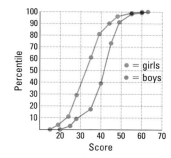

a. Obtain examples of data sets each with at least 25 numbers, but different distributions. For instance, collect examples of data sets that are approximately uniform, binomial, and normal. Calculate percentile ranks for the scores in each data set and plot the corresponding percentile curve. If you have software that can draw percentile curves, draw some graphs using it. Compare and contrast the shapes of the percentile curves.

b. Galton (see Project 1) called such a percentile curve an ogive (pronounced "oh'-jive") based on an architectural term. Find pictures of ogives in architecture books and compare and contrast them to the curves you drew in part **a**.

Chapter 10   *Projects*   **687**

Chapter 10 Projects

The projects relate chiefly to the content of the lessons of this chapter as follows:

Project	Lesson(s)
1	10-1, 10-2, 10-3
2	10-1, 10-4, 10-5
3	10-5, 10-6, 10-7, 10-8
4	10-8
5	10-5, 10-6, 10-7
6	10-3, 10-5, 10-6, 10-7, 10-8

1 The Quincunx This project is appropriate for someone who is handy with tools.

2 Cumulative Percentile Curves For **part a**, data sets with the appropriate characteristics are described in this chapter. The drawings can be done by hand and compared with the computer drawings in **part c**.

4. a. Sample: Open to a page in Chapter 10 and point randomly. Then, count the first 30 characters to the right. Open to another page in the same chapter and do the same thing again. Repeat the above procedure 10 times in total. We got $\bar{x} = 13\%$, and $\sigma_{\bar{x}} = .07$.
b. We found $0 \le x \le 26.7\%$
c. Sample: Another book had $\bar{x} = 14\%$, $\sigma = .07$, $2\% \le x \le 26\%$.
d. Sample: The answers are very close.

(Responses continue on page 688.)

Responses begin on page 686
2. a. (Continued)

Poisson

b. Answers will vary.

3. a. Sample: Students are chosen by surveying every 5th person that walks into school.
b. Answers will vary. Students discuss the mean and spread of each variable. The Central Limit Theorem might be applied.
c. Answers will vary. Students should discuss the mean and spread of the data sets relative to each other.
d. Answers will vary.

687

3 Is Your Class Typical? To answer **part d**, the Central Limit Theorem should be used.

4 How Common Is the Letter *e*? Other letters could be used, of course. The letter *T* is, on the average, the second most common letter.

5 Sums of Random Digits Students should not be surprised by now to see probabilities represented by areas.

6 Design a Study This project is very open-ended, which is its appeal for many students. If students have some motivating concern, they are likely to put more time into the project. Consider allowing individuals, small groups, or the class as a whole to do the project.

Additional responses
5. a. Sample:

n	$P(s \le n)$
0	0
1	.02
2	.04
3	.14
4	.18
5	.26
6	.32
7	.36
8	.42
9	.5
10	.62
11	.70
12	.72
13	.86
14	.96
15	.98
16	.98
17	1.00
18	1.00

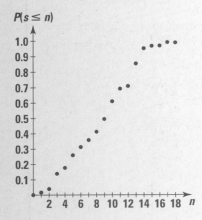

(Responses continue on page 689.)

(continued)

3 Is Your Class Typical?
Refer to Project 6 of Chapter 1 (p. 69) and the related projects in Chapters 2 and 3.
a. Determine a way to choose a random sample of at least 30 students in your school. Conduct a survey of that sample with the same variables.
b. Use displays and descriptive statistics to describe a typical student in the random sample.
c. Make inferences to describe a typical student in your school.
d. Compare your results from part **b** above to the results you obtained in earlier chapters. How typical is your class of the school as a whole?

4 How Common Is the Letter *e*?
a. Describe a way to pick letters at random from this chapter, and pick 30 such letters. Calculate the relative frequency of occurrence of the letter *e*.
b. Repeat part **a** at least 9 times and use your collected data to determine a 95% confidence interval for the percentage of *e*'s in the English language.
c. Repeat parts **a** and **b** with another book.
d. Compare your answers to parts **b** and **c**.

5 Sums of Random Digits
a. Use a computer, calculator, or table of random numbers to choose two random *digits* from 0 to 9. Then calculate their sum. Repeat this until you have 50 such random sums. For instance, your first ten sums might be
14 10 5 3 15 3 6 7 7 12.
Let s = the sum of the two random digits. Then s can be any integer from 0 to 18. Find $P(s \le 5)$, $P(s \le 12)$, and $P(s \le n)$ for any $n \in \{0, 1, 2, \ldots, 18\}$. Express your answer as a table of values and as a graph.

b. Modify part **a** to choose two random *numbers* from 0 to 9. That is, consider the analogous *continuous* random variable *s*. To calculate $P(s \le 5)$ in this case it will help to think geometrically. For instance, to calculate $P(s \le 5)$ and $P(s \le 12)$ you will need to consider the areas of the figures below.

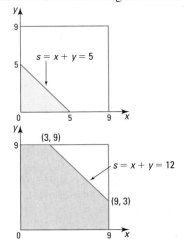

Use areas to find $P(s \le n)$ for all integers n between 0 and 18. Again, describe the probability distribution with a table and with a graph.
c. Compare and contrast the functions $(n, P(s \le n))$ in parts **a** and **b**.

6 Design a Study
Consider a problem that concerns you: crime, drug abuse, air pollution, poverty, etc. Design a study to investigate some aspect of the problem. Use descriptive and inferential statistics, as appropriate, to report the results of your study.

SUMMARY

Binomial probabilities are used to analyze events with repeated independent trials. A binomial distribution function gives the probability of getting exactly k successes in n binomial trials, each of which has probability p of success. Usually computers or calculators are used to calculate the necessary binomial probabilities.

The mean μ and standard deviation σ of a binomial probability distribution are given by $\mu = np$ and $\sigma = \sqrt{npq}$, respectively. For large n, graphs of binomial probability distributions resemble a bell-shaped curve.

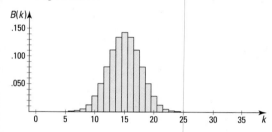

A commonly observed continuous distribution is the normal distribution, characterized by bell-shaped distribution curves. Many naturally occurring phenomena can be approximated by normal distributions. The parent of all these curves is given by $f(x) = e^{-x^2}$. The standard normal distribution has a mean of 0 and a standard deviation of 1; its equation is $f(z) = \frac{1}{\sqrt{2\pi}} e^{-z^2/2}$.

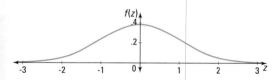

Areas under any normal curve can be calculated using calculus or closely approximated using computer programs, tables, or some calculators. The area between this curve and the x-axis is 1. Probabilities of events in any normal distribution can be estimated by first standardizing the variable with z-scores, where $z = \frac{x - m}{s}$, and then using the tabulated values for the standard normal distribution.

Binomial and normal distributions are often used to make judgments or inferences about issues. Assuming a binomial or normal distribution, one can determine how probable a certain observed event is. Then, based on predefined significance levels, one can decide whether the calculated probability supports the null hypothesis that the event *is* a reasonable result given the assumed distribution, or it supports the alternative hypothesis that the assumed distribution is *not* a proper one.

The Central Limit Theorem states that if a large number of random samples of size n are selected from any population with mean μ and standard deviation σ, then as n increases, the distribution of sample means has the following properties:

(1) its mean approaches μ; (2) its standard deviation approaches $\frac{\sigma}{\sqrt{n}}$; and (3) it approaches a normal distribution.

The theorem can be applied if the original population is itself normally distributed, or if the sample size $n \geq 30$.

Based on the Central Limit Theorem, confidence interval estimates can be determined for the mean of a population using sample results. The intervals may be narrow or wide, depending on the preset confidence level.

Additional responses, page 688
5. b. Sample

n	$P(s \leq n)$
0	0
	.006
2	.025
3	.056
4	.099
5	.154
6	.222
7	.302
8	.395
9	.500
10	.605
11	.698
12	.778
13	.846
14	.90144
15	.94
16	.975
17	.994
18	1.000

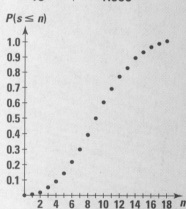

c. **The graphs are very similar. In fact, if the graph in part a did not depend on experiment, but was theoretical, the graphs would be the same.**

6. **Sample: The goal of the study is to see whether Dullsville has a lower daily crime rate than the national average for towns of a similar population. The statistics gathered provided a z-score of -5. Thus, it was concluded that Dullsville has a lower daily crime rate.**

689

Vocabulary

Terms, symbols, and properties are listed by lesson to provide a checklist of concepts a student must know. Emphasize to students that they should read the vocabulary list carefully before starting the Progress Self-Test. If students do not understand the meaning of a term, they should refer back to the indicated lesson.

VOCABULARY

Below are the most important terms and phrases for this chapter. You should be able to give a general description and a specific example of each and a precise definition for those marked with an asterisk (*).

Lesson 10-1
*binomial distribution function, $B(k)$
parameters of the binomial distribution
mode (of a probability distribution)
cumulative binomial probability table

Lesson 10-2
Mean of a Binomial Distribution Theorem
variance of a probability distribution
Variance and Standard Deviation of a Binomial
   Distribution Theorem

Lesson 10-3
hypothesis
significance level
hypothesis testing
null hypothesis, H_0
alternative hypothesis, H_1

Lesson 10-4
concave down, concave up
inflection points
*normal distribution
normal curve
parent normal curve
*standard normal curve
*standard normal distribution

Lesson 10-5
Standard Normal Distribution Table

Lesson 10-6
standard score
standardizing (a variable)

Lesson 10-7
sample/sampling distribution
mean of a sampling distribution, $\mu_{\bar{x}}$
standard deviation of a sampling distribution, $\sigma_{\bar{x}}$
Central Limit Theorem

Lesson 10-8
confidence interval
margin of error

PROGRESS SELF-TEST

1, 2, 5, 9a, 9b, 10) See margin.

Take this test as you would take a test in class. You will need Appendix D and a calculator or computer that generates binomial probabilities. Then check the test yourself using the solutions at the back of the book.

1. Suppose the probability is 0.89 that a randomly selected patient with a particular heart condition will survive more than one year. Draw a histogram of the binomial probability distribution that x of 10 heart patients will survive a year or more.

2. Describe how the domain, range, and the shape of the binomial distribution in Question 1 would change if 100 patients are studied.

3. A binomial probability distribution has $p = 0.2$ and $n = 60$. What are the mean μ and standard deviation σ of the distribution? **12; ≈ 3.1**

4. In the product specification sheet for their 1.5 kΩ resistors, a manufacturer reports the 99% confidence interval as 1500 ohms ± 5%. Assuming their data are normally distributed, what are the mean and standard deviation of the resistances for these resistors? **1500 ohms; ≈ 29 ohms**

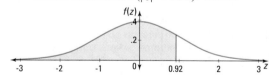

In 5 and 6, consider the function f with equation $f(x) = \frac{1}{2} e^{-x^2}$.

5. Is the graph of f reflection-symmetric? If yes, give an equation for the line of symmetry. If not, explain why not.

6. *True or false.* The equation for f is an equation for the standard normal curve. **False**

In 7 and 8, find the probability that a randomly chosen observation z from a standard normal distribution is in the given interval.

7. less than 1.3 **.9032**

8. between –1.5 and 1.5 **0.8664**

9. It is commonly thought that average "normal" body temperature is 98.6°F. A study of the temperatures of 130 healthy adults revealed a normal distribution of temperatures with an average of 98.2°F and a standard deviation of 0.7°F.

    a. State a null hypothesis H_0 and an alternative hypothesis H_1 that could be used to test whether average "normal" body temperature is 98.6°F.

    b. Test the null hypothesis at the 0.01 level. (Assume that the standard deviations of the sample and the entire population are the same.)

10. The heights of all 946 girls in one high school are measured and the girls are found to have a mean height of 170 cm with a standard deviation of 7.2 cm. Would it be unusual for a sample of 40 girls from this high school to have a mean height of over 180 cm? Explain your answer.

11. Complete: 95% of all observations on a normal distribution fall within __?__ standard deviations of the mean. **1.96**

12. If a variable x has a normal distribution with mean m and standard deviation s, then the transformed variable $z = \frac{x - m}{s}$ has what distribution? **standard normal**

13. A survey of the students at Peaks High School shows that they travel an average of 2.15 miles to school every day with a standard deviation of 0.36 miles. Assuming a normal distribution, determine the probability that a randomly chosen student at Peaks High travels over 3 miles to school. **0.0091**

14. The area shaded below, which lies between the standard normal curve and the z-axis, is about 0.8212. Determine $P(|z| < 0.92)$. **0.6424**

Additional Answers

1.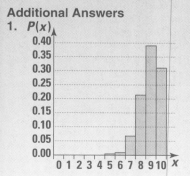

2. The domain would increase; the range would "flatten" or decrease; and the shape would approach a normal distribution.

5. Yes, $x = 0$, because
$$f(-x) = \frac{1}{2} e^{-(-x)^2} = \frac{1}{2} e^{-x^2} = f(x).$$

9. a. H_0: Average "normal" body temperature is 98.6°F.
   H_1: Average "normal" body temperature is not 98.6°F.

Progress Self-Test

For the development of mathematical competence, feedback and correction, along with the opportunity to practice, are necessary. The Progress Self-Test provides the opportunity for feedback and correction; the Chapter Review provides additional opportunities and practice. We cannot overemphasize the importance of these end-of-chapter materials. It is at this point that the material "gels" for many students, allowing them to solidify skills and understanding. In general, student performance should be markedly improved after these pages.

Assign the Progress Self-Test as a one-night assignment. Worked-out *solutions* for all questions are in the Selected Answers section of the student book. Encourage students to take the Progress Self-Test honestly, grade themselves, and then be prepared to discuss the test in class.

Advise students to pay special attention to those Chapter Review questions (pages 692–695) that correspond to questions missed on the Progress Self-Test.

9. b. $z = \dfrac{98.2 - 98.6}{\frac{.7}{\sqrt{130}}} \approx$ **-6.52,**

   $P(z < -6.52) = 0 < 0.01$
   Thus, we reject the null hypothesis H_0 in favor of the alternative H_1 that average normal body temperature is not 98.6°F.

10. Using the Central Limit Theorem, we would expect a sample of 40 girls from this high school to have a mean height of about 170 cm with a standard deviation of about $\frac{7.2}{\sqrt{40}}$ cm, or 1.14 cm. A sample mean of 180 cm is about 6 standard deviations from the population mean. A Standard Normal Distribution Table shows even 3.09 standard deviations from the mean to have a probability of less than 0.001. So the event is quite unusual.

Chapter 10 Review

Resources

From the _Teacher's Resource File_
- Answer Master for Chapter 10 Review
- Assessment Sourcebook:
  - Chapter 10 Test, Forms A–D
  - Chapter 10 Test, Cumulative Form

Additional Resources
- Quiz and Test Writer

The main objectives for the chapter are organized in the Chapter Review under the four types of understanding this book promotes—Skills, Properties, Uses, and Representations.

Whereas end-of-chapter material may be considered optional in some texts, in _UCSMP Functions, Statistics, and Trigonometry_ we have selected these objectives and questions with the expectation that they will be covered. Students should be able to answer these questions with about 85% accuracy after studying the chapter.

You may assign these questions over a single night to help students prepare for a test the next day, or you may assign the questions over a two-day period. If you work the questions over two days, we recommend assigning the _evens_ for homework the first night so that students get feedback in class the next day and then assigning the _odds_ the night before the test, because answers are provided to the odd-numbered questions.

CHAPTER REVIEW

Questions on SPUR Objectives

SPUR stands for **S**kills, **P**roperties, **U**ses, and **R**epresentations. The Chapter Review questions are grouped according to the SPUR Objectives for this chapter.
1, 2, 8–12, 17a) See margin.

SKILLS DEAL WITH THE PROCEDURES USED TO GET ANSWERS.

Objective A: _Calculate the mean and standard deviation of a binomial probability distribution._ (Lesson 10-2)

In 1 and 2, find the mean and standard deviation for the distribution.

1. a binomial distribution with $p = .6$, $n = 60$
2. a binomial distribution with $q = .3$, $n = 100$

In 3 and 4, consider a test with 20 items.

3. If all items are True-False and students guess randomly, what is the expected mean and standard deviation? $\mu = 10$, $\sigma = \sqrt{5} \approx 2.24$

4. If all items are multiple choice with four options and students guess randomly, what is the expected mean and standard deviation?

5. How many questions with five options should there be on a multiple-choice test to have an expected mean of 20 when students guess randomly? **100**

4) $\mu = 5$, $\sigma = \sqrt{3.75} \approx 1.94$

6. If $\mu = 158$ and $\sigma = 5$ for a binomial probability distribution, determine n and p (with three-digit accuracy).
$p = 0.842$, $n = 188$

Objective B: _Use the Standard Normal Distribution to find probabilities._ (Lesson 10-5)

In Questions 7–11, use the table in Appendix D.

7. **a.** What is the probability that a random variable z with the standard normal distribution takes on a value between -1.28 and 1.28? **0.7994   b) 0.7994 units²**
   b. Determine the area under the standard normal curve from $z = -1.28$ to $z = 1.28$.

In 8–11, evaluate the given probability.

8. $P(z < 2)$
9. $P(1 < z < 2)$
10. $P(z < -2.34)$
11. $P(z > 3.01)$
12. Verify the statement that 99.7% of the area under the standard normal curve is between $z = -3$ and $z = 3$.

PROPERTIES DEAL WITH THE PRINCIPLES BEHIND THE MATHEMATICS.

Objective C: _Compare and contrast characteristics of different binomial probability distribution graphs._ (Lesson 10-1)

In 13–15, consider binomial probability distributions with n trials and a probability p of success of any trial. _True or false._

13. The graph of any binomial distribution is symmetric to the line $x = m$, where m is the mode of the distribution. **False**

14. With fixed p, as n increases, the graphs of binomial distributions "spread out." **True**

16) $B(x) = \binom{n}{x} (p)^x (1 - p)^{n-x}$

15. With fixed n, as p increases, the mode of a binomial distribution moves to the right along the x-axis. **True**

16. Give an equation for $B(x)$, the probability of exactly x successes. **See below left.**

Objective D: _Use properties of normal distributions and their parent function._ (Lessons 10-4, 10-5, 10-6)

17. **a.** Show that $f(x) = e^{-x^2}$ is an even function.
    b. What kind of symmetry does this imply for the graph of any normal distribution with mean μ and standard deviation σ?
    reflection symmetry over the y-axis

Additional Answers

1. Mean $= 36$, $\sigma = \sqrt{14.4} \approx 3.8$
2. Mean $= 70$, $\sigma = \sqrt{21} \approx 4.58$
8. ≈ 0.9772
9. ≈ 0.1359
10. ≈ 0.0096
11. ≈ 0.0013

12. $P(-3 < z < 3)$
    $= 2P(0 < z < 3)$
    $= 2(.9987 - .5)$
    $= 2(.4987)$
    $= 0.9974 \approx 99.7\%$

17. **a.** $f(-x) = e^{-(-x)^2} = e^{-x^2} = f(x)$

In 18–20, *true or false*.   **True**

18. The graph of $y = e^{-x^2}$ never intersects the x-axis.

19. The area between the graph of $y = e^{-x^2}$ and the x-axis is infinite. **False**

20. The area between the standard normal curve and the x-axis is 1. **True**

26) P(97 or more recoveries) $\approx$ 0.00497 < .05; reject H_0 in favor of H_1.

USES DEAL WITH APPLICATIONS OF MATHEMATICS IN REAL SITUATIONS.

Objective E: *Solve probability problems using binomial or normal distributions.*
(Lessons 10-1, 10-2, 10-6)

21) $\approx$ 0.35

21. 20% of the deer in a wildlife preservation park are believed to have a certain antler infection. A zoologist randomly captures 15 deer and checks their antlers. Assuming the prediction is accurate, determine the probability that more than three of the deer will have infected antlers.

22. An allergy test requires that small samples of chemicals be injected under the skin of the patient. Individuals sensitive to any one of the chemicals have a reaction time that is approximately normally distributed with a mean of 11 hours and a standard deviation of 3 hours. How often can one expect a reaction time of more than 18 hours with such individuals? **about 1% of the cases**

23. A new test of extroversion-introversion was administered to a large group of adults, and found to yield scores that were approximately normally distributed with a mean of 35 and a standard deviation of 8. For the instruction manual, various scores are to be interpreted as in the table below. Determine the highest and the lowest scores for each of these five groups.

highly extroverted	top 5%	≥ 49
extroverted	next to top 15%	42–48
average	middle 60%	29–41
introverted	next to bottom 15%	22–28
highly introverted	bottom 5%	< 22

24. Based on factory and field tests, a car company determines that the trouble-free mileage for their new model is normally distributed with a mean of 31,600 miles and a standard deviation of 16,200 miles. The car is marketed with a 60,000-mile guarantee. Determine the percentage of cars of this make the company should expect to repair due to malfunctioning before 60,000 miles. **about 96%**

Objective F: *Use binomial and normal distributions to test hypotheses.* *(Lessons 10-3, 10-7)*

In 25 and 26, a certain disease has a recovery rate of 70%. A researcher has developed a new treatment for the disease and tests it on 120 patients. She finds that 97 of the 120 patients recovered from the disease. The researcher claims that her new treatment is effective against the disease.

25. *Multiple choice.* To test this claim, what is the most appropriate set of hypotheses? **c**

(a) H_0: The new treatment is effective against the disease.

  H_1: The new treatment is not effective against the disease.

(b) H_0: The recovery rate for patients receiving the new treatment is greater than 70%.

  H_1: The recovery rate for patients receiving the new treatment is not greater than 70%.

(c) H_0: The new treatment has no effect on the disease.

  H_1: The new treatment is effective against the disease.

26. Test the researcher's claim at the 0.05 significance level. **See above.**

27. The average weight of checked luggage allowed per person on a domestic flight must be 20 kg. For flight safety purposes, one airline randomly samples 450 of its customers and studies the weight of their checked luggage. The mean weight is found to be 27.8 kg and the sample standard deviation to be 5.3 kg. Can the airline officers claim that the average weight of checked luggage is heavier than 20 kilograms? Use a 0.01 significance level. (Because the sample size is large, assume that the standard deviation of the sample and the standard deviation of the population are approximately the same.) P(weight > 27.8) $\approx$ 0.0708 ≥ 0.01; **the null hypothesis cannot be rejected at the 0.01 significance level.**

It is effective to ask students which questions they still do not understand and use the day or days as a total class discussion of the material which the class finds most difficult.

Assessment

Evaluation The Assessment Sourcebook provides five forms of the Chapter 10 Test. Forms A and B present parallel versions in a short-answer format. Forms C and D offer performance assessment. The fifth test is Chapter 10 Test, Cumulative Form. About 50% of this test covers Chapter 10, 25% of it covers Chapter 9, and 25% of it covers earlier chapters.

For information on grading, see *General Teaching Suggestions; Grading* in the *Professional Sourcebook*, which begins on page T20 in the Teacher's Edition.

Feedback After students have taken the test for Chapter 10 and you have scored the results, return the tests to students for discussion. Class discussion of the questions that caused trouble for the most students can be very effective in identifying and clarifying misunderstandings. You might want to have them write down the items they missed and work, either in groups or at home, to correct them. It is important for students to receive feedback on every chapter test, and we recommend that students see and correct their mistakes before proceeding too far into the next chapter.

28. A highway patrol group decides to check the results they have read in a report which claimed that the speed of cars in their region of the highway has a mean of 63 and standard deviation of 15 miles per hour. They track 100 cars every day for a month and record the average speed observed at the end of each day. Suppose that, based on the total of 3000 cars they track in a month, they calculate an average speed of 58.75 mph. Can they claim that the results in the report are wrong using a 0.05 significance level? **See below.**

31, 34) See below right.

Objective G: *Apply the Central Limit Theorem.*
(Lesson 10-7)

In 29 and 30, *true or false*.

29. If the distribution of population data is not known to be normal, one needs to pick large samples ($n \geq 30$) to apply the Central Limit Theorem. **True**

30. Given a population with mean μ and standard deviation σ, the standard deviation of the means of k samples of size n from this population is approximately $\frac{\sigma}{\sqrt{k}}$. **False**

31. Suppose that the weights of full-grown oranges in a citrus grove are normally distributed with mean 7.3 ounces and standard deviation 2.1 ounces. Determine the probability that 50 oranges randomly picked from this grove have a mean weight greater than 10.5 ounces.

32. A vitamin manufacturer reports that the average weight of their vitamin C tablets is 500 mg with a standard deviation of 2 mg. To check the veracity of this claim, a consumer protection group randomly samples 100 tablets from each lot produced and records the mean weight of each sample. If the numbers reported by the manufacturer are correct, describe the distribution of the data collected by this group.
The weights will be normally distributed with a mean of 500 mg and a standard deviation of .2.

28) $P\left(z < \dfrac{58.75 - 63}{\dfrac{15}{\sqrt{3000}}} \right) = P(z < \text{-}15.5) \approx 0.$

The highway patrol group can claim the report is wrong.

Objective H: *Apply confidence intervals to real-world problems.*   *(Lesson 10-8)*

33. Otto is traveling down the highway when the gas indicator of his car goes on, warning him that he has only 1 gallon of gas left. The manufacturer of Otto's car reports that the 95% confidence interval for the car's highway fuel efficiency is 36 ± 5 mpg. If Otto knows he is 41 miles from the next gas station, what is the probability of his making it? $\approx$ **0.025**

34. Dr. Al Kali, an environmental chemist, measures the pH of numerous samples of water collected from a polluted lake. His data are normally distributed with a mean pH of 8.25 and a standard deviation of 0.35. What should Dr. Kali report as the margin of error for the 90% confidence interval for his data?

35. A manufacturer of contact lenses measures the radius of 225 randomly sampled lenses from their inventory of a certain size lens. The mean and standard deviation of this sample are 0.625 cm and 0.015 cm, respectively. Because the sample size is large, the manufacturer assumes the standard deviation of the sampled lenses is the same as the standard deviation for the entire inventory.

   a. What would the manufacturer report as a 68% confidence interval for the mean radius of its lenses? **0.624 ≤ radius ≤ 0.626**

   b. Suppose the manufacturer wants to change its sampling procedure so that it can estimate the mean radius of its lenses with 95% confidence to within 0.001 cm. How many lenses would they need to sample?
   about 864

31) very close to zero
34) ± 0.5758

694

REPRESENTATIONS DEAL WITH PICTURES, GRAPHS, OR OBJECTS THAT ILLUSTRATE CONCEPTS.

37b, 38a, 38b, 39, 41) See margin.

Objective I: *Graph and interpret a binomial probability distribution.*   *(Lesson 10-1)*

36. Tell why this table does *not* show a probability distribution. **Sum of probabilities ≠ 1.**

x	-1	0	1	4
P(x)	$\frac{1}{2}$	$\frac{1}{4}$	$\frac{1}{8}$	$\frac{1}{5}$

37. Assuming that the births of boys and girls are equally likely, the probability of x boys in a family with 4 children is given below.

x = number of boys	0	1	2	3	4
P(x)	$\frac{1}{16}$	$\frac{1}{4}$	$\frac{3}{8}$	$\frac{1}{4}$	$\frac{1}{16}$

  a. Finish the table of probabilities.

  b. Graph the distribution as a histogram.

38. Let x be the number of items a person gets right (by guessing) on a 3-item multiple-choice test. If each question has three possible choices, then the probability $P(x)$ of getting x items correct is

$$P(x) = {}_3C_x\left(\frac{1}{3}\right)^x\left(\frac{2}{3}\right)^{3-x}.$$

  a. Construct a table of probabilities for x = 0, 1, 2, 3.

  b. Graph the probability distribution as a scatterplot.

39. Construct a graph of the probability distribution for the function P where $P(x)$ is the probability of getting k heads in 5 tosses of a coin that is biased with p(heads) =.6.

40. The graph of a binomial probability distribution is given below.

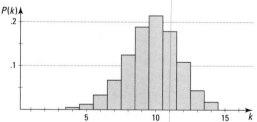

  a. Approximate the mean of the distribution. **10**

  b. Estimate $P(3 \le k \le 7)$. **0.125**

41. Give two reasons why the graph below *cannot* represent a binomial probability distribution.

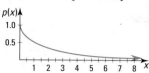

Objective J: *Graph and interpret normal distributions.*   *(Lessons 10-5, 10-6)*

42. Below are the graphs of three normal distributions. Identify each.

  a. the standard normal distribution **ii**

  b. the distribution with σ = 2 **iii**

  c. the distribution with $\sigma = \frac{1}{2}$ **i**

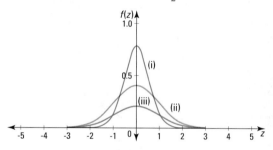

In 43–45, the area shaded below, between the standard normal curve and the z-axis, is about .9544. Determine the following probabilities.

43. $P(z \le 2)$ **44.** $P(0 < z < 2)$ **45.** $P(-2 < z < 2)$
  ≈ 0.9772   **≈ 0.4772**   **≈ 0.9544**

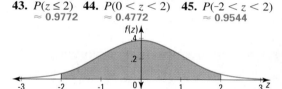

In 46–48, suppose that the variable z is normally distributed with a mean of 0 and standard deviation 1, and that the probability that z is between -a and a is r. Express each of the following in terms of r.

46. $P(z \ge a)$ **(1 − r)/2**

47. $P(0 < z < a)$ **r/2**

48. $P(|z| > a)$
  1 − r

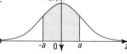

Additional Answers

37. b. P(x)

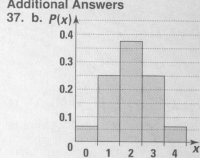

38. a.

x	0	1	2	3
p(x)	$\frac{8}{27}$	$\frac{4}{9}$	$\frac{2}{9}$	$\frac{1}{27}$

b. P(x)

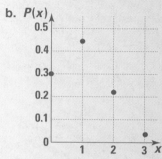

39. P(x)

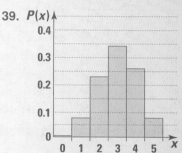

41. Samples: It is continuous; $p(x) > 0$ **for arbitrarily large values of x.**

Chapter 10   *Chapter Review*   **695**

Chapter **11** Planner

Adapting to Individual Needs

The student text is written for the vast majority of students. The chart at the right suggests two pacing plans to accommodate the needs of your students. Students in the Full Course should complete the entire text by the end of the year. Students in the Minimal Course will spend more time when there are quizzes and more time on the Chapter Review. Therefore, these students may not complete all of the chapters in the text.

Options are also presented to meet the needs of a variety of teaching and learning styles. For each lesson, the Teacher's Edition provides a section entitled *Adapting to Individual Needs*. This section regularly includes **Optional Activities, Challenge** problems, **English Language Development** suggestions, and suggestions for providing **Extra Help.** The Teacher's Edition also frequently includes an **Error Alert,** an **Extension,** and an **Assessment** alternative. The options available in Chapter 11 are summarized in the chart below.

Chapter 11 Pacing Chart

Day	Full Course	Minimal Course
1	11-1	11-1
2	11-2	11-2
3	11-3	11-3
4	Quiz*; 11-4	Quiz*; begin 11-4.
5	11-5	Finish 11-4.
6	11-6	11-5
7	Quiz*; 11-7	11-6
8	11-8	Quiz*; begin 11-7.
9	Self-Test	Finish 11-7.
10	Review	11-8
11	Test*	Self-Test
12		Review
13		Review
14		Test*

*in the Teacher's Resource File

In the Teacher's Edition...

Lesson	Optional Activities	Extra Help	Challenge	English Language Development	Error Alert	Extension	Cooperative Learning	Ongoing Assessment
11-1	●	●	●	●		●	●	Written
11-2	●	●	●	●	●	●		Written
11-3	●	●	●		●	●		Quiz
11-4	●	●	●			●		Written
11-5	●	●	●		●	●		Written
11-6	●	●	●			●		Quiz
11-7	●	●	●		●	●	●	Written
11-8	●	●			●	●	●	

Chapter 11 Block Schedule

Day	Recommended Pacing
1	Lesson 11-1
2	Lessons 11-2, 11-3
3	Lesson 11-4
4	Lessons 11-5, 11-6
5	Lesson 11-7
6	Lesson 11-8, Self-Test, Chapter Review
7	Chapter Review, Chapter Test

In the Additional Resources...

Lesson	In the Teacher's Resource File					Visual Aids**	Technology	Explorations Software
	Lesson Masters	Teaching Aids*	Answer Masters	Technology Sourcebook	Assessment Sourcebook			
11-1	11-1	95	11-1			95, AM		
11-2	11-2	95, 98	11-2			95, 98, AM		11-2
11-3	11-3	96, 99, 100	11-3		Quiz	96, 99, 100, AM		
11-4	11-4	96, 101	11-4			96, 101, AM		11-4
11-5	11-5	96	11-5			96, AM		
11-6	11-6	97	11-6	Comp 12	Quiz	97, AM	Auto Grapher	
11-7	11-7	97	11-7			97, AM		
11-8		97, 102	11-8			97, 102, AM		
End of chapter					Tests			

*Teaching Aids, except Warm-ups, are pictured on page 696C.

**Visual Aids provide transparencies for all Teaching Aids and all Answer Masters.

Also available is the Study Skills Handbook which includes study-skill tips related to reading, note-taking, and comprehension.

Integrating Strands and Applications

	11-1	11-2	11-3	11-4	11-5	11-6	11-7	11-8
Mathematical Connections								
Number Sense							●	●
Algebra	●	●	●	●	●	●	●	●
Geometry	●	●	●	●				
Measurement		●	●					
Logic and Reasoning		●			●	●	●	●
Probability	●							
Statistics/Data Analysis	●			●		●	●	
Patterns and Functions	●		●		●	●	●	
Discrete Mathematics	●	●	●	●	●	●		●
Interdisciplinary and Other Connections								
Art				●				
Science								●
Social Studies	●					●	●	
Technology		●		●	●	●	●	●
Career				●	●			●
Consumer	●	●		●				
Sports	●					●		

Teaching and Assessing the Chapter Objectives

Chapter 11 Objectives (Organized into the SPUR categories—Skills, Properties, Uses, and Representations)	Lessons	Progress Self-Test Questions	Chapter Review Questions	Chapter Test, Forms A and B	Chapter Test, Forms C	Chapter Test, Forms D
Skills						
A: Multiply matrices when possible.	11-1	2,4	1-4	1, 2	1	✓
B: Use matrices to solve systems of equations.	11-7	18	5-9	9	2	
C: Find the inverse of a 2×2 matrix.	11-7	9, 16, 17	10-13	3, 4	3	
Properties						
D: Apply properties of matrices and matrix multiplication.	11-1, 11-3, 11-7	5	14-17	7, 8	1	
E: Apply the Addition and Double Angle Formulas.	11-5, 11-6	13, 14, 15	18-29	5, 6	4	
Uses						
F: Use a matrix to organize information.	11-1	1, 3	30-33	12	3	
Representations						
G: Represent reflections, rotations, scale changes, and size changes as matrices.	11-2, 11-3, 11-4	9, 10	34-43	10, 11, 13	5	✓
H: Represent composites of transformations as matrix products.	11-3, 11-4	11	44-47	14, 16	5	✓
I: Use matrices to find the image of a figure under a transformation.	11-2, 11-3, 11-4	6, 7, 8, 12	48-51	15	5	✓

In the Teacher's Resource File

Multidimensional Assessment

Quiz for Lessons 11-1 through 11-3   Chapter 11 Test, Forms A–D

Quiz for Lessons 11-4 through 11-6   Chapter 11 Test, Cumulative Form

 Quiz and Test Writer

Teaching Aids

TEACHING AID 95

Warm-up — Lesson 11-1

1. A person buys a apples at A¢ an apple, b bananas at B¢ per banana, and c cucumbers at C¢ for each cucumber. What is the total amount (in cents) spent?

2. Give another situation whose answer is the same as that in Question 1.

Warm-up — Lesson 11-2

Find the image of the point (x, y) under the transformation.

1. $r_{x\text{-axis}}$

2. $r_{y = x}$

3. The size change with magnitude 6

4. The composite of a horizontal scale change of magnitude $\frac{1}{5}$ and a vertical scale change of magnitude 2

TEACHING AID 96

Warm-up — Lesson 11-3

In 1–3, describe the composite of the pair of transformations.

1. A reflection over the line $y = x$ followed by a reflection over the y-axis

2. A size change of magnitude 3 followed by a size change of magnitude 4 with the same center

3. A rotation of $\frac{\pi}{6}$ followed by a rotation of $\frac{5\pi}{6}$ with the same center

Warm-up — Lesson 11-4

To the nearest thousandth, give the coordinates of the image of $(\cos 72°, \sin 72°)$ under a rotation of 100° about the origin.

Warm-up — Lesson 11-5

In 1–6, let $x = -\frac{\pi}{4}$ and let $y = \frac{3\pi}{2}$. Give the value of:

1. $\cos x$ **2.** $\sin x$

3. $\cos y$ **4.** $\sin y$

5. $\cos (x + y)$ **6.** $\sin (x + y)$

These values can be used to confirm the Addition Formulas for the Cosine and Sine.

TEACHING AID 97

Warm-up — Lesson 11-6

1. Consider a sequence s in which $s_1 = \frac{1}{2}$ and for all $n > 1$, $s_n = 2s_{n-1}^2 - 1$. Give the first five terms of this sequence.

2. Give the values of $\cos\left(2^n \cdot \frac{\pi}{3}\right)$ for $n = 0, 1, 2, 3,$ and 4.

3. Compare your results to Questions 1 and 2 and explain what has happened.

Warm-up — Lesson 11-7

Solve this system for (x, y):
$$ax + by = 1$$
$$cx + dy = 0$$

Warm-up — Lesson 11-8

Multiply these matrices.

$$\begin{bmatrix} a & b & e \\ c & d & f \\ 0 & 0 & 1 \end{bmatrix} \begin{bmatrix} 1 & 2 & 5 \\ 3 & 4 & 6 \\ 0 & 0 & 1 \end{bmatrix}$$

TEACHING AID 98 — Lesson 11-2

Graphs in Examples

Example 2

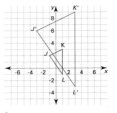

Example 3

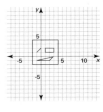

TEACHING AID 99 — Lesson 11-3

Matrices and Graph for Example 1

Let $\triangle ABC = \begin{bmatrix} 2 & 6 & 6 \\ 1 & 1 & 3 \end{bmatrix}$.

The matrix for r_x is $\begin{bmatrix} 1 & 0 \\ 0 & -1 \end{bmatrix}$. So $\triangle A'B'C'$ is represented by the matrix

$$\begin{bmatrix} 1 & 0 \\ 0 & -1 \end{bmatrix} \cdot \begin{bmatrix} 2 & 6 & 6 \\ 1 & 1 & 3 \end{bmatrix} = \begin{bmatrix} 2 & 6 & 6 \\ -1 & -1 & -3 \end{bmatrix}.$$

The matrix for $r_{y = x}$ is $\begin{bmatrix} 0 & 1 \\ 1 & 0 \end{bmatrix}$. Apply this matrix to $\triangle A'B'C'$ to get a matrix for $\triangle A''B''C''$.

$$\begin{bmatrix} 0 & 1 \\ 1 & 0 \end{bmatrix} \cdot \begin{bmatrix} 2 & 6 & 6 \\ -1 & -1 & -3 \end{bmatrix} = \begin{bmatrix} -1 & -1 & -3 \\ 2 & 6 & 6 \end{bmatrix}.$$

TEACHING AID 100 — Lesson 11-3

Theorems

Theorem

If M is the matrix associated with a transformation t, and N is the matrix associated with a transformation u, then NM is the matrix associated with the transformation $u \circ t$.

Matrices for Rotations Theorem

$\begin{bmatrix} 0 & -1 \\ 1 & 0 \end{bmatrix}$ is the matrix for R_{90}, rotation of 90° around the origin.

$\begin{bmatrix} -1 & 0 \\ 0 & -1 \end{bmatrix}$ is the matrix for R_{180}, rotation of 180° around the origin.

$\begin{bmatrix} 0 & 1 \\ -1 & 0 \end{bmatrix}$ is the matrix for R_{270}, rotation of 270° around the origin.

Matrix Basis Theorem

Suppose T is a transformation represented by a 2×2 matrix.

If $T(1, 0) = (x_1, y_1)$ and $T(0, 1) = (x_2, y_2)$, then T has the matrix $\begin{bmatrix} x_1 & x_2 \\ y_1 & y_2 \end{bmatrix}$.

TEACHING AID 101 — Lesson 11-4

Rotation Matrix Theorem

Rotation Matrix Theorem

The matrix R_θ, the rotation of magnitude θ about the origin, is

$$\begin{bmatrix} \cos \theta & -\sin \theta \\ \sin \theta & \cos \theta \end{bmatrix}.$$

Example 2

TEACHING AID 102 — Lesson 11-8

The Matrix for $T_2 \circ R_{-22.5} \circ T_1$

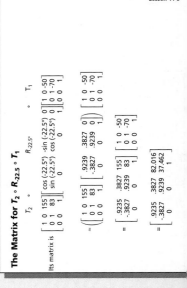

$T_2 \circ R_{-22.5°} \circ T_1$

$$\begin{bmatrix} 1 & 0 & 155 \\ 0 & 1 & 83 \\ 0 & 0 & 1 \end{bmatrix} \begin{bmatrix} \cos (-22.5°) & -\sin (-22.5°) & 0 \\ \sin (-22.5°) & \cos (-22.5°) & 0 \\ 0 & 0 & 1 \end{bmatrix} \begin{bmatrix} 1 & 0 & -50 \\ 0 & 1 & -70 \\ 0 & 0 & 1 \end{bmatrix}$$

$$= \begin{bmatrix} 1 & 0 & 155 \\ 0 & 1 & 83 \\ 0 & 0 & 1 \end{bmatrix} \begin{bmatrix} .9239 & .3827 & 0 \\ -.3827 & .9239 & 0 \\ 0 & 0 & 1 \end{bmatrix} \begin{bmatrix} 1 & 0 & -50 \\ 0 & 1 & -70 \\ 0 & 0 & 1 \end{bmatrix}$$

Its matrix is $\begin{bmatrix} .9235 & .3827 & 82.016 \\ -.3827 & .9239 & 37.462 \\ 0 & 0 & 1 \end{bmatrix}$

696C

696D

Chapter Opener

Pacing

All lessons in this chapter are designed to be covered in one day. At the end of the chapter, you should plan to spend 1 day to review the Progress Self-Test, 1–2 days for the Chapter Review, and 1 day for a test. You may wish to spend a day on projects, and possibly a day is needed for quizzes. This chapter should therefore take 11–14 days. Spending more than 15 days on this chapter is not recommended.

Using Pages 696–697

The drawings of the frogs on page 697 were made using a computer program with a built-in rotation feature. One figure was drawn and the program used a version of the techniques described in this chapter to reproduce the other images.

Matrices are taught even in some junior high classes. Informally assess your students' knowledge of matrices. If they remember matrix multiplication and have had matrices for transformations, the first three lessons of this chapter will be easy, and you may be able to do them in two days.

Chapter 11 Overview

The use of matrices in algebra, geometry, discrete mathematics, finance, computing, biology, differential equations, linear algebra, and statistics make it necessary for today's students to become familiar with them.

Different aspects of matrices are studied in three UCSMP texts. The use of matrices to solve systems of equations is covered in UCSMP *Advanced Algebra*. The use of matrices to represent networks and to describe transition states is discussed in *Precalculus and Discrete Mathematics*.

This chapter reviews multiplication of matrices and how they represent geometric transformations, and then uses matrices to develop the formulas for cos $(\alpha + \beta)$ and sin $(\alpha + \beta)$. If you have never seen this approach before, be ready for a treat. It is among the most beautiful, elegant, and easiest developments in all of high school mathematics. Various applications of these formulas and of the connection between transformations and matrices close out the chapter.

Lesson 11-1 presents the language, symbols, and rules for multiplying matrices. The next three lessons then apply matrix multiplication to generate geometric transformations. In Lesson 11-2, students learn about matrices for some of the transformations

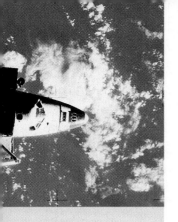

MATRICES AND TRIGONOMETRY

Have you ever wondered how computer games produce animated images? A standard programming technique uses matrices and trigonometry. A *matrix* (plural *matrices*) is a rectangular arrangement of objects.

For instance, to generate an animation with frogs, a single frog might be described by a set of points. These data are stored in a matrix in which each column represents a key point on the frog. Then the figure is changed by transformations such as scale changes, translations, or rotations. These transformations can also be stored as matrices. Multiplying the matrix representing a figure by a matrix representing a transformation gives a matrix for the image of the original figure. For example, the following matrix represents a transformation that translates the figure and rotates it 22.5° clockwise.

$$\begin{bmatrix} .9239 & .3827 & 82.016 \\ -.3827 & .9239 & 37.462 \\ 0 & 0 & 1 \end{bmatrix}$$

In this chapter you will study matrices for many transformations, including rotations of any magnitude around the origin. You will also apply matrices to derive some trigonometric identities, and to illustrate some elementary computer graphics techniques.

Photo Connections

The photo collage makes real-world connections to the content of this chapter: matrices and trigonometry.

Computer Chips: Many computer games that produce animated images apply a programming technique that uses matrices and trigonometry.

Shuttle: Computer simulations can be used to show the take-offs and landings of a space shuttle. In Lesson 11-8 there is a discussion of how matrices are used in computer graphics.

Road: The number of direct routes between a pair of cities can be determined by applying matrix multiplication, the topic of Lesson 11-1.

Canoeing: Clear surfaces can show reflection images. In Lesson 11-2 students learn to use matrices to show reflection images.

Baseball: A formula for determining the path of an object thrown or kicked into the air from ground level is given at the beginning of Lesson 11-6. This formula involves a double angle expression.

Chapter 11 Projects

At this time, you might want to have students look over the projects on pages 745–746.

they studied in Chapter 3. These include matrices for reflections through either axis or the line $y = x$, size changes of magnitude k, and scale changes $S(x, y) = (ax, by)$. Lesson 11-3 develops matrices for rotations through angles of 90°, 180°, or 270° about the origin.

Lesson 11-4 uses the trigonometry of Chapter 5 to produce a matrix for any rotation about the origin. The general rotation matrix is then applied in Lesson 11-5 to deduce the Addition Identities for Cosine and Sine. These identities are then used in Lesson 11-6 to prove the Double Angle Identities. The emphasis on these identities is their practical utility—students are asked to calculate accurately and decide which formula is appropriate in a given situation.

In Lesson 11-7, the chapter further connects matrices with transformations in the finding of inverses of 2 × 2 matrices. Lesson 11-8 describes how matrices can be used in computer programs to manipulate graphics.

The trigonometric identities in this chapter are all covered in *Precalculus and Discrete Mathematics*. For students who will take that course, you do not need to spend much time on the proofs of the identities and can stress the matrix representations and arithmetic calculations.

Teaching Lesson 11-1

Warm-up

1. A person buys *a* apples at *A¢* an apple, *b* bananas at *B¢* per banana, and *c* cucumbers at *C¢* for each cucumber. What is the total amount (in cents) spent? ***Aa + Bb + Cc* cents**

2. Give another situation whose answer is the same as that in Question 1. **Sample: A person travels for *A* hours at *a* miles per hour, *B* hours at *b* miles per hour, and *C* hours at *c* miles per hour. What is the total distance (in miles) traveled?**

LESSON 11-1

Matrix Multiplication

What Is a Matrix?

The Math Team holds an autumn and a spring fund raiser. Below are the numbers of each item sold at each sale last year.

	Trail Treats	Carob Chews	Fruit Clusters	Nut Bars
Autumn	40	100	0	40
Spring	75	108	80	65

The numbers are presented in a **matrix**, a rectangular array. We identify a matrix by enclosing the array in square brackets. Each object in a matrix is called an **element**. The matrix above has 2 rows (labeled autumn and spring) and 4 columns (one for each item). The labels are not part of the matrix. Each element may be identified by giving its row and column. For instance, the element in row 2, column 1 is 75. This matrix is said to have *dimensions* 2 by 4, written 2×4. In general, a matrix with m rows and n columns has **dimensions $m \times n$**. It is sometimes called an $m \times n$ matrix.

Example 1

The prices for trail treats, carob chews, fruit clusters, and nut bars are 1.00, 1.00, .50, and 1.50 dollars, respectively. Present these values in a matrix.

Solution

There are two possible matrices. One is a 4×1 matrix. It has 4 rows and 1 column, and is shown below.

$$\begin{bmatrix} 1.00 \\ 1.00 \\ 0.50 \\ 1.50 \end{bmatrix}$$

The other is the 1×4 matrix shown below.

$$\begin{bmatrix} 1.00 & 1.00 & 0.50 & 1.50 \end{bmatrix}$$

Multiplying a Row and a Column

To calculate the total amount of money (*the revenue*) received from each fund raiser, the club treasurer multiplies the cost of each item by the quantity sold, and then adds the results. For the autumn sale the revenue is $200 because

$$40(1.00) + 100(1.00) + 0(0.50) + 40(1.50) = 200.$$

Lesson 11-1 Overview

Broad Goals This lesson reviews matrix multiplication and its basic properties: associativity yet non-commutativity.

Perspective Matrix multiplication is an easy operation to learn if one begins with multiplication of one row (on the left) by one column (on the right). This immediately indicates when the rows and columns will be compatible—the number of elements in the left matrix's row must equal the number of elements in the right matrix's column. Then, if a matrix with m rows is multiplied by a compatible matrix with n columns, there are mn possible products and the only question is where to put them. The obvious answer: put the product of the ith row and the jth column in the ith row and jth column in the product.

We do not start by teaching matrix addition. In part this is because matrix addition is done in an element-by-element mode (that is, corresponding elements are added), and this easily leads students into expecting that multiplication is also element-by-element. So by beginning their study of matrices with multiplication, students do not need to "unlearn" an inappropriate algorithm. The other reason for focusing on multiplication is that there are more interesting applications of matrix multiplication than of matrix addition.

This can be considered as the product of a matrix of quantities and a matrix of prices. The first matrix, the quantity matrix, is called a **row matrix**, because it consists of a single row. The second matrix, the price matrix, is a **column matrix**, because it consists of a single column.

$$[40 \quad 100 \quad 0 \quad 40] \cdot \begin{bmatrix} 1.00 \\ 1.00 \\ 0.50 \\ 1.50 \end{bmatrix} = [200.00]$$

The product of a row matrix and a column matrix is a matrix with a single element.

Similarly, the revenue received in the spring sale is $320.50 .

$$75(1.00) + 108(1.00) + 80(.50) + 65(1.50) = 320.50$$

This can be represented as the following product of matrices.

$$[75 \quad 108 \quad 80 \quad 65] \cdot \begin{bmatrix} 1.00 \\ 1.00 \\ 0.50 \\ 1.50 \end{bmatrix} = [320.50]$$

Multiplying Entire Matrices

The two sets of products can be written as a single product by multiplying the 4×1 cost matrix from Example 1 by the original 2×4 matrix for quantities. If Q is the matrix with quantities sold, and U is the matrix with the unit prices, then $Q \cdot U = R$ represents the revenue.

	Trail Treats	Carob Chews	Fruit Clusters	Nut Bars
Autumn	40	100	0	40
Spring	75	108	80	65

$$\begin{bmatrix} 40 & 100 & 0 & 40 \\ 75 & 108 & 80 & 65 \end{bmatrix} \cdot \begin{bmatrix} 1.00 \\ 1.00 \\ 0.50 \\ 1.50 \end{bmatrix} \begin{matrix} \text{Trail Treats} \\ \text{Carob Chews} \\ \text{Fruit Clusters} \\ \text{Nut Bars} \end{matrix}$$

$$\qquad\qquad Q \qquad\qquad\qquad \cdot \quad U$$

In general, *matrix multiplication* is done using rows from the left matrix and columns from the right matrix. Multiply the first element in the row by the first element in the column, the second element in the row by the second element in the column, and so on. Finally, add the resulting products. The shading below shows the first row times the column, which gave a total of $200.00. Similarly, the second row times the column gives $320.50. These results may be represented in a 2×1 matrix.

$$\begin{bmatrix} 40 & 100 & 0 & 40 \\ 75 & 108 & 80 & 65 \end{bmatrix} \cdot \begin{bmatrix} 1.00 \\ 1.00 \\ 0.50 \\ 1.50 \end{bmatrix} = \begin{bmatrix} 200.00 \\ 320.50 \end{bmatrix}$$

$$\qquad Q \qquad\qquad\qquad \cdot \quad U \quad = \quad R$$

Notes on Reading
Emphasize that matrices are a type of short hand—they represent ideas in a rectangular array. Students are likely familiar with the phrase "dot-matrix printer" or the matrix of the screen of a computer monitor or television. These are more general uses of the word *matrix* to mean "any rectangular array." Newspapers contain many examples of matrices (**Question 26**).

Error Alert A common error among beginning students of matrix multiplication is to get the matrices in the wrong order. To help avoid this mistake, emphasize the arrows in the dimensions shown on page 700 and the shading in the row-column pattern in the solution to **Example 2.** Encouraging this attention to setting up a multiplication will also help students correctly translate applications into matrix form more quickly.

Even when students learn what sizes of matrices *may* be multiplied, it may take them a while to learn that for most square matrices A and B, $AB \neq BA$. One notable exception is that $AS = SA$, where S is a matrix with 0's in elements that are not on the main diagonal (from upper left to lower right) and its non-zero elements are equal. (S is a matrix for a scale change.) However, we recommend that, at this point, the properties of matrices should not be overemphasized. The focus should remain on the meaning and skills of matrix multiplication.

In the definition of matrix multiplication, the notation c_{ij} for an element of matrix C may take some time for students to understand.

Some calculators can perform operations with matrices. If your students have their own calculators, you may suggest that they also have their owner's handbooks with them. Then, when they ask you questions about using this technology, you can have them refer to the handbook for their specific calculators.

Optional Activities

Ask students to explain the statement on page 699 which states "The product of a row matrix (at the left) and a column matrix (on the right) is a matrix with a single element." [Sample: Each element in a product matrix is the result of the sum of the products of a set of row elements of the first matrix and the corresponding set of column elements of the second matrix. Thus, in effect, a single row and column produce one element in the product matrix. So, if the two matrices to be multiplied consist of a single row on the left and a single column on the right, the product will be a single element in a 1×1 matrix.]

Additional Examples

1. Give the dimensions of each matrix.
   a. The standard multiplication table from 0×0 through 9×9; 10×10
   b. A basketball game box score, in which scores are given for each quarter and for the entire game. 2×5

2. Let $D = \begin{bmatrix} 5 & -2 \\ 3 & 9 \end{bmatrix}$ and

   $C = \begin{bmatrix} 1 & 8 & 2 & -6 \\ 0 & 4 & 5 & 7 \end{bmatrix}$

   Find CD and DC.
   CD does not exist.

   $DC = \begin{bmatrix} 5 & 32 & 0 & -44 \\ 3 & 60 & 51 & 45 \end{bmatrix}.$

3. A school district has three high schools A, B, and C with enrollments as follows:

	Fr.	So.	Jr.	Sr.
A	500	500	450	400
B	480	470	450	420
C	370	380	350	420

   From past records, it is estimated that all freshmen, 95% of sophomores, 90% of juniors, and 80% of seniors take mathematics courses in the district. Put that information into a second matrix, multiply the two matrices, and interpret the product.

   $\begin{bmatrix} 1 \\ .95 \\ .90 \\ .80 \end{bmatrix}$; multiply with this

   matrix on the right to yield the

   product $\begin{bmatrix} 1700 \\ 1667.5 \\ 1382 \end{bmatrix}$. **This product**

   contains estimates of the total number of students enrolled in mathematics courses in each school.

Notice how the dimensions of the original matrices relate to the product matrix: The product of a 2×4 matrix and a 4×1 matrix is a 2×1 matrix.

(must be equal)

In general, the product, $A \cdot B$, of two matrices A and B exists if and only if the number of columns of A equals the number of rows of B.

> **Definition**
> Suppose A is an $m \times n$ matrix and B is an $n \times p$ matrix. Then the **product matrix** $A \cdot B$ is an $m \times p$ matrix whose element in row i and column j is the sum of the products of elements in row i of A and corresponding elements in column j of B.

As usual, often we write AB for the product $A \cdot B$.

Example 2

Consider $A = \begin{bmatrix} 3 & 0 \\ 1 & 2 \end{bmatrix}$ and $B = \begin{bmatrix} 4 & 3 & 2 \\ 1 & 0 & 5 \end{bmatrix}$. Find the product matrix, if it exists.

a. AB b. BA

Solution

a. By definition, the product of a 2×2 and a 2×3 matrix is a 2×3 matrix. This means you should expect to find 6 elements. The product of row 1 of A and column 1 of B is
$$3 \cdot 4 + 0 \cdot 1 = 12.$$
Write this in the 1st row and 1st column of the product matrix.

$$\begin{bmatrix} 3 & 0 \\ 1 & 2 \end{bmatrix} \cdot \begin{bmatrix} 4 & 3 & 2 \\ 1 & 0 & 5 \end{bmatrix} = \begin{bmatrix} 12 & - & - \\ - & - & - \end{bmatrix}$$

The product of row 1 of A and column 2 of B is $3 \cdot 3 + 0 \cdot 0 = 9$. This is the element in row 1 and column 2 of the product.

$$\begin{bmatrix} 3 & 0 \\ 1 & 2 \end{bmatrix} \cdot \begin{bmatrix} 4 & 3 & 2 \\ 1 & 0 & 5 \end{bmatrix} = \begin{bmatrix} 12 & 9 & - \\ - & - & - \end{bmatrix}$$

The other four elements of the product matrix are found by using the same row ____ by column ____ pattern. For instance, the element in the 2nd row, 3rd column of the product is found by multiplying the 2nd row of A by the 3rd column of B, shown here along with the final result.

$$\begin{bmatrix} 3 & 0 \\ 1 & 2 \end{bmatrix} \cdot \begin{bmatrix} 4 & 3 & 2 \\ 1 & 0 & 5 \end{bmatrix} = \begin{bmatrix} 12 & 9 & 6 \\ 6 & 3 & 12 \end{bmatrix}$$

b. To calculate the element in the 1st row, 1st column of BA you would have to multiply the shaded numbers.

$$\begin{bmatrix} 4 & 3 & 2 \\ 1 & 0 & 5 \end{bmatrix} \cdot \begin{bmatrix} 3 & 0 \\ 1 & 2 \end{bmatrix}$$

The row by column multiplication cannot be done. The product BA does not exist.

Adapting to Individual Needs

Extra Help
If students have difficulty with matrix multiplication, they may benefit from a step-by-step approach. Before doing a multiplication, ask students to give the dimensions of the product. Then put in blanks in each place in the product matrix and fill each blank by multiplying a row by a column. Pick the blank before picking the row and column so students see that for the element in row i and column j, row i and

column j are multiplied. Encourage students to use this approach in **Questions 9–12.**

Properties of Matrix Multiplication

As Example 2 illustrates, matrix multiplication is not commutative. However, matrix multiplication is associative. That is, for matrices A, B, C where multiplication exists, $(AB)C = A(BC)$. In Example 3 one product of three matrices is calculated. In the Questions you will verify associativity for this case.

Example 3

Suppose that the Math Team mentioned earlier is permitted to keep 40% of its sales in the autumn and 50% in the spring. Let $P = [.4\ .5]$ represent the percents kept. Calculate $P(QU)$, and describe what this product represents.

Solution

Earlier we calculated

$$QU = \begin{bmatrix} 40 & 100 & 0 & 40 \\ 75 & 108 & 80 & 65 \end{bmatrix} \cdot \begin{bmatrix} 1.00 \\ 1.00 \\ 0.50 \\ 1.50 \end{bmatrix} = \begin{bmatrix} 200.00 \\ 320.50 \end{bmatrix}.$$

Thus

$$P(QU) = \begin{bmatrix} .4 & .5 \end{bmatrix} \cdot \begin{bmatrix} 200.00 \\ 320.50 \end{bmatrix}$$

$$= [80 + 160.25]$$

$$= [240.25].$$

The product represents the total amount of profit earned by the Math Team on its two fund raisers.

4. If $A = \begin{bmatrix} 3 & 4 \\ 5 & 6 \end{bmatrix}$,

$B = \begin{bmatrix} 1 & 0 & 2 \\ -1 & 3 & 1 \end{bmatrix}$, and

$C = \begin{bmatrix} 7 & 6 \\ 5 & 2 \\ 3 & 4 \end{bmatrix}$, verify that

$AB(C) = A(BC)$. **Both products**

equal $\begin{bmatrix} 83 & 58 \\ 131 & 94 \end{bmatrix}$.

QUESTIONS

Covering the Reading

1. What is a *matrix*? **a rectangular arrangement of objects**

In 2–5, use the matrix at the right below which shows the numbers of members of the House of Representatives of each gender for the 102nd–105th Congresses.

2. What are the dimensions of this matrix? **4 × 2**

3. What is the element in row 3, column 2? **47**

4. If a_{ij} represents the element in row i and column j, what is a_{21}? **388**

	male	female
1991	407	28
1993	388	47
1995	388	47
1997	384	51

5. What does the sum of the elements in each row represent? **the total number of male and female representatives for each indicated congress**

6. If A and B are matrices, under what circumstances does the product AB exist ? **The number of columns in A equals the number of rows in B.**

In 7 and 8, give the dimensions of AB.

7. A is 3×2, B is 2×4 **3 × 4**

8. A is 5×1, B is 1×7 **5 × 7**

Lesson 11-1 *Matrix Multiplication* **701**

In Congressional hearing rooms, Senatorial or House committees listen to testimony covering topics such as human rights, the budget, farming, or education.

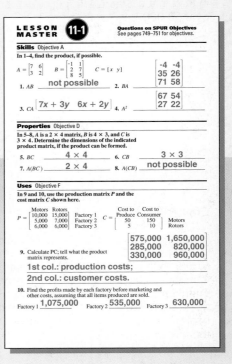

Notes on Questions

Question 14 Many students do not understand associativity of an operation until they see it with matrix multiplication. They have a way of adding or multiplying three numbers at a time, they have no algorithm for multiplying three matrices. Thus they are forced to take a product like *PQU* and do one of the multiplications first. Explain that it is because of associativity that no parentheses are needed in a product like *PQU*. Associativity of addition and multiplication is why, if *a*, *b*, and *c* are numbers, we can write $a + b + c$ or *abc* unambiguously. But subtraction is not associative, so if we write $a - b - c$ we need a rule telling us which subtraction is done first, and if we don't want the left subtraction to be done first, we need parentheses $a - (b - c)$.

Questions 15–16 These questions help students think of translating matrix equations into systems of linear equations. Solving systems using matrices is studied in UCSMP *Advanced Algebra*.

Question 18 This is an example of a matrix used to represent a network. These representations are explored in some detail in *Precalculus and Discrete Mathematics*.

Social Studies Connection The National System of Interstate and Defense Highways is a 42,770-mile network of freeways designed to connect more than 75% of the cities in the United States with populations over 50,000.

In 9–12, multiply.

9. $[8 \quad 2] \cdot \begin{bmatrix} 9 \\ 1 \end{bmatrix}$ [74]

10. $\begin{bmatrix} 7 & 3 & 1 \\ 0 & 4 & 2 \end{bmatrix} \cdot \begin{bmatrix} -1 \\ 1 \\ -2 \end{bmatrix}$ $\begin{bmatrix} -6 \\ 0 \end{bmatrix}$

11. $\begin{bmatrix} a & b \\ c & d \end{bmatrix} \cdot \begin{bmatrix} x \\ y \end{bmatrix}$ $\begin{bmatrix} ax + by \\ cx + dy \end{bmatrix}$

12. $\begin{bmatrix} 1 & 0 \\ 2 & 3 \end{bmatrix} \cdot \begin{bmatrix} -2 & 3 \\ 1 & 4 \end{bmatrix}$ $\begin{bmatrix} -2 & 3 \\ -1 & 18 \end{bmatrix}$

13. Give the dimensions of two matrices which cannot be multiplied.
   Sample: 3 × 2 and 3 × 4

14. Refer to the Math Team fund raiser described in the Lesson. In Example 3, the matrix $P(QU)$ was calculated. Calculate $(PQ)U$. That is, find the product matrix PQ, then multiply this result by U. Does $P(QU) = (PQ)U$? See left.

14) $PQ = [0.4 \quad 0.5] \cdot \begin{bmatrix} 40 & 100 & 0 & 40 \\ 75 & 108 & 80 & 65 \end{bmatrix} =$
$[53.5 \quad 94 \quad 40 \quad 48.5]$
$(PQ)U =$
$[53.5 \quad 94 \quad 40 \quad 48.5] \cdot \begin{bmatrix} 1.00 \\ 1.00 \\ 0.50 \\ 1.50 \end{bmatrix} = [240.25]$
Yes; $P(QU) = (PQ)U$.

Applying the Mathematics

In 15 and 16, solve for the variables.

15. $\begin{bmatrix} 3 & 4 \\ 1 & 2 \end{bmatrix} \cdot \begin{bmatrix} x \\ 1 \end{bmatrix} = \begin{bmatrix} -2 \\ 0 \end{bmatrix}$ $x = -2$

16. $\begin{bmatrix} 2 & a \\ 3 & b \end{bmatrix} \cdot \begin{bmatrix} 5 \\ 6 \end{bmatrix} = \begin{bmatrix} 7 \\ 8 \end{bmatrix}$ $a = -\frac{1}{2}, b = -\frac{7}{6}$

17. For square matrices, $M^2 = M \cdot M$. Let $M = \begin{bmatrix} 0 & -2 \\ -2 & 0 \end{bmatrix}$.
   a. Calculate M^2. $\begin{bmatrix} 4 & 0 \\ 0 & 4 \end{bmatrix}$
   b. Calculate M^3. $\begin{bmatrix} 0 & -8 \\ -8 & 0 \end{bmatrix}$

18. The diagram below shows the major highways connecting four cities.
   a. Write the number of direct routes (not through any other city on the diagram) between each pair of cities into a matrix as begun below. (Note that U.S. 41–U.S. 52 is considered to be one road.) See left.

18a) $\begin{bmatrix} 0 & 1 & 1 & 2 \\ 1 & 0 & 1 & 1 \\ 1 & 1 & 0 & 1 \\ 2 & 1 & 1 & 0 \end{bmatrix}$

b) $\begin{bmatrix} 6 & 3 & 3 & 2 \\ 3 & 3 & 2 & 3 \\ 3 & 2 & 3 & 3 \\ 2 & 3 & 3 & 6 \end{bmatrix}$
The matrix represents the number of ways to travel from one city to another, or from a city back to itself, through exactly one other city.

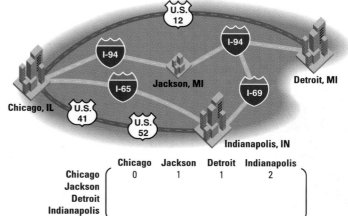

	Chicago	Jackson	Detroit	Indianapolis
Chicago	0	1	1	2
Jackson				
Detroit				
Indianapolis				

   b. Multiply the matrix from part **a** by itself and interpret what it signifies. See left.

702

Adapting to Individual Needs

Challenge

Matrix $P = \begin{bmatrix} .75 & .15 & .10 \\ .20 & .60 & .20 \\ .05 & .35 & .60 \end{bmatrix}$ is an example of a probability matrix, a type of matrix used in many settings. Each entry of a probability matrix must be a probability, that is, a number p such that $0 \le p \le 1$, and the sum of each row must be 1. Have students answer the following questions.

1. What happens if you raise P to higher and higher powers? [The limit of each row is the same.]
2. Give an example of a 4 × 4 probability matrix. [Answers will vary.]
3. Raise your matrix to higher and higher powers. Does the same thing happen that happened for matrix P? [Yes]

Beauty and the Beast

19a) $\begin{bmatrix} 2860 \\ 2918 \\ 2640 \end{bmatrix}$

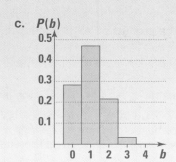

In 19 and 20, the matrix N gives the number of tickets sold for a Children's Theater performance. The matrix C gives the unit cost in dollars for each ticket.

$$N = \begin{array}{l} \text{Weekday matinee} \\ \text{Weekend matinee} \\ \text{Weekend evening} \end{array} \begin{array}{cc} \text{Adults} & \text{Children} \\ \begin{bmatrix} 250 & 340 \\ 273 & 320 \\ 170 & 405 \end{bmatrix} \end{array} \qquad C = \begin{bmatrix} 6.00 \\ 4.00 \end{bmatrix} \begin{array}{l} \text{Adults} \\ \text{Children} \end{array}$$

19. **a.** Find NC. **See left.**
   b. What was the theater's total revenue for the weekday performance? **$2860**

20. A portion of the receipts for each performance goes to a children's health charity: 50% for the weekday performance and 40% for each of the weekend performances. Let $P = \begin{bmatrix} .50 & .40 & .40 \end{bmatrix}$. Find the total contribution to charity for all three performances. **$3653.20**

Review

21. Five pairs each of red, blue, yellow, and green socks are in a drawer. Four pairs are selected randomly. Let b = number of blue pairs selected. *(Lesson 7-6)* **b, c) See margin.**
   a. List all possible values of b. **{0, 1, 2, 3, 4}**
   b. Make a probability distribution table for the random variable b.
   c. Construct a histogram of the probability distribution.

22. Let (x, y) be the image of the point $(1, 0)$ under a rotation of magnitude θ about the origin. Then $x =$ __?__ and $y =$ __?__. *(Lesson 4-3)*
   $x = \cos\theta, y = \sin\theta$

23. Let f and g be functions whose equations are given by $f(x) = x^2 + 2$ and $g(x) = 3x - 1$. Find a rule for $f(g(x))$. *(Lesson 3-7)* $f(g(x)) = 9x^2 - 6x + 3$

24a, b)

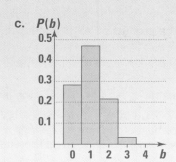

24. **a.** Draw $\triangle SAD$, where $S = (3, 7)$, $A = (0, 5)$, and $D = (2, -3)$.
   b. Draw $\triangle S'A'D'$, the reflection image of $\triangle SAD$ over the y-axis.
   c. If r_y represents reflection over the y-axis, then r_y: $(x, y) \rightarrow$ __?__. $(-x, y)$
   (Lesson 3-4) **a, b) See left.**

25. Match each transformation with the *best* description. *(Lessons 3-2, 3-4, 3-5)*
   a. $M(x, y) = (x + 3, y - 2)$ **v**   (i) reflection over the x-axis
   b. $N(x, y) = (x, -y)$ **i**   (ii) reflection over the line $y = x$
   c. $P(x, y) = (y, x)$ **ii**   (iii) scale change
   d. $Q(x, y) = \left(\frac{x}{3}, \frac{y}{3}\right)$ **iv**   (iv) size change
   e. $V(x, y) = (0.1x, 10y)$ **iii**   (v) translation

Exploration

26. Matrices frequently appear in the business and sports sections of newspapers, though they are not usually identified with brackets.
   a. Find an example of a matrix in a newspaper.
   b. State its dimensions.
   c. Describe what each row and column represents.
   Answers will vary.

Question 20 From the way the question is written, its answer is the matrix $P(NC)$. You might have students multiply $(PN)C$ to verify that matrix multiplication is associative.

Questions 22–25 These questions are review for Lessons 11-2 to 11-4 and should be discussed.

Follow-up for Lesson **11-1**

Practice
For more questions on SPUR Objectives, use **Lesson Master 11-1** (shown on page 701).

Assessment
Written Communication Have students **work in pairs.** Have each student write 3 or 4 matrix multiplication problems. Ask students to solve their partner's problems. Then have students write a pair of matrices that cannot be multiplied and explain to their partner why the multiplication is not possible. [Students multiply matrices and give examples of matrices that can be multiplied as well as those that cannot.]

Extension
Have students find a pair of 2×2 matrices that are commutative under multiplication. [Sample: Let one matrix be of the form $\begin{bmatrix} a & 0 \\ 0 & a \end{bmatrix}$.]

Project Update Project 4, *Matrix Codes*, on page 746, relates to the content of this lesson.

Additional Answers

21. **b.**

b	0	1	2	3	4
$P(b)$	0.3164	0.4219	0.2109	0.0469	0.0039

c. $P(b)$

Setting Up Lesson 11-2
Discuss **Question 24**, whose skill is needed for Lesson 11-2.

Objectives
G Represent reflections, scale changes, and size changes as matrices.
I Use matrices to find the image of a figure under a transformation.

Resources

From the *Teacher's Resource File*
■ Lesson Master 11-2
■ Answer Master 11-2
■ Teaching Aids
　95 Warm-up
　98 Graphs in Examples 2–3

Additional Resources
■ Visuals for Teaching Aids 95, 98
■ Exploration 11-2

Teaching Lesson 11-2

Warm-up
Give the image of the point (x, y) under the transformation.
1. $r_{x\text{-axis}}$ $(x, -y)$
2. $r_{y = x}$ (y, x)
3. The size change with magnitude 6 $(6x, 6y)$
4. The composite of a horizontal scale change of magnitude $\frac{1}{5}$ and a vertical scale change of magnitude 2. $(\frac{x}{5}, 2y)$

LESSON 11-2

Matrices for Transformations

Representing a Geometric Figure by a Matrix

Matrices can represent geometric figures as well as numerical data. To do so, let the point (a, b) be written as the matrix $\begin{bmatrix} a \\ b \end{bmatrix}$. Such a matrix is sometimes called a **point matrix**. Then a polygon with n sides can be represented by a $2 \times n$ matrix in which the columns are the coordinates of consecutive vertices. For instance, $\triangle QRS$ below can be represented by the matrix $\begin{bmatrix} -1 & 3 & 3 \\ -1 & -1 & 2 \end{bmatrix}$. If named $\triangle SRQ$, the triangle is represented by $\begin{bmatrix} 3 & 3 & -1 \\ 2 & -1 & -1 \end{bmatrix}$.

$\underset{Q}{\uparrow} \quad \underset{R}{\uparrow} \quad \underset{S}{\uparrow}$

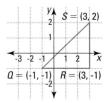

Representing a Transformation by a Matrix

Matrices may also represent transformations.

Example 1
a. Multiply the matrix for $\triangle QRS$ above by the matrix $\begin{bmatrix} 1 & 0 \\ 0 & -1 \end{bmatrix}$ and graph the resulting image, $\triangle Q'R'S'$.
b. Describe the transformation represented by the matrix.

Solution
a. $\begin{bmatrix} 1 & 0 \\ 0 & -1 \end{bmatrix} \cdot \begin{bmatrix} -1 & 3 & 3 \\ -1 & -1 & 2 \end{bmatrix} = \begin{bmatrix} -1 & 3 & 3 \\ 1 & 1 & -2 \end{bmatrix}$

$\underset{Q}{\uparrow} \quad \underset{R}{\uparrow} \quad \underset{S}{\uparrow} \qquad \underset{Q'}{\uparrow} \quad \underset{R'}{\uparrow} \quad \underset{S'}{\uparrow}$

b. $\triangle Q'R'S'$ is the reflection image of $\triangle QRS$ over the x-axis.

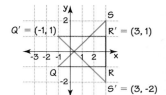

In general, multiplying any point matrix $\begin{bmatrix} x \\ y \end{bmatrix}$ by $\begin{bmatrix} 1 & 0 \\ 0 & -1 \end{bmatrix}$ gives

$$\begin{bmatrix} 1 & 0 \\ 0 & -1 \end{bmatrix} \cdot \begin{bmatrix} x \\ y \end{bmatrix} = \begin{bmatrix} x \\ -y \end{bmatrix}.$$

Lesson 11-2 Overview

Broad Goals This lesson uses matrix multiplication to represent transformations in the coordinate plane. We expect students to see how matrix representations of reflections and scale changes can be used to transform figures.

Perspective All the matrices for transformations in this lesson have dimensions 2×2. The general idea is this:

The product of a 2×2 matrix $\begin{bmatrix} a & b \\ c & d \end{bmatrix}$ and a 2×1 matrix $\begin{bmatrix} x \\ y \end{bmatrix}$ is the 2×1 matrix $\begin{bmatrix} ax + by \\ cx + dy \end{bmatrix}$. Thus, if the image of (x, y) under a transformation is given by a formula of the form $(ax + by, cx + dy)$. Then we can think of (x, y) as represented by the matrix $\begin{bmatrix} x \\ y \end{bmatrix}$ and the transformation as represented by the matrix $\begin{bmatrix} a & b \\ c & d \end{bmatrix}$. This lesson does *not* attempt to answer the question "If I have a transformation, how do I find its matrix?". That question is discussed in Lesson 11-4.

This means that multiplication by $\begin{bmatrix} 1 & 0 \\ 0 & -1 \end{bmatrix}$ maps (x, y) to $(x, -y)$. You should recognize this transformation as r_x, the reflection over the x-axis.

The above result can be generalized. Let F be a matrix for a geometric figure. Whenever multiplication of F by matrix M produces a matrix for the image of F under a transformation T, then M is called the **matrix representing the transformation T**, or the matrix for T.

Matrices for Reflections

Below are matrices for r_x and other reflections.

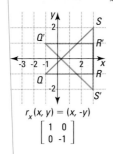 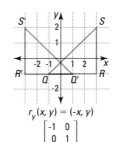 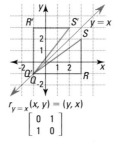

$r_x(x, y) = (x, -y)$ $r_y(x, y) = (-x, y)$ $r_{y=x}(x, y) = (y, x)$

$\begin{bmatrix} 1 & 0 \\ 0 & -1 \end{bmatrix}$ $\begin{bmatrix} -1 & 0 \\ 0 & 1 \end{bmatrix}$ $\begin{bmatrix} 0 & 1 \\ 1 & 0 \end{bmatrix}$

Theorem (Matrices for Reflections)

$\begin{bmatrix} 1 & 0 \\ 0 & -1 \end{bmatrix}$ is the matrix for r_x, reflection over the x-axis.

$\begin{bmatrix} -1 & 0 \\ 0 & 1 \end{bmatrix}$ is the matrix for r_y, reflection over the y-axis.

$\begin{bmatrix} 0 & 1 \\ 1 & 0 \end{bmatrix}$ is the matrix for $r_{y=x}$, reflection over the line $y = x$.

Matrices for Certain Other Transformations

What transformation does the matrix $\begin{bmatrix} 1 & 0 \\ 0 & 1 \end{bmatrix}$ represent? Since $\begin{bmatrix} 1 & 0 \\ 0 & 1 \end{bmatrix} \cdot \begin{bmatrix} x \\ y \end{bmatrix} = \begin{bmatrix} x \\ y \end{bmatrix}$, the transformation represented by this matrix maps any point (x, y) to itself, and is the identity transformation. Futhermore, since $\begin{bmatrix} 1 & 0 \\ 0 & 1 \end{bmatrix} \cdot \begin{bmatrix} a & b \\ c & d \end{bmatrix} = \begin{bmatrix} a & b \\ c & d \end{bmatrix} \cdot \begin{bmatrix} 1 & 0 \\ 0 & 1 \end{bmatrix} = \begin{bmatrix} a & b \\ c & d \end{bmatrix}$ for all a, b, c, and d, $\begin{bmatrix} 1 & 0 \\ 0 & 1 \end{bmatrix}$ is an identity for the set of 2×2 matrices under multiplication.

There is no other 2×2 matrix with this property. Thus, the matrix $\begin{bmatrix} 1 & 0 \\ 0 & 1 \end{bmatrix}$ is called the **2×2 identity matrix**.

Transformations other than reflections or the identity transformation can be represented by matrices.

A bonus of studying this application of matrices is that prior to this point, many students will have thought of transformations as objects that connect preimages to images, not as objects that exist in their own right. Matrices make the latter conception automatic and give students new insight into the transformations they used in previous chapters.

Additional Examples

1. Suppose $\triangle QRS$ has the matrix $\begin{bmatrix} 1 & 3 & 3 \\ -1 & -1 & 2 \end{bmatrix}$. Multiply this matrix on the left by $\begin{bmatrix} 0 & -1 \\ -1 & 0 \end{bmatrix}$.

   a. What is the product matrix?
   $\begin{bmatrix} 1 & 1 & -2 \\ -1 & -3 & -3 \end{bmatrix}$

   b. What transformation does the matrix seem to represent?
   Reflection over the line $y = -x$

2. Multiply the matrix $\begin{bmatrix} 0 & 5 & 10 & 10 \\ 0 & 5 & 15 & 20 \end{bmatrix}$ by $\begin{bmatrix} .2 & 0 \\ 0 & .2 \end{bmatrix}$.

   a. What is the product matrix?
   $\begin{bmatrix} 0 & 1 & 2 & 2 \\ 0 & 1 & 3 & 4 \end{bmatrix}$

   b. Interpret the multiplication geometrically. **A size change of magnitude .2 on the quadrilateral with vertices (0, 0), (5, 5), (10, 15), and (10, 20)**

Is It Really Larger?
The full moon nearest the autumnal equinox is called the Harvest Moon. Near the horizon, the moon appears enlarged by a scale change, but it is an illusion.

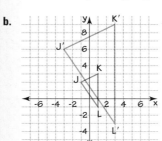

Example 2

a. Multiply the matrix for $\triangle JKL$ with $J = (-1, 2)$, $K = (1, 3)$, and $L = (1, -1)$ by $\begin{bmatrix} 3 & 0 \\ 0 & 3 \end{bmatrix}$.

b. Graph the preimage and image.

c. What transformation does $\begin{bmatrix} 3 & 0 \\ 0 & 3 \end{bmatrix}$ represent?

Solution

a. Write the matrix for $\triangle JKL$ and multiply it by the given matrix.
$$\begin{bmatrix} 3 & 0 \\ 0 & 3 \end{bmatrix} \cdot \begin{bmatrix} -1 & 1 & 1 \\ 2 & 3 & -1 \end{bmatrix} = \begin{bmatrix} -3 & 3 & 3 \\ 6 & 9 & -3 \end{bmatrix}$$

b.

c. The matrix $\begin{bmatrix} 3 & 0 \\ 0 & 3 \end{bmatrix}$ represents a size change of magnitude 3.

In general, a size change of magnitude k for $k \neq 0$ is represented by the matrix $\begin{bmatrix} k & 0 \\ 0 & k \end{bmatrix}$. Similarly, a matrix of the form $\begin{bmatrix} a & 0 \\ 0 & b \end{bmatrix}$ with $a \neq 0$, $b \neq 0$ represents the scale change $S(x, y) = (ax, by)$. This is the transformation that stretches a preimage horizontally by a and vertically by b and is symbolized by $S_{a,b}$.

Example 3

a. Apply $\begin{bmatrix} 3 & 0 \\ 0 & 2 \end{bmatrix}$ to the figure at the left.   **b.** Identify the transformation.

Solution

a. Here is the product that represents the image of the square.
$$\begin{bmatrix} 3 & 0 \\ 0 & 2 \end{bmatrix} \cdot \begin{bmatrix} 4 & 4 & -2 & -2 \\ 4 & -2 & -2 & 4 \end{bmatrix} = \begin{bmatrix} 12 & 12 & -6 & -6 \\ 8 & -4 & -4 & 8 \end{bmatrix}$$

The images of the interior figures are found with the following products.

segment $\begin{bmatrix} 3 & 0 \\ 0 & 2 \end{bmatrix} \cdot \begin{bmatrix} -1 & 0 \\ 1 & 2 \end{bmatrix} = \begin{bmatrix} -3 & 0 \\ 2 & 4 \end{bmatrix}$

rectangle $\begin{bmatrix} 3 & 0 \\ 0 & 2 \end{bmatrix} \cdot \begin{bmatrix} 1 & 1 & 3 & 3 \\ 1 & 2 & 2 & 1 \end{bmatrix} = \begin{bmatrix} 3 & 3 & 9 & 9 \\ 2 & 4 & 4 & 2 \end{bmatrix}$

triangle $\begin{bmatrix} 3 & 0 \\ 0 & 2 \end{bmatrix} \cdot \begin{bmatrix} -1 & 3 & 2 \\ -1 & 0 & -1 \end{bmatrix} = \begin{bmatrix} -3 & 9 & 6 \\ -2 & 0 & -2 \end{bmatrix}$

Adapting to Individual Needs

Extra Help
Point out as you discuss the theorem on page 705 that only reflections over lines containing the origin can have 2 × 2 matrices. This is because (0, 0) is its own image under every transformation with a 2 × 2 matrix. The matrices in the theorem represent reflections over all the symmetry lines of the square with vertices (1, 1), (1, -1), (-1, -1), and (-1, 1) except the line $y = -x$. That line is given as Additional Example 1.

English Language Development
Some students will say "matrixes" instead of "matrices." They are applying probability, because most words that end in x do take plurals by adding –es. In fact, matrixes is occasionally used as the plural of matrix, but not in mathematics. The mathematical plural uses the Latin plural of words that end in –ix or –ex, changing the x to a c, such as is done with the plurals of index (indices), radix (radices), and vertex (vertices).

Challenge
The matrix $\begin{bmatrix} 0 & -2 \\ 2 & 0 \end{bmatrix}$ is a matrix for a composite of three transformations studied in this lesson. What can those transformations be?
[Sample: $S_2 \circ r_{y = x} \circ r_{x\text{-axis}}$]

b. Graph the image.

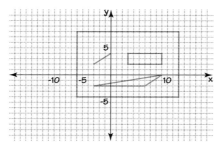

Notice that the image is a distortion, not a simple enlargement of the original figure. **Every part of the original figure is stretched 3 times horizontally and twice vertically. The transformation is the scale change $S_{3,2}$.**

3. Apply $\begin{bmatrix} -4 & 0 \\ 0 & 3 \end{bmatrix}$ to the
quadrilateral given in Additional Example 2.
a. What is the image?
$\begin{bmatrix} 0 & -20 & -40 & -40 \\ 0 & 15 & 45 & 60 \end{bmatrix}$
b. Describe the transformation.
A transformation that stretches the figure 4 times horizontally, reflects it over the y-axis, and stretches it 3 times vertically

Notes on Questions
Question 3 Students should be able to match a matrix with its transformation without referring to the theorem in the lesson. Take a couple of points and find their images under each transformation.

QUESTIONS

Covering the Reading

1. *Multiple choice.* Which matrix represents the point $(5, -2)$? **c**

(a) $\begin{bmatrix} 5 & -2 \end{bmatrix}$
(b) $\begin{bmatrix} -2 & 5 \end{bmatrix}$
(c) $\begin{bmatrix} 5 \\ -2 \end{bmatrix}$
(d) $\begin{bmatrix} -2 \\ 5 \end{bmatrix}$

2a) $\begin{bmatrix} 4 & 2 & -2 \\ -2 & 3 & 2 \end{bmatrix}$

b) $\begin{bmatrix} -2 & 3 & 2 \\ 4 & 2 & -2 \end{bmatrix}$

2. Refer to the figure at the right. **a, b, see left.**
   a. Write $\triangle XYZ$ as a matrix.
   b. Multiply the matrix for $\triangle XYZ$ by $\begin{bmatrix} 0 & 1 \\ 1 & 0 \end{bmatrix}$.

   c. The matrix in part **b** represents what transformation?
   reflection over the line $y = x$

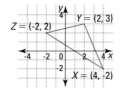

3. Match the matrix with the transformation it represents.

   a. $\begin{bmatrix} -1 & 0 \\ 0 & 1 \end{bmatrix}$ iii   (i) identity

   b. $\begin{bmatrix} 0 & -1 \\ -1 & 0 \end{bmatrix}$ v   (ii) reflection over x-axis

   c. $\begin{bmatrix} 1 & 0 \\ 0 & -1 \end{bmatrix}$ ii   (iii) reflection over y-axis

   d. $\begin{bmatrix} 1 & 0 \\ 0 & 1 \end{bmatrix}$ i   (iv) reflection over $y = x$

   e. $\begin{bmatrix} 0 & 1 \\ 1 & 0 \end{bmatrix}$ iv   (v) none of these

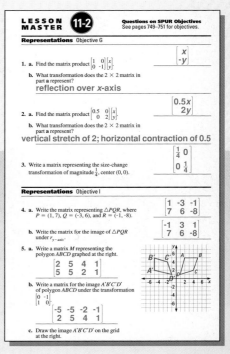

4a)

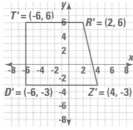

T' = (-4.5, 3)   R' = (1.5, 3)
D' = (-4.5, -1.5)   Z' = (3, -1.5)

b) It is a size change of magnitude 1.5.

5a)

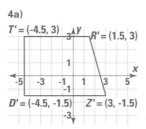

T' = (-6, 6)   R' = (2, 6)
D' = (-6, -3)   Z' = (4, -3)

b) It is a scale change of magnitude 2 horizontally and of magnitude 3 vertically.

9a) $\begin{bmatrix} 0 & 1 \\ 1 & 0 \end{bmatrix}$ b) $\begin{bmatrix} 1 & 0 \\ 0 & 1 \end{bmatrix}$

12a) $\begin{bmatrix} 2 & 0 \\ 0 & 2 \end{bmatrix}$

b) Sample: $\begin{bmatrix} 3 & 0 \\ 0 & \frac{1}{2} \end{bmatrix}$

c) Sample: $\begin{bmatrix} \frac{1}{2} & 0 \\ 0 & 3 \end{bmatrix}$

13a) A' = $\begin{bmatrix} 30 \\ -17 \end{bmatrix}$,

B' = $\begin{bmatrix} 14 \\ -8 \end{bmatrix}$,

C' = $\begin{bmatrix} -18 \\ 10 \end{bmatrix}$

In 4 and 5, use the trapezoid *TRZD* at the right.
  a. Find the image of *TRZD* under the transformation with the given matrix.
  b. Describe the transformation.

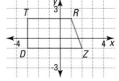

4. $\begin{bmatrix} 1.5 & 0 \\ 0 & 1.5 \end{bmatrix}$ See left. **5.** $\begin{bmatrix} 2 & 0 \\ 0 & 3 \end{bmatrix}$ See left.

In 6 and 7, state a matrix for the transformation.
6. size change of magnitude *a* 6) $\begin{bmatrix} a & 0 \\ 0 & a \end{bmatrix}$ 7) $\begin{bmatrix} a & 0 \\ 0 & b \end{bmatrix}$
7. scale change $S_{a,b}$

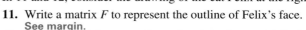

Applying the Mathematics

8. Prove that $\begin{bmatrix} -1 & 0 \\ 0 & 1 \end{bmatrix}$ is the matrix for r_y, reflection over the y-axis.
See margin.

9. a. Write the matrix for $r_{y=x}$. See left.
  b. Square the matrix. See left.
  c. What transformation does the matrix in part **b** represent?
  The identity transformation

10. a. Find the image of $\triangle ABC = \begin{bmatrix} 2 & 3 & 0 \\ -1 & 2 & 4 \end{bmatrix}$ under the transformation
  T with matrix $\begin{bmatrix} -1 & 0 \\ 0 & -1 \end{bmatrix}$. $\begin{bmatrix} -2 & -3 & 0 \\ 1 & -2 & -4 \end{bmatrix}$
  b. Describe *T*. **a rotation of 180° about the origin**

In 11 and 12, consider the drawing of the cat Felix at the right.

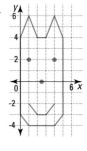

11. Write a matrix *F* to represent the outline of Felix's face.
  See margin.
12. Find a matrix for a transformation that when multiplied by *F* produces the desired image. See left.
  a. a face similar to Felix's with four times the area
  b. a face that is shorter and wider than Felix's
  c. a face that is longer and thinner than Felix's

13. Here are matrices for three collinear points *A*, *B*, and *C*, and a matrix *T* for a transformation:
$$A = \begin{bmatrix} 1 \\ 4 \end{bmatrix}, B = \begin{bmatrix} 0 \\ 2 \end{bmatrix}, C = \begin{bmatrix} -2 \\ -2 \end{bmatrix}; T = \begin{bmatrix} 2 & 7 \\ -1 & -4 \end{bmatrix}.$$
  a. Find the images of the points under the transformation. See left.
  b. Are the images collinear? **Yes**
  c. Does this transformation preserve distance? **No**

14. The matrix $\begin{bmatrix} \frac{\sqrt{3}}{2} & \frac{1}{2} \\ \frac{1}{2} & -\frac{\sqrt{3}}{2} \end{bmatrix}$ is associated with the reflection over a line ℓ
which contains the origin. What is the measure of the acute angle formed by ℓ and the x-axis? You may need to experiment with graph paper and a protractor. **15°**

Additional Answers

8. $\begin{bmatrix} -1 & 0 \\ 0 & 1 \end{bmatrix} \begin{bmatrix} x \\ y \end{bmatrix} = \begin{bmatrix} -x \\ y \end{bmatrix}$. So the matrix $\begin{bmatrix} -1 & 0 \\ 0 & 1 \end{bmatrix}$ maps each point (*x, y*) to the point (-*x, y*), which is its reflection image over the *y*-axis.

11. $\begin{bmatrix} 0 & 1 & 2 & 3 & 4 & 5 & 5 & 4 & 1 & 0 \\ 4 & 6 & 4 & 4 & 6 & 4 & -3 & -4 & -4 & -3 \end{bmatrix}$

15. Matrix X has dimensions 3×5 and matrix Y has dimensions 5×4.
   a. What are the dimensions of XY? **3 × 4**
   b. How many elements are in XY? *(Lesson 11-1)* **12**

In 16 and 17, multiply, if the product exists. *(Lesson 11-1)*

16. $\begin{bmatrix} 2 & 3 \\ 0 & 4 \end{bmatrix} \begin{bmatrix} x \\ y \end{bmatrix}$ $\begin{bmatrix} 2x + 3y \\ 0x + 4y \end{bmatrix}$
     17. $\begin{bmatrix} 3 & 0 & 1 \\ 2 & -1 & -2 \end{bmatrix} \cdot \begin{bmatrix} 4 & 0 \\ 1 & -3 \end{bmatrix}$ **Product does not exist.**

18. A clothing manufacturer has factories in Oakland, CA, and Charleston, SC. The quantities (in thousands) of each of three products manufactured are given in the production matrix P below. The costs in dollars for producing each item during three years are given in the cost matrix C below.

	Coats	Pants	Shirts	
Oakland	10	10	22	
Charleston	20	15	0	$= P$,

	1994	1995	1996	
Coats	30	30	32	
Pants	5	7	8	$= C$
Shirts	2	3	3.5	

   a. Calculate PC. **See left.**
   b. Interpret PC by telling what each element represents. **See margin.**
   c. Does CP exist? Why or why not? *(Lesson 11-1)* **No; the number of columns of C does not equal the number of rows of P.**

19. Consider $X = \begin{bmatrix} 1 & 2 \\ 3 & -1 \end{bmatrix}$, $Y = \begin{bmatrix} 4 & 3 \\ 0 & -1 \end{bmatrix}$, and $Z = \begin{bmatrix} -2 & 0 \\ 1 & -1 \end{bmatrix}$.

   a. Find $(XY)Z$.   a) $\begin{bmatrix} -7 & -1 \\ -14 & -10 \end{bmatrix}$ b) $\begin{bmatrix} -7 & -1 \\ -14 & -10 \end{bmatrix}$
   b. Find $X(YZ)$.
   c. What property of matrix multiplication do the results of parts **a** and **b** illustrate? *(Lesson 11-1)* **the Associative Property**

In 20 and 21, solve for θ. *(Lesson 4-4)*

20. $\cos(-\theta) = -\cos\theta$ **See left.**
     21. $\tan\theta = \sin\theta$
           $\theta = k\pi$ for all integers k

22. Let $k(x) = \sqrt{x}$ and $n(x) = 3x + 1$. *True or false.*
   $(k \circ n)(x) = (n \circ k)(x)$. Justify your answer. *(Lesson 3-7)* **False;** $(k \circ n)(x) =$
   $k(n(x)) = k(3x + 1) = \sqrt{3x + 1};$ $(n \circ k)(x) = n(\sqrt{x}) = 3\sqrt{x} + 1.$

18a) $\begin{bmatrix} 394 & 436 & 477 \\ 675 & 705 & 760 \end{bmatrix}$

20) $\theta = \frac{\pi}{2} + k\pi$ for all integers k

23a)

23. A cube in a three-dimensional coordinate system can be represented by the matrix C below.

$$C = \begin{bmatrix} 1 & 1 & 1 & 1 & -1 & -1 & -1 & -1 \\ 1 & 1 & -1 & -1 & -1 & 1 & 1 & -1 \\ 1 & -1 & -1 & 1 & 1 & 1 & -1 & -1 \end{bmatrix}$$

   a. Graph the cube. **See left.**
   b. Let T be the transformation represented by the matrix

$$M = \begin{bmatrix} 2 & 0 & 0 \\ 0 & 2 & 0 \\ 0 & 0 & 2 \end{bmatrix}.$$ Calculate and graph MC. **See margin.**

   c. Describe the transformation T.
   It is a size change of magnitude 2.

Lesson 11-2 *Matrices for Transformations* **709**

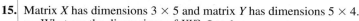

Practice
For more questions on SPUR Objectives, use **Lesson Master 11-2** (shown on page 707).

Assessment
Written Communication Have students work in pairs. Ask each student to make up a problem like that in **Questions 11–12**, designing a picture similar to Felix. Have students solve their partner's problem. [Students use matrices to represent points in the coordinate plane and find their images under transformations.]

Extension
Students who are adept at deductive proofs might be able to prove that an matrix that has a 2×2 transformation preserves collinearity. The key is to identify three general points on the same general line and then show that their images are also on a line. Let the line be $y = mx + b$. Then the points can be $(x_1, mx_1 + b)$, $(x_2, mx_2 + b)$, and $(x_3, mx_3 + b)$. Let the matrix be $\begin{bmatrix} c & d \\ e & f \end{bmatrix}$. Then show that the images of these points all lie on a line by showing that the slopes of the segments connecting them are equal.

Project Update Project 1, *Programming 2-D Graphics*, and Project 4, *Matrix Codes*, on pages 745–746, relate to the content of this lesson.

Additional Answers
18. b. The first row represents the production costs (in thousands of dollars) in Oakland for the years 1994, 1995, and 1996. The second row represents the corresponding costs for Charleston.

23. b. $MC = \begin{bmatrix} 2 & 2 & 2 & 2 & -2 & -2 & -2 & -2 \\ 2 & 2 & -2 & -2 & -2 & 2 & 2 & -2 \\ 2 & -2 & -2 & 2 & 2 & 2 & -2 & -2 \end{bmatrix}$

The graph is shown at the right.

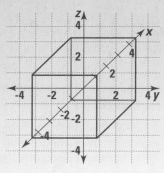

Setting Up Lesson 11-3
Question 25 of Lesson 11-1 and **Question 22** of Lesson 11-2 are helpful to review.

Objectives

D Apply properties of matrices and matrix multiplication.
G Represent rotations as matrices.
H Represent composites of transformations as matrix products.
I Use matrices to find the image of a figure under a transformation.

Resources

From the *Teacher's Resource File*
- Lesson Master 11-3
- Answer Master 11-3
- Assessment Sourcebook: Quiz for Lessons 11-1 through 11-3
- Teaching Aids
  - 96 Warm-up
  - 99 Matrices and Graph for Example 1
  - 100 Theorems

Additional Resources
- Visuals for Teaching Aids 96, 99, 100

Teaching Lesson **11-3**

Warm-up

In 1–3, describe the composite of the pair of transformations.
1. A reflection over the line $y = x$ followed by a reflection over the y-axis R_{90}
2. A size change of magnitude 3 followed by a size change of magnitude 4 with the same center **A size change of magnitude 12 with that center**
3. A rotation of $\frac{\pi}{6}$ followed by a rotation of $\frac{5\pi}{6}$ with the same center **A rotation of π with that center**

11-3

Matrices for Composites of Transformations

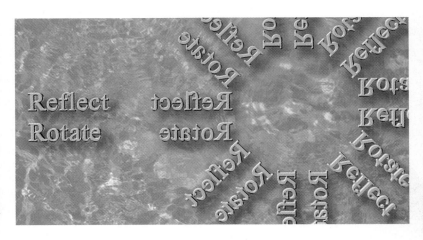

Using Matrices to Find the Image of a Figure Under a Composite of Transformations

As you know, when two transformations are composed, the result is another transformation. In this lesson, composites of transformations are represented using matrices.

Example 1

Let $\triangle ABC = \begin{bmatrix} 2 & 6 & 6 \\ 1 & 1 & 3 \end{bmatrix}$.

a. Find $\triangle A'B'C'$, the image of $\triangle ABC$ under a reflection over the x-axis.
b. Reflect the image over $y = x$ to obtain $\triangle A''B''C''$.

Solution

a. The matrix for r_x is $\begin{bmatrix} 1 & 0 \\ 0 & -1 \end{bmatrix}$. So $\triangle A'B'C'$ is represented by the matrix

$$\begin{bmatrix} 1 & 0 \\ 0 & -1 \end{bmatrix} \cdot \begin{bmatrix} 2 & 6 & 6 \\ 1 & 1 & 3 \end{bmatrix} = \begin{bmatrix} 2 & 6 & 6 \\ -1 & -1 & -3 \end{bmatrix}.$$

b. The matrix for $r_{y=x}$ is $\begin{bmatrix} 0 & 1 \\ 1 & 0 \end{bmatrix}$. Apply this matrix to the matrix for $\triangle A'B'C'$ to get a matrix for $\triangle A''B''C''$.

$$\begin{bmatrix} 0 & 1 \\ 1 & 0 \end{bmatrix} \cdot \begin{bmatrix} 2 & 6 & 6 \\ -1 & -1 & -3 \end{bmatrix} = \begin{bmatrix} -1 & -1 & -3 \\ 2 & 6 & 6 \end{bmatrix}$$

At the right is a graph of the three triangles.

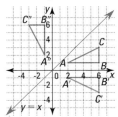

Lesson 11-3 Overview

Broad Goals This lesson has three goals: to show how to find the image of a figure under a composite of transformations, to use that idea to develop the matrices for several rotations, and to provide a means by which matrices for a variety of transformations can be remembered.

Perspective UCSMP *Geometry* students, in their study of congruence, learn a Two-Reflection Theorem: the composite of

two reflections over intersecting lines is a rotation whose center is the point of intersection of the lines and whose magnitude is twice the acute angle between the lines measured from the first line to the second. Here that theorem is recalled and verified (but not deduced) for the special case where the first line is the x-axis and the second is the line $y = x$. Students know a formula for each of these reflections and so can obtain a formula for the composite.

In Example 1, $\triangle A''B''C''$ is the image of $\triangle ABC$ under the *composite* of the reflections $r_{y=x}$ and r_x. That is, $\triangle A''B''C'' = r_{y=x}(r_x(\triangle ABC))$. To find a single matrix for the composite $r_{y=x} \circ r_x$, notice that the matrix for $\triangle A''B''C''$ came from the product

$$\begin{bmatrix} 0 & 1 \\ 1 & 0 \end{bmatrix} \cdot \left(\begin{bmatrix} 1 & 0 \\ 0 & -1 \end{bmatrix} \begin{bmatrix} 2 & 6 & 6 \\ 1 & 1 & 3 \end{bmatrix} \right).$$

Because matrix multiplication is associative, the preceding expression may be rewritten as

$$\left(\begin{bmatrix} 0 & 1 \\ 1 & 0 \end{bmatrix} \cdot \begin{bmatrix} 1 & 0 \\ 0 & -1 \end{bmatrix} \right) \cdot \begin{bmatrix} 2 & 6 & 6 \\ 1 & 1 & 3 \end{bmatrix}.$$

Thus, multiplying the matrices for $r_{y=x}$ and r_x gives the matrix for the composite $r_{y=x} \circ r_x$.

$$\begin{bmatrix} 0 & 1 \\ 1 & 0 \end{bmatrix} \cdot \begin{bmatrix} 1 & 0 \\ 0 & -1 \end{bmatrix} = \begin{bmatrix} 0 & -1 \\ 1 & 0 \end{bmatrix}$$

Compare the preimage and the final image in Example 1. The transformation that maps $\triangle ABC$ to $\triangle A''B''C''$ is R_{90}, the *rotation* of 90° counterclockwise with the origin as its center. (Note: We usually omit the degree symbol in the subscript for rotations.) So $R_{90} = r_{y=x} \circ r_x$.

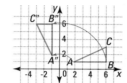

The results of Example 1 can be generalized:

A Good Turn. *This wheel has 90° rotation symmetry.*

Theorem

If M is the matrix associated with a transformation t, and N is the matrix associated with a transformation u, then NM is the matrix associated with the transformation $u \circ t$.

How to Find the Matrix for a Composite of Transformations

❶ **Example 2**

Use the fact that a rotation of 180° is the composite of a 90° rotation with a 90° rotation to find a matrix for R_{180}.

Solution

$R_{180} = R_{90} \circ R_{90}$. Thus, the product of the matrix for R_{90} with itself equals the matrix for R_{180}.

$$\begin{bmatrix} 0 & -1 \\ 1 & 0 \end{bmatrix} \cdot \begin{bmatrix} 0 & -1 \\ 1 & 0 \end{bmatrix} = \begin{bmatrix} -1 & 0 \\ 0 & -1 \end{bmatrix}$$

So $\begin{bmatrix} -1 & 0 \\ 0 & -1 \end{bmatrix}$ is a matrix for R_{180}.

▶

Error Alert As with the notation for composition of functions, the matrices in a representation of a composite transformation are in order from right to left. Although the notation for composite functions, using parentheses, makes this right-to-left process relatively obvious, the straightforward notation of matrix multiplication hides it altogether. So students may need to be continually reminded that the order of transformations represented in a matrix multiplication is right to left.

Some students may confuse the symbol ∘ for composition with the symbol · for multiplication. We feel that the distinction should be carefully maintained. However, students may start to call the matrices by the names for the transformations. That is, they may use R to name both the transformation (the rotation of 90° about the origin) and the matrix $\begin{bmatrix} 0 & -1 \\ 1 & 0 \end{bmatrix}$. We feel that this double meaning is acceptable. As long as students know the difference between a matrix and a transformation; it's much simpler and quite convenient to call the matrix by its transformation name.

Teaching Aid 99 is provided with the matrices and graph of **Example 1.** You may wish to have students redraw the line $y = x$ on the graph to help emphasize the reflection of $\triangle A'B'C'$ over that line to its image $\triangle A''B''C''$.

❶ The general rotation matrix is presented in Lesson 11-4, and the matrix for R_{90} is needed for its development. Students should know the matrix for R_{90}. In UCSMP *Advanced Algebra*, students will have seen R_{90} used to show that two oblique lines

Optional Activities

Have students find a composition of reflections that produces R_{180} and R_{270}. $[r_x \circ r_y = r_y \circ r_x = R_{180}$, while $r_{y=x} \circ r_y = r_x \circ r_{y=x} = R_{270}.]$

But this composite of transformations is represented by the product of the matrices for the reflections. Then, products of matrices for 90° rotations then lead to matrices for rotations of 180° and 270°. Thus, by the end of this lesson, students have a matrix for any rotation about the origin whose magnitude is a multiple of 90°.

To help in remembering all of these matrices, it is proved that if a 2 × 2 matrix

exists for a transformation, then the image of (1, 0) is the first column of the matrix and the image of (0, 1) is the second column.

The name "Matrix Basis Theorem" comes not only from the fact that the matrix is informally "based" on the images of (1, 0) and (0, 1), but also because in linear algebra these points form an orthonormal basis for the vector space in two dimensions.

in the coordinate plane are perpendicular if and only if the product of their slopes is -1. The idea is that a rotation of 90° geometrically maps a line onto a line perpendicular to it. Algebraically, the coordinates are switched and one of them is changed to its opposite. If this algebra is done with the slope formula, then the numerator and denominator are switched, and one of them is changed to its opposite. Thus the slope of the image is the opposite of the reciprocal of the slope of the preimage.

Stress the general property of rotations: $R_\alpha \circ R_\beta = R_{\alpha + \beta}$. This property is applied in the next lesson.

Emphasize the use of the Matrix Basis Theorem to facilitate remembering matrices for transformations. We recommend that you go over its proof, but do not expect students to understand it. The proof is so short that many students do not see what has occurred.

Teaching Aid 100 contains the three theorems presented in this lesson.

Check

Apply this matrix to △ABC of Example 1.

$$\begin{bmatrix} -1 & 0 \\ 0 & -1 \end{bmatrix} \cdot \begin{bmatrix} 2 & 6 & 6 \\ 1 & 1 & 3 \end{bmatrix} = \begin{bmatrix} -2 & -6 & -6 \\ -1 & -1 & -3 \end{bmatrix}$$

The product should represent the image of △ABC under a rotation of 180° around the origin. The graph below illustrates that it does.

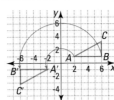

Similarly, a matrix for R_{270} can be found by using $R_{270} = R_{180} \circ R_{90}$. In the Questions you are asked to prove that R_{270} is represented by $\begin{bmatrix} 0 & 1 \\ -1 & 0 \end{bmatrix}$.

The following theorem summarizes these results.

Matrices for Rotations Theorem

$\begin{bmatrix} 0 & -1 \\ 1 & 0 \end{bmatrix}$ is the matrix for R_{90}, rotation of 90° around the origin.

$\begin{bmatrix} -1 & 0 \\ 0 & -1 \end{bmatrix}$ is the matrix for R_{180}, rotation of 180° around the origin.

$\begin{bmatrix} 0 & 1 \\ -1 & 0 \end{bmatrix}$ is the matrix for R_{270}, rotation of 270° around the origin.

Remembering Matrices for Transformations

You may wonder how you will ever remember matrices for each of the transformations you have studied. The key is a simple but beautiful result: if a transformation can be represented by a 2 × 2 matrix, then the first column of the matrix is the image of (1, 0), and the second column of the matrix is the image of (0, 1).

For instance, suppose you forget the matrix for R_{90}. Visualize the 90° rotation of (1, 0) and (0, 1). Note that $R_{90}(1, 0) = (0, 1)$ and $R_{90}(0, 1) = (-1, 0)$. So the matrix for R_{90} is

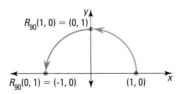

Adapting to Individual Needs

Extra Help
Some students may be troubled by the use of the equality sign between the notations for triangle and matrix in **Example 1**. Point out that this is the customary use of that sign to indicate that two symbols name the same object. Obviously the triangle (a set of points) and the matrix (a rectangular array of numbers) are not the same thing. But then, neither are 1.5 and $\frac{3}{2}$, yet we write $1.5 = \frac{3}{2}$.

Challenge
Ask students to explore compositions of three transformations. Have them start by finding out whether there is a single transformation that is represented by $r_{y = x} \circ r_y \circ r_x$. [Yes, the result is a matrix that represents reflection over the line $y = -x$, $\begin{bmatrix} 0 & -1 \\ -1 & 0 \end{bmatrix}$.]

Have them explore the composition in different orders. [Four produce $r_{y = -x}$ and

two produce $r_{y = x}$.] Then have them explore compositions of rotations, and compositions of reflections and rotations. [Samples: $R_{90} \circ R_{180} \circ R_{270}$ produces R_{180}; $R_{90} \circ r_x \circ r_y$ produces R_{270}; students should begin to notice that three reflections produce another reflection while two reflections and a rotation produce a rotation. An even number of reflections produces a rotation and an odd number of reflections produces a reflection.]

712

This relation is called the **Matrix Basis Theorem** because the matrix is *based* on the images of the points (1, 0) and (0, 1).

Matrix Basis Theorem

Suppose T is a transformation represented by a 2×2 matrix.

If $T(1, 0) = (x_1, y_1)$ and $T(0, 1) = (x_2, y_2)$, then T has the matrix $\begin{bmatrix} x_1 & x_2 \\ y_1 & y_2 \end{bmatrix}$.

Proof

Let M be the 2×2 matrix for T. Because $T(1, 0) = (x_1, y_1)$ and $T(0, 1) = (x_2, y_2)$,

$$M \cdot \begin{bmatrix} 1 & 0 \\ 0 & 1 \end{bmatrix} = \begin{bmatrix} x_1 & x_2 \\ y_1 & y_2 \end{bmatrix}.$$

    ↑ 1st point   ↑ 2nd point   ↑ image of 1st point   ↑ image of 2nd point

But $\begin{bmatrix} 1 & 0 \\ 0 & 1 \end{bmatrix}$ is the 2×2 identity matrix for multiplication, so $M = \begin{bmatrix} x_1 & x_2 \\ y_1 & y_2 \end{bmatrix}$.

Example 3

Use the Matrix Basis Theorem to verify that $\begin{bmatrix} -1 & 0 \\ 0 & -1 \end{bmatrix}$ represents the transformation R_{180}.

Solution

Under a 180° rotation, the image of (1, 0) is (-1, 0) and the image of (0, 1) is (0, -1). Thus, by the Matrix Basis Theorem,

$$R_{180} = \begin{bmatrix} -1 & 0 \\ 0 & -1 \end{bmatrix}.$$

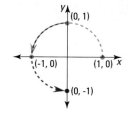

QUESTIONS

Covering the Reading

1. In the composite $r_{y=x} \circ r_x$, which reflection is done first? r_x

2. What is a single transformation for $r_{y=x} \circ r_x$? R_{90}

3. What is a matrix for R_{90}? $\begin{bmatrix} 0 & -1 \\ 1 & 0 \end{bmatrix}$

1. Let $\triangle DEF = \begin{bmatrix} 0 & 2 & 0 \\ 0 & 0 & 6 \end{bmatrix}$.

   a. Use matrices to find the image of this triangle under the transformation $r_{x=y} \circ r_y$.
   $\begin{bmatrix} 0 & 0 & 6 \\ 0 & -2 & 0 \end{bmatrix}$

   b. Describe the composite transformation. **The matrix for the composite is** $\begin{bmatrix} 0 & 1 \\ -1 & 0 \end{bmatrix}$, **which is the matrix for R_{-90}.**

2. a. Show that the square of the matrix for R_{180} is the identity matrix.
   $\begin{bmatrix} -1 & 0 \\ 0 & -1 \end{bmatrix}\begin{bmatrix} -1 & 0 \\ 0 & -1 \end{bmatrix}$
   $= \begin{bmatrix} 1 & 0 \\ 0 & 1 \end{bmatrix}$

   b. Explain why this is so. **The composite of R_{180} with itself is R_{360}, the identity transformation.**

3. Use the Matrix Basis theorem to find a matrix for the transformation $r_{x=-y}$. **Under $r_{x=-y}$, the image of (1, 0) is (0, -1) and the image of (0, 1) is (-1, 0). Thus a matrix for the transformation is** $\begin{bmatrix} 0 & -1 \\ -1 & 0 \end{bmatrix}$.

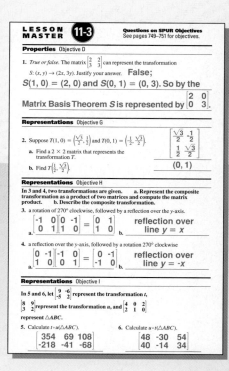

Notes on Questions

Question 6 Students can be asked to generalize the idea of this question.

Questions 9–11 Stress these questions, since the Matrix Basis Theorem is applied in Lesson 11-4.

Questions 12–15 Stress that the order in which the matrices are applied is the same as the order in which the transformations are applied, namely, right to left.

Question 17 The process here becomes quite easy for students after they have seen a few cases.

Question 22 Another way to word this question: If $\sin t = 0.8$ and $\frac{\pi}{2} \le t \le \pi$, find $\cos t$.

Additional Answers

6. a. $R_{90} \cdot R_{180} =$
$$\begin{bmatrix} 0 & -1 \\ 1 & 0 \end{bmatrix}\begin{bmatrix} -1 & 0 \\ 0 & -1 \end{bmatrix} =$$
$$\begin{bmatrix} 0 & 1 \\ -1 & 0 \end{bmatrix} = R_{270}$$

b. No, the order does not matter. A rotation of 270° can be considered as a rotation of 180° followed by a rotation of 90°, or vice versa.

7. a.

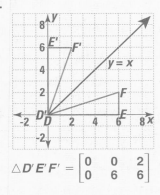

$$\triangle D'E'F' = \begin{bmatrix} 0 & 0 & 2 \\ 0 & 6 & 6 \end{bmatrix}$$

4a) $\triangle A'B'C' = \begin{bmatrix} 2 & 6 & 6 \\ -1 & -1 & -3 \end{bmatrix}$

$\triangle A''B''C'' = \begin{bmatrix} -2 & -6 & -6 \\ -1 & -1 & -3 \end{bmatrix}$

c) $\begin{bmatrix} -1 & 0 \\ 0 & -1 \end{bmatrix}$

9a) $R_{-90}\,(1, 0) = (0, -1)$
b) $R_{-90}\,(0, 1) = (1, 0)$
c) $\begin{bmatrix} 0 & 1 \\ -1 & 0 \end{bmatrix}$

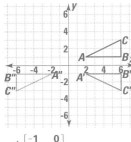

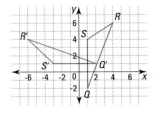

Which Way is Up?
This photograph of beach bungalows in Bali, Indonesia, has been rotated 90°. Which side is the preimage?

10a) $r_{x=-y}\,(1, 0) = (0, -1)$
b) $r_{x=-y}\,(0, 1) = (-1, 0)$
c) $\begin{bmatrix} 0 & -1 \\ -1 & 0 \end{bmatrix}$

11a) $S_{4, 3}\,(1, 0) = (4, 0)$
b) $S_{4, 3}\,(0, 1) = (0, 3)$
c) $\begin{bmatrix} 4 & 0 \\ 0 & 3 \end{bmatrix}$

---

4. Refer to Example 1.
  a. Reflect $\triangle ABC$ over the x-axis. Then reflect its image $\triangle A'B'C'$ over the y-axis to get a second image $\triangle A''B''C''$. **See left.**
  b. What transformation can take you directly from $\triangle ABC$ to $\triangle A''B''C''$? R_{180}
  c. The composite $r_y \circ r_x$ is represented by $\begin{bmatrix} -1 & 0 \\ 0 & 1 \end{bmatrix} \cdot \begin{bmatrix} 1 & 0 \\ 0 & -1 \end{bmatrix}$. Find this product. **See left.**
  d. What transformation is represented by the product in part **c**? R_{180}

5. Refer to the figures graphed at the right.
  a. What transformation you have studied maps $\triangle RQS$ to $\triangle R'Q'S'$? R_{90}
  b. Write a matrix for that transformation.
  $$\begin{bmatrix} 0 & -1 \\ 1 & 0 \end{bmatrix}$$

6. a. Derive the matrix for R_{270} by multiplying matrices for R_{90} and R_{180}.
  b. Does the order in which you multiply the matrices matter? Why or why not?
  a, b, see margin.

7. Let $\triangle DEF$ be represented by the matrix $\begin{bmatrix} 0 & 6 & 6 \\ 0 & 0 & 2 \end{bmatrix}$. **See margin.**
  a. Find the reflection image of $\triangle DEF$ over the line with equation $y = x$.
  b. Transform the image in part **a** by the scale change $S_{2, 0.6}$.
  c. Give a matrix for the composite $S_{2, 0.6} \circ r_{y=x}$.

8. Solve for a, b, c, and d. $\begin{bmatrix} a & b \\ c & d \end{bmatrix} \cdot \begin{bmatrix} 1 & 0 \\ 0 & 1 \end{bmatrix} = \begin{bmatrix} w & x \\ y & z \end{bmatrix}$ $a = w, b = x,$ $c = y, d = z$

In 9–11, a transformation is given. **a.** Find the image of $(1, 0)$ under the transformation. **b.** Find the image of $(0, 1)$ under the transformation. **c.** Find the 2×2 matrix for the transformation derived from the Matrix Basis Theorem.

9. R_{-90} **10.** $r_{x=-y}$ **11.** $S_{4, 3}$
   See above left.   See left.   See left.

Applying the Mathematics

In 12 and 13, a transformation t has matrix $\begin{bmatrix} 2 & 5 \\ 1 & 3 \end{bmatrix}$ and a transformation u has matrix $\begin{bmatrix} 4 & 2 \\ -1 & 3 \end{bmatrix}$. Let $\triangle ABC$ be represented by $\begin{bmatrix} 8 & 3 & 2 \\ -2 & 0 & -5 \end{bmatrix}$. Calculate and graph $\triangle ABC$ and the indicated image. **See margin.**

12. $t \circ u\,(\triangle ABC)$

13. $u \circ t\,(\triangle ABC)$ **14)** $R_{90} \circ R_{270} = \begin{bmatrix} 0 & -1 \\ 1 & 0 \end{bmatrix}\begin{bmatrix} 0 & 1 \\ -1 & 0 \end{bmatrix} = \begin{bmatrix} 1 & 0 \\ 0 & 1 \end{bmatrix}$

14. Use matrices to verify that $R_{90} \circ R_{270}$ is the identity transformation. **See above.**

15. a. Calculate a matrix for $r_x \circ r_{y=x}$. **See below.**
  b. Describe the composite transformation. R_{270}

  a) $r_x \circ r_{y=x} = \begin{bmatrix} 1 & 0 \\ 0 & -1 \end{bmatrix}\begin{bmatrix} 0 & 1 \\ 1 & 0 \end{bmatrix} = \begin{bmatrix} 0 & 1 \\ -1 & 0 \end{bmatrix}$

---

7. b.

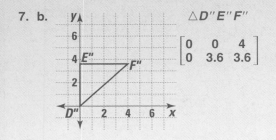

$\triangle D''E''F''$
$$\begin{bmatrix} 0 & 0 & 4 \\ 0 & 3.6 & 3.6 \end{bmatrix}$$

c. $\begin{bmatrix} 0 & 2 \\ 0.6 & 0 \end{bmatrix}$

12.

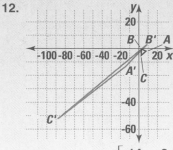

$$t \circ u\,(\triangle ABC) = \begin{bmatrix} -14 & 9 & -89 \\ -14 & 3 & -53 \end{bmatrix}$$

13.

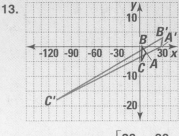

$$u \circ t\,(\triangle ABC) = \begin{bmatrix} 28 & 30 & -110 \\ 0 & 3 & -18 \end{bmatrix}$$

16a) R_{90} (3, 4) = (-4, 3);
R_{180} (3, 4) = (-3, -4);
R_{270} (3, 4) = (4, -3)
b)
R_{90} (3, 4) = (-4, 3)

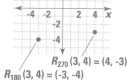

R_{270} (3, 4) = (4, -3)
R_{180} (3, 4) = (-3, -4)

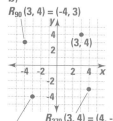

16. a. Find the image of (3, 4) under each of R_{90}, R_{180}, and R_{270}. **See left.**
  b. Graph (3, 4) and its three images. **See left.**
  c. The four points are vertices of what kind of polygon? **a square**
  d. Find the center and radius of a circle that passes through these four points. **center: (0, 0), radius = 5**

17. Find a 2 × 2 matrix for T if $T(x, y) = (3x - y, x + y)$. $\begin{bmatrix} 3 & -1 \\ 1 & 1 \end{bmatrix}$

Review

18. Write a matrix for the size change of magnitude 6. *(Lesson 11-2)* $\begin{bmatrix} 6 & 0 \\ 0 & 6 \end{bmatrix}$

19. Find x and y so that the following is true. *(Lesson 11-1)* $x = -2, y = 7$

$$\begin{bmatrix} 1 & -1 \\ x & 3 \end{bmatrix} \cdot \begin{bmatrix} 2 & y \\ 0 & 1 \end{bmatrix} = \begin{bmatrix} 2 & 6 \\ -4 & -11 \end{bmatrix}$$

20. A child's swing is mounted 12 ft off the ground. If the ropes supporting the swing are 10'6" long, and the swing rotates through a vertical angle of 40°, as shown at the left, how high off the ground is the bottom of the swing in the position shown? *(Lesson 5-1)* $12 - 10.5 \cos 40° \approx 4$ ft

10'6"
40°
12 ft

21. *Multiple choice.* The point (1, 0) is rotated 30° counterclockwise around the origin. Which statement is false? *(Lessons 4-2, 4-3, 4-5)* **d**
  (a) Its image is (cos 30°, sin 30°).
  (b) Its image is $\left(\frac{\sqrt{3}}{2}, \frac{1}{2}\right)$.
  (c) The arc length from (1, 0) to the image is $\frac{\pi}{6}$.
  (d) The arc length from (1, 0) to the image is tan 30°.

22. The point $(x, 0.8)$ is in the second quadrant and on the unit circle. Find x. *(Lesson 4-3)* $x = -0.6$

23a, b)
$y = \cos 2\theta$ $y = 2\cos \theta$

23. a. Graph $f(\theta) = 2 \cos \theta$. **See left.**
  b. On the same set of axes, graph $g(\theta) = \cos 2\theta$. **See left.**
  c. Identify a scale change S which maps the graph of f onto the graph of g. *(Lessons 3-5, 4-7)* $S:(x, y) \to \left(\frac{x}{2}, \frac{y}{2}\right)$

In 24 and 25, simplify. *(Previous course)*

24. $\frac{\sqrt{2}}{2}\left(-\frac{\sqrt{2}}{2}\right)$ $-\frac{1}{2}$

25. $\frac{3}{2} \cdot \frac{\sqrt{3}}{2} + \frac{\sqrt{3}}{2}$ $\frac{5\sqrt{3}}{4}$

Exploration

26. Write a Matrix Basis Theorem for three dimensions. Verify your theorem with an example.
See margin.

Practice
For more questions on SPUR Objectives, use **Lesson Master 11-3** (shown on page 713).

Assessment
Quiz A quiz covering Lessons 11-1 through 11-3 is provided in the *Assessment Sourcebook.*

Extension
Project Update Project 1, *Programming 2-D Graphics,* and Project 4, *Matrix Codes,* on pages 745–746, relate to the content of this lesson.

26. Sample: Suppose t is a transformation represented by a 3 × 3 matrix. If $t(1, 0, 0) = (x_1, y_1, z_1)$, $t(0, 1, 0) = (x_2, y_2, z_2)$, and $t(0, 0, 1) = (x_3, y_3, z_3)$, then t has the matrix $\begin{bmatrix} x_1 & x_2 & x_3 \\ y_1 & y_2 & y_3 \\ z_1 & z_2 & z_3 \end{bmatrix}$.

Example: Let t be the reflection over the *xy*-plane; that is $t(x, y, z) = (x, y, -z)$ for all points (x, y, z).

Then $t(1, 0, 0) = (1, 0, 0)$, $t(0, 1, 0) = (0, 1, 0)$, and $t(0, 0, 1) = (0, 0, -1)$.

The matrix of t is $\begin{bmatrix} 1 & 0 & 0 \\ 0 & 1 & 0 \\ 0 & 0 & -1 \end{bmatrix}$.

To verify that this represents t, compute the product

$$\begin{bmatrix} 1 & 0 & 0 \\ 0 & 1 & 0 \\ 0 & 0 & -1 \end{bmatrix}\begin{bmatrix} x \\ y \\ z \end{bmatrix} = \begin{bmatrix} x \\ y \\ -z \end{bmatrix}.$$

Setting Up Lesson 11-4
You might use **Question 21** as a lead-in to Lesson 11-4. You could say: "You know the image of (1, 0) under R_{30}. Now the question is: How can you find the image of all other points under this transformation? Read the next lesson to find out."

You have seen that size changes with center at (0, 0), scale changes, reflections over the *x*- and *y*-axes and the line *y* = *x*, rotations of 90°, 180°, and 270°, and several other transformations can all be represented by 2 × 2 matrices. For what other transformations do 2 × 2 matrices exist?

Finding the Matrix for R_θ

Perhaps surprisingly, all rotations around (0, 0) can be represented by 2 × 2 matrices. To develop a general rotation matrix requires only the Matrix Basis Theorem and a little trigonometry.

Let θ be the magnitude of a rotation around the origin. In this discussion, we assume θ is in degrees. First, note that composition of rotations with the same center is commutative, so $R_\theta \circ R_{90} = R_{90} \circ R_\theta$.

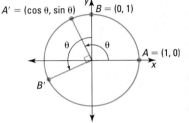

Consider the images *A'* and *B'* of the points *A* = (1, 0) and *B* = (0, 1) under R_θ. By definition of the cosine and sine, $A' = R_\theta(1, 0) = (\cos\theta, \sin\theta)$. Since $B' = R_{90}(B)$ and $B = R_{90}(A)$, then $B' = (R_\theta \circ R_{90})(A) = (R_{90} \circ R_\theta)(A) = R_{90}(A')$. Thus, if $B' = (x, y)$, then

$$\begin{bmatrix} x \\ y \end{bmatrix} = \begin{bmatrix} 0 & -1 \\ 1 & 0 \end{bmatrix} \cdot \begin{bmatrix} \cos\theta \\ \sin\theta \end{bmatrix} = \begin{bmatrix} -\sin\theta \\ \cos\theta \end{bmatrix}.$$

$$B' \quad = \quad R_{90} \quad \cdot \quad A'$$

Thus, $R_\theta(0, 1) = (-\sin\theta, \cos\theta)$.

From the images of (1, 0) and (0, 1) and the Matrix Basis Theorem, the matrix for R_θ follows.

Rotation Matrix Theorem
The matrix for R_θ, the rotation of magnitude θ about the origin, is

$$\begin{bmatrix} \cos\theta & -\sin\theta \\ \sin\theta & \cos\theta \end{bmatrix}.$$

Proof
The first column is $R_\theta(1, 0)$. The second column is $R_\theta(0, 1)$.

Lesson 11-4 Overview

Broad Goals In this lesson, we assume that there is a 2 × 2 matrix for R_θ, the rotation of magnitude θ about the origin. From this assumption and the theorem of the previous lesson, the matrix
$$\begin{bmatrix} \cos\theta & -\sin\theta \\ \sin\theta & \cos\theta \end{bmatrix}$$ for R_θ is derived and applied.

Perspective At this point, students have seen matrices for transformations for which

they already knew formulas. It is natural for students to wonder at this point which transformations have 2 × 2 matrices. The answer: any transformation of the plane that maps the origin to itself and maps lines onto lines.

The derivation of the Rotation Matrix Theorem is quite simple: the first column is the image of (1, 0) under this rotation (from the definition of cosine and sine).

The second column is shown to be the image of the first under a rotation of 90°.

Because most people do not have as good intuition for rotations as they have for reflections, if you have technology that can do rotations, this is an appropriate time to use it.

In the Questions you are asked to verify that the matrices for R_{90}, R_{180}, and R_{270} are special cases of this theorem.

Example 1

Find a 2×2 rotation matrix for R_{30}.

Solution

Use the Rotation Matrix Theorem.

$$R_{30} = \begin{bmatrix} \cos 30° & -\sin 30° \\ \sin 30° & \cos 30° \end{bmatrix} = \begin{bmatrix} \frac{\sqrt{3}}{2} & -\frac{1}{2} \\ \frac{1}{2} & \frac{\sqrt{3}}{2} \end{bmatrix}$$

Check

Triangle ABC below is represented by $\begin{bmatrix} 1 & 2 & 2 \\ 3 & 3 & 6 \end{bmatrix}$. Its image, $\triangle A'B'C'$, is represented by the product

$$\begin{bmatrix} \frac{\sqrt{3}}{2} & -\frac{1}{2} \\ \frac{1}{2} & \frac{\sqrt{3}}{2} \end{bmatrix} \cdot \begin{bmatrix} 1 & 2 & 2 \\ 3 & 3 & 6 \end{bmatrix} = \begin{bmatrix} \frac{\sqrt{3}}{2} - \frac{3}{2} & \sqrt{3} - \frac{3}{2} & \sqrt{3} - 3 \\ \frac{1}{2} + \frac{3\sqrt{3}}{2} & 1 + \frac{3\sqrt{3}}{2} & 1 + 3\sqrt{3} \end{bmatrix}$$

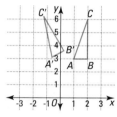

You are asked to verify that $AO = A'O$ and m $\angle AOA' = 30°$ in the Questions.

Computer animators use matrices to produce rotation images. Points are identified as ordered pairs on a coordinate grid. To rotate a set of points around the origin, a matrix for the points is multiplied by a matrix for the rotation.

An Application to Animation

Example 2

In a computer game, the wheel at the right (pictured on a coordinate grid) spins counterclockwise around the origin at the rate of π radians per second. The T (in the word TO) has endpoints at (1.7, 4.8), (1.8, 8), and (4, 7). Approximate the coordinates of the endpoints of T if someone playing the game hits a key to stop the wheel in 5.43 seconds.

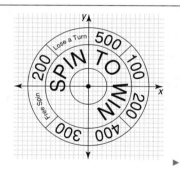

▶

Lesson 11-4 *The General Rotation Matrix* **717**

Notes on Reading

The proof of the Rotation Matrix Theorem is important because understanding it will save time in the next lesson. **Teaching Aid 101** can be used for discussing the theorem.

In **Example 1,** we use the equal sign between a name for a transformation and its matrix. Again the idea is that these are two names for the same transformation, not that they are the same object.

Example 2 shows how computers can simulate a spinning wheel.

Optional Activities
Technology Connection
Materials: Explorations software

Students may use *Exploration 11-4, The General Rotation Matrix*, as an alternative to **Example 1.** Students can investigate the numerical and graphical results when the general rotation matrix is multiplied by a 2×3 matrix representing a triangle. The computer will display the numerical and graphical results of the multiplied matrices.

Adapting to Individual Needs
Extra Help
Some students may be unsure about a matrix for a transformation. Remind them that a specific example, like that in the Check for **Example 1**, can be very helpful. For this check, you might use 0.866 as an approximation to $\frac{\sqrt{3}}{2}$ and have students graph the points.

Additional Examples

1. **a.** Give a matrix for R_{-45}.

$$\begin{bmatrix} \frac{\sqrt{2}}{2} & \frac{\sqrt{2}}{2} \\ -\frac{\sqrt{2}}{2} & \frac{\sqrt{2}}{2} \end{bmatrix}$$

   b. Check the answer by multiplying that matrix by the matrix for R_{45}. The product of the matrices is $\begin{bmatrix} 1 & 0 \\ 0 & 1 \end{bmatrix}$, the matrix for R_0, the identify.

2. In the computer game of **Example 2** of the lesson, what are the coordinates of the endpoints of the letter T if the wheel is stopped after 1.2 seconds?

$$\begin{bmatrix} \cos 1.2\pi & -\sin 1.2\pi \\ \sin 1.2\pi & \cos 1.2\pi \end{bmatrix}$$

$$\begin{bmatrix} 1.7 & 1.8 & 4.0 \\ 4.8 & 8.0 & 7.0 \end{bmatrix}$$

$$\begin{bmatrix} 1.4 & 3.2 & 0.9 \\ -4.9 & -7.5 & -8.0 \end{bmatrix}$$

Notes on Questions

Question 12 The vertices are the graphs of the fifth roots of the complex number $100,000i$. Students will see other examples of this type in Lesson 13-8.

Question 13b You might ask students if this part could have been done without **part a**. [Yes.] How? [By substituting -90° for θ in the general rotation matrix.]

(Notes on Questions continue on page 720.)

---

1) $\begin{bmatrix} \cos t & -\sin t \\ \sin t & \cos t \end{bmatrix}$

2a) $\begin{bmatrix} \frac{\sqrt{2}}{2} & -\frac{\sqrt{2}}{2} \\ \frac{\sqrt{2}}{2} & \frac{\sqrt{2}}{2} \end{bmatrix}$

b) $\begin{bmatrix} \frac{\sqrt{2}}{2} & -\frac{\sqrt{2}}{2} \\ \frac{\sqrt{2}}{2} & \frac{\sqrt{2}}{2} \end{bmatrix}\begin{bmatrix} 1 & 2 & 2 \\ 3 & 3 & 6 \end{bmatrix} =$

$\begin{bmatrix} -\sqrt{2} & -\frac{\sqrt{2}}{2} & -2\sqrt{2} \\ 2\sqrt{2} & \frac{5\sqrt{2}}{2} & 4\sqrt{2} \end{bmatrix}$

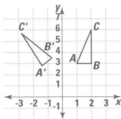

3) $\begin{bmatrix} 0.891 & -0.454 \\ 0.454 & 0.891 \end{bmatrix}$

4) $\begin{bmatrix} 0.978 & 0.208 \\ -0.208 & 0.978 \end{bmatrix}$

5) $R_{90} = \begin{bmatrix} \cos 90° & -\sin 90° \\ \sin 90° & \cos 90° \end{bmatrix}$
$= \begin{bmatrix} 0 & -1 \\ 1 & 0 \end{bmatrix}$

6) $R_{180} = \begin{bmatrix} \cos 180° & -\sin 180° \\ \sin 180° & \cos 180° \end{bmatrix}$
$= \begin{bmatrix} -1 & 0 \\ 0 & -1 \end{bmatrix}$

7) $R_{270} =$
$\begin{bmatrix} \cos 270° & -\sin 270° \\ \sin 270° & \cos 270° \end{bmatrix}$
$= \begin{bmatrix} 0 & 1 \\ -1 & 0 \end{bmatrix}$

718

Solution

Here we consider everything in radians. In 5.43 seconds, the wheel covers 5.43π radians. As any multiple of 2π revolutions preserves the image, it is the last 1.43π of a revolution that should be considered.

The matrix for $R_{1.43\pi}$ is

$$\begin{bmatrix} \cos 1.43\pi & -\sin 1.43\pi \\ \sin 1.43\pi & \cos 1.43\pi \end{bmatrix} \approx \begin{bmatrix} -.218 & .976 \\ -.976 & -.218 \end{bmatrix}$$

Multiply the matrix for the preimage by this matrix.

$$\begin{bmatrix} -.218 & .976 \\ -.976 & -.218 \end{bmatrix} \cdot \begin{bmatrix} 1.7 & 1.8 & 4 \\ 4.8 & 8 & 7 \end{bmatrix} = \begin{bmatrix} 4.3 & 7.4 & 6.0 \\ -2.7 & -3.5 & -5.4 \end{bmatrix}$$

Thus, the coordinates of the endpoints of T in its new position are (4.3, -2.7), (7.4, -3.5), and (6.0, -5.4).

Check

1.43π radians is about $\frac{7}{10}$ of a full revolution, or about 260°. The image is shown at the right.

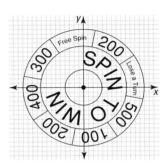

QUESTIONS

Covering the Reading

1. What is the matrix for R_t, the rotation of magnitude t about the origin? **See left.**
2. **a.** Give the 2×2 matrix for R_{45}. **See left.**
   b. Check your result by multiplying the matrix for the triangle in Example 1 by the matrix for R_{45}, and plotting the preimage and image on the same set of axes. **See left.**
3. If $\sin 27° \approx 0.454$ and $\cos 27° \approx 0.891$, what is an approximate matrix for R_{27}? **See left.**
4. If $\sin (-12°) \approx -0.208$ and $\cos (-12°) \approx 0.978$, what is an approximate matrix for R_{-12}? **See left.**

In 5–7, verify the Rotation Matrix Theorem for these special cases. **See left.**

5. R_{90} 6. R_{180} 7. R_{270}

8. For Example 1, verify the following. **See margin.**
   a. $AO = A'O$ **b.** $m\angle AOA' = 30°$

Additional Answers

8. **a.** $A = (1, 3)$; $A' = \left(\frac{\sqrt{3}}{2} - \frac{3}{2}, \frac{1}{2} + \frac{3\sqrt{3}}{2}\right)$; $AO = \sqrt{(1-0)^2 + (3-0)^2} = \sqrt{1+9} = \sqrt{10}$;

$A'O = \sqrt{\left(\frac{\sqrt{3}}{2} - \frac{3}{2} - 0\right)^2 + \left(\frac{1}{2} + \frac{3\sqrt{3}}{2} - 0\right)^2} = \sqrt{\frac{12 - 6\sqrt{3} + 28 + 6\sqrt{3}}{4}} = \sqrt{\frac{40}{4}} = \sqrt{10}$.

Therefore $AO = A'O$.

b. Let P be a point on the positive y-axis. Then $\tan \angle AOP = \frac{1}{3}$; so $\angle AOP = \tan^{-1}\left(\frac{1}{3}\right) \approx 18.435°$.

$\tan \angle A'OP = \frac{\left|\frac{\sqrt{3}}{2} - \frac{3}{2}\right|}{\frac{1}{2} + \frac{3\sqrt{3}}{2}} \approx .2046$, so $\angle A'OP \approx 11.565°$.

$\angle AOA' = \angle AOP + \angle A'OP = 18.435° + 11.565° = 30°$.

10a) $R_{60} = \begin{bmatrix} \cos 60° & -\sin 60° \\ \sin 60° & \cos 60° \end{bmatrix}$

$= \begin{bmatrix} \frac{1}{2} & -\frac{\sqrt{3}}{2} \\ \frac{\sqrt{3}}{2} & \frac{1}{2} \end{bmatrix}$

b) $(R_{60})^3 = \left(\begin{bmatrix} \frac{1}{2} & -\frac{\sqrt{3}}{2} \\ \frac{\sqrt{3}}{2} & \frac{1}{2} \end{bmatrix} \cdot \right.$

$\begin{bmatrix} \frac{1}{2} & -\frac{\sqrt{3}}{2} \\ \frac{\sqrt{3}}{2} & \frac{1}{2} \end{bmatrix} =$

$\begin{bmatrix} \frac{1}{2} & -\frac{\sqrt{3}}{2} \\ \frac{\sqrt{3}}{2} & \frac{1}{2} \end{bmatrix}$

$\begin{bmatrix} -\frac{1}{2} & -\frac{\sqrt{3}}{2} \\ \frac{\sqrt{3}}{2} & -\frac{1}{2} \end{bmatrix} \cdot$

$\begin{bmatrix} \frac{1}{2} & -\frac{\sqrt{3}}{2} \\ \frac{\sqrt{3}}{2} & \frac{1}{2} \end{bmatrix} =$

$\begin{bmatrix} -1 & 0 \\ 0 & -1 \end{bmatrix} = R_{180}$

11a) $\begin{bmatrix} 0 & -4\sqrt{3} & -2\sqrt{3} \\ 0 & -4 & -6 \end{bmatrix}$

b)

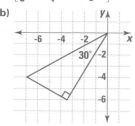

13a) A clockwise rotation of θ is equivalent to a counterclockwise rotation of −θ. So $R_{-\theta}$

$= \begin{bmatrix} \cos(-\theta) & -\sin(-\theta) \\ \sin(-\theta) & \cos(-\theta) \end{bmatrix}$

$= \begin{bmatrix} \cos\theta & \sin\theta \\ -\sin\theta & \cos\theta \end{bmatrix}$.

---

9. Refer to Example 2. The endpoints of the I in "SPIN" are given by the matrix $\begin{bmatrix} -4.2 & -6.8 \\ 3.4 & 5 \end{bmatrix}$. Approximate the coordinates of the I after it is turned 3.2π radians counterclockwise. $\begin{bmatrix} 5.4 & 8.4 \\ -0.28 & -0.05 \end{bmatrix}$

Applying the Mathematics

10. a. Use the Rotation Matrix Theorem to find a matrix for R_{60}. **See left.**
   b. Verify your result in part **a** by showing that the cube of the matrix for R_{60} is the matrix for R_{180}. **See left.**

11. The 30°-60°-90° triangle shown at the right may be represented by the matrix $\begin{bmatrix} 0 & 8 & 6 \\ 0 & 0 & 2\sqrt{3} \end{bmatrix}$.
   a. Find a matrix for its image under R_{210}. (Use exact values.) **See left.**
   b. Graph the image. **See left.**

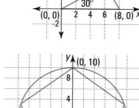

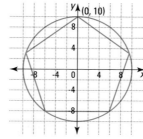

12. A student is designing a club logo to be produced on a computer screen. The outline is a regular pentagon inscribed in a circle with radius 10. One vertex is at (0, 10). Find (to the nearest thousandth) the coordinates of the other vertices.
(−9.511, 3.090); (−5.878, −8.090); (5.878, −8.090); (9.511, 3.090)

13. a. Show that a matrix for $R_{-\theta}$, a clockwise rotation of θ around the origin, is $\begin{bmatrix} \cos\theta & \sin\theta \\ -\sin\theta & \cos\theta \end{bmatrix}$. **See left.**
   b. Use part **a** to determine the matrix for a clockwise rotation of 90° around the origin. $\begin{bmatrix} \cos 90° & \sin 90° \\ -\sin 90° & \cos 90° \end{bmatrix} = \begin{bmatrix} 0 & 1 \\ -1 & 0 \end{bmatrix}$

Review

14. Use the Matrix Basis Theorem to determine the matrix for the reflection over the line $y = -x$. *(Lesson 11-3)* $\begin{bmatrix} 0 & -1 \\ -1 & 0 \end{bmatrix}$

15. Is the given transformation the identity transformation; that is, does it map a figure to itself? *(Lesson 11-2)*
   a. rotation of 360° **Yes**   **b.** reflection over the y-axis **No**
   c. size change of magnitude 1 **Yes**   **d.** size change of magnitude −1 **No**

16. For a standard normal distribution, find each of the following. *(Lesson 10-5)*
   a. the mean **0**   **b.** the standard deviation **1**
   c. the area between the curve and the x-axis **1**

Practice
For more questions on SPUR Objectives, use **Lesson Master 11-4** (shown below).

Assessment
Written Communication Give students a problem like **Question 3**. After students solve the problem, have them check their result using the method given in **Question 2b**. [Students represent a rotation by a matrix and use the matrix to find the rotation image of a triangle.]

(Follow-up continues on page 720.)

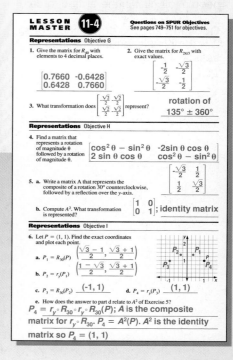

Adapting to Individual Needs
Challenge
Find the image of (7, 3) under a rotation of magnitude $\frac{\pi}{3}$ about the point (-2, 0).
[This rotation is the composite of the translation 2 units to the right, the rotation of magnitude $\frac{\pi}{3}$ about the origin, and the translation 2 units to the left. The image is $(2.5 - 1.5\sqrt{3}, 1.5 + 4.5\sqrt{3})$]

720

Extension

Refer students to **Question 12**. Suppose the logo is a regular hexagon instead of a regular pentagon, with a vertex at (0, 10). Have students find the *exact* coordinates of the other vertices. [(-5√3, 5); (-5√3, -5); (0, -10); (5√3, -5); (5√3, 5)] Have students find the exact coordinates of the other vertices of the logo if it is a regular octagon with a vertex at (0, 10). [(-5√2, 5√2); (-10, 0); (-5√2, -5√2); (0, -10); (5√2, -5√2); (10, 0); (5√2, 5√2)]

Project Update Project 1, *Programming 2-D Graphics*, and Project 4, *Matrix Codes*, on pages 745–746, relate to the content of this lesson.

Notes on Questions

Questions 19–20 Point out that, although these formulas are incorrect, there are general formulas for cos (α + β) and sin (2β) and that students will learn these in the next two lessons.

Question 25 Art Connection The first advertising posters appeared in the 1870s. Numerous artists, such as Pablo Picasso and Toulouse Lautrec, elevated poster design to an art form. Perhaps the most famous United States poster produced in the United States is the picture of Uncle Sam pointing his finger, with the caption "I want you." The purpose of this poster was to encourage young people to enlist in the armed forces.

Question 26 The determinant of a 2 × 2 matrix is formally defined in Lesson 11-7.

17b) There is not a unique cubic function through three points. **Sample:** Using (0, 0) as a fourth point, the function containing these four points is

$$y = \frac{1}{3}x^3 + 2x^2 - \frac{7}{3}x.$$

18b) **Sample:** The parent sine curve contains the point $\left(\frac{\pi}{4}, \frac{\sqrt{2}}{2}\right)$. Under the transformation $(x, y) \rightarrow \left(x + \frac{\pi}{4}, 3y\right)$, the preimage is mapped onto $\left(\frac{\pi}{2}, \frac{3\sqrt{2}}{2}\right)$.

Many people collect posters such as this classic.

---

17. Consider the points (1, 0), (-1, 4), and (-3, 16). *(Lessons 2-6, 9-2, 9-3)*
   a. Find an equation for the quadratic function that passes through these points. $y = x^2 - 2x + 1$
   b. Find an equation for a cubic function that passes through these points. See left.

18. a. Determine an equation for a sine curve *s* which has an amplitude of 3 and a phase shift of $\frac{\pi}{4}$ from the parent sine curve. $y = 3 \sin\left(x - \frac{\pi}{4}\right)$
   b. Explain why the point $\left(\frac{\pi}{2}, \frac{3\sqrt{2}}{2}\right)$ should be on *s*. *(Lesson 4-8)* See left.

In 19–21, *true or false*. *(Lessons 4-4, 4-5, 5-1)*

19. cos (30° + 60°) = cos 30° + cos 60°. **False**

20. sin 90° = 2 sin 45°. **False**

21. $\cos\frac{\pi}{3} + \sin\frac{\pi}{3} = 1$. **False**

In 22–24, *multiple choice*. For the graph of the given data set, determine which of the following best describes the correlation coefficient *r* of the line of best fit.
   (a) strongly positive   (b) strongly negative
   (c) approximately zero   *(Lesson 2-2)*

22. c 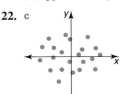   **23.** a 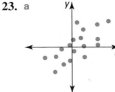   **24.** b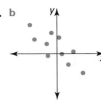

25. Suppose a print shop states that it costs $65 to print 500 posters and $125 to print 1000 posters. Assume that the cost *c* is linearly related to the number *n* of copies made.
   a. Find an equation relating *c* to *n*. $c = 0.12n + 5$
   b. How much should the print shop charge to print 2000 posters? *(Lesson 2-2)* $245

Exploration

26. The *determinant* of the matrix $M = \begin{bmatrix} a & b \\ c & d \end{bmatrix}$ is $ad - bc$. Apply the matrix *M* to the square $S = \begin{bmatrix} 0 & 1 & 1 & 0 \\ 0 & 0 & 1 & 1 \end{bmatrix}$. How is the area of the figure *MS* related to the determinant of *M*?

$M \cdot S = \begin{bmatrix} 0 & a & a+b & b \\ 0 & c & c+d & d \end{bmatrix}$

The figure represented by the matrix *MS* is a parallelogram whose area is equal to the absolute value of the determinant of *M*.

Setting Up Lesson 11-5
Note that although the statement in **Question 19** is false, a formula for cos (α + β) will be derived in the next lesson. Be sure that students remember how α and β are read (alpha and beta).

Formulas for $\cos\ (\alpha + \beta)$ *and* $\sin\ (\alpha + \beta)$

Image Rotation. *Images created by a CAD/CAM program can be rotated on screen to simulate the movements of parts of the car or passengers. Engineers use this in designing automobiles and their safety features.*

The Point ($\cos\ (\alpha + \beta)$, $\sin\ (\alpha + \beta)$)

Suppose that a computer animator wishes to rotate the point $P = (\cos \alpha, \sin \alpha)$ counterclockwise $\beta°$ around the origin. The image of P will be Q, where $Q = R_{\alpha + \beta}(1, 0)$. Thus, $Q = (\cos\ (\alpha + \beta), \sin\ (\alpha + \beta))$, as illustrated here.

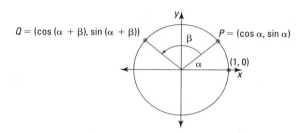

As you know, in general, $\cos\ (\alpha + \beta) \neq \cos \alpha + \cos \beta$ and $\sin\ (\alpha + \beta) \neq \sin \alpha + \sin \beta$. For instance, when $\alpha = 45°$ and $\beta = 30°$,

$$\sin\ (45° + 30°) = \sin 75° \quad \text{but} \quad \sin 45° + \sin 30° \approx 0.707 + 0.5$$
$$\approx 0.966 \qquad\qquad = 1.207.$$

Still, the coordinates of Q can be stated in terms of cosines and sines of α and β. Formulas for these coordinates can be found by using rotation matrices to compute $(R_\alpha \circ R_\beta)\ (1, 0)$.

Lesson 11-5

Objectives

E Apply the Addition Formulas for the Cosine and Sine.

Resources

From the **Teacher's Resource File**
■ Lesson Master 11-5
■ Answer Master 11-5
■ Teaching Aid 96: Warm-up

Additional Resources
■ Visual for Teaching Aid 96

Teaching Lesson 11-5

Warm-up

In 1–6, let $x = -\frac{\pi}{4}$ and let $y = \frac{3\pi}{2}$.
Give the value of:
1. $\cos x$ $\frac{\sqrt{2}}{2}$
2. $\sin x$ $-\frac{\sqrt{2}}{2}$
3. $\cos y$ **0**
4. $\sin y$ **-1**
5. $\cos\ (x + y)$ $-\frac{\sqrt{2}}{2}$
6. $\sin\ (x + y)$ $-\frac{\sqrt{2}}{2}$

These values can be used to confirm the Addition Formulas for the Cosine and Sine.

Lesson 11-5 Overview

Broad Goals This brief lesson develops the Addition Formulas for the Cosine and Sine and applies them to deduce Subtraction Formulas, some other theorems students have seen before, and new exact values of these functions.

Perspective The image of (1, 0) under the rotation R_β is ($\cos \beta$, $\sin \beta$). The image of that point under R_α is ($\cos\ (\alpha + \beta)$, $\sin\ (\alpha + \beta)$). When this is done with

matrices, we simply multiply:
$\begin{bmatrix} \cos \alpha & -\sin \alpha \\ \sin \alpha & \cos \alpha \end{bmatrix} \begin{bmatrix} \cos \beta \\ \sin \beta \end{bmatrix}$. This gives the familiar formulas for $\cos\ (\alpha + \beta)$ and $\sin\ (\alpha + \beta)$ both in one line.

This derivation seems to have been discovered in the first decade of this century. The "wrapping function" approach found in some textbooks is newer, having

been invented in the 1940s. In the wrapping function approach $\cos\ (\alpha - \beta)$ is found by equating distances, and $\cos\ (\alpha + \beta)$ is found, then $\sin\ (\alpha - \beta)$ is found by using the identity $\sin x = \cos\left(\frac{\pi}{2} - x\right)$. In *Precalculus and Discrete Mathematics* we combine the transformation definitions of cosine and sine with the equating of distances.

Notes on Reading

The approach found in many books to find a formula for cos $(x - y)$, using the unit circle and equating distances between points, is so long that students do not have to be convinced of the importance of the identity. Here the proof is so short that you may need to point out why these identities are important. Three reasons are found in the examples in this lesson. **Example 1** shows how to find some new exact values of sines and cosines. **Example 2** shows how new identities can be deduced. **Example 3** shows that some old identities are merely special cases of the Addition Identities.

Encourage your students to learn the Addition Identities and then change the sign for the Subtraction Identities.

Example 3 proves the Supplements Theorem for the sine function, and students are asked to prove the corresponding theorem for cosine in **Question 8. Question 9** asks for a proof of the Complements Theorem for cosine, and a proof of the corresponding theorem for sine is a good example for class discussion (see Additional Example 3).

cos (84° + 17°) =
cos 84° cos 17° −
sin 84° sin 17°;
cos 101° = -0.1908;
cos 84° cos 17° −
sin 84° sin 17° =
(0.1045)(0.9563) −
(0.9945)(0.2924) =
0.09996 − 0.29077 =
-0.1908

Theorem (Addition Formulas for the Cosine and Sine)
For all real numbers α and β,

$$\cos (\alpha + \beta) = \cos \alpha \cos \beta - \sin \alpha \sin \beta$$
$$\sin (\alpha + \beta) = \sin \alpha \cos \beta + \cos \alpha \sin \beta.$$

Proof
By definition of the sine and cosine functions,

$$(\cos (\alpha + \beta), \sin (\alpha + \beta)) = R_{\alpha+\beta} (1, 0).$$

But it is also true that
$$R_{\alpha+\beta} = R_\alpha \circ R_\beta.$$

Thus,
$$(\cos (\alpha + \beta), \sin (\alpha + \beta)) = R_\alpha \circ R_\beta (1, 0)$$
$$= R_\alpha (R_\beta (1, 0))$$
$$= R_\alpha(\cos \beta, \sin \beta).$$

Now translate this last sentence into matrices.

$$\begin{bmatrix} \cos(\alpha + \beta) \\ \sin (\alpha + \beta) \end{bmatrix} = \begin{bmatrix} \cos \alpha & -\sin \alpha \\ \sin \alpha & \cos \alpha \end{bmatrix} \begin{bmatrix} \cos \beta \\ \sin \beta \end{bmatrix}$$

$$= \begin{bmatrix} \cos \alpha \cos \beta - \sin \alpha \sin \beta \\ \sin \alpha \cos \beta + \cos \alpha \sin \beta \end{bmatrix}$$

Two matrices are equal if and only if their corresponding elements are equal, so

$$\cos (\alpha + \beta) = \cos \alpha \cos \beta - \sin \alpha \sin \beta$$

and
$$\sin (\alpha + \beta) = \sin \alpha \cos \beta + \cos \alpha \sin \beta.$$

The Addition Formulas for the Cosine and Sine are very useful in mathematics. You should either memorize them or be able to reconstruct them.

Activity

Verify the formula for cos $(\alpha + \beta)$ by letting $\alpha = 84°$ and $\beta = 17°$. **See left.**

Using the exact values of cosine and sine of 30°, 45°, 60°, and 90°, these formulas lead to the exact values for the sine and cosine of many other angles.

Example 1

Find an exact value for sin 75°.

Solution
Let $\alpha = 45°$ and $\beta = 30°$. Then
$$\sin 75° = \sin (45° + 30°)$$
$$= \sin 45° \cos 30° + \cos 45° \sin 30°$$
$$= \frac{\sqrt{2}}{2} \cdot \frac{\sqrt{3}}{2} + \frac{\sqrt{2}}{2} \cdot \frac{1}{2}$$
$$= \frac{\sqrt{6} + \sqrt{2}}{4}.$$

Check
Evaluate $\frac{\sqrt{6} + \sqrt{2}}{4}$ and sin 75° on your calculator. You should get approximately 0.966 for each value.

Optional Activities

As a class activity, ask students to provide as many exact values of cosines and sines of whole number degrees as they can between 0° and 360°. (Sines and cosines for any multiple of 15° can be found.) Give the coordinates of the corresponding points on the unit circle.

Adapting to Individual Needs

Extra Help
Some students may have difficulty following the proof of the theorem on page 722. Students might have a better understanding if you discuss **Question 1** in detail with the class.

There are also formulas for sin $(\alpha - \beta)$ and cos $(\alpha - \beta)$. Example 2 shows how to derive a formula for sin $(\alpha - \beta)$. You are asked to verify that cos $(\alpha - \beta) = \cos \alpha \cos \beta + \sin \alpha \sin \beta$ in the Questions.

Example 2

Derive a formula for sin $(\alpha - \beta)$ in terms of sines and cosines of α and β.

Solution

Rewrite $\alpha - \beta$ as $\alpha + (-\beta)$. Then for all α and β,

$\sin (\alpha - \beta) = \sin (\alpha + (-\beta))$	Algebraic definition of subtraction
$= \sin \alpha \cos(-\beta) + \cos \alpha \sin(-\beta)$	Addition Formula for the Sine
$= \sin \alpha \cos \beta + \cos \alpha\, (-\sin \beta)$	Opposites Theorem
$= \sin \alpha \cos \beta - \cos \alpha \sin \beta.$	Simplify

The formulas for cos $(\alpha + \beta)$ and sin $(\alpha + \beta)$ provide another way to prove some theorems about circular functions, such as the Supplements and Complements Theorems in Lesson 4-4.

Example 3

Prove the Supplements Theorem for the sine function:

$$\sin (\pi - \theta) = \sin \theta \text{ for all real numbers } \theta.$$

Solution

From the formula derived in Example 2, for all real numbers θ,
$$\sin(\pi - \theta) = \sin \pi \cos \theta - \cos \pi \sin \theta$$
$$= 0 \cdot \cos \theta - (-1)\sin \theta$$
$$= \sin \theta.$$

QUESTIONS

Covering the Reading

1. In the proof of the theorem in the lesson it is stated that $R_\alpha \circ R_\beta(1, 0) = R_\alpha(\cos \beta, \sin \beta)$. Explain why this is true. **See left.**

2. Consider the statement: *For all α and β, cos $(\alpha + \beta) = \cos \alpha + \cos \beta$.*
   a. Give one pair of values for α and β for which the statement is true.
   b. Give a counterexample to the statement.
   a, b, see left.

In 3 and 4, simplify without using a calculator.

3. $\sin 75° \cos 15° + \cos 75° \sin 15°$ $\sin (75° + 15°) = \sin (90°) = 1$

4. $\cos\left(\frac{11\pi}{12}\right) \cos\left(\frac{7\pi}{12}\right) - \sin\left(\frac{11\pi}{12}\right) \sin\left(\frac{7\pi}{12}\right)$ $\cos\left(\frac{11\pi}{12} + \frac{7\pi}{12}\right) = \cos\left(\frac{3\pi}{2}\right) = 0$

In 5 and 6, give an exact value.

5. $\cos 75°$ $\frac{\sqrt{6} - \sqrt{2}}{4}$

6. $\sin 15°$ $\frac{\sqrt{6} - \sqrt{2}}{4}$

Lesson 11-5 Formulas for cos$(\alpha + \beta)$ and sin $(\alpha + \beta)$ **723**

Additional Examples

1. Use the sine of a sum to find an exact value for sin 105°.
   sin (60° + 45°)
   = sin 60° cos 45°
     + cos 60° sin 45°
   $= \left(\frac{\sqrt{3}}{2} \cdot \frac{\sqrt{2}}{2} + \frac{1}{2} \cdot \frac{\sqrt{2}}{2}\right) = \frac{\sqrt{6} + \sqrt{2}}{4}$. You might have students check this value with their calculators.

2. Derive a formula for cos (30° + x) in terms of cos x and sin x.
   cos (30° + x)
   = cos 30° cos x − sin 30° sin x
   $= \frac{\sqrt{3}}{2}\cos x - \frac{1}{2}\sin x$

3. Prove the Complements Theorem for the sine function.
   $\sin\left(\frac{\pi}{2} - \theta\right)$
   $= \sin \frac{\pi}{2} \cos \theta - \cos \frac{\pi}{2} \sin \theta$
   $= 1 \cdot \cos \theta - 0 \cdot \sin \theta = \cos \theta$

Notes on Questions

Question 2 It is difficult to find even one set of values of α and β for which the statement is true.

Left margin answers:

1) We know $R_\beta(1, 0) =$ (cos β, sin β). So $R_\alpha \circ R_\beta(1, 0) = R_\alpha(R_\beta(1, 0)) = R_\alpha(\cos \beta, \sin \beta)$.

2a) Sample: $\alpha = \frac{3\pi}{2}$, $\beta = \frac{\pi}{4}$;
$\cos\left(\frac{3\pi}{2} + \frac{\pi}{4}\right) =$
$\cos\left(\frac{7\pi}{4}\right) = \frac{\sqrt{2}}{2}$;
$\cos\frac{3\pi}{2} + \cos\frac{\pi}{4} =$
$0 + \frac{\sqrt{2}}{2} = \frac{\sqrt{2}}{2}$.

b) Sample: $\alpha = \frac{\pi}{4}$, $\beta = \pi$;
$\cos\left(\frac{\pi}{4} + \pi\right) =$
$\cos\left(\frac{5\pi}{4}\right) = -\frac{\sqrt{2}}{2} \approx$
−0.707; but $\cos\frac{\pi}{4} +$
$\cos \pi = \frac{\sqrt{2}}{2} - 1 =$
$\frac{\sqrt{2} - 2}{2} \approx$ −0.293.

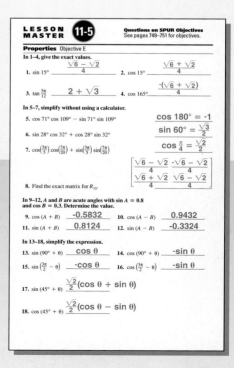

Adapting to Individual Needs

Challenge

Have students use the results for the Exploration Question in this lesson to answer the following.

1. Derive a formula for tan $(A + B + C)$ in terms of tan A, tan B, and tan C.
   [tan $(A + B + C) =$
   $\frac{\tan A + \tan B + \tan C - \tan A \tan B \tan C}{1 - \tan A \tan B - \tan A \tan C - \tan B \tan C}$]

2. Show that if A, B, and C are the angles of $\triangle ABC$, then tan A + tan B + tan C = tan A tan B tan C. [Setting the formula from Question 1 equal to zero, since tan 180° = 0, gives the result.]

Questions 10–11 You may have to supply the hints: $255° = 180° + 75°$ and $-\frac{13\pi}{12} = -\left(\frac{3\pi}{4} + \frac{\pi}{3}\right)$.

Question 18 Error Alert Some students forget to write the second term in each row.

Question 28 This tends to be a difficult question for most students.

Additional Answers

14. True. We can find exact values of $\sin\theta$ and $\cos\theta$ for all integral multiples of $\frac{\pi}{4}$ and $\frac{\pi}{3}$. Since $\frac{\pi}{12} = \frac{\pi}{3} - \frac{\pi}{4}$, then $k\cdot\frac{\pi}{12} = k\cdot\frac{\pi}{3} - k\cdot\frac{\pi}{4}$ for all integers k. So, we can find exact values of $\sin\theta$ and $\cos\theta$ $(0 \le \theta \le 2\pi)$ for all integral multiples $k = \{1, 2, \ldots, 24\}$ of $\frac{\pi}{12}$ by using the exact values for multiples of $\frac{\pi}{3}$ and $\frac{\pi}{4}$ in the Addition Formulas.

---

7) $\cos(\alpha - \beta) =$
$\cos(\alpha + (-\beta)) =$
$\cos\alpha\cos(-\beta) -$
$\sin\alpha\sin(-\beta) =$
$\cos\alpha\cos\beta +$
$\sin\alpha\sin\beta$

13)
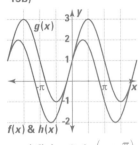

15b)

c) $f(x) = 2\sin\left(x + \frac{\pi}{6}\right) =$
$2\left(\sin x\cos\frac{\pi}{6} + \cos x\sin\frac{\pi}{6}\right) =$
$2\left(\frac{\sqrt{3}}{2}\sin x + \frac{1}{2}\cos x\right)$
$= \sqrt{3}\sin x + \cos x =$
$h(x)$

16) $\sin(x + 2\pi n) =$
$\sin x\cos 2\pi n + \cos x\sin 2\pi n =$
$\sin x\cdot 1 + \cos x\cdot 0 =$
$\sin x$

17) $\sin\left(x - \frac{\pi}{2}\right) =$
$\sin\left(x + \left(-\frac{\pi}{2}\right)\right) =$
$\sin x\cos\left(-\frac{\pi}{2}\right) +$
$\cos x\sin\left(-\frac{\pi}{2}\right) =$
$\sin x\cdot 0 + \cos x\cdot -1 =$
$-\cos x$

19c) Sample:
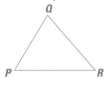

724

In 7–9, use the formula for $\cos(\alpha + \beta)$ to prove the stated theorem.

7. $\cos(\alpha - \beta) = \cos\alpha\cos\beta + \sin\alpha\sin\beta$ **See left.**

8. Supplements Theorem for the cosine function
$\cos(\pi - \theta) = \cos\pi\cos\theta + \sin\pi\sin\theta = -\cos\theta$

9. Complements Theorem for the cosine function
$\cos\left(\frac{\pi}{2} - \theta\right) = \cos\frac{\pi}{2}\cos\theta + \sin\frac{\pi}{2}\sin\theta = \sin\theta$

Applying the Mathematics

In 10–12, give exact values.

10. $\sin 255°$ $\frac{-\sqrt{2} - \sqrt{6}}{4}$ 11. $\cos\left(-\frac{13\pi}{12}\right)$ $\frac{-\sqrt{2} - \sqrt{6}}{4}$ 12. $\tan 75°$ $2 + \sqrt{3}$

13. Give an exact matrix for $R_{5\pi/12}$. (Hint: $\frac{5\pi}{12} = \frac{3\pi}{12} + \frac{2\pi}{12}$.) **See left.**

14. *True or false.* Exact values of $\sin\theta$ and $\cos\theta$ can be found for all integral multiples of $\frac{\pi}{12}$ between 0 and 2π. Justify your answer. **See margin.**

15. **a.** Without graphing the equations, tell which graph will be different from the others. $g(x)$
$$f(x) = 2\sin\left(x + \frac{\pi}{6}\right)$$
$$g(x) = 2\sin x + 2\sin\left(\frac{\pi}{6}\right)$$
$$h(x) = \sqrt{3}\sin x + \cos x$$
   b. Check your prediction by graphing $y = f(x)$, $y = g(x)$, and $y = h(x)$ on the same set of axes. **See left.**
   c. Explain your results using a theorem in this lesson. **See left.**

16. Use the formula for $\sin(\alpha + \beta)$ to show that $\sin(x + 2\pi n) = \sin x$ for all integers n. **See left.**

17. Prove: For all x, $\sin\left(x - \frac{\pi}{2}\right) = -\cos x$. **See left.**

18. Give the elements of the matrix for $R_{\alpha + \beta}$ in terms of sines and cosines of α and β. **See margin.**

19. $\triangle PQR$ has acute angles P and Q with $\cos P = \frac{1}{2}$ and $\cos Q = \frac{1}{3}$.
   a. Find $\cos(P + Q)$. a) $\frac{1 - 2\sqrt{6}}{6}$ b) $\frac{2\sqrt{6} - 1}{6}$
   b. Find $\cos R$.
   c. Draw a possible $\triangle PQR$.
   See left.

Review

20. Determine the coordinates of the image of point $(2, 5)$ under a counterclockwise rotation about the origin of $42°$. *(Lesson 11-4)* $\approx (-1.86, 5.05)$

---

18. $R_{\alpha + \beta} = \begin{bmatrix} \cos\alpha\cos\beta - \sin\alpha\sin\beta & -\sin\alpha\cos\beta - \cos\alpha\sin\beta \\ \sin\alpha\cos\beta + \cos\alpha\sin\beta & \cos\alpha\cos\beta - \sin\alpha\sin\beta \end{bmatrix}$

21b) It is a scale change:
$(x, y) \rightarrow (2x, -y)$

22a) $P'' =$
$$\begin{bmatrix} 0 & \frac{5\sqrt{2}}{2} & 2\sqrt{2} & -\frac{\sqrt{2}}{2} \\ \sqrt{2} & \frac{7\sqrt{2}}{2} & 6\sqrt{2} & \frac{7\sqrt{2}}{2} \end{bmatrix}$$

In 21 and 22, consider the polygon represented by the matrix
$$P = \begin{bmatrix} 1 & 6 & 8 & 3 \\ 1 & 1 & 4 & 4 \end{bmatrix}.$$

21. a. Calculate $P' = \begin{bmatrix} 2 & 0 \\ 0 & -1 \end{bmatrix} \cdot P.$ $P' = \begin{bmatrix} 2 & 12 & 16 & 6 \\ -1 & -1 & -4 & -4 \end{bmatrix}$

b. Describe the transformation mapping P onto P'. *(Lessons 11-2, 11-3)*
See left.

22. a. Calculate $P'' = \begin{bmatrix} \cos 45° & -\sin 45° \\ \sin 45° & \cos 45° \end{bmatrix} \cdot P.$
See left.

b. Describe the transformation mapping P onto P''. *(Lessons 11-2, 11-4)*
It is a counterclockwise rotation of 45° about the origin.

23. Kevin, Laura, and Sergio work part-time after school. The matrix R below gives the hourly payment each one earns. The matrix H shows the number of hours each worked on the days of a certain week. *(Lesson 11-1)*

	Kevin	Laura	Sergio
Monday	3	4	4
Tuesday	5	5	4
Wednesday	2	4	4
Thursday	4	2	4
Friday	3	0	4

$R = \begin{bmatrix} 5.25 \\ 4.90 \\ 5.50 \end{bmatrix}$

$= H$

a. How many hours did Laura work in this week? **15**

b. On which day was the combined time of the three the least? **Friday**

c. Which matrix, HR or RH, gives the total earnings of Kevin, Laura, and Sergio for each day of this week? **HR**

d. How much did the three of them earn on Thursday? **$52.80**

24. Solve $x^4 - 2x^3 - 13x^2 - 4x - 30 = 0$ completely, given that one of the solutions is $\sqrt{2}\,i$. *(Lessons 9-6, 9-7)* $x = \sqrt{2}i, -\sqrt{2}i, -3, 5$

25. Consider the graph of a polynomial function g pictured at the left.

a. How many real zeros does g seem to have? **3**

b. What is the smallest possible degree g can have? **4**

c. *True or false.* The factorization of g over the set of polynomials with real number coefficients has at least four factors. Explain your answer. *(Lessons 9-5, 9-6, 9-7)* See left.

25c) True. There are four observable solutions to $g(x) = 0$, counting the double root twice. By the Factor Theorem, each solution c implies $(x - c)$ is a factor of g.

26. Give an exact value.

a. $\log 1000$ **3**
b. $\log_2 8 - \log_8 2$ $\frac{8}{3}$
c. $\log 2 \cdot \log_2(.1)$ **-1**

(Lessons 6-3, 6-5)

27. *Multiple choice.* Which correlation coefficient indicates the strongest linear relationship? *(Lesson 2-2)* **c**

(a) 0.43   (b) 0.16   (c) -0.79   (d) 0.1

Exploration

28. a. Use the fact that $\tan (\alpha + \beta) = \frac{\sin (\alpha + \beta)}{\cos (\alpha + \beta)}$ to derive a formula for $\tan (\alpha + \beta)$ in terms of tangents of α and β. (Hint: divide both numerator and denominator of the fraction by $\cos \alpha \cos \beta$.)

b. Check your answer to part **a** by using some values of tangents known to you.
See margin.

Additional Answers

28. a. $\tan (\alpha + \beta) = \dfrac{\sin (\alpha + \beta)}{\cos (\alpha + \beta)} = \dfrac{\sin \alpha \cos \beta + \cos \alpha \sin \beta}{\cos \alpha \cos \beta - \sin \alpha \sin \beta} =$

$\dfrac{\frac{\sin \alpha \cos \beta}{\cos \alpha \cos \beta} + \frac{\cos \alpha \sin \beta}{\cos \alpha \cos \beta}}{\frac{\cos \alpha \cos \beta}{\cos \alpha \cos \beta} - \frac{\sin \alpha \sin \beta}{\cos \alpha \cos \beta}} = \dfrac{\frac{\sin \alpha}{\cos \alpha} + \frac{\sin \beta}{\cos \beta}}{1 - \frac{\sin \alpha}{\cos \alpha} \cdot \frac{\sin \beta}{\cos \beta}} = \dfrac{\tan \alpha + \tan \beta}{1 - \tan \alpha \tan \beta}$

b. Sample: If $\alpha = 30°$ and $\beta = 45°$,

$\tan(30° + 45°) = \tan 75° \approx 3.732$, and $\dfrac{\tan 30° + \tan 45°}{1 - \tan 30° \tan 45°} = \dfrac{\frac{\sqrt{3}}{3} + 1}{1 - \frac{\sqrt{3}}{3}} \approx 3.732.$

Follow-up for Lesson 11-5

Practice
For more questions on SPUR Objectives, use **Lesson Master 11-5** (shown on page 723).

Assessment
Written Communication Have students write the addition and subtraction formulas for sine and cosine either from memory or by reconstructing them. [Students give the addition and subtraction formulas for sine and cosine.]

Extension
An alternate proof of the Addition Identities follows. Since
$R_{\alpha + \beta} = R_\alpha \circ R_\beta$,
$$\begin{bmatrix} \cos(\alpha + \beta) & -\sin(\alpha + \beta) \\ \sin(\alpha + \beta) & \cos(\alpha + \beta) \end{bmatrix}$$
$$= \begin{bmatrix} \cos \alpha & -\sin \alpha \\ \sin \alpha & \cos \alpha \end{bmatrix}$$
$$\cdot \begin{bmatrix} \cos \beta & -\sin \beta \\ \sin \beta & \cos \beta \end{bmatrix}$$
$$= \begin{bmatrix} \cos \alpha \cos \beta - \sin \alpha \sin \beta & -\sin \alpha \cos \beta - \cos \alpha \sin \beta \\ \sin \alpha \cos \beta + \cos \alpha \sin \beta & \cos \alpha \cos \beta - \sin \alpha \sin \beta \end{bmatrix}$$
and the Addition Formulas for the Cosine and Sine follow because corresponding elements of matrices are equal. Although this proof is even more elegant than the proof given in the lesson, we have found that students are more satisfied with the one we give there.

Students working together can use the alternate approach given above to prove theorems in this lesson. For instance, an alternate approach for **Example 3** is to use the matrix form of the transformation identity $R_{\pi - \theta} = R_\pi \circ R_{-\theta}.$

725

Objectives

E Apply the Double Angle Formulas for the Cosine and Sine.

Resources

From the *Teacher's Resource File*
- Lesson Master 11-6
- Answer Master 11-6
- Assessment Sourcebook: Quiz for Lessons 11-4 through 11-6
- Teaching Aid 97: Warm-up
- Technology Sourcebook Computer Master 12

Additional Resources
- Visual for Teaching Aid 97
- Automatic grapher

Teaching Lesson **11-6**

Warm-up

1. Consider a sequence s in which $s_1 = \frac{1}{2}$ and for all $n > 1$, $s_n = 2(s_{n-1})^2 - 1$. Give the first five terms of this sequence.
$\frac{1}{2}, -\frac{1}{2}, -\frac{1}{2}, -\frac{1}{2}, -\frac{1}{2}$

2. Give the values of $\cos\left(2^n \cdot \frac{\pi}{3}\right)$ for $n = 0, 1, 2, 3,$ and 4.
$\frac{1}{2}, -\frac{1}{2}, -\frac{1}{2}, -\frac{1}{2}, -\frac{1}{2}$

3. Compare your results to Questions 1 and 2 and explain what has happened. **The results are the same. The recursive rule in Question 1 is of the same form as the formula for cos 2n in terms of cos n. So the consecutive terms of the sequence are consecutive cosines of numbers that keep doubling. That is what is sought in Question 2.**

Formulas for cos 2θ and sin 2θ

A Use for sin 2θ

Ignoring air resistance and wind, the path of an object thrown or kicked into the air from ground level will be part of a parabolic trajectory. Specifically, if a golf ball is driven off the ground with velocity v m/sec at an angle of θ degrees to the ground, the horizontal distance d that the ball travels is given by $d = \frac{v^2 \sin 2\theta}{g}$, where g is the acceleration due to gravity.

Thus, a golf ball leaving a tee at 45 meters per second at an angle of 30° to the ground will travel about

$$\frac{\left(45 \ \frac{m}{sec}\right)^2 \cdot \sin(2 \cdot 30°)}{9.81 \ \frac{m}{sec^2}} \approx 179m.$$

Proving the Double Angle Formulas

Expressions like sin 2θ and cos 2θ occur often in mathematics and science. Formulas expressing sin 2θ and cos 2θ as functions of θ are often called Double Angle or Double Argument Formulas. They can be derived using the Addition Formulas for the sine and cosine functions.

Theorem (Double Angle Formulas)
For all real numbers θ,

$$\sin 2\theta = 2 \sin \theta \cos \theta;$$
and
$$\cos 2\theta = \cos^2\theta - \sin^2\theta$$
$$= 2 \cos^2\theta - 1$$
$$= 1 - 2 \sin^2\theta.$$

Proof
Set $\alpha = \theta$ and $\beta = \theta$ in the formulas for sin $(\alpha + \beta)$ and cos $(\alpha + \beta)$.
Then
$$\sin 2\theta = \sin (\theta + \theta)$$
$$= \sin \theta \cos \theta + \cos \theta \sin \theta$$
$$= 2 \sin \theta \cos \theta.$$
Similarly,
$$\cos 2\theta = \cos (\theta + \theta)$$
$$= \cos \theta \cos \theta - \sin \theta \sin \theta$$
$$= \cos^2\theta - \sin^2\theta.$$
Substituting $\sin^2\theta = 1 - \cos^2\theta$ from the Pythagorean Identity yields the second form of the Double Angle Formula for the cosine function.
$$\cos 2\theta = \cos^2\theta - (1 - \cos^2\theta)$$
$$= \cos^2\theta - 1 + \cos^2\theta$$
$$= 2 \cos^2\theta - 1$$

Lesson 11-6 Overview

Broad Goals This is a straightforward lesson in which formulas for sin 2θ and cos 2θ are derived and applied.

Perspective Regardless of the approach used to find the Addition Formulas for the Cosine and Sine, by letting θ stand for both α and β, the Double Angle Formulas are derived quite easily. They are called "double angle" formulas because of their historical origin, not because α and β must be angles.

Some teachers prefer to call them "double argument" formulas. Some teachers also prefer the word "identity" to "formula."

You are asked to derive the third form of the Double Angle Formula for the cosine function in the Questions.

Picturing the Double Angle Formula

Graphically, the first Double Angle Formula means that the graphs of $y = \sin 2x$ and $y = 2 \sin x \cos x$ coincide. The graphs of these functions are shown below. You are asked to verify the formulas for $\cos 2x$ graphically in the Questions.

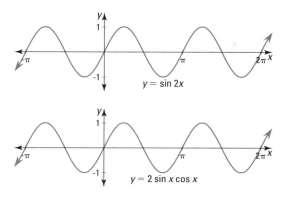

$y = \sin 2x$

$y = 2 \sin x \cos x$

Verifying the Double Angle Formulas

Since the Double Angle Formulas are true for all θ, you can use a specific value of θ to check them.

Example 1

For $\theta = \frac{\pi}{6}$, verify the formula for $\sin 2\theta$.

Solution

When $\theta = \frac{\pi}{6}$, $\sin 2\theta = 2 \sin \theta \cos \theta$ becomes

$\sin \left(2 \cdot \frac{\pi}{6}\right) = 2 \sin \frac{\pi}{6} \cos \frac{\pi}{6}$. Is this true?

$$\sin \left(2 \cdot \frac{\pi}{6}\right) = \sin \frac{\pi}{3} \qquad \text{and} \qquad 2 \sin \frac{\pi}{6} \cos \frac{\pi}{6} = 2 \cdot \frac{1}{2} \cdot \frac{\sqrt{3}}{2}$$

$$= \frac{\sqrt{3}}{2} \qquad\qquad\qquad = \frac{\sqrt{3}}{2}$$

The identity is verified.

Extending the Double Angle Formulas

From the identities for $\cos 2\theta$ and $\sin 2\theta$, identities for the cosine and sine of other multiples of θ can be found.

The major reasons for having double angle identities are (1) the existence of certain formulas that involve expressions with them, as in the first paragraph of this lesson, (2) the ability to deduce formulas for $\cos (n\theta)$ and $\sin (n\theta)$ from them, as **Example 2** demonstrates, and (3) to use them to deduce the half-angle formulas given in **Questions 18–19**. Today the last reason is not particularly important, as values of any of the trigonometric functions can be found to great accuracy with technology. Still, in theory, by halving and adding as appropriate, you can with these identities get as close as you wish to the value of these functions for any argument.

Additional Examples

1. When $\theta = \frac{\pi}{4}$, verify the identity for $\sin 2\theta$ and the first identity for $\cos 2\theta$. $\sin 2\theta = \sin \frac{\pi}{2} = 1$ and

   $2 \sin \theta \cos \theta = 2 \cdot \frac{\sqrt{2}}{2} \cdot \frac{\sqrt{2}}{2} = 1$.

   $\cos 2\theta = \cos \frac{\pi}{2} = 0$ and

   $\cos^2\theta - \sin^2\theta =$

   $\left(\frac{\sqrt{2}}{2}\right)^2 - \left(\frac{\sqrt{2}}{2}\right)^2 = 0$

2. Express $\cos 3\theta$ as a function of $\cos \theta$.
   $\cos 3\theta = \cos(\theta + 2\theta)$
   $= \cos \theta \cos 2\theta - \sin \theta \sin 2\theta$
   $= \cos \theta(2 \cos^2\theta - 1) - \sin \theta(2 \sin \theta \cos \theta)$
   $= 2 \cos^3\theta - \cos \theta - 2 \sin^2\theta \cos \theta$
   $= 2 \cos^3\theta - \cos \theta - 2(1 - \cos^2\theta) \cos \theta$
   $= 2 \cos^3\theta - \cos \theta - 2 \cos \theta + 2 \cos^3\theta$
   $= 4 \cos^3\theta - 3 \cos \theta$

Optional Activities

Activity 1 Technology Connection
In *Technology Sourcebook, Computer Master 12,* students use an automatic grapher to examine graphs of various trigonometric functions and use these graphs to identify possible identities.

Activity 2 Ask students to identify why the answer to **Question 13** could be predicted to be rational numbers. [A right triangle is similar to a 3-4-5 right triangle; 3-4-5 is a Pythagorean triple.] Have students make up problems similar to **Question 13**, using other common Pythagorean triples. [Sample: Use a 5-12-13 right triangle. For instance, assume $\angle A$ is acute and $\sin A = \frac{5}{13}$. Then $\cos A = \frac{12}{13}$ and

$\sin 2A = \frac{120}{169}$. Other Pythagorean triples with small integers are 8, 15, 17; 7, 24, 25; 9, 40, 41; and any multiples of these.]

Notes on Questions

Question 2 It is instructive to see if the formula works in this extreme case. [It does.]

Question 11 Whereas cos $(n\theta)$ can always be expressed as a polynomial function of cos θ (see **Example 2** and Additional Example 2 for the cases $n = 3$ and $n = 4$), sin $(n\theta)$ cannot be expressed as a polynomial function of sin θ. The proof is beyond the scope of this course, but students can see that even for $n = 2$, the formula for sin 2θ is not given in terms of sin θ only.

Question 12 The result here shows that the soccer ball of **Question 1** is being kicked at the best angle. The answer to **part b** is quite large, but friction due to air (which is ignored in the formula) is a significant barrier to the golf ball.

Questions 15–17 A proof that
$\begin{bmatrix} \cos 2\theta & \sin 2\theta \\ \sin 2\theta & -\cos 2\theta \end{bmatrix}$ is the matrix for r_L is as follows. Because the angle between the lines L and x-axis is θ, the composite $r_L \circ r_x = R_{2\theta}$. That is, the composite of reflections over intersecting lines is the rotation whose center is the intersection of the lines and whose magnitude is twice the angle between the lines measured from the first line to the second. Students who have studied from UCSMP *Geometry* should be familiar with this theorem. Now, in matrix language, the transformation equation is equivalent to
$\begin{bmatrix} a & b \\ c & d \end{bmatrix}\begin{bmatrix} 1 & 0 \\ 0 & -1 \end{bmatrix} = \begin{bmatrix} \cos 2\theta & -\sin 2\theta \\ \sin 2\theta & \cos 2\theta \end{bmatrix}$
where a, b, c, and d need to be found. Multiplying the matrices on the left side shows that $a = \cos 2\theta$, $b = \sin 2\theta$, $c = \sin 2\theta$, and $d = -\cos 2\theta$ as required.

Example 2

Express cos 4θ as a function of cos θ only.

Solution

First, express cos 4θ as a function of cos 2θ.
$$\cos 4\theta = \cos 2(2\theta)$$
$$= 2\cos^2(2\theta) - 1$$
Now use the Double Angle Formula again.
$$\cos 4\theta = 2(2\cos^2\theta - 1)^2 - 1$$
$$= 2(4\cos^4\theta - 4\cos^2\theta + 1) - 1$$
$$= 8\cos^4\theta - 8\cos^2\theta + 2 - 1$$
$$= 8\cos^4\theta - 8\cos^2\theta + 1$$

Check

Substitute a value for θ for which the values of cos θ and cos 4θ are known. We use $\theta = 45°$. Then
$$\cos 4\theta = \cos (4 \cdot 45°) \quad \text{and} \quad 8\cos^4\theta - 8\cos^2\theta + 1 = 8\left(\frac{\sqrt{2}}{2}\right)^4 - 8\left(\frac{\sqrt{2}}{2}\right)^2 + 1$$
$$= \cos 180° \qquad\qquad\qquad\qquad\qquad = 8\left(\frac{4}{16}\right) - 8\left(\frac{2}{4}\right) + 1$$
$$= -1 \qquad\qquad\qquad\qquad\qquad\qquad\quad = -1.$$

QUESTIONS

Covering the Reading

In 1 and 2, use the formula $d = \frac{v^2 \sin 2\theta}{g}$.

1. About how far will a soccer ball travel with respect to the ground if you kick it at 34 $\frac{m}{sec}$ at an initial angle of 45° to the ground? $\approx$ **118 m**

2. How far will a tennis ball travel horizontally if it leaves the ground at 25 $\frac{m}{sec}$ at an angle of 90°? **0 m**

3. Prove that cos $2\theta = 1 - 2\sin^2\theta$. **See left.**

4. Find a value of θ for which cos $2\theta \neq 2$ cos θ. **Sample:** $\theta = 45°$

5. **a.** Graph the functions f, g, and h on the same set of axes. **See left.**
   $$f(x) = \cos^2 x - \sin^2 x$$
   $$g(x) = 2\cos^2 x - 1$$
   $$h(x) = 1 - 2\sin^2 x$$
   b. Find another equation whose graph coincides with those of f, g, and h.
   $$y = \cos (2x)$$

6. Use $\theta = 60°$ and a formula for cos 2θ to find an exact value for cos 120°. **See left.**

In 7–10, simplify each expression using the appropriate Double Angle Formula.

7. $2\cos^2 25° - 1$ **cos 50°**

8. $2\sin 35° \cos 35°$ **sin 70°**

9. $1 - 2\sin^2\left(\frac{3\pi}{8}\right)$ **cos $\left(\frac{3\pi}{4}\right)$**

10. $\cos^2\left(\frac{4\pi}{9}\right) - \sin^2\left(\frac{4\pi}{9}\right)$ **cos $\left(\frac{8\pi}{9}\right)$**

11. Express sin 4θ as a function of cos θ and sin θ.
    Sample: $4\sin\theta\cos^3\theta - 4\sin^3\theta\cos\theta$

Side notes

3) $\cos 2\theta = \cos (\theta + \theta) = \cos\theta\cos\theta - \sin\theta\sin\theta = \cos^2\theta - \sin^2\theta = (1 - \sin^2\theta) - \sin^2\theta = 1 - 2\sin^2\theta$

5a)

6) $\cos 120° = \cos (2 \cdot 60°)$
$= \cos^2 60° - \sin^2 60°$
$= \left(\frac{1}{2}\right)^2 - \left(\frac{\sqrt{3}}{2}\right)^2$
$= \frac{1}{4} - \frac{3}{4} = -\frac{1}{2}$

Additional Answers, page 729

18. **a.**
$$\cos 2\theta = \cos^2\theta - \sin^2\theta$$
$$\underline{+\ 1\qquad = \cos^2\theta + \sin^2\theta}$$
$$1 + \cos 2\theta = 2\cos^2\theta$$
$$\frac{1 + \cos 2\theta}{2} = \cos^2\theta$$

$$\cos\theta = \pm\sqrt{\frac{1 + \cos 2\theta}{2}}$$

b. According to the formula,
$$\cos\frac{\pi}{8}$$
$$= \pm\sqrt{\frac{1 + \cos\frac{\pi}{4}}{2}} = \pm\sqrt{\frac{1 + \frac{\sqrt{2}}{2}}{2}}$$
$$= \pm\sqrt{\frac{2 + \sqrt{2}}{4}} = \pm\frac{\sqrt{2 + \sqrt{2}}}{2}. \text{ Since}$$
$\frac{\pi}{8}$ is in the first quadrant, cos $\frac{\pi}{8} > 0$, therefore cos $\frac{\pi}{8} = \frac{\sqrt{2 + \sqrt{2}}}{2}$.

19. **a.**
$$-\cos 2\theta = \sin^2\theta - \cos^2\theta$$
$$\underline{+\ 1\qquad = \sin^2\theta + \cos^2\theta}$$
$$1 - \cos 2\theta = 2\sin^2\theta$$
$$\frac{1 - \cos 2\theta}{2} = \sin^2\theta$$

$$\sin\theta = \pm\sqrt{\frac{1 - \cos 2\theta}{2}}$$

Example 1

Show that $\begin{bmatrix} 3 & 0 \\ 0 & 5 \end{bmatrix}$ and $\begin{bmatrix} \frac{1}{3} & 0 \\ 0 & \frac{1}{5} \end{bmatrix}$ are inverses.

Solution

Because 2×2 matrix multiplication is not commutative, you should check the multiplications in both orders.

$$\begin{bmatrix} 3 & 0 \\ 0 & 5 \end{bmatrix}\begin{bmatrix} \frac{1}{3} & 0 \\ 0 & \frac{1}{5} \end{bmatrix} = \begin{bmatrix} 1 & 0 \\ 0 & 1 \end{bmatrix}, \qquad \begin{bmatrix} \frac{1}{3} & 0 \\ 0 & \frac{1}{5} \end{bmatrix}\begin{bmatrix} 3 & 0 \\ 0 & 5 \end{bmatrix} = \begin{bmatrix} 1 & 0 \\ 0 & 1 \end{bmatrix}$$

Finding the Inverse of a 2 × 2 Matrix

If the transformation for a matrix is not known, you can find its inverse using algebra.

Example 2

Find the inverse of $\begin{bmatrix} 3 & 7 \\ 2 & 5 \end{bmatrix}$.

Solution

The task is to find a matrix $\begin{bmatrix} w & x \\ y & z \end{bmatrix}$ such that

$$\begin{bmatrix} 3 & 7 \\ 2 & 5 \end{bmatrix}\begin{bmatrix} w & x \\ y & z \end{bmatrix} = \begin{bmatrix} w & x \\ y & z \end{bmatrix}\begin{bmatrix} 3 & 7 \\ 2 & 5 \end{bmatrix} = \begin{bmatrix} 1 & 0 \\ 0 & 1 \end{bmatrix}.$$

Multiply the left two matrices.

$$\begin{bmatrix} 3 & 7 \\ 2 & 5 \end{bmatrix}\begin{bmatrix} w & x \\ y & z \end{bmatrix} = \begin{bmatrix} 3w + 7y & 3x + 7z \\ 2w + 5y & 2x + 5z \end{bmatrix}.$$

So

$$3w + 7y = 1,$$
$$3x + 7z = 0,$$
$$2w + 5y = 0,$$

and

$$2x + 5z = 1.$$

To solve this system, note that the first and third equations have the same two variables. Multiply the first equation by 2 and the third by –3 and add the resulting sentences. This yields $y = -2$. Substituting this value into the first equation gives $w = 5$. Similarly, multiplying the second equation by 2 and the fourth by –3 and adding the results yields $z = 3$. Substituting this value into the second equation gives $x = -7$. So the inverse of $\begin{bmatrix} 3 & 7 \\ 2 & 5 \end{bmatrix}$ is $\begin{bmatrix} 5 & -7 \\ -2 & 3 \end{bmatrix}$.

Check

$$\begin{bmatrix} 3 & 7 \\ 2 & 5 \end{bmatrix} \cdot \begin{bmatrix} 5 & -7 \\ -2 & 3 \end{bmatrix} = \begin{bmatrix} 15 - 14 & -21 + 21 \\ 10 - 10 & -14 + 15 \end{bmatrix} = \begin{bmatrix} 1 & 0 \\ 0 & 1 \end{bmatrix}$$

$$\begin{bmatrix} 5 & -7 \\ -2 & 3 \end{bmatrix} \cdot \begin{bmatrix} 3 & 7 \\ 2 & 5 \end{bmatrix} = \begin{bmatrix} 15 - 14 & 35 - 35 \\ -6 + 6 & -14 + 15 \end{bmatrix} = \begin{bmatrix} 1 & 0 \\ 0 & 1 \end{bmatrix}$$

In **Example 1,** we check both products because the definition requires that both $MN = \begin{bmatrix} 1 & 0 \\ 0 & 1 \end{bmatrix}$ and

$NM = \begin{bmatrix} 1 & 0 \\ 0 & 1 \end{bmatrix}$ in order for M and N

to be inverses. It is possible, however, to prove that a check only one way is needed. (See the Challenge in *Adapting to Individual Needs* on page 734.)

In the first edition to *Functions, Statistics, and Trigonometry* we included material on coding matrices in this lesson. Here that material is found in Project 4, *Matrix Codes*, on page 746.

History Connection British scientist Arthur Cayley (1821–1895) was the first major contributor to the theory of matrices. The development of quantum mechanics in 1925 and the theory of relativity depend heavily on his work with matrices and invariance.

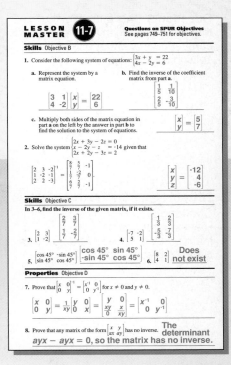

Adapting to Individual Needs

Extra Help

Some students will wonder where the formula for the inverse of a 2×2 matrix came from. Point out that the process of **Example 2** can be generalized using *a, b, c,* and *d* in the place of 3, 7, 2, and 5. The result is the theorem.

733

Additional Examples

1. Show that $\begin{bmatrix} 6 & 11 \\ 2 & 4 \end{bmatrix}$ and

   $\begin{bmatrix} 2 & -5.5 \\ -1 & 3 \end{bmatrix}$ are inverses of each

   other. **The product in both**

   orders is $\begin{bmatrix} 1 & 0 \\ 0 & 1 \end{bmatrix}$.

2. Find the inverse of $\begin{bmatrix} 1 & 5 \\ -3 & 4 \end{bmatrix}$.

   $\begin{bmatrix} \frac{4}{19} & -\frac{5}{19} \\ \frac{3}{19} & \frac{1}{19} \end{bmatrix}$

3. Show that $\begin{bmatrix} 3 & -15 \\ -4 & 20 \end{bmatrix}$ has no

   inverse. **Its determinant**
   $3 \cdot 20 - (-15)(-4) = 0.$

Notes on Questions

Question 3 Error Alert Some students will feel that a size change of magnitude 1 is the identity, and a different identity from a rotation of magnitude 0. You can point out that these are two ways to think of the identity transformation, just as $\frac{0}{5}$ and $3 - 3$ are two different ways of expressing the additive identity for real number addition.

Question 7 Point out the use of the Pythagorean Identity $\sin^2 \theta + \cos^2 \theta = 1$, which may come as a surprise to students.

Question 9 This question shows that, at times, the inverse of a matrix can be found without a formula or solving an equation.

If the inverse of a 2×2 matrix exists, you can generalize the procedure used in Example 2, or you can use the following theorem. Here we use the symbol M^{-1} to stand for the inverse of M.

> **Theorem (Inverse of a 2 × 2 Matrix)**
> If $ad - bc \neq 0$, then
> $$\begin{bmatrix} a & b \\ c & d \end{bmatrix}^{-1} = \begin{bmatrix} \frac{d}{ad-bc} & \frac{-b}{ad-bc} \\ \frac{-c}{ad-bc} & \frac{a}{ad-bc} \end{bmatrix}.$$

Proof

It must be shown that the product of the matrix $\begin{bmatrix} a & b \\ c & d \end{bmatrix}$ with its inverse in either order is the identity matrix. Here is one order.

$$\begin{bmatrix} a & b \\ c & d \end{bmatrix}\begin{bmatrix} \frac{d}{ad-bc} & \frac{-b}{ad-bc} \\ \frac{-c}{ad-bc} & \frac{a}{ad-bc} \end{bmatrix} = \begin{bmatrix} \frac{ad}{ad-bc} - \frac{bc}{ad-bc} & \frac{-ab}{ad-bc} + \frac{ab}{ad-bc} \\ \frac{cd}{ad-bc} - \frac{cd}{ad-bc} & \frac{-bc}{ad-bc} + \frac{ad}{ad-bc} \end{bmatrix}$$

$$= \begin{bmatrix} \frac{ad-bc}{ad-bc} & \frac{0}{ad-bc} \\ \frac{0}{ad-bc} & \frac{ad-bc}{ad-bc} \end{bmatrix}$$

$$= \begin{bmatrix} 1 & 0 \\ 0 & 1 \end{bmatrix}$$

You are asked to verify multiplication in the other order in the Questions.

Example 3

Use the Inverse of a 2×2 Matrix Theorem to find $\begin{bmatrix} 2 & -3 \\ 6 & -1 \end{bmatrix}^{-1}$.

Solution

In $\begin{bmatrix} 2 & -3 \\ 6 & -1 \end{bmatrix}$, $a = 2$, $b = -3$, $c = 6$, and $d = -1$. So,

$ad - bc = (2)(-1) - (-3)(6) = 16.$

Therefore, $\begin{bmatrix} 2 & -3 \\ 6 & -1 \end{bmatrix}^{-1} = \begin{bmatrix} -\frac{1}{16} & \frac{3}{16} \\ -\frac{6}{16} & \frac{2}{16} \end{bmatrix}.$

Check

$$\begin{bmatrix} 2 & -3 \\ 6 & -1 \end{bmatrix}\begin{bmatrix} -\frac{1}{16} & \frac{3}{16} \\ -\frac{6}{16} & \frac{2}{16} \end{bmatrix} = \begin{bmatrix} -\frac{2}{16} + \frac{18}{16} & \frac{6}{16} - \frac{6}{16} \\ -\frac{6}{16} + \frac{6}{16} & \frac{18}{16} - \frac{2}{16} \end{bmatrix} = \begin{bmatrix} 1 & 0 \\ 0 & 1 \end{bmatrix}$$

$$\begin{bmatrix} -\frac{1}{16} & \frac{3}{16} \\ -\frac{6}{16} & \frac{2}{16} \end{bmatrix}\begin{bmatrix} 2 & -3 \\ 6 & -1 \end{bmatrix} = \begin{bmatrix} -\frac{2}{16} + \frac{18}{16} & \frac{3}{16} - \frac{3}{16} \\ -\frac{12}{16} + \frac{12}{16} & \frac{18}{16} - \frac{2}{16} \end{bmatrix} = \begin{bmatrix} 1 & 0 \\ 0 & 1 \end{bmatrix}$$

Adapting to Individual Needs

Challenge
Have students prove that, if I is the identity matrix, $MN = I$, and M has an inverse, then $NM = I$. [Proof shown at right.]

Let $I = \begin{bmatrix} 1 & 0 \\ 0 & 1 \end{bmatrix}$ and suppose $MN = I$. Then

$(MN)M = IM$	Substitution
$(MN)M = M$	Property of Identity Transformation
$M(NM) = M$	Associative Property
$M^{-1}M(NM) = M^{-1}M$	M^{-1} exists
$I(NM) = I$	Property of Inverses
$NM = I$	Property of Identity Transformation

Not all 2×2 matrices have inverses. If $M = \begin{bmatrix} a & b \\ c & d \end{bmatrix}$ and $ad - bc = 0$,

then $\frac{1}{ad - bc}$ is undefined, so M^{-1} cannot exist. The expression $ad - bc$ is called the **determinant** of the matrix because it can be used to determine whether the matrix has an inverse. The word *determinant* is abbreviated as **det**, and we write

$$\det \begin{bmatrix} a & b \\ c & d \end{bmatrix} = ad - bc.$$

Thus, if $M = \begin{bmatrix} a & b \\ c & d \end{bmatrix}$, and $ad - bc \neq 0$, another way to write the formula

for M^{-1} is $M^{-1} = \begin{bmatrix} \frac{d}{\det M} & \frac{-b}{\det M} \\ \frac{-c}{\det M} & \frac{a}{\det M} \end{bmatrix}$.

In general, only square ($n \times n$) matrices can have inverses, because both products MM^{-1} and $M^{-1}M$ must exist. For matrices where $n > 2$, inverses also exist, but are not always easy to calculate by hand. However, some calculators and computer software packages will find them easily.

QUESTIONS

Covering the Reading

In 1–4, give the identity for each set under the indicated operation.

1. $+$, set of real numbers
   0

2. $\circ$, set of real functions
   $I(x) = x$

3. $\circ$, set of transformations of the plane
   $I(P) = P$

4. $\bullet$, set of 2×2 matrices $\begin{bmatrix} 1 & 0 \\ 0 & 1 \end{bmatrix}$

5. In the set of real numbers, what is the sum of the additive and multiplicative inverses of 12? $-\frac{143}{12}$

6. Complete this statement. Two transformations S and T are inverses if and only if ___?___. $S \circ T = T \circ S = I$

7. **a.** Use the Inverse of a 2×2 Matrix Theorem to find
   $$\begin{bmatrix} \cos \theta & -\sin \theta \\ \sin \theta & \cos \theta \end{bmatrix}^{-1} . \quad \begin{bmatrix} \cos \theta & \sin \theta \\ -\sin \theta & \cos \theta \end{bmatrix}$$
   b. *True or false.* $R_\theta^{-1} = R_{-\theta}$. **True**

8. **a.** What is the matrix for the scale change $S_{3,0.5}$? **See left.**
   b. Find the matrix for the inverse of this scale change and prove that your answer is correct. **See left.**

9. **a.** Write a matrix for the size change $S(x, y) = (4x, 4y)$. **See left.**
   b. What transformation T undoes S? $T(x, y) = \left(\frac{1}{4}x, \frac{1}{4}y\right)$
   c. Write a matrix for T. **See left.**
   d. *True or false.* The matrices for S and T are inverses. Justify your answer. **See left.**

Lesson 11-7 *Inverses of 2×2 Matrices* **735**

(margin answers, left side)

8a) $S = \begin{bmatrix} 3 & 0 \\ 0 & 0.5 \end{bmatrix}$

b) $S^{-1} = \begin{bmatrix} \frac{1}{3} & 0 \\ 0 & 2 \end{bmatrix}$;

$\begin{bmatrix} 3 & 0 \\ 0 & 0.5 \end{bmatrix}\begin{bmatrix} \frac{1}{3} & 0 \\ 0 & 2 \end{bmatrix} = \begin{bmatrix} 1 & 0 \\ 0 & 1 \end{bmatrix}$ and

$\begin{bmatrix} \frac{1}{3} & 0 \\ 0 & 2 \end{bmatrix}\begin{bmatrix} 3 & 0 \\ 0 & 0.5 \end{bmatrix} = \begin{bmatrix} 1 & 0 \\ 0 & 1 \end{bmatrix}$

9a) $S = \begin{bmatrix} 4 & 0 \\ 0 & 4 \end{bmatrix}$

c) $T = \begin{bmatrix} \frac{1}{4} & 0 \\ 0 & \frac{1}{4} \end{bmatrix}$

d) True; $ST = \begin{bmatrix} 4 & 0 \\ 0 & 4 \end{bmatrix}\begin{bmatrix} \frac{1}{4} & 0 \\ 0 & \frac{1}{4} \end{bmatrix} = \begin{bmatrix} 1 & 0 \\ 0 & 1 \end{bmatrix}$ and $TS = \begin{bmatrix} \frac{1}{4} & 0 \\ 0 & \frac{1}{4} \end{bmatrix}\begin{bmatrix} 4 & 0 \\ 0 & 4 \end{bmatrix} = \begin{bmatrix} 1 & 0 \\ 0 & 1 \end{bmatrix}$

Question 20 This question reviews an idea covered in USCMP *Advanced Algebra*. In general, a linear system of the form

$$\begin{cases} ax + by = c \\ dx + ey = f \end{cases}$$ can be written as

$AX = B$, where $A = \begin{bmatrix} a & b \\ d & e \end{bmatrix}$,

$X = \begin{bmatrix} x \\ y \end{bmatrix}$, and $B = \begin{bmatrix} c \\ f \end{bmatrix}$. When A has an inverse, $X = A^{-1}B$. If A does not have an inverse, then there is no unique solution.

17c) $\det \begin{bmatrix} W & X \\ Y & Z \end{bmatrix} = WZ - XY$ and

$-\det \begin{bmatrix} Y & Z \\ W & X \end{bmatrix} = -(XY - WZ) = WZ - XY$

19a) $\begin{bmatrix} 1 & 2 \\ 3 & -1 \end{bmatrix}\begin{bmatrix} x \\ y \end{bmatrix} = \begin{bmatrix} x + 2y \\ 3x - y \end{bmatrix}$

c) $\begin{bmatrix} x \\ y \end{bmatrix} = \begin{bmatrix} 5 \\ 3 \end{bmatrix}$

20a) $AB = \begin{bmatrix} 13 & 16 \\ 11 & 14 \end{bmatrix}$

b) $(AB)^{-1} = \begin{bmatrix} \frac{7}{3} & -\frac{8}{3} \\ -\frac{11}{6} & \frac{13}{6} \end{bmatrix}$

c) $A^{-1} = \begin{bmatrix} \frac{4}{3} & -\frac{5}{3} \\ -\frac{1}{3} & \frac{2}{3} \end{bmatrix}$

d) $B^{-1} = \begin{bmatrix} 2 & 1 \\ -\frac{3}{2} & -\frac{1}{2} \end{bmatrix}$

e) $A^{-1}B^{-1} = \begin{bmatrix} \frac{31}{6} & \frac{13}{6} \\ -\frac{5}{3} & -\frac{2}{3} \end{bmatrix}$;

$B^{-1}A^{-1} = \begin{bmatrix} \frac{7}{3} & -\frac{8}{3} \\ -\frac{11}{6} & \frac{13}{6} \end{bmatrix}$

10. Complete the proof of the Inverse of a 2 × 2 Matrix Theorem. **See margin.**

11. Find $\det \begin{bmatrix} 3 & -12 \\ 6 & 5 \end{bmatrix}$. **87**

12. In order for the inverse of a 2 × 2 matrix to exist, what must be true about its determinant? **It must be nonzero.**

In 13 and 14, find the inverse of the matrix.

13. $\begin{bmatrix} -3 & 7 \\ 6 & -14 \end{bmatrix}$ **The inverse does not exist.**

14. $\begin{bmatrix} 8 & 3 \\ 2 & 7 \end{bmatrix}$ $\begin{bmatrix} 0.14 & -0.06 \\ -0.04 & 0.16 \end{bmatrix}$

In 15 and 16, explain why the matrix does not have an inverse.

15. $\begin{bmatrix} 4 & 2 \\ 2 & 1 \end{bmatrix}$ **Its determinant is zero.**

16. $\begin{bmatrix} 1 & 2 & 3 \\ 4 & 5 & 6 \end{bmatrix}$ **It is not an $n \times n$ matrix.**

Applying the Mathematics

17. a. *True or false.* $\det \begin{bmatrix} 90 & -75 \\ 63 & 112 \end{bmatrix} = -\det \begin{bmatrix} 63 & 112 \\ 90 & -75 \end{bmatrix}$. **True**

b. Generalize the result of part **a**: $\det \begin{bmatrix} W & X \\ Y & Z \end{bmatrix} = \underline{\ ?\ }$. $-\det \begin{bmatrix} Y & Z \\ W & X \end{bmatrix}$

c. Prove the generalization in part **b**. **See left.**

18. Find the determinant for the matrix representing R_θ. **1**

19. Consider the following system.

$$\begin{cases} x + 2y = 11 \\ 3x - y = 12 \end{cases}$$

a. Multiply $\begin{bmatrix} 1 & 2 \\ 3 & -1 \end{bmatrix}\begin{bmatrix} x \\ y \end{bmatrix}$. (The answer means that it is possible to represent the left side of the system by a matrix product.) **See left.**

b. Find $\begin{bmatrix} 1 & 2 \\ 3 & -1 \end{bmatrix}^{-1} \cdot \begin{bmatrix} \frac{1}{7} & \frac{2}{7} \\ \frac{3}{7} & -\frac{1}{7} \end{bmatrix}$

c. Multiply both sides of the equation $\begin{bmatrix} 1 & 2 \\ 3 & -1 \end{bmatrix}\begin{bmatrix} x \\ y \end{bmatrix} = \begin{bmatrix} 11 \\ 12 \end{bmatrix}$ on the left by the answer to part **b**. **See left.**

d. What is the solution to the system of equations? **$x = 5$, $y = 3$**

e. Use the method of parts **a–d** to solve the following system.
$x = -\frac{1}{2}$, $y = \frac{7}{3}$
$$\begin{cases} -8x + 3y = 11 \\ 4x + 3y = 5 \end{cases}$$

20. Let $A = \begin{bmatrix} 2 & 5 \\ 1 & 4 \end{bmatrix}$ and $B = \begin{bmatrix} -1 & -2 \\ 3 & 4 \end{bmatrix}$. **a–e, see left.**

a. Find AB. **b.** Find $(AB)^{-1}$.
c. Find A^{-1}. **d.** Find B^{-1}.
e. Find $A^{-1}B^{-1}$ and $B^{-1}A^{-1}$.
f. Generalize from the results of parts **b** and **e**.
$(AB)^{-1} = B^{-1}A^{-1} \neq A^{-1}B^{-1}$

Additional Answers

10. $\begin{bmatrix} \frac{d}{ad - bc} & \frac{-b}{ad - bc} \\ \frac{-c}{ad - bc} & \frac{a}{ad - bc} \end{bmatrix}\begin{bmatrix} a & b \\ c & d \end{bmatrix} = \begin{bmatrix} \frac{ad}{ad - bc} - \frac{bc}{ad - bc} & \frac{bd}{ad - bc} - \frac{bd}{ad - bc} \\ \frac{-ac}{ad - bc} + \frac{ac}{ad - bc} & \frac{-bc}{ad - bc} + \frac{ad}{ad - bc} \end{bmatrix}$

$= \begin{bmatrix} \frac{ad - bc}{ad - bc} & \frac{0}{ad - bc} \\ \frac{0}{ad - bc} & \frac{ad - bc}{ad - bc} \end{bmatrix} = \begin{bmatrix} 1 & 0 \\ 0 & 1 \end{bmatrix}$

21c) Sample:
$y = 3 \sin (2x)$
d) $y = 3 \sin (2x) =$
$3(2 \sin x \cos x) =$
$6 \sin x \cos x$

26) False; $M_1 M_2 =$
$\begin{bmatrix} \cos a & -\sin a \\ \sin a & \cos a \end{bmatrix}\begin{bmatrix} 1 & 0 \\ 0 & -1 \end{bmatrix}$
$= \begin{bmatrix} \cos a & \sin a \\ \sin a & -\cos a \end{bmatrix}$;
$M_2 M_1 =$
$\begin{bmatrix} 1 & 0 \\ 0 & -1 \end{bmatrix}\begin{bmatrix} \cos a & -\sin a \\ \sin a & \cos a \end{bmatrix}$
$= \begin{bmatrix} \cos a & -\sin a \\ -\sin a & -\cos a \end{bmatrix}$

27b)

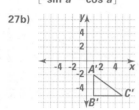

d)

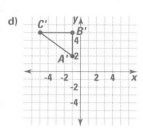

28) $x = 7, -\frac{7}{2} + \frac{7\sqrt{3}}{2} i,$
$-\frac{7}{2} - \frac{7\sqrt{3}}{2} i$

Review

21. Consider the graph of the function $y = 6 \sin x \cos x$.
  a. What is its amplitude? **3**   **b.** What is its period? π
  c. Use parts **a** and **b** to write another equation for the function. **See left.**
  d. Use a Double Angle Formula to rewrite the formula for the function and verify your answers in parts **a** and **b**. *(Lessons 4-7, 11-6)* **See left.**

In 22 and 23, rewrite each expression as the cosine or sine of a single argument. *(Lessons 11-5, 11-6)*

22. $\cos^2 \frac{\pi}{30} - \sin^2 \frac{\pi}{30}$ $\cos\left(\frac{\pi}{15}\right)$ **23.** $\cos 2\theta \cos \theta - \sin 2\theta \sin \theta$ $\cos 3\theta$

24. Simplify $\sin (a + b) + \sin (a - b)$. *(Lesson 11-5)* **2 sin a cos b**

In 25 and 26, let $M_1 = \begin{bmatrix} \cos a & -\sin a \\ \sin a & \cos a \end{bmatrix}$ and $M_2 = \begin{bmatrix} 1 & 0 \\ 0 & -1 \end{bmatrix}$.

25. What transformation is represented by each matrix?
  a. M_1 R_a **b.** M_2 *(Lessons 11-2, 11-4)* r_x

26. *True or false.* $M_1 M_2 = M_2 M_1$. Justify your answer. *(Lessons 11-1, 11-2)* **See left.**

27. Let $A = (2, -1)$, $B = (5, -1)$, and $C = (5, -5)$.
  a. Write a matrix M representing $\triangle ABC$. $M = \begin{bmatrix} 2 & 5 & 5 \\ -1 & -1 & -5 \end{bmatrix}$
  b. Draw $r_x \circ R_{90}(\triangle ABC)$. **See left.**
  c. Write a matrix M' representing $r_x \circ R_{90}(\triangle ABC)$. $M' = \begin{bmatrix} 1 & 1 & 5 \\ -2 & -5 & -5 \end{bmatrix}$
  d. Draw $R_{90} \circ r_x(\triangle ABC)$. **See left.**
  e. Write a matrix representing $R_{90} \circ r_x(\triangle ABC)$. $\begin{bmatrix} -1 & -1 & -5 \\ 2 & 5 & 5 \end{bmatrix}$
  (Previous course, Lessons 11-2, 11-3)

28. Find all three solutions to the equation $x^3 = 343$. *(Lesson 9-8)* **See left.**

In 29 and 30, an equation is given.
  a. Give all real solution(s) exactly.
  b. Estimate all real solution(s) to the nearest hundredth. *(Lessons 6-1, 6-6)*

29. $x^{2/3} = 81$
  a) $x = 729$ b) $x = 729.00$

30. $3^x = 20$
  a) $x = \log_3 20$ b) $x \approx 2.73$

Exploration

31. The matrix $\begin{bmatrix} 1 & 0 & 0 \\ 0 & 1 & 0 \\ 0 & 0 & 1 \end{bmatrix}$ is the identity for multiplication of 3×3 matrices.

Solve systems of equations to find the inverse of $\begin{bmatrix} 10 & 3 & 4 \\ -2 & 1 & 5 \\ 0 & 2 & -4 \end{bmatrix}$ in the set of 3×3 matrices.
$\begin{bmatrix} \frac{7}{90} & -\frac{1}{9} & \frac{11}{180} \\ \frac{2}{45} & \frac{2}{9} & \frac{29}{90} \\ \frac{1}{45} & \frac{1}{9} & -\frac{4}{45} \end{bmatrix}$

Practice
For more questions on SPUR Objectives, use **Lesson Master 11-7** (shown on page 733).

Assessment
Written Communication Have students **work in pairs.** Have Partner A write a 2×2 matrix that has an inverse and ask Partner B to find it. Then Partner A should check Partner B's answer by following the method of the check to **Example 1.** Have partners switch roles and repeat the activity. [Students demonstrate understanding of which 2×2 matrices have inverses and find the inverse of a 2×2 matrix.]

Extension
Project Update Project 3, *Inverse 3 × 3 Matrices*, and Project 4, *Matrix Codes*, on pages 745–746, relate to the content of this lesson.

Setting Up Lesson 11-8
Discuss **Question 31** to get students into matrices larger than 2×2.

737

Teaching **11-8**
Lesson

Warm-up
Multiply these matrices.

$$\begin{bmatrix} a & b & e \\ c & d & f \\ 0 & 0 & 1 \end{bmatrix} \begin{bmatrix} 1 & 2 & 5 \\ 3 & 4 & 6 \\ 0 & 0 & 1 \end{bmatrix}$$

$$\begin{bmatrix} a+3b & 2a+4b & 5a+6b+e \\ c+3d & 2c+4d & 5c+6d+f \\ 0 & 0 & 1 \end{bmatrix}$$

Notice that the third row is unaffected by the elements in the first two rows.

Notes on Reading
The purpose of this lesson is to introduce students to the mathematics of computer animation, without attempting to teach the topic for mastery. Therefore, Questions Covering the Reading are included, but there are no Questions Applying the Mathematics.

LESSON

11-8

Matrices in Computer Graphics

computer simulation of a space shuttle landing (Courtesy Evans & Sutherland)

The four pictures of the space shuttle above are a small part of a computer simulation of take-offs and landings. To make the shuttle appear to the human eye to be in smooth motion, at least 15 pictures must appear each second, each one showing the new position of the shuttle, its shadow, and any changes in background. The screen that produced this simulation has about 1024×1024 pixels. Thus, to change every pixel 15 times a second requires $15 \times 1024 \times 1024 \approx 15,700,000$ computations of images of points.

How do computer graphics terminals perform these operations fast enough to fool the human eye? One way is to make sure the hardware operates as fast as possible. Another is to use mathematics to make the computations for each picture as efficient as possible. Matrices play a role in accomplishing both. This lesson shows how ideas from this chapter form the foundation of computer graphics.

An Example of Animation
On page 697, you saw various images of a frog. Suppose you want to change the frog from the position on the left to the position on the right.

Every point of the frog, his eyes, nose, hands, feet, etc., must be transformed in a consistent manner. To produce such an image, graphics programmers generate a point matrix for the frog, just as you have done for simple geometric figures in this chapter, and then multiply that matrix by a matrix representing the transformation.

Lesson 11-8 Overview

Broad Goals This reading lesson covers three topics: the use of 3×3 matrices to represent transformations that map (x, y) onto $(ax + by + e, cx + dy + f)$; the rotation about a point other than the origin; the application of these first two ideas to computer graphics.

Perspective The importance of matrices in virtually every field of study and every industry has caused computer designers to incorporate matrix operations into their computer hardware. For three-dimensional graphics, the techniques outlined in this lesson are typical of "graphics engines" currently on the market.

To obtain a matrix for transformations in the plane that do not fix the origin, we represent

(x, y) as $\begin{bmatrix} x \\ y \\ 1 \end{bmatrix}$ and the transformation as

$\begin{bmatrix} a & b & e \\ c & d & f \\ 0 & 0 & 1 \end{bmatrix}$. This makes it possible to find

matrices for all isometries and similarity transformations in the plane, though that is not done here.

Specifically, this helps us find a matrix for a rotation whose center is not the origin. The idea is to translate the center to the origin;

Three steps describe the transformation of the frog. Take any point of the picture, say the spot on the frog at (50, 70).

1. Translate the spot from (50, 70) to the origin. Call this transformation T_1.
2. Rotate the image about the origin 22.5° clockwise. This is $R_{-22.5}$.
3. Translate the rotated frog so that the spot is at (155, 83). Call this second translation T_2.

If you can write each transformation as a matrix, then you can find a single matrix which represents the composite $T_2 \circ R_{-22.5} \circ T_1$. (Note: multiplication of matrices is associative, so grouping parentheses are not needed.)

(50, 70)   (155, 83)

Representing Translations by Matrices

Unfortunately, a translation cannot be represented by a 2×2 matrix. This is because any 2×2 matrix maps the origin onto the origin,

$$\begin{bmatrix} a & b \\ c & d \end{bmatrix}\begin{bmatrix} 0 \\ 0 \end{bmatrix} = \begin{bmatrix} 0 \\ 0 \end{bmatrix},$$

whereas under a translation with nonzero magnitude, the image of the origin is not the origin.

Computer graphics programs get around this dilemma by expressing matrices for points, translations, and rotations in *homogeneous form*. The **homogeneous form** for any point (x, y) is $(x, y, 1)$. Thus, the origin is $(0, 0, 1)$ in homogeneous form. The spot on the frog has homogeneous coordinates $(50, 70, 1)$, and the tip of the frog's right foot is $(59, 14, 1)$.

You may think that appending a 1 to the coordinates of every point doesn't gain much information. However, it allows you to write every translation of the plane as a 3×3 matrix. Consider the translation h units horizontally and k units vertically. This translation has the rule $T: (x, y) \rightarrow (x + h, y + k)$. In matrix form

$$T: \begin{bmatrix} x \\ y \end{bmatrix} \rightarrow \begin{bmatrix} x + h \\ y + k \end{bmatrix}.$$

T can be expressed using homogeneous coordinates with the matrix

$\begin{bmatrix} 1 & 0 & h \\ 0 & 1 & k \\ 0 & 0 & 1 \end{bmatrix}$, because $\begin{bmatrix} 1 & 0 & h \\ 0 & 1 & k \\ 0 & 0 & 1 \end{bmatrix}\begin{bmatrix} x \\ y \\ 1 \end{bmatrix} = \begin{bmatrix} x + h \\ y + k \\ 1 \end{bmatrix}$. In particular, the image

of the origin is $\begin{bmatrix} 1 & 0 & h \\ 0 & 1 & k \\ 0 & 0 & 1 \end{bmatrix}\begin{bmatrix} 0 \\ 0 \\ 1 \end{bmatrix} = \begin{bmatrix} h \\ k \\ 1 \end{bmatrix}$, as needed.

Now you can find matrices for the translations applied to the frog. The translation to the origin, T_1, requires a shift of 50 left and 70 down. Thus,

$$T_1 = \begin{bmatrix} 1 & 0 & -50 \\ 0 & 1 & -70 \\ 0 & 0 & 1 \end{bmatrix}.$$

The four-step process for producing three-dimensional graphics, which is described on page 741, is an over-simplification of the process actually used. It does, however, relate the major steps in the process to matrix multiplication.

To review Lesson 11-7 while in this lesson, you might wish to discuss the inverse $(T_{a,b})^{-1} = T_{-a,-b}$ of a translation $T_{a,b}$. In matrix form,

$$(T_{a,b})^{-1} = \begin{bmatrix} 1 & 0 & a \\ 0 & 1 & b \\ 0 & 0 & 1 \end{bmatrix}^{-1}$$

$$= \begin{bmatrix} 1 & 0 & -a \\ 0 & 1 & -b \\ 0 & 0 & 1 \end{bmatrix}.$$

You can check by multiplying that $(T_{a,b})^{-1} \circ T_{a,b} = I$, where here I is the identity for multiplication of 3×3 matrices.

Teaching Aid 102 contains the matrix $T_2 \circ R_{-22.5} \circ T_1$.

---

rotate there (since a formula is known for that), and then translate back.

The computer graphics in this lesson include the problem of picturing three-dimensional objects on a two-dimensional computer screen via the use of world coordinates.

Optional Activities

Have students find out more about how vector processors work by interviewing someone in the computer field or by researching the topic in an encyclopedia or on the internet. If a student in your class has a parent who works in the hardware computer field, you may want to see if that person would be willing to talk to the class about computers and his or her work.

Adapting to Individual Needs

Extra Help
As you discuss the composite transformation that moves the frog, point out that multiplication of matrices is associative. Thus, we would get the same results if we first multiplied the matrices for $R_{-22.5} \circ T_1$. Remind students, however, that multiplication of matrices is not generally commutative. Therefore, the order of the matrices representing $T_2 \circ R_{-22.5} \circ T_1$ cannot be changed.

T_2 translates 155 right and 83 up. So

$$T_2 = \begin{bmatrix} 1 & 0 & 155 \\ 0 & 1 & 83 \\ 0 & 0 & 1 \end{bmatrix}.$$

Now the rotation matrix must be made into a 3×3 matrix. In general, the 2×2 transformation matrix $\begin{bmatrix} a & b \\ c & d \end{bmatrix}$ has homogeneous form $\begin{bmatrix} a & b & 0 \\ c & d & 0 \\ 0 & 0 & 1 \end{bmatrix}$. So, the rotation matrix for the frog is

$$R_{-22.5^\circ} = \begin{bmatrix} \cos(-22.5^\circ) & -\sin(-22.5^\circ) & 0 \\ \sin(-22.5^\circ) & \cos(-22.5^\circ) & 0 \\ 0 & 0 & 1 \end{bmatrix}.$$

The composite transformation which moves the frog all at one time is

$$T_2 \qquad \circ \qquad R_{-22.5^\circ} \qquad \circ \qquad T_1.$$

Its matrix is $\begin{bmatrix} 1 & 0 & 155 \\ 0 & 1 & 83 \\ 0 & 0 & 1 \end{bmatrix} \begin{bmatrix} \cos(-22.5^\circ) & -\sin(-22.5^\circ) & 0 \\ \sin(-22.5^\circ) & \cos(-22.5^\circ) & 0 \\ 0 & 0 & 1 \end{bmatrix} \begin{bmatrix} 1 & 0 & -50 \\ 0 & 1 & -70 \\ 0 & 0 & 1 \end{bmatrix}$

$$\approx \left(\begin{bmatrix} 1 & 0 & 155 \\ 0 & 1 & 83 \\ 0 & 0 & 1 \end{bmatrix} \begin{bmatrix} .9239 & .3827 & 0 \\ -.3827 & .9239 & 0 \\ 0 & 0 & 1 \end{bmatrix} \right) \begin{bmatrix} 1 & 0 & -50 \\ 0 & 1 & -70 \\ 0 & 0 & 1 \end{bmatrix}$$

$$= \begin{bmatrix} .9239 & .3827 & 155 \\ -.3827 & .9239 & 83 \\ 0 & 0 & 1 \end{bmatrix} \begin{bmatrix} 1 & 0 & -50 \\ 0 & 1 & -70 \\ 0 & 0 & 1 \end{bmatrix}$$

$$= \begin{bmatrix} .9239 & .3827 & 82.016 \\ -.3827 & .9239 & 37.462 \\ 0 & 0 & 1 \end{bmatrix}.$$

The calculations can be checked by considering the spot, which moves from (50, 70) to (155, 83).

$$\begin{bmatrix} .9239 & .3827 & 82.016 \\ -.3827 & .9239 & 37.462 \\ 0 & 0 & 1 \end{bmatrix} \begin{bmatrix} 50 \\ 70 \\ 1 \end{bmatrix} = \begin{bmatrix} 155 \\ 83 \\ 1 \end{bmatrix}$$

To find the image of any point (x, y) on the frog, then, you would multiply the 3×3 matrix for $T_2 \circ R_{-22.5} \circ T_1$ by $\begin{bmatrix} x \\ y \\ 1 \end{bmatrix}$. Notice that the difficulty of the multiplication is not greatly increased by going from 2×2 form to homogeneous form. The last row of all 3×3 homogeneous form matrices is $[0 \quad 0 \quad 1]$, so that row contributes very little to the complexity of calculations.

Representing Three-Dimensional Transformations by Matrices

A generalization of this idea is used to picture three-dimensional objects on a two-dimensional computer screen. Just as 3×3 matrices are used for homogeneous coordinates of 2×2 matrices, 4×4 matrices can be used to transform the position and orientation of any 3-D object. The point (x, y, z) in 3-space has homogeneous coordinates $(x, y, z, 1)$, and a translation of 5 units in x, -3 units in y, and 2.5 units in z is represented by the matrix

$$\begin{bmatrix} 1 & 0 & 0 & 5 \\ 0 & 1 & 0 & -3 \\ 0 & 0 & 1 & 2.5 \\ 0 & 0 & 0 & 1 \end{bmatrix}.$$

Coordinate systems which are used for representing 3-D objects are called **world coordinates**. Modeling an object's change in position can be achieved by multiplying its world coordinates by a 4×4 transformation matrix. In this way, world coordinates for an object maintain a record of where the object is in space.

When viewing a 3-D object, someone must choose the viewing point. Where should the viewer be stationed? This is a separate issue from computing world coordinates. A viewer on the right side of the classroom has a different view of your teacher than a person on the left side. But the teacher's world coordinates are the same for both viewing positions. Once the viewing position is determined, then the view must be restricted, or clipped, to fit into the boundary of a computer screen, as though the computer screen were a window. Finally, the projection of coordinates must be accomplished, to determine where on the 2-D screen the 3-D points are to appear.

All of these steps can be performed with 4×4 matrices. Here is a summary.

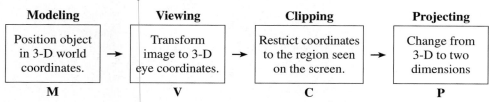

Modeling	**Viewing**	**Clipping**	**Projecting**
Position object in 3-D world coordinates.	Transform image to 3-D eye coordinates.	Restrict coordinates to the region seen on the screen.	Change from 3-D to two dimensions
M	**V**	**C**	**P**

The matrix product $P \cdot C \cdot V \cdot M$ is applied to the world coordinates to give points on the screen. (Note the order of the matrices—M represents the first-applied transformation.) Each frame of an animated sequence has a different product matrix.

The Role of High-Speed Computers

The complexity of three-dimensional graphics makes it difficult to do high-quality work on personal computers. The multiplications needed to perform the transformations take a long time. However, supercomputers and high-quality graphics workstations do matrix operations with great speed. *Vector processors* are designed to multiply a row times a column in

Setting Up Lesson 12-1

Homework Assign Lesson 12-1 to be read and at least the Questions Covering the Reading to be completed.

Notes on Questions

Question 10 There would be little point to having these matrices represent transformations if the matrix for the composite was not of the same form.

Question 11 Career Connection Most video games have been aimed at men and boys—probably because most software designers have been men. Recently video games have been designed specifically to appeal to women and girls, some with an eye to keeping girls interested in technology.

(Notes on Questions continue on page 744.)

Follow-up for Lesson **11-8**

Extension

Cooperative Learning Groups of students might want to use the ideas of this lesson to find a 3 × 3 matrix for every reflection and every rotation. The 3-step process on page 739 can be employed to do this. For reflections, translate a point on the reflecting line to the origin, next reflect over the line using the formula in **Questions 15–17** of Lesson 11-6, then translate back to the original point. For rotations, translate the center to the origin, rotate using the Rotation Matrix Theorem, and then translate back.

one step. On supercomputers these vector processors vastly shorten the time needed for each 4-matrix product. On graphics workstations, more than one processor might be devoted to the matrix multiplications. Here is how the work can be shared among processors. Consider the following multiplication.

$$\begin{bmatrix} 3 & -1 & 2 & 7 \\ 5 & 8 & 4 & 3 \\ 2 & 9 & -6 & 4 \\ 0 & 0 & 0 & 1 \end{bmatrix} \begin{bmatrix} 33 \\ 27 \\ 11 \\ 1 \end{bmatrix} = \begin{bmatrix} x' \\ y' \\ z' \\ 1 \end{bmatrix}$$

A human or microcomputer would have to perform 12 multiplications and 9 additions to find x', y', and z'. If there were three processors sharing the task, each could have 4 multiplications and 3 additions. For example, the first processor could find $x' = 3 \cdot 33 + -1 \cdot 27 + 2 \cdot 11 + 7 \cdot 1$. The second processor could find y', and the third, z'. So three processors would cut the computational time to $\frac{1}{3}$ that of a single processor. If the processors are vector processors, they can further reduce the time to that of a single multiplication step.

High-powered computers for graphics are organized to perform matrix multiplications quickly so that the motion they represent appears smooth and natural. When combined with shadows and light reflections, also computable with matrices, you can get the realism which fascinates viewers, as in the picture below.

scene from the Star Wars *trilogy*

QUESTIONS

Covering the Reading

1. A commercial film has 24 frames a second; a computer simulation has 5000 × 5000 pixels for each frame. How many point calculations must be performed per second for computer simulation of the commercial film?
   600,000,000
2. Write the homogeneous form of (3, −7). (3, −7, 1)

Additional Answers, page 743

10. Let $A = \begin{bmatrix} a_1 & a_2 & a_3 & 0 \\ a_4 & a_5 & a_6 & 0 \\ a_7 & a_8 & a_9 & 0 \\ 0 & 0 & 0 & 1 \end{bmatrix}$ and $B = \begin{bmatrix} b_1 & b_2 & b_3 & 0 \\ b_4 & b_5 & b_6 & 0 \\ b_7 & b_8 & b_9 & 0 \\ 0 & 0 & 0 & 1 \end{bmatrix}$.

Then $AB = \begin{bmatrix} a_1b_1 + a_2b_4 + a_3b_7 & a_1b_2 + a_2b_5 + a_3b_8 & a_1b_3 + a_2b_6 + a_3b_9 & 0 \\ a_4b_1 + a_5b_4 + a_6b_7 & a_4b_2 + a_5b_5 + a_6b_8 & a_4b_3 + a_5b_6 + a_6b_9 & 0 \\ a_7b_1 + a_8b_4 + a_9b_7 & a_7b_2 + a_8b_5 + a_9b_8 & a_7b_3 + a_8b_6 + a_9b_9 & 0 \\ 0 & 0 & 0 & 1 \end{bmatrix}$, which is also of homogeneous form.

4) $\begin{bmatrix} \frac{\sqrt{3}}{2} & -\frac{1}{2} & 0 \\ \frac{1}{2} & \frac{\sqrt{3}}{2} & 0 \\ 0 & 0 & 1 \end{bmatrix}$

6) $\begin{bmatrix} 1 & 0 & 0 \\ 0 & 1 & 0 \\ 0 & 0 & 1 \end{bmatrix}$

8) $\begin{bmatrix} 1 & 0 & 0 & -4 \\ 0 & 1 & 0 & 0.3 \\ 0 & 0 & 1 & 0 \\ 0 & 0 & 0 & 1 \end{bmatrix}$

9) **The bottom row of a 4 × 4 matrix that represents 3-D graphics has 3 zeros and a 1, so when such a matrix is multiplied by a point in homogeneous coordinates, the last number in the result is a 1 and does not have to be calculated. So, there are only 3 vector multiplications that need to be made — one each for x′, y′, and z′.**

12a) $\begin{bmatrix} 0.985 & 0.174 \\ -0.174 & 0.985 \end{bmatrix}$

b) $R_{10} =$
$\begin{bmatrix} 0.985 & -0.174 \\ 0.174 & 0.985 \end{bmatrix}$

14) **Sample:** $\begin{bmatrix} 1 & 2 \\ 3 & 6 \end{bmatrix}$

15) **If T_1 and T_2 are scale changes with $T_1: (x, y) \rightarrow (3x, y/2)$ and $T_2: (x, y) \rightarrow (x/3, 2y)$, then $T_1 \circ T_2 = I$, where I is the identity transformation.**

---

3. Write the nonhomogeneous form of (2, 0, -1, 1). **(2, 0, -1)**

4. Write the homogeneous form of the matrix for R_{30}, using exact values. **See left.**

5. Give the 2 × 2 matrix which has homogeneous form $\begin{bmatrix} -1 & 0 & 0 \\ 0 & -1 & 0 \\ 0 & 0 & 1 \end{bmatrix}$. $\begin{bmatrix} -1 & 0 \\ 0 & -1 \end{bmatrix}$

6. What is the homogeneous form of the 2 × 2 identity matrix? **See left.**

7. Find the image of the tip of the frog's right foot under the composite transformation in the lesson. **≈ (142, 28)**

8. Give a 4 × 4 matrix which represents a translation of -4 units in x, 0.3 units in y, and 0 units in z. **See left.**

9. Why are 3 processors, not 4, used to speed the multiplication of 4 × 4 matrices representing 3-D graphics? **See left.**

10. Prove that if A and B are 3 × 3 matrices in homogeneous form, then so is the product AB. **See margin.**

11. A microcomputer with a single processor runs a 3-D computer game with 10 frames per second. In an analysis of the computation steps, the designers found that the processor was doing computations involved in the matrix operations of 3-D graphics 60% of the time and running the video display 40% of the time. If they replace the single processor with a graphics "engine" that has three processors to handle matrix multiplications and if they don't change the speed of the video display, how many frames per second can they expect? (Assume that the three processors can do real-number multiplications and additions no faster than a single processor.) **≈ 16.7 frames per second**

Review

12. a. Give the entries of the matrix for R_{-10}, rounded to the nearest thousandth. **See left.**
    b. What matrix is the inverse of the matrix in part **a**? *(Lessons 11-4, 11-7)* **See left.**

13. Let $A = \begin{bmatrix} 1 & 0 \\ 0 & -1 \end{bmatrix}$.
    a. What transformation does A represent? r_x b) $\begin{bmatrix} 1 & 0 \\ 0 & -1 \end{bmatrix}$
    b. Find A^{-1}.
    c. What transformation does A^{-1} represent? *(Lessons 11-2, 11-7)* r_x

14. Give an example of a 2 × 2 matrix with a zero determinant. *(Lesson 11-7)* **See left.**

15. State a corresponding sentence involving transformations. **See left.**
$\begin{bmatrix} 3 & 0 \\ 0 & \frac{1}{2} \end{bmatrix} \cdot \begin{bmatrix} \frac{1}{3} & 0 \\ 0 & 2 \end{bmatrix} = \begin{bmatrix} 1 & 0 \\ 0 & 1 \end{bmatrix}$ *(Lessons 11-2, 11-7)*

16. Use matrices to solve the system $\begin{cases} 4x + y = 11 \\ -5x + 2y = 7 \end{cases}$. *(Lesson 11-7)*
$x = \frac{15}{13}, y = \frac{83}{13}$

Possible responses, page 745
1. (Continued)
Draw the figure. Input the type of transformation. GOSUB to appropriate subroutine. Draw the transformed figure.
Translation Subroutine
Input the horizontal and vertical translations; H, K. Define a 3 × 3 array to represent the translation

matrix $M = \begin{bmatrix} 1 & 0 & H \\ 0 & 1 & K \\ 0 & 0 & 1 \end{bmatrix}$.

Multiply $M \times$ VERT and store results in VERT. Return to main program.

Reflection subroutine
Input the axis of reflection (i.e., x-axis, y-axis, x = y). Define a 3 × 3 array to represent the appropriate reflection matrix (i.e.,

$M = \begin{bmatrix} 1 & 0 & 0 \\ 0 & -1 & 0 \\ 0 & 0 & 1 \end{bmatrix}$,

$M = \begin{bmatrix} -1 & 0 & 0 \\ 0 & 1 & 0 \\ 0 & 0 & 1 \end{bmatrix}$, or

$M = \begin{bmatrix} 0 & 1 & 0 \\ 1 & 0 & 0 \\ 0 & 0 & 1 \end{bmatrix}$.

Multiply $M \times$ VERT and store results in VERT. Return to main program.

Scale change subroutine
Input the size of the scale change; S. Define a 3 × 3 array to represent the scale change.

Matrix $M = \begin{bmatrix} S_a & 0 & 0 \\ 0 & S_b & 0 \\ 0 & 0 & 1 \end{bmatrix}$.

Multiply $M \times$ VERT and store results in VERT. Return to main program.

(Responses continue on page 744.)

Possible responses, page 745
1. The program should allow the user to input the vertices of a figure and the kind of transformation to be applied (i.e., translation, reflection, scale change, or rotation). It should contain a subroutine for each type of transformation. You may also want to have separate subroutines to multiply the matrices and to draw the figure. Here is an outline of the program. For reasons discussed in Lesson 11-8, the matrices have three rows even though the figure is two-dimensional. The third row contains only 0 0 1.

Main body of program
Input the number of vertices for the figure; N.
Input the vertices in a 3 × N array VERT (i.e., $x_j =$ VERT(1, J), $y_j =$ VERT(2, J), $z_j = 1 =$ VERT(3, J).

(Continued at the top of next column.)

Notes on Questions

Question 20 Error Alert Students may think they need to multiply the matrices to answer the question. This is not the case.

Question 24 A projection matrix does not represent a transformation because it is not one-to-one.

Additional Responses, page 745
1. (Continued)
Rotation subroutine
Input the angle of rotation in radians; ANGLE.
Define a 3 × 3 array to represent the rotation matrix
$M =$
$$\begin{bmatrix} \cos\,(\text{ANGLE}) & -\sin\,(\text{ANGLE}) & 0 \\ \sin\,(\text{ANGLE}) & \cos\,(\text{ANGLE}) & 0 \\ 0 & 0 & 1 \end{bmatrix}.$$
Multiply $M \times$ VERT and store results in VERT.
Return to main program.

2. a.

θ	d
20	14.95
25	16.48
30	17.71
35	18.57
40	19.01
45	18.97
50	18.45

Using intervals of 0.5°, we find that the maximum distance is approximately 19.05 meters and occur when $\theta = 42°$.
b. ≈ 18.87 meters
c. Answers will vary. The Olympic shot-putting record is 22.47 m ≈ 73'8¾".

744

---

17) $\sin 3\theta = 3 \sin \theta - 4 \sin^3 \theta$

18) $f(x) = 5(2 \cos^2 x - 1) = 5 \cos 2x$, so the graph has amplitude 5.

21a) $\begin{bmatrix} 3 & 5 \\ -1 & 4 \end{bmatrix}$

22a) $\begin{bmatrix} 1 & 0 \\ -\frac{1}{f_1} - \frac{1}{f_2} & 1 \end{bmatrix}$

b) $\begin{bmatrix} 1 - \frac{d}{f_2} & d \\ \frac{d - f_1 - f_2}{f_1 f_2} & 1 - \frac{d}{f_1} \end{bmatrix}$

744

---

17. Give a formula for $\sin 3\theta$ in terms of $\sin \theta$. *(Lesson 11-6)* **See left.**

18. Use a Double Angle Formula to show that the graph of the function $f(x) = 10 \cos^2 x - 5$ has amplitude 5. *(Lesson 11-6)* **See left.**

19. Give an exact value. *(Lessons 4-7, 11-5)*
  a. $\cos 255°$ $\frac{\sqrt{2} - \sqrt{6}}{4}$
  b. $\sin \frac{29\pi}{2}$ **1**

20. Suppose that a triangle is represented by the matrix $\begin{bmatrix} a & c & e \\ b & d & f \end{bmatrix}$. Tell what the following product represents.
$$\begin{bmatrix} \cos 25° & -\sin 25° \\ \sin 25° & \cos 25° \end{bmatrix} \cdot \begin{bmatrix} a & c & e \\ b & d & f \end{bmatrix} \quad \textit{(Lesson 11-4)}$$
a counterclockwise rotation of 25° about the origin

21. Suppose a 2 × 2 matrix is used to transform a figure. (1, 0) has image (3, -1), and (0, 1) has image (5, 4).
  a. What is the 2 × 2 matrix? **See left.**
  b. What is the image of (0, 0)? **(0, 0)**
  c. What is the image of (1, 1)? *(Lesson 11-3)* **(8, 3)**

22. Consider two thin lenses with focal lengths f_1 and f_2 at a distance d apart in the air. Physicists and engineers studying optics have shown that the product
$$\begin{bmatrix} 1 & 0 \\ -\frac{1}{f_1} & 1 \end{bmatrix}\begin{bmatrix} 1 & d \\ 0 & 1 \end{bmatrix}\begin{bmatrix} 1 & 0 \\ -\frac{1}{f_2} & 1 \end{bmatrix}$$
describes the image of light passing through this system. *(Lesson 11-1)*
  a. Calculate this product for the special case when the lenses touch each other, that is, when $d = 0$. **See left.**
  b. Calculate this product for the general case given above. **See left.**

Exploration

23. Estimate your world coordinates in your math class with relation to the front door of where you live. Let x be feet north; y be feet east; and z be feet up. (If you are 2 miles west of your house, for instance, you would have a y-coordinate of $-2 \cdot 5280 = -10560$. If you are on the third floor of your school and your front door is at the level of the school entrance, $z \approx 24$ for you.) **Answers will vary.**

24. One kind of projection matrix is $\begin{bmatrix} 1 & 0 & 0 & 0 \\ 0 & 1 & 0 & 0 \\ 0 & 0 & 0 & 0 \\ 0 & 0 & 0 & 1 \end{bmatrix}$. In what way does this matrix transform a 3-D object?
This matrix represents the projection of a 3-D object onto the xy-plane. It makes the z-coordinate 0 because the third row of the matrix contains all zeros.

---

3. a.

$$\begin{bmatrix} 2 & 1 & 1 \\ 1 & 4 & -3 \\ -1 & -3 & 3 \end{bmatrix} \cdot \begin{bmatrix} \frac{3}{7} & -\frac{6}{7} & -1 \\ 0 & 1 & 1 \\ \frac{1}{7} & \frac{5}{7} & 1 \end{bmatrix} = \begin{bmatrix} 1 & 0 & 0 \\ 0 & 1 & 0 \\ 0 & 0 & 1 \end{bmatrix};$$

$$\begin{bmatrix} \frac{3}{7} & -\frac{6}{7} & -1 \\ 0 & 1 & 1 \\ \frac{1}{7} & \frac{5}{7} & 1 \end{bmatrix} \cdot \begin{bmatrix} 2 & 1 & 1 \\ 1 & 4 & -3 \\ -1 & -3 & 3 \end{bmatrix} = \begin{bmatrix} 1 & 0 & 0 \\ 0 & 1 & 0 \\ 0 & 0 & 1 \end{bmatrix}$$

b.

$$\begin{bmatrix} 2 & 1 & 1 \\ 1 & 4 & -3 \\ -1 & -3 & 3 \end{bmatrix} \cdot \begin{bmatrix} x \\ y \\ z \end{bmatrix} = \begin{bmatrix} 0 \\ 5 \\ 7 \end{bmatrix} \Rightarrow \begin{bmatrix} 2x + y + z \\ x + 4y - 3z \\ -x - 3y + 3z \end{bmatrix} = \begin{bmatrix} 0 \\ 5 \\ 7 \end{bmatrix}$$

$\Rightarrow 2x + y + z = 0$, $x + 4y - 3z = 5$, and $-x - 3y + 3z = 7$

A project presents an opportunity for you to extend your knowledge of a topic related to the material of this chapter. You should allow more time for a project than you do for a typical homework question.

1 Programming 2-D Graphics

Write a program to display a figure and its images under some of the transformations described in this chapter. Include the images under a reflection, rotation, translation, and scale change.

2 Maximizing Shot-Put Distance

The formula $d = \frac{v^2 \sin 2\theta}{9.8}$, for the distance d in meters at which an object projected from ground level with an initial velocity v (in meters per second) at an angle θ to the horizontal will land, only applies if the points of release and landing are at the same horizontal level. This assumption is often not satisfied. For instance, in the shot put an athlete propels a shot, a heavy metal sphere, and tries to maximize the horizontal distance it travels. But a shot-putter releases the shot at about shoulder level, not at ground level. It can be shown that when the shot is released at a height h meters above the ground with a velocity of v meters per second at an angle θ with the horizontal, its horizontal displacement d is given by

$$d = \frac{v^2 \sin 2\theta}{19.6} + \frac{v^2 \cos \theta}{9.58} \sqrt{\sin^2 \theta + \frac{19.6\,h}{v^2}}.$$

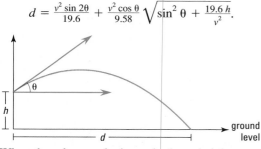

When the release velocity and release height are given, d is solely a function of θ.

a. World-class shot-putters can achieve a release velocity of 13 meters per second. Suppose for such a shot-putter $h = 1.90$ m. Construct a table of values for d as a function of θ for angles between 20° and 50°, in increments of 5°. Then, using smaller increments, find the angle θ to the nearest degree at which the shot should be released so as to achieve the maximum value of d. According to this model, what is the maximum distance possible for this shot-putter?

b. Consider a shorter athlete who releases the shot from a height of 1.7 m at the same velocity. What is the maximum distance this shot-putter can attain?

c. How do the data in parts **a** and **b** above compare to all-time records in the shot put for your school or local area? for the Olympics?

3 Inverse 3 × 3 Matrices

a. Two 3 × 3 matrices M and N are inverse matrices if and only if their product MN is the 3 × 3 identity matrix. Verify that

$$\begin{bmatrix} 2 & 1 & 1 \\ 1 & 4 & -3 \\ -1 & -3 & 3 \end{bmatrix}^{-1} = \begin{bmatrix} 3/7 & -6/7 & -1 \\ 0 & 1 & 1 \\ 1/7 & 5/7 & 1 \end{bmatrix}$$

b. Consider the system

$$2x + y + z = 0$$
$$x + 4y - 3z = 5$$
$$-x - 3y + 3z = 7.$$

Verify that you can represent this system with the matrix equation

Chapter 11 *Projects* **745**

Chapter 11 Projects

The projects relate chiefly to the content of the lessons of this chapter as follows:

Project	Lesson(s)
1	11-2, 11-3, 11-4
2	11-6
3	11-7
4	11-1, 11-2, 11-3, 11-4, 11-7

1 Programming 2-D Graphics
Students who do this project should be reminded to use the ideas of Lesson 11-8, so that they can use translations and other transformations that do not map (0,0) onto (0,0).

2 Maximizing Shot-Put Distance
This project extends the application of sin 2θ in the formula for the horizontal distance traveled by an object thrown at an angle. The extension is to the more realistic situation where the initial height of the object is not equal to its final height. Students who were interested in the simpler case in Lesson 11-6 might be encouraged to work on this project.

3 Inverse 3 × 3 Matrices This
project extends the use of matrices to solving systems of three equations in three unknowns. Students should do **Question 19** of Lesson 11-7 before beginning this project. The computer program in the project uses two-dimensional arrays.

Responses begin on page 743.

3. c. $\begin{bmatrix} \frac{3}{7} & -\frac{6}{7} & -1 \\ 0 & 1 & 1 \\ \frac{1}{7} & \frac{5}{7} & 1 \end{bmatrix} \cdot \begin{bmatrix} 2 & 1 & 1 \\ 1 & 4 & -3 \\ -1 & -3 & 3 \end{bmatrix} \cdot \begin{bmatrix} x \\ y \\ z \end{bmatrix} = \begin{bmatrix} \frac{3}{7} & -\frac{6}{7} & -1 \\ 0 & 1 & 1 \\ \frac{1}{7} & \frac{5}{7} & 1 \end{bmatrix} \begin{bmatrix} 0 \\ 5 \\ 7 \end{bmatrix}$;

$\begin{bmatrix} 1 & 0 & 0 \\ 0 & 1 & 0 \\ 0 & 0 & 1 \end{bmatrix} \cdot \begin{bmatrix} x \\ y \\ z \end{bmatrix} = \begin{bmatrix} -\frac{79}{7} \\ 12 \\ \frac{74}{7} \end{bmatrix} \Rightarrow \begin{bmatrix} x \\ y \\ z \end{bmatrix} = \begin{bmatrix} -\frac{79}{7} \\ 12 \\ \frac{74}{7} \end{bmatrix}$

$\Rightarrow x = -\frac{79}{7}, y = 12, z = \frac{74}{7}$

3. d. $\begin{bmatrix} 2 & 1 & 1 \\ 1 & 4 & -3 \\ -1 & -3 & 3 \end{bmatrix}^{-1} \approx \begin{bmatrix} .42857 & -.85714 & -1 \\ 0 & 1 & 1 \\ .14286 & .71428 & 1 \end{bmatrix} \approx$

$\begin{bmatrix} \frac{3}{7} & -\frac{6}{7} & -1 \\ 0 & 1 & 1 \\ \frac{1}{7} & \frac{5}{7} & 1 \end{bmatrix}$ **which verifies the program.**

(Responses continue on page 746.)

4 Matrix Codes The code is based on modular arithmetic; students who take *Precalculus and Discrete Mathematics* will study that arithmetic. Students may not realize why the matrix method provides a particularly nice way to devise a secret code. They may be familiar with simple substitutions. For example, if
W X Y Z A B C D E F G H I J K L M
N O P Q R S T U V
are substituted for
A B C D E F G H I J K L M N O P Q
R S T U V W X Y Z,
you could code MATH TEAM as IWPD PAWI, but then each letter always translates into the same code. Since E and T are the most common letters of the English alphabet, these translation-substitution ciphers are trivial for code-breakers to decode. They can quickly determine the codes for E and T and deduce the rest of the message from common words such as THE or THEN. Matrices provide an easy way of getting around this problem.

In serious use of codes, such as those used by the military or by business to secure messages, documents, or moneys, even matrix coding and decoding is too simple. More complex mathematical schemes are needed. Mainly for this reason, the National Security Agency is the largest U.S. employer of mathematicians with Ph.D.'s.

ZIVOGQWSCSLV

$$\begin{bmatrix} 2 & 1 & 1 \\ 1 & 4 & -3 \\ -1 & -3 & 3 \end{bmatrix} \cdot \begin{bmatrix} x \\ y \\ z \end{bmatrix} = \begin{bmatrix} 0 \\ 5 \\ 7 \end{bmatrix}.$$

c. Multiply both sides of the matrix representation for the system by the inverse matrix in part **a**. What is the solution to the system?

d. Use a calculator to compute the inverse of $\begin{bmatrix} 2 & 1 & 1 \\ 1 & 4 & -3 \\ -1 & -3 & 3 \end{bmatrix}$, and verify that it is equal to the matrix in part **a**.

e. Solve the system

$$\begin{aligned} 3x + \ \ y + z &= 4 \\ 2x - 2y - z &= 2 \\ 3x - \ \ y - z &= 1 \end{aligned}$$

using a calculator. Check your results by solving the system through adding or subtracting equations.

4 Matrix Codes

An application of matrices to codes was found in 1929–31 by the mathematician Lester Hill. To encode a message, put its letters into 2×2 matrices four at a time. For instance, to encode the message HELP ME PLEASE, use the matrices $\begin{bmatrix} H & E \\ L & P \end{bmatrix}$, $\begin{bmatrix} M & E \\ P & L \end{bmatrix}$, and $\begin{bmatrix} E & A \\ S & E \end{bmatrix}$. Now assign an integer to each letter using A = 1, B = 2, C = 3, … , Z = 26. This yields the matrices $\begin{bmatrix} 8 & 5 \\ 12 & 16 \end{bmatrix}$, $\begin{bmatrix} 13 & 5 \\ 16 & 12 \end{bmatrix}$, and $\begin{bmatrix} 5 & 1 \\ 19 & 5 \end{bmatrix}$. Next, multiply each matrix on the left by an *encoding matrix*, one whose determinant is 1 or -1. We choose the matrix $\begin{bmatrix} 3 & -2 \\ 1 & -1 \end{bmatrix}$. The product of this encoding matrix with the first matrix of the message is $\begin{bmatrix} 0 & -17 \\ -4 & -11 \end{bmatrix}$. Now translate the numbers back to letters, adding or subtracting multiples of 26 to each number if it is not from 1 to 26. For instance, the first coded matrix becomes $\begin{bmatrix} 26 & 9 \\ 22 & 15 \end{bmatrix}$, which is $\begin{bmatrix} Z & I \\ V & O \end{bmatrix}$.

a. Multiply matrices to verify that the second and third coded matrices are $\begin{bmatrix} G & Q \\ W & S \end{bmatrix}$ and $\begin{bmatrix} C & S \\ L & V \end{bmatrix}$. So the coded message is ZIVOGQWSCSLV.

b. Notice that, by using matrices, the same letter in the original message HELPMEPLEASE is replaced by different letters in the coded message. This is what makes the matrix coding more difficult to decipher. But, if you know the encoding matrix, you can decipher the message using its inverse, the *decoding matrix*. In this case, the decoding matrix is $\begin{bmatrix} 3 & -2 \\ 1 & -1 \end{bmatrix}^{-1}$, or $\begin{bmatrix} 1 & -2 \\ 1 & -3 \end{bmatrix}$. Multiplying each of the coded matrices by this inverse gets you back to the original message. For instance, $\begin{bmatrix} 1 & -2 \\ 1 & -3 \end{bmatrix} \cdot \begin{bmatrix} 26 & 9 \\ 22 & 15 \end{bmatrix} = \begin{bmatrix} -18 & -21 \\ -40 & -36 \end{bmatrix}$ which becomes (after adding multiples of 26) $\begin{bmatrix} 8 & 5 \\ 12 & 16 \end{bmatrix} = \begin{bmatrix} H & E \\ L & P \end{bmatrix}$. Verify that multiplication of the second and third coded matrices by the decoding matrix retrieves the rest of the message.

c. Make up your own message of at least 24 letters in length and encode it using a different coding matrix than the one shown here.

d. Show that your message can be decoded by using the inverse of your encoding matrix.

e. Why is it important that the determinant of the coding matrix be 1 or -1?

Additional responses, page 746

e. We get $\begin{bmatrix} 3 & 1 & 1 \\ 2 & -2 & -1 \\ 3 & -1 & -1 \end{bmatrix}^{-1} \approx \begin{bmatrix} .16667 & 0 & .16667 \\ -.16667 & -1 & .83333 \\ .66667 & 1 & -1.33333 \end{bmatrix} \approx \begin{bmatrix} \frac{1}{6} & -\frac{1}{6} & -1 \\ -\frac{1}{6} & -1 & \frac{5}{6} \\ \frac{2}{3} & 1 & -\frac{4}{3} \end{bmatrix}$.

Since $\begin{bmatrix} \frac{1}{6} & -\frac{1}{6} & -1 \\ -\frac{1}{6} & -1 & \frac{5}{6} \\ \frac{2}{3} & 1 & -\frac{4}{3} \end{bmatrix} \cdot \begin{bmatrix} 4 \\ 2 \\ 1 \end{bmatrix} = \begin{bmatrix} \frac{5}{6} \\ -\frac{11}{6} \\ \frac{10}{3} \end{bmatrix}$, the solution to the system is $x = \frac{5}{6}$, $y = -\frac{11}{6}$, and $z = \frac{10}{3}$.

Substituting these values into the left side of each original equation we get
$3\left(\frac{5}{6}\right) + -\frac{11}{6} + \frac{10}{3} = 4$,
$2\left(\frac{5}{6}\right) - 2\left(-\frac{11}{6}\right) - \frac{10}{3} = 2$, and
$3\left(\frac{5}{6}\right) - \left(-\frac{11}{6}\right) - \frac{10}{3} = 1$.
So our solution checks.

SUMMARY

An $m \times n$ matrix is a rectangular array of elements arranged in m rows and n columns. If $m = n$, the matrix is a square matrix.

If A and B are matrices, the product $C = AB$ exists if the number of columns of A equals the number of rows of B. The element in the ith row and jth column of C is the sum of the term-by-term products of the ith row of A and the jth row of B. Matrix multiplication has many applications. If the elements of A represent coefficients, the elements of B are variables, and C is a column matrix of constants, then $AB = C$ represents a linear system of equations. If A contains numbers of items and B represents corresponding unit values of the items, then AB gives total values of the items.

Some geometric figures and some transformations can be represented by 2×2 matrices. Any n-gon can be represented by a $2 \times n$ matrix whose columns are its vertices. If M represents a transformation T and P represents a polygon, then the product MP represents $T(P)$. This enables transformations to be performed by using matrices. If M_1 and M_2 are matrices for transformations T_1 and T_2, then M_1M_2 represents $T_1 \circ T_2$. Thus composites of transformations can also be represented by matrices. Lifelike computer animations

can be performed by multiplying a large number of points by successive matrices representing the transformations desired of the animated figure.

Some of the transformations for which 2×2 matrices exist are: reflections over the x-axis, y-axis, and line $x = y$; all rotations with center at the origin; all size changes with center $(0, 0)$; all scale changes of the form $(x, y) \rightarrow (ax, by)$. The Matrix Basis Theorem provides an easy way to recall the matrix for a given transformation; you need only know the images of $(1, 0)$ and $(0, 1)$ under that transformation.

If a matrix with a non-zero determinant exists for a transformation, then the multiplicative inverse of that matrix is the matrix for the inverse of the transformation. Matrices and their inverses are useful for solving systems of equations. Any 2×2 matrix will have an inverse if its determinant is not equal to zero.

From the matrix for a rotation, formulas for $\cos (x + y)$ and $\sin (x + y)$ can be rather quickly derived. From these formulas, formulas for $\cos (x - y)$, $\sin (x - y)$, $\cos 2x$, and $\sin 2x$ follow. These formulas enable exact values for certain cosines and sines to be determined.

VOCABULARY

Below are the most important terms and phrases for this chapter. You should be able to give a general description and a specific example of each and a precise definition for those marked with an asterisk (*).

Lesson 11-1
matrix
element
*dimensions of a matrix
row matrix
column matrix
matrix multiplication
product matrix

Lesson 11-2
point matrix
matrix representing a transformation
2×2 Identity Matrix

Lesson 11-3
Matrices for Rotations Theorem
Matrix Basis Theorem

Lesson 11-4
Rotation Matrix Theorem

Lesson 11-5
Addition Identities for the Cosine and Sine

Lesson 11-6
Double Angle Formulas
Half Angle Formulas

Lesson 11-7
*inverse transformations
*inverse matrices
Inverse of a 2×2 Matrix Theorem
determinant, det

Chapter 11 *Summary and Vocabulary* **747**

4. a. $\begin{bmatrix} 3 & -2 \\ 1 & -1 \end{bmatrix}\begin{bmatrix} 13 & 5 \\ 16 & 12 \end{bmatrix} = \begin{bmatrix} 7 & -9 \\ -3 & -7 \end{bmatrix} \Rightarrow \begin{bmatrix} 7 & 17 \\ 23 & 19 \end{bmatrix} \Rightarrow \begin{bmatrix} G & Q \\ W & S \end{bmatrix}$

$\begin{bmatrix} 3 & -2 \\ 1 & -1 \end{bmatrix}\begin{bmatrix} 5 & 1 \\ 19 & 5 \end{bmatrix} = \begin{bmatrix} -23 & -7 \\ -14 & -4 \end{bmatrix} \Rightarrow \begin{bmatrix} 3 & 19 \\ 12 & 22 \end{bmatrix} \Rightarrow \begin{bmatrix} C & S \\ L & V \end{bmatrix}$

b. $\begin{bmatrix} 1 & -2 \\ 1 & -3 \end{bmatrix}\begin{bmatrix} 7 & 17 \\ 23 & 19 \end{bmatrix} = \begin{bmatrix} -39 & -21 \\ -62 & -40 \end{bmatrix} \Rightarrow \begin{bmatrix} 13 & 5 \\ 16 & 12 \end{bmatrix} \Rightarrow \begin{bmatrix} M & E \\ P & L \end{bmatrix}$

$\begin{bmatrix} 1 & -2 \\ 1 & -3 \end{bmatrix}\begin{bmatrix} 3 & 19 \\ 12 & 22 \end{bmatrix} = \begin{bmatrix} -21 & -25 \\ -33 & -47 \end{bmatrix} \Rightarrow \begin{bmatrix} 5 & 1 \\ 19 & 5 \end{bmatrix} \Rightarrow \begin{bmatrix} E & A \\ S & E \end{bmatrix}$

c. **Answers will vary.**
d. **Answers will vary.**
e. **The determinant must be 1 or -1 so that the inverse of the matrix is composed of integers and not rational numbers. If the inverse had rational numbers, the product with the decoding matrix will yield rational numbers which may not correspond to a single letter of the alphabet.**

Progress Self-Test

For the development of mathematical competence, feedback and correction, along with the opportunity to practice, are necessary. The Progress Self-Test provides the opportunity for feedback and correction; the Chapter Review provides additional opportunities and practice. We cannot overemphasize the importance of these end-of-chapter materials. It is at this point that the material "gels" for many students, allowing them to solidify skills and understanding. In general, student performance should be markedly improved after these pages.

Assign the Progress Self-Test as a one-night assignment. Worked-out *solutions* for all questions are in the Selected Answers section of the student book. Encourage students to take the Progress Self-Test honestly, grade themselves, and then be prepared to discuss the test in class.

Advise students to pay special attention to those Chapter Review questions (pages 749–751) that correspond to questions missed on the Progress Self-Test.

Additional Answers

2. $VP = \begin{bmatrix} 2.591 \\ 2.45 \\ 1.059 \end{bmatrix}$

3. To obtain the first row of *VP*, we multiplied the percentage of urban voters that are expected to vote Democrat by the total number of registered urban voters, added the percentage of rural voters that are expected to vote Democrat times the total number of rural voters, and then added the percentage of suburban voters that are expected to vote Democrat times the total number of suburban voters. Thus the entry in the first row is the total number of registered voters expected to vote Democrat. Similarly, the second and third rows represent the total number of voters expected to vote Republican and Independent, respectively.

748

PROGRESS SELF-TEST

Take this test as you would take a test in class. You will need graph paper and a calculator. Then check the test yourself using the solutions at the back of the book.

In 1–3, use the following matrices. *P* gives the number of registered voters (in millions) in each part of a state. *V* represents the percent of registered voters in those areas telling how they would expect to vote in an election.

$$\begin{array}{l} \text{Urban} \\ \text{Rural} \\ \text{Suburban} \end{array} \begin{bmatrix} 3.4 \\ 0.6 \\ 2.1 \end{bmatrix} = P$$

	Urban	Rural	Suburban
Democrat	.50	.47	.29
Republican	.29	.41	.58
Independent	.21	.12	.13

$= V$

1. How many people in the state are expected to vote Republican? **2.45 million**

2. Find *VP*. **See margin.**

3. What does the matrix *VP* represent? **See margin.**

4. Find the product $\begin{bmatrix} 5 & -1 \\ 2 & 0 \end{bmatrix}\begin{bmatrix} 3 & 8 \\ -1 & 1 \end{bmatrix}$. $\begin{bmatrix} 16 & 39 \\ 6 & 16 \end{bmatrix}$

5. Suppose *M* is a 3 × 4 matrix, *N* is a 4 × *t* matrix, and *Z* is a 3 × 5 matrix. If *MN* = *Z*, find the value of *t*. **t = 5**

In 6–8 use the figure below.

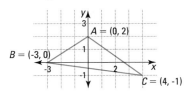

6. Write a matrix *M* for △*ABC*. $\begin{bmatrix} 0 & -3 & 4 \\ 2 & 0 & -1 \end{bmatrix}$

7. Find *XM*, where $X = \begin{bmatrix} -1 & 0 \\ 0 & 2 \end{bmatrix}$. $\begin{bmatrix} 0 & 3 & -4 \\ 4 & 0 & -2 \end{bmatrix}$

8. Graph the image represented by *XM*. **See margin.**

748

---

9) See margin.

9. **a.** Give a matrix representing the transformation for the reflection over the line $y = x$.
   b. Use the matrix in part **a** to show that the transformation $r_{y=x}$ is its own inverse.

10. *Multiple choice.* Which matrix represents R_{30}? **b**

    (a) $\begin{bmatrix} \sqrt{3}/2 & 1/2 \\ 1/2 & \sqrt{3}/2 \end{bmatrix}$ (b) $\begin{bmatrix} \sqrt{3}/2 & -1/2 \\ 1/2 & \sqrt{3}/2 \end{bmatrix}$

    (c) $\begin{bmatrix} -\sqrt{3}/2 & -1/2 \\ 1/2 & -\sqrt{3}/2 \end{bmatrix}$ (d) $\begin{bmatrix} 1/2 & -\sqrt{3}/2 \\ \sqrt{3}/2 & 1/2 \end{bmatrix}$

    (e) $\begin{bmatrix} 1/2 & \sqrt{3}/2 \\ -\sqrt{3}/2 & 1/2 \end{bmatrix}$

11. A figure is transformed by $R_{180} \circ r_x$.
    a. What transformation is done first? r_x
    b. What single matrix represents the composite? $\begin{bmatrix} -1 & 0 \\ 0 & 1 \end{bmatrix}$

12. Let $P = (0, 0)$, $Q = (1, 0)$ and $R = (0, 1)$. What is the image of △*PQR* under a rotation of magnitude θ? **See margin.**

13. Write the following expression as the sine or cosine of a single argument:
    $\sin 83° \cos 42° - \cos 83° \sin 42°$ **sin 41°**

14. Using a formula for $\cos(\alpha + \beta)$, simplify $\cos(\pi + \theta)$. **−cos θ**

15. If $\sin A = 0.40$ and *A* is acute, find $\sin 2A$. **≈ 0.733**

16. Find the inverse of $C = \begin{bmatrix} 1 & -1 \\ 3 & 5 \end{bmatrix}$. $\begin{bmatrix} \frac{5}{8} & \frac{1}{8} \\ -\frac{3}{8} & \frac{1}{8} \end{bmatrix}$

17. Show that $G = \begin{bmatrix} 3x & 6 \\ 5x & 10 \end{bmatrix}$ has no inverse. **See margin.**

18. **a.** Write a matrix equation to represent the system.
    $\begin{cases} 3x - y = 6 \\ 5x - 2y = 11 \end{cases}$ $\begin{bmatrix} 3 & -1 \\ 5 & -2 \end{bmatrix}\begin{bmatrix} x \\ y \end{bmatrix} = \begin{bmatrix} 6 \\ 11 \end{bmatrix}$
    b. Solve the system in part **a**.
    $\begin{bmatrix} x \\ y \end{bmatrix} = \begin{bmatrix} 1 \\ -3 \end{bmatrix}$

8.

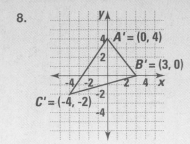

9. **a.** $\begin{bmatrix} 0 & 1 \\ 1 & 0 \end{bmatrix}$

   b. $\begin{bmatrix} 0 & 1 \\ 1 & 0 \end{bmatrix}\begin{bmatrix} 0 & 1 \\ 1 & 0 \end{bmatrix} = \begin{bmatrix} 1 & 0 \\ 0 & 1 \end{bmatrix}$, the identity matrix. So $r_{y=x} \circ r_{y=x} = I$.

12. $\begin{bmatrix} 0 & \cos\theta & -\sin\theta \\ 0 & \sin\theta & \cos\theta \end{bmatrix}$.

17. $\det G = 3x \cdot 10 - 6 \cdot 5x = 30x - 30x = 0$. A matrix with a zero determinant has no inverse.

CHAPTER REVIEW

Questions on SPUR Objectives

SPUR stands for **S**kills, **P**roperties, **U**ses, and **R**epresentations. The Chapter Review questions are grouped according to the SPUR Objectives for this chapter.

SKILLS DEAL WITH THE PROCEDURES USED TO GET ANSWERS.

Objective A: *Multiply matrices, when possible.*
(Lesson 11-1)

In 1–4, use the following matrices.

$$A = \begin{bmatrix} 1/2 & 3 \\ 5 & -1 \end{bmatrix} \qquad B = \begin{bmatrix} 1 & 5 & -1 \\ -1 & 0 & 1 \end{bmatrix}$$

$$C = \begin{bmatrix} x \\ 3 \end{bmatrix} \qquad D = \begin{bmatrix} 1 & -7 \end{bmatrix}$$

1. *Multiple choice.* Which of the following products is not possible? **c**
   (a) AC (b) CD
   (c) BA (d) A^2C

2. Find AB. **See below.**

3. Find DC. **$[x - 21]$**

4. Find A^2. **See below.**

Objective B: *Use matrices to solve systems of equations.* *(Lesson 11-7)*

5. Solve for x: $\begin{bmatrix} 1 & 2 \\ -1 & 1 \end{bmatrix}\begin{bmatrix} x \\ 1 \end{bmatrix} = \begin{bmatrix} 7 \\ -4 \end{bmatrix}$.
   $x = 5$

6. Consider the system $\begin{cases} x + 3y = 11 \\ 2x - y = 8 \end{cases}$.
   a. Represent the system by a matrix equation.
   b. Find the inverse of the coefficient matrix in part **a**.
   c. Multiply on the left both sides of the matrix equation by the answer in part **b**.
   d. What is the solution to the system of equations? **$x = 5$, $y = 2$**
   a–c) See margin.

2) $\begin{bmatrix} -\frac{5}{2} & \frac{5}{2} & \frac{5}{2} \\ 6 & 25 & -6 \end{bmatrix}$ 4) $\begin{bmatrix} \frac{61}{4} & -\frac{3}{2} \\ -\frac{5}{2} & 16 \end{bmatrix}$

In 7 and 8, solve the given system of equations using matrices.

7. $\begin{cases} 5x + 2y = 6 \\ 10x - 10y = -9 \end{cases}$ $x = \frac{3}{5}, y = \frac{3}{2}$

8. $\begin{cases} 8x + 3y = 10 \\ x + 8y = -14 \end{cases}$ $x = 2, y = -2$

9. Solve the system $\begin{cases} x + 2y + 3z = 10 \\ 3x + y + 2z = 13, \\ 2x + 3y + z = 13 \end{cases}$
   given that

   $$\begin{bmatrix} 1 & 2 & 3 \\ 3 & 1 & 2 \\ 2 & 3 & 1 \end{bmatrix}^{-1} = \begin{bmatrix} -\frac{5}{18} & \frac{7}{18} & \frac{1}{18} \\ \frac{1}{18} & -\frac{5}{18} & \frac{7}{18} \\ \frac{7}{18} & \frac{1}{18} & -\frac{5}{18} \end{bmatrix}.$$

   $x = 3, y = 2, z = 1$

Objective C: *Find the inverse of a 2 × 2 matrix.*
(Lesson 11-7)   **See margin.**
In 10 and 11, find the inverse of the given matrix.

10. $\begin{bmatrix} 2 & 1 \\ -5 & 4 \end{bmatrix}$ 11. $\begin{bmatrix} \cos 40° & -\sin 40° \\ \sin 40° & \cos 40° \end{bmatrix}$

12. Find $\begin{bmatrix} \frac{2}{9} & \frac{1}{9} \\ -\frac{1}{3} & \frac{4}{3} \end{bmatrix}^{-1} \cdot \begin{bmatrix} 4 & -\frac{1}{3} \\ 1 & \frac{2}{3} \end{bmatrix}$

13. *Multiple choice.* Tell which two of the following matrices have no inverses. **a, e**
    (a) $\begin{bmatrix} 0 & 0 \\ 0 & 0 \end{bmatrix}$ (b) $\begin{bmatrix} 1 & 0 \\ 0 & 1 \end{bmatrix}$
    (c) $\begin{bmatrix} 0 & 1 \\ 1 & 0 \end{bmatrix}$ (d) $\begin{bmatrix} -2 & 4 \\ -6 & 8 \end{bmatrix}$
    (e) $\begin{bmatrix} -2 & 4 \\ -1 & 2 \end{bmatrix}$

Additional Answers

6. a. $\begin{bmatrix} 1 & 3 \\ 2 & -1 \end{bmatrix}\begin{bmatrix} x \\ y \end{bmatrix} = \begin{bmatrix} 11 \\ 8 \end{bmatrix}$

   b. $\begin{bmatrix} \frac{1}{7} & \frac{3}{7} \\ \frac{2}{7} & -\frac{1}{7} \end{bmatrix}$

   c. $\begin{bmatrix} \frac{1}{7} & \frac{3}{7} \\ \frac{2}{7} & -\frac{1}{7} \end{bmatrix}\begin{bmatrix} 1 & 3 \\ 2 & -1 \end{bmatrix}\begin{bmatrix} x \\ y \end{bmatrix}$

   $= \begin{bmatrix} \frac{1}{7} & \frac{3}{7} \\ \frac{2}{7} & -\frac{1}{7} \end{bmatrix}\begin{bmatrix} 11 \\ 8 \end{bmatrix}$

   $\Rightarrow \begin{bmatrix} x \\ y \end{bmatrix} = \begin{bmatrix} 5 \\ 2 \end{bmatrix}$

10. $\begin{bmatrix} \frac{4}{13} & -\frac{1}{13} \\ \frac{5}{13} & \frac{2}{13} \end{bmatrix}$

11. $\begin{bmatrix} \cos 40° & \sin 40° \\ -\sin 40° & \cos 40° \end{bmatrix}$

Chapter 11 Review

Resources

From the ***Teacher's Resource File***
■ Answer Master for Chapter 11 Review
■ Assessment Sourcebook: Chapter 11 Test, Forms A-D Chapter 11 Test, Cumulative Form

Additional Resources
■ Quiz and Test Writer

The main objectives for the chapter are organized in the Chapter Review under the four types of understanding this book promotes—Skills, Properties, Uses, and Representations.

Whereas end-of chapter material may be considered optional in some texts, in *UCSMP Functions, Statistics, and Trigonometry* we have selected these objectives and questions with the expectation that they will be covered. Students should be able to answer these questions with about 85% accuracy after studying the chapter.

You may assign these questions over a single night to help students prepare for a test the next day, or you may assign the questions over a two-day period. If you work the questions over two days, then we recommend assigning the *evens* for homework the first night so that students get feedback in class the next day, then assigning the *odds* the night before the test, because answers are provided to the odd-numbered questions.

It is effective to ask students which questions they still do not understand and use the day or days as a total class discussion of the material which the class finds most difficult.

Assessment

Evaluation The Assessment Sourcebook provides five forms of the Chapter 11 Test. Forms A and B present parallel versions in a short-answer format. Forms C and D offer performance assessment. The fifth test is Chapter 11 Test, Cumulative Form. About 50% of this test covers Chapter 11, 25% of it covers Chapter 10, and 25% of it covers earlier chapters.

For information on grading, see *General Teaching Suggestions; Grading* in the *Professional Sourcebook*, which begins on page T20 in the Teacher's Edition.

Feedback After students have taken the test for Chapter 11 and you have scored the results, return the tests to students for discussion. Class discussion of the questions that caused trouble for the most students can be very effective in identifying and clarifying misunderstandings. You might want to have them write down the items they missed and work, either in groups or at home, to correct them. It is important for students to receive feedback on every chapter test, and we recommend that students see and correct their mistakes before proceeding too far into the next chapter.

Additional Answers

17. Sample: a rotation about the origin, a reflection over a line containing the origin, and the identity transformation.

20. $\frac{3 + 4\sqrt{3}}{10}$

24. $\cos 4\theta = 8 \cos^4\theta - 8 \cos^2\theta + 1$

25. $\sin 2A$

PROPERTIES DEAL WITH THE PRINCIPLES BEHIND THE MATHEMATICS.
20, 24–26, 28, 29) See margin.

Objective D: *Apply properties of matrices and matrix multiplication.* (*Lessons 11-1, 11-3, 11-7*)

In 14 and 15, an equation relating the matrices M, N, and P is given. The matrix M has dimensions 4×2, and the matrix P has dimensions 4×5. Give the dimensions of N.

14. $MN = P$ **2 × 5**

15. $PN = M$ **5 × 2**

16. *Multiple choice.* Which of the following statements about 2×2 matrices R, S, and T is false? **d**

   (a) RS is also a 2×2 matrix.

   (b) $(RS)T = R(ST)$

   (c) There is a matrix I such that $RI = IR = R$

   (d) $RS = SR$

17. Name three types of transformations that can be represented by 2×2 matrices.
   See margin.

Objective E: *Apply the Addition and Double Angle Formulas.* (*Lessons 11-5, 11-6*)

In 18 and 19, state the exact value.

18. $\sin 105°$ $\frac{\sqrt{6} + \sqrt{2}}{4}$ 19. $\cos \frac{5\pi}{12}$ $\frac{\sqrt{6} - \sqrt{2}}{4}$

In 20 and 21, A and B are acute angles with $\sin A = .8$ and $\cos B = .5$. Find each.

20. $\cos (A - B)$ 21. $\sin 2A$ **0.96**

In 22 and 23, simplify.

22. $\cos (\pi - \theta)$ **-cos θ** 23. $\sin \left(\theta - \frac{\pi}{2}\right)$ **-cos θ**

24. Give a formula for $\cos 4\theta$ in terms of $\cos \theta$ only.

In 25–27, write as the sine or cosine of a single argument.

25. $2 \sin A \cos A$ 26. $\cos \frac{\pi}{5} \cos \frac{\pi}{3} + \sin \frac{\pi}{5} \sin \frac{\pi}{3}$

27. $2 \cos^2 25° - 1$ **cos 50°**

In 28–29, explain how the formula was derived.

28. $\sin (\alpha + \beta)$ 29. $\cos 2\theta$

USES DEAL WITH APPLICATIONS OF MATHEMATICS IN REAL SITUATIONS.
30a, b, d, 32a) See margin.

Objective F: *Use a matrix to organize information.* (*Lessons 11-1*)

In 30 and 31, use the production matrix P and the cost matrix C shown here.

$$P = \begin{bmatrix} 1000 & 10,000 \\ 2000 & 10,000 \\ 500 & 20,000 \\ 500 & 5,000 \end{bmatrix} \begin{matrix} \text{Farm A} \\ \text{Farm B} \\ \text{Farm C} \\ \text{Farm D} \end{matrix}$$

with column headers: Melons, Lettuce (heads)

$$C = \begin{bmatrix} .45 & .90 \\ .65 & 1.00 \end{bmatrix} \begin{matrix} \text{Melons} \\ \text{Lettuce} \end{matrix}$$

with column headers: Cost to Produce, Cost to Consumer

30. **a.** Calculate PC.   **b.** What does PC represent?

   c. Find the total cost of producing melons and lettuce on Farm C. **$13,225**

   d. What element of PC contains this cost?

31. Find the total cost to the consumer of the melons and lettuce produced on Farm A.
   $10,900

In 32 and 33, use the following matrix of Foreign Exchange rates.

	United Kingdom (pound)	Canada (dollar)	Japan (yen)	United States (dollar)	
1975	2.22	0.98	0.0034	1.00	
1980	2.32	0.86	0.0044	1.00	
1985	1.30	0.73	0.0042	1.00	= F
1990	1.78	0.86	0.0069	1.00	
1995	1.58	0.73	0.0106	1.00	

32. **a.** Describe the data given by each row of F.

   b. How many U.S. dollars were 1000 Japanese yen worth in 1995? **$10.60**

33. **a.** If a tourist entered the U.S. in 1995 with 150 pounds U.K., 212 dollars Canadian, and 100 dollars U.S., what is the U.S. equivalent of that cash? **$491.76**

   b. *True or false.* To compare the total cash value of the tourist in part **a** at five-year intervals between 1975 and 1995, one would look at the product matrix FC. (C is shown at the right.) **True**

   $$C = \begin{bmatrix} 150 \\ 212 \\ 0 \\ 100 \end{bmatrix}$$

---

26. $\cos \left(\frac{2\pi}{15}\right)$

28. The rotation image of the point $(1, 0)$ about the origin $(\alpha + \beta)°$ is $(\cos (\alpha + \beta), \sin (\alpha + \beta))$. But, $R_{\alpha+\beta}$ is also $R_\alpha \circ R_\beta$. So $R_\alpha \circ R_\beta (1, 0) = (\cos (\alpha + \beta), \sin (\alpha + \beta))$. $R_\alpha (\cos \beta, \sin \beta) = (\cos (\alpha + \beta), \sin (\alpha + \beta))$.
In matrix form,

$$\begin{bmatrix} \cos \alpha & -\sin \alpha \\ \sin \alpha & \cos \alpha \end{bmatrix} \begin{bmatrix} \cos \beta \\ \sin \beta \end{bmatrix} = \begin{bmatrix} \cos (\alpha + \beta) \end{bmatrix}$$

$$\begin{bmatrix} \cos \alpha \cos \beta - \sin \alpha \sin \beta \end{bmatrix} = \begin{bmatrix} \cos (\alpha + \beta) \end{bmatrix}$$

Therefore, $\sin (\alpha + \beta) = \sin \alpha \cos \beta + \cos \alpha \sin \beta$.

29. By the derivation in **28.**, $\cos (\alpha + \beta)$ $= \cos \alpha \cos \beta - \sin \alpha \sin \beta$.
So, if $\alpha = \theta$ and $\beta = \theta$,
$\cos (\theta + \theta) = \cos \theta \cos \theta - \sin \theta \sin \theta$
$\cos 2\theta = \cos^2\theta - \sin^2\theta$
Also, from the identity
$\sin^2\theta + \cos^2\theta = 1$, $\sin^2\theta = 1 - \cos^2\theta$
and $\cos^2\theta = 1 - \sin^2\theta$. So, by substitution, $\cos 2\theta = 1 - 2 \sin^2\theta$, and $\cos 2\theta = 2 \cos^2\theta - 1$.

REPRESENTATIONS DEAL WITH PICTURES, GRAPHS, OR OBJECTS THAT ILLUSTRATE CONCEPTS.

34–36) See below.   40–42, 43a) See margin.

Objective G: *Represent reflections, rotations, scale changes, and size changes as matrices.*
(Lesson 11-2, 11-3, 11-4)

34. Write the matrix representing r_x, reflection over the x-axis.

35. Write the matrix for the scale change $T: (x, y) \rightarrow \left(x, \frac{1}{3}y\right)$.

36. Write the matrix which represents a 90° rotation counterclockwise about the origin.

In 37 and 38, describe the transformation represented by the matrix.

37. $\begin{bmatrix} 11 & 0 \\ 0 & 11 \end{bmatrix}$ a size change of magnitude 11

38. $\begin{bmatrix} 0 & 1 \\ 1 & 0 \end{bmatrix}$ a reflection over the line $y = x$

39. Tell what rotation is represented by $\begin{bmatrix} -1 & 0 \\ 0 & -1 \end{bmatrix}$. R_{180}

40. Give the rotation matrix for R_{32}.

41. Give exact values of the matrix for R_{120}.

42. If $T(1, 0) = (q, t)$, $T(0, 1) = (e, z)$, and T can be represented by a 2 × 2 matrix, what is this matrix?

43. A transformation which can be represented by a matrix takes $(0, 0)$ to $(0, 0)$, $(1, 0)$ to $(5, 0)$, and $(0, 1)$ to $(0, -1)$.

  a. What is the matrix for the transformation?

  b. What is the image of $(1, 1)$? (5, -1)

44, 45, 46a, 47a) See margin.

Objective H: *Represent composites of transformations as matrix products.*
(Lessons 11-3, 11-4)

44. A figure is rotated 90° clockwise, then reflected over the y-axis.

  a. Write a matrix product for the composite transformation.

  b. Compute the matrix product from part **a.**

45. Tell, in words, what composition of transformations is represented by
$\begin{bmatrix} \cos 32° & -\sin 32° \\ \sin 32° & \cos 32° \end{bmatrix} \cdot \begin{bmatrix} 0 & 1 \\ 1 & 0 \end{bmatrix} \cdot \begin{bmatrix} 0 & -1 \\ 1 & 0 \end{bmatrix}$.

34) $\begin{bmatrix} 1 & 0 \\ 0 & -1 \end{bmatrix}$ 35) $\begin{bmatrix} 1 & 0 \\ 0 & \frac{1}{3} \end{bmatrix}$ 36) $\begin{bmatrix} 0 & -1 \\ 1 & 0 \end{bmatrix}$

46. The matrix representing R_{135} is
$A = \begin{bmatrix} -\sqrt{2}/2 & -\sqrt{2}/2 \\ \sqrt{2}/2 & -\sqrt{2}/2 \end{bmatrix}$.

  a. Compute A^2.

  b. What transformation does A^2 represent? R_{270}

47. Let Y be the matrix representing r_y.

  a. Compute Y^3.

  b. What transformation does Y^3 represent? r_y

48b, 49b, 50, 51) See margin.

Objective I: *Use matrices to find the image of a figure under a transformation.*
(Lessons 11-2, 11-3, 11-4)

48. Refer to $\triangle ABC$ below.

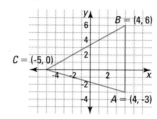

  a. Find a matrix for the image $\triangle A'B'C'$ under the transformation represented by
$\begin{bmatrix} 1 & 1 \\ 0 & -1 \end{bmatrix} \cdot \begin{bmatrix} 1 & 10 & -5 \\ 3 & -6 & 0 \end{bmatrix}$.

  b. Draw the image.

49. **a.** Find a matrix for the vertices of the image of the square having opposite vertices $(0, 0)$ and $(1, 1)$ under the transformation with matrix $\begin{bmatrix} 7 & 0 \\ -1 & 1 \end{bmatrix}$. Sample: $\begin{bmatrix} 0 & 7 & 7 & 0 \\ 0 & -1 & 0 & 1 \end{bmatrix}$

  b. Draw the square and its image on the same axes.

50. Let $A = (7, 0)$, $B = (0, 2)$, and $C = (-1, -1)$.

  a. Describe $(r_x \circ R_{90})(\triangle ABC)$ as the product of three matrices.

  b. Find a single matrix for the image triangle.

51. A two-dimensional figure has been rotated counterclockwise around the origin by 75°. Write the matrix for the transformation which returns the figure to its original orientation.

41. $\begin{bmatrix} -\frac{1}{2} & -\frac{\sqrt{3}}{2} \\ \frac{\sqrt{3}}{2} & -\frac{1}{2} \end{bmatrix}$

42. $\begin{bmatrix} q & e \\ t & z \end{bmatrix}$

43. a. $\begin{bmatrix} 5 & 0 \\ 0 & -1 \end{bmatrix}$

44. a. $\begin{bmatrix} -1 & 0 \\ 0 & 1 \end{bmatrix} \begin{bmatrix} 0 & -1 \\ 1 & 0 \end{bmatrix}$

  b. $\begin{bmatrix} 0 & 1 \\ 1 & 0 \end{bmatrix}$

45. A counterclockwise rotation of 90°, followed by a reflection over the line $y = x$, followed by a counterclockwise rotation of 32°

46. a. $\begin{bmatrix} 0 & 1 \\ -1 & 0 \end{bmatrix}$

47. a. $\begin{bmatrix} -1 & 0 \\ 0 & 1 \end{bmatrix}$

48. b.

49. b.

Additional Answers, pages 750–751.

30. a. $PC = \begin{bmatrix} 6950 & 10900 \\ 7400 & 11800 \\ 13225 & 20450 \\ 3475 & 5450 \end{bmatrix}$

  b. It is the total cost of production (first column) and total cost to the consumer (second column) resulting from the produce from each farm (the rows).

  d. The element in row 3, column 1

32. a. For each respective year, each row gives the exchange rates in terms of U.S. dollars for English pounds, Canadian dollars, and Japanese yen.

40. $\begin{bmatrix} \cos 32° & -\sin 32° \\ \sin 32° & \cos 32° \end{bmatrix}$

(Responses continue at the top of the next column.)

50. a. $\begin{bmatrix} 1 & 0 \\ 0 & -1 \end{bmatrix} \begin{bmatrix} 0 & -1 \\ 1 & 0 \end{bmatrix} \begin{bmatrix} 7 & 0 & -1 \\ 0 & 2 & -1 \end{bmatrix}$

  b. $\begin{bmatrix} 0 & -2 & 1 \\ -7 & 0 & 1 \end{bmatrix}$

51. $R_{-75} = \begin{bmatrix} \cos(-75°) & -\sin(-75°) \\ \sin(-75°) & \cos(-75°) \end{bmatrix} =$

$\begin{bmatrix} \cos 75° & \sin 75° \\ -\sin 75° & \cos 75° \end{bmatrix}$

751

Chapter 12 Planner

Adapting to Individual Needs

The student text is written for the vast majority of students. The chart at the right suggests two pacing plans to accommodate the needs of your students. Students in the Full Course should complete the entire text by the end of the year. Students in the Minimal Course will spend more time when there are quizzes and more time on the Chapter Review. Therefore, these students may not complete all of the chapters in the text.

   Options are also presented to meet the needs of a variety of teaching and learning styles. For each lesson, the Teacher's Edition provides a section entitled *Adapting to Individual Needs.* This section regularly includes **Optional Activities, Challenge** problems, **English Language Development** suggestions, and suggestions for providing **Extra Help.** The Teacher's Edition also frequently includes an **Error Alert,** an **Extension,** and an **Assessment** alternative. The options available in Chapter 12 are summarized in the chart below.

Chapter 12 Pacing Chart

Day	Full Course	Minimal Course
1	12-1	12-1
2	12-2	12-2
3	12-3	12-3
4	Quiz*; 12-4	Quiz*; begin 12-4.
5	12-5	Finish 12-4.
6	12-6	12-5
7	Self-Test	12-6
8	Review	Self-Test
9	Test*	Review
10		Review
11		Test*

*in the Teacher's Resource File

In the Teacher's Edition...

Lesson	Optional Activities	Extra Help	Challenge	English Language Development	Error Alert	Extension	Cooperative Learning	Ongoing Assessment
12-1	●	●		●		●	●	Written
12-2	●	●	●		●	●	●	Written
12-3	●	●	●		●	●	●	Quiz
12-4	●	●	●		●	●	●	Written
12-5	●	●	●		●	●	●	Written
12-6	●	●	●			●	●	

Chapter 12 Block Schedule

Day	Recommended Pacing
1	Lessons 12-1, 12-2
2	Lesson 12-3
3	Lesson 12-4
4	Lesson 12-5
5	Lesson 12-6, Self-Test, Chapter Review
6	Chapter Review, Chapter Test

In the Additional Resources...

Lesson	In the Teacher's Resource File							Explorations Software
	Lesson Masters	Teaching Aids*	Answer Masters	Technology Sourcebook	Assessment Sourcebook	Visual Aids**	Technology	
12-1	12-1	103, 105, 106	12-1			103, 105, 106, AM		12-1
12-2	12-2	103, 107	12-2			103, 107, AM		12-2
12-3	12-3	103, 106, 108	12-3	Comp 13	Quiz	103, 106, 108, AM	GraphExplorer	12-3
12-4	12-4	104, 109	12-4			104, 109, AM		12-4
12-5	12-5	104, 110	12-5			104, 110, AM		
12-6		104, 111	12-6			104, 111, AM		
End of chapter					Tests			

*Teaching Aids are pictured on pages 752C and 752D.

**Visual Aids provide transparencies for all Teaching Aids and all Answer Masters.

Also available is the Study Skills Handbook which includes study-skill tips related to reading, note-taking, and comprehension.

Integrating Strands and Applications

	12-1	12-2	12-3	12-4	12-5	12-6
Mathematical Connections						
Number Sense				●	●	
Algebra	●	●	●	●	●	●
Geometry	●	●	●	●	●	●
Measurement	●	●	●	●		●
Logic and Reasoning			●	●	●	
Statistics/Data Analysis	●			●		
Patterns and Functions	●	●			●	
Discrete Mathematics	●	●	●	●		
Interdisciplinary and Other Connections						
Literature	●					
Science	●	●	●	●		●
Social Studies	●			●		●
Technology	●	●	●	●	●	
Sports						●

Teaching and Assessing the Chapter Objectives

Chapter 12 Objectives (Organized into the SPUR categories—Skills, Properties, Uses, and Representations)	Lessons	Progress Self-Test Questions	Chapter Review Questions	Chapter Test, Forms A and B	Chapter Test, Forms	
					C	D
Skills						
A: Use properties of ellipses and hyperbolas to write equations describing them.	12-2, 12-3	5	1-4	2	2, 4	✓
B: Find equations for rotation images of figures.	12-4	8	5-10	5	4	
C: Rewrite equations of conic sections in the general form of a quadratic relation in two variables.	12-5	10	11-14	13	4	✓
Properties						
D: State and apply properties of ellipses and hyperbolas to draw or describe them.	12-1, 12-3, 12-4	6, 7, 9	15-20	1, 8, 12	1	✓
E: Describe the intersections of a plane and a cone of 2 nappes.	12-1, 12-5	1	21-24	7	3	
Uses						
F: Determine information about elliptical orbits.	12-2	13	25-26	14		
Representations						
G: Graph or identify graphs of ellipses and hyperbolas given their equations.	12-2, 12-3	2, 3	27-34	3, 4	2	✓
H: Graph transformation images of parent ellipses and hyperbolas.	12-2, 12-3, 12-5	4	35-38	6	1, 4	✓
I: Describe graphs of quadratic equations.	12-5	11, 12	39-42	9, 10, 11		

In the Teacher's Resource File

Multidimensional Assessment
Quiz for Lessons 12-1 through 12-3   Chapter 12 Test, Forms A–D
                                       Chapter 12 Test, Cumulative Form

Quiz and Test Writer

Teaching Aids

TEACHING AID 103

Warm-up   Lesson 12-1

In 1–3, draw the figure.

1. A plane and a cube that intersect in a triangle
2. A plane and a cube that intersect in a quadrilateral
3. A plane and a cube that intersect in a pentagon
4. Can a cross section of a cube be a hexagon? Why or why not?

Warm-up   Lesson 12-2

1. What equation arises from squaring both sides of $\sqrt{m} + t = \sqrt{n}$?
2. What equation results from squaring both sides of $a\sqrt{k} = a^2 + v$?

Warm-up   Lesson 12-3

1. Solve each of the following equations.
   a. $p^2 + 12^2 = 13^2$
   b. $q^2 + 12^2 = 15^2$
   c. $r^2 + 12^2 = 20^2$
2. Use the solutions to Question 1 to help graph the relation $y^2 - x^2 = 12^2$.

TEACHING AID 104

Warm-up   Lesson 12-4

Simplify each expression.

1. $\sin \frac{\pi}{4}$
2. $\sin 60°$
3. $\cos 60°$
4. $\begin{bmatrix} \cos 30° & -\sin 30° \\ \sin 30° & \cos 30° \end{bmatrix} \begin{bmatrix} 4 \\ 0 \end{bmatrix}$

Warm-up   Lesson 12-5

Write each of these equations for conic sections in the form $Ax^2 + Bxy + Cy^2 + Dx + Ey + F = 0$. Give the values of A, B, C, D, E, and F.

1. $y = x^2$
2. $(x - 7)^2 + y^2 = 25$
3. $y + 2 = \frac{1}{x + 17}$

Warm-up   Lesson 12-6

1. Name several games or sports that involve bouncing a ball off a wall or floor.
2. Have you ever read about or visited a whispering gallery? If so, briefly describe why the name is appropriate.

TEACHING AID 105
Lesson 12-1

Sections of a Cone

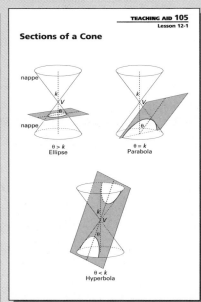

θ > k
Ellipse

θ = k
Parabola

θ < k
Hyperbola

TEACHING AID 106
Lesson 12-1

Dandelin Spheres for the Ellipse

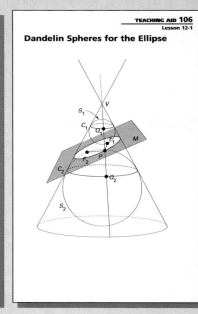

TEACHING AID 107
Lesson 12-2

Developing a Equation for an Ellipse

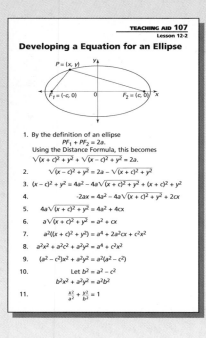

1. By the definition of an ellipse
   $PF_1 + PF_2 = 2a$.
   Using the Distance Formula, this becomes
   $\sqrt{(x + c)^2 + y^2} + \sqrt{(x - c)^2 + y^2} = 2a$.

2. $\sqrt{(x - c)^2 + y^2} = 2a - \sqrt{(x + c)^2 + y^2}$

3. $(x - c)^2 + y^2 = 4a^2 - 4a\sqrt{(x + c)^2 + y^2} + (x + c)^2 + y^2$

4. $-2ax = 4a^2 - 4a\sqrt{(x + c)^2 + y^2} + 2cx$

5. $4a\sqrt{(x + c)^2 + y^2} = 4a^2 + 4cx$

6. $a\sqrt{(x + c)^2 + y^2} = a^2 + cx$

7. $a^2((x + c)^2 + y^2) = a^4 + 2a^2cx + c^2x^2$

8. $a^2x^2 + a^2c^2 + a^2y^2 = a^4 + c^2x^2$

9. $(a^2 - c^2)x^2 + a^2y^2 = a^2(a^2 - c^2)$

10. Let $b^2 = a^2 - c^2$
    $b^2x^2 + a^2y^2 = a^2b^2$

11. $\frac{x^2}{a^2} + \frac{y^2}{b^2} = 1$

TEACHING AID 108
Lesson 12-3

Dandelin Spheres for the Hyperbola

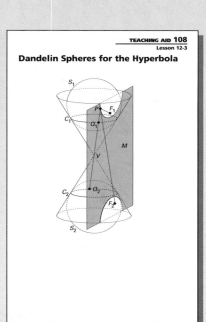

TEACHING AID 109
Lesson 12-4

Rotating $y = x^2$ Twenty Degrees about (5, 8)

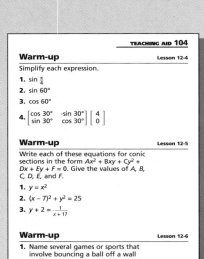

$T_{5, 8} \circ R_{20} \circ T_{-5, -8} =$ rotation of 20° about (5, 8)

$R_{20} \circ T_{-5, -8}$ applied to $y = x^2$

$T_{-5, -8}$ applied to $y = x^2$

TEACHING AID 110
Lesson 12-5

Degenerate Conic Sections

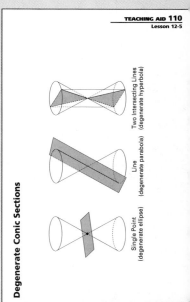

Two Intersecting Lines (degenerate hyperbola)

Line (degenerate parabola)

Single Point (degenerate ellipse)

752C

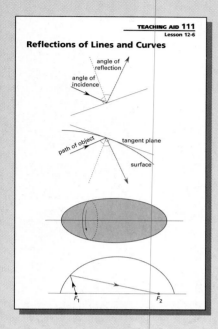

Pacing

All lessons in this chapter are designed to be covered in one day. At the end of the chapter, you should plan to spend 1 day to review the Progress Self-Test, 1–2 days for the Chapter Review, and 1 day for a test. Lesson 12-3 may be a two-day lesson. You may wish to spend a day on projects, and possibly a day is needed for quizzes. This chapter should therefore take 10–12 days.

Using Pages 752–753

In his book *A History of Mathematics*, Carl Boyer points out that 129 Greek mathematicians named Apollonius are listed in a particular German encyclopedia he consulted. The mathematician mentioned here is Apollonius of Perga. Boyer calls him one of the three mathematicians in the "golden age of Greek mathematics," the 3rd century B.C., who stood head and shoulders above their contemporaries. The other two of these three are far more famous today: Euclid and Archimedes. But in his day, Apollonius, not Euclid, was called "The Great Geometer." Sadly, most of the works of Apollonius are lost, and we only know of their existence because some extant writings refer to them.

CHAPTER
12

752

Chapter 12 Overview

This chapter examines quadratic relations (those with the form $Ax^2 + Bxy + Cy^2 + Dx + Ey + F = 0$). The applications include two famous examples of mathematical modeling, Kepler's modeling of the orbits of planets and Galton's modeling of the relationship between the heights of parents and their children.

Compared to linear relations, quadratic relations are more varied. In the rectangular

coordinate plane, the graph of a quadratic relation may be a parabola, an ellipse (including circles), a hyperbola, two lines, a single line, a single point, or even the empty set. Parabolas, ellipses, and hyperbolas constitute the conic sections, and often a chapter like this one is titled Conic Sections.

Since students have already studied parabolas, the first attention in the chapter is given to ellipses. We first address the link

between the three-dimensional geometry of the cone that gives rise to a conic section and the equation for the two-dimensional section. The move from the cone to the geometric two-dimensional definition of an ellipse is made in Lesson 12-1. Lesson 12-2 finishes the steps from the geometry to the algebra. By using translations, we arrive at an equation for any ellipse with horizontal and vertical lines of symmetry.

QUADRATIC RELATIONS

In the 3rd century B.C., only about 25 years after the appearance of Euclid's *Elements*, another Greek mathematician, Appollonius, wrote a set of books entitled *Conics*, dealing with the curves formed by intersecting a cone with a plane: ellipses, parabolas, and hyperbolas.

Apollonius did not consider any applications of these curves, but 1800 years later, in the 10-year period from 1609 to 1619, the German scholar Johannes Kepler performed one of the greatest examples of mathematical modeling of all time. Until Kepler, almost all people thought that the planets moved in circles (either around the earth or the sun) and the stars were fixed on a celestial sphere. Using the measurements of the positions of the planets obtained by his teacher, the Danish astronomer Tycho Brahe, Kepler found that the orbits of the planets around the sun were ellipses and that these ellipses satisfied several simple but not obvious properties.

At about the same time, Descartes applied his new coordinates (the rectangular coordinates you know very well) to the geometry of the *conic sections* and found that all conics could be described by equations of the form $Ax^2 + Bxy + Cy^2 + Dx + Ey + F = 0$. Because the greatest degree of any term in this equation is 2, the sets of ordered pairs (x, y) satisfying it are called *quadratic relations*.

This chapter explores the relationships between the graphs of conic sections and equations of quadratic relations. Along the way, you will encounter a variety of applications of these curves.

Students should already know about some topics of this chapter, for example, equations for parabolas and for circles. Ask if they have studied equations for ellipses and if they remember any equations for hyperbolas. (They should know at least those that are offspring of the parent with equation $y = \frac{1}{x}$.) Point out that these are special kinds of quadratic relations.

Photo Connections
The photo collage makes real-world connections to the content of the chapter: Quadratic Relations.

Car Headlight: Most car headlights include parabolic mirrors. Parabolas are discussed in Lesson 12-6.

Hockey: When a hockey puck hits a hard surface, it bounces off at a predictable angle. Such angles are discussed in Lesson 12-6.

Comet: The path of a comet about the sun is an ellipse. Lessons 12-1 and 12-2 discuss ellipses.

Dinosaur: Theories about why dinosaurs became extinct introduce Lesson 12-3. That lesson deals with the hyperbola.

Autumn Leaves: Some people mistakenly think that seasonal changes are related to the distance that Earth is from the Sun. The real reason is discussed in Lesson 12-2.

Chapter 12 Projects
At this time, you might want to have students look over the projects on pages 797–798.

753

Although hyperbolas look quite different from ellipses, their geometric and algebraic properties are quite analogous. So what took two lessons for the ellipse is presented in one lesson for the hyperbola.

We can now "turn" our attention to Lesson 12-4; that lesson discusses how to rotate any relation about the origin. Because rotations do not change the degree of any relation, this establishes that all conic sections have equations of the second degree. In Lesson 12-5, the problem is reversed, and we show that the graph of every quadratic relation is either a conic section or a degenerate conic section (two lines, a single line, a single point, or the null set). Lesson 12-6 examines the special reflection properties of each conic section.

For some classes, this will be the last chapter of the book that is covered. For some students, it may be their last mathematics in high school. It is fitting that the chapter combines algebra, two- and three-dimensional geometry, trigonometry, relations and functions, and statistics, and includes some beautiful proofs and wonderful applications. Thus not only are all the themes of this course included, but the most important themes of all of high school mathematics are juxtaposed.

Objectives

D State and apply properties of ellipses to draw or describe them.
E Describe the intersections of a plane and a cone of 2 nappes.

Resources

From the *Teacher's Resource File*
- Lesson Master 12-1
- Answer Master 12-1
- Teaching Aids
   103 Warm-up
   105 Sections of a Cone
   106 Dandelin Spheres for the Ellipse

Additional Resources
- Visuals for Teaching Aids 103, 105, 106
- Exploration 12-1

Warm-up

In 1–3, draw the figure.
Sample drawings shown below and in the next column.

1. A plane and a cube that intersect in a triangle
2. A plane and a cube that intersect in a quadrilateral
3. A plane and a cube that intersect in a pentagon
4. Can a cross section of a cube be a hexagon? Why or why not?
Yes. See drawing 4.

1. Triangle   2. Quadrilateral

12-1

The Geometry of the Ellipse

The Three Conic Sections

The "cone" that gives rise to a conic section is not the same as the cones studied in geometry. The conic section cone is formed by rotating one of two intersecting, non-perpendicular lines about the other. The fixed line is called the **axis** of the cone; the point of intersection of these lines is the cone's **vertex**. Any position of the rotating line is an **edge** of the cone. The conic section cone has two parts, called **nappes**, one on each side of its vertex, as shown in the figure below at the left.

❶ In general, a **cross section** or **section** of a three-dimensional figure is the intersection of a plane with that figure. The three figures below are the sections of a cone formed when a plane intersects the cone but does not contain the cone's vertex.

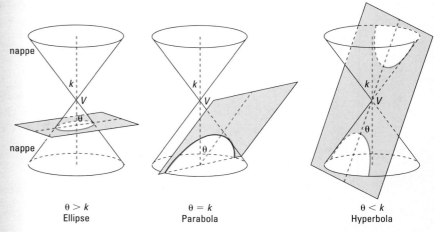

| $\theta > k$ | $\theta = k$ | $\theta < k$ |
| Ellipse | Parabola | Hyperbola |

Because drawings can only show a part of a cone, it may not be obvious that every cone intersects every plane in space. Let k be the measure of the angle between the lines that formed the cone (that is, between its axis and the rotating line). Let θ be the measure of the smallest angle between the cone's axis and the plane. (This angle cannot be obtuse, so $\theta \le 90°$.) If $\theta > k$, the plane intersects only one nappe of the cone and the section is an *ellipse*. If $\theta = k$, the plane is parallel to an edge of the cone, the conic section is unbounded, and the section is a *parabola*. If $\theta < k$ or if the axis and plane are parallel, the plane intersects both nappes of the cone, the conic section is unbounded in opposite directions, and a *hyperbola* is formed.

Lesson 12-1 Overview

Broad Goals The purpose of this lesson is to connect the three-dimensional and two-dimensional characterizations of ellipses.

Perspective There are two common ways to characterize ellipses. One is three-dimensional, as the intersection of a plane and a single nappe of a cone. The other is the two-dimensional locus definition as the set of points in a plane such that the sum of the distances of each point from two given

points is a constant. Shown in this lesson is the gorgeous connection between the two definitions discovered by the French mathematician Dandelin less than 200 years ago. This enables us to be confident that the locus definition indeed describes the same ellipses that the conic sections describe. Often books show the three-dimensional definition, the far more intuitive one, but do not connect it with the two-dimensional form that leads to equations.

From the locus definition, without benefit of equations in x and y, it can be shown that every ellipse has two symmetry lines. The significance of this is that symmetry is seen to be a geometric property; we do not want students to feel that they have to have an equation for the curve to know of its symmetry.

Question 12 of this lesson is to reconstruct the data that led Kepler to discover that the

Dandelin Spheres and the Ellipse

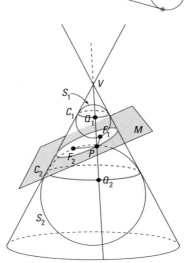

❷The three-dimensional descriptions of conic sections in the previous paragraph are like those used by Apollonius to define the three types of conic sections. The French mathematician Germinal Pierre Dandelin (1794–1847) gave an elegant way to obtain a two-dimensional algebraic characterization for one of the conic sections, the ellipse, from the above three-dimensional description. Dandelin's method involves spheres that are nested inside the cone and applies the following properties.

1. The intersection of a cone and a sphere nested in the cone is a circle (in blue at the left) whose points are all the same distance from the vertex of the cone.

2. The intersection of a sphere and a plane tangent to the sphere is a single point. (Think of a hard ball resting on a flat surface; there is, in theory, one point in common.)

3. The lengths of all tangents from a given point to a given sphere are equal.

Now consider the ellipse formed by a plane M intersecting a cone as drawn at the right. There are only two spheres that can be nested in the cone and that are tangent to the plane M. One sphere S_1 is between the plane and the vertex. A larger sphere S_2 is on the other side of M. Let F_1 and F_2 be the points of tangency of the spheres with the plane, and let C_1 and C_2 be the circles of intersection of the spheres and the cone. Notice that the cone and the plane determine an ellipse; then, all of these named spheres, circles, and points are determined by the ellipse and are fixed.

To describe the ellipse, we will find a property that relates any point on the ellipse to the fixed points F_1 and F_2. Let P be any point on the ellipse. P is on an edge $\overleftrightarrow{PV}$ of the cone and that edge intersects the circles C_1 and C_2 at Q_1 and Q_2, respectively. Notice that Q_1Q_2 is the distance along the cone between the circles, and since VQ_2 and VQ_1 are constant distances (property 3 above),

$$Q_1Q_2 = VQ_2 - VQ_1 = \text{a constant.}$$

So the distance between circles C_1 and C_2 along any edge of the cone is the same.

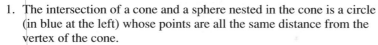
3. Pentagon   4. Hexagon

This activity gives students some idea of the variety of figures that can arise from the intersection of a plane and even a simple 3-dimensional figure.

Notes on Reading

The conic sections shown on page 754 are on **Teaching Aid 105** and the Dandelin spheres for the ellipse are on **Teaching Aid 106.**

❶ We expect that students are familiar with ellipses, though they may know very little about them. How do we know that the intersection of the cone in the left drawing on page 754 is the same ellipse as that given by the definition on page 756? We could get three-dimensional equations for the cone and for the plane, and solve the system, and then get a two-dimensional curve in 3-space and somehow prove it is an ellipse. But it is easier to use the elegant method of Dandelin.

❷ **Reading Mathematics** Like all elegant methods, the method of Dandelin requires that the explanation be read slowly. You may wish to go through page 755 with your students line by line. Plastic models of Dandelin's spheres have been available for some time, and such a model is an excellent visual aid if it is possible for you to locate one.

Optional Activities

Activity 1 Technology Connection
Materials: Explorations software

You may use *Exploration 12-1, Sections of a Cone Formed with a Plane*, as an introduction to this lesson. Students can explore the relationship between a cone and an intersecting plane. They can change the angle measure between the cone and the plane, or the angle between the cone's axis and the rotating line forming the cone. An

animation feature allows students to see how different conic sections (a parabola, ellipse, or hyperbola) are formed.

ratio of the cube of the radius of a planetary orbit to the square of the time of revolution is a constant. It is to our knowledge the first example of logarithmic modeling.

Emphasize the logic: We prove that the intersection of the cone and the plane has the property described in the definition on page 756. Then we are justified in defining ellipse as a curve that has that property. Refer to the drawing on page 755, or **Teaching Aid 106**. The idea of the proof is that $PF_1 + PF_2$ equals the distance (as measured along an edge of the cone) between the circles of intersection of the spheres and the cone. Since the circles are parallel, that distance is constant.

Some students may have learned that the ellipse with equation $\frac{x^2}{a^2} + \frac{y^2}{b^2} = 1$ is symmetric to the x- and y-axes by noting that if (x, y) is on the graph, so is $(x, -y)$ and $(-x, y)$. This algebraic proof has two weaknesses: It does not apply to all ellipses and it uses algebra on a property that is fundamentally geometric. The proof given on page 757 relies on the fact that reflections preserve distance, a property that should be known to students who have studied UCSMP *Geometry* or UCSMP *Advanced Algebra*.

a) Check students' drawings.
b) The ellipse becomes fatter, with its dimension in the direction of $\overleftrightarrow{F_1F_2}$ becoming smaller, and its dimension in the direction of the perpendicular bisector of $\overline{F_1F_2}$ becoming larger.

Now notice that both $\overline{PF}_1$ and $\overline{PQ}_1$ are tangents to sphere S_1, so $PF_1 = PQ_1$. Similarly, both $\overline{PF}_2$ and $\overline{PQ}_2$ are tangents to sphere S_2, so $PF_2 = PQ_2$. Thus $PF_1 + PF_2 = PQ_1 + PQ_2 = Q_1Q_2$, (since P is on Q_1Q_2), which is a constant. That means that the sum of the distances from any point P on the ellipse to the points F_1 and F_2 is constant. In this way, Dandelin proved that the three-dimensional definition of an ellipse is the same as the normal two-dimensional definition of an ellipse with *foci* F_1 and F_2 and a given focal constant. (The word *foci* [pronounced "foe sigh"] is the plural of the word *focus*.)

A Two-dimensional Definition of the Ellipse

Definition
Let F_1 and F_2 be two given points in a plane and k be a positive real number with $k > F_1F_2$. Then the **ellipse with foci F_1 and F_2 and focal constant k** is the set of all points in the plane which satisfy

$$PF_1 + PF_2 = k.$$

This definition of an ellipse can be used to draw an ellipse.

Activity

a. Mark two points on a sheet of paper, put pins (or tacks) at each of the foci. Tie string to the pins so that the string is not tight. Then, keeping the string taut, trace out the ellipse with a pencil.
b. Move the two pins closer together, and draw a new ellipse. How is this ellipse different than the one you drew in part **a**?
c. Describe what happens to the ellipse when the foci F_1 and F_2 are the same point. The ellipse becomes a circle.

Some people call an ellipse an oval, and the word "oval" comes from the Latin word for egg, "ovum," so they think of an ellipse as egg-shaped. But the cross sections of many eggs have only one symmetry line. Eggs are often more pointed at one end than the other, while every ellipse has two symmetry lines.

Theorem
An ellipse with foci F_1 and F_2 is reflection-symmetric to $\overleftrightarrow{F_1F_2}$ and to the perpendicular bisector of $\overline{F_1F_2}$.

Optional Activities
Activity 2
Materials: Flashlight

Have students use a flashlight to outline a conic section. One student should shine a flashlight on a flat wall. Then he or she should turn the flashlight so the outline is a hyperbola, an ellipse, and a parabola. Have other students determine the angle between the line containing the flashlight's axis and the wall when the conic sections change

type. [If the outline lies entirely on the wall, the outline is an ellipse. If an edge of the beam is parallel to the wall, then the outline is a parabola. If the flashlight is turned still farther, the outline is a hyperbola.]

Adapting to Individual Needs
Extra Help
Some students may labor under the misconception that all cones have only one nappe. This will prevent them from understanding how a hyperbola can have two parts. Emphasize the description of the cone given at the beginning of the lesson, and check for students' understanding in **Question 1.**

Proof

Let F_1 and F_2 be the foci of an ellipse with focal constant k and let $m = \overleftrightarrow{F_1F_2}$. Then, by definition, for any point P on the ellipse, $PF_1 + PF_2 = k$. To show that the ellipse is reflection-symmetric to m, it must be shown that the ellipse coincides with its reflection image over that line. Let $P' = r_m(P)$. Because F_1 and F_2 are on the reflecting line, $r_m(F_1) = F_1$ and $r_m(F_2) = F_2$. Because reflections preserve distance, $P'F_1 = PF_1$ and $P'F_2 = PF_2$. So for all P, $P'F_1 + P'F_2 = PF_1 + PF_2 = k$. Thus P' is on the ellipse. So the image of each point on the ellipse is also on the ellipse.

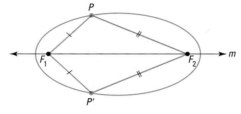

To show that the image is the entire ellipse, let Q be any point on the original ellipse. Then its image, $r_m(Q)$, is on the original ellipse (using the argument above). But $r_m(r_m(Q)) = Q$. So Q is also on the image, and thus all points of the ellipse are on the image.

A similar argument can be written to show that the perpendicular bisector of F_1F_2 is also a symmetry line for the ellipse.

Ellipses in Astronomy

One discovery by Kepler about planetary orbits, known as his first law, was that the orbit of each planet is an ellipse with the sun at one focus. Another discovery was that a planet does not go around the sun at a constant speed, but that a segment from the sun to the planet sweeps out equal areas in equal times. This is now known as Kepler's second law. His third discovery, called his third law, related the distance of the planet from the sun to its period, the length of time it takes to make one revolution. You are asked to investigate Kepler's third law in the Questions.

Johannes Kepler discussing planetary motion with his sponsor Emperor Rudolph II

> 1) The cone studied in geometry is the set of all points between the points on a given circle and a given point not in the plane of the circle. The cone that gives rise to conic sections is formed by rotating one of two intersecting lines about the other. It is infinite in extent and it consists of two nappers.

QUESTIONS

Covering the Reading

1. What is the difference between the cones studied in geometry and the cones that give rise to the conic sections? **See left.**

2. Refer to the figures on page 754. Use k and θ to describe how a plane intersects a given cone to result in the given figure.
   a. parabola $\theta = k$
   b. ellipse $\theta > k$
   c. hyperbola $\theta < k$
   d. exactly one point at the vertex of the cone; $m \angle \theta > k$
   e. no points not possible

Lesson 12-1 *The Geometry of the Ellipse* **757**

Notes on Questions

Question 1 This is an important distinction. See Extra Help In *Adapting to Individual Needs* on page 756 for a more complete discussion.

Question 2 Error Alert Students are likely to miss **parts d and e** most often.

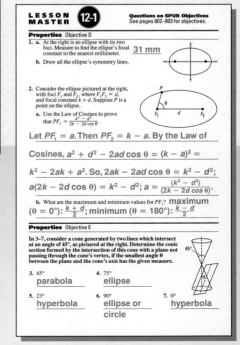

LESSON MASTER 12-1   Questions on SPUR Objectives See pages 802–803 for objectives.

Properties Objective D

1. a. At the right is an ellipse with its two foci. Measure to find the ellipse's focal constant to the nearest millimeter. **31 mm**
   b. Draw all the ellipse's symmetry lines.

2. Consider the ellipse pictured at the right, with foci F_1 and F_2, where $F_1F_2 = d$, and focal constant $k > d$. Suppose P is a point on the ellipse.
   a. Use the Law of Cosines to prove that $PF_1 = \frac{k^2 - d^2}{2k - 2d \cos \theta}$.

   Let $PF_1 = a$. Then $PF_2 = k - a$. By the Law of Cosines, $a^2 + d^2 - 2ad \cos \theta = (k - a)^2 = k^2 - 2ak + a^2$. So, $2ak - 2ad \cos \theta = k^2 - d^2$; $a(2k - 2d \cos \theta) = k^2 - d^2$; $a = \frac{(k^2 - d^2)}{(2k - 2d \cos \theta)}$.

   b. What are the maximum and minimum values for PF_1? **maximum** $(\theta = 0°): \frac{k+d}{2}$; **minimum** $(\theta = 180°): \frac{k-d}{2}$

Properties Objective E

In 3–7, consider a cone generated by two lines which intersect at an angle of 45°, as pictured at the right. Determine the conic section formed by the intersection of this cone with a plane not passing through the cone's vertex, if the smallest angle θ between the plane and the cone's axis has the given measure.

3. 45° **parabola**
4. 75° **ellipse**
5. 23° **hyperbola**
6. 90° **ellipse or circle**
7. 0° **hyperbola**

Adapting to Individual Needs

English Language Development

Apollonius gave the names ellipse, parabola, and hyperbola to the conic sections. "Ellipse" is related to the word "ellipsis," which describes the three dots (...) used when something is left out. "Parabola" literally means "to throw right up to." "Hyperbola" is related to the word "hyperbole," which literally means "to throw over," but which today means an exaggeration. Interested students may wish to explore the mathematical properties of these curves which led Apollonius to give them these names.

Question 12 Science Connection
These were the only planets known to the ancients because they are the only ones visible from the earth without a telescope. It was only a short time before Kepler that Galileo had first looked at the sky through a telescope. The planet Uranus was not discovered until 1781, over 150 years after Kepler.

Question 14 This question is preparation for work with the expression $a^2 - c^2$, used in the next lesson to derive an equation for an ellipse.

Questions 21–23 These questions give practice with manipulations like those found in the next lesson.

Question 24 History Connection
Hypatia is the earliest known famous female mathematician.

Additional Answers
3. a. The center of the sphere is on the axis of the cone. The intersection of the cone and the sphere is a circle whose points are all the same distance from the vertex of the cone.

b.

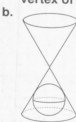

---

5) **Sample:** An ellipse is the set of all points in a plane the sum of whose distances to two fixed points in the same plane is a constant.

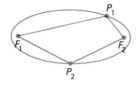

8b) One line of symmetry contains the foci, and the other is the perpendicular bisector of the line segment between the foci.

9) The area swept out by the line segment reaching from the sun to Earth is equal for an equal time.

11) True. The center of the circle is the location of both foci. The focal constant is twice the radius of the circle.

13b) As the focal constant gets larger, the ellipse looks more and more like a circle.

758

---

3. a. If a sphere is *nested* in a cone, how are these figures related?
   b. Draw a picture of a sphere nested in a cone.
   a, b) See margin.
4. a. Draw a cone and a plane whose intersection is an ellipse.
   b. Describe the location of the Dandelin spheres for this ellipse.
   c. How are the foci of the ellipse related to the location of the Dandelin spheres?
   a–c) See margin.
5. State the two-dimensional definition for *ellipse*.
   See left.
6. Consider P_1 and P_2 on the ellipse at the left, $F_1F_2 = 4$ and $P_1F_1 + P_1F_2 = 5$. Find $P_2F_1 + P_2F_2$. **5**
7. Answer the questions in parts **b** and **c** of the Activity in the lesson.
   See page 756.
8. a. At least how many symmetry lines does every ellipse have? **two**
   b. How are they related to the foci of the ellipse?
   See left.
9. Apply Kepler's second law to describe the orbit of Earth.
   See left.
10. Prove that the perpendicular bisector of the segment joining the foci of an ellipse is a symmetry line for the ellipse.
    See margin.

Applying the Mathematics

11. *True or false.* A circle is a special type of ellipse. Explain your thinking.
    See left.
12. In Kepler's day, the orbits of the six known planets around the sun were thought to be circular, and the radii of these circles were calculated in **astronomical units (a.u.)**, where 1 astronomical unit was the radius of the Earth's orbit. Here are the values that Kepler had for these radii and for the periods of the planets. **See margin.**

Planet	Radius r (a.u.)	Period t (days)
Mercury	0.389	87.77
Venus	0.724	224.70
Earth	1.000	365.25
Mars	1.524	686.98
Jupiter	5.200	4,332.62
Saturn	9.510	10,759.20

a. Kepler discovered that $\frac{r^3}{t^2}$ is nearly a constant. Verify Kepler's calculations. What is the mean value that you get for $\frac{r^3}{t^2}$?
b. Graph the points $(\log_{10} r, \log_{10} t)$ for the six planets. What property of this scatterplot verifies that $\frac{r^3}{t^2}$ is nearly a constant?

a) There is no smallest focal constant, but it must be larger than 1 meter.

13. Suppose the two foci of an ellipse are 1 meter apart.
    a. What is the smallest possible focal constant for this ellipse?
    b. As the focal constant gets larger, what happens to the shape of the ellipse? **See left.**
    c. Is there a largest possible focal constant for this ellipse? If so, what is it? **There is no largest focal constant; it can be arbitrarily large as long as it is larger than 1 meter.**

758

---

4. a.

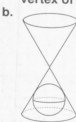

b. The smaller of the spheres is between the plane and the vertex of the cone, tangent to the plane at one focus of the ellipse. The plane is between the vertex and the larger of the spheres; it is tangent to the sphere at the other focus of the ellipse.
c. Each Dandelin sphere is tangent to the plane. The foci are the points of tangency.

10. For an ellipse with foci F_1 and F_2 and focal constant k, let l be the perpendicular bisector of $\overline{F_1F_2}$. By definition, for any point P on the ellipse, $PF_1 + PF_2 = k$. To prove that the ellipse is reflection-symmetric to l, let $P' = r_l(P)$. By the definition of reflection, $r_l(F_1) = F_2$ and $r_l(F_2) = F_1$. Because reflections preserve distance, $P'F_1 = PF_2$, and $P'F_2 = PF_1$. So for all P, $P'F_1 + P'F_2 = PF_2 + PF_1 = k$, proving that all

19) False.
   Counterexample:
   $g(f(-2)) =$
   $((-2)^6)^{\frac{1}{6}} = 2$, but
   $f(g(-2))$ is undefined.

20a, b)

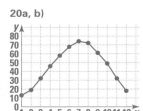

c) Sample: $t = 31.025$
   $\sin(.483\,x - 1.845) +$
   42.679
   where t = average
   monthly temperature
   in °F and x = month of
   the year.

Review

14. Suppose a and c are real numbers and $a^2 - b^2 = c^2$. How must a and c be
related in order for b to be a real number?   *(Lesson 9-6)*
   $a > c > 0$ or $a < c < 0$ or $a = c$

In 15–17, consider the 4th degree
polynomial function graphed at the right with
relative extrema at B, D, and F. *(Lessons 2-4, 9-2)*

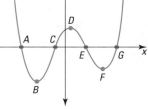

15. Identify all intervals on which the
function is increasing.
   $\{x: B < x < D\}$, $\{x: x > F\}$
16. Identify all intervals on which the
function is positive.
   $\{x: x < A\}$, $\{x: C < x < E\}$, $\{x: G < x\}$
17. Does the function have any asymptotes?
If yes, identify them.
   No
18. Determine the sum of the first 100 multiples of 3. *(Lesson 8-3)*
   15,150
19. Let $f(x) = x^6$ and $g(x) = x^{1/6}$. *True or false.* $f(g(x)) = g(f(x))$ for all real
numbers x. Justify your answer. *(Lesson 6-1)*
   See left.
20. The following are the average monthly temperatures in °F for Huron,
South Dakota.

Jan	Feb	Mar	Apr	May	June	July	Aug	Sep	Oct	Nov	Dec
13	19	32	46	58	68	74	72	61	49	32	18

a–c) See left.
a. Draw a scatterplot of the data.
b. Sketch a sine curve to fit the data.
c. Determine an equation for the curve in part **b** to model the data.
   (Lessons 1-2, 4-10)

In 21 and 22, expand the binomials and combine like terms. *(Previous course)*

21. $(a+b)^2 - (a-b)^2$
   $4ab$
22. $(2p - \sqrt{d})^2 - d^2$
   $4p^2 - 4p\sqrt{d} + d - d^2$
23. Find the distance between the points (a, b) and (x, y). *(Previous course)*
   $\sqrt{(a-x)^2 + (b-y)^2}$

Exploration

24. The mathematician Hypatia wrote a book, *On the Conics of Apollonius*,
around 400 A.D. Find out something else about Hypatia.
   Sample: Hypatia, an Alexandrian mathematician of note, was the
daughter of Theon of Alexandria, a Greek geometrician. She also wrote
commentaries on the work of Diophantus.

*This small statuette of Hypatia
is in the Greco-Roman Museum
of Alexandria in Egypt.*

Lesson 12-1 *The Geometry of the Ellipse* **759**

Q is any point on the ellipse, then
$Q = r_l(r_l(Q))$. By the above argument, $r_l(Q)$ is on the ellipse, therefore the entire ellipse is the image.
Thus, the entire ellipse coincides
with its reflection image over l,
making l a symmetry line for the
ellipse, by definition.

12. a.

Planet	$\frac{r^3}{t^2}$
Mercury	7.64×10^{-6}
Venus	7.52×10^{-6}
Earth	7.50×10^{-6}
Mars	7.50×10^{-6}
Jupiter	7.49×10^{-6}
Saturn	7.43×10^{-6}

The mean value of $\frac{r^3}{t^2} \approx 7.51 \times 10^{-6}$.
b. See next column.

Follow-up 12-1
for Lesson

Practice
For more questions on SPUR
Objectives, use **Lesson Master 12-1**
(shown on page 757).

Assessment
Written Communication Have students write a paragraph explaining
how the angle at which a plane intersects a cone determines which conic
section is formed. [Students describe
the intersection of a plane and a
cone of 2 nappes.]

Extension
Cooperative Learning Have students **work in groups** to construct
a model of Dandelin's spheres.
About the only materials needed are
spheres of two sizes and transparent
plastic material for constructing a
cone and an intersecting plane.

Project Update Project 2, *Using
Paper-folding to Make Conic Sections*
and Project 3, *Using Drawing to
Make Conic Sections,* on page 797,
relate to the content of this lesson.

12. b.

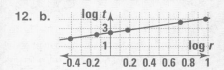

The fact that this graph is
linear with a slope very
nearly equal to $\frac{3}{2}$ indicates
that $\frac{r^3}{t^2}$ is approximately
constant.

Setting Up Lesson 12-2
Discuss **Questions 14 and 21–23.**

759

Objectives

A Use properties of ellipses to write equations describing them.
F Determine information about elliptical orbits.
G Graph or identify graphs of ellipses given their equations.
H Graph transformation images of parent ellipses.

Resources

From the Teacher's Resource File
■ Lesson Master 12-2
■ Answer Master 12-2
■ Teaching Aids
103 Warm-up
107 Developing an Equation for an Ellipse

Additional Resources
■ Visuals for Teaching Aids 103, 107
■ Exploration 12-2

Teaching Lesson 12-2

Warm-up

1. What equation arises from squaring both sides of $\sqrt{m} + t = \sqrt{n}$?
   $m + 2t\sqrt{m} + t^2 = n$
2. What equation results from squaring both sides of $a\sqrt{k} = a^2 + v$?
   $a^2k = a^4 + 2a^2v + v^2$

LESSON

12-2

The Algebra of the Ellipse

From the two-dimensional definition of an ellipse in Lesson 12-1, an equation for any ellipse in the plane can be found. If the foci are $F_1 = (a, b)$ and $F_2 = (c, d)$ and the focal constant is k, then, by definition, any point $P = (x, y)$ on the ellipse must satisfy the equation

$$PF_1 \quad + \quad PF_2 \quad = k.$$

Applying the distance formula gives

$$\sqrt{(x - a)^2 + (y - b)^2} + \sqrt{(x - c)^2 + (y - d)^2} = k.$$

This is an equation for the ellipse. But this equation is rather unwieldy and it does not lend itself to graphing, even with an automatic grapher. A more common approach is to begin with an ellipse that is symmetric to the x- and y-axes, find its equation, and then transform the ellipse as needed to find equations for other ellipses. This is the approach we take.

Developing an Equation for an Ellipse

To simplify the algebraic manipulations, the focal constant is called $2a$, and the foci are on the x-axis, symmetric to the origin. So let $F_1 = (-c, 0)$, $F_2 = (c, 0)$, and $P = (x, y)$. The following eleven steps are numbered for reference.

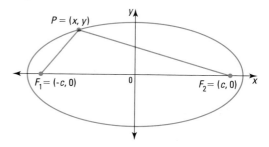

1. By the definition of an ellipse

$$PF_1 + PF_2 = 2a.$$

Using the Distance Formula, this becomes

$$\sqrt{(x + c)^2 + y^2} + \sqrt{(x - c)^2 + y^2} = 2a.$$

2. Subtract one of the square roots from both sides.

$$\sqrt{(x - c)^2 + y^2} = 2a - \sqrt{(x + c)^2 + y^2}$$

Lesson 12-2 Overview

Broad Goals By conveniently locating the foci at $(c, 0)$ and $(-c, 0)$, so that the lines of symmetry of an ellipse are the axes, the equation $\frac{x^2}{a^2} + \frac{y^2}{b^2} = 1$ for an ellipse can be derived and properties of a, b, and c are easily seen.

Perspective Students who have studied Chapter 12 of UCSMP *Advanced Algebra* will have studied this content.

In the equation $\frac{x^2}{a^2} + \frac{y^2}{b^2} = 1$, when the foci are on the x-axis, as they are above, then $a > b$. In contrast, if the foci of the ellipse are on the y-axis at $(0, c)$ and $(0, -c)$, then an equation of the same form arises but $b > a$. (If $a = b$, then the circle with center $(0, 0)$ and radius a results.) In both cases, the relationship between a, b, and c is quite simple: $c^2 = |a^2 - b^2|$.

Here $2a$ is the length of the major axis, $2b$ the length of the minor axis, and $2c$ the distance between the foci. Seldom do we have such nice traditional use of letters in mathematics. In **Questions 17–19**, the eccentricity $\frac{c}{a}$ of an ellipse is introduced. The relationships between these quantities enables information to be deduced about orbits of planets.

3. Square both sides (the right side is like a binomial) to eliminate one radical.

$$(x - c)^2 + y^2 = 4a^2 - 4a\sqrt{(x + c)^2 + y^2} + (x + c)^2 + y^2$$

4. Expand the binomials and do appropriate subtractions.

$$-2cx = 4a^2 - 4a\sqrt{(x + c)^2 + y^2} + 2cx$$

5. Use the Addition Property of Equality and rearrange terms.

$$4a\sqrt{(x + c)^2 + y^2} = 4a^2 + 4cx$$

6. Multiply both sides by $\frac{1}{4}$.

$$a\sqrt{(x + c)^2 + y^2} = a^2 + cx$$

7. Square both sides again to eliminate the radical.

$$a^2((x + c)^2 + y^2) = a^4 + 2a^2cx + c^2x^2$$

8. Expand $(x + c)^2$ and subtract $2a^2cx$ from both sides.

$$a^2x^2 + a^2c^2 + a^2y^2 = a^4 + c^2x^2$$

9. Subtract a^2c^2 and c^2x^2 from both sides, then factor.

$$(a^2 - c^2)x^2 + a^2y^2 = a^2(a^2 - c^2)$$

10. Since $c > 0$, $F_1F_2 = 2c$; and since $2a > F_1F_2$, $2a > 2c$. So $a > c > 0$. Thus $a^2 > c^2$ and $a^2 - c^2$ is positive. So $a^2 - c^2$ can be considered as the square of some real number, say b. Now let $b^2 = a^2 - c^2$ and substitute.

$$b^2x^2 + a^2y^2 = a^2b^2$$

11. Dividing both sides by a^2b^2 gives

$$\frac{x^2}{a^2} + \frac{y^2}{b^2} = 1.$$

This argument yields the **standard form** for an equation of this ellipse.

Theorem (Equation for an Ellipse)

The ellipse with foci $(c, 0)$ and $(-c, 0)$ and focal constant $2a$ has equation $\frac{x^2}{a^2} + \frac{y^2}{b^2} = 1$, where $b^2 = a^2 - c^2$.

Notes on Reading

The derivation of an equation for an ellipse is long, but such a clean result comes out of such a messy first equation that it is worth doing. The derivation is also shown on **Teaching Aid 107**.

As you go through the derivation you may have to recap periodically what is being done. Either equation in Step 1 is an equation for an ellipse, but we would like an equation in terms of a (half the focal constant) and c that does not have any square roots. In Step 7, we finally reach such an equation, but it is rather complicated. By some maneuvering, we are able to get the standard form found in the Equation for an Ellipse Theorem.

The theorem on page 762 applies both to ellipses with foci $(c, 0)$ and $(-c, 0)$ and to ellipses with foci $(0, c)$ and $(0, -c)$. It is for this reason that we use the terms *horizontal axis* and *vertical axis* rather than *major axis* and *minor axis*. The major axis is always the longer axis; it is the axis that contains the foci.

The equation for the translation image of an ellipse in standard form (near the top of page 765) is important for students to know, but it is simply a special case of the Graph Translation Theorem, so we do not state it as a separate theorem. You could call it a corollary of the Equation for an Ellipse Theorem.

In general, when one body in space rotates around another that we think of as fixed, the orbit of the first body is an ellipse with one focus at the fixed second body. (See **Example 2** on page 764.)

Optional Activities

Activity 1 Technology Connection
Materials: Explorations software

Students may use *Exploration 12-2, Algebra of an Ellipse*, as a review of this lesson. Students can explore the relationship between the standard equation for an ellipse and its graphical representation. Students can change the elements of the standard equation and observe the results on a coordinate grid. An animation feature allows students to see the results as the values change over a given interval.

1. Consider the ellipse with equation $\frac{x^2}{100} + 4y^2 = 1$.
   a. Determine the endpoints of the major and minor axes.
      (10, 0), (-10, 0), (0, 0.5), (0, -0.5)
   b. Give coordinates of the foci.
      $(\sqrt{99.75}, 0)$ and $(-\sqrt{99.75}, 0)$; This ellipse is very thin.

2. Saturn ranges from 838 to 938 million miles from the Sun. How far from the Sun is the second focus of its elliptical orbit?
   50 million miles (farther from the Sun than the planet Mercury)

Properties of an Ellipse

By substitution into the equation, it is easy to verify that the points $A_1 = (a, 0)$, $A_2 = (-a, 0)$, $B_1 = (0, b)$, and $B_2 = (0, -b)$ are on this ellipse. Notice that in the equation for an ellipse $|x|$ cannot be greater than a, nor can $|y|$ be greater than b; otherwise the left side would be greater than 1. This shows that those four points are extreme points for the ellipse. These points help to sketch a graph of the ellipse.

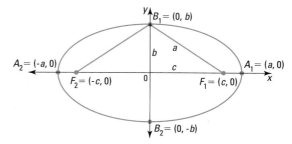

This figure illustrates the following theorem.

> **Theorem**
> In the ellipse with equation $\frac{x^2}{a^2} + \frac{y^2}{b^2} = 1$,
> $2a$ is the length of the horizontal axis,
> $2b$ is the length of the vertical axis, and
> $2c$ is the distance between the foci, where $c^2 = a^2 - b^2$.

Because $2a$ is the focal constant, $B_1F_1 + B_1F_2 = 2a$. Also, $B_1F_1 = B_1F_2$, so each of these distances is a. You can also see in the drawing that $b^2 + c^2 = a^2$, as was used in step 10 of the argument yielding the equation. Thus $a > b$.

The segments $\overline{A_1A_2}$ and $\overline{B_1B_2}$ and their lengths are called, respectively, the **major axis** and **minor axis** of the ellipse. The major axis contains the foci and is never shorter than the minor axis. (If $a = b$, the ellipse becomes a circle.) The two axes lie on the symmetry lines and intersect at the **center** of the ellipse.

If $a \geq b$, as in the proof of the equation for an ellipse, then $(c, 0)$ and $(-c, 0)$ are the foci, the focal constant is $2a$, and $c^2 = a^2 - b^2$. However, if $a < b$, then the major axis of the ellipse is vertical. In this case, the foci are $(0, c)$ and $(0, -c)$, the focal constant is $2b$, and $c^2 = b^2 - a^2$.

762

Activity 2 You can use this activity after students have completed **Questions 17–19.** Have students draw as many ellipses as they can with eccentricity $\frac{3}{5}$. They should see quickly that all ellipses with a certain eccentricity are not congruent. However, we do say that they are similar. See if students can write a general equation(s) for all ellipses with eccentricity $\frac{3}{5}$. [All ellipses with horizontal a axes and eccentricity $\frac{3}{5}$

are of the form $\frac{(x - h)^2}{25m} + \frac{(y - k)^2}{16m} = 1$, or $\frac{(x - h)^2}{16m} + \frac{(y - k)^2}{25m} = 1$, where m is a positive real number, h and k are real numbers.]

Using Properties of the Ellipse

Example 1 illustrates both cases.

Example 1

Determine the foci of the ellipse with the given equation and sketch its graph.

a. $\frac{x^2}{36} + \frac{y^2}{9} = 1$ **b.** $\frac{x^2}{9} + \frac{y^2}{36} = 1$

Solution

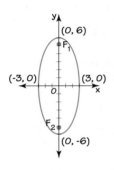

a. The equation is in standard form

$\frac{x^2}{a^2} + \frac{y^2}{b^2} = 1$ with $a = 6$ and $b = 3$.

Because $a > b$, the foci are on the horizontal axis. So let the foci be $(c, 0)$ and $(-c, 0)$, where $c^2 = a^2 - b^2 = 36 - 9 = 27$. So $c = \sqrt{27}$. Thus, $(\sqrt{27}, 0) \approx (5.2, 0)$ and $(-\sqrt{27}, 0) \approx (-5.2, 0)$ are the foci.
The extreme points for this ellipse are $(6, 0)$, $(-6, 0)$, $(0, 3)$, and $(0, -3)$. This enables the ellipse to be sketched rather easily.

b. The ellipse in part **b** is the reflection image of the ellipse in part **a** over the line $y = x$. So its foci are $(0, \sqrt{27})$ and $(0, -\sqrt{27})$. The extreme points are $(3, 0)$, $(-3, 0)$, $(0, 6)$, and $(0, -6)$. Its graph is sketched at the left.

Activity

a. Check the graph in part **b** of Example 1 by finding a fifth pair of numbers x and y satisfying the equation and showing that (x, y) is on the graph.

b. Check the foci by showing that the sum of the distances from this point to the two foci is 12. **See margin on page 765.**

The theorems about ellipses can be used to answer questions about the orbits of planets.

Adapting to Individual Needs

Extra Help

Some students may be confused by the theorem on page 762 where $2a$ is given as the length of the horizontal axis because on the previous page $2a$ is the focal constant. Point out that the focal constant equals the length of the major axis. You might want to verify this using the diagram on page 762 and applying the definition of ellipse to point $A_1 = (a, 0)$.

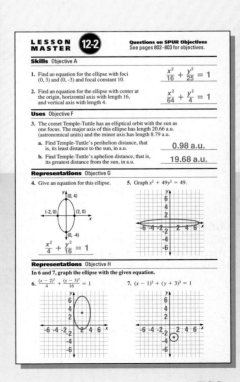

Example 2

The closest Earth gets to the sun is approximately 91.4 million miles and the farthest is 94.6 million miles. Given that the orbit is an ellipse with the sun at one focus, how far from the sun is the other focus?

Solution

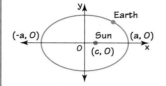

A picture, even as exaggerated as the one at the left, helps. Think of the center of the orbit as being the origin and place the sun at $(c, 0)$, where the unit is one million miles. The maximum and minimum distances from the sun occur when Earth's orbit intersects the *x*-axis. **From the given information, $a - c = 91.4$ and $c - (-a) = 94.6$.** This is a system of two linear equations in two variables and is easily solved. Adding these equations $2a = 186.0$, so $a = 93.0$. Thus $c = 1.6$. So the second focus is $(-1.6, 0)$ and is 3.2 million miles from the sun.

The sun itself has a radius of about 433,000 miles, so the second focus is about 2.8 million miles from the surface of the sun.

Not long after Kepler, Isaac Newton (1642–1727) *deduced* that the orbits of the planets were ellipses from assumed principles of force and mass. Newton worked backwards from Kepler's third law to discover these principles, and then worked forward to apply them to explain how the planets moved. The mathematics of his time was insufficient to deal with these ideas, so Newton developed calculus to solve the problem. This is another one of the greatest mathematical achievements of all time. Newton understood the generality of his results, that any body moves around any other body in an elliptical orbit. The orbits of the moon or artificial satellites around Earth, of comets around the sun, and even of particles around the centers of atoms obey these laws; they are ellipses.

Hail! Hale-Bopp. *The comet Hale-Bopp, shown here in 1997, was for a time one of the brightest objects in the sky. It has a very eccentric elliptical orbit and will make its next appearance in about 2400 years.*

Using Technology to Graph an Ellipse

An ellipse is not the graph of a function in the *xy*-plane, so automatic graphers need special routines to graph ellipses. Some graphers allow you to plot ellipses centered at the origin and their translation images. On some of these graphers you must enter the constants *a* and *b* in the standard form of the equation for an ellipse. At the right are the graphs of $\frac{x^2}{49} + \frac{y^2}{16} = 1$ and $\frac{(x - 5)^2}{49} + \frac{(y + 2)^2}{16} = 1$ as produced by an automatic grapher. Notice that each has major axis of length $2 \cdot 7 = 14$ and minor axis of $2 \cdot 4 = 8$.

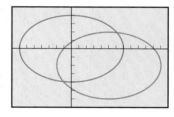

$-8 \le x \le 13$, *x*-scale = 1
$-7 \le y \le 5$, *y*-scale = 1

Adapting to Individual Needs

Challenge
A *latus rectum* of an ellipse is the line segment through a focus perpendicular to the major axis with endpoints on the ellipse. Find a formula the length of a latus rectum in terms of *a* and *b*. $[\frac{2b^2}{a}]$

In general, because translations preserve distance, the graph of the ellipse with equation

$$\frac{(x-h)^2}{a^2} + \frac{(y-k)^2}{b^2} = 1$$

has center (h, k), horizontal axis of length $2a$, and vertical axis of length $2b$.

When an automatic grapher does not have a special program to graph an ellipse, you can solve the equation of the ellipse for y. This is explored in Question 16.

2a) $\frac{x^2}{169} + \frac{y^2}{144} = 1$

6a)

QUESTIONS

Covering the Reading

1. Use the distance formula to write an equation for the ellipse with foci $(11, 6)$ and $(-2, 7)$ and focal constant 15. (The equation does not have to be in standard form.) $\sqrt{(x-11)^2 + (y-6)^2} + \sqrt{(x+2)^2 + (y-7)^2} = 15$

2. a. Find an equation in standard form for the ellipse with foci $(5, 0)$ and $(-5, 0)$ and focal constant 26 by going through the steps that led to the first theorem of this lesson. **See left.**
   b. Give the distance between foci, length of major axis, and length of minor axis for this ellipse.
      distance between the foci = 10;   major axis = 26;   minor axis = 24

3. Consider the ellipse drawn at the left. Identify each of the following.
   a. the major axis $\overline{RP}$
   b. the minor axis $\overline{SQ}$
   c. the axis which contains the foci $\overline{RP}$

In 4 and 5, consider the ellipse with equation $\frac{x^2}{a^2} + \frac{y^2}{b^2} = 1$.

4. Identify each of the following.
   a. the center **(0, 0)**
   b. the endpoints of the horizontal axis $(a, 0)$ and $(-a, 0)$
   c. the length of the horizontal axis $2a$

5. If the horizontal axis is the major axis, what is true about a and b?
   $a \geq b$

In 6 and 7, an equation for an ellipse is given. **a.** Sketch a graph of the ellipse. **b.** Determine its foci. **c.** Determine the length of the major axis.

6. $\frac{x^2}{25} + \frac{y^2}{16} = 1$ a) See left.   b) $(-3, 0)$ and $(3, 0)$ c) 10

7. $\frac{x^2}{16} + \frac{y^2}{25} = 1$ a) See left.   b) $(0, -3)$ and $(0, 3)$ c) 10

8. Give your work for the Activity in this lesson. **See margin.**

9. Consider the ellipse with equation $\frac{(x-1)^2}{36} + \frac{(y+7)^2}{9} = 1$.
   a. Explain how its graph is related to the graph of one of the ellipses in Example 1.
   b. Graph this ellipse. **See margin.**
   a) **The graph is the translation image of the graph in Example 1a under** $T: (x, y) \rightarrow (x + 1, y - 7)$.

7a)

Lesson 12-2   *The Algebra of the Ellipse*   **765**

Additional Answers
8. a. **Sample: Let $x = 2$. Then**
   $\frac{4}{9} + \frac{y^2}{36} = 1$
   $y^2 = \frac{180}{9} = 20$
   $y = \sqrt{20} \approx 4.47$

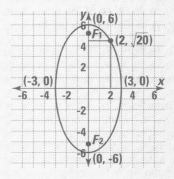

The point $(2, \sqrt{20})$ seems to be on the graph.

b. **The sum of the distances from the point $(2, \sqrt{20})$ to the two foci, $(0, \sqrt{27})$ and $(0, -\sqrt{27})$, is**
   $\sqrt{(2-0)^2 + (\sqrt{20} - \sqrt{27})^2} +$
   $\sqrt{(2-0)^2 + (\sqrt{20} + \sqrt{27})^2}$
   $= 12$

9. b.
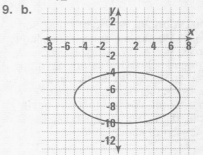

Question 10 Error Alert Some students find it difficult to believe that Pluto is not always the farthest from the Sun. This may be because they learn an order of the planets quite early in elementary school.

Question 16 This question demonstrates that even with technology, algebraic skills can be quite helpful.

Questions 17–19 Eccentricity is a means by which the shape of conic sections can be determined. For ellipses, since $c < a$, the eccentricity is always less than 1. Parabolas have eccentricity 1, and all hyperbolas have eccentricity greater than 1. Two conics are similar (in the strict geometric sense of the word) if and only if they have the same eccentricity.

Question 20 This question is meant to clarify the difference between the terms *focal distance* and *focal constant*.

Question 23 This is an important review for Lesson 12-4.

Question 26 Why is this question here? Because a survey of college graduates at a prestigious Ivy League school indicated that many of them thought summer was warmer because Earth was closer to the Sun. We feel that all people should be aware of such basic knowledge about Earth.

The planet Neptune was named after Neptune, the Roman god of the sea, well before its blue color was revealed by the Hubble Space Telescope.

13) Dividing both sides of the equation $2x^2 + 3y^2 = 12$ by 12 gives the equation $\frac{x^2}{6} + \frac{y^2}{4} = 1$, which is an equation of an ellipse in standard form.

15a) $\frac{x^2}{100} + \frac{y^2}{49} = 1$

b) $\frac{(x-3)^2}{100} + \frac{(y+6)^2}{49} = 1$

17a) Eccentricity $= \frac{c}{a}$, where $c^2 = a^2 - b^2$

10. The closest distance the planet Pluto comes to the sun is about 2759 million miles, and its farthest distance from the sun is about 4599 million miles. In fact, it was "inside" Neptune's orbit for most of the 1990s and only in 1999 will again become farther from the sun than Neptune. Is the second focus of Pluto's orbit nearer or farther from the sun than Earth? **farther**

11. Consider the ellipse with equation $\frac{(x-h)^2}{a^2} + \frac{(y-k)^2}{b^2} = 1$.
    a. What are the coordinates of its center? **(h, k)**
    b. What is the length of the vertical axis? **2b**
    c. How is this ellipse related to the ellipse with equation $\frac{x^2}{a^2} + \frac{y^2}{b^2} = 1$?
       It is the translation image under $T: (x, y) \to (x + h, y + k)$.

Applying the Mathematics

12. Find an equation for the ellipse pictured below.
    $\frac{x^2}{9} + y^2 = 1$

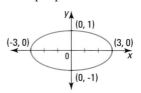

13. Explain why the set of points (x, y) satisfying $2x^2 + 3y^2 = 12$ is an ellipse. **See left.**

14. Consider the curve with equation $\frac{x^2}{25} + \frac{y^2}{25} = 1$ as an ellipse. State the length of the major and minor axes, and the focal constant.
    major axis = 10   minor axis = 10   focal constant = 10

15. a. Give an equation for the ellipse whose center is the origin, whose horizontal axis has length 20, and whose vertical axis has length 14.
    b. Give an equation for the image of the ellipse in part **a** under the translation $(x, y) \to (x + 3, y - 6)$.
    a, b) See left.

16. Even if an automatic grapher does not have a special feature for graphing conics, you can still graph an ellipse by following these steps.

    Step 1: Solve $\frac{x^2}{a^2} + \frac{y^2}{b^2} = 1$ for y.
    Step 2: Graph one of the solutions.
    Step 3: Graph the other solution. The union of the graphs is the ellipse.
    a, b) See margin.
    a. Graph the ellipse with equation $\frac{x^2}{4} + \frac{y^2}{9} = 1$ on an automatic grapher.
    b. Give the coordinates of four points on the ellipse other than the endpoints of the axes.

    In 17–19, the **eccentricity** of an ellipse is the ratio of the distance between the foci to the length of its major axis.

17. a. What is the eccentricity of the ellipse with equation $\frac{x^2}{a^2} + \frac{y^2}{b^2} = 1$?
       (Assume $a \geq b$; give a formula in terms of a, b, and/or c.) **See left.**
    b. Is the eccentricity of a long thin ellipse greater or less than the eccentricity of an ellipse that is more like a circle? **greater**

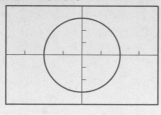

22a) $\cos\left(2\cdot\frac{\pi}{4}\right) =$

$\cos\left(\frac{\pi}{2}\right) = 0$

$\sin^2\left(\frac{\pi}{4}\right) - \cos^2\left(\frac{\pi}{4}\right) =$

$\left(\frac{\sqrt{2}}{2}\right)^2 - \left(\frac{\sqrt{2}}{2}\right)^2 = 0$

b) Sample: Let $\theta = \frac{\pi}{3}$.

Then $\cos 2\theta = -\frac{1}{2}$,

but $\sin^2\theta - \cos^2\theta =$

$\left(\frac{\sqrt{3}}{2}\right)^2 - \left(\frac{1}{2}\right)^2 =$

$\frac{3}{4} - \frac{1}{4} = \frac{1}{2}$

c)

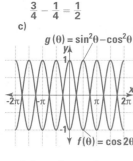

$g(\theta) = \sin^2\theta - \cos^2\theta$

$f(\theta) = \cos 2\theta$

d) Sample: $\cos 2\theta = \cos^2\theta - \sin^2\theta$

24) Sample: $\begin{bmatrix} \sqrt{5} & 0 \\ 0 & \sqrt{5} \end{bmatrix}$

Overachiever. *Pioneer 10, completed and launched in 1972, was still transmitting signals in 1997 when it was over 10 billion kilometers from Earth. At that distance, radio signals, traveling at the speed of light, took almost ten hours to reach Earth.*

---

18. a. What is the eccentricity of a circle? **0**

  b. What are the largest and smallest possible values of the eccentricity?
  $0 \le$ eccentricity < 1

19. Refer to Question 10. Pluto has the most eccentric orbit of the planets. What is the eccentricity of Pluto's orbit?
  ≈ 0.25

Review

20. Draw an ellipse in which the distance between the foci is 2 inches and the focal constant is 4 inches. *(Lesson 12-1)*
  Check student's drawings.

21. If a cone with two nappes is cut by a plane which is parallel to its axis, and does not contain the axis, what kind of figure can the intersection be?
  (Lesson 12-1)
  hyperbola

22. Consider the equation $\cos 2\theta = \sin^2\theta - \cos^2\theta$. **See left.**

  a. Show that the equation is true when $\theta = \frac{\pi}{4}$.

  b. Give an example to show that the equation is *not true* for all values of θ.

  c. Sketch the graphs of $f(\theta) = \cos 2\theta$ and $g(\theta) = \sin^2\theta - \cos^2\theta$ on the same set of axes to explain the results in parts **a** and **b**.

  d. Replace one side of the equation with another expression so that the resulting sentence is an identity. *(Lessons 4-5, 4-6, 11-6)*

23. Given that $R_\theta = \begin{bmatrix} -.5736 & -.8192 \\ .8192 & -.5736 \end{bmatrix}$, estimate θ if $0° < \theta < 360°$.
  (Lesson 11-4) $\approx 125°$

24. Write a matrix which represents a similarity transformation that results in an image whose area is five times the area of the preimage.
  (Previous course, Lesson 11-2) **See left**.

25. A certain space probe can transmit 500 megabytes (1 megabyte $= 10^6$ bytes) of electronic information during the first year of its mission. Due to decrease in energy sources and increasing distance, the transmission drops by $\frac{1}{10}$ every year. Determine how many megabytes of information this probe will transmit in the given time period.
  a. in 15 years **about 3971 megabytes**
  b. if it operates "forever" *(Lessons 8-4, 8-5)*
    5000 megabytes

Exploration

26. Although Earth is closer to the sun at some times than others, it is not this aspect of Earth's orbit that determines whether it is winter or summer. (It could not be, for when it is winter in one hemisphere, it is summer in the other.) What aspect of Earth's orbit causes the seasons?
  The inclination of the earth's axis of rotation causes one hemisphere of the earth to receive the most light at one point in the orbit, and the other hemisphere to receive the most light on the other side of the orbit.

Follow-up **12-2**
for Lesson

Practice

For more questions on SPUR Objectives, use **Lesson Master 12-2** (shown on page 763).

Assessment

Written Communication Have students **work in pairs**. Ask each student to make up a problem like **Example 1**, in which the given equations are for ellipses which are reflection images of each other over the line $x = y$. Have students solve their partner's problem and check one another's work. [Students use the equations of ellipses to determine their foci and sketch their graphs.]

Extension

Have students experiment to see how much information must be given to determine the equation for a unique ellipse. For example, the focal distance alone will not determine a unique ellipse, but the focal distance and the coordinates of the foci will. Have students make up problems containing certain given information, with the goal of finding the specific equation of a unique ellipse. Then have them exchange and work each others' problems. Discuss the different amounts and types of given information as a class. [Samples: the length of the major axis and the coordinates of the end-points of the minor axis; the coordinates of the foci and the length of the minor or major axis; the eccentricity and coordinates of the end-points of one of the axes.]

Project Update Project 1, *Orbits of Celestial Bodies,* Project 2, *Using Paper-folding to Make Conic Sections,* and Project 5, *Quadric Sections*, on pages 797–798, relate to the content of this lesson.

767

Objectives

A Use properties of hyperbolas to write equations describing them.
D State and apply properties of hyperbolas to draw or describe them.
G Graph or identify graphs of hyperbolas given their equations.
H Graph transformation images of parent hyperbolas.

Resources

From the Teacher's Resource File
■ Lesson Master 12-3
■ Answer Master 12-3
■ Assessment Sourcebook: Quiz for Lessons 12-1 through 12-3
■ Teaching Aids
 103 Warm-up
 107 Developing an Equation for an Ellipse
 108 Dandelin Spheres for the Hyperbola
■ Technology Sourcebook Computer Master 13

Additional Resources
■ Visuals for Teaching Aids 103, 107, 108
■ GraphExplorer
■ Exploration 12-3

Teaching Lesson 12-3

Warm-up

1. Solve each of the following equations.
 a. $p^2 + 12^2 = 13^2$ ± 5
 b. $q^2 + 12^2 = 15^2$ ± 9
 c. $r^2 + 12^2 = 20^2$ ± 16

12-3

The Hyperbola

It is not known for certain how or why the dinosaurs became extinct, but about 65 million years ago, after nearly 140 million years of roaming the earth, they suddenly disappeared. One theory is that a large asteroid hit Earth, raising so much dust that sunlight was blocked out for a time. Another theory is that a star came close to the sun and spewed dangerous radiation, and the dinosaurs, being so large, could not avoid it. If that star swerved past the sun, not to return, then its orbit would not be an ellipse. In the neighborhood of the sun, its orbit would be one branch of a hyperbola.

Because both hyperbolas and ellipses are conic sections, the hyperbola is a relative of the ellipse. That certain orbits are hyperbolas suggests other similarities between these two quite different-looking figures. In fact, much of what you have seen in the previous two lessons can be adapted to the hyperbola.

Dandelin Spheres and the Hyperbola

Here is Dandelin's way of relating the three-dimensional definition of a hyperbola as a conic section to a two-dimensional definition in terms of foci and a focal constant.

Consider a hyperbola formed by a plane M intersecting both nappes of a cone, as shown at the right. As with the ellipse, two spheres are tangent to the cone and to the plane M, but now one is in each nappe. Let F_1 and F_2 be the points of tangency of the spheres with the plane and let C_1 and C_2 be the circles of intersection of the spheres and the cone.

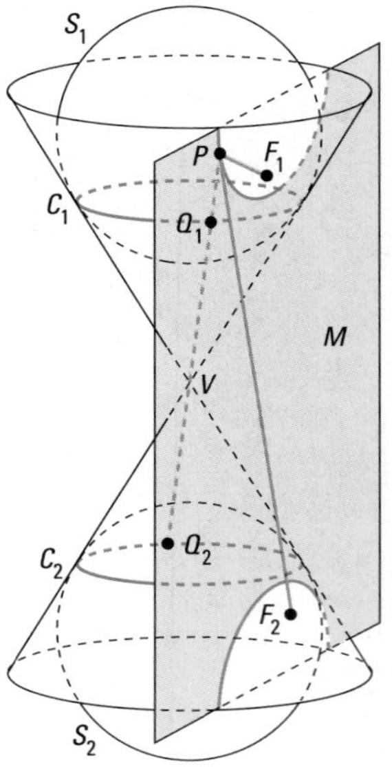

There is a property that relates any point P on the hyperbola to the fixed points F_1 and F_2. Suppose P is on the nappe of the cone containing sphere S_1. P is on an edge $\overrightarrow{PV}$ of the cone and that edge intersects the circles at Q_1 and Q_2. Since Q_1Q_2 is the distance along the edge between the circles, and the circles lie in parallel planes, Q_1Q_2 is a constant, regardless of the position of P.

Now notice that $\overline{PF_1}$ and $\overline{PQ_1}$ are tangents to sphere S_1 from point P, and $\overline{PF_2}$ and $\overline{PQ_2}$ are tangents from P to sphere S_2, so $PF_1 = PQ_1$ and $PF_2 = PQ_2$. So $PF_2 - PF_1 = PQ_2 - PQ_1 = Q_1Q_2$, a constant. That means that the difference $PF_2 - PF_1$ is a constant.

Lesson 12-3 Overview

Broad Goals This lesson recapitulates the previous two lessons, but with the changes required to cause the subject to be the hyperbola rather than the ellipse.

Perspective The hyperbola is formed by a plane intersecting *both* nappes of the cone and not being parallel to an edge. The locus is the set of points in a plane such that the *absolute difference* of the distances from two given points is a constant.

The hyperbola has the same two symmetry lines as the ellipse (namely, the line through its foci and the perpendicular bisector of the segment whose endpoints are the foci), and the proof is virtually identical. So is the derivation of an equation for the hyperbola with foci $(c, 0)$ and $(-c, 0)$: $\frac{x^2}{a^2} - \frac{y^2}{b^2} = 1$. If the foci are on the y-axis at $(0, c)$ and $(0, -c)$, an equation is $\frac{y^2}{a^2} - \frac{x^2}{b^2} = 1$. In both cases, $c^2 = a^2 + b^2$. The hyperbola has one major

feature that distinguishes it from the ellipse, its asymptotes. The classic transformation strategy is utilized to deal with these. That is, we consider the simplest hyperbola with an equation of one of the above forms, $x^2 - y^2 = 1$. (It is akin to the unit circle.) We find its asymptotes. Then we scale change it—and along with it, its asymptotes—to the other hyperbolas of that form.

If P were located on the other nappe of the cone, then the argument on page 768 would result in the difference $PF_1 - PF_2 = PQ_1 - PQ_2 = Q_1Q_2$, the same constant.

Thus either $PF_2 - PF_1 = Q_1Q_2$ or $PF_1 - PF_2 = Q_1Q_2$. These two equations are equivalent to the single equation $|PF_2 - PF_1| = Q_1Q_2$. That is, the absolute value of the difference of the distances from any point P on the hyperbola to the foci is a constant. This property is normally taken as the two-dimensional definition of a hyperbola.

A Two-dimensional Definition of the Hyperbola

$PF_2 - PF_1 = 10$

Definition
Let F_1 and F_2 be two given points in a plane and k be a positive real number with $k < F_1F_2$. Then the **hyperbola with foci F_1 and F_2 and focal constant k** is the set of all points in the plane which satisfy $|PF_1 - PF_2| = k$.

For instance, here is a hyperbola with foci F_1 and F_2 that are 14 units apart and $k = 10$. Notice that, unlike the ellipse, this hyperbola is unbounded. A point can be farther than any specified distance from either focus and still be 10 units closer to one focus than to the other.

a, b, d, e)
Sample: 6 points
$P_1: \left(\frac{1}{2}, 0\right) = (.5, 0)$
$P_2: \left(1, \frac{3}{2}\right) = (1, 1.5)$
$P_3: \left(1, -\frac{3}{2}\right) = (1, -1.5)$
$P_4: \left(2, \frac{3\sqrt{5}}{2}\right) \approx (2, 3.4)$
$P_5: \left(2, -\frac{3\sqrt{5}}{2}\right) \approx (2, -3.4)$
$P_6: \left(3, \frac{\sqrt{105}}{2}\right) \approx (3, 5.1)$

Activity
a. Draw two points F_1 and F_2, 2 units apart. See left for a, b, d, e.
b. Draw six points that are 1 unit closer to F_1 than to F_2.
c. *True or false.* All six points must lie on the same branch of a hyperbola with foci F_1 and F_2. **True**
d. Sketch the set of all points P such that $|PF_1 - PF_2| = 1$.
e. Draw all lines of symmetry of the curve in part **d**.

Hyperbolas possess the same symmetries as ellipses.

Theorem
A hyperbola with foci F_1 and F_2 is reflection-symmetric to $\overleftrightarrow{F_1F_2}$ and to the perpendicular bisector of the segment $\overline{F_1F_2}$.

Proof
The proof follows the ideas of the corresponding proof for the ellipse found in Lesson 12-1 and is left to you.

Developing an Equation for a Hyperbola

From the two-dimensional definition of a hyperbola, an equation for any hyperbola in the plane can be found, again by a method similar to that used for the ellipse. If the foci are $F_1 = (a, b)$ and $F_2 = (c, d)$ and the focal

2. Use the solutions to Question 1 to help graph the relation $y^2 - x^2 = 12^2$. **The graph is a hyperbola which contains the points $(0, \pm 12)$, $(\pm 5, \pm 13)$, $(\pm 9, \pm 15)$, $(\pm 12, \pm 16)$, $(\pm 22.5, \pm 25.5)$.**

Notes on Reading

Pacing You may wish to treat this as a two-day lesson. Students can do the reading and **Questions 1–7 and 16** for the first day. Then the remainder of the questions can be covered on the second day and students can begin the long reading of Lesson 12-4.

The orbit of one body with respect to another is an ellipse if the objects revolve about one another, a hyperbola if they do not. However, because of the gravitational influences of other bodies, no orbits are exactly ellipses or hyperbolas either. There are always wobbles. Such wobbles in planetary orbits led to the discovery of the planet Neptune.

Students who had difficulty following the mathematical developments in Lessons 12-1 and 12-2 have an opportunity for a review here. Emphasize that everything (except the existence of asymptotes) is analogous. Still, it is wise to take the same care here as before. Again, you may wish to go through the material on the Dandelin spheres for the hyperbola as you did for the ellipse, line by line. You can use **Teaching Aid 108** for this discussion. The basic idea is that the difference $PF_1 - PF_2$ between PF_1 and PF_2 is equal to the distance Q_1Q_2 between the circles of intersection of the spheres and the cone, measured along an edge of the cone.

Optional Activities

Activity 1 Technology Connection
Materials: Explorations software

You may use *Exploration 12-3, The Hyperbola,* as an alternative to the example in this lesson. Students can explore the relationship between the standard equation for a hyperbola and its graphical representation. Students can change the elements of the standard equation and observe the results on a coordinate grid. An animation feature allows students to see the results as the values change over a given interval.

Activity 2 Technology Connection
You may wish to use *Technology Sourcebook, Computer Master 13.* Students use *GraphExplorer* or similar software to explore various relationship between the graphs of conic sections and the corresponding equations.

Error Alert Be sure students understand the distinction between **parts b and d** in the **Activity** on page 769. You might want to interpret the absolute value sign in **part d** to mean that all the points fitting the description in **part b** are to be included as well as all the points that are 1 unit closer to F_2 than to F_1.

The symmetry of the ellipse and hyperbola to the line containing its foci and to the perpendicular bisector of the segment joining the foci can be easily explained. Switching the foci leads to the same conic section. Thus the symmetry of the conic is the same as the symmetry of the figure with just the two points.

❶ You might wish to go through the derivation of the equation $\frac{x^2}{a^2} - \frac{y^2}{b^2} = 1$ for a hyperbola using **Teaching Aid 107**, which was given for the ellipse in Lesson 12-2. Then you can make changes in Step 10 as needed, and the similarities and differences become obvious.

The hyperbola with equation $x^2 - y^2 = 1$ is quite analogous to the unit circle. The values of the *hyperbolic trigonometric functions* cosh and sinh are coordinates of points on this hyperbola just as (cos θ, sin θ) is a point on the unit circle. Beginning with this hyperbola and stretching it into the more general hyperbola $\frac{x^2}{a^2} - \frac{y^2}{b^2} = 1$ ought to be expected by students.

constant is k, then any point $P = (x, y)$ on the hyperbola must satisfy the equation

$$|PF_1 - PF_2| = k$$

or $\quad \sqrt{(x - a)^2 + (y - b)^2} - \sqrt{(x - c)^2 + (y - d)^2} = \pm k.$

This is an equation for the hyperbola. Again, it is unwieldy and it does not lend itself to graphing even with an automatic grapher. What we will do is to begin with a hyperbola whose foci are particularly well-chosen and find an equation for that hyperbola. Then we will apply transformations to generate equations for other hyperbolas.

Theorem (Equation for a Hyperbola)
The hyperbola with foci $(c, 0)$ and $(-c, 0)$ and focal constant $2a$ has equation $\frac{x^2}{a^2} - \frac{y^2}{b^2} = 1$, where $b^2 = c^2 - a^2$.

---

❶ **Proof**
The proof is identical to the proof of the equation for an ellipse in standard form, with two exceptions. In Step 1, by the definition of hyperbola,

$$|PF_1 - PF_2| = 2a.$$

Now if $P = (x, y)$, $F_1 = (c, 0)$, and $F_2 = (-c, 0)$, then using the Distance Formula,

$$\sqrt{(x - c)^2 + y^2} - \sqrt{(x - -c)^2 + y^2} = \pm 2a.$$

Steps 2–9 are identical to those in the proof of the theorem for the ellipse. A difference comes in Step 10. Because for the hyperbola $c > a > 0$, then $c^2 > a^2$, so we let $b^2 = c^2 - a^2$. This accounts for the minus sign in the equation for the hyperbola (see Step 11), where there is a plus sign for the ellipse.

The equation $\frac{x^2}{a^2} - \frac{y^2}{b^2} = 1$ is said to be the **standard form** for an equation of a hyperbola.

The Hyperbola $x^2 - y^2 = 1$

The simplest equation in standard form is $x^2 - y^2 = 1$, which occurs when $a = b = 1$. Then, since $b^2 = c^2 - a^2$, $1 = c^2 - 1$, so $c = \pm\sqrt{2}$. Thus the hyperbola with foci $(\sqrt{2}, 0)$ and $(-\sqrt{2}, 0)$ and focal constant 2 is the set of points (x, y) that satisfy the equation $x^2 - y^2 = 1$. Every other hyperbola with an equation of the form $\frac{x^2}{a^2} - \frac{y^2}{b^2} = 1$ is a scale-change image of this hyperbola. So it helps to study the hyperbola $x^2 - y^2 = 1$ in some detail.

Here is a table of some values. Notice that it contains the points $(1, 0)$ and $(-1, 0)$. Other points can be found by solving for y. Since $y^2 = x^2 - 1$,

$y = \pm\sqrt{x^2 - 1}$. The two lines of symmetry of the hyperbola enable points to be found in all four quadrants. This hyperbola is graphed on page 771.

Optional Activities

Activity 3 After discussing this lesson, you might have students explain how the equations for the asymptotes of a hyperbola change when the center of the hyperbola is moved away from the origin to a point (h, k). [The intersection point of the asymptotes is also moved off the origin to the point (h, k). Therefore, the equations of the asymptotes can be written $y - k = \pm m(x - h)$, where $\pm m$ are the slopes of the asymptotes, determined by the values of a and b. This form of

a linear equation is point-slope form, which students will remember, although it is also seen easily as a translation the image of $y = \pm mx$.]

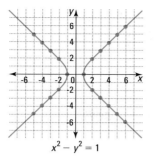

x	$y = \pm\sqrt{x^2 - 1}$	
1	0	
2	$\pm\sqrt{3}$	$\approx \pm 1.7$
3	$\pm\sqrt{8}$	$\approx \pm 2.8$
4	$\pm\sqrt{15}$	$\approx \pm 3.9$
5	$\pm\sqrt{24}$	$\approx \pm 4.9$
6	$\pm\sqrt{35}$	$\approx \pm 5.9$
-1	0	
-2	$\pm\sqrt{3}$	$\approx \pm 1.7$
-3	$\pm\sqrt{8}$	$\approx \pm 2.8$
-4	$\pm\sqrt{15}$	$\approx \pm 3.9$
-5	$\pm\sqrt{24}$	$\approx \pm 4.9$

$$x^2 - y^2 = 1$$

Unique among the conic sections, every hyperbola has asymptotes, lines it approaches as x gets farther from the foci. The asymptotes for the hyperbola $x^2 - y^2 = 1$ are $y = x$ and $y = -x$. This is because as x gets larger, $\sqrt{x^2 - 1}$ becomes closer and closer to $\sqrt{x^2}$, which is $|x|$. So y gets closer and closer to $\pm x$. You can verify this by examining the above table. Even for as small a value as $x = 6$, $y \approx \pm 5.92$, which is close to $\pm x$. Alternately, you can also use an automatic grapher to investigate the asymptotes of this hyperbola. Below are two views of the hyperbola $x^2 - y^2 = 1$ and its asymptotes in two different windows.

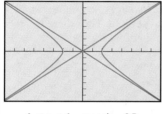

$-4 \le x \le 4$, x-scale = 0.5
$-4 \le y \le 4$, y-scale = 0.5

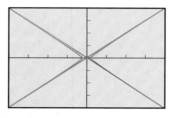

$-20 \le x \le 20$, x-scale = 5
$-20 \le y \le 20$, y-scale = 5

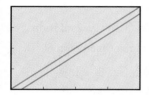

$14.8 \le x \le 15.2$, x-scale = 0.1
$14.8 \le y \le 15.2$, y-scale = 0.1

Note that as you look at larger values of $|x|$ in each window, the hyperbola gets closer to its asymptote.

It is important to realize, however, that the hyperbola never reaches its asymptotes. If you zoom or rescale around a point that appears to be on $y = \pm x$, you will see that there is always some distance between the graphs. For instance, at the left is a view of the graphs of $x^2 - y^2 = 1$ and $y = x$ near the point (15, 15). The graph of $y = x$ (in orange) does not intersect the graph of $x^2 - y^2 = 1$ (in blue).

The Hyperbola $\dfrac{x^2}{a^2} - \dfrac{y^2}{b^2} = 1$

Other hyperbolas are scale-change images of the parent $x^2 - y^2 = 1$. The scale change $(x, y) \rightarrow (ax, by)$ maps $x^2 - y^2 = 1$ onto $\dfrac{x^2}{a^2} - \dfrac{y^2}{b^2} = 1$. The asymptotes $y = \pm x$ are mapped onto the lines $\dfrac{y}{b} = \pm\dfrac{x}{a}$ or, solving for y,

Lesson 12-3 *The Hyperbola* **771**

Students may wonder why we did not begin with the unit circle and stretch it to get equations for ellipses. The reason is that typically the foci of a conic do not stretch into the foci of its image. A circle has only one focus (its center) and that focus could never be mapped onto the two foci of any noncircular ellipse.

However, the asymptotes do stretch with the hyperbola itself, so the stretch argument works quite well in finding equations for asymptotes.

In the **Example,** at the bottom of page 772, because the equation of **part b** is identical to the equation of **part a** except with x and y switched, it should be obvious that each is the reflection image of the other over the line $y = x$. Note that the asymptotes also are reflection images of each other.

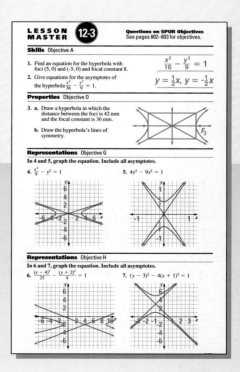

Additional Examples

1. Name the vertices and asymptotes of each hyperbola.

a. $\frac{x^2}{100} - \frac{y^2}{36} = 1$.
Vertices (10, 0) and (-10, 0); asymptotes $\frac{y}{6} = \pm\frac{x}{10}$, or equivalently, $y = \frac{3}{5}x$ and $y = -\frac{3}{5}x$

b. $\frac{y^2}{100} - \frac{x^2}{36} = 1$.
Vertices (0, 10) and (0, -10); asymptotes $\frac{y}{10} = \pm\frac{x}{6}$, or equivalently, $y = \frac{5}{3}x$ and $y = -\frac{5}{3}x$; notice that the answers to part b are easily found from the answers to part a.

(Notes on Questions begin on page 774.)

$y = \pm\frac{b}{a}x$. With this information, the hyperbola with equation in standard form $\frac{x^2}{a^2} - \frac{y^2}{b^2} = 1$ can be sketched easily.

Each asymptote contains the origin. One asymptote goes through the points (a, b) and $(-a, -b)$; the other goes through $(a, -b)$ and $(-a, b)$. Drawing the rectangle with these four points as vertices, and the lines determined by its diagonals, helps to position the hyperbola. Notice that since $b^2 = c^2 - a^2$, then $a^2 + b^2 = c^2$, and so the sides and diagonals of the guiding rectangle have lengths $2a$, $2b$, and $2c$.

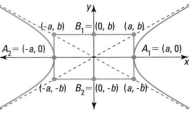

By substitution, you can verify that $(a, 0)$ and $(-a, 0)$ are on this hyperbola. These points are the **vertices** of the hyperbola. Now sketch the hyperbola with vertices at $(\pm a, 0)$ and the diagonals of the rectangle as asymptotes.

Notice that when $|x| < a$, y is not a real number. Thus the hyperbola $\frac{x^2}{a^2} - \frac{y^2}{b^2} = 1$ contains no points with x-coordinates between $-a$ and a.

The segments $\overline{A_1A_2}$ and $\overline{B_1B_2}$ of the guiding rectangle are the **axes** of the hyperbola. The two axes lie on the symmetry lines and intersect at the **center** of the hyperbola. Thus there is a theorem for hyperbolas that corresponds to that for ellipses.

> **Theorem**
> In the hyperbola with equation $\frac{x^2}{a^2} - \frac{y^2}{b^2} = 1$,
> $2a$ is the length of the horizontal axis,
> $2b$ is the length of the vertical axis, and
> $2c$ is the distance between the foci, where $c^2 = a^2 + b^2$.

If x and y are switched in the equation for a hyperbola, the general form becomes $\frac{y^2}{a^2} - \frac{x^2}{b^2} = 1$. Its graph is the reflection image of the graph of $\frac{x^2}{a^2} - \frac{y^2}{b^2} = 1$ over the line $y = x$, and the foci of the image hyperbola are on the y-axis. In this case, $2a$ is the length of the vertical axis, and $2b$ is the length of the horizontal axis.

> **Example**
> Sketch a graph of the hyperbola, and determine equations of its asymptotes.
> a. $\frac{x^2}{9} - \frac{y^2}{16} = 1$
> b. $\frac{y^2}{9} - \frac{x^2}{16} = 1$

Adapting to Individual Needs

Challenge
The challenge for Lesson 4-6 introduced students to equations in parametric form. Have students use identities to determine the description of the following graphs.

1. $x = a \cos t$; $y = a \sin t$; $0 \le t \le 2\pi$.
[A circle centered at the origin with radius a: $x^2 + y^2 = (a \cos t)^2 + (a \sin t)^2 = a^2 (\cos^2 t + \sin^2 t) = a^2$, ...]

2. $x = a \cos t$; $y = b \sin t$; $0 \le t \le 2\pi$.
[An ellipse centered at the origin with axes endpoints at $(\pm a, 0)$ and $(0, \pm b)$: $\frac{x}{a} = \cos t$ and $\frac{y}{b} = \sin t$, so $(\frac{x}{a})^2 + (\frac{y}{b})^2 = \cos^2 t + \sin^2 t = 1$, ...]

3. $x = a \sec t$; $y = b \tan t$; $0 \le t \le 2\pi$.
[A hyperbola centered at the origin with axes endpoints at $(\pm a, 0)$ and $(0, \pm b)$: $\frac{x}{a} = \sec t$ and $\frac{y}{b} = \tan t$. Since $\tan^2 t + 1 = \sec^2 t$, $(\frac{y}{b})^2 + 1 = (\frac{x}{a})^2$, or $(\frac{x}{a})^2 - (\frac{y}{b})^2 = 1$, ...]

4. $x = a \cos t$; $y = a^2 \sin^2 t$; $0 \le t \le 2\pi$.
[A parabola, vertex at $(0, a^2)$, pointing down: $\frac{x}{a} = \cos t$ and $\frac{y}{a^2} = \sin^2 t$. Thus $(\frac{x}{a})^2 + \frac{y}{a^2} = \cos^2 t + \sin^2 t = 1$, from which $x^2 + y = a^2$, so $y = a^2 - x^2$, ...]

Solution

a. In this hyperbola **the foci are on the x-axis, and a = 3 and b = 4.**
Thus the vertices of the hyperbola are (3, 0) and (-3, 0). To sketch the
hyperbola, draw a rectangle centered at the origin with horizontal axis of
length 2 · 3 = 6, and vertical axis of length 2 · 4 = 8. The diagonals of this
rectangle are the asymptotes. **They have equations** $\frac{y}{4} = \pm\frac{x}{3}$ **or,**
equivalently $y = \pm\frac{4}{3}x$. **The hyperbola has vertices (± 3, 0) and**
is bounded by these asymptotes. A sketch is at the left below.

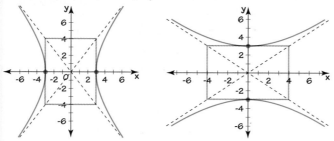

b. In this hyperbola, **a = 3 and b = 4. However, the foci and vertices**
are on the y-axis. The vertices of this hyperbola are (0, 3) and
(0, -3). The asymptotes have equations $\frac{y}{3} = \pm\frac{x}{4}$ **or equivalently,**
$y = \pm\frac{3x}{4}$. **A graph is at the right above.**

Check

a. Analyze the equation for values excluded from the domain or range. In
part **a**, $\frac{x^2}{9} - 1 = \frac{y^2}{16}$ or $y = \pm\sqrt{16\left(\frac{x^2}{9} - 1\right)}$. The expression under the
radical sign is a real number if and only if $\frac{x^2}{9} - 1 \geq 0$ or $x^2 \geq 9$. That is,
all points on the hyperbola must have $|x| \geq 3$. This agrees with the
sketch we drew.

b. You are asked to check the work for part **b** in the Questions.

Using Hyperbolas to Locate Objects

Hyperbolas can be and are used to
locate objects that emit sound
waves. The idea comes directly
from the definition of hyperbola.
Suppose a whale at an unknown
point W emits a sound. Let A and B
be locations of two underwater
devices that can receive the sound,
and suppose A and B are 10,000

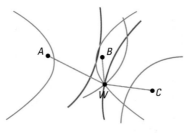

feet apart. Suppose a sound from the whale is received 0.5 seconds later at
point A than at point B. The speed of sound in water is known to be about
5000 feet per second. So the difference of the distances WA and WB is
2500 feet. Thus the position of the whale must be on a hyperbola with foci
A and B and with focal constant 2500 feet.

Lesson 12-3   *The Hyperbola*   **773**

Practice

For more questions on SPUR
Objectives, use **Lesson Master 12-3**
(shown on page 771).

Assessment

Quiz A quiz covering Lessons 12-1
through 12-3 is provided in the
Assessment Sourcebook.

Extension

Cooperative Learning If students
did the Extension for Lesson 12-1,
they might adapt their model of Dandelin's spheres for the hyperbola.

Project Update Project 2, *Using
Paper-folding to Make Conic Sections*,
Project 3, *Using Drawing to Make
Conic Sections*, and Project 5,
Quadric Sections, on pages 797–798,
relate to the content of this lesson.

Setting Up Lesson 12-4

Discuss **Question 18** and determine the
image of (x, y) under the corresponding
transformations.

Question 4 This idea is used in the derivation of an equation for a hyperbola.

Question 10 This is a proof of part of the theorem on page 769.

Question 21 You might ask students for a generalization:
$(x + y)^2 + (x - y)^2 = 2x^2 + 2y^2.$

Additional Answers

7. a. Sample:
$P_1 = (5, 0)$
$P_2 = (-5, 0)$
$P_3 = (10, 7\sqrt{3})$
$P_4 = (10, -7\sqrt{3})$
$P_5 = (-10, 7\sqrt{3})$
$P_6 = (-10, -7\sqrt{3})$

b. $y = \frac{7}{5}x,\ y = -\frac{7}{5}x$

c.
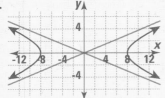

8. a.
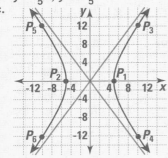

b.

c. They are reflection images of each other over the line $y = x$.

9. In the equation for part b,
$\frac{y^2}{9} = \frac{x^2}{16} + 1$ or $y \pm \sqrt{9(\frac{x^2}{16} + 1)}$.

For all x, $\frac{x^2}{16} + 1 \geq 1$ so $|y| \geq 3$. This agrees with the graph.

3a, b)
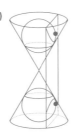

If another device receives the same sound at point C and the time is recorded, then the position of the whale can be located on two other hyperbolas (one with foci A and C, the other with foci B and C). The whale's position at the time of emitting the sound, which is the solution of two equations in two variables, can be located quite precisely.

QUESTIONS

Covering the Reading

1. *True or false.* The path of an object in space may be hyperbolic in shape.
   True
2. Suppose ℓ and m are intersecting lines and m is rotated around ℓ to form a cone. Now a plane P intersects the cone. Which position of P gives a hyperbola, which an ellipse, which a parabola?
   a. P is parallel to m. **parabola**   **b.** P is perpendicular to ℓ.
   c. P is parallel to ℓ.   **ellipse**
   hyperbola
3. **a.** Draw a plane intersecting a cone to form a hyperbola. **See left.**
   b. Draw the Dandelin spheres for this hyperbola. **See left.**
   c. How are the Dandelin spheres related to the foci of the hyperbola?
   The spheres are tangent to the plane at the foci of the hyperbola.
4. If $|m - n| = k > 0$, what are the possible values of $m - n$?
   $m - n = k$ **or** $m - n = -k$
5. Show your work from the Activity in the lesson.
   See page 769.
6. **a.** Graph $x^2 - y^2 = 1$.   **b.** Graph $y^2 - x^2 = 1$.
   c. Write several sentences comparing and contrasting the graphs in parts **a** and **b**.
   a–c) See left.
7. Consider the hyperbola $\frac{x^2}{25} - \frac{y^2}{49} = 1$. **See margin.**
   a. Find the coordinates of six points on the graph.
   b. Give equations for its asymptotes.
   c. Use the results of parts **a** and **b** to sketch a graph of the hyperbola.
8. **a.** Graph the hyperbola with equation $\frac{x^2}{64} - \frac{y^2}{9} = 1$. **a–c) See margin.**
   b. Graph the hyperbola with equation $\frac{y^2}{64} - \frac{x^2}{9} = 1$.
   c. How are the graphs of parts **a** and **b** related?
9. Check part **b** of the Example of this lesson. **See margin.**

Applying the Mathematics

10. Prove that every hyperbola is symmetric to the line containing its foci. **See margin.**
11. Use the definition of hyperbola to verify that $(1, 0)$ is on the hyperbola with foci $(\sqrt{2}, 0)$ and $(-\sqrt{2}, 0)$ and focal constant 2. **See margin.**
12. Let A and B be points on the x-axis 10,000 units apart. Find an equation for a hyperbola on which the whale of this lesson lies.
    Let $A = (5000, 0)$ and $B = (-5000, 0)$. An equation for the hyperbola is
    $$\frac{x^2}{1{,}562{,}500} - \frac{y^2}{23{,}437{,}500} = 1.$$

6a)
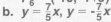

b)

c) Sample: The graph of $x^2 - y^2 = 1$ is the reflection image of the graph of $y^2 - x^2 = 1$ over the line $y = x$. Both graphs have the same shape, the same focal constant, and the same asymptotes. However, the foci and vertices of the graph of $x^2 - y^2 = 1$ lie on the x-axis, while those of the graph of $y^2 - x^2 = 1$ lie on the y-axis.

774

---

10. Let F_1 and F_2 be the foci of a hyperbola with focal constant k. If P is any point on the hyperbola then $|PF_1 - PF_2| = k$. Let P' be the image of P under the reflection r over $\overline{F_1F_2}$. Since $r(F_1) = F_1$ and $r(F_2) = F_2$ and reflections preserve distance, $P'F_1 = PF_1$ and $P'F_2 = PF_2$. So $|P'F_1 - P'F_2| = |PF_1 - PF_2| = k$ and P' is on the hyperbola. This shows that the image of any point on the hyperbola

is also on the hyperbola. To show that the image is the entire hyperbola, note that if Q is on the hyperbola, then $r(r(Q)) = Q$ and $r(Q)$ is on the hyperbola by the above argument. Thus any point on the hyperbola is the image of some point on the hyperbola.

13a) Dividing both sides of the equation $x^2 - 2y^2 = 2$ by 2 gives the equivalent equation $\frac{x^2}{2} - y^2 = 1$.

14c)

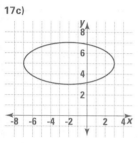

17c)

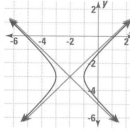

18a) $\begin{bmatrix} 0 & 1 \\ -1 & 0 \end{bmatrix}$

b) $\begin{bmatrix} \cos\theta & -\sin\theta \\ \sin\theta & \cos\theta \end{bmatrix}$

c) $\begin{bmatrix} \cos\theta & \sin\theta \\ -\sin\theta & \cos\theta \end{bmatrix}$

---

13. a. Explain why the graph of $x^2 - 2y^2 = 2$ is a hyperbola. **See left.**
   b. Find the foci and focal constant of this hyperbola.
   foci $(\sqrt{3}, 0), (-\sqrt{3}, 0)$; focal constant: $2\sqrt{2}$
14. Consider the hyperbola with equation $(x + 2)^2 - (y + 3)^2 = 1$.
   a. Name its vertices. $(-1, -3), (-3, -3)$
   b. Give equations for its asymptotes. $y = x - 1, y = -x - 5$
   c. Sketch a graph of the hyperbola. **See left.**

15. Consider the hyperbola with equation $\frac{(x - h)^2}{a^2} - \frac{(y - k)^2}{b^2} = 1$. Identify each of the following.
   a. its center (h, k)
   b. its vertices $(a + h, k), (-a + h, k)$
   c. its foci
   d. its asymptotes
   $\left(\sqrt{a^2 + b^2} + h, k\right), \left(-\sqrt{a^2 + b^2} + h, k\right)$
   $\frac{y - k}{b} = \frac{x - h}{a}, \frac{y - k}{b} = -\frac{(x - h)}{a}$

Review

16. a. What is an equation for the ellipse shown $\frac{x^2}{4} + \frac{y^2}{9} = 1$ at the right?
   b. Where are its foci? *(Lesson 12-2)*
   $\left(0, \sqrt{5}\right), \left(0, -\sqrt{5}\right)$
17. Consider the ellipse with equation
   $\frac{(x + 2)^2}{25} + \frac{(y - 5)^2}{4} = 1$.   **a.** center: $(-2, 5)$ foci $\left(\sqrt{21} - 2, 5\right),$ $\left(-\sqrt{21} - 2, 5\right)$
   a. Determine the center and the foci of this ellipse.
   b. How long are its major and minor axes? major axis: 10 minor axis 4
   c. Graph this ellipse. *(Lesson 12-2)*
   See left.
18. Give the matrix for the rotation of the given magnitude around the origin. *(Lesson 11-4)* **See left.**
   a. $\frac{3\pi}{2}$ **b.** θ **c.** $-\theta$

19. The operational life span of a certain brand of toner for laser printers is known to be normally distributed with mean 4500 pages of text and standard deviation 500 pages. If a printing office is buying 50 of these toners, how many of them should they expect to last for less than 4000 pages? *(Lesson 10-6)* **about 8**

20. a. Use the Binomial Theorem to write out the terms of the following powers of $(1 + 1)$. **a–b) See margin.**
   i. $(1 + 1)^0$ **ii.** $(1 + 1)^1$
   iii. $(1 + 1)^2$ **iv.** $(1 + 1)^3$
   b. *True or false.* The binomial expansion of $(1 + 1)^n$ for any n gives the elements in the nth row of Pascal's Triangle. Justify your answer. *(Lessons 8-6, 8-7, 8-8)*

21. Simplify $\left(\sqrt{2}\, a + b\right)^2 + \left(\sqrt{2}\, a - b\right)^2$. *(Previous course)*
   $4a^2 + 2b^2$

Exploration

a–c) See margin.
22. a. Describe the graph of the set of points (x, y) satisfying $x^2 - y^2 < 1$.
   b. Describe the graph of the set of points (x, y) satisfying $x^2 - y^2 > 1$.
   c. Generalize parts **a** and **b** to apply to any hyperbola in standard form.

---

20. b. True; by definition, the elements of the nth row of Pascal's triangle are $_nC_r$ for $0 \le r \le n$. By the Binomial Theorem, the terms in the binomial expansion of $(1 + 1)^n$ are $_nC_r \cdot 1^n \cdot 1^{n-r} = _nC_r$. The terms are the same.

22. a.

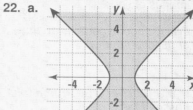

$\{(x, y): x^2 - y^2 < 1\}$
The set of points satisfying $x^2 - y^2 < 1$ is the set of points between the branches of the hyperbola $x^2 - y^2 = 1$. It is shaded above.

b.

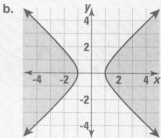

$\{(x, y): x^2 - y^2 > 1\}$
The set of points satisfying $x^2 - y^2 > 1$ is the set of points outside the branches of the hyperbola $x^2 - y^2 = 1$. It is shaded above.

c. Given a hyperbola $\frac{x^2}{a^2} - \frac{y^2}{b^2} = 1$, the set of points satisfying $\frac{x^2}{a^2} - \frac{y^2}{b^2} < 1$ is the set of points between the branches of the hyperbola. The set of points satisfying $\frac{x^2}{a^2} - \frac{y^2}{b^2} > 1$ is the set of points outside the branches of the hyperbola.

---

11. Let $F_1 = (\sqrt{2}, 0), F_2 = (-\sqrt{2}, 0)$, the focal constant $k = 2$, and $P = (1, 0)$.
We have to show $\left|PF_1 - PF_2\right| = 2$, or, equivalently, $(PF_1 - PF_2)^2 = 4$.

$$(PF_1 - PF_2)^2 = \left(\sqrt{(1 - \sqrt{2})^2 + (0 - 0)^2} - \sqrt{(1 + \sqrt{2})^2 + (0 - 0)^2}\right)^2$$

$$= \left(\sqrt{(3 - 2\sqrt{2})} - \sqrt{(3 + 2\sqrt{2})}\right)^2$$

$$= 3 - 2\sqrt{2} - 2\sqrt{(3 - 2\sqrt{2})(3 + 2\sqrt{2})} + 3 + 2\sqrt{2} = 6 - 2\sqrt{9 - 8} = 4$$

20. a. i. $(1 + 1)^0 = {_0C_0} \cdot 1^0 = 1$
   ii. $(1 + 1)^1 = {_1C_0} \cdot 1^1 + {_1C_1} \cdot 1^1 = 1 + 1 = 2$
   iii. $(1 + 1)^2 = {_2C_0} \cdot 1^2 + {_2C_1} \cdot 1^1 \cdot 1^1 + {_2C_2} \cdot 1^2 = 1 + 2 + 1 = 4$
   iv. $(1 + 1)^3 = {_3C_0} \cdot 1^3 + {_3C_1} \cdot 1^2 \cdot 1^1 + {_3C_2} \cdot 1^1 \cdot 1^2 + {_3C_3} \cdot 1^3 = 1 + 3 + 3 + 1 = 8$

775

Objectives

B Find equations for rotation images of figures.
D State and apply properties of ellipses and hyperbolas to draw or describe them.

Resources

From the *Teacher's Resource File*
■ Lesson Master 12-4
■ Answer Master 12-4
■ Teaching Aids
   104 Warm-up
   109 Rotating $y = x^2$ Twenty Degrees about (5, 8)

Additional Resources
■ Visuals for Teaching Aids 104, 109
■ Exploration 12-4

Teaching Lesson 12-4

Warm-up

Simplify each expression.

1. $\sin \frac{\pi}{4}$ $\frac{1}{2}\sqrt{2}$
2. $\sin 60°$ $\frac{1}{2}\sqrt{3}$
3. $\cos 60°$ $\frac{1}{2}$
4. $\begin{bmatrix} \cos 30° & -\sin 30° \\ \sin 30° & \cos 30° \end{bmatrix} \begin{bmatrix} 4 \\ 0 \end{bmatrix}$ $\begin{bmatrix} 2\sqrt{3} \\ 2 \end{bmatrix}$

LESSON

12-4

Rotating Relations

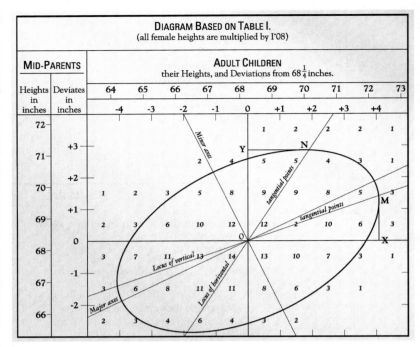

DIAGRAM BASED ON TABLE I.
(all female heights are multiplied by 1'08)

In Lesson 12-1, it was noted that Kepler's discovery that the planets go around the sun in elliptical orbits is one of the great examples of mathematical modeling of all time. Another brilliant example of mathematical modeling, which also involved ellipses, occurred only a little over a century ago, in 1886. It came as the result of the work of Francis Galton (1822–1911), an English scientist and statistician.

❶ Galton was attempting to show the influences of heredity on height. He tabulated the heights of 928 adult children from 205 families against the mean heights of their parents (which he called the *mid-parent height*). He then grouped the data to plot frequencies as shown in the graph above. He discovered that, in this grouped data, the frequencies with the same values lay roughly on a series of similar ellipses with the same center and whose axes were at the same angle of inclination. For instance, the eleven points with frequency 3 lie on an ellipse slightly larger than the one drawn.

He showed his findings to a mathematician, J. Hamilton Dickson, who proved that Galton's discovery was the result of these heights being related by a *bivariate normal distribution*, that is, a three-dimensional curve with two planes of symmetry in which each cross section parallel to a plane of symmetry is a normal curve. The ellipses are the contour lines of equal probabilities, as shown on page 777.

776

Lesson 12-4 Overview

Broad Goals This lesson shows how equations for conic sections whose axes are neither horizontal nor vertical can be derived by rotating conic sections with horizontal or vertical axes.

Perspective A generation ago, during the study of analytic geometry, axes would be translated and rotated while the graphs of relations were kept in the same place. Now it is considered far easier to translate and

rotate the graphs of relations. The Graph Rotation Theorem of this lesson is another in the mold of the Graph Translation Theorem and the Graph Scale Change Theorem. It enables a sentence for the rotation image of any graph to be found if you know a sentence for the preimage.

Thus, to find an equation for any conic section, one determines how much their axes are tilted to the horizontal and vertical,

rotates a curve in standard position that amount, and then translates it. The algebraic manipulation is still quite formidable, so the examples given in this lesson are simple. Still, they are telling. Rotating the hyperbola $x^2 - y^2 = 1$ an amount $\frac{\pi}{4}$ about the origin gives a hyperbola of the form $xy = k$ as its image. Thus these hyperbolas that students have seen in previous years are in fact congruent to the hyperbolas that have been studied in the previous lesson.

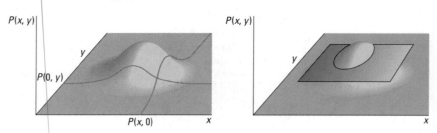
$P(x, y)$ $P(x, y)$

$P(0, y)$ y

$P(x, 0)$ x y x

This work of Galton led to the development of the ideas of correlation and variance and their connection with regression and the line of best fit. While those details are beyond the scope of this course, you can determine the equations of ellipses that are rotated so that their axes are no longer horizontal or vertical, like Galton's ellipse pictured on page 776. The techniques for finding rotation images of graphs are developed in this lesson.

The Graph-Rotation Theorem

Recall that if the point (x, y) is rotated through magnitude θ about the origin, then its image (x', y') can be found by matrix multiplication.

$$\begin{bmatrix} x' \\ y' \end{bmatrix} = \begin{bmatrix} \cos \theta & -\sin \theta \\ \sin \theta & \cos \theta \end{bmatrix} \begin{bmatrix} x \\ y \end{bmatrix}$$

The inverse of the matrix for R_θ is the matrix for $R_{-\theta}$. To obtain an equation for (x, y) in terms of (x', y'), multiply each side of the preceding matrix equation by that inverse.

$$\begin{bmatrix} \cos \theta & \sin \theta \\ -\sin \theta & \cos \theta \end{bmatrix} \begin{bmatrix} x' \\ y' \end{bmatrix} = \begin{bmatrix} \cos \theta & \sin \theta \\ -\sin \theta & \cos \theta \end{bmatrix} \begin{bmatrix} \cos \theta & -\sin \theta \\ \sin \theta & \cos \theta \end{bmatrix} \begin{bmatrix} x \\ y \end{bmatrix}$$

$$= \begin{bmatrix} 1 & 0 \\ 0 & 1 \end{bmatrix} \begin{bmatrix} x \\ y \end{bmatrix}$$

So $$\begin{bmatrix} \cos \theta & \sin \theta \\ -\sin \theta & \cos \theta \end{bmatrix} \begin{bmatrix} x' \\ y' \end{bmatrix} = \begin{bmatrix} x \\ y \end{bmatrix}$$

Now multiply the two matrices on the left side to get the following equation.

$$\begin{bmatrix} x' \cos \theta + y' \sin \theta \\ -x' \sin \theta + y' \cos \theta \end{bmatrix} = \begin{bmatrix} x \\ y \end{bmatrix}$$

Equating the two matrices above gives the following.

$$x = x' \cos \theta + y' \sin \theta$$
$$y = -x' \sin \theta + y' \cos \theta$$

Now, if a sentence involving x and y is known, then the above expressions can be substituted for x and y and the result will be a sentence involving x' and y'. The new sentence describes the rotation image. Once the sentence for the rotation image is found, the primes in x' and y' are removed so that the resulting sentence is in the variables x and y. The result is the following theorem on page 778.

Notes on Reading

This lesson has more reading than most, so it is a good idea to summarize it. There are five parts:
1. The description of Galton's statistical work, which shows a reason for rotating ellipses;
2. A proof and an example of the Graph Rotation Theorem;
3. A second example of that theorem, leading to the fact that relations with equations of the form $xy = k$ are hyperbolas;
4. A verbal argument explaining how any isometry in the plane can be performed on a relation, and why the equation for the image will have the same degree as the preimage; and
5. An example of performing an isometry on a parabola. We suggest that you begin with the questions and discuss the parts of the lesson as needed.

❶ Students may not understand how Galton's table on page 776 relates to the contour graphs on page 777. They should think of Galton's table as being in the xy-plane of a three-dimensional coordinate system. Then think of the frequencies as being the values of z for each pair (x, y). The values of z will be highest in the middle and taper off in all directions. If heights are normally distributed for each weight, and vice versa, then the bivariate normal distribution is the theoretical distribution that occurs. The cross-sections could be circles if x and y were converted into standard scores, but when they are not standardized the cross-sections are most likely to be noncircular ellipses.

The proof of the Graph Rotation Theorem follows the same pattern as its counterparts, the Graph Translation Theorem in Lesson 3-2 and the Graph Scale Change Theorem in Lesson 3-5. Begin with the formula for the image under the transformation that gives x' and y' in terms of x and y. Then solve the system (here represented by matrices) for x and y in terms of x' and y'. Make those substitutions for x and y to rotate the given graph.

Two graphs are shown on the automatic grapher screen on page 779. Students should be careful in choosing the window if they use their own automatic grapher. If they use the window $-3 \le x \le 3$ and $-3 \le y \le 3$, the ellipse would appear short and wide instead of tall and narrow (as it actually is). Point out that students can have their graphics calculator adjust and redraw the graph immediately by using the zoom menu and choosing the option that will square the screen. This command adjusts the screen in only one direction so that 1 unit on the x-axis is the same length as 1 unit on the y-axis.

In **Example 2,** students may wonder what hyperbola would have given $xy = 1$. The answer is $y^2 - x^2 = 2$. (See Additional Example 2 on page 781.)

Graph-Rotation Theorem
In a relation described by a sentence in x and y, the following two processes yield the same graph:
1. replacing x by $x \cos \theta + y \sin \theta$ and y by $-x \sin \theta + y \cos \theta$;
2. applying the rotation of magnitude θ about the origin to the graph of the original equation.

Using the Graph-Rotation Theorem

Example 1

Find an equation for the image of the ellipse $\frac{x^2}{4} + \frac{y^2}{9} = 1$ under a rotation of 30° about the origin.

Solution

To simplify computation, first multiply each side of the given equation by 36. The equation becomes $9x^2 + 4y^2 = 36$. Now, to find an equation for the image, use part (1) of the Graph-Rotation Theorem.

Replace x by $x \cos 30° + y \sin 30°$, or $\frac{\sqrt{3}}{2}x + \frac{1}{2}y$. Replace y by $-x \sin 30° + y \cos 30°$, or $-\frac{1}{2}x + \frac{\sqrt{3}}{2}y$.

$$9\left(\frac{\sqrt{3}}{2}x + \frac{1}{2}y\right)^2 + 4\left(-\frac{1}{2}x + \frac{\sqrt{3}}{2}y\right)^2 = 36$$

$$\frac{9}{4}\left(\sqrt{3}x + y\right)^2 + \left(-x + \sqrt{3}y\right)^2 = 36$$

$$\frac{9}{4}\left(3x^2 + 2\sqrt{3}xy + y^2\right) + \left(x^2 - 2\sqrt{3}xy + 3y^2\right) = 36$$

$$\frac{31}{4}x^2 + \frac{5}{2}\sqrt{3}xy + \frac{21}{4}y^2 = 36$$

For a simpler expression, multiply each side by 4.

$$31x^2 + 10\sqrt{3}xy + 21y^2 = 144$$

Check

Find a point on the preimage. Check that the coordinates of its image under R_{30} satisfy the equation. We take (2, 0). Its image under a rotation of 30° is

$$\begin{bmatrix} \cos 30° & -\sin 30° \\ \sin 30° & \cos 30° \end{bmatrix}\begin{bmatrix} 2 \\ 0 \end{bmatrix} = \begin{bmatrix} \frac{\sqrt{3}}{2} & -\frac{1}{2} \\ \frac{1}{2} & \frac{\sqrt{3}}{2} \end{bmatrix}\begin{bmatrix} 2 \\ 0 \end{bmatrix} = \begin{bmatrix} \sqrt{3} \\ 1 \end{bmatrix}$$

Is $\left(\sqrt{3}, 1\right)$ a solution to the equation found for the image? Substitute $\sqrt{3}$ for x and 1 for y.

$$31x^2 + 10\sqrt{3}xy + 21y^2 = 144$$

Does $31\left(\sqrt{3}\right)^2 + 10\sqrt{3}\left(\sqrt{3}\right)(1) + 21(1)^2 = 144$?

Does $93 + 30 + 21 = 144$?

Yes, it checks.

Optional Activities
Activity 2 Refer students to **Question 11**. Ask them to find the equation for the y-axis under a rotation of θ, *without* using the Graph-Rotation Theorem. [$y = -x \cot \theta$; students should know that since the x- and y-axes are perpendicular, their slopes should be opposite reciprocals. The opposite reciprocal of $\tan \theta = -\cot \theta$.] Have them verify their result with the Graph-Rotation Theorem.

Adapting to Individual Needs
Extra Help
Some students may not realize that the degree of xy is 2. Mention that the equations in **Examples 1 and 2** are all of the second degree. Point out that the degree of the original ellipse or hyperbola did not change under the rotation. This is critical knowledge for the analyses of the next lesson, in which all quadratic relations are considered.

Some automatic graphers allow you to graph any equation of the form $Ax^2 + Bxy + Cy^2 + Dx + Ey + F = 0$. If you have access to such a grapher, you can also check the solution to Example 1 by graphing. Below are the graphs of $9x^2 + 4y^2 - 36 = 0$ and $31x^2 + 10\sqrt{3}\,xy + 21y^2 - 144 = 0$ produced by such a grapher.

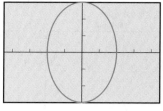

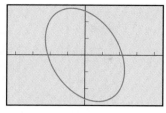

$-4.5 \le x \le 4.5$, x-scale = 1
$-3 \le y \le 3$, y-scale = 1

$-4.5 \le x \le 4.5$, x-scale = 1
$-3 \le y \le 3$, y-scale = 1

The second appears to be the image of the first under a rotation of 30° around the origin.

In the solution of Example 1 notice that an xy term appears. This is typical of quadratic relations that are not symmetric to the coordinate axes. Example 2 shows that rotation of the parent hyperbola can result in a hyperbola whose equation contains *only* an xy term.

Example 2

Rotate the hyperbola $x^2 - y^2 = 1$ a magnitude $-\frac{\pi}{4}$ about the origin.

Solution

Use the Graph-Rotation Theorem.

Replace x by $x \cos\left(-\frac{\pi}{4}\right) + y \sin\left(-\frac{\pi}{4}\right)$ and replace y by $-x \sin\left(-\frac{\pi}{4}\right) + y \cos\left(-\frac{\pi}{4}\right)$. Note that $\sin\left(-\frac{\pi}{4}\right) = -\frac{\sqrt{2}}{2}$ and $\cos\left(-\frac{\pi}{4}\right) = \frac{\sqrt{2}}{2}$. Thus an equation for the image is

$$\left(\frac{\sqrt{2}}{2}x - \frac{\sqrt{2}}{2}y\right)^2 - \left(\frac{\sqrt{2}}{2}x + \frac{\sqrt{2}}{2}y\right)^2 = 1.$$

Since $\left(\frac{\sqrt{2}}{2}\right)^2 = \frac{1}{2}$, the computation is easier than in Example 1.

$$\frac{1}{2}x^2 - xy + \frac{1}{2}y^2 - \left(\frac{1}{2}x^2 + xy + \frac{1}{2}y^2\right) = 1$$
$$-2xy = 1$$
$$xy = -\frac{1}{2}$$

▶

Lesson 12-4 *Rotating Relations* **779**

Adapting to Individual Needs

Challenge

Have students answer the following questions.

1. What happens if R_θ is applied to a circle centered at the origin? [The result is the same circle.]

2. What happens if R_θ is applied to a circle centered at (h, k)? [The result is a circle with the same radius but centered at $(h \cos\theta - k \sin\theta, h \sin\theta + k \cos\theta)$.]

3. If the image of a circle centered at (h, k) under a translation $T_{a,b}$ is the same circle as the image under R_θ, find a and b in terms of θ, h, and k.
[$a = h \cos\theta - k \sin\theta - h$;
$b = h \sin\theta + k \cos\theta - k$]

779

Point out that the answer in **Example 3** is approximate because of substituting .34 for sin 20° and .94 for cos 20°. **Teaching Aid 109** is also provided showing the graphs of preimage and image.

The strategy in **Example 3** can be applied to other transformations whose center is not the origin. For instance, to apply a size change of magnitude 3 with center (5, 8), translate that point to the origin, then apply the size change with center (0, 0), then translate back. That is, perform the composite $T_{5,8} \circ S_3 \circ T_{-5,-8}$.

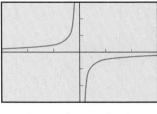

Check

Draw graphs of the preimage and image. The graph of $xy = -\frac{1}{2}$, on the right below, is known to be a hyperbola whose graph lies entirely in the 2nd and 4th quadrants and whose asymptotes are the x- and y-axes. This is what would be expected from rotating the hyperbola $x^2 - y^2 = 1$, on the left below, a magnitude $\frac{\pi}{4}$ clockwise.

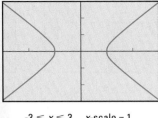

$-3 \leq x \leq 3$, x-scale = 1
$-3 \leq y \leq 3$, y-scale = 1

$-3 \leq x \leq 3$, x-scale = 1
$-3 \leq y \leq 3$, y-scale = 1

When the asymptotes of a hyperbola are perpendicular, as in Example 2, the hyperbola is called a **rectangular hyperbola**. Also, each is a rotation image of the other, so they are congruent. Now if a size change of magnitude $\sqrt{2}$ is applied to the hyperbola $xy = -\frac{1}{2}$, the result is a third hyperbola $\frac{x}{\sqrt{2}} \cdot \frac{y}{\sqrt{2}} = -\frac{1}{2}$, which simplifies to $xy = -1$. When this hyperbola is reflected over the x-axis, its image is a fourth hyperbola $xy = 1$. All of these transformations give rise to similar figures, so this reasoning shows that the hyperbolas $x^2 - y^2 = 1$ and $xy = 1$ are similar. More generally, all rectangular hyperbolas are similar. Still more generally, two hyperbolas are similar if and only if the angles between their asymptotes are congruent.

Composites of Rotations and Translations

Recall that an **isometry** is a composite of translations, rotations, and reflections. Some isometries need no reflections; for example, rotations of magnitude θ around a point (a, b) can be accomplished by translating the figure using $T_{-a,-b}$, rotating θ about the origin, then translating back using $T_{a,b}$. It can be proved that if all translations and rotations are possible, then any isometry needs a maximum of one reflection. Specifically, only the reflection over the line $y = x$ is needed. Thus the Graph-Translation Theorem and the Graph-Rotation Theorem, together with reflection over the line $y = x$, give the means to perform any isometry in the plane on any relation.

Example 3 illustrates a composite of transformations applied to a parabola.

Example 3

Find an equation for the image of the parabola $y = x^2$ when rotated 20° about the point (5, 8).

Solution

Following the discussion above, first translate the parabola using $T_{-5, -8}$. (This maps (5, 8) onto the origin.)

The image of $y = x^2$ under $T_{-5, -8}$ is

$$y + 8 = (x + 5)^2.$$

Then, rotate this curve 20° about the origin.

Replace x by   x cos 20° + y sin 20° ≈ .94x + .34y, and

y by -x sin 20° + y cos 20° ≈ -.34x + .94y.

Then $y + 8 = (x + 5)^2$ becomes

$$-.34x + .94y + 8 \approx (.94x + .34y + 5)^2$$

Now, translate back using $T_{5, 8}$. That is, replace x by x − 5 and y by y − 8.

$$-.34(x - 5) + .94(y - 8) + 8 \approx (.94(x - 5) + .34(y - 8) + 5)^2$$

This simplifies to

$$.88x^2 + .64xy + .12y^2 - 4.21x - 2.59y + 3.68 \approx 0.$$

Check

The images of the original parabola after each of the three transformations are graphed below.

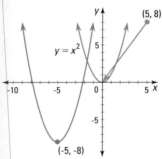

$T_{-5, -8}$ applied to $y = x^2$

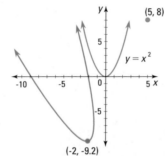

$R_{20} \circ T_{-5, -8}$ applied to $y = x^2$

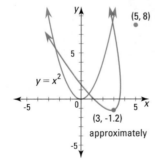

$T_{5, 8} \circ R_{20} \circ T_{-5, -8}$ = rotation of 20° about (5, 8)

Additional Examples

1. Find an equation for the image of the ellipse $\frac{x^2}{4} + \frac{y^2}{9} = 1$ under a rotation of $\frac{\pi}{3}$ about the origin. Substitute $\frac{x}{2} + \frac{\sqrt{3}y}{2}$ for x and $-\frac{\sqrt{3}x}{2} + \frac{y}{2}$ for y to get $21x^2 + 10\sqrt{3}xy + 31y^2 = 144$.

2. Rotate the hyperbola $xy = 1$, 45° about the origin. Substitute $\frac{\sqrt{2}}{2}x + \frac{\sqrt{2}}{2}y$ for x and $-\frac{\sqrt{2}}{2}x + \frac{\sqrt{2}}{2}y$ for y to get $y^2 - x^2 = 2$.

3. Consider the parabola $y = x^2 + 2x - 6$. Rotate this parabola -35° about its vertex. Apply $T_{-1,-7} \circ R_{-35} \circ T_{1,7}$; An exact result is $-(x + 1) \sin (-35°) + (y + 7) \cos (-35°) = [(x + 1) \cos (-35°) + (y + 7) \sin (-35°)]^2$; An approximate result is $.67x^2 - .94xy + .33y^2 - 5.81x + 2.85y + 3.91 = 0$.

Notes on Questions

Question 4 Notice that the equation in the answer looks like it might be an equation for a hyperbola or ellipse; in the next lesson students will see how to determine the type of conic from its equation. Obviously the equation here is for a parabola, because rotating a conic does not change its type.

Question 6 A way of showing that these hyperbolas are *not* congruent is to note that the distance between the vertices of $x^2 - y^2 = 1$ is 2, while the distance between the vertices of $xy = 1$ is $2\sqrt{2}$. Since isometries preserve distance, these hyperbolas cannot be related by an isometry.

Question 7 Error Alert Some students might go blindly into substitutions rather than first examine the particular relation that is given. The image of the circle is the circle itself. If you would like to emphasize this point, you might forge ahead with the substitution as if you were a student who did not sufficiently think about the problem. That is, substitute $x \cos 40° + y \sin 40°$ for x and $-x \sin 40° + y \cos 40°$ for y. Show that it all works out at the end. You could even do it in general, with θ in place of 40°, or have students do this.

Question 8 Students first need to find an equation for this ellipse as if it were untilted. Then they should rotate that ellipse 30°.

Question 9 This question generalizes Additional Example 2.

Question 20 Completing the square is needed for the next lesson.

10) The equation of the image of the ellipse is found by substituting linear combinations of x and y for x and y. Since the original equation is of degree 2, the resulting equation also has degree 2.

11) An equation for the x-axis is $y = 0$. By the Graph Rotation Theorem, the image of the x-axis under R_θ has equation $-x \sin \theta + y \cos \theta = 0$. Solving for y yields $y = x \tan \theta$.

Sir Francis Galton, the subject of an oil painting by Charles Wellington Furse

QUESTIONS

Covering the Reading

1. What situation was Galton trying to model when he found that ellipses described the points with equal probability of occurrence?
   the influence of heredity on height
2. If a figure F is the image of a figure G under R_θ, then G is the image of F under what transformation? $R_{-\theta}$

In 3 and 4, find an equation for the image of the given figure under the given rotation. 3) Sample: $91x^2 - 18\sqrt{3}xy + 73y^2 = 1600$

3. $\frac{x^2}{25} + \frac{y^2}{16} = 1$; R_{60}
4. $y = x^2 + 4$; $R_{\pi/4}$
   4) Sample: $-x^2 - 2xy - y^2 - \sqrt{2}x + \sqrt{2}y = 8$
5. Tell whether or not the hyperbola is a rectangular hyperbola.
   a. $xy = -2$ **rectangular**
   b. $x^2 - y^2 = 8$ **rectangular**
   c. $y^2 - x^2 = 8$ **regtangular**
   d. $\frac{x^2}{4} - \frac{y^2}{9} = 1$ **not rectangular**
6. *Multiple choice.* The hyperbolas $x^2 - y^2 = 1$ and $xy = 1$ are which of the following? b
   (a) congruent
   (b) similar but not congruent
   (c) neither similar nor congruent
7. Find an equation for the image of $x^2 + y^2 = 10$ under a rotation of 40° around the origin without using the Graph-Rotation Theorem.
   $x^2 + y^2 = 10$

Applying the Mathematics

8. Galton's ellipse, pictured on page 776, has a major axis with length about 8 and a minor axis of length about 5, and the major axis makes an angle of about 30° with the x-axis. a) Sample: $139x^2 - 78\sqrt{3}xy + 217y^2 = 1600$
   a. Find an equation for this ellipse.
   b. Find equations for the lines containing its major and minor axes.
      major axis: $y = \frac{\sqrt{3}}{3}x$ minor axis $y = -\sqrt{3}x$
9. Suppose the hyperbola $xy = k$ is rotated $\frac{\pi}{4}$ about the origin.
   a. What is an equation for its image? Sample: $y^2 - x^2 = 2k$
   b. *True or false.* Both $xy = k$ and its rotation image in part **a** are rectangular hyperbolas.
      True
10. Explain why, if an ellipse is rotated, its image must have an equation of degree 2.
    See left.
11. Suppose the x-axis is rotated θ about the origin. Prove that an equation for its image is $y = x \tan \theta$. (This provides another way of showing that the slope of a line that makes an angle of θ measured counterclockwise from the positive x-axis is tan θ.) **See left.**

12. a. Find an equation for the image of the parabola $y = (x - 2)^2 + 3$ when rotated 30° about the point (2, 3).
    b. Check your work by graphing the image and preimage with an automatic grapher.
    a, b) See margin.

Additional Answers

12. a. Sample: $-\frac{3}{4}x^2 - \frac{\sqrt{3}}{2}xy - \frac{1}{4}y^2 + \frac{3\sqrt{3} + 5}{2}x + \frac{3\sqrt{3} + 3}{2}y - \frac{18\sqrt{3} + 17}{4} = 0$.

b.

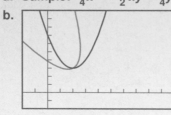

$-2 \le x \le 10$, x-scale = 1
$-2 \le y \le 10$, y-scale = 1

13a)

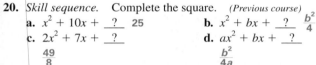

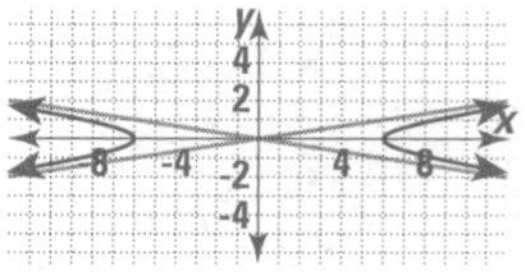

14) $\frac{4x^2}{13} + \frac{4y^2}{49} = 1$

15a) an equation which is true for all values in the domain of the variables
b) Sample: $\cos^2\theta + \sin^2\theta = 1$
c) Sample: $\cos\theta + \sin\theta = 1$

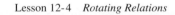

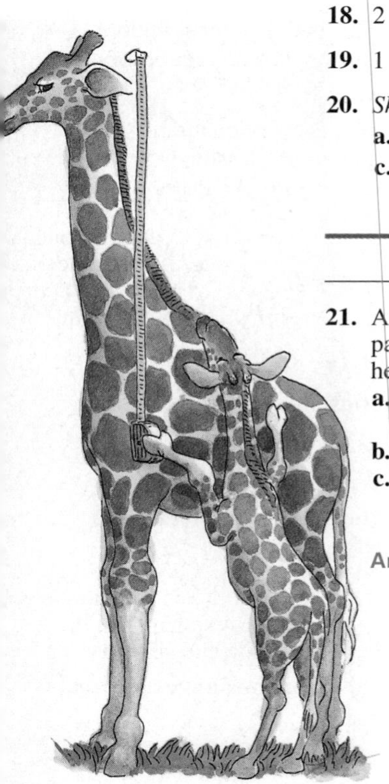

Review

13. Consider the hyperbola with equation $\frac{x^2}{36} - y^2 = 1$.

a. Sketch its graph. **See left.**

b. Give equations for its asymptotes. $y = \frac{1}{6}x$, $y = -\frac{1}{6}x$

c. State an equation for the image of this curve under reflection over the line $y = x$. *(Lesson 12-3)* $\frac{y^2}{36} - x^2 = 1$

14. Find an equation for the ellipse with foci (0, 3) and (0, -3) and focal constant 7. *(Lesson 12-2)* **See left.**

15. a. What is an identity? **a–c) See left.**

b. Give an example of a statement that is an identity.

c. Give an example of a statement that is not an identity. *(Lesson 4-4)*

In 16–19, *multiple choice*. Which expression below equals the given expression? *(Lessons 4-4, 11-6)*

(a) 1 (b) $\sin\theta$ (c) $\sin 2\theta$ (d) $\cos 2\theta$

16. $\cos^2\theta - \sin^2\theta$ **d**

17. $\cos^2\theta + \sin^2\theta$ **a**

18. $2\sin\theta\cos\theta$ **c**

19. $1 - 2\sin^2\theta$ **d**

20. *Skill sequence.* Complete the square. *(Previous course)*

a. $x^2 + 10x +$ _?_ **25**

b. $x^2 + bx +$ _?_ $\frac{b^2}{4}$

c. $2x^2 + 7x +$ _?_ $\frac{49}{8}$

d. $ax^2 + bx +$ _?_ $\frac{b^2}{4a}$

Exploration

21. Ask each of about 25 students for the height of his or her biological parents. Graph the ordered pairs of the form (height of student, mid-parent height). As Galton did, multiply heights of mothers by 1.08.

a. Find the center of gravity (mean student height, mean mid-parent height) of this bivariate distribution.

b. Find an equation for the line of best fit.

c. The line from part **b** estimates the major axis of the ellipse which contain points of equal probability in the distribution. Derive an equation for an ellipse that seems to contain about $\frac{2}{3}$ of the data points.
Answers will vary.

Question 21 This exploration replicates Galton's work. Have students either multiply the heights of the mothers by 1.08, as Galton did, or treat mothers and fathers separately.

Social Studies Connection
English mathematician-statistician Francis Galton was Charles Darwin's cousin. He was among the last of the gentleman scientists, and was best known for his work on the inheritance of talent. He also established a method of fingerprinting still in use today.

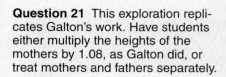

Follow-up for Lesson 12-4

Practice

For more questions on SPUR Objectives, use **Lesson Master 12-4** (shown on page 779).

Assessment

Written Communication Have students **work in pairs.** Ask students to make up a problem like **Example 1 or 2**. Have students solve their partner's problem and check it as was done in **Example 1**. [Students find an equation for the rotation images of an ellipse or a hyperbola.]

Extension

Project Update Project 1, *Orbits of Celestial Bodies*, and Project 4, *Eccentricity*, on page 797–798, relate to the content of this lesson.

Setting Up Lesson 12-5

In discussing **Question 4**, ask the reverse question. What if you had the equation that is the answer? How could you determine the type of conic? That is the major question discussed in Lesson 12-5.

Objectives

C Rewrite equations of conic sections in the general form of a quadratic relation in two variables.
E Describe the intersections of a plane and a cone of 2 nappes.
H Graph transformation images of parent ellipses and hyperbolas.
I Describe graphs of quadratic equations.

Resources

From the *Teacher's Resource File*
■ Lesson Master 12-5
■ Answer Master 12-5
■ Teaching Aids
  104 Warm-up
  110 Degenerate Conic Sections

Additional Resources
■ Visuals for Teaching Aids 104, 110

Teaching **12-5**
Lesson

Warm-up

Write each of these equations for conic sections in the form $Ax^2 + Bxy + Cy^2 + Dx + Ey + F = 0$. Give the values of A, B, C, D, E, and F.

1. $y = x^2$
$x^2 - y = 0$; $A = 1$, $B = C = D = 0$, $E = -1$, $F = 0$

2. $(x - 7)^2 + y^2 = 25$
$x^2 + y^2 - 14x + 24 = 0$; $A = 1$, $B = 0$, $C = 1$, $D = -14$, $E = 0$, $F = 24$

3. $y + 2 = \frac{1}{x + 17}$
$xy + 2x + 17y + 33 = 0$; $A = 0$, $B = 1$, $C = 0$, $D = 2$, $E = 17$, $F = 33$

LESSON

12-5

The General Quadratic Equation

You have learned that any conic section has an equation that is a polynomial of degree 2. That is, every conic section has an equation of the form

$$Ax^2 + Bxy + Cy^2 + Dx + Ey + F = 0,$$

where at least one of A, B, and C is not zero. This is the **general form of a quadratic relation in two variables**. Thus every conic section is a quadratic relation.

In this lesson, the converse question is discussed. Is every quadratic relation a conic? The answer, which is developed in this lesson, is "Usually, but not always." We separate our analysis into two cases: When $B = 0$ and $B \neq 0$.

The General Quadratic Equation When B = 0

If $B = 0$, the equation $Ax^2 + Bxy + Cy^2 + Dx + Ey + F = 0$ has the form

$$Ax^2 + Cy^2 + Dx + Ey + F = 0$$

We say it has no xy term. By reordering the terms, this equation can be rewritten as

$$Ax^2 + Dx + Cy^2 + Ey + F = 0.$$

In this form, the equation is set up for completing the square. First factor out A and C from the x and y terms, respectively.

$$A\left(x^2 + \tfrac{D}{A}x + \quad\right) + C\left(y^2 + \tfrac{E}{C}y + \quad\right) + F = 0$$

Then add the appropriate constants $\frac{D^2}{4A^2}$ and $\frac{E^2}{4C^2}$ to each side and simplify. Example 1 applies this technique to show that a certain quadratic equation represents a hyperbola.

Broad Goals The goal of this lesson is for the student to be able to determine the type of conic from its equation, by rewriting it in standard form and using the discriminant of the conic.

Perspective Any conic section in the plane can be mapped by a rotation onto a conic section with horizontal and/or vertical symmetry. A further translation can get a key point (normally a center or vertex of the

conic) to be at the origin. The logic of this lesson is as follows. First we note that if $B = 0$ in the general quadratic $Ax^2 + Bxy + Cy^2 + Dx + Ey + F = 0$, then one can complete the square to get equations for ellipses, hyperbolas, and parabolas with horizontal or vertical symmetry lines, and which type we get can thus be determined. Unless we get a degenerate conic, we find that the graph is an ellipse, parabola, or hyperbola, depending on whether AC is

positive, zero, or negative. To consider the cases when $B \neq 0$, we determine the magnitude θ of a rotation under which there will be no xy term in an equation for the image of the quadratic relation above. This magnitude is such that $\tan 2\theta = \frac{B}{C - A}$.

Next is an amazing fact: under a rotation or a translation, the value of $B^2 - 4AC$ in $Ax^2 + Bxy + Cy^2 + Dx + Ey + F = 0$ is

Example 1

Show that the equation $3x^2 - y^2 + 6x + 7y - 12 = 0$ represents a hyperbola.

Solution

Rewrite the given equation in the standard form of a hyperbola. First, reorder the terms to group the terms in x and the terms in y.

$$3x^2 + 6x - y^2 + 7y - 12 = 0$$

Factor out the coefficients of x^2 and y^2 from the terms in x and y.

$$3(x^2 + 2x + \quad) - (y^2 - 7y + \quad) - 12 = 0$$

Complete the square. Be careful to add the same amount to each side, and to watch out for the numbers that have been factored out.

$$3(x^2 + 2x + 1) - (y^2 - 7y + 12.25) - 12 = 0 + 3 - 12.25$$

Rewrite the binomials as squares and simplify the constant.

$$3(x + 1)^2 - (y - 3.5)^2 = 2.75$$

This is actually far enough to see what is going on. **By dividing both sides by 2.75, an equation of the form**

$$\frac{(x + 1)^2}{a^2} - \frac{(y - 3.5)^2}{b^2} = 1$$

is obtained. This is an equation for a hyperbola with center at (-1, 3.5).

Check

Use an automatic grapher that graphs equations of the form $Ax^2 + Bxy + Cy^2 + Dx + Ey + F = 0$. Input $A = 3$, $B = 0$, $C = -1$, $D = 6$, $E = 7$, and $F = -12$. At the right is the output from such a grapher. The graph is a hyperbola with $x = -1$ and $y = 3.5$ as axes of symmetry.

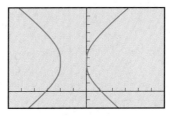

-6 ≤ x ≤ 6,   x-scale = 1
-2 ≤ y ≤ 10,   y-scale = 1

Example 1 illustrates the graph of a quadratic relation $Ax^2 + Bxy + Cy^2 + Dx + Ey + F = 0$ where $B = 0$ and A and C have opposite signs. In such a case $AC < 0$. For such values of A, B, and C, the graph is typically a hyperbola. If A and C have the same sign, that is, if $AC > 0$, then it is possible that no points may satisfy the equation. But if more than one point satisfies the equation, then the graph of the quadratic relation is an ellipse. (The special case of a circle occurs when $A = C$.)

Activity 1

Explain why there are no ordered pairs of real numbers (x, y) which satisfy $3x^2 + 4y^2 + 5 = 0$. **Sample: If x and y are real numbers, then x^2 and y^2 are never negative, so $3x^2 + 4y^2 + 5 \geq 5$ and so $3x^2 + 4y^2 + 5 \neq 0$.**

After students have read the lesson, you may wish to summarize as follows. Put a table on the board with the following six columns: equation, type of conic, A, B, C, B² − 4AC. Then use a variety of equations known to the students, for instance:

Equation	Conic	A	B	C	B² − 4AC
$y = 3x^2$	para-bola	3	0	0	0
$x^2 + y^2 = 9$	circle	1	0	1	-4
$\frac{x^2}{4} + \frac{y^2}{9} = 1$	ellipse	$\frac{1}{4}$	0	$\frac{1}{9}$	$-\frac{1}{9}$
$x^2 - y^2 = 1$	hyper-bola	1	0	-1	4
$xy = 100$	hyper-bola	0	1	0	1

Point out that the type of the conic and whether the value of $B^2 - 4AC$ is positive, negative, or zero corresponds exactly as predicted by the last theorem of the lesson. The goal of the entire lesson is to prove that rather amazing theorem.

Notice in **Example 1** that the solution stops when the equation is in a form that allows it to be recognized as a hyperbola. There is no point in going through manipulations that are not needed.

In the determination of the angle in **Example 2,** on page 788, if θ is a solution, then so is $\theta + \frac{\pi}{2}$. A proof is simple: $\tan 2(\theta + \frac{\pi}{2}) = \tan(2\theta + \pi) = \tan 2\theta$ since the period of the tangent function is π.

the same as the value of $B'^2 - 4A'C'$ in its image $A'x^2 + B'xy + C'y^2 + D'x + E'y + F' = 0$. Thus, if $B' = 0$, $B^2 - 4AC = -4A'C'$. Thus the sign of $B^2 - 4AC$ is the opposite of the sign of $A'C'$, and we know what conics are determined by any given value of $A'C'$. Thus unless we get a degenerate conic, the graph of the general quadratic relation is an ellipse, parabola, or hyperbola, depending on whether $B^2 - 4AC$ is negative, zero, or positive, the signs opposite those found when just considering AC.

Refer students to **Question 16**. Ask them how they could alter the given equation to make its graph each of the following curves.
1. Parabola [Sample: $x^2 - xy + \frac{1}{4}y^2 = 6$]
2. Ellipse [Sample: $x^2 - xy + y^2 = 6$]

Then ask students whether they can use an xy term and only one squared term to write the equation for the given conic section. [Parabola: no; if one squared term is 0, then

either A or $C = 0$, and $B^2 - 4AC = B^2$. The discriminant must be zero for a parabola, so $B = 0$, which eliminates the xy term. Ellipse: if one squared term is 0, then either A or $C = 0$, and $B^2 - 4AC = B^2 > 0$ always. The discriminant must be less than zero for an ellipse.]

❶ Geometrically, it is easy to see when a conic section is degenerate; the intersecting plane contains the vertex of the cone. The drawings on page 786 show the possibilities. (**Teaching Aid 110** also contains these drawings.) However, the algebraic counterpart is not so simple, and students are likely to ask how you can determine whether an equation graphs as a degenerate conic or some other conic. One way to decide is to graph the conic. But this may not be easy to do if the available technology does not accept conics in standard form. Algebraically, you can try to solve for one variable in terms of the other and try to find five points on the conic. If it is impossible to find five points, then the conic either consists of a single point or it is the null set. If three of the five points are on the same line, then there is a degenerate conic of intersecting or parallel lines (use the $B^2 - 4AC$ criterion to determine which), because no line can intersect an ellipse, hyperbola, or parabola in more than two points.

Students may ask if it is coincidence that the discriminant $b^2 - 4ac$ for a quadratic has the same form as the expression $B^2 - 4AC$ used to discriminate conics. A reasonable response is that it seems to be coincidence, but perhaps someone will find that there is a connection, similar to the way that Dandelin connected the two-dimensional and three-dimensional characterizations of conics.

a)

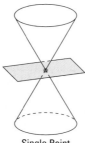

$3x+2y-5=0$ $3x+2y+6=0$

b) **Sample: This graph goes off to infinity in four directions, and has two axes of symmetry, much like a hyperbola. In fact, it looks much like the asymptotes for a hyperbola. But the two halves of the graph intersect, unlike a hyperbola.**

786

If one of A or C is zero, that is, if $AC = 0$, and there are points which satisfy the equation, then the graph of $Ax^2 + Cy^2 + Dx + Ey + F = 0$ is typically a parabola.

Notice the word "typically" occurs in the preceding discussion twice. The reason is that, on occasion, the graph of

$$Ax^2 + Cy^2 + Dx + Ey + F = 0$$

is not an ellipse, parabola, or hyperbola. When this happens, the graph is called a *degenerate conic section*. For instance, the left side of

$$9x^2 - 4y^2 + 3x + 22y - 30 = 0$$

can be factored by grouping, leading to

$$(3x + 2y - 5)(3x - 2y + 6) = 0.$$

But if the product of two numbers is zero, then one or the other (or both) is zero. So

$$3x + 2y - 5 = 0 \quad \text{or} \quad 3x - 2y + 6 = 0.$$

These are equations of lines. So a point satisfies the first quadratic relation if and only if it is on one or both of the two lines. These two intersecting lines form a *degenerate hyperbola*.

Activity 2

a. Graph the lines $3x + 2y - 5 = 0$ and $3x - 2y + 6 = 0$ on the same set of axes. See left.

b. Describe some ways that the graph is like a hyperbola. How is this graph different from a hyperbola? See left.

❶ There are five possible degenerate conic sections. Three of them may be thought of as the intersection of a cone and a plane containing the vertex of the cone.

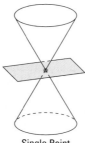

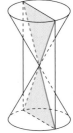

Single Point
(degenerate ellipse)

Line
(degenerate parabola)

Two Intersecting Lines
(degenerate hyperbola)

The other possibilities are two parallel lines (which is sometimes considered a degenerate parabola), and the null set (which is sometimes considered a degenerate ellipse). This information is summarized in the following theorem.

Adapting to Individual Needs
Extra Help
Some students have difficulty completing the square because they forget to consider the numbers that have been factored out. For instance, in **Example 1**, the first square $x^2 + 2x + \underline{}$ is completed with a 1. However, have students notice that 3, not 1, is added to the right side of the equation. This is because 3 had first been factored out, causing 3, not 1, to be added on the left.

Now do you see why we wrote "Usually, but not always" to answer the question of whether the graph of a quadratic relation is always a conic section?

The General Quadratic Equation When $B \neq 0$

When B is not zero, the equation $Ax^2 + Bxy + Cy^2 + Dx + Ey + F = 0$ has an xy term. In the last lesson, you saw that such equations occur by rotating a conic section so that its axes are no longer horizontal or vertical. Consequently, one way to classify such a conic section is to rotate it back in order to eliminate the xy term and then apply the above theorem. The argument is long, so read carefully.

Begin with the general quadratic relation

$$Ax^2 + Bxy + Cy^2 + Dx + Ey + F = 0.$$

We need to find θ so that under a rotation of θ about the origin, the image has no xy term, so we substitute $x \cos\theta + y \sin\theta$ for x, and $-x \sin\theta + y \cos\theta$ for y. The expressions become rather complicated, but you do not have to worry about the substitutions for x and y in Dx and Ey because they do not yield a term in xy.

$$A(x \cos\theta + y \sin\theta)^2 + B(x \cos\theta + y \sin\theta)(-x \sin\theta + y \cos\theta)$$
$$+ C(-x \sin\theta + y \cos\theta)^2 + \ldots + F = 0$$

We are looking for the xy-coefficient of the image, so consider only the terms in xy that will result from the squaring and multiplication of the binomials.

$$A(2xy \cos\theta \sin\theta) + B(xy \cos^2\theta - xy \sin^2\theta)$$
$$+ C(-2xy \sin\theta \cos\theta) + \ldots + F = 0$$

Factoring out xy from each of these terms gives

$$xy\,[2A \cos\theta \sin\theta + B(\cos^2\theta - \sin^2\theta) - 2C \sin\theta \cos\theta] + \ldots + F = 0.$$

Thus the coefficient of the xy term in the rotation image is

$$B' = 2A \cos\theta \sin\theta + B(\cos^2\theta - \sin^2\theta) - 2C \sin\theta \cos\theta.$$

Notice that each expression in θ is related to a double angle formula.

$$B' = A \sin 2\theta + B \cos 2\theta - C \sin 2\theta$$

So $\qquad B' = (A - C) \sin 2\theta + B \cos 2\theta.$

Lesson 12-5 *The General Quadratic Equation* **787**

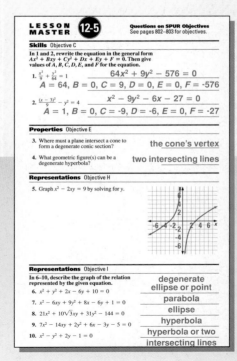

787

Practice

For more questions on SPUR Objectives, use **Lesson Master 12-5** (shown on page 787).

Assessment

Written Communication Have students give an equation of the form $Ax^2 + Cy^2 + Dx + Ey + F = 0$ to illustrate each of the three cases of the theorem on page 787. Then have students give an equation of the form $Ax^2 + Bxy + Cy^2 + Dx + Ey + F = 0$ to illustrate each of the three cases of the theorem on page 789. [Students give examples of quadratic equations in two variables for conic sections.]

Remember that you want a value of θ so that there is no xy term. That means $B' = 0$. So consider this equation.

$$0 = (A - C)\sin 2\theta + B\cos 2\theta$$

This is equivalent to

$$B\cos 2\theta = (C - A)\sin 2\theta.$$

There are now two possibilities. If $C = A$, then solve $B\cos 2\theta = 0$ to find the magnitude of the rotation θ under which the image of the original quadratic has no xy term. That equation always has the solution $2\theta = \frac{\pi}{2}$, or $\theta = \frac{\pi}{4}$. If $C \neq A$, then neither B nor $C - A$ is 0 and so neither $\sin 2\theta$ nor $\cos 2\theta$ is 0. Then divide by $(C - A)\cos 2\theta$ to get

$$\frac{B}{C - A} = \frac{\sin 2\theta}{\cos 2\theta}$$

That is,

$$\frac{B}{C - A} = \tan 2\theta.$$

This can be solved for 2θ to find the value of θ that will rotate the quadratic relation into one that has no xy term.

Example 2

What rotation will cause the image of the graph of

$$x^2 - 3xy + 4y^2 + 2x - y + 5 = 0$$

to have an equation with no xy term?

Solution

Here $A = 1$, $B = -3$, and $C = 4$. So $\tan 2\theta = \frac{-3}{4 - 1} = -1$, and thus $2\theta = \tan^{-1}(-1) = -\frac{\pi}{4}$ and so $\theta = -\frac{\pi}{8}$. A rotation of magnitude $-\frac{\pi}{8}$ will cause the image to have no xy term.

To find an equation in standard form for the image in Example 2, values for $\cos \theta$ and $\sin \theta$ must be found and then substitutions made as in Lesson 12-4. This can require a great deal of algebraic manipulation. Fortunately, if all that is desired is to know whether the quadratic relation is a parabola, ellipse, or hyperbola, there is a criterion that does not require finding this equation. It is based on the following theorem: under a rotation, the value of the **discriminant** $B^2 - 4AC$ does not change.

Theorem
Let S be the set of ordered pairs (x, y) satisfying

$$Ax^2 + Bxy + Cy^2 + Dx + Ey + F = 0,$$

and let $S' = R_\theta(S)$. Furthermore, suppose that

$$A'x^2 + B'xy + C'y^2 + D'x + E'y + F' = 0$$

is an equation for S'. Then $B^2 - 4AC = (B')^2 - 4A'C'$.

Proof

The proof requires quite a bit of algebraic manipulation. It is begun here, and you are asked to fill in some other details as one of the questions. To perform the rotation R_θ, $x \cos \theta + y \sin \theta$ is substituted for x in the equation for S, and $-x \sin \theta + y \cos \theta$ is substituted for y. After some algebraic manipulation, the result is the equation for S', and you should verify that

$$A' = A \cos^2\theta - B \cos \theta \sin \theta + C \sin^2\theta,$$
$$B' = 2(A - C) \sin \theta \cos \theta + B(\cos^2\theta - \sin^2\theta) \text{ (as stated on page 787),}$$

and
$$C' = A \sin^2\theta + B \cos \theta \sin \theta + C \cos^2\theta.$$

Now we have to find $(B')^2 - 4A'C'$. This too requires quite a bit of manipulation. To shorten the writing, let $s = \sin \theta$ and $t = \cos \theta$. Then

$$A' = At^2 - Bts + Cs^2,$$
$$B' = 2(A - C)ts + B(t^2 - s^2),$$

and
$$C' = As^2 + Bts + Ct^2.$$

Now calculate $B'^2 - 4A'C'$ and use the fact that $s^2 + t^2 = 1$ to finish the proof.

The above theorem holds for *any* rotation, so it certainly holds for the rotation for which $B' = 0$. Thus for the equation of the rotation image that has no xy term, $B^2 - 4AC = (B')^2 - 4A'C' = -4A'C'$. But, from the first theorem of this lesson, the type of conic section is determined by the sign of $A'C'$. The sign of $-4A'C'$ is just the opposite of the sign of $A'C'$. Putting this all together, the following theorem is obtained.

Theorem

Let S be the set of ordered pairs (x, y) satisfying

$$Ax^2 + Bxy + Cy^2 + Dx + Ey + F = 0.$$

Then:

if $B^2 - 4AC < 0$, then S is an ellipse, a single point, or the null set;
if $B^2 - 4AC > 0$, then S is a hyperbola or a pair of intersecting lines;
if $B^2 - 4AC = 0$, then S is a parabola, two parallel lines, a line, or the null set.

Example 3

What kind of conic section is the graph of the quadratic relation

$$2x^2 + 3xy - y^2 + 2x - 2y - 5 = 0?$$

Solution

Use the theorem above with $A = 2$, $B = 3$, and $C = -1$.
$B^2 - 4AC = 9 + 8 = 17 > 0$. Thus the conic is either a hyperbola or a pair of intersecting lines. To determine which, try to find some points on the graph. Begin with the given equation

$$2x^2 + 3xy - y^2 + 2x - 2y - 5 = 0.$$

If $x = 0$, then $-y^2 - 2y - 5 = 0$ or $y^2 + 2y + 5 = 0$, for which there is no real solution. This tells us that the graph does not cross the y-axis. This is impossible if the lines are intersecting, so the graph of $2x^2 + 3xy - y^2 + 2x - 2y - 5 = 0$ must be a hyperbola.

Extension

Cooperative Learning You might have the class **work in groups** and have them work on the following questions:

1. What is an equation for the conic whose graph is the single point $(3, 4)$? $[(x - 3)^2 + (y - 4)^2 = 0]$
2. What is an equation for the conic whose graph is the union of the intersecting lines $3x - 4y = 2$ and $x + y = 7$?
$[(3x - 4y - 2)(x + y - 7) = 0]$
3. Generalize both of the questions above and the answers. For example, what is an equation for a relation whose graph is the union of two lines? [Sample: If the lines are $a_1x + b_1y = c_1$ and $a_2x + b_2y = c_2$, the equation of the relation is
$(a_1x + b_1y - c_1)(a_2x + b_2y - c_2) = 0.$]

Project Update Project 5, *Quadric Sections*, on page 798, relates to the content of this lesson.

Question 9 Error Alert Some students may answer that this is an ellipse. It is, more specifically, a degenerate ellipse, which can be thought of as an ellipse whose focal constant and focal distance are both 0.

Questions 12–13: Any integer multiple of $\frac{\pi}{2}$ can be added to the magnitude, because a rotation of an integer multiple of $\frac{\pi}{2}$ maps horizontal and vertical lines onto themselves or each other.

Question 25 If students have any difficulty, you might suggest that they start with $C = 0$ or $C = 1$. This question can also be done as a class or group activity.

Additional Answers
8. Since $B = 0$ and $AC = 15 > 0$, the graph is an ellipse, a point, or the null set. Let $x = 0$. $5y^2 + 2y - 9 = 0$ has a positive discriminant, so there are two solutions. Thus, the graph must be an ellipse. The equation is equivalent to
$$\frac{(x-1)^2}{\frac{61}{15}} + \frac{(y+\frac{1}{5})^2}{\frac{61}{25}} = 1.$$

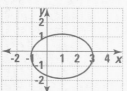

9. Since $B = 0$ and $AC > 0$, the graph is an ellipse, a point, or the null set. The equation is equivalent to $(x - 7)^2 + (y + 1)^2 = 0$, a degenerate ellipse, whose graph is the point $\{(7, -1)\}$.

If in Example 3 we found points on the graph, then we would have had to find a total of at least three points. The reasoning is as follows: If the graph is a pair of intersecting lines, then at least two of these points must be on one of the lines. If all three points are on the same line, then the graph must be a pair of intersecting lines. If all three points are not on the same line, then try some other point (perhaps the midpoint) on each of the three lines connecting them. If the graph contains a straight line, then one of these lines must be one of the intersecting lines. If none of the midpoints satisfies the equation, then the graph does not contain any lines; the only possibility is that it is a hyperbola. Similar reasoning can be used to distinguish ellipses and parabolas from their degenerate forms.

QUESTIONS

Covering the Reading

1a) $9x^2 + 4y^2 - 36 = 0$
b) $A = 9, B = 0, C = 4,$
   $D = 0, E = 0, F = -36$
c) ellipse

2a) $x^2 + y^2 - 10x - 4y + 23 = 0$
b) $A = 1, B = 0, C = 1,$
   $D = -10, E = -4, F = 23$
c) ellipse (circle)

3a) $xy - 1 = 0$
b) $A = 0, B = 1, C = 0,$
   $D = 0, E = 0, F = -1$
c) hyperbola

4a) $\dfrac{(x+1)^2}{\frac{109}{12}} + \dfrac{\left(y+\frac{7}{2}\right)^2}{\frac{109}{4}} = 1$

In 1–3, an equation for a quadratic relation is given. **See left.**
  a. Rewrite the equation in the general form of a quadratic relation in two variables.
  b. Give values for A, B, C, D, E, and F in that form.
  c. Identify the conic section.

1. $\dfrac{x^2}{4} + \dfrac{y^2}{9} = 1$ 2. $(x-5)^2 + (y-2)^2 = 6$ 3. $xy = 1$

4. **a.** Rewrite the equation $3x^2 + y^2 + 6x + 7y - 12 = 0$ in the standard form of an ellipse. **See left.**
   b. Find the center of the ellipse. $\left(-1, -\frac{7}{2}\right)$

5. What is a degenerate conic section? A degenerate conic section is the graph of a quadratic relation that is not an ellipse, parabola, or hyperbola.

6. **a.** Write your answer to Activity 1. **See page 785.**
   b. Which type of degenerate conic section is this equation? the null set

7. Write your answers to Activity 2. **See page 786.**

In 8–11, without graphing, name the conic section whose equation is given. Whenever possible, check by graphing. **See margin.**

8. $3x^2 + 5y^2 - 6x + 2y - 9 = 0$

9. $x^2 - 14x + y^2 + 2y + 50 = 0$

10. $x + y + xy = 8$

11. $3x^2 - 6xy + 3y^2 - 7x + 2y + 5 = 0$

In 12 and 13, what is the magnitude of the rotation which will cause an equation for the image of the graph of the given equation to have no term in xy?

12. $x^2 + 3xy + y^2 = 8$ $\frac{\pi}{4}$

13. $-2x^2 - 4xy - 5y^2 + 4x - 3y + 27 = 0.$
   $\frac{1}{2}\tan^{-1}\left(\frac{4}{3}\right) \approx 0.464$

---

10. Hyperbola. $B \neq 0$, $B^2 - 4AC = 1 > 0$. So the graph is a hyperbola or a pair of intersecting lines. From the original equation, $(x + 1)(y + 1) = 9$. Its graph is the image of the graph of $xy = 9$ under the translation one unit to the left and one unit down.

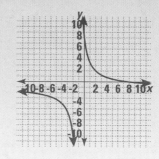

14) Multiplying the factors shows this is an equation for a quadratic relation. $(2x + 5y - 7) \cdot (3x - 7y + 11) = 0$ if and only if $2x + 5y - 7 = 0$ or $3x - 7y + 11 = 0$. The graph of each of the latter two equations is a line, so the graph of the relation is a pair of lines. Since the slopes of the lines are not equal, the lines intersect. The equation represents a degenerate hyperbola.

18) A hyperbola is called a rectangular hyperbola when its asymptotes are perpendicular.

23) False; if $x = 0$, then $\sin\left(\frac{\pi}{2} - x\right) = \sin\left(\frac{\pi}{2}\right) = 1$, but $\sin\left(x - \frac{\pi}{2}\right) = \sin\left(0 - \frac{\pi}{2}\right) = \sin\left(-\frac{\pi}{2}\right) = -1$.

14. Explain why $(2x + 5y - 7)(3x - 7y + 11) = 0$ is an equation for a degenerate conic. **See left.**

15. Examine the proof of the theorem on page 789. Do the algebraic manipulation to show that $(B')^2 - 4A'C' = B^2 - 4AC$. **See margin.**

16. Consider the graph of $x^2 - xy = 6$. **See margin.**
   a. Use the $B^2 - 4AC$ criterion to determine the type of conic this is.
   b. Solve for y and graph this conic.
   c. At what angle are the axes of this conic inclined to the x-axis?

Review

17. Find an equation for the image of $x^2 - y^2 = 1$ under the rotation R_{-30}. *(Lesson 12-4)* Sample: $x^2 - 2\sqrt{3}\,xy - y^2 = 2$

18. What makes a hyperbola a rectangular hyperbola? *(Lesson 12-4)* **See left.**

In 19 and 20, conditions for a quadratic relation are given. **a.** Sketch the curve satisfying the conditions. **b.** Find an equation for the curve. *(Lessons 12-2, 12-3)*

19. ellipse with vertices $(\pm 5, 0)$ and minor axis of length 4 **See margin.**

20. hyperbola with vertices $(0, \pm 6)$ and asymptotes $y = \pm 4x$ **See margin.**

In 21 and 22 simplify each expression. *(Lessons 4-4, 11-5)*

21. $\cos(\pi - \theta)$
   $-\cos\theta$

22. $\cos\left(\frac{\pi}{2} + \theta\right)$
   $-\sin\theta$

23. *True or false.* For all real numbers x, $\sin\left(\frac{\pi}{2} - x\right) = \sin\left(x - \frac{\pi}{2}\right)$. Justify your answer. *(Lessons 4-4, 11-5)* **See left.**

24. Given $z = 3 + 2i$ and $w = 5 - i$, find each. *(Lesson 9-6)*
   a. $z + 4w$
      $23 - 2i$
   b. zw
      $17 + 7i$
   c. $\frac{z}{w}$
      $\frac{1}{2} + \frac{1}{2}i$

Exploration

25. Explore the graph of the equation $x^2 + 2xy + Cy^2 - 12 = 0$ for various values of C. How many different types of conics are possible? What values of C lead to degenerate conics? Are there any properties that all members of this family of quadratic relations satisfy?
   Sample: Three types of conics are possible, one of them degenerate. If $C = 1$, the conic is a pair of parallel lines. If $C > 1$, the conic is an ellipse. If $C < 1$, the conic is a hyperbola.

16. a. $B^2 - 4AC = (-1)^2 - 4(1)(0) = 1 > 0$, so the conic is a hyperbola or a pair of intersecting lines.
   b. $y = \frac{x^2 - 6}{x} = x - \frac{6}{x}$

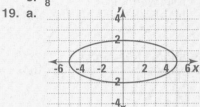

   c. $\frac{\pi}{8}$

19. a.

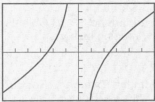

   b. $\frac{x^2}{25} + \frac{y^2}{4} = 1$

20. a.

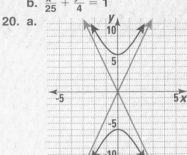

   b. $\frac{y^2}{36} - \frac{4x^2}{9} = 1$

11. Parabola

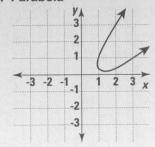

15. Let $s = \sin\theta$ and $t = \cos\theta$.
$$B'^2 - 4A'C' = (2(A - C)ts + B(t^2 - s^2))^2 - 4(At^2 - Bts + Cs^2)(As^2 + Bts + Ct^2)$$
$$= 4(A - C)^2t^2s^2 + 4(A - C)B(t^2 - s^2)ts + B^2(t^2 - s^2)^2 - 4(A^2s^2t^2 - B^2s^2t^2 + C^2s^2t^2 + AB(st^3 - s^3t) + AC(s^4 + t^4) + BC(s^3t - st^3))$$
$$= 4A^2t^2s^2 - 8ACt^2s^2 + 4AB(t^3s - ts^3) - 4BC(t^3s - ts^3) + B^2t^4 - 2B^2t^2s^2 + B^2s^4 - 4A^2s^2t^2 + 4B^2s^2t^2 - 4C^2s^2t^2 - 4AB(st^3 - s^3t) - 4AC(s^4 + t^4) - 4BC(s^3t - st^3) = B^2(t^2 + s^2)^2 - 4AC(t^2 + s^2)^2$$
$$= B^2(t^4 + 2t^2s^2 + s^4) - 4AC(t^4 + 2t^2s^2 + s^4)$$
$$= B^2 - 4AC$$

LESSON

12-6

It's All Done With Mirrors

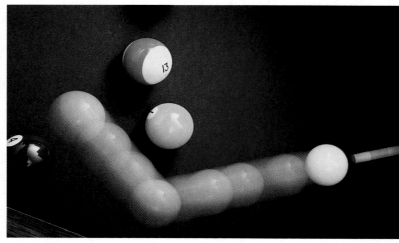

Follow the Bouncing Ball. *A typical shot in billiards involves banking the ball off at least one cushion. Knowing where the ball will carom is the key to winning.*

Reflecting Properties of a Plane

An object that hits a flat hard surface without spin will bounce off that surface in a path that is the reflection image of what its path would have been if the wall were not there. This reflection principle is often seen in handball, tennis, basketball, baseball, hockey, and many other sports.

In physics this principle is stated as *the angle of incidence equals the angle of reflection*, where the two angles in question are measured from the ray perpendicular to the surface at the point of contact. Furthermore, the two rays of the path of the object and the third perpendicular ray all lie in the same plane, so that the mathematics of this situation can be analyzed using plane geometry.

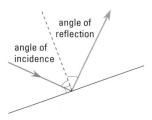

These reflection principles apply also to electromagnetic radiation (such as light waves and radio waves) and sound waves. When you look in a mirror and see the image of an object, the actual object is located in the position of the reflection image of the image you see. Acoustical engineers use these principles to design concert halls so that the sounds from the stage are not distorted as they bounce off the walls, ceiling, seats, and floor.

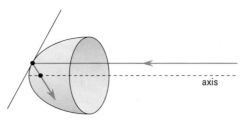

axis

This property makes the paraboloid a particularly appropriate surface for collecting light or radio waves that come from a far distance; the waves are close to parallel, so after reflection they concentrate together at the focus where they can be collected. For this reason, satellite dishes to receive television or radio transmissions, and most telescope mirrors to collect light from stars, are parts of paraboloids.

Automobile headlights use this property in reverse. The light bulb is placed at the focus of a parabolic (actually, *paraboloidal*) mirror. Most of the light from the bulb that hits the surface of the mirror bounces off in a direction parallel to the axis of the paraboloid. Usually the only difference between "brights" and normal headlights in a car is that the paraboloidal mirror is turned so that its axis is parallel to the ground, and so the light travels without hitting the ground.

Beaming. *The inner reflector of the headlights of many automobiles, such as this one from a 1940 LaSalle, are paraboloids.*

4)

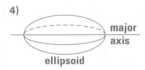

major axis

ellipsoid

5)

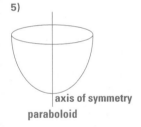

axis of symmetry

paraboloid

6a) Any ray emitted from one focus of an ellipsoid will reflect back through the other focus.

b) Sample: Ellipsoids can form "whispering galleries" where even soft noises made at one focus can be heard at the other focus quite a distance away.

QUESTIONS

Covering the Reading

In 1–3, suppose a laser beam hits the mirror at point *P*. Trace the picture and draw the path of the beam after it hits the mirror.

1.

Plane Mirror

2.  F_1 F_2

P

Elliptical Mirror

3.

F *P*

Parabolic Mirror

In 4 and 5, sketch and identify the three-dimensional figure obtained by each of the following. **See left.**

4. rotating an ellipse 360° around the major axis

5. rotating a parabola around its axis of symmetry

6. a. State a reflecting property of an ellipsoid.
b. Give a practical application of this property. **See left.**

7. a. State a reflecting property of a paraboloid.
b. Give a practical application of this property. **See margin.**

8. Find an equation for the line tangent to the circle $x^2 + y^2 = 25$ at the point (3, 4). (*Hint:* The tangent is perpendicular to the radius at the point of tangency.)
$y = -\frac{3}{4}x + \frac{25}{4}$

Lesson 12-6 *It's All Done With Mirrors* **795**

10. Using the figure to the left of Question 10, define m∠*TPQ* as α and m∠*FPQ* as θ. Now
$PQ = 9, TQ = 1.5$;
so $\tan \alpha = \frac{1.5}{9} = \frac{1}{6}$; $\alpha =$
$\tan^{-1}\left(\frac{1}{6}\right) \approx 9.46°$.

For θ, we have
$\tan \theta = \frac{3}{9 - \frac{1}{4}} = \frac{12}{35}$, therefore

$\theta = \tan^{-1}\frac{12}{35} \approx 18.92°$.
So $\alpha \approx \frac{1}{2}\theta$.

14. a.

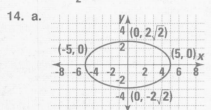

b. $(\sqrt{17}, 0), (-\sqrt{17}, 0)$
c. 10

15. a.

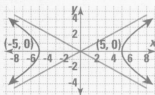

b. $(-\sqrt{33}, 0), (\sqrt{33}, 0)$
c. 10

19. If *H* is a hyperbola with foci F_1 and F_2 and *P* is any point on *H*, let ℓ be the tangent line to *H* through *P*, and let *m* be the line perpendicular to ℓ through *P*. Then, the angle between *m* and $\overrightarrow{PF_1}$ is equal to the angle between *m* and $\overrightarrow{PF_2}$

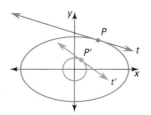

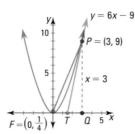

Earthrise photographed from Apollo 17 as it orbited the Moon in 1972

9. An equation for the tangent line *t* to a parent ellipse $\frac{x^2}{a^2} + \frac{y^2}{b^2} = 1$ at any point *P* on it can be found using the following procedure.

Step 1: By a scale change, map the ellipse onto the unit circle, and let *P'* be the image of *P* under this scale change.

Step 2: Use the idea of Question 8 to find an equation for *t'*, the tangent to the circle at *P'*.

Step 3: Use the inverse of the transformation used in Step 1 to find an equation for the original tangent.

Use this procedure to find an equation for the tangent line *t* to the ellipse $\frac{x^2}{200} + \frac{y^2}{450} = 1$ at the point (14, 3). $y = -\frac{21}{2}x + 150$

10. The focus *F* of the parabola $y = x^2$ is at the point $\left(0, \frac{1}{4}\right)$. It can be shown that the tangent to this parabola at the point $P = (3, 9)$ has equation $y = 6x - 9$. By drawing triangles and using trigonometry, show that $\overline{FP}$ and the vertical line $x = 3$ make equal angles with the tangent.
See margin.

Review

In 11 and 12, name the conic section whose equation is given.

11. $4x^2 + 5xy - 6y^2 + 12x + 36 = 0$ **hyperbola**

12. $x^2 + xy + y^2 + x + y - 5 = 0$ *(Lesson 12-5)*
ellipse

13. Suppose the curve with equation $xy = -6$ is rotated $\frac{\pi}{4}$ about the origin.
a. What is an equation for the image? $y^2 - x^2 = -12$
b. *True or false.* Both the preimage and image are rectangular hyperbolas. *(Lesson 12-4)*
True

In 14 and 15, an equation for a quadratic relation is given. **a.** Sketch a graph.
b. Identify the foci. **c.** Identify the focal constant. *(Lessons 12-2, 12-3)*

14. $\frac{x^2}{25} + \frac{y^2}{8} = 1$ **15.** $\frac{x^2}{25} - \frac{y^2}{8} = 1$
14, 15) See margin.

16. Name the conic section(s) with the following symmetry. *(Lessons 12-1, 12-3)*
a. exactly one line of symmetry   **b.** at least two lines of symmetry
c. 90° rotation symmetry **circle**   **ellipse; hyperbola**
a) parabola

17. The elliptical orbit of the moon has the center of Earth as one focus. If the closest distance from the center of the moon to the center of Earth is 216,000 miles and the largest distance to the center of Earth is 248,000 miles, how far from the center of Earth is the second focus? *(Lesson 12-2)*
32,000 miles

18. Find all complex solutions to $x^3 - 1000 = 0$. *(Lesson 9-8)*
$10, -5 + 5\sqrt{3}i, -5 - 5\sqrt{3}i$

Exploration

19. There is a reflection property for the hyperbola. Find out what this is.
See margin.

Possible Responses, page 797

1. a.

Planet	Eccentricity
Venus	.007
Neptune	.009
Earth	.017
Uranus	.047
Jupiter	.048
Saturn	.056
Mars	.093
Mercury	.206
Pluto	.254

b. Here is some data relating period to eccentricity for several comets:

e	period (yr)	*e*	period (yr)
.379	7.35	.810	5.46
.463	5.98	.821	13.61
.553	6.42	.847	3.3
.559	6.8	.919	27.87
.600	6.82	.955	70.87
.604	7.02	.967	76.04
.761	10.99	.969	164.3
.774	17.97		

Overall, periods seem to get longer as eccentricity increases. In particular, there is a large jump in period length as the eccentricities become larger than .900.

c. A heavenly body can travel in a path that is hyperbolic or nearly parabolic. In fact, a majority of the newly discovered comets have nearly parabolic orbits. If an object is traveling fast enough, it can

A project presents an opportunity for you to extend your knowledge of a topic related to the material of this chapter. You should allow more time for a project than you do for a typical homework question.

1 Orbits of Celestial Bodies

a. Collect data on the elliptical orbits of the planets. Arrange the eccentricities (see Project 4) of the orbits of the planets from smallest to largest.

b. Find data on the elliptical orbits of comets or other celestial bodies. Does there appear to be any relation between the period of the comet (i.e., how long it takes to complete one trip) and the eccentricity of its path? If so, what is it?

c. Can a heavenly body travel in a path that is parabolic? hyperbolic? Why or why not?

2 Using Paper-folding to Make Conic Sections

Using wax paper, determine the curve that results from each of the following.

a. Draw a line ℓ and a point P not on the line. Fold and crease the paper so a point Q on the line coincides with P. Repeat at least a dozen times for different points Q. How does the distance between P and ℓ affect the resulting curve?

b. Draw a circle and a point P in the interior of the circle (but not the center of it). Make different folds where a point on the circle coincides with P. How does the distance between P and the center of the circle affect the resulting curve?

c. Draw a circle and a point P in the exterior of the circle. Make different folds where a point on the circle coincides with P. Discuss the effect of the distance between P and the center of the circle on the resulting curve.

3 Using Drawing to Make Conic Sections

The following methods always generate conic sections. For each of the following methods below, draw the curve, name the curve, and explain why the method always produces a certain conic section.

a. Tie a pencil near the middle of a piece of string and pass the string around two pins inserted on a piece of paper. Using the pencil to keep the string taut, hold the two ends of the string together and draw them toward you around one of the pins, as shown below. Repeat by interchanging the roles of the two pins.

b. Place a piece of string of length AB as shown below on a T-square. Place the T-square perpendicular to a line ℓ on the paper and place the ends of the string at B and at a point C on the paper. As the T-square slides on ℓ, draw the curve by keeping the pencil firmly on the edge of the T-square.

Chapter 12 Projects

The projects relate chiefly to the content of the lessons of this chapter as follows:

Project	Lesson(s)
1	12-2, 12-4
2	12-1, 12-3
3	12-1, 12-3
4	12-2, 12-4
5	12-2, 12-3, 12-5

1 Orbits of Celestial Bodies This project should involve some manipulation of data on the planets and comets. Comets that are visible from Earth, such as Halley's comet or the Hale-Bopp comet of 1997, have quite eccentric orbits.

2 Using Paper-folding to Make Conic Sections The paper folds determine *envelopes* for the conic sections, that is, sets of lines that are tangent to the particular conic section being generated. That these lines so clearly determine a conic is usually a surprise to students.

3 Using Drawing to Make Conic Sections This project uses the 2-dimensional locus definitions of the conic sections presented in Lesson 12-1 for the ellipse and Lesson 12-3 for the hyperbola.

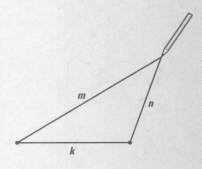

---

escape from the gravitational pull of the sun and follow a nearly parabolic or hyperbolic path.

2. a. The curve is a parabola. When P is farther from the line, the parabola is wider and flatter. When P is nearer to the line, the parabola is more curved.

b. The curve is an ellipse. When P is farther from the center, the ellipse is more elongated. When P is closer to the center, the ellipse is more circular.

c. The curve is a branch of a hyperbola. When P is farther from the circle, the hyperbola is wider and flatter. When P is nearer to the circle, the hyperbola is more curved.

3. a. The curve is a hyperbola. In the drawing above at the right, we let k, m, and n be the lengths of the sides of the triangle formed by the string. Since the pencil is at the midpoint of the string, $k + n = m$. As you pull the string toward you, m and n change, but k (distance between the pins) is constant. Thus any point on the curve lies on a hyperbola with the pins as foci and with focal constant k.

(Responses continue on page 798.)

4 Eccentricity The eccentricity definition is the third definition students have seen for the ellipse and hyperbola, and is the same as the 2-dimensional definition of the parabola with which they should be familiar. It has the advantage of applying easily to all conics, a property it shares with their definitions as sections of a cone, but it has the further advantage of not giving rise to any degenerate conics.

5 Quadric Sections The shape of Earth is sometimes described as an *oblate spheroid*. This project might be appropriate for a group of students working together. Some calculus textbooks give attention to quadric surfaces.

Possible responses, page 797

3. b. **Use the drawing below. If the distance from *B* to the pencil point is *n*, then the distance from the pencil point to *A* must be *AB* − *n*. Since the string has length *AB*, then the distance from *C* to the pencil point is also *AB* − *n*. Thus at any point on the resulting curve, the distance from *C* to the point is the same as the distance from the point to *I*. So, by definition, the curve must be a parabola with focus *C* and directrix *I*.**

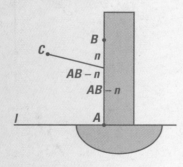

4 Eccentricity

It is possible to define a conic section in terms of distances from a fixed point and a fixed line. If the curve has its major axis along the *x*-axis, then the distance from a point on the curve to the focus $(c, 0)$ divided by the distance from a point on the curve to the directrix line with equation $x = \frac{a^2}{c}$ is $\frac{c}{a}$. The ratio $\frac{c}{a}$ is called the **eccentricity** of the conic and is denoted as *e*.

a. Calculate the value of the eccentricity *e* for some conic sections you have drawn before.

b. Both the ellipse and hyperbola have two foci and two *directrices*. Give equations for both directrices of ellipses and hyperbolas in standard form.

c. Draw curves with increasing eccentricities such as .25, .5, .75, .9, 1.0, 1.5, 2, 2.5, 3, 4, 5, and 10. *Multiple choice.* Match the following equations with their curves.

   i. $0 < e < 1$ (I) ellipse
   ii. $e = 1$ (II) hyperbola
   iii. $e > 1$ (III) parabola

d. What is the eccentricity of the ellipse most pleasing to your eye? Some people believe it to be the reciprocal of the golden ratio or the reciprocal of the number *e*. Do you agree?

5 Quadric Sections

As the circle has three-dimensional analogs in the sphere and cylinder, the other conic sections have three-dimensional analogs as well. These are called **quadric surfaces** and can be expressed by the following general second degree equation in three variables:

$Ax^2 + By^2 + Cz^2 + Dxy + Exz + Fyz + Gx + Hy + Iz + J = 0$,

where the coefficients are real numbers. Do either parts **a** and **b**, or part **c**.

a. For instance, an **ellipsoid** has as its general equation

$$\frac{x^2}{a^2} + \frac{y^2}{b^2} + \frac{z^2}{c^2} = 1.$$

If two of *a*, *b*, and *c* in the above equation are equal, then the surface is a **spheroid**. A *prolate spheroid*, somewhat like a football, is created by rotating an ellipse about its major axis. An *oblate spheroid*, somewhat like a doorknob, is created by rotating an ellipse about its minor axis. Draw some ellipsoids and spheroids.

b. Other quadric surfaces have the following general equations.

hyperboloid of one sheet: $\frac{x^2}{a^2} + \frac{y^2}{b^2} - \frac{z^2}{c^2} = 1$

hyperboloid of two sheets: $-\frac{x^2}{a^2} - \frac{y^2}{b^2} + \frac{z^2}{c^2} = 1$

elliptic paraboloid: $z = \frac{x^2}{a^2} + \frac{y^2}{b^2}$

hyperbolic paraboloid (the "saddle-shaped" surface): $z = \frac{y^2}{b^2} - \frac{x^2}{a^2}$

Graph examples of each of these curves.

c. Many quadric surfaces can be approximated by string models.

Use string to build a quadric surface such as the one pictured here.

4. a. Examples: For the ellipse in Lesson 12-2, Question 6:
$\frac{x^2}{25} + \frac{y^2}{16} = 1$, $e = \frac{3}{5}$.
For the hyperbola in Lesson 12-3, Question 7a:
$\frac{x^2}{64} - \frac{y^2}{9} = 1$, $e = \frac{\sqrt{73}}{8} \approx 1.068$.

   b. $x = \pm\frac{a^2}{c}$

4. c. $e = .25$ $e = 1.5$ $e = .5$ $e = 2$

SUMMARY

When one of two intersecting lines is rotated about the other, an unbounded cone of two nappes is formed. The sections of this cone lead to the three primary conic sections: the parabola (which was studied earlier), the ellipse, and the hyperbola.

Both the ellipse and the hyperbola have two foci. An ellipse is the set of all points where the sum of the distances to each of the foci is constant. A hyperbola is the set of all points where the absolute value of the difference of the distances to the foci is constant. Relating these definitions to the description of the conic sections as intersections can be done elegantly by the use of Dandelin spheres.

Both the ellipse and hyperbola have two symmetry lines which contain the major axis and the minor axis of the curves. The major axis is the one containing the foci. If these symmetry lines are the x- and y-axes, then the ellipse can be described by the standard form equation $\frac{x^2}{a^2} + \frac{y^2}{b^2} = 1$, and the hyperbola can be described by the standard form equation $\frac{x^2}{a^2} - \frac{y^2}{b^2} = 1$ or $\frac{y^2}{a^2} - \frac{x^2}{b^2} = 1$.

When the asymptotes of a hyperbola are perpendicular, the hyperbola is called rectangular. Translation images can be described by applying the theorems studied earlier in this course.

When one symmetry line of an ellipse or hyperbola is not horizontal, the conic is a rotation image of an ellipse or hyperbola in standard form. If the center of the rotation is the origin, then the Graph-Rotation Theorem can be applied to find an equation for the conic. For instance, $xy = 1$ is an equation for the image of the rectangular hyperbola with equation $x^2 - y^2 = 1$ under R_{45}.

Graphs of the general quadratic equation

$$Ax^2 + Bxy + Cy^2 + Dx + Ey + F = 0$$

include all conic sections and the degenerate conic sections. The discriminant $B^2 - 4AC$ tells you the possible shapes of the curve. If $B^2 - 4AC < 0$, the curve is an ellipse, a single point, or the null set. If $B^2 - 4AC > 0$, the curve is a hyperbola or a pair of intersecting lines. If $B^2 - 4AC = 0$, the curve is a parabola, two parallel lines, a line, or the null set. By using the identity $\frac{B}{C - A} = \tan 2\theta$ or $B\cos\theta = 0$, you can determine the magnitude of rotation needed to map the curve onto a conic with a horizontal line of symmetry.

The reflection property of an ellipse—that a path through one focus will reflect off the ellipse through the other focus—is used in constructing whispering galleries. The reflection property of a parabola—that a path parallel to the axis will reflect off the parabola through the focus—is used in constructing satellite dishes and headlights. Systems of hyperbolas are used in locating and tracking objects that emit sound waves.

Chapter 12 *Summary and Vocabulary* **799**

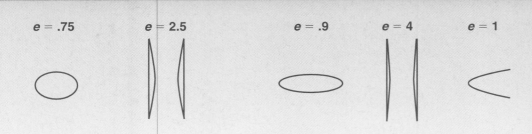

e = .75   e = 2.5   e = .9   e = 4   e = 1

4. c. (Continued)
   Samples: When the eccentricity of an ellipse ($0 \le e \le 1$) is close to 0, it is nearly circular. When the eccentricity is close to 1, the ellipse is long and narrow. When $e = 1$, the curve becomes a parabola. When the eccentricity of a hyperbola ($e > 1$) is close to one, the branches of the hyperbola are very curved. When the eccentricity is larger, the branches become straighter.
   i. I   ii. III   iii. II
5. a. **Sample:** $\frac{x^2}{4} + \frac{y^2}{25} + z^2 = 1$

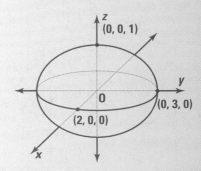

   b. **Sample:**
   $\frac{x^2}{9} + \frac{y^2}{4} - \frac{z^2}{16} = 1$

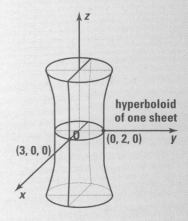

   hyperboloid of one sheet

(Responses continue on page 800.)

Vocabulary

Terms, symbols, and properties are listed by lesson to provide a checklist of concepts a student must know. Emphasize to students that they should read the vocabulary list carefully before starting the Progress Self-Test. If students do not understand the meaning of a term, they should refer back to the indicated lesson.

Possible responses, page 798
5. b. (Continued)

$$-\frac{x^2}{4} - y^2 + \frac{z^2}{9} = 1$$

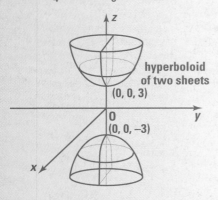

hyperboloid
of two sheets
$(0, 0, 3)$

$(0, 0, -3)$

$$z = \frac{x^2}{4} + \frac{y^2}{25}$$

elliptic
paraboloid

$$z = \frac{y^2}{16} - \frac{x^2}{4}$$

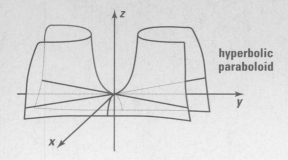

hyperbolic
paraboloid

VOCABULARY

Below are the most important terms and phrases for this chapter. You should be able to give a general description and a specific example of each and a precise definition for those marked with an asterisk (*).

Lesson 12-1
*conic section
quadratic relation
axis, vertex, nappes of cone
cross section, section
edge (of a cone)
*ellipse
focus, foci of an ellipse
focal constant for an ellipse
astronomical units (a.u.)

Lesson 12-2
*standard form equation for an ellipse
center of an ellipse
horizontal axis, vertical axis
major axis, minor axis
eccentricity (of an ellipse)

Lesson 12-3
*hyperbola
focus, foci, focal constant of a hyperbola
*standard form equation for a hyperbola
vertices
axes, center of a hyperbola

Lesson 12-4
Graph-Rotation Theorem
rectangular hyperbola
isometry

Lesson 12-5
general form of a quadratic relation in two variables
degenerate conic sections
discriminant

800

c. Each point where the strings intersect is the intersection of two lines
(the strings) which lie entirely on
the surface.

PROGRESS SELF-TEST

1–4, 6) See margin.   5, 7–10) See below.

Take this test as you would take a test in class. You will need an automatic grapher. Then, check the test yourself using the solutions at the back of the book.

1. a. Explain how to obtain an ellipse from a cone.

   b. Draw a figure to illustrate your description.

In 2–4, graph.

2. $\frac{x^2}{25} + \frac{y^2}{81} = 1$

3. $x^2 - 9y^2 = 9$

4. $\frac{(x-2)^2}{36} + \frac{(y+1)^2}{20} = 1$

5. Find an equation for the hyperbola with foci (7, 0) and (-7, 0) and focal constant 10.

6. Draw an ellipse for which the distance between the foci is 8 cm and the focal constant is 10 cm.

7. a. Consider the hyperbola $\frac{x^2}{81} - \frac{y^2}{100} = 1$. Give equations for its asymptotes.

   b. Give equations for its symmetry lines.

8. Find an equation for the image of $y = x^2 - 3x - 4$ under $R_{\pi/3}$.

9. Tell whether or not $\frac{y^2}{30} - \frac{x^2}{4} = 1$ is a rectangular hyperbola. Justify your answer.

10. Rewrite $\frac{x^2}{9} - \frac{y^2}{64} = 1$ in the general quadratic form, and give values of $A, B, C, D, E,$ and F in that form.

5) $\frac{x^2}{25} - \frac{y^2}{24} = 1$.

7a) $y = \frac{10}{9}x$ and $y = -\frac{10}{9}x$
 b) $x = 0, y = 0$.

8) $\frac{1}{4}x^2 + \frac{\sqrt{3}}{2}xy + \frac{3}{4}y^2 + \frac{-3+\sqrt{3}}{2}x + \frac{-1-3\sqrt{3}}{2}y - 4 = 0$

9) No; the asymptotes $y = \frac{\sqrt{30}}{2}x$ and $y = -\frac{\sqrt{30}}{2}x$ are not perpendicular, thus the hyperbola is not rectangular.

10) $64x^2 - 9y^2 - 576 = 0$
 $A = 64, B = 0, C = -9,$
 $D = 0, E = 0, F = -576$

In 11 and 12, describe the graph of the relation represented by the given equation. See below.

11. $2x^2 - 6xy + 18y^2 - 14x + 6y - 110 = 0$
12. $9x^2 - 2xy + y^2 - 4x + 22 = 0$

13. The elliptical orbit of the planet Jupiter has the center of the sun as one focus. If the closest distance to the center of the sun is 460 million miles and the farthest distance is 508 million miles, how far from the center of the sun is the second focus? The second focus is (-24, 0) and is 48 million miles from the sun.

The planet Jupiter was named after the Roman king of the gods before it was known to be the largest planet.

11) The graph is an ellipse.
12) The graph is the null set.

Progress Self-Test
For the development of mathematical competence, feedback and correction, along with the opportunity to practice, are necessary. The Progress Self-Test provides the opportunity for feedback and correction; the Chapter Review provides additional opportunities and practice. We cannot overemphasize the importance of these end-of-chapter materials. It is at this point that the material "gels" for many students, allowing them to solidify skills and understanding. In general, student performance should be markedly improved after these pages.

Assign the Progress Self-Test as a one-night assignment. Worked-out *solutions* for all questions are in the Selected Answers section of the student book. Encourage students to take the Progress Self-Test honestly, grade themselves, and then be prepared to discuss the test in class.

Advise students to pay special attention to those Chapter Review questions (pages 802–803) that correspond to questions missed on the Progress Self-Test.

3.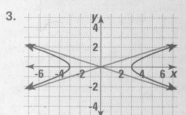

4.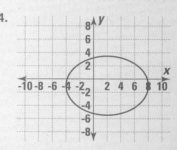

6. The ellipse should have the shape of the ellipse below, where the distance between the foci is 8 cm and the minor axis is 6 cm.

Additional Answers
1. a. By taking the intersection of the cone with a plane while the angle formed by the cone's axis and the plane is greater than the angle between the axis and the rotating line.

2.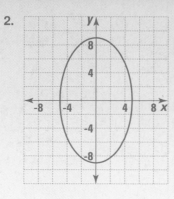

801

Chapter 12 Review

Resources

From the ***Teacher's Resource File***

- Answer Master for Chapter 12 Review
- Assessment Sourcebook: Chapter 12 Test, Forms A–D Chapter 12 Test, Cumulative Form

Additional Resources

- Quiz and Test Writer

The main objectives for the chapter are organized in the Chapter Review under the four types of understanding this book promotes—Skills, Properties, Uses, and Representations.

Whereas end-of chapter material may be considered optional in some texts, in *UCSMP Functions, Statistics, and Trigonometry* we have selected these objectives and questions with the expectation that they will be covered. Students should be able to answer these questions with about 85% accuracy after studying the chapter.

You may assign these questions over a single night to help students prepare for a test the next day, or you may assign the questions over a two-day period. If you work the questions over two days, then we recommend assigning the *evens* for homework the first night so that students get feedback in class the next day, then assigning the *odds* the night before the test, because answers are provided to the odd-numbered questions.

CHAPTER REVIEW

Questions on SPUR Objectives

SPUR stands for **S**kills, **P**roperties, **U**ses, and **R**epresentations. The Chapter Review questions are grouped according to the SPUR Objectives for this chapter.

SKILLS DEAL WITH THE PROCEDURES USED TO GET ANSWERS.

1–3, 5–7, 10–16, 19–20) See margin.

Objective A: *Use properties of ellipses and hyperbolas to write equations describing them.* *(Lessons 12-2, 12-3)*

1. Find an equation for the ellipse with foci (0, 15) and (0, -15) and focal constant 34.

2. Find an equation for the hyperbola with foci (4, 0) and (-4, 0) and focal constant 6.

3. Give an equation for the ellipse whose center is the origin, whose horizontal axis has length 18, and whose vertical axis has length 7.

4. Give equations for the asymptotes of the hyperbola $\frac{x^2}{16} - \frac{y^2}{4} = 1$. **$y = \frac{1}{2}x$, $y = -\frac{1}{2}x$**

Objective B: *Find equations for rotation images of figures.* *(Lesson 12-4)*

In 5–8, find an equation for the image of the given figure under the given rotation.

5. $\frac{x^2}{9} + \frac{y^2}{36} = 1$; R_{45}

6. $9x^2 - y^2 = 1$; $R_{\pi/3}$

7. $y = x^2 - 8$; $R_{\pi/6}$

8. $x^2 + y^2 = 20$; R_{55} **$x^2 + y^2 = 20$**

9. Suppose the hyperbola $xy = 120$ is rotated $\frac{\pi}{4}$ about the origin. What is an equation for the image hyperbola? **Sample: $y^2 - x^2 = 240$**

10. Find an equation for the image of the parabola $y = (x + 4)^2 + 5$ when rotated 60° about the point (-4, 5).

Objective C: *Rewrite equations of conic sections in the general form of a quadratic relation in two variables.* *(Lesson 12-5)*

In 11–14, rewrite the equation in the general form of a quadratic relation in two variables and give values of *A*, *B*, *C*, *D*, *E*, and *F* in that form.

11. $\frac{x^2}{25} + \frac{y^2}{49} = 1$

12. $(x + 3)^2 + (y - 8)^2 = 35$

13. $7xy = 8$

14. $\frac{(x - 2)^2}{4} - y^2 = 1$

PROPERTIES DEAL WITH THE PRINCIPLES BEHIND THE MATHEMATICS.

Objective D: *State and apply properties of ellipses and hyperbolas to draw or describe them.* *(Lessons 12-1, 12-3, 12-4)*

15. Draw an ellipse in which the distance between the foci is 6 cm and the focal constant is 8 cm.

16. Draw a hyperbola in which the distance between the foci is 2 inches and the focal constant is 1 inch.

17. At least how many symmetry lines does every ellipse have? **2**

18. At most how many symmetry lines does every hyperbola have? **2**

In 19 and 20, tell whether or not the hyperbola is a rectangular hyperbola. Justify your answer.

19. $\frac{x^2}{6} - \frac{y^2}{12} = 1$

20. $5xy = 80$

Additional Answers

1. $\frac{x^2}{64} + \frac{y^2}{289} = 1$
2. $\frac{x^2}{9} - \frac{y^2}{7} = 1$
3. $\frac{x^2}{81} + \frac{4y^2}{49} = 1$
5. Sample: $5x^2 + 6xy + 5y^2 = 72$
6. Sample: $3x^2 + 10\sqrt{3}xy + 13y^2 = 2$
7. Sample: $3x^2 + 2\sqrt{3}xy + y^2 + 2x - 2\sqrt{3}y - 32 = 0$
10. Sample: $x^2 + 2\sqrt{3}xy + 3y^2 + (8 - 8\sqrt{3})x + (8\sqrt{3} - 32)y - 32\sqrt{3} + 101 = 0$
11. $49x^2 + 25y^2 - 1225 = 0$; $A = 49$, $B = 0$, $C = 25$, $D = 0$, $E = 0$, $F = -1225$
12. $x^2 + y^2 + 6x - 16y + 38 = 0$; $A = 1$, $B = 0$, $C = 1$, $D = 6$, $E = -16$, $F = 38$
13. $7xy - 8 = 0$; $A = 0$, $B = 7$, $C = 0$, $D = 0$, $E = 0$, $F = -8$
14. $x^2 - 4y^2 - 4x = 0$; $A = 1$, $B = 0$, $C = -4$, $D = -4$, $E = 0$, $F = 0$
15. The ellipse should have the shape of the ellipse at the right with 6 cm between the foci and a minor axis of $2\sqrt{7}$ cm.

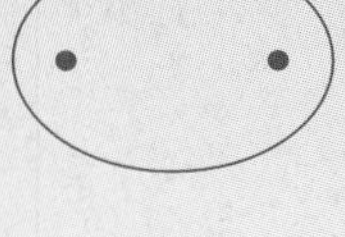

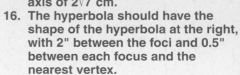

16. The hyperbola should have the shape of the hyperbola at the right, with 2" between the foci and 0.5" between each focus and the nearest vertex.

21–24, 27–32, 35–37) See margin.

Objective E: *Describe the intersections of a plane and a cone of 2 nappes.* *(Lessons 12-1, 12-5)*

21. How is the "cone" in conic sections generated?

22. Name the three degenerate conic sections.

23. Draw a plane intersecting a cone in a hyperbola.

24. *True or false.* Justify your thinking. Any given plane must intersect a given cone.

USES DEAL WITH APPLICATIONS OF MATHEMATICS IN REAL SITUATIONS.

Objective F: *Determine information about elliptical orbits.* *(Lesson 12-2)*

25. The elliptical orbit of the planet Mercury has the center of the sun as one focus. If the closest distance to the center of the sun is 28,440,000 miles and the farthest distance is 43,560,000 miles, how far from the center of the sun is the second focus?
15,120,000 miles

26. The closest distance the planet Mars gets to the sun is 129 million miles and the farthest distance is 154 million miles. Is the second focus of Mars's orbit nearer or farther from the sun than the planet Mercury (use the information of Question 25)?
closer

REPRESENTATIONS DEAL WITH PICTURES, GRAPHS, OR OBJECTS THAT ILLUSTRATE CONCEPTS.

Objective G: *Graph or identify graphs of ellipses and hyperbolas given their equations.* *(Lessons 12-2, 12-3)*

In 27–32, graph.

27. $x^2 + \dfrac{y^2}{16} = 1$

28. $16x^2 - y^2 = 16$

29. $\dfrac{y^2}{40} - \dfrac{x^2}{9} = 1$

30. $20x^2 + 49y^2 = 980$

31. $y^2 - x^2 = 1$

32. $\dfrac{x^2}{100} - \dfrac{y^2}{9} = 1$

In 33 and 34, give an equation for the ellipse.

33.

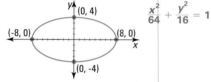

$\dfrac{x^2}{64} + \dfrac{y^2}{16} = 1$

34.

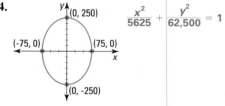

$\dfrac{x^2}{5625} + \dfrac{y^2}{62,500} = 1$

Objective H: *Graph transformation images of parent ellipses and hyperbolas.* *(Lessons 12-2, 12-3, 12-5)*

In 35 and 36, graph.

35. $\dfrac{(x-4)^2}{25} + \dfrac{(y+2)^2}{4} = 1$

36. $\dfrac{(x+8)^2}{16} - (y-3)^2 = 1$

37. Graph $xy = 20$.

38. Graph $x^2 - xy = 8$ by solving for y.
$y = \dfrac{x^2 - 8}{x}$; See margin for graph.

Objective I: *Describe graphs of quadratic equations.* *(Lesson 12-5)*

In 39–42, describe the graph of the relation represented by the given equation.

39. $8x^2 + 3y^2 - 12x + 6y + 18 = 0$

40. $8x + 8y - 4xy = -12$

41. $x^2 + 4xy + 4y^2 + 8x + 2y + 9 = 0$

42. $3y^2 - 4y = 2x^2 + 9x - 3$

39) the null set
40) hyperbola
41) parabola
42) hyperbola

It is effective to ask students which questions they still do not understand and use the day or days as a total class discussion of the material which the class finds most difficult.

Assessment

Evaluation The Assessment Sourcebook provides six forms of the Chapter 12 Test. Forms A and B present parallel versions in a short-answer format. Forms C and D offer performance assessment. The fifth test is Chapter 12 Test, Cumulative Form. About 50% of this test covers Chapter 12, 25% of it covers Chapter 11, and 25% of it covers earlier chapters.

For information on grading, see *General Teaching Suggestions; Grading* in the *Professional Sourcebook*, which begins on page T20 in the Teacher's Edition.

Feedback After students have taken the test for Chapter 12 and you have scored the results, return the tests to students for discussion. Class discussion of the questions that caused trouble for the most students can be very effective in identifying and clarifying misunderstandings. You might want to have them write down the items they missed and work, either in groups or at home, to correct them. It is important for students to receive feedback on every chapter test, and we recommend that students see and correct their mistakes before proceeding too far into the next chapter.

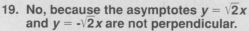

19. No, because the asymptotes $y = \sqrt{2}x$ and $y = -\sqrt{2}x$ are not perpendicular.

20. Yes, because the asymptotes are the x- and y-axes.

21. The cone is formed by rotating one of two intersecting, non-perpendicular lines about the other.

22. A point, a line, two intersecting lines

23.

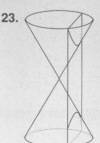

24. True, since the cone is infinite in extent.

(See Additional Answers which begin on page T170 of this Teacher's Edition.)

Adapting to Individual Needs

The student text is written for the vast majority of students. The chart at the right suggests two pacing plans to accommodate the needs of your students. Students in the Full Course should complete the entire text by the end of the year. Students in the Minimal Course will spend more time when there are quizzes and more time on the Chapter Review. Therefore, these students may not complete all of the chapters in the text.

Options are also presented to meet the needs of a variety of teaching and learning styles. For each lesson, the Teacher's Edition provides a section entitled *Adapting to Individual Needs*. This section regularly includes **Optional Activities, Challenge** problems, **English Language Development** suggestions, and suggestions for providing **Extra Help.** The Teacher's Edition also frequently includes an **Error Alert,** an **Extension,** and an **Assessment** alternative. The options available in Chapter 13 are summarized in the chart below.

Chapter 13 Pacing Chart

Day	Full Course	Minimal Course
1	13-1	13-1
2	13-2	13-2
3	13-3	13-3
4	Quiz*; 13-4	Quiz*; begin 13-4.
5	13-5	Finish 13-4.
6	13-6	13-5
7	Quiz*; 13-7	13-6
8	13-8	Quiz*; begin 13-7.
9	13-9	Finish 13-7.
10	Self-Test	13-8
11	Review	13-9
12	Test*	Self-Test
13	Comprehensive Test*	Review
14		Review
15		Test*
16		Comprehensive Test*

*in the Teacher's Resource File

In the Teacher's Edition...

Lesson	Optional Activities	Extra Help	Challenge	English Language Development	Error Alert	Extension	Cooperative Learning	Ongoing Assessment
13-1	●	●	●	●		●	●	Written
13-2	●	●	●		●	●	●	Written
13-3	●	●	●		●	●		Quiz
13-4	●	●	●		●	●	●	Written
13-5	●	●	●		●	●		Group
13-6	●	●	●		●	●		Quiz
13-7	●	●	●		●	●	●	Written
13-8	●	●	●		●	●		Written
13-9	●	●	●			●		

In the Additional Resources...

Lesson	In the Teacher's Resource File					Visual Aids**	Technology	Explorations Software
	Lesson Masters	Teaching Aids*	Answer Masters	Technology Sourcebook	Assessment Sourcebook			
13-1	13-1	112, 115, 116	13-1			112, 115, 116, AM		
13-2	13-2	112, 117	13-2	Calc 10		112, 117, AM		
13-3	13-3	112	13-3		Quiz	112, AM		
13-4	13-4	113, 118, 119	13-4			113, 118, 119, AM		
13-5	13-5	113, 120–122	13-5			113, 120–122, AM		13-5
13-6	13-6	113, 123	13-6		Quiz	113, 123, AM		
In-class Activity			13-7			AM		13-7
13-7	13-7	114, 124	13-7			114, 124, AM		
13-8	13-8	114, 125	13-8			114, 125, AM		
13-9		114	13-9	Calc 11		114, AM		
End of chapter					Tests			

*Teaching Aids are pictured on pages 804C and 804D.

**Visual Aids provide transparencies for all Teaching Aids and all Answer Masters.

Also available is the Study Skills Handbook which includes study-skill tips related to reading, note-taking, and comprehension.

Integrating Strands and Applications

	13-1	13-2	13-3	13-4	13-5	13-6	13-7	13-8	13-9
Mathematical Connections									
Number Sense	●					●	●		●
Algebra	●	●	●	●	●	●	●	●	●
Geometry	●	●		●	●	●	●		
Measurement						●	●		
Logic and Reasoning	●	●	●				●		
Probability	●		●				●		
Statistics/Data Analysis	●					●			
Patterns and Functions	●	●	●	●	●		●	●	●
Discrete Mathematics	●	●	●	●		●	●	●	●
Interdisciplinary and Other Connections									
Art				●					
Science	●		●				●		
Social Studies				●				●	●
Multicultural				●		●		●	
Technology	●	●	●	●	●			●	●
Consumer			●						

Teaching and Assessing the Chapter Objectives

Chapter 13 Objectives (Organized into the SPUR categories—Skills, Properties, Uses, and Representations)	Lessons	Progress Self-Test Questions	Chapter Review Questions	In the Teacher's Resource File		
				Chapter Test, Forms A and B	Chapter Test, Forms	
					C	D
Skills						
A: Evaluate the reciprocal trigonometric functions.	13-1	1, 2	1-6	3, 4, 5	1	
B: Perform operations with complex numbers in polar or trigonometric form.	13-7	15, 16	7-12	14, 15		
C: Represent complex numbers in different forms.	13-6, 13-7	11	13-18	9, 10	4	
D: Find powers and roots of complex numbers.	13-8	12, 13	19-22	16, 17	5	
Properties						
E: Apply properties of the reciprocal trigonometric functions.	13-1	3	23-26	1, 2		
F: Prove trigonometric identities.	13-2, 13-3	6, 17	27-30	18	2	
G: Describe singularities of functions.	13-3	4, 6	31-34	6, 18	2	
Uses						
There are no objectives relating to uses in this chapter.						
Representations						
H: Use an automatic grapher to test a proposed identity.	13-2, 13-3	5	35-38	18	2	
I: Given polar coordinates of a point, determine its rectangular coordinates and vice versa.	13-4	10	39-44	7	3	✓
J: Plot points in a polar coordinate system.	13-4	7	45-48	8	3	✓
K: Graph and interpret graphs of polar equations	13-5	14, 18	49-54	11, 13	3	✓
L: Graph complex numbers.	13-6, 13-7	8, 9	55-58	12	4	

Multidimensional Assessment
Quiz for Lessons 13-1 through 13-3   Chapter 13 Test, Forms A–D   Comprehensive Test, Chapters 1–13
Quiz for Lessons 13-4 through 13-6   Chapter 13 Test, Cumulative Form

Quiz and Test Writer

Teaching Aids

Warm-up
Lesson 13-1

In right triangle ABC, angle C is the right angle, $AC = 7$, and $AB = 13$. Give exact values and estimate to the nearest thousandth for each.

1. $\sin A$ 2. $\cos A$ 3. $\tan A$
4. $\frac{1}{\sin A}$ 5. $\frac{1}{\cos A}$ 6. $\frac{1}{\tan A}$
7. Explain why the answer to Warm-up Question 6 is the answer to Question 4 divided by the answer to Question 5.

Warm-up
Lesson 13-2

Three functions are described here. Graph each function over the interval $\{x: -1 < x < 1\}$ (for the trigonometric function with x in radians). Describe what happens.

$f(x) = \frac{x^2 - x}{1 - x}$

$g(x) = -\sin x$

$h(x) = -x$

Warm-up
Lesson 13-3

Explain the difference between the graphs of $y = (x - 1)^2$ and $y = \frac{(x - 1)^7}{(x - 1)^5}$.

Warm-up
Lesson 13-4

Give the image of the point $(1, 0)$ under each of the following transformations.

1. $R_{\frac{3\pi}{4}}$ 2. $R_{\frac{3\pi}{4}} \circ S_2$ 3. $S_2 \circ R_{\frac{3\pi}{4}}$

Warm-up
Lesson 13-5

Examine your calculator to determine if and how it can plot points in polar coordinates. Be ready to explain how to others.

Warm-up
Lesson 13-6

Suppose * is an operation on ordered pairs, with $(a, b) * (c, d) = (a + c, b + d)$.

1. Calculate $(2, 5) * (7, -1)$.
2. Graph $(0, 0)$, $(2, 5)$, $(7, -1)$, and your answer to Question 1.
3. Generalize the result of Question 2.

Warm-up
Lesson 13-7

Consider the point $(2, 3)$.
1. Find polar coordinates for this point.
2. What complex number does this point represent?
3. Square the complex number in part b, and graph it.
4. Write polar coordinates for the complex number in part c.

Warm-up
Lesson 13-8

1. Find the three solutions to $x^3 - 1 = 0$.
2. Square each of the non-real solutions and describe the result.

Warm-up
Lesson 13-9

Consider the sequence defined by $z_1 = \frac{i}{\sqrt{2}}$ and $z_n = (z_{n-1})^2 + \frac{i}{2}$.

1. Calculate the next five terms of this sequence.
2. Do you think that the limit of this sequence is infinity?

Lesson 13-1

Definitions and Right Triangle Theorem for Reciprocal Functions

Definitions

Let θ be any real number, then

secant of θ = **sec** $\theta = \frac{1}{\cos \theta}$, for $\cos \theta \neq 0$;

cosecant of θ = **csc** $\theta = \frac{1}{\sin \theta}$, for $\sin \theta \neq 0$;

cotangent of θ = **cot** $\theta = \frac{\cos \theta}{\sin \theta}$, for $\sin \theta \neq 0$.

Theorem

Given a right triangle with angle θ, then

$\sec \theta = \frac{\text{hypotenuse}}{\text{side adjacent to } \theta}$;

$\csc \theta = \frac{\text{hypotenuse}}{\text{side opposite } \theta}$;

$\cot \theta = \frac{\text{side adjacent to } \theta}{\text{side opposite } \theta}$.

Lesson 13-1

Cosine and Secant Function

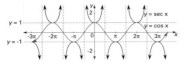

Tangent and Cotangent Function

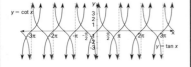

Lesson 13-2

Proofs in Examples 1-3

Example 1
Expand the expression.
$(\cos x - \sin x)^2 = \cos^2 x - 2\cos x \sin x + \sin^2 x$
$= \cos^2 x + \sin^2 x - 2\cos x \sin x$
Recall two identities: for all x,
$\cos^2 x + \sin^2 x = 1$ and
$2\cos x \sin x = \sin 2x$.
So, $(\cos x - \sin x)^2 = 1 - \sin 2x$.

Example 2
Substitute into the left expression and rewrite until you get the right. For all x with $\cos x \neq 0$.

$1 + \tan^2 x = 1 + \frac{\sin^2 x}{\cos^2 x}$ Definition of tangent

$= \frac{\cos^2 x}{\cos^2 x} + \frac{\sin^2 x}{\cos^2 x}$ Forming a common denominator

$= \frac{\cos^2 x + \sin^2 x}{\cos^2 x}$ Adding fractions with a common denominator

$= \frac{1}{\cos^2 x}$ Pythagorean Identity

$= \sec^2 x$.

So, $1 + \tan^2 x = \sec^2 x$ for all x in the domain of $\tan x$ and $\sec x$.

Example 3
Use the Addition Identities for the sine and cosine.

$\sin\left(x + \frac{\pi}{4}\right)$ | $\cos\left(x - \frac{\pi}{4}\right)$

$= \sin x \cos \frac{\pi}{4} + \cos x \sin \frac{\pi}{4}$ | $= \cos x \cos \frac{\pi}{4} + \sin x \sin \frac{\pi}{4}$

$= \sin x \cdot \frac{\sqrt{2}}{2} + \cos x \cdot \frac{\sqrt{2}}{2}$ | $= \cos x \cdot \frac{\sqrt{2}}{2} + \sin x \cdot \frac{\sqrt{2}}{2}$

So $\sin\left(x + \frac{\pi}{4}\right) = \cos\left(x - \frac{\pi}{4}\right)$

Lesson 13-4

Polar Coordinate Grid

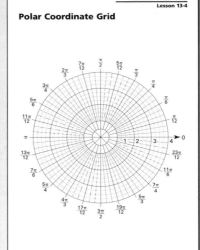

Lesson 13-4

Polar Coordinate Grids

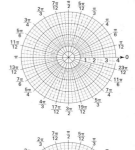

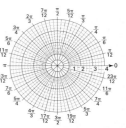

Table and Graph for Example 1

θ	0	$\frac{\pi}{6}$	$\frac{\pi}{4}$	$\frac{\pi}{3}$	$\frac{\pi}{2}$	$\frac{2\pi}{3}$	$\frac{3\pi}{4}$	$\frac{5\pi}{6}$	π
r	1	0.866	0.707	0.500	0	-0.500	-0.707	-0.866	-1

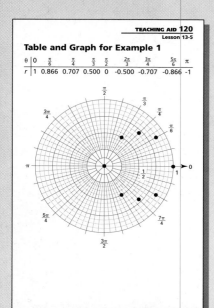

Rose Curves

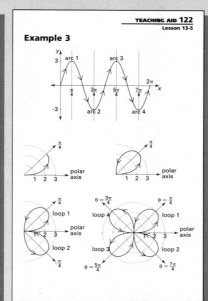

$r = \cos 2\theta$

$0 \le \theta \le 360,\quad \theta\ \text{step} = 7.5$
$-2.25 \le x \le 2.25,\quad x\text{-scale} = 1$
$-1.5 \le y \le 1.5,\quad y\text{-scale} = 1$

$r = \cos 3\theta$

$0 \le \theta \le 180,\quad \theta\ \text{step} = 7.5$
$-2.25 \le x \le 2.25,\quad x\text{-scale} = 1$
$-1.5 \le y \le 1.5,\quad y\text{-scale} = 1$

$r = \cos 4\theta$

$0 \le \theta \le 360,\quad \theta\ \text{step} = 7.5$
$-2.25 \le x \le 2.25,\quad x\text{-scale} = 1$
$-1.5 \le y \le 1.5,\quad y\text{-scale} = 1$

Example 3

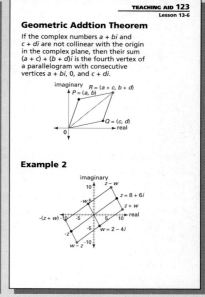

Geometric Addtion Theorem

If the complex numbers $a + bi$ and $c + di$ are not collinear with the origin in the complex plane, then their sum $(a + c) + (b + d)i$ is the fourth vertex of a parallelogram with consecutive vertices $a + bi$, 0, and $c + di$.

Example 2

Product of Complex Numbers Theorem

Proof

The proof applies, perhaps surprisingly, the sum formulas for the cosine and sine.

$z_1 z_2 = (r_1(\cos\theta_1 + i\sin\theta_1))(r_2(\cos\theta_2 + i\sin\theta_2))$
$= r_1 r_2(\cos\theta_1 + i\sin\theta_1)(\cos\theta_2 + i\sin\theta_2)$
$= r_1 r_2(\cos\theta_1\cos\theta_2 + i\cos\theta_1\sin\theta_2 + i\sin\theta_1\cos\theta_2 + i^2\sin\theta_1\sin\theta_2)$
$= r_1 r_2(\cos\theta_1\cos\theta_2 + i^2\sin\theta_1\sin\theta_2) + i(\cos\theta_1\sin\theta_2 + \sin\theta_1\cos\theta_2)$
$= r_1 r_2(\cos\theta_1\cos\theta_2 - \sin\theta_1\sin\theta_2) + (\sin\theta_1\cos\theta_2 + \cos\theta_1\sin\theta_2)$
$= r_1 r_2(\cos(\theta_1 + \theta_2)\ i\sin(\theta_1 + \theta_2))$

This is the trigonometric form for a complex number with absolute value $r_1 r_2$ and argument $\theta_1 + \theta_2$.

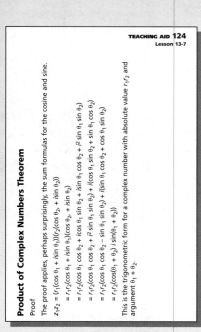

Graph for Example 1

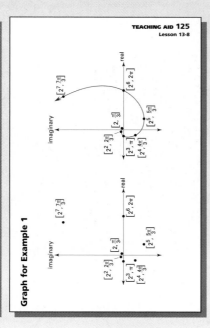

Chapter Opener 13

Pacing

All lessons in this chapter are designed to be covered in one day. At the end of the chapter, you should plan to spend 1 day to review the Progress Self-Test, 1–2 days for the Chapter Review, and 1 day for a test. You may wish to spend a day on projects, and possibly a day is needed for quizzes and the In-class Activity. This chapter should therefore take 12–15 days. Spending more than 16 days on this chapter is not recommended.

Using Pages 804–805

The three graphs on this page are examples of rose curves. Students will study them in Lesson 13-5. They strike many people as quite beautiful. There is other beautiful mathematics in this chapter, ranging from the relationships among the trigonometric functions to the graphs of the nth powers and nth roots of a complex number.

You might ask students: If you had to pick a piece of mathematics that you have studied as being beautiful, what would you pick? Note that beauty does not have to be geometric beauty; it could be the beauty of a logical argument or the beauty in the way ideas fit together.

Chapter 13 Overview

This chapter is necessary to provide a complete course in trigonometry. It covers the reciprocals of the sine, cosine, and tangent functions, the proofs of trigonometric identities, the use of trigonometry in polar coordinates and polar graphs, and the relationships between trigonometry and complex numbers, culminating in DeMoivre's Theorem and its applications. All of these topics are covered in detail in UCSMP *Precalculus and Discrete Mathematics*, so

if students will be taking that course next, this chapter can be omitted.

Introduction of the secant, cosecant, and cotangent functions begins this chapter. Relations among them and the other trigonometric functions are found in Lessons 13-2 and 13-3 as students examine trigonometric and other identities. An automatic grapher is employed to determine if an equation appears to be an identity. If it

appears to be an identity, then an algebraic proof is worth pursuing; if not, then students are instructed to find a counterexample.

The topic of Lesson 13-4 and 13-5 is the polar coordinate system. In the former, students apply their knowledge of trigonometry to plot points in the polar plane and convert between the rectangular and polar systems. In the latter, students graph simple polar equations and verify their shapes by

FURTHER WORK WITH TRIGONOMETRY

This chapter covers three topics in trigonometry. First, three more trigonometric functions are introduced—the *secant*, *cosecant*, and *cotangent*—and identities involving them and the original three trigonometric functions are proved.

The second topic is an introduction to a coordinate system different from rectangular coordinates, the *polar coordinate system*. When plotted with polar coordinates, the graphs of trigonometric functions often are quite beautiful. Patterns like those below are examples.

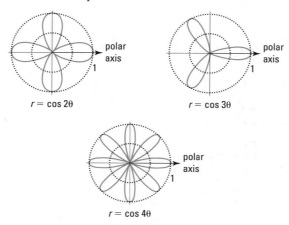

$r = \cos 2\theta$

$r = \cos 3\theta$

$r = \cos 4\theta$

Lastly, complex numbers are graphed in both the rectangular and polar coordinate systems. Operations with complex numbers can be expressed simply and elegantly in these systems, and the trigonometric functions play a major role.

805

rewriting the equations in rectangular form. A function grapher with a polar graphing option is a very useful tool in these lessons.

Lessons 13-6 through 13-8 present properties and graphs of complex numbers, and develop theorems to aid in calculations with complex numbers. In Lesson 13-6, complex numbers and the sum of two complex numbers are graphed. In Lesson 13-7, complex numbers are rewritten in polar form and in

trigonometric form, and the product of two complex numbers can be expressed in either form. In Lesson 13-8, students generalize the product of two complex numbers to obtain DeMoivre's Theorem for calculating powers of a complex number. This theorem is then used to generalize a theorem for calculating roots of complex numbers.

Lesson 13-9 presents a beautiful and recent (since 1980) application of complex numbers

and computers, in describing what is now known as the Mandelbrot Set. The lesson combines algebra, geometry, and sequences in a fitting way to end this book.

Objectives

A Evaluate the reciprocal trigono-metric functions.
E Apply properties of the reciprocal trigonometric functions.

Resources

From the Teacher's Resource File
■ Lesson Master 13-1
■ Answer Master 13-1
■ Teaching Aids
  112 Warm-up
  115 Definitions and Right Triangle Theorem for Reciprocal Functions
  116 Cosine and Secant Functions/Tangent and Cotangent Functions

Additional Resources
■ Visuals for Teaching Aids 112, 115, 116

Teaching Lesson 13-1

Warm-up

In right triangle *ABC*, angle *C* is the right angle, *AC* = 7, and *AB* = 13. Give exact values and estimate to the nearest thousandth for each.

1. $\sin A$ $\frac{2\sqrt{30}}{13} \approx .843$

2. $\cos A$ $\frac{7}{13} \approx .538$

3. $\tan A$ $\frac{2\sqrt{30}}{7} \approx 1.565$

4. $\frac{1}{\sin A}$ $\frac{13}{2\sqrt{30}} \approx 1.187$

5. $\frac{1}{\cos A}$ $\frac{13}{7} \approx 1.857$

6. $\frac{1}{\tan A}$ $\frac{7}{2\sqrt{30}} \approx .639$

LESSON

13-1

The Secant, Cosecant, and Cotangent Functions

Three More Trigonometric Functions

The definition of $\tan \theta$ is in terms of $\sin \theta$ and $\cos \theta$, namely $\tan \theta = \frac{\sin \theta}{\cos \theta}$. Three other common circular functions, *secant*, *cosecant*, and *cotangent*, can also be defined in terms of the sine and cosine. As with the definition of tangent, division by zero must be avoided.

Definitions
Let θ be any real number. Then

secant of θ = $\sec \theta = \frac{1}{\cos \theta}$, for $\cos \theta \neq 0$;

cosecant of θ = $\csc \theta = \frac{1}{\sin \theta}$, for $\sin \theta \neq 0$;

cotangent of θ = $\cot \theta = \frac{\cos \theta}{\sin \theta}$, for $\sin \theta \neq 0$.

Notice that $\frac{\cos \theta}{\sin \theta} = \frac{1}{\frac{\sin \theta}{\cos \theta}}$, except when $\sin \theta = 0$ or $\cos \theta = 0$. So $\cot \theta = \frac{1}{\tan \theta}$ except when $\cos \theta = 0$ or $\tan \theta = 0$. Because each of the secant, cosecant, and cotangent functions can be expressed as the reciprocal of a parent trigonometric function, these functions are sometimes called **reciprocal trigonometric functions**.

Example 1

a. Find $\sec \frac{7\pi}{6}$ exactly.
b. Find $\sec \frac{7\pi}{6}$ approximately, using a calculator.

Solution

a. By definition of secant,
$$\sec \frac{7\pi}{6} = \frac{1}{\cos \frac{7\pi}{6}} = \frac{1}{-\frac{\sqrt{3}}{2}} = \frac{-2}{\sqrt{3}} = \frac{-2\sqrt{3}}{3}.$$

b. There is no $\boxed{\text{sec}}$ key on most calculators. So you need to use the reciprocal key, $\boxed{1/x}$. On some calculators you may use the key sequence (in radian mode) $7 \boxed{\times} \boxed{\pi} \boxed{\div} 6 \boxed{=} \boxed{\cos} \boxed{1/x}$. On others, use $\boxed{\cos} 7 \boxed{\times} \boxed{\pi} \boxed{\div} 6 \boxed{\text{ENTER}} \boxed{x^{\text{-}1}} \boxed{\text{ENTER}}$. Either sequence leads to the display $\approx$ -1.1547005 ... .

Check
$\frac{-2\sqrt{3}}{3} \approx$ -1.1547005..., so it checks.

Lesson 13-1 Overview

Broad Goals This lesson introduces students to the reciprocal circular functions: secant (reciprocal of cosine), cosecant (reciprocal of sine), and cotangent (recipro-cal of tangent).

Perspective The reciprocal functions are presented in the same manner as the func-tions sine, cosine, and tangent were pre-sented in Chapter 5. They are used in right-triangle situations, and then analyzed

as functions. Students are expected to be able to give domain, range, maximum and minimum points, and graphs of the parent reciprocal functions.

Using the Reciprocal Functions in Right Triangles

For values of θ between 0 and $\frac{\pi}{2}$, values of the reciprocal trigonometric functions can be expressed in terms of the sides of a right triangle.

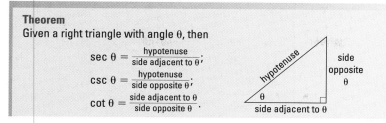

Theorem

Given a right triangle with angle θ, then

$$\sec \theta = \frac{\text{hypotenuse}}{\text{side adjacent to } \theta};$$

$$\csc \theta = \frac{\text{hypotenuse}}{\text{side opposite } \theta};$$

$$\cot \theta = \frac{\text{side adjacent to } \theta}{\text{side opposite } \theta}.$$

The proof of this theorem follows from the definitions of the trigonometric ratios given in Lesson 5-1 and the property that $\frac{1}{\frac{a}{b}} = \frac{b}{a}$.

Example 2

A safe angle for a fire ladder is 65° to the ground. To the nearest foot, how long must the ladder be to reach 19 feet up the side of a building?

Solution

In the diagram, the side opposite the 65° angle is known and the hypotenuse is unknown. Use the cosecant ratio.

$$\csc 65° = \frac{d}{19}$$

$$d = 19 \csc 65°$$

Set a calculator to degree mode. On some calculators you may use the key sequence 19 $\times$ (65 sin 1/x) $=$, which displays 20.9642. The *ladder needs to be about 21 feet long.*

Check

Check using the sine ratio. Is $\frac{19}{21} \approx \sin 65°$? Yes, because $\frac{19}{21} \approx .905$ and $\sin 65° \approx .906$.

Graphs of the Reciprocal Functions

Because the expressions $\sec \theta$ and $\cos \theta$ are reciprocals, you can use the properties of the cosine function to determine characteristics of the secant function. These characteristics enable you to graph the function $y = \sec x$.

Function Properties	Graph Properties
When $\cos x$ is positive, $\sec x$ is positive. When $\cos x$ is negative, $\sec x$ is negative.	For a given value of x, the graphs of $y = \cos x$ and $y = \sec x$ are on the same side of the x-axis.
When $\cos x = 0$, $\sec x$ is undefined.	If $\cos k = 0$, then there is a vertical asymptote of $y = \sec x$ at $x = k$.
Because $|\cos x| \le 1$ for all x, $|\sec x| \ge 1$ for all x. The smaller $|\cos x|$ is, the larger $|\sec x|$ is.	The closer the graph of $y = \cos x$ is to the x-axis, the farther the graph of $y = \sec x$ is.
$\sec x = \cos x$ when $\cos x = \pm 1$.	The graphs intersect when $\cos x = \pm 1$.

---

7. Explain why the answer to Warm-up Question 6 is the answer to Question 4 divided by the answer to Question 5.

$$\frac{\frac{1}{\sin A}}{\frac{1}{\cos A}} = \frac{\cos A}{\sin A} = \frac{1}{\frac{\sin A}{\cos A}} = \frac{1}{\tan A}$$

Note: In Question 7 students are being asked to prove a trigonometric identity not unlike those they will see in Lessons 13-2 and 13-3.

Notes on Reading

Historically, the secant and cosecant functions were employed for much the same reason as rationalizing the denominator of a radical expression—to avoid division by a decimal. For instance, the hypotenuse in **Example 2** is equal to $\frac{19}{\sin 65°}$, but division by $\sin 65°$ is more difficult than multiplication by $\csc 65°$. Today, however, the secant and cosecant functions are seldom used for finding lengths or angle measures. They still appear in some formulas in calculus (for example, if $y = \tan x$, then $\frac{dy}{dx} = \sec^2 x$) but they have lost much of their importance. For this reason, we restrict the study of these functions to the parents and do not devote much attention to their offspring (**Questions 19, 20, and 31**). **Teaching Aid 115** is provided giving the definitions and right triangle theorem for reciprocal functions.

The cotangent function appears a little more often in formulas because it is the cofunction of the tangent. That is, $\tan x = \cot \left(\frac{\pi}{2} - x\right)$.

Optional Activities

After discussing the lesson, you might play a version of "20 Questions" with students, but limit their questions to five. Tell them you are thinking of the graph of one of the six trigonometric functions they now know (one of the three parent functions or one of the three reciprocal functions.) They are allowed to ask five yes-or-no questions to determine which function's graph you have in mind. They may not ask directly whether the function is sine, cosine, tangent, etc. Encourage them to ask

questions such as: Is the domain of the function all real numbers? (An answer of *yes* would limit the choices to sine or cosine.) Are there asymptotes at $x = 0 + n\pi$? (An answer of *yes* would limit the choices to cosecant or cotangent.) Are there function values between -1 and 1? (An answer of *no* would limit the choices to secant or cosecant.) Note how few questions about the features of the graph are required to determine the specific trigonometric function.

Adapting to Individual Needs

Extra Help

Some students might gain a better understanding of the cosecant function if you help them develop a table for the sine and cosecant functions like the table given for the cosine and secant functions on page 807. You might want to have students work on this before they attempt **Question 18**.

A function grapher is an important tool for studying these functions because graphing the curves by hand is too time-consuming. However, students should be able to draw quick sketches of these functions to indicate that they understand their basic characteristics as listed in the chart on page 807. **Teaching Aid 116,** with the graphs of the cosine, secant, tangent, and cotangent functions is provided.

Example 3 considers the secant function in some detail. **Question 18** asks for similar properties of the cosecant.

Most of the graphers we have used require entering the functions as reciprocals of sine, cosine, and tangent. Some, however, give the reciprocals as options in a menu of functions.

Error Alert Caution students not to mistake the inverse functions of sine, cosine, and tangent on their calculators for the reciprocal functions. It is natural for a student to get confused and think $\sin^{-1}$ means csc.

Additional Examples

1. Find each value.
   a. $\csc \frac{\pi}{6}$ **2**
   b. $\sec \frac{\pi}{6}$ $\frac{2}{\sqrt{3}} = \frac{2\sqrt{3}}{3}$
   c. $\cot \frac{\pi}{6}$ $\sqrt{3}$
2. A regular polygon is inscribed in a circle of radius R and circumscribed about a circle of radius r. If an angle of the polygon has measure θ, what is the ratio of R to r in terms of θ? $\frac{R}{r} = \csc \frac{\theta}{2}$

These properties are exhibited in the graphs below. The graph of $y = \cos x$ is in blue; the graph of $y = \sec x$ is in orange.

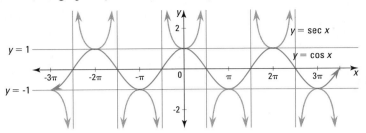

Example 3

Consider the function with equation $y = \sec x$.
a. Identify its domain and range.
b. Find its period.
c. Identify any minimum or maximum values.

Solution

a. **The domain consists of all real numbers except $x = \frac{\pi}{2} + n\pi$, for any integer n.** From both the definition and the graph above, you can see that **the range is $\{y: y \leq -1 \text{ or } y \geq 1\}$.**
b. **The period of $y = \cos x$ is 2π. The graph of $y = \sec x$ also has period 2π.**
c. **There are no maximum or minimum values of sec x. However, 1 is a relative minimum and -1 is a relative maximum of the secant function.**

In the Questions, you are asked to analyze the graph of $y = \csc x$ in relation to the graph of $y = \sin x$.

The graph of $y = \cot x$ is shown below in orange. It is a reflection image, over any vertical line with equation $x = \frac{\pi}{4} + n\pi$ where n is an integer, of the graph of $y = \tan x$, which is drawn in blue.

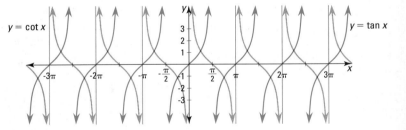

Adapting to Individual Needs

English Language Development

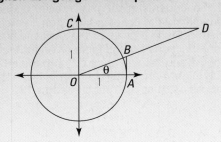

This diagram may help students understand the origin of the terms *cotangent, secant,* and *cosecant.* Consider angle θ in the unit circle. The length of $\overline{AB}$, a tangent to the circle, is $\tan \theta$. The length of $\overline{CD}$, another tangent to the circle, is the tangent of the complement of θ, from which we get the term cotangent. It is the cotangent of θ. In the language of geometry, line $\overleftrightarrow{DB}$ is a secant to the circle, and it is from this that

the trigonometric functions secant and cosecant get their names. Notice that OB is the reciprocal of $\cos \theta$; that is, $OB = \sec \theta$. OD is the reciprocal of the cosine of the complement; it is the secant of the complement of θ, hence it is the cosecant of θ.

QUESTIONS

Covering the Reading

8a) $\cot 73° = \dfrac{x}{8}$
$x = 8 \cdot \cot 73°$
$x = 8 \cdot \dfrac{1}{\tan 73°}$
$x \approx 2.4$ in.
b) $\tan 73° = \dfrac{8}{x}$
$x = \dfrac{8}{\tan 73°}$
$x \approx 2.4$ in.

9a) $\sec 48° = \dfrac{x}{10}$
$x = 10 \cdot \sec 48°$
$x = 10 \cdot \dfrac{1}{\cos 48°}$
$x \approx 14.9$ cm
b) $\cos 48° = \dfrac{10}{x}$
$x = \dfrac{10}{\cos 48°}$
$x \approx 14.9$ cm

1. Find the exact value of each.
  a. $\csc 45°$ $\sqrt{2}$ **b.** $\sec 45°$ $\sqrt{2}$ **c.** $\cot 45°$ **1**

In 2–7, evaluate without using a calculator.

2. $\csc 90°$ **1**   **3.** $\sec 150°$ $-\dfrac{2\sqrt{3}}{3}$ **4.** $\cot(-135°)$ **1**

5. $\sec\left(-\dfrac{11\pi}{6}\right)$ $\dfrac{2\sqrt{3}}{3}$ **6.** $\cot\dfrac{17\pi}{3}$ $-\dfrac{\sqrt{3}}{3}$ **7.** $\csc\left(-\dfrac{5\pi}{2}\right)$ **-1**

In 8 and 9, find x to the nearest tenth in two ways. **a.** Use a reciprocal trigonometric function. **b.** Use a parent trigonometric function. **See left.**

8.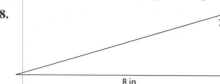

9.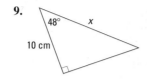

10. *Multiple choice.* The base of a ladder is placed so that it makes an angle of 56° with the ground. If it reaches 40 ft up the side of a building, how long must the ladder be? **d**
  (a) $40 \sin 56°$ (b) $40 \cos 56°$ (c) $40 \sec 56°$ (d) $40 \csc 56°$

In 11 and 12, consider the function defined by the given equation on the interval $0 \le x < 2\pi$. **a.** Identify all values at which the function is undefined. **b.** Identify all x-intercepts.

11. $y = \sec x$
  a) $\dfrac{\pi}{2}$ and $\dfrac{3\pi}{2}$ b) none

12. $y = \cot x$
  a) 0 and π b) $\dfrac{\pi}{2}$ and $\dfrac{3\pi}{2}$

Applying the Mathematics

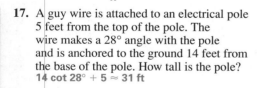

In 13–16, consider the triangle at the left. Evaluate the function in terms of x, y, and z.

13. $\csc \theta$ $\dfrac{z}{x}$ **14.** $\cot \theta$ $\dfrac{y}{x}$

15. $\sec(90° - \theta)$ $\dfrac{z}{x}$ **16.** $\cot(90° - \theta)$ $\dfrac{x}{y}$

17. A guy wire is attached to an electrical pole 5 feet from the top of the pole. The wire makes a 28° angle with the pole and is anchored to the ground 14 feet from the base of the pole. How tall is the pole?
14 cot 28° + 5 ≈ 31 ft

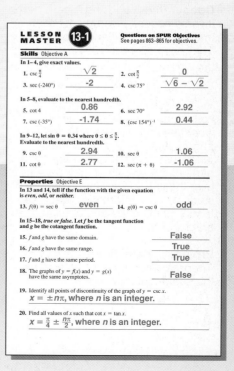

Lesson 13-1 *The Secant, Cosecant, and Cotangent Functions* **809**

---

3. Consider the function $y = \cot x$.
  a. What is its period, and why?
    π; It has the same period as the tangent function.
  b. Identify any relative maximum or relative minimum values.
    There are no relative maximum or relative minimum values on its entire domain.

Notes on Questions

Questions 8–9 These questions may be solved using either a reciprocal function or one of the parent functions. Students can use one as a check of the other.

Question 17 Science Connection Many electrical and communication cables installed now are buried. This offers protection from weather damage, and helps keep the landscape uncluttered.

Adapting to Individual Needs

Challenge
You may wish to have students **work in groups** to answer the following questions.
1. Explain how you can use a calculator to find the following, then find the value.
  a. $\csc^{-1} 1.5$ $[\sin^{-1}\left(\dfrac{1}{1.5}\right) \approx .730]$
  b. $\cot^{-1} 7$ $[\tan^{-1}\left(\dfrac{1}{7}\right) \approx .142]$
  c. $\sec^{-1} 2.1$ $[\cos^{-1}\left(\dfrac{1}{2.1}\right) \approx 1.074]$

2. Find the exact value of each of the following, without using a calculator. [Hint: Use a right triangle.]
  a. $\sin\left(\sec^{-1}\dfrac{10}{9}\right)$ $\left[\dfrac{\sqrt{19}}{10}\right]$
  b. $\cos\left(\sec^{-1}\dfrac{9}{4}\right)$ $\left[\dfrac{4}{9}\right]$
3. Use the identity for $\sin(\alpha + \beta)$ to find the exact value of:
  $\sin\left(\sec^{-1}\left(\dfrac{6}{5}\right) + \sec^{-1}\left(\dfrac{7}{4}\right)\right)$ $\left[\dfrac{4\sqrt{11} + 5\sqrt{33}}{42}\right]$

Notes on Questions

Questions 19–21 Perhaps the most important generalization students can make from this lesson is that some properties of a function transfer to its reciprocal function. Among these properties are its period and its evenness or oddness.

Questions 22–23 These numerical questions are designed to prepare students for some of the identities they will encounter in the next two lessons.

Follow-up for Lesson 13-1

Practice

For more questions on SPUR Objectives, use **Lesson Master 13-1** (shown on page 809).

Assessment

Written Communication Have students **work in pairs**. Give students three problems like **Example 1**, one involving secant, one involving cosecant, and one involving cotangent. Ask one partner to solve **part a** of the problem and the other to solve **part b**. Then have students switch roles and give them three more problems. [Students evaluate secant, cosecant, and cotangent functions.]

Extension

Cooperative Learning There are inverse secant, inverse cosecant, and inverse cotangent functions. They are defined on $0 < x < \pi$ for the cotangent; $0 \le x < \frac{\pi}{2}$ and $\pi \le x < \frac{3\pi}{2}$ for the secant; and $-\pi < x \le -\frac{\pi}{2}$ and $0 < x \le \frac{\pi}{2}$ for the cosecant. (See the Challenge in *Adapting to Individual Needs* on page 809.) The graphs of these functions are reflection images of parts of the graphs of their parents over the line $y = x$. Small groups of students can determine what these functions might be and provide graphs of them.

Project Update Project 1, *Euler's Theorem*, on page 858, relates to the content of this lesson.

18a)

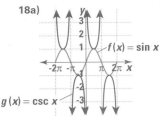

$g(x) = \csc x$

c) domain = the set of all real numbers except $x = n\pi$ for all integers n; range = $\{y: |y| \ge 1\}$

19a)

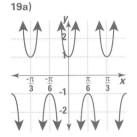

20a)

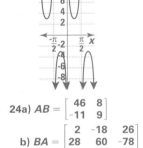

24a) $AB = \begin{bmatrix} 46 & 8 \\ -11 & 9 \end{bmatrix}$

b) $BA = \begin{bmatrix} 2 & -18 & 26 \\ 28 & 60 & -78 \\ 6 & 6 & -7 \end{bmatrix}$

---

18. Let $f(x) = \sin x$ and $g(x) = \csc x$.
   a. Graph both functions on the same set of axes on the interval $-2\pi \le x \le 2\pi$. **See left.**
   b. *True or false.* For a given value of x, the graphs of $y = f(x)$ and $y = g(x)$ are on the same side of the x-axis. **True**
   c. Give the domain and range of g. **See left.**
   d. State equations of all asymptotes of $y = g(x)$.
   e. For what values of x between 0 and 2π does $f(x) = g(x)$?
   d) $x = n\pi$ for all integers n e) $\pi/2$ and $(3\pi)/2$

In 19 and 20, an equation for a function is given. **a.** Sketch the graph of the function. **b.** Give the period of the function. **a) See left.**

19. $y = \sec 6x$ **b)** $\frac{\pi}{3}$

20. $y = 3 \csc 2x$ **b)** π

21. Prove that $y = \cot x$ is an odd function.
$$\cot(-x) = \frac{\cos(-x)}{\sin(-x)} = \frac{\cos x}{-\sin x} = -\cot x$$

Review

In 22 and 23, let $\cos \alpha = 0.8$ and $\sin \beta = -0.6$, where $0 < \alpha < \frac{\pi}{2}$ and $\pi < \beta < \frac{3\pi}{2}$. Evaluate. *(Lessons 4-4, 11-5, 11-6)*

22. $\cos 2\alpha$ **0.28**

23. $\sin(\alpha + \beta)$ **-0.96**

24. Let $A = \begin{bmatrix} 2 & 6 & -8 \\ 4 & 0 & 1 \end{bmatrix}$ and $B = \begin{bmatrix} -3 & 2 \\ 10 & 2 \\ 1 & 1 \end{bmatrix}$. Find the product, if it exists. *(Lesson 11-1)* **See left.**
   a. AB
   b. BA

25. What is the 99% confidence interval for a normally distributed set of data with a mean of 23.9 and a standard deviation of 2.3? *(Lesson 10-8)* **18 to 29.8**

26. Tell whether the infinite series $\sum_{k=0}^{\infty} (-.25)^k 6$ is convergent or divergent. If it is convergent, give its sum. *(Lesson 8-5)* **convergent with sum 4.8**

27. Consider the equation $2 \sin^2 \theta - \sin \theta - 3 = 0$.
   a. Find the solution(s) between 0 and 2π. $\theta = (3\pi)/2$
   b. Find the general solution. *(Lesson 5-7)* $\theta = (3\pi)/2 + 2\pi n$ for all integers n

In 28 and 29, evaluate in degrees. *(Lessons 5-3, 5-6)*

28. $\tan^{-1} 1$ **45°**

29. $\cos^{-1}(-0.5)$ **120°**

30. a. *True or false.* The graphs of $f(x) = 6^x$ and $p(x) = x^6$ are reflection images of each other over the y-axis. **False**
   b. Use an automatic grapher to justify your answer to part **a**. *(Lesson 2-4)* **See margin.**

Exploration

31. Analyze the graph of $\frac{y - k}{b} = \sec\left(\frac{x - h}{a}\right)$. **See margin.**

Additional Answers

30. b. $p(x) = x^6$ $f(x) = 6^x$

$-2 \le x \le 2$, x-scale = 1
$-1 \le y \le 10$, y-scale = 2

31. $\left(\frac{y - k}{b}\right) = \sec\left(\frac{x - h}{a}\right)$ is a rubberband transformation image of the graph of $y = \sec x$. It has asymptotes at $x = a\left(\frac{\pi}{2} + n\pi\right) + h$ and relative extrema at $(2\pi na + h, b + k)$ and $((\pi + 2\pi n)a + h, -b + k)$.

In this lesson you will see various ways to derive and prove trigonometric identities. Although the proof techniques are illustrated using only trigonometric functions, they are applicable to any function.

Testing Whether an Equation Might Be an Identity

You have seen many instances where graphs are used to decide whether or not a particular statement is true. In particular, if you want to see whether an equation in one variable is an identity, you can consider each side of the equation as a separate function of x, and graph the two functions. If the graphs coincide, the original equation is likely to be an identity.

As an example, consider the Pythagorean Identity,

$$\cos^2 x + \sin^2 x = 1.$$

If each side of this equation is considered as a separate function of x, specifically if $f(x) = \cos^2 x + \sin^2 x$ and $g(x) = 1$, the following graphs result.

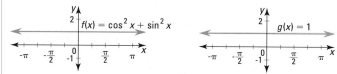

As expected, the graphs are identical. Had they been plotted on the same set of axes, the graphs would have coincided.

In contrast, the equation $(\cos x - \sin x)^2 = \cos^2 x - \sin^2 x$ is not an identity. The graphs of $f(x) = (\cos x - \sin x)^2$ and $g(x) = \cos^2 x - \sin^2 x$ are shown below. It is apparent that f and g are not the same function.

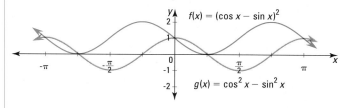

Notice that the graph of g appears to be a cosine function with amplitude 1 and period π. This suggests that an expression identically equal to $\cos^2 x - \sin^2 x$ is $\cos 2x$. This agrees with what was proved in Lesson 11-6: $\cos 2x = \cos^2 x - \sin^2 x$ for all x.

Deducing New Identities by Manipulating Expressions

Using identities you already know, you can derive new identities.

Lesson 13-2

Objectives

F Prove trigonometric identities.
H Use an automatic grapher to test a proposed identity.

Resources

From the *Teacher's Resource File*
■ Lesson Master 13-2
■ Answer Master 13-2
■ Teaching Aids
   112 Warm-up
   117 Proofs in Examples 1-3
■ Technology Sourcebook
   Calculator Master 10

Additional Resources
■ Visuals for Teaching Aids 112, 117

Teaching 13-2
Lesson

Warm-up

Three functions are described here. Graph each function over the interval $\{x: -1 < x < 1\}$ (for the trigonometric function with x in radians). Describe what happens.

$f(x) = \frac{x^2 - x}{1 - x}$ $g(x) = -\sin x$
$h(x) = -x$

Sample: *f* and *g* are very close to each other when *x* is close to zero. *f* and *h* are identical except when *x* = 1, in which case *f* is undefined.

Lesson 13-2 Overview

Broad Goals One objective in this lesson is to determine whether an equation of the form $f(x) = g(x)$, where f and g may involve trigonometric functions, is true for all x in the domains of f and g. A second objective of the lesson is for students to realize that a graph *does not prove or disprove* the identity.

Perspective There is no special logic to finding or proving trigonometric identities. One can begin by examining the graphs of

$y = f(x)$ and $y = g(x)$ over a reasonably wide domain. If the graphs are identical, then one can proceed to attempt to prove that the equation $f(x) = g(x)$ is an identity. To prove that $f(x) = g(x)$, three techniques are offered. The first technique is to rewrite the expression $f(x)$, perhaps by using definitions of the trigonometric functions, or by the distributive property, until it is the same as $g(x)$. The second technique is to rewrite both $f(x)$ and $g(x)$ until they are each equal

to the same third expression. The third technique is to begin with a known identity (the example uses the Pythagorean Identity $\cos^2 x + \sin^2 x = 1$) and from it deduce a new identity. All of these techniques are commonly employed by those who work with trigonometry, and all are found throughout the chapter.

Notes on Reading

Graphing $y = f(x)$ and $y = g(x)$ to analyze $f(x) = g(x)$ is exceedingly useful; it points out the reasonableness of constructing a proof in the former case, and indicates counterexamples and solutions to the equations in the latter. The *Warm-up* can be used as evidence that careful analysis of functions is helpful, because none of the functions are identical even though over the domain $\{x: -0.3 \leq x \leq 0.3\}$ the graphs may look the same.

The graphs at the beginning of this lesson are identical; they are given twice because of the limitations of having to write on paper. Students using an automatic grapher should graph one function on top of the other, and see dynamically that the second function does not appear to get graphed at all. If any new points are added, yet the identity really is true, then the computer has displayed round-off error.

The proofs in **Examples 2–4** illustrate three distinct approaches to proving identities. In **Example 2**, one side of the identity is manipulated until the other side is obtained. In **Example 3** both sides of the identity are manipulated until they are identical. In **Example 4**, a known identity, the Pythagorean Identity, is manipulated to generate the desired identity. All of these methods are legitimate proof techniques and in our opinion, none of these methods should be discounted in favor of another. The proofs in **Examples 1–3** are shown on **Teaching Aid 117**.

In all the Examples, identities can be deduced without students worrying about singularities. The idea of singularities is covered in Lesson 13-3.

$f(x) = 1 + \tan^2 x$

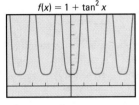

$-\dfrac{5\pi}{2} \leq x \leq \dfrac{5\pi}{2}$, x-scale $= \dfrac{\pi}{2}$
$-1 \leq y \leq 8$,   y-scale $= 1$

$g(x) = \sec^2 x$

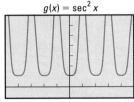

$-\dfrac{5\pi}{2} \leq x \leq \dfrac{5\pi}{2}$, x-scale $= \dfrac{\pi}{2}$
$-1 \leq y \leq 8$,   y-scale $= 1$

812

Example 1

Find an identity involving $(\cos x - \sin x)^2$.

Solution

Expand the expression.
$$(\cos x - \sin x)^2 = \cos^2 x - 2 \cos x \sin x + \sin^2 x$$
$$= \cos^2 x + \sin^2 x - 2 \cos x \sin x$$
Recall two identities: for all x, $\cos^2 x + \sin^2 x = 1$ and $2 \cos x \sin x = \sin 2x$.
So, $(\cos x - \sin x)^2 = 1 - \sin 2x$.

Check

Graph $f(x) = (\cos x - \sin x)^2$ and $g(x) = 1 - \sin 2x$. Check that the graphs coincide. As shown below, they do.

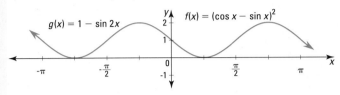

Proving Identities by Working with One Side

In Example 1, one expression was manipulated to equal a second expression. This technique can often be employed to prove that an equation is an identity. Start with one side of a proposed identity, and rewrite it using definitions, known identities, or algebraic properties, until it equals the other side.

Example 2

Prove that $1 + \tan^2 x = \sec^2 x$, for all x in the domains of these expressions.

Solution

Substitute into the left expression and rewrite until you get the right. For all x with $\cos x \neq 0$,

$$1 + \tan^2 x = 1 + \frac{\sin^2 x}{\cos^2 x}$$ Definition of tangent

$$= \frac{\cos^2 x}{\cos^2 x} + \frac{\sin^2 x}{\cos^2 x}$$ Forming a common denominator

$$= \frac{\cos^2 x + \sin^2 x}{\cos^2 x}$$ Adding fractions with a common denominator

$$= \frac{1}{\cos^2 x}$$ Pythagorean Identity

$$= \sec^2 x.$$ Definition of secant

So, $1 + \tan^2 x = \sec^2 x$ for all x in the domain of $\tan x$ and $\sec x$.

Check

Let $f(x) = 1 + \tan^2 x$ and $g(x) = \sec^2 x$. At the left, each function is shown on a separate set of axes. In practice, you should graph both on the same set of axes. Because the graphs appear to be identical, it checks.

Proving Identities by Working with Both Sides

A second proof technique is to rewrite each side of a proposed identity independently until equal expressions are obtained. When using this technique, because you cannot be sure that the proposed identity is true until you have finished, you should not write an equal sign between the two sides until the end. We draw a vertical line between the two sides as a reminder of this restriction. Thus, a proof that $A = B$ is an identity based on this technique has the following form.

$$
\begin{array}{c|c}
A & B \\
= \ldots & = \ldots \\
= \ldots & = \ldots \\
= E & = E
\end{array}
$$

So $\qquad A = B.$

Example 3

Prove: For all x, $\sin\left(x + \frac{\pi}{4}\right) = \cos\left(x - \frac{\pi}{4}\right).$

Solution

Use the Addition Identities for the sine and cosine.

$$
\begin{array}{c|c}
\sin\left(x + \frac{\pi}{4}\right) & \cos\left(x - \frac{\pi}{4}\right) \\
= \sin x \cos\frac{\pi}{4} + \cos x \sin\frac{\pi}{4} & = \cos x \cos\frac{\pi}{4} + \sin x \sin\frac{\pi}{4} \\
= \sin x \cdot \frac{\sqrt{2}}{2} + \cos x \cdot \frac{\sqrt{2}}{2} & = \cos x \cdot \frac{\sqrt{2}}{2} + \sin x \cdot \frac{\sqrt{2}}{2}
\end{array}
$$

So $\qquad\qquad \sin\left(x + \frac{\pi}{4}\right) = \cos\left(x - \frac{\pi}{4}\right).$

Deducing New Identities from Known Identities

A third proof technique is to begin with a known identity and derive statements equivalent to it until the proposed identity appears.

Example 4

Prove that $1 + \cot^2 x = \csc^2 x$ for $x \neq n\pi$, n an integer.

Solution

Begin with the Pythagorean Identity.
For all real numbers x,

$$\cos^2 x + \sin^2 x = 1.$$

$$\frac{\cos^2 x}{\sin^2 x} + \frac{\sin^2 x}{\sin^2 x} = \frac{1}{\sin^2 x}$$
Divide both sides by $\sin^2 x$.
(Note that $\sin^2 x \neq 0$ when $x \neq n\pi$.)

$$\cot^2 x + 1 = \csc^2 x$$
Definitions of $\cot x$ and $\csc x$

Check

At the left is a graph of both $f(x) = 1 + \cot^2 x$ and $g(x) = \csc^2 x$. They appear to coincide.

$-\frac{5\pi}{2} \le x \le \frac{5\pi}{2}$, x-scale $= \frac{\pi}{2}$

$-1 \le y \le 8$, y-scale $= 1$

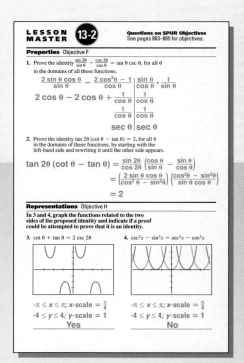

Adapting to Individual Needs

Challenge

Have students answer the following. A student got $2 + 2\tan^2 x + C$ for the answer to a calculus question, where C is a constant. The answer manual said the answer was $2\sec^2 x + C$. Should the student worry? [No] Why or why not? [For all x, $2 + 2\tan^2 x = 2\sec^2 x$.]

Setting Up Lesson 13-3

Begin with the statement of **Question 7**. Ask which values of x are excluded. [Multiples of $\frac{\pi}{2}$] Why are they excluded? [For integer multiples of π, the right side is not defined; for odd integer multiples of $\frac{\pi}{2}$, the left side is not defined.]

Question 3 Error Alert Some students may include graphing each side of the equation as a separate function. Point out that while this technique can verify an identity, it is not considered a proof.

Practice

For more questions on SPUR Objectives, use **Lesson Master 13-2** (shown on page 813).

Assessment

Written Communication Have students **work in pairs.** Ask each student to solve and check **Example 1**, but give one partner the expression tan $x(\sin 2x)$ and the other cot $x(\sin 2x)$. Then have students prove their partner's identity for all x in the domain of the functions. [Students generate, verify, and prove trigonometric identities.]

Extension

Cooperative Learning Groups of students can apply the following procedure to construct their own identities. Then they can prove each other's identities.
1. Start with a statement that is always true. [Sample: 1 = 1.]
2. Replace a part(s) of the beginning statement with an equivalent trigonometric expression. [Sample: $\sin^2 \theta + \cos^2 \theta = 1$.]
3. Repeat step 2. [$\sin^2 \theta + \cos^2 \theta = \frac{\sin \theta}{\sin \theta}$ (if $\sin \theta \neq 0$).]

2a)

$y = (\cos x + \sin x)^2$

$y = \cos^2 x + \sin^2 x$

3) Manipulate one expression to equal a second; rewrite each side independently until equal expressions are obtained; begin with a known identity and derive statements equivalent to it until the proposed identity appears.

4) $1 + \cot^2 x = 1 + \frac{\cos^2 x}{\sin^2 x} = \frac{\sin^2 x}{\sin^2 x} + \frac{\cos^2 x}{\sin^2 x}$

$= \frac{\sin^2 x + \cos^2 x}{\sin^2 x} = \frac{1}{\sin^2 x} = \csc^2 x$

814

As shown in the solution to Example 4, the identity $1 + \cot^2 x = \csc^2 x$ can be derived quickly from the Pythagorean Identity. Hence, it is sometimes called a *corollary* to the Pythagorean Identity. In the Questions you are asked to use this technique to show that $1 + \tan^2 x = \sec^2 x$ is also a corollary to the Pythagorean Identity.

QUESTIONS

Covering the Reading

1. *True or false.* $(\cos x - \sin x)^2 = \cos^2 x - \sin^2 x$. **False**

2. **a.** Is the sentence $(\cos x + \sin x)^2 = \cos^2 x + \sin^2 x$ an identity? Justify your answer with a graph. **No. See left.**
   b. Find an expression involving a single circular function equal to $(\cos x + \sin x)^2$. **1 + sin (2x)**

3. State three different techniques for proving that an equation is an identity. **See left.**

In 4 and 5, prove the following statement using the specified technique:
For all x such that $x \neq n\pi$, $1 + \cot^2 x = \csc^2 x$.

4. Use the technique of Example 2. **See left.**

5. Use the technique of Example 3. **See margin.**

6. Show that $1 + \tan^2 x = \sec^2 x$ is a corollary to the Pythagorean Identity. That is, prove the identity $1 + \tan^2 x = \sec^2 x$, for all x such that $x \neq \frac{\pi}{2} + n\pi$, using the technique of Example 4. **See margin.**

Applying the Mathematics

7. Prove: For all x for which all the functions are defined,
   $\sin x \cdot \cos x \cdot \tan x = \frac{1}{\csc^2 x}$. **See margin.**

In 8 and 9, the graph of a product of trigonometric functions is drawn.
a. What identity is suggested by the graph? (Hint: The answer involves one of the six parent trigonometric functions.)
b. Prove your answer to part **a**. **See margin.**
c. Over what domain is the identity true? **See margin.**

8. $y = \cot x \sec x$

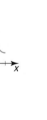

a) cot x sec x = csc x

9. $y = \sec x \tan x \cos x$

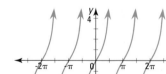

a) sec x tan x cos x = tan x

Additional Answers

5. $1 + \cot^2 x$
   $= 1 + \frac{\cos^2 x}{\sin^2 x}$
   $= \frac{\sin^2 x}{\sin^2 x} + \frac{\cos^2 x}{\sin^2 x}$
   $= \frac{\sin^2 x + \cos^2 x}{\sin^2 x}$
   $= \frac{1}{\sin^2 x}$
   So, $1 + \cot^2 x = \csc^2 x$

   $\csc^2 x$
   $= \frac{1}{\sin^2 x}$

6. $\cos^2 x + \sin^2 x = 1$
   $\frac{\cos^2 x}{\cos^2 x} + \frac{\sin^2 x}{\cos^2 x} = \frac{1}{\cos^2 x}$
   $1 + \tan^2 x = \sec^2 x$, for all x such that $x \neq \frac{\pi}{2} + n\pi$, for all integers n.

7. $\sin x \cdot \cos x \cdot \tan x$
   $= \sin x \cdot \cos x \cdot \frac{\sin x}{\cos x}$
   $= \sin^2 x$

   $\frac{1}{\csc^2 x}$
   $= \frac{1}{\frac{1}{\sin^2 x}}$
   $= \sin^2 x$

   So, $\sin x \cdot \cos x \cdot \tan x = \frac{1}{\csc^2 x}$ for $x \neq \frac{n\pi}{2}$, for all integers n.

8. **b.** $\cot x \sec x = \frac{\cos x}{\sin x} \cdot \frac{1}{\cos x} = \frac{1}{\sin x}$
   $= \csc x$
   c. For all x such that $x \neq \frac{n\pi}{2}$, for all integers n

9. **b.** $\sec x \tan x \cos x = \frac{1}{\cos x} \cdot \cos x \cdot \tan x = \tan x$
   c. For all x such that $x \neq \frac{\pi}{2} + n\pi$, for all integers n

10a)

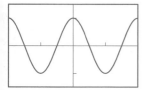

$-2\pi \le x \le 2\pi, \quad x\text{-scale} = \pi$
$-1.5 \le y \le 1.5, \quad y\text{-scale} = 1$

b) For all x,
$-\cos(\pi - x) =$
$-(-\cos x) = \cos x$.

11a)
$y = 3\sin x \cos x \quad y = \sin 3x$

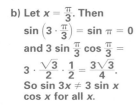

$-2\pi \le x \le 2\pi, \quad x\text{-scale} = \pi$
$-2 \le y \le 2, \quad y\text{-scale} = 1$

b) Let $x = \frac{\pi}{3}$. **Then**
$\sin\left(3 \cdot \frac{\pi}{3}\right) = \sin \pi = 0$
and $3 \sin \frac{\pi}{3} \cos \frac{\pi}{3} =$
$3 \cdot \frac{\sqrt{3}}{2} \cdot \frac{1}{2} = \frac{3\sqrt{3}}{4}$.
So $\sin 3x \ne 3 \sin x$
$\cos x$ **for all** x.

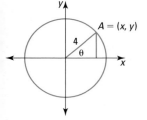

$A = (x, y)$

4

θ

In 10–13, a trigonometric equation is given. **a.** Use an automatic grapher to test whether the equation may be an identity. **b.** Prove the identity or give a counterexample.

10. $\cos x = -\cos(\pi - x)$ **See left.**　　**11.** $\sin 3x = 3 \sin x \cos x$ **See left.**

12. $\frac{\csc x}{\sec x} = \cot x$. **See margin.**　　**13.** $\tan^2 x \cos^2 x = 1 - \cos^2 x$
　　　　　　　　　　　　　　　　　　　　　　　See margin.

14. Let θ be in the interval $270° < \theta < 360°$, and $\tan \theta = -\frac{3}{8}$. Use the Pythagorean Identity or one of its corollaries to find the following.

　a. $\cot \theta$　　　　**b.** $\sec \theta$　　　　**c.** $\sin \theta$
　　　$-8/3$　　　　　　$\frac{\sqrt{73}}{8}$　　　　$-3\sqrt{73}/73$

15. Prove: For all x, $\cos^4 x + \sin^2 x = \sin^4 x + \cos^2 x$.
　　See margin.

In 16 and 17, use the techniques in this lesson to test whether the statement is or is not an identity. Justify your answer. **See margin.**

16. $x^3 + x^4 = x^7$　　　　　　**17.** $\log x^3 + \log x^4 = \log x^7$

Review

In 18 and 19, let $\triangle ABC$ be a right triangle with right angle C. Express each function in terms of the side a, b, or c. *(Lesson 13-1)*

18. $\csc A$　$\frac{c}{a}$　　　　　　**19.** $\cot B$　$\frac{a}{b}$

20. a. Write the first six terms of the sequence *(Lesson 8-1)*

$$\begin{cases} a_1 = 1 \\ a_n = 2a_{n-1} + 1 \end{cases}. \; 1, 3, 7, 15, 31, 63$$

　b. Tell whether the sequence is arithmetic, geometric, or neither.
　　neither

In 21 and 22, evaluate in radians. *(Lessons 5-5, 5-6)*

21. $\sin^{-1}(-1)$　$-\frac{\pi}{2}$　　　　**22.** $\tan^{-1}(\sqrt{3})$　$\frac{\pi}{3}$

23. A is a point on a circle of radius 4, as shown at the left. Give the coordinates of A in terms of θ. *(Lesson 4-3)* **(4 cos θ, 4 sin θ)**

24. If a sector of a circle has a central angle of $\frac{\pi}{8}$ and an area of 5π square inches, what is the radius of the circle? *(Lesson 4-2)*
　$4\sqrt{5} \approx 8.94$ inches

Exploration

25. Refer to Questions 8 and 9. **See margin.**
　a. Find another pair of parent functions whose product seems to be a parent function, and prove the identity.
　b. Find another set of three parent functions whose product seems to be another parent function, and prove the identity.

---

4. Apply procedures for changing an equation to an equivalent equation. [$\sin^2 \theta + 2 \sin \theta \cos \theta + \cos^2 \theta = \frac{\sin \theta}{\sin \theta} + 2 \sin \theta \cos \theta$;
so
$(\sin \theta + \cos \theta)^2$
$= \sin \theta(\frac{1}{\sin \theta} + 2 \cos \theta)$; so
$(\sin \theta + \cos \theta)^2$
$= \sin \theta (\csc \theta + 2 \cos \theta)$.]

Project Update Project 1, *Euler's Theorem*, on page 858, relates to the content of this lesson.

13. a.

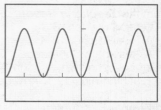

$-2\pi \le x \le 2\pi, \quad x\text{-scale} = \frac{\pi}{2}$

$-0.5 \le y \le 1.5, \quad y\text{-scale} = 1$

b. $\tan^2 x \cos^2 x$　　$\Big|$　$1 - \cos^2 x$
$= \frac{\sin^2 x}{\cos^2 x} \cdot \cos^2 x$　$\Big|$　$= \sin^2 x$
$= \sin^2 x$
So, $\tan^2 x \cos^2 x =$
$1 - \cos^2 x$, for all x such that $x \ne \frac{\pi}{2} + n\pi$ for all integers n.

15. Begin with the Pythagorean Identity: for all x,
$\cos^2 x + \sin^2 x = 1$
$(\cos^2 x + \sin^2 x)(\cos^2 x - \sin^2 x)$
$= \cos^2 x - \sin^2 x$
$\cos^4 x - \sin^4 x = \cos^2 x - \sin^2 x$
$\cos^4 x + \sin^2 x = \sin^4 x + \cos^2 x$

16. Let $x = 1$. Then $x^3 + x^4 = 1^3 + 1^4 = 2$ and $x^7 = 1^7 = 1$. So, $x^3 + x^4 = x^7$ is not an identity.

17. For all x, $\log x^3 + \log x^4 = \log(x^3 \cdot x^4) = \log x^7$, so it is an identity.

25. a. Sample: $\sin x \sec x = \tan x$, for $x \ne \frac{\pi}{2} + n\pi$, n an integer. Proof:
$\sin x \sec x = \sin x \cdot \frac{1}{\cos x}$
$= \tan x$
b. Sample:
$\csc x \cot x \sin x = \cot x$, for $x \ne n\pi$, n an integer. Proof: $\csc x \cot x \sin x$
$= \frac{1}{\sin x} \cdot \frac{\cos x}{\sin x} \cdot \sin x$
$= \frac{\cos x}{\sin x} = \cot x$

---

12. a.

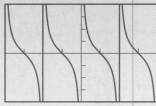

$-2\pi \le x \le 2\pi, \quad x\text{-scale} = \frac{\pi}{2}$

$-4 \le y \le 4, \quad y\text{-scale} = 1$

b. $\frac{\csc x}{\sec x} = \frac{\frac{1}{\sin x}}{\frac{1}{\cos x}} = \frac{1}{\sin x} \cdot \frac{\cos x}{1} = \frac{\cos x}{\sin x}$

$= \cot x$, for all x such that $x \ne \frac{n\pi}{2}$ for all integers n.

815

Objectives
F Prove trigonometric identities.
G Describe singularities of functions.
H Use an automatic grapher to test a proposed identity.

Resources

From the _Teacher's Resource File_
- Lesson Master 13-3
- Answer Master 13-3
- Assessment Sourcebook: Quiz for Lessons 13-1 through 13-3
- Teaching Aid 112: Warm-up

Additional Resources
- Visual for Teaching Aid 112

Teaching Lesson 13-3

Warm-up
Explain the difference between the graphs of $y = (x - 1)^2$ and $y = \frac{(x - 1)^7}{(x - 1)^5}$. The latter graph is identical to the former except that it does not contain the point $(1, 0)$ because y is not defined when $x = 1$.

Notes on Reading
There are two kinds of singularities, *essential* and *removable*. Every singularity is a value of the domain variable. An essential singularity is signaled by a vertical asymptote at that value and can usually be determined from a graph.

This lesson is concerned more with removable singularities, those which are not represented by vertical asymptotes, but by holes in a graph. An automatic grapher typically can represent such holes only if the domain is very carefully chosen so that the x-value at the pixel is exactly one of the singularities. So a critical analysis of the symbolic form of an identity is the safest way to identify singularities.

LESSON

13-3

Restrictions on Identities

Restrictions on the Domains of the Trigonometric Functions

Only two of the parent trigonometric functions—the sine and cosine—are defined for all real numbers. The others have the following restrictions on their domains.

Function	Not defined when $x =$	
tan	$\frac{\pi}{2} + n\pi$	
cot	$n\pi$	n an integer
sec	$\frac{\pi}{2} + n\pi$	
csc	$n\pi$	

Recall that an identity is a statement that is true for *all* values of a variable in a particular domain. In general, when trying to prove an identity you should consider the largest domain on which all the relevant functions are defined. Thus, the identity $1 + \cot^2 x = \csc^2 x$ is true for all real numbers x except where $\cot x$ and $\csc x$ are not defined. That is, $1 + \cot^2 x = \csc^2 x$ for all real numbers x except when $x = n\pi$, where n is an integer.

What Is a Singularity?

An isolated value for which a function is undefined is called a **singularity**. The singularities of the parent tangent, cotangent, secant, and cosecant functions are signaled graphically by vertical asymptotes. For instance, when n is an integer and $x = n\pi$, x is a singularity of $f(x) = \cot x$ and the lines with equations $x = n\pi$ are vertical asymptotes of the graph of $\cot x$. Singularities of other functions may not be represented by asymptotes, and may not be obvious on a graph. Thus, when using an automatic grapher to test a potential identity, you need to consider the restrictions on the domain.

Example 1

Consider the equation $\cos x \tan x = \sin x$. Use an automatic grapher to test whether or not the equation seems to be an identity. If it seems to be, prove the identity over the largest possible domain.

Solution

The graphs of $f(x) = \cos x \tan x$ and $g(x) = \sin x$, as they appear on one automatic grapher, are shown at the right. It appears that the graphs coincide, so an algebraic proof of the identity is worth pursuing. Rewrite the left side.

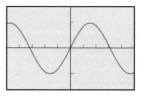

$-5 \leq x \leq 5$, x-scale = 1
$-2 \leq y \leq 2$, y-scale = 1

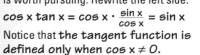
$$\cos x \tan x = \cos x \cdot \frac{\sin x}{\cos x} = \sin x$$
Notice that **the tangent function is defined only when $\cos x \neq 0$.**

So $\cos x \tan x = \sin x$ for all x except when $x = \frac{\pi}{2} + n\pi$, n an integer.

Lesson 13-3 Overview

Broad Goals This lesson is a brief lesson designed to give more time to practice proving identities. Its purpose is to examine the domain for which an identity is true.

Perspective Many identities are not true for all real numbers. Determining the values for which an identity $f(x) = g(x)$ is not true often is equivalent to finding the singularities of the functions f and g. For instance, even $\frac{\sin x}{\cos x} = \tan x$ is not true for all x

because the functions $f(x) = \frac{\sin x}{\cos x}$ and $g(x) = \tan x$ have singularities at each value of x such that $\cos x = 0$. Algebra needs to be used to find these singularities because they can be impossible to locate in graphs generated by technology.

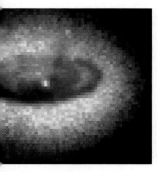

Nonremovable Singularity. *Because of its special properties, the center of a black hole is called a singularity. The bright point at the center of this image of a galaxy is theorized to be the final flare of heated matter as it disappears into a black hole.*

Removable Singularities

Notice that although the graph in Example 1 suggested that $\cos x \tan x = \sin x$ is an identity for all x, it is an identity only when $\tan x$ is defined. Geometrically, you can think of the singularities of the function $f(x) = \cos x \tan x$ as signaling "holes" in the graph of $f(x) = \sin x$ at the points where x is an odd multiple of $\frac{\pi}{2}$. A singularity of this type, where the break in the graph can be "removed" by adding a single point, is called a **removable singularity**. On some automatic graphers, if you plot $f(x) = \cos x \tan x$ and repeatedly zoom in around the point $\left(\frac{\pi}{2}, 1\right)$, you may eventually see a small hole in the graph. Try this with your technology.

Example 2 also involves an identity on a restricted domain.

Example 2

Consider the statement $\sin 2\theta = \frac{2 \cot \theta}{1 + \cot^2 \theta}$.
a. Determine any restrictions on the domain.
b. Prove the statement over the restricted domain in part **a**.

Solution

a. Singularities occur where $\cot \theta$ is undefined, so $\theta \neq n\pi$, for n an integer. Since $1 + \cot^2 \theta > 0$ for all θ, there are no other restrictions due to the denominator of the fraction.

b. Rewrite both sides of the equation until equivalent expressions remain. (In the Questions, you are asked to give justifications for each step, so they are numbered here.)

$$\sin 2\theta \quad \Big| \quad \frac{2 \cot \theta}{1 + \cot^2 \theta}$$

1. $= 2 \sin \theta \cos \theta \quad \Big| \quad = \frac{2 \cot \theta}{\csc^2 \theta}$ 2.

$$= \frac{\frac{2 \cos \theta}{\sin \theta}}{\frac{1}{\sin^2 \theta}} \quad 3.$$

$$= 2 \sin \theta \cos \theta \quad 4.$$

So $\qquad \sin 2\theta \quad = \quad \frac{2 \cot \theta}{1 + \cot^2 \theta}$ for all $\theta \neq n\pi$.

QUESTIONS

Covering the Reading

1. What is a *singularity* of a function? **A singularity is an isolated value for which a function is not defined.**

In 2 and 3, identify any singularities of the function described.

2. $f(x) = \cot x$
$n\pi$ for all integers n

3. $g(x) = \cos x \tan x$
$\pi/2 + n\pi$ for all integers n

4. *True or false.* All singularities of functions are signaled by asymptotes.
False

Lesson 13-3 *Restrictions on Identities* **817**

In both **Examples 1–2**, the restrictions on the domain of the identity are the singularities of the trigonometric functions involved. The only other possible restrictions arise when a denominator is zero, as in **Questions 9–11 and 13**.

Additional Examples

1. Consider the equation $\frac{\cos \theta + 1}{\cot \theta + \csc \theta} = \sin \theta$.
   a. Use an automatic grapher to test whether or not the equation seems to be an identity. The graph of $f(\theta) = \frac{\cos \theta + 1}{\cot \theta + \csc \theta}$ does seem to be like the graph of the sine function.
   b. If it seems to be, prove the identity over the largest possible domain. If not, find a value of θ for which the equation is defined but the two sides are not equal. **The left side is not defined when $\cot \theta = 0$ or $\csc \theta = 0$ or $\cot \theta + \csc \theta = 0$, that is, when $\sin \theta = 0$, which is when $\theta = n\pi$ for any integer n.**
   $\frac{\cos \theta + 1}{\cot \theta + \csc \theta} = \frac{\cos \theta + 1}{\frac{\cos \theta}{\sin \theta} + \frac{1}{\sin \theta}} = \sin \theta.$
   When $\cos \theta + 1 = 0$, the left side is not defined, but then $\cos \theta = -1$, and this is taken care of by the restriction $\sin \theta \neq 0$.

2. Prove the identity $\sin^2 x + \cos^2 x + \tan^2 x = \sec^2 x$ over the largest possible domain.
   $\sin^2 x + \cos^2 x + \tan^2 x = 1 + \tan^2 x = \sec^2 x$ **(using the Pythagorean Identities twice). Since $\tan^2 x$ and $\sec^2 x$ are not defined when $\cos x = 0$, the largest possible domain is the set of real numbers x such that $x \neq n\pi + \frac{\pi}{2}$ for any integer n.**

Optional Activities

After completing the lesson you might have students make up functions that meet the following descriptions:
1. a line with a hole (removable singularity).
   [Sample: $y = \frac{x^2 - x - 6}{x + 2}$]
2. a parabola with a hole.
   [Sample: $y = \frac{(x - 5)^3}{x - 5}$]
3. a parabola with two holes.
   [Sample: $y = \frac{x^4 + 3x^2 - 4}{x^2 - 1}$]

4. a cubic with a hole.
   [Sample: $y = \frac{(x - 5)^4}{x - 5}$]
5. a sine curve with holes at $x = \pi + n \cdot 2\pi$ (i.e., at odd multiples of π).
   [Sample: $y = \frac{\sin x - \sin x \cos x}{1 - \cos x}$]
Have students discuss how to "create" holes in functions, in general. [One way is to multiply by a fraction with identical numerator and denominator where each can take on the value 0.]

Adapting to Individual Needs

Extra Help
Some students may be confused by the analysis of the denominator in **Example 2**. Explain that $1 + \cot^2 \theta > 0$ for all θ because $\cot^2 \theta \geq 0$ (a squared quantity is never negative).

817

Questions 7–8 You might point out that these could not both be identities. In **Question 8** the tangent is the product of the cosecant and secant; in **Question 7** it is the quotient.

Question 13 Error Alert Be sure students find both kinds of restrictions: the denominator cannot be zero and the functions must be defined.

Question 14 This question emphasizes that identities exist in other than trigonometric contexts.

Question 20 A false positive is likely to be traumatic to the person; he or she does not have AIDS-contaminated blood but the test indicates otherwise. Thus the accuracy of this test, even though it is 98%, is not high enough.

Question 21 The kind of thinking in this question is similar to that found in limit proofs in calculus.

5) (1) double angle formula;
(2) Pythagorean Identity corollary;
(3) definition of cotangent, cosecant;
(4) operation of division

6a)

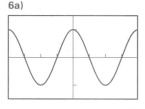

$-2\pi \le x \le 2\pi$,   x-scale = $\frac{\pi}{2}$
$-1.5 \le y \le 1.5$,   y-scale = 1

b) $\sin x \cot x =$
$\sin x \cdot \dfrac{\cos x}{\sin x} = \cos x$,
for all x such that
$x \ne n\pi$ for all integers n.

7a)

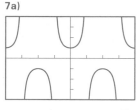

$-2\pi \le x \le 2\pi$,   x-scale = $\frac{\pi}{2}$
$-4 \le y \le 4$,   y-scale = 1

b) $\tan x \csc x =$
$\dfrac{\sin x}{\cos x} \cdot \dfrac{1}{\sin x} =$
$\dfrac{1}{\cos x} = \sec x$, for all
x such that $x \ne \dfrac{n\pi}{2}$
for all integers n.

5. Give a justification for each numbered step in Example 2. **See left.**

In 6–9, a trigonometric equation is given. **a.** Use an automatic grapher to test whether the equation may be an identity. **b.** If the equation is an identity, prove it and give its domain.

6. $\sin x \cot x = \cos x$
6–7) See left.

7. $\sec x = \tan x \csc x$

8. $\csc x = \dfrac{\tan x}{\sec x}$
8–9) See margin.

9. $\sin 2x = \dfrac{2\tan x}{1 + \tan^2 x}$

Applying the Mathematics

In 10 and 11, an equation for a function is given. **a.** Graph the function. **b.** Identify its domain. **c.** Propose an identity based on this graph. **d.** Prove the identity. **See margin.**

10. $f(x) = \dfrac{1 - \tan^2 x}{1 + \tan^2 x}$

11. $g(x) = \dfrac{1 + \cos 2x}{\sin 2x}$

In 12 and 13, a trigonometric equation is given. **a.** State any restrictions on the domain of the proposed identity. **b.** Prove or disprove the proposed identity over the domain you state in part **a**. b) See margin.

12. $\tan x + \cot x = \sec x \csc x$ a) $x \ne (n\pi)/2$ for all integers n

13. $\csc^2 x \sin x = \dfrac{\sec^2 x - \tan^2 x}{\sin x}$ a) $x \ne (n\pi)/2$ for all integers n

14. a. Graph $f(x) = \dfrac{x^2 - x - 12}{x - 4}$ and $g(x) = x + 3$ on the same set of axes.
b. Find the singularity in the graph of $y = f(x)$. x = 4
c. What is the domain for the identity $\dfrac{x^2 - x - 12}{x - 4} = x + 3$?
d. Prove the identity. a, d) See margin.
c) the set of all real numbers such that $x \ne 4$

Review

15. Suppose α is in the interval $\frac{\pi}{2} < \alpha < \pi$, and $\cot \alpha = -4$. Determine each of the following. *(Lessons 11-6, 13-1, 13-2)*
a. $\csc \alpha$ $\sqrt{17}$
b. $\sin \alpha$ $\sqrt{17}/17$
c. $\sin 2\alpha$ $-\frac{8}{17}$

16. Suppose $\dfrac{x^2}{16} - \dfrac{y^2}{9} = 1$ and $\dfrac{x^2}{16} + \dfrac{y^2}{9} = 1$.
a. Solve this system graphically.
b. Solve this system algebraically. *(Lessons 12-2, 12-3)*
a, b) See margin.

17. *True or false.* The matrix $\begin{bmatrix} 1 & 0 \\ 0 & 1 \end{bmatrix}$ does not have an inverse. *(Lesson 11-7)*
False

18. Find the number z such that 75% of the area under the standard normal curve lies between $-z$ and z. *(Lesson 10-5)* **z ≈ 1.15**

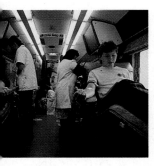

Gift of Life. *About 14 million pints of blood are donated each year in the U.S. These college students are donating blood in a bloodmobile.*

In 19 and 20, consider the ELISA test, which was introduced in the mid-1980s to screen donated blood for the presence of antibodies to the AIDS virus. *(Lessons 10-1, 10-2, 10-6)*

19. When presented with AIDS-contaminated blood, ELISA gives a positive response in about 98% of all cases. Suppose that among the blood that passes through a blood bank in a year there are 25 units containing AIDS antibodies. **a) $(0.98)^{25} \approx 0.60$**
   a. What is the probability that ELISA will detect all 25 of these units?
   b. What is the probability that more than 2 of the 25 contaminated units will escape detection? **≈ 0.013**
   c. What is the mean number of units among the 25 that will be detected by ELISA? **24.5 units**
   d. What is the standard deviation of the number detected? **0.7**

20. ELISA claims that AIDS antibodies are present in uncontaminated blood about 7% of the time. Such a result is called a *false positive*. Suppose a blood bank contains 20,000 units of blood.
   a. What is the expected number of false positives among this group?
   b. What is the standard deviation of the number of false positives?
   a) 1400   b) ≈ 36

21. Consider the row of Pascal's Triangle that begins with 1, 12, ...
   a. What is the next entry in the row? **66**
   b. What is the sum of all the numbers in the row? *(Lesson 8-7)* **4096**

In 22 and 23, solve to the nearest tenth. *(Lessons 6-6, 6-7)*

22. $2 = (1.07)^{y/100}$
   $y \approx 1024.5$

23. $100 = 12.2 \ln t + 4.8$
   $t \approx 2448.6$

24. Solve the equation $\tan \theta = 2.5$ on the given domain. *(Lesson 5-7)*
   a. $\{\theta: -\frac{\pi}{2} \le \theta \le \frac{\pi}{2}\}$ **$\theta \approx 1.19$**
   b. $\{\theta: 0 \le \theta \le 2\pi\}$ **$\theta \approx 1.19$ or 4.33**
   c. the set of all real numbers
   $\theta \approx 1.19 + n\pi$, for all integers n

Exploration

25. The sentence $\sqrt{x^2 - 1} = x - \frac{1}{2x}$ is not an identity for $x \ge 1$. In fact, the expressions on the two sides never have the same value.
   a. Evaluate the two expressions in the sentence at $x = 1$, $x = 5$, $x = 9$, and $x = 10$ to support the preceding claims. **See margin.**
   b. Notice that the two expressions $\sqrt{x^2 - 1}$ and $x - \frac{1}{2x}$ have closer and closer values as x gets bigger. Use an automatic grapher to determine the values of x for which $\sqrt{x^2 - 1}$ is within .01 of $x - \frac{1}{2x}$.
   all values of x larger than about 2.395

Lesson 13-3 *Restrictions on Identities* **819**

25. a.

x	$\sqrt{x^2 - 1}$	$x - \frac{1}{2x}$
1	0	0.5
5	4.899	4.9
9	8.9443	8.9444
10	9.9499	9.95

Follow-up for Lesson 13-3

Practice
For more questions on SPUR Objectives, use **Lesson Master 13-3** (shown below).

Assessment
Quiz A quiz covering Lesson 13-1 through 13-3 is provided in the *Assessment Sourcebook*.

Extension
Have students prove the following identity.
$$\frac{\cos^4 \theta - \sin^4 \theta}{1 - \tan^4 \theta} = \frac{1}{\sec^4 \theta}$$
$$\left[\frac{\cos^4 \theta - \sin^4 \theta}{1 - \tan^4 \theta} = \frac{\cos^4 \theta - \sin^4 \theta}{1 - \frac{\sin^4 \theta}{\cos^4 \theta}}\right.$$
$$= \cos^4 \theta$$
$$\left. = \frac{1}{\sec^4 \theta}\right]$$

Project Update Project 1, *Euler's Theorem*, on page 858, relates to the content of this lesson.

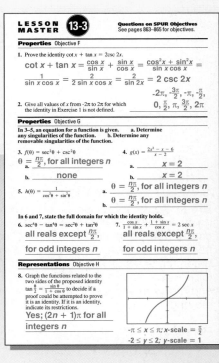

LESSON MASTER 13-3

Questions on SPUR Objectives
See pages 863–865 for objectives.

Properties Objective F

1. Prove the identity $\cot x + \tan x = 2\csc 2x$.
$$\cot x + \tan x = \frac{\cos x}{\sin x} + \frac{\sin x}{\cos x} = \frac{\cos^2 x + \sin^2 x}{\sin x \cos x} =$$
$$\frac{1}{\sin x \cos x} = \frac{2}{2 \sin x \cos x} = \frac{2}{\sin 2x} = 2 \csc 2x$$

2. Give all values of x from -2π to 2π for which the identity in Exercise 1 is not defined. $-2\pi, -\frac{3\pi}{2}, -\pi, -\frac{\pi}{2}, 0, \frac{\pi}{2}, \pi, \frac{3\pi}{2}, 2\pi$

Properties Objective G

In 3–5, an equation for a function is given. a. Determine any singularities of the function. b. Determine any removable singularities of the function.

3. $f(\theta) = \sec^2\theta + \csc^2\theta$
   a. $\theta = \frac{n\pi}{2}$, for all integers n
   b. none

4. $g(x) = \frac{2x^2 - x - 6}{x - 2}$
   a. $x = 2$
   b. $x = 2$

5. $h(\theta) = \frac{1}{\cos^2\theta + \sin^2\theta}$
   a. $\theta = \frac{n\pi}{2}$, for all integers n
   b. $\theta = \frac{n\pi}{2}$, for all integers n

In 6 and 7, state the full domain for which the identity holds.

6. $\sec^4\theta - \tan^4\theta = \sec^2\theta + \tan^2\theta$
   all reals except $\frac{n\pi}{2}$, for odd integers n

7. $\frac{\cos x}{1 + \sin x} + \frac{1 + \sin x}{\cos x} = 2 \sec x$
   all reals except $\frac{n\pi}{2}$, for odd integers n

Representations Objective H

8. Graph the functions related to the two sides of the proposed identity $\tan \frac{\theta}{2} = \frac{\sin \theta}{1 + \cos \theta}$ to decide if a proof could be attempted to prove it is an identity. If it is an identity, indicate its restrictions.
   Yes; $(2n + 1)\pi$ for all integers n

$-\pi \le x \le \pi$; x-scale $= \frac{\pi}{2}$
$-2 \le y \le 2$; y-scale $= 1$

819

I Given polar coordinates of a point, determine its rectangular coordinates, and vice versa.

J Plot points in a polar coordinate system.

Resources

From the Teacher's Resource File
- Lesson Master 13-4
- Answer Master 13-4
- Teaching Aids
  - 113 Warm-up
  - 118 Polar Coordinate Grid
  - 119 Polar Coordinate Grids

Additional Resources
- Visuals for Teaching Aids 113, 118, 119

Teaching Lesson 13-4

Warm-up

Give the image of the point (1, 0) under each of the following transformations.

1. $R_{\frac{3\pi}{4}}$ $\left(-\frac{\sqrt{2}}{2}, \frac{\sqrt{2}}{2}\right)$

2. $R_{\frac{3\pi}{4}} \circ S_2$ $(-\sqrt{2}, \sqrt{2})$

3. $S_2 \circ R_{\frac{3\pi}{4}}$ $(-\sqrt{2}, \sqrt{2})$

LESSON 13-4

Polar Coordinates

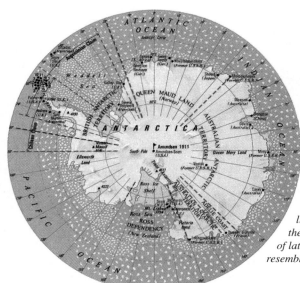

Don't Be Square. *On this map of Antarctica, the rays emanating from the pole are lines of longitude; the circles are lines of latitude. The grid resembles a polar grid.*

The rectangular coordinate system that you have been using for many years dates back to the early 1600s, when René Descartes and Pierre de Fermat worked to develop analytic geometry. Later in that same century, other mathematicians, notably Isaac Newton and Jakob Bernoulli, introduced other coordinate systems. This lesson introduces you to the system of *polar coordinates*.

The Polar Coordinate System

Recall that in a rectangular coordinate system, every point in the plane can be identified by a unique ordered pair of numbers (x, y) representing the point's distances and direction from two perpendicular axes. In a **polar coordinate system**, a pair of numbers $[r, \theta]$ again represent a unique point. Square brackets [,] are used to distinguish polar coordinates from rectangular coordinates. Here r or $-r$ is a distance, but θ is a magnitude of rotation measured in degrees or radians.

To construct a polar coordinate system, first select a point O as the **pole** of the system. Then select any line through O as the **polar axis**. Usually the polar axis is drawn horizontally as shown below. Coordinatize this line so O has coordinate 0. Any point P has **polar coordinates $[r, \theta]$** if and only if P is the image, under a rotation θ about the pole O, of the point on the polar axis with coordinate r. Below it seems as if $P = [4, 40°]$.

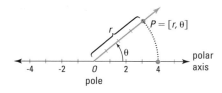

Lesson 13-4 Overview

Broad Goals In this lesson students graph points in the polar coordinate system and convert back and forth from polar coordinates to rectangular coordinates. They also graph the simplest polar equations $r = k$ for $k > 0$ (a circle with center at the origin and radius k) and $\theta = k$ (a line containing the origin).

Perspective We study polar coordinates to expand the horizons of students regarding

coordinate systems, so that students will be able to consider other systems later. Also, they afford a very useful representation of complex numbers, and certain relations graphed in this system are enjoyable and pleasing to see.

The use of a polar reference system is quite old. It is the basis of a compass used for orientation and map making. It is also the basis of radar and satellite communication and

detection systems, navigation procedures, and astronomical representations. In general, a polar reference system determines position in a plane based on distance from an origin at some angle to a fixed ray (the polar axis).

It is important to realize that polar coordinates provide simply an alternate way of naming a point. They, and rectangular coordinates, are to points as decimals and

Example 1

Plot each point $[r, \theta]$, where θ is in radians.

a. $\left[2, \frac{\pi}{3}\right]$ **b.** $\left[1.4, -\frac{\pi}{2}\right]$ **c.** $\left[-2, \frac{7\pi}{5}\right]$

Solution

a. Rotate the point on the polar axis with coordinate 2 counterclockwise by $\frac{\pi}{3}$ radians.

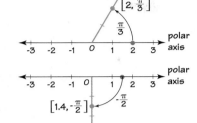

b. Rotate the point on the polar axis with coordinate 1.4 clockwise by $\frac{\pi}{2}$ radians.

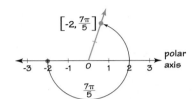

c. Rotate the point on the polar axis with coordinate –2 counterclockwise by $\frac{7\pi}{5}$ radians.

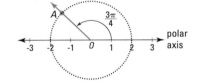

Every Point Has Many Polar Coordinates

A particular ordered pair $[r, \theta]$ identifies a unique point in the polar plane. However, there are an infinite number of polar coordinates for any given point. Example 2 illustrates how some of those pairs of coordinates can be found.

Example 2

Give four different polar coordinate pairs for the point A graphed at the right.

Solution

There are an infinite number of answers. One of them is $\left[2, \frac{3\pi}{4}\right]$ because A is the image of the point on the polar axis with coordinate 2 under a rotation of $\frac{3\pi}{4}$ radians. Rotating A another 2π yields $\left[2, \frac{11\pi}{4}\right]$. Point A can also be considered as the image of the point –2 on the polar axis under a rotation of either $-\frac{\pi}{4}$ or $\frac{7\pi}{4}$, so $\left[-2, -\frac{\pi}{4}\right]$ and $\left[-2, \frac{7\pi}{4}\right]$ also are polar coordinates for it.

Notes on Reading

Because of their background using the unit circle, students should be able to plot points in the polar plane, as in **Example 1**.

Error Alert Most difficulties seem to occur when r is negative. Also, some students don't immediately accept that any point in the polar plane has an infinite number of polar coordinate pairs which describe it. **Examples 2 and 5** and **Questions 1–7** help confront these difficulties.

Example 3 and **Questions 8, 15, and 16** involve equations to be plotted in the polar coordinate system and are appropriate lead-ins into the next lesson.

While converting from polar to rectangular coordinates in **Example 4** and **Questions 11–12** involves exact values of sine and cosine, you may wish to include some problems with points where θ is not a multiple of 30° or 45°, as in Additional Example 4.

Polar coordinate grids are provided on **Teaching Aid 118** (1 grid) and **Teaching Aid 119** (2 grids). You might want to copy these grids for your class.

Optional Activities

fractions are to rational numbers. We use brackets [ ] to avoid confusion with rectangular coordinates. If $[r, \theta] = (x, y)$ in the sense that they refer to the same point, then $x = r \cos \theta$ and $y = r \sin \theta$, $|r| = \sqrt{x^2 + y^2}$, and $\tan \theta = \frac{y}{x}$. Because neither the values of r nor θ are unique, a single point has many polar coordinate representations.

To help students practice plotting and naming polar coordinates, have them form groups of four. Give each group a transparency of a polar grid, a marker, and a list of points to be plotted on the grid. Students should take turns plotting the list of points with the marker. To check the understanding of the class, layer the transparencies on the overhead a couple at a time—all points should coincide! To extend this activity, give each group a polar grid with points

A–P plotted. Have them take turns writing down four different representations for each point in polar coordinates, with $-2\pi \leq \theta \leq 2\pi$. To check, call up individual group members at random to read off some of the answers.

Additional Examples

1. Plot the following points on a polar coordinate system.
   a. [6, 0]
   b. [2.5, $\frac{2\pi}{3}$]
   c. [-1, -40°]

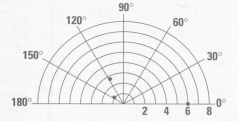

2. Give four additional pairs of polar coordinates for the point [5, $\frac{\pi}{3}$].

   [5, $\frac{7\pi}{3}$], [5, $\frac{13\pi}{3}$], and [5, $\frac{19\pi}{3}$],
   [-5, $\frac{4\pi}{3}$]; in general any pair of
   the form [5, $\frac{\pi}{3}$ + 2nπ], or
   [-5, $\frac{4\pi}{3}$ + 2nπ]

3. Sketch all solutions [r, θ] to each equation.
   a. θ = π The line containing the polar axis
   b. r = π A circle with center at the pole and radius π

4. Find rectangular coordinates for the point with polar coordinates [1.3, $\frac{\pi}{5}$]. (1.3 cos $\frac{\pi}{5}$, 1.3 sin $\frac{\pi}{5}$) ≈ (1.05, .76)]

5. Find a set of polar coordinates for the point (6, -1). Sample:
   [$\sqrt{37}$, tan⁻¹ ($\frac{-1}{6}$)] ≈ [6.1, -9.46°]

The following theorem summarizes the possible polar coordinates for a point in the plane.

> **Theorem**
> For any particular values of r and θ, the following polar coordinate pairs name the same point.
> a. [r, θ]
> b. [r, θ + 2πn], for all integers n
> c. [-r, θ + (2n + 1)π], for all integers n

The Polar Grid

Polar coordinate graph paper, with grids like the *polar grid* pictured at the right, is very helpful for plotting points and sketching curves in the polar plane. Each of the concentric circles in the grid represents a value of r, and each ray from the pole represents a value of θ.

When plotting polar coordinates, you should identify the positive polar axis with an arrow and put a scale on it to indicate values of r.

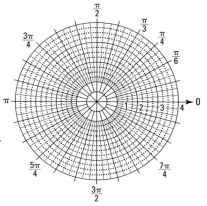

Example 3

a. Sketch all solutions [r, θ] to the equation r = 3;
b. Sketch all solutions [r, θ] to the equation θ = $-\frac{\pi}{3}$.

Solution

a. The equation r = 3 describes all points 3 units from the pole. The graph is a circle of radius 3 centered at the pole. This circle is drawn in blue at the right.

b. θ = $-\frac{\pi}{3}$ is the line obtained by rotating the polar axis by $-\frac{\pi}{3}$. This line is drawn in orange at the right.

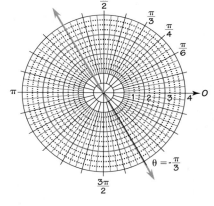

Adapting to Individual Needs

Extra Help
Some students may have difficulty remembering how to convert between rectangular and polar coordinates. It may be helpful to give students the following table.

Polar to Rectangular	Rectangular to Polar
1 pair of rectangular coordinates per point	Infinite pairs of polar coordinates per point
$x = r\cos θ$	$r = \pm \sqrt{x^2 + y^2}$
$y = r\sin θ$	$θ = \tan^{-1} \frac{y}{x} + n\pi$

Challenge
Have students use a graphing calculator in polar mode to graph each equation and then identify the shape of each curve.

1. $r = \dfrac{3}{2 - \cos θ}$ [Ellipse]
2. $r = \dfrac{4}{1 + \sin θ}$ [Parabola]
3. $r = \dfrac{4}{2 - 3\cos θ}$ [Hyperbola]

Converting from Polar to Rectangular Coordinates

Often polar and rectangular coordinate systems are superimposed on the same plane. Then the polar axis coincides with the *x*-axis and the pole is the origin. When this is done, you can use trigonometry to find the unique rectangular coordinate representation for any point for which polar coordinates are known.

Consider the diagram at the right. When the point on the polar axis with coordinate 1 is rotated θ about the origin, the rectangular coordinates of its image are (cos θ, sin θ). A size change of magnitude *r* maps this image onto (*r* cos θ, *r* sin θ). But this final image has polar coordinates [*r*, θ].

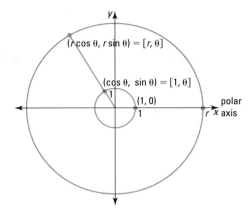

This proves the following theorem, which is true even when $r = 0$.

> **Theorem**
> If *P* has polar coordinates [*r*, θ], then the rectangular coordinates (*x*, *y*) of *P* are given by $x = r \cos θ$ and $y = r \sin θ$.

Example 4

Find the rectangular coordinates for the point with polar coordinates [4, 300°].

Solution

By the preceding theorem, the coordinates are **x = 4 cos 300° and y = 4 sin 300°.** So

$$(x, y) = \left(4 \cdot \frac{1}{2}, 4 \cdot -\frac{\sqrt{3}}{2}\right)$$
$$= (2, -2\sqrt{3}).$$

Check

Use a graph. Both [4, 300°] and $\left(2, -2\sqrt{3}\right)$ are in the 4th quadrant, and the points agree.

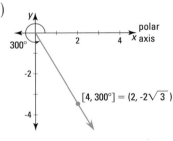

Lesson 13-4 *Polar Coordinates* **823**

Notes on Questions

Questions 1–4 If students do not have protractors and rulers, suggest that they copy the drawing for **Questions 1–4** onto polar graph paper. Do not underestimate the difficulty some students may have measuring the angles.

Questions 5, 8, and 20 Polar graph paper is needed. **Teaching Aids 118–119** are provided from which you can copy grids for your class.

Questions 9–10 You could write $(x, y) = [r, \theta]$ here, as they are two different names for the same point.

(Notes on Questions continue on page 826.)

Converting from Rectangular to Polar Coordinates

Converting from rectangular coordinates to polar coordinates is a little trickier. Suppose a point has polar coordinates $[r, \theta]$ and rectangular coordinates (x, y). Squaring and adding the equations in the theorem on page 823,

$$x^2 + y^2 = r^2\cos^2 \theta + r^2\sin^2 \theta$$
$$= r^2(\cos^2 \theta + \sin^2 \theta)$$
$$= r^2.$$

So
$$|r| = \sqrt{x^2 + y^2},$$
or
$$r = \pm\sqrt{x^2 + y^2}.$$

To find θ, again use the theorem on page 823. Start with $x = r \cos \theta$ and $y = r \sin \theta$. If $x \neq 0$, then you can divide the second equation by the first.

$$\frac{y}{x} = \frac{r \sin \theta}{r \cos \theta} = \tan \theta.$$

Notice that r may be positive or negative and that there are infinitely many values of θ for which $\tan \theta = \frac{y}{x}$. These correspond to the infinitely many polar coordinates which exist for any given point.

If $x = 0$, then $r \cos \theta = 0$ and the point (x, y) lies on the y-axis. If $(x, y) = (0, 0)$, so that (x, y) is the origin, then $r = \sqrt{0^2 + 0^2} = 0$. In this case, θ can have any value. Otherwise when $(x, y) = (0, y)$ with $y \neq 0$, then $r = \sqrt{0^2 + y^2} = \pm y$ and it must be that $\cos \theta = 0$. So $\theta = \pm\frac{\pi}{2}$. In this case you can pick either the positive or negative value for r and then determine whether θ is positive or negative.

Example 5

Find two different sets of polar coordinates for the point whose rectangular coordinates are (-2, -5).

Solution

Plot the point and draw a triangle.

$$r^2 = 5^2 + 2^2$$

So
$$r = \pm\sqrt{5^2 + 2^2}$$
$$= \pm\sqrt{29}.$$

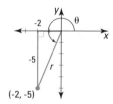

Also $\tan \theta = \frac{-5}{-2} = 2.5$. So one value of θ is $\tan^{-1} 2.5 \approx 68°$.

Thus $\theta \approx 68° \pm n \cdot 180°$. Now the choice of particular values of θ and r depend on matching the angle to the quadrant. If you use $r = \sqrt{29}$, then because (-2, -5) is in the third quadrant, a value of θ that can be used is $68° + 180° = 248°$. So one set of polar coordinates for (-2, -5) is about $[\sqrt{29}, 248°]$. If the value $-\sqrt{29}$ for r is used, the pair $[-\sqrt{29}, 68°]$ is another set of polar coordinates for this point.

QUESTIONS

Covering the Reading

In 1–4, O is the pole and $\overrightarrow{OA}$ is the polar axis of a polar coordinate system. Use a protractor and ruler to estimate the polar coordinates $[r, \theta]$ of the point. Measure r in cm and θ in degrees.

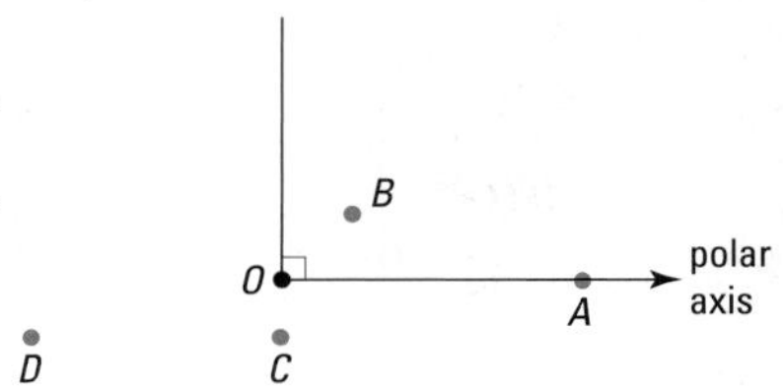

Samples:

1. A $\approx [2.4, 0°]$ **2.** B $\approx [0.8, 44°]$

3. C $\approx [0.5, 270°]$ **4.** D $\approx [2.0, 193°]$

5. Plot all the points on the same polar grid. **See left.**

a. $P = \left[1, \frac{\pi}{2}\right]$ **b.** $Q = \left[-1, \frac{\pi}{4}\right]$ **c.** $R = \left[3.25, -\frac{5\pi}{6}\right]$ **d.** $S = [-4, -75°]$

6. Suppose $P = \left[4, \frac{5\pi}{6}\right]$. **See left.**

a. Give another set of polar coordinates for P with $r = 4$, $\theta \neq \frac{5\pi}{6}$.

b. Give another set of polar coordinates for P with $r = -4$.

7. *Multiple choice.* Which polar coordinates do not identify the same point as $[6, -40°]$? **c**

(a) $[6, 320°]$ (b) $[6, -400°]$ (c) $[-6, 40°]$ (d) $[-6, 140°]$

8. On the same polar grid sketch all solutions to the following equations.

a. $r = 5$ **b.** $\theta = \frac{5\pi}{6}$

a, b) See left.

In 9 and 10, suppose (x, y) in a rectangular coordinate system names the same point as $[r, \theta]$ in a polar coordinate system. *True or false.*

9. $x = r\cos\theta$ **True** **10.** $|r| = \sqrt{x^2 + y^2}$ **True**

In 11 and 12, find the rectangular coordinates for the point P whose polar coordinates are given.

11. $\left[10, \frac{3\pi}{2}\right]$ **(0, -10)** **12.** $[8, -60°]$ **$(4, -4\sqrt{3})$**

In 13 and 14, give one pair of polar coordinates for the (x, y) pair. **Samples:**

13. $(5, 5\sqrt{3})$ **[10, 60°]** **14.** $(-6, -8)$ $\left[10, \tan^{-1}\left(\frac{4}{3}\right)\right] \approx [10, 233°]$

Applying the Mathematics

15. The point $[r, \theta]$ has $r = 8$. On what geometric figure must this point lie? **a circle with radius 8 and center at the pole**

16. The point $[r, \theta]$ has $\theta = \frac{3\pi}{4}$ radians. On what geometric figure must this point lie? **the line that is the image of the polar axis under a rotation of $(3\pi)/4$ about the pole**

In 17 and 18, consider the point $P = \left[6, \frac{\pi}{3}\right]$. State one pair of polar coordinates for the image of P under the given transformation. **See left.**

17. reflection over the polar axis **18.** reflection over the line $\theta = \frac{\pi}{2}$

5a–d)

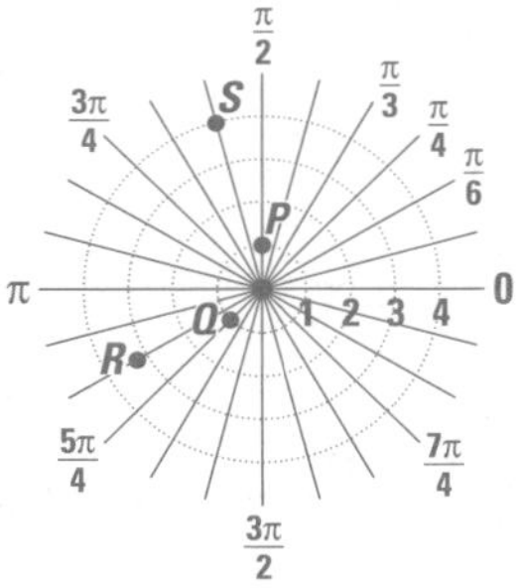

6a) Samples: $\left[4, \frac{17\pi}{6}\right]$, $\left[4, \frac{29\pi}{6}\right]$, $\left[4, -\frac{7\pi}{6}\right]$

b) Samples: $\left[-4, \frac{11\pi}{6}\right]$, $\left[-4, -\frac{\pi}{6}\right]$

8a, b)

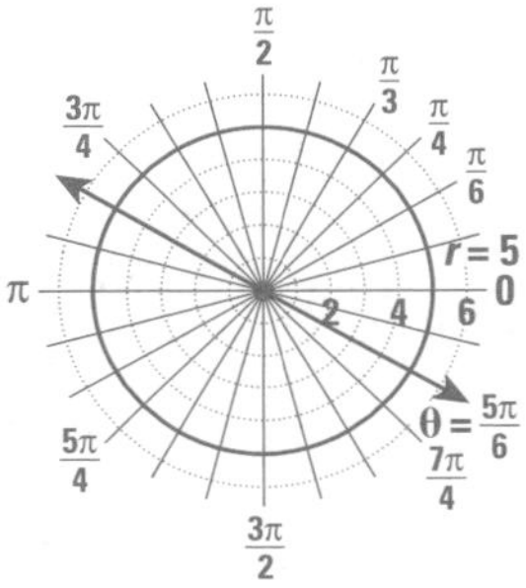

17) Samples: $\left[6, -\frac{\pi}{3}\right]$, $\left[-6, \frac{2\pi}{3}\right]$

18) Samples: $\left[6, \frac{2\pi}{3}\right]$, $\left[-6, -\frac{\pi}{3}\right]$

Follow-up for Lesson 13-4

Practice

For more questions on SPUR Objectives, use **Lesson Master 13-4** (shown on page 823).

Assessment

Written Communication Have students **work in pairs**. Ask students to make up one problem like **Example 4** and one like **Example 5**. Have students solve their partner's problems and plot each point on the appropriate graph. [Students convert between polar and rectangular coordinates and plot the points described.]

Extension

Refer students to **Example 3.** Have them determine the equations for the two geometric figures shown in rectangular coordinates. [a. $x^2 + y^2 = 9$; b. $y = -\sqrt{3}x$] Then ask them to generalize to any circle $r = k$ and any line passing through the pole, $\theta = m$. [Since $|r| = \sqrt{x^2 + y^2}$, $\sqrt{x^2 + y^2} = k$ and thus $x^2 + y^2 = k^2$. You may want to point out here, if students do not ask, that $r = -k$ and $r = k$ produce the same graph. Since $\tan\theta = \frac{y}{x}$, $\tan m = \frac{y}{x}$, and so $y = (\tan m)x$.]

Project Update Project 2, *Famous Polar Equations*, on page 858, relates to the content of this lesson.

Additional Answers

22. The graphs do not coincide in the domain tested. Counterexample:
Let $x = 30°$. Then
$\sec x + \cot x \cdot \csc x$
$= \sec 30° + \cot 30° \csc 30°$
$= \dfrac{1}{\cos 30°} + \dfrac{\cos 30°}{\sin 30°} \cdot \dfrac{1}{\sin 30°}$
$= \dfrac{2}{\sqrt{3}} + \sqrt{3} \cdot 2 \approx 4.6$
and $\sec x \csc x$
$= \sec 30° \csc 30°$
$= \dfrac{1}{\cos 30°} \cdot \dfrac{1}{\sin 30°} = \dfrac{2}{\sqrt{3}} \cdot 2 \approx 2.3$.
So, $\sec x + \cot x \csc x$
$\neq \sec x \csc x$ for all x

26. a, b.

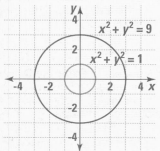

27. a, b.

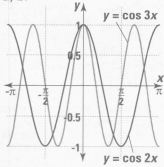

28. a. Slope connecting $(0, 0)$
and $(m, n) = \dfrac{n - 0}{m - 0} = \dfrac{n}{m}$
Slope connecting (m, n)
and $(p, q) = \dfrac{q - n}{p - m}$
Slope connecting (p, q)
and $(p - m, q - n) =$
$\dfrac{q - n - q}{p - m - p} = \dfrac{n}{m}$
Slope connecting
$(p - m, q - n)$ and $(0, 0) =$
$\dfrac{q - n - 0}{p - m - 0} = \dfrac{q - n}{p - m}$
Since both pairs of opposite sides are parallel, the figure is a parallelogram.

19. Airport runways are often numbered in a way that is related to polar coordinates. If you land from the north, you see a runway numbered 0. If you land from the west, you see a runway numbered 9. Each additional unit corresponds to 10° counterclockwise, the highest being 35. From what direction do you land on a runway with the given number?
   a. 18   b. 1   c. 22   d. 16
   south   10° W of N   40° E of S   20° W of S

20. a. Plot on polar graph paper. **See left.**

r	0	$\frac{1}{2}(\sqrt{6} - \sqrt{2})$	1	$\sqrt{2}$	$\sqrt{3}$	$\frac{1}{2}(\sqrt{2} + \sqrt{6})$	2
$\theta°$	0	15	30	45	60	75	90

b. The points above all satisfy the equation $r = 2 \sin \theta$. Let $\theta = 105°, 120°, \dots$, and find six more points satisfying this equation. Plot these points. **See left.**

c. Make a conjecture about the graph of all points $[r, \theta]$ satisfying $r = 2 \sin \theta$. **It is a circle with center $[1, 90°]$ and radius 1.**

20a)

b) $\left[\frac{1}{2}(\sqrt{6} + \sqrt{2}), 105°\right]$,
$[\sqrt{3}, 120°]$,
$[\sqrt{2}, 135°], [1, 150°]$,
$\left[\frac{1}{2}(\sqrt{6} - \sqrt{2}), 165°\right]$,
$[0, 180°]$. See graph above.

21) $\sin\left(\frac{\pi}{2} + x\right) =$
$\sin \frac{\pi}{2} \cos x +$
$\cos \frac{\pi}{2} \sin x =$
$1 \cdot \cos x + 0 \cdot \sin x =$
$\cos x$ for all x

Review

In 21 and 22, if the equation is an identity, give a proof and state the domain on which it is true. If the equation is not an identity, provide a counterexample. *(Lessons 11-5, 13-3)*

21. $\sin\left(\frac{\pi}{2} + x\right) = \cos x$ 22. $\sec x + \cot x \csc x = \sec x \csc x$
   See left.   **See margin.**

In 23 and 24, simplify using trigonometric identities. *(Lessons 4-4, 13-2)*

23. a. $\sin^2 \theta + \cos^2 \theta$ **1**   b. $25 \sin^2 \theta + 25 \cos^2 \theta$ **25**

24. a. $1 + \tan^2 \theta$ **$\sec^2 \theta$**   b. $r^2 + r^2 \tan^2 \theta$ **$r^2 \sec^2 \theta$**

25. Give the center and radius of the circle with equation
$x^2 + 2x + y^2 + 8y = 8$. *(Lesson 12-5)* **center: $(-1, -4)$; radius: 5**

In 26 and 27, graph the two equations on the same set of axes. *(Lessons 4-7, 12-2)* **See margin.**

26. a. $x^2 + y^2 = 1$ b. $x^2 + y^2 = 9$

27. a. $y = \cos 2x$ b. $y = \cos 3x$

28. a. Prove that the quadrilateral with consecutive vertices $(0, 0)$, (m, n), (p, q), and $(p - m, q - n)$ is a parallelogram.
   b. Draw such a parallelogram. *(Previous course)*
   a, b) See margin.

Exploration

29. How might points be described in three-dimensional space using polar coordinates? **Sample: One way is by using cylindrical coordinates. A point (x, y, z) would be described by $[r, \theta, z]$ in cylindrical coordinates, where, as in polar coordinates, $x = r \cos \theta$ and $y = r \sin \theta$.**

28. b. Sample:

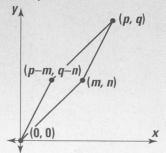

Setting Up Lesson 13-5

Questions 8, 15, 16, and 20 of this lesson give basic ideas for the next lesson.
Question 20 is particularly important, in that it involves the type of thinking used throughout the next lesson.

Any equation which involves only the variables r and θ can be graphed using polar coordinates. For instance, in the previous lesson the equations $r = 3$ and $\theta = -\frac{\pi}{3}$ were graphed. Some automatic graphers allow you to graph polar relations. The relation is usually entered in the form $r = f(\theta)$ or $r = f(t)$.

You should be able to draw by hand graphs of relatively simple equations of the form $r = f(\theta)$. In particular, you should study the patterns that emerge when graphs of the parent circular functions are made.

The Graph of the Cosine Function in Polar Coordinates

Example 1

Sketch a graph of the polar equation $r = \cos \theta$.

Solution

Make a table of values for $[r, \theta]$ for $0 \le \theta \le 2\pi$, and plot the points. A table for some values of θ between 0 and π is below, and the corresponding graph is below. When making the table it is usual to consider θ to be the independent variable and r to be the dependent variable.

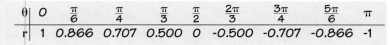

θ	0	$\frac{\pi}{6}$	$\frac{\pi}{4}$	$\frac{\pi}{3}$	$\frac{\pi}{2}$	$\frac{2\pi}{3}$	$\frac{3\pi}{4}$	$\frac{5\pi}{6}$	π
r	1	0.866	0.707	0.500	0	-0.500	-0.707	-0.866	-1

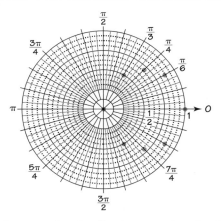

Notice that as θ increases from 0 to $\frac{\pi}{2}$, r decreases from 1 to 0, and points above the polar axis are generated. As θ increases from $\frac{\pi}{2}$ to π, r decreases from 0 to -1, which produces points below the polar axis.

Lesson 13-5 *Polar Graphs* **827**

Lesson 13-5

Objectives
K Graph and interpret graphs of polar equations.

Resources
From the *Teacher's Resource File*
■ Lesson Master 13-5
■ Answer Master 13-5
■ Teaching Aids
  113 Warm-up
  120 Table and Graph for Example 1
  121 Rose Curves
  122 Graphs for Example 3

Additional Resources
■ Visuals for Teaching Aids 113, 120, 121, 122
■ Explorations 13-5

Teaching Lesson 13-5

Warm-up
Examine your calculator to determine if and how it can plot points in polar coordinates. Be ready to explain how to others.

Notes on Reading
Even if you do not have access to a polar grapher, we have designed the questions so that students are asked to graph only equations whose graphs have relatively simple shapes—probably the most difficult are the cardioid and spiral in **Questions 11–12**.

Lesson 13-5 Overview

Broad Goals This lesson provides only an introduction to polar graphs, concentrating on the circles with equations of the form $r = a \cos \theta$ and $r = a \sin \theta$ and the rose curves of the form $r = a \sin b\theta$ and $r = a \cos b\theta$, though other curves are considered in the questions.

Perspective The mechanics of graphing in polar coordinates are nearly the same as graphing in rectangular coordinates. The

differences are that the variables are customarily r and θ rather than x and y and that different values of r and θ may give rise to the same point.

The graphs of equations in the polar plane can be as simple as a circle, or as delightful as a rose. Unfortunately, these graphs have not been part of the secondary curriculum in large part because of the difficulty of drawing them with pencil and paper. Indeed,

the topic is often minimized in college calculus classes. An automatic grapher with the option to graph polar curves takes the tedium away and opens this beautiful bit of mathematics to students.

We do not expect students to be able to graph equations more complicated than the following:
$r = k$ (circle)
$\theta = k$ (line through origin)
$r = a \sin \theta$ (circle)
$r = a \cos \theta$ (circle)
$r = a \sin b\theta$ (rose curve)
$r = a \cos b\theta$ (rose curve)
$r \sin \theta = k$ (horizontal line)
$r \cos \theta = k$ (vertical line).
Rose curves of the above forms have b petals when b is odd but $2b$ petals when b is even. (See **Question 10b**.) **Teaching Aid 121** contains rose curves.

Alternate Approach There are two general ways to graph polar equations. One is to plot points, as in **Example 1. Teaching Aid 120** is provided with this table and graph. The other is to utilize the corresponding graph in rectangular coordinates, as in **Example 3. Teaching Aid 122** is provided with all the graphs from this example.

The method of **Example 1** has the advantage of being more direct; the method of **Example 3** can help one see some of the larger features of the curve.

Point out that we can do **Example 2** because we know rectangular coordinate descriptions of a circle.

Additional Examples

1. Sketch a graph of the polar equation $r = 4 \sin \theta$.

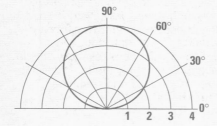

When θ is between π and $\frac{3\pi}{2}$, $r = \cos \theta$ is negative. All such points are in the first quadrant, and coincide with the points generated when $0 \leq \theta \leq \frac{\pi}{2}$. For instance, if $\theta = \frac{5\pi}{4}$, $r = \cos \frac{5\pi}{4} \approx -0.707$. The point $\left[-0.707, \frac{5\pi}{4}\right]$ coincides with the point $\left[0.707, \frac{\pi}{4}\right]$, which has already been plotted.

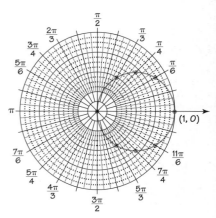

Similarly, when $\frac{3\pi}{2} \leq \theta \leq 2\pi$, the points generated coincide with those generated by $\frac{\pi}{2} \leq \theta \leq \pi$. The complete graph is drawn above. The graph appears to be a circle.

By converting from polar to rectangular coordinates, the graph of $r = \cos \theta$ can be proved to be a circle. The idea is to derive a rectangular equation for $r = \cos \theta$, and show that it is of the form $(x - h)^2 + (y - k)^2 = r^2$.

Example 2

Prove that the graph of $r = \cos \theta$ is a circle.

Solution

Since $x = r \cos \theta$, $\cos \theta = \frac{x}{r}$.
Now substitute $\frac{x}{r}$ for $\cos \theta$ in $r = \cos \theta$ and rewrite.

If
$$r = \cos \theta,$$
then
$$r = \frac{x}{r}.$$
So
$$r^2 = x.$$
But $r^2 = x^2 + y^2$, and substituting for r^2 in the preceding equation gives
$$x^2 + y^2 = x.$$
Subtracting x from each side of the equation gives
$$x^2 - x + y^2 = 0.$$
Now complete the square in x.
$$\left(x^2 - x + \frac{1}{4}\right) + y^2 = \frac{1}{4}$$
$$\left(x - \frac{1}{2}\right)^2 + y^2 = \frac{1}{4}$$

This equation, $\left(x - \frac{1}{2}\right)^2 + y^2 = \frac{1}{4}$, is an equation in the rectangular coordinate system for the circle with center at $\left(\frac{1}{2}, 0\right)$ and radius $\frac{1}{2}$. It is the same circle as graphed in Example 1 (shown here smaller).

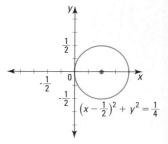

828

Optional Activities

Activity 1 Technology Connection
Materials: Explorations software

Students may use *Exploration 13-5, Polar Graphs*, as a review of Lesson 13-5. Students can explore polar graphs by choosing a polar equation. The computer will show some of the coordinate points and the graph on polar coordinates. An animation feature allows students to see how the polar coordinates for the point

change as θ changes over the interval $0 \leq \theta \leq 2\pi$. Students can also enter their own values into the table.

Activity 2
You might use this activity after students complete the lesson. Tell them that the graph of $r = b + a \cos \theta$ is called a *limaçon*. Have them graph some limaçons on their automatic graphers, using different values for a and b such as
1. $b = 3$; $a = 2$.
2. $b = 1$; $a = 2$.
3. $b = 1$; $a = -2$.
4. $b = 3$; $a = -2$.

In the Questions you are asked to show that any equation of the form $r = a \cos \theta$, where $a \neq 0$, is a circle.

Rose Curves

Recall that in the rectangular coordinate system, graphs of functions of the form $y = \cos b\theta$, where b is a positive integer, are sine waves with amplitude 1 and period $\frac{2\pi}{b}$. The graphs of polar equations in the form $r = \cos b\theta$, where b is a positive integer, are quite different and beautiful. Below are graphs for $b = 2$, 3, and 4 made by an automatic grapher.

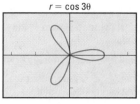

$r = \cos 2\theta$

$0 \leq \theta \leq 360$, θ step = 7.5
$-2.25 \leq x \leq 2.25$,   x-scale = 1
$-1.5 \leq y \leq 1.5$,   y-scale = 1

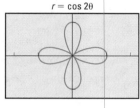

$r = \cos 3\theta$

$0 \leq \theta \leq 180$, θ step = 7.5
$-2.25 \leq x \leq 2.25$,   x-scale = 1
$-1.5 \leq y \leq 1.5$,   y-scale = 1

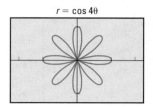

$r = \cos 4\theta$

$0 \leq \theta \leq 360$, θ step = 7.5
$-2.25 \leq x \leq 2.25$,   x-scale = 1
$-1.5 \leq y \leq 1.5$,   y-scale = 1

These graphs are part of a family of polar graphs called *rose curves* or *petal curves*. The following example shows how to draw a rose curve by hand without having to plot too many points.

dogwood

trillium

clematis

Example 3

Sketch a graph of all $[r, \theta]$ with $r = 3 \sin 2\theta$.

Solution

First sketch a graph of $y = 3 \sin 2x$ for $0 \leq x \leq 2\pi$ in rectangular coordinates. As shown at the right, it has amplitude 3 and period $\frac{2\pi}{2} = \pi$.

Since $y = 3 \sin 2x$ and $r = 3 \sin 2\theta$, the possible y values of the function on the rectangular coordinate graph are the possible values of r in the polar coordinate graph. Thus, $-3 \leq r \leq 3$.

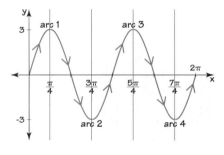

The x-intercepts of the rectangular graph indicate when $r = 0$, that is, when the polar graph passes through the pole. Notice also that when $0 \leq x \leq 2\pi$, the rectangular coordinate graph has 4 congruent arcs, each symmetric to a vertical line where x is an odd multiple of $\frac{\pi}{4}$. In the polar graph, this reflection symmetry gives rise to symmetry in the "petals."

▶

Lesson 13-5   *Polar Graphs*   **829**

---

2. Prove that the graph in Additional Example 1 is a circle. Substitute for r and $\frac{y}{r} = \frac{y}{\sqrt{x^2 + y^2}}$ for sin θ. This yields $\sqrt{x^2 + y^2} = 4 \cdot \frac{y}{\sqrt{x^2 + y^2}}$, which is equivalent to $x^2 + y^2 = 4y$, or $x^2 + y^2 - 4y = 0$. From completing the square, or from the theorem about quadratic relations in Lesson 12-6, this is seen to be a circle. If we wished to be more specific, we complete the square to obtain the equivalent equation $x^2 + (y - 2)^2 = 4$, which is an equation for the circle with center (0, 2) and radius 2, verifying the answer to Additional Example 1.

3. Graph all $[r, \theta]$ with $r = 2 \cos 3\theta$.

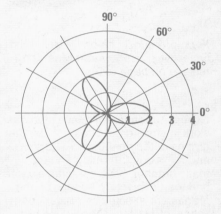

This is a rose curve with 3 petals, twice the size of the middle graph on the opening page of this chapter.

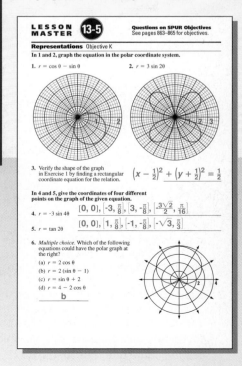
Adapting to Individual Needs

Have students conjecture when the limaçon will have a loop and when it will have a dimple. [The limaçon has a dimple if $|b| > |a|$; it has a loop if $|b| < |a|$. Incidentally, when $|a| = |b|$, the limaçon becomes a cardioid.] Finally, ask students to look up the etymology of limaçon to see why it was chosen as the name of this curve. [The name goes back to old French, *limaz*, which meant slug or snail.]

Extra Help

Point out as you discuss **Example 1** that when working in the polar plane it is customary to consider the second coordinate, θ, to be the independent value, and the first coordinate, r, to be the dependent variable. This is the opposite of what is customarily done with rectangular coordinates where the first coordinate is the independent variable and y is the dependent variable.

Notes on Questions

Question 4b Error Alert Since the equation should be for rectangular coordinates, it should involve only x and y, not r and θ. However, the equation need not be in standard form.

Question 10 Have students use the zoom menu and choose the option that will square the screen. This command adjusts the screen in only one direction so that 1 unit on the x-axis is the same length as 1 unit on the y-axis. Otherwise the graphs will be distorted.

Follow-up 13-5
for Lesson

Practice

For more questions on SPUR Objectives, use **Lesson Master 13-5** (shown on page 829).

Assessment

Group Assessment Have students work in small groups to consider the graphs of the equations $r = a \sin b\theta$ and $r = a \cos b\theta$. Using an automatic grapher, have students explore and then conjecture about how the graphs are affected by (1) various values of b, (2) various values of a, and (3) whether the function is sine or cosine. [Students graph rose curves and make generalizations.]

stained-glass rose window in Notre Dame Cathedral, Chartres, France

▶ To sketch the polar graph, begin with the point $[0, \theta]$. As θ increases from 0 to $\frac{\pi}{4}$, r increases from 0 to 3. This part of the graph of $r = 3 \sin 2\theta$ is pictured at the right.

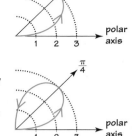

As θ continues to increase from $\frac{\pi}{4}$ to $\frac{\pi}{2}$, the value of r decreases from 3 to 0. The reflection symmetry in arc 1 above results in symmetry over the line $\theta = \frac{\pi}{4}$ for the corresponding arc in the polar plane. Thus, the loop shown at the right has been completed.

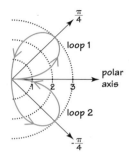

Similarly, as θ increases from $\frac{\pi}{2}$ to $\frac{3\pi}{4}$, r decreases from 0 to -3; and as θ goes from $\frac{3\pi}{4}$ to π, r increases from -3 to 0. These points are on loop 2, as noted on the sketch at the right.

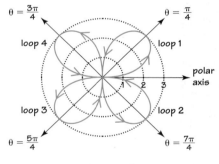

A similar analysis of arcs 3 and 4 indicates that there are two more loops in the polar graph. A complete graph of $r = 3 \sin 2\theta$ is sketched below. It is a 4-petaled rose.

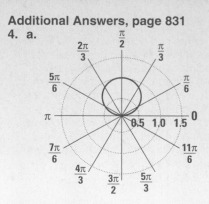

In general, polar graphs of trigonometric functions with equations of the form $r = c + a \sin b\theta$ or $r = c + a \cos b\theta$, where b is a positive integer and $a \neq 0$, are beautiful curves. You are asked to draw some of these in the Questions.

Adapting to Individual Needs

Challenge

1. Compare the spiral $r\theta = \pi$ with the one in **Question 11**. [$r\theta = \pi$ does not go through the pole. It has an asymptote; the horizontal line π units above the polar axis.]

2. Explain why the point $[0, 0]$ lies on the circle graphed in **Example 1** but it doesn't satisfy the equation. [The polar coordinate pair graphed is $[0, \frac{\pi}{2}]$, which has the same graph as $[0, 0]$.]

Setting Up Lesson 13-6

Discuss **Questions 19–20** to refresh students' minds about complex numbers.

Additional Answers, page 831

4. a.

QUESTIONS

Covering the Reading

1. Consider the polar equation $r = 2$.
  a. Sketch a graph of the equation. **See left.**
  b. Give an equation in rectangular coordinates x and y for this graph.
  $x^2 + y^2 = 4$

1a)

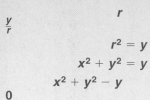

2. Describe the graph of $r = a$, where a is a constant nonzero real number.
It is a circle with center at the pole and radius a.

3. Consider the equation $r = 2 \cos \theta$ in the polar plane.
  a. Find and plot at least six points on its graph.
  b. Prove that the graph is a circle.
  a, b) See left.

4. Consider $r = \sin \theta$.
  a. Sketch a graph of this function in a polar coordinate system.
  b. Derive an equation for this curve in rectangular coordinates.
  a, b) See margin.

In 5 and 6, refer to the rose curves on page 829. *True or false.*

5. The point $[4, \pi]$ is on the graph of $r = \cos 4\theta$. **False**

6. The point $[0, 0]$ is on the graph of $r = \cos 2\theta$. **True**

3a) $[2, 0], \left[\sqrt{3}, \frac{\pi}{6}\right],$
$\left[-\sqrt{3}, \frac{5\pi}{6}\right], \left[1, \frac{\pi}{3}\right],$
$\left[0, \frac{\pi}{2}\right], \left[-1, \frac{2\pi}{3}\right]$

7. Consider the equation $r = 3 \cos 2\theta$.
  a. Sketch a graph of this equation in the rectangular plane.
  b. What are the maximum and minimum values of r? **3, -3**
  c. Find r when $\theta = 0, \frac{\pi}{6}$, and $\frac{\pi}{2}$, and plot these points in the polar plane.
  d. Use the technique described in Example 3 to sketch a complete graph of this equation in polar coordinates. **a, d) See margin.**
  c) $[3, 0], \left[1.5, \frac{\pi}{6}\right], \left[-3, \frac{\pi}{2}\right].$ **See d) in margin for art.**

Applying the Mathematics

8. At the right is a graph of $r = \sin 2\theta$. Give the coordinates of four points on the graph.

Samples: $\left[1, \frac{\pi}{4}\right], [0, \pi], \left[-1, \frac{3\pi}{4}\right], [0, 2\pi]$

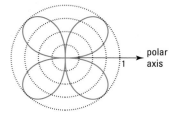

polar axis

b) For $r \neq 0$; $r = 2 \cos \theta$
$$r = 2\left(\frac{x}{r}\right)$$
$$r^2 = 2x$$
$$x^2 + y^2 = 2x$$
$$x^2 - 2x + y^2 = 0$$
$$(x - 1)^2 + y^2 = 1,$$
which is the equation of a circle with center (1, 0) and radius 1. If $r = 0$, $x = y = 0$, so the origin is also included.

9. Sketch a graph in polar coordinates of $r = a \sin 2\theta$, where a is a positive real number. **See margin.**

10. Refer to the graphs of $r = \cos 2\theta$, $r = \cos 3\theta$, and $r = \cos 4\theta$ in the reading.
  a. Make a conjecture regarding the number of petals on the polar curve $r = \cos n\theta$, where n is a positive integer. **See left.**
  b. Test your conjecture by drawing polar graphs of $r = \cos 5\theta$ and $r = \cos 6\theta$ with an automatic grapher. **See margin.**

10a) If n is odd, there are n petals. If n is even, there are $2n$ petals.

Lesson 13-5 *Polar Graphs* **831**

Extension

Refer students to **Question 10.** They should have discovered that $r = a \cos(n\theta)$ or $r = a \sin(n\theta)$ produce $2n$ petals if n is even and n petals if n is odd. Ask students how they could produce a rose curve with 6 petals, 10 petals, and 2 petals. To produce $2(2n - 1)$ petals is tricky at first because these numbers are all twice an odd number, and using an odd number will produce that number of odd petals. Have students experiment to see if they can find an alteration to the rose curve equations that will produce $2(2n - 1)$ petals.
$[r = a\sqrt{\sin^2(2n - 1)\theta}$ will produce the desired $2(2n - 1)$ number of petals. For the case $n = 1$, this equation is sometimes referred to as a *lemniscate*.]

Project Update Project 2, *Famous Polar Equations*, on page 858, relates to the content of this lesson.

9.

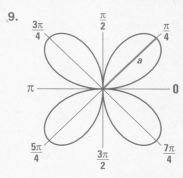

10. b. $r = \cos 5\theta$

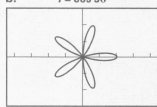

$0° \leq \theta \leq 360°, \quad \theta \text{ step} = 7.5°$
$-2.25 \leq x \leq 2.25, \ x\text{-scale} = 0.5$
$-1.5 \leq y \leq 1.5, \quad y\text{-scale} = 0.5$

$r = \cos 6\theta$

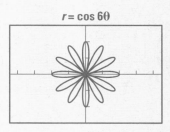

$0° \leq \theta \leq 360°, \quad \theta \text{ step} = 7.5°$
$-2.25 \leq x \leq 2.25, \ x\text{-scale} = 0.5$
$-1.5 \leq y \leq 1.5, \quad y\text{-scale} = 0.5$

4. b. For $r \neq 0$, $r = \sin \theta$

$$r = \frac{y}{r}$$
$$r^2 = y$$
$$x^2 + y^2 = y$$
$$x^2 + y^2 - y = 0$$
$$x^2 + \left(y - \frac{1}{2}\right)^2 = \frac{1}{4}$$

If $r = 0$, $x = y = 0$, so the origin is also included.

7. a.

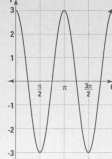

7. d.

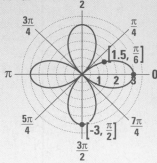

$[1.5, \frac{\pi}{6}]$

$[-3, \frac{\pi}{2}]$

831

13. b.

14. a.

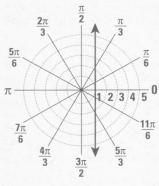

16. a. Seems to be an identity.

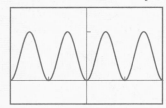

-2π ≤ x ≤ 2π, x-scale = π
-0.5 ≤ y ≤ 1.5, y-scale = 1

b. For all x, $\frac{1}{2}(1 - \cos 2x)$
$= \frac{1}{2}(1 - (\cos^2 x - \sin^2 x))$
$= \frac{1}{2}(1 - \cos^2 x + \sin^2 x)$
$= \frac{1}{2}(\sin^2 x + \sin^2 x)$
$= \frac{1}{2}(2\sin^2 x) = \sin^2 x.$

17. a. Not an identity

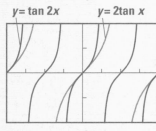

$y = \tan 2x$ $y = 2\tan x$

-π ≤ x ≤ π, x-scale = $\frac{\pi}{4}$
-4 ≤ y ≤ 4, y-scale = 2

832

With All My Cardioid.
Hearts are a traditional decoration for Valentine's Day cards. This Victorian valentine dates from about 1900.

11)

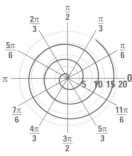

12a)

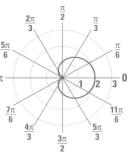

832

---

11. The graph of $r = \theta$, for $\theta > 0$, in the polar plane is called an *Archimedean spiral*, named after Archimedes. Graph this curve. **See left.**

12. The graph of $r = a(\cos \theta - 1)$ in the polar plane is called a *cardioid*.
a. Graph this curve for $a = 1$. **See left.**
b. Why is *cardioid* an appropriate name for this curve?
It is shaped like a heart.

13. The graph of $r = a^\theta$, where $a > 0$, is called a *logarithmic spiral*.
a. For $r = 2^\theta$, find the coordinates of the points in the interval $0 \le \theta < 2\pi$ where θ is a multiple of $\frac{\pi}{4}$. **See below.**
b. Graph the curve. **See margin.**

14. Consider the equation $r = \sec \theta$.
a. Graph the equation in polar coordinates. **See margin.**
b. Give an equation of the graph in rectangular coordinates. **x = 1**

Review

15. Which polar pairs describe the same point? *(Lesson 13-4)* **a, b, and c**
(a) $\left[0.5, \frac{5\pi}{6}\right]$ (b) $\left[-\frac{1}{2}, -\frac{\pi}{6}\right]$ (c) $\left[\frac{1}{2}, -\frac{7\pi}{6}\right]$ (d) $\left[-0.5, -\frac{5\pi}{6}\right]$

In 16 and 17, a trigonometric equation is given. **a.** Use an automatic grapher to test whether the equation seems to be an identity. **b.** Prove your conclusion in part **a**. *(Lessons 13-2, 13-3)* **See margin.**

16. $\sin^2 x = \frac{1}{2}(1 - \cos 2x)$ **17.** $\tan 2x = 2 \tan x$

18. Show that multiplication of 2×2 matrices is not always commutative. *(Lesson 11-1)* **See margin.**

19. Suppose $f(x) = x^3 - 729$. Find all complex numbers such that $f(x) = 0$. *(Lesson 9-8)* $9, -\frac{9}{2} + \frac{9\sqrt{3}}{2}i, -\frac{9}{2} - \frac{9\sqrt{3}}{2}i$

20. Let $u = 3 - 4i$ and $v = 5 + i$. Write each of the following in $a + bi$ form. *(Lesson 9-6)*
a. $u + v$ **b.** uv **c.** $\frac{u}{v}$
  $8 - 3i$ $19 - 17i$ $\frac{11}{26} - \frac{23}{26}i$

Exploration

21. Consider equations of the form $r = a + b \sin \theta$, where $a > 0$ and $b > 0$. Experiment with an automatic grapher using various values of a and b.
a. Find an equation whose graph looks like the one at the right.
b. In general, what is true about a and b if the graph of $r = a + b \sin \theta$ has a loop as above? **b > a**
a) Sample: $r = 1 + 2 \sin \theta$

13a) $[1, 0], \left[1.72, \frac{\pi}{4}\right], \left[2.97, \frac{\pi}{2}\right], \left[5.12, \frac{3\pi}{4}\right], [8.82, \pi], \left[15.21, \frac{5\pi}{4}\right],$ $\left[26.22, \frac{3\pi}{2}\right], \left[45.19, \frac{7\pi}{4}\right]$

---

17. b. When $x = 30°$, then
$\tan 2x = \tan 60°$
$= \sqrt{3}$ and
$2 \tan x = 2 \tan 30°$
$= 2 \cdot \frac{1}{\sqrt{3}} = \frac{2\sqrt{3}}{3}.$
So $\tan 2x = 2 \tan x$
is not an identity.

18. Sample:

$\begin{bmatrix} 1 & 2 \\ 1 & 2 \end{bmatrix} \cdot \begin{bmatrix} 3 & 4 \\ 3 & 4 \end{bmatrix} = \begin{bmatrix} 9 & 12 \\ 9 & 12 \end{bmatrix}$

but

$\begin{bmatrix} 3 & 4 \\ 3 & 4 \end{bmatrix} \cdot \begin{bmatrix} 1 & 2 \\ 1 & 2 \end{bmatrix} = \begin{bmatrix} 7 & 14 \\ 7 & 14 \end{bmatrix}$

Therefore, multiplication of 2×2 matrices is not commutative.

Graphing Complex Numbers in the Rectangular Coordinate Plane

About 1800, Caspar Wessel, a Norwegian surveyor, and Jean Robert Argand, a Swiss mathematician, independently invented a geometric representation of complex numbers. Their diagrams, sometimes called *Argand diagrams*, involve graphs in a *complex plane*. As you will see in the remainder of this chapter, these graphs can be useful, illuminating, and beautiful.

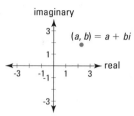

In a complex plane, the horizontal axis is called the **real axis** and the vertical axis is called the **imaginary axis**. To graph the complex number $a + bi$ in the complex plane, first write it as the ordered pair (a, b). Then plot (a, b) as you normally would in a rectangular coordinate system.

Each real number is of the form $a + 0i$, so it equals $(a, 0)$ and is plotted on the real axis in the complex plane. Similarly, every imaginary number is of the form $0 + bi$ and $(0, b)$ is plotted on the imaginary axis. The complex number $0 = 0 + 0i = (0, 0)$, and is graphed at the origin.

Example 1

Graph in the complex plane.
a. $-6i$
b. $2 + 5i$
c. $-4 - i$

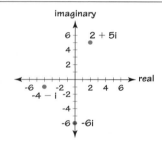

Solution
a. $-6i$ can be rewritten as $0 - 6i$, which equals the ordered pair $(0, -6)$.
b. $2 + 5i = (2, 5)$
c. $-4 - i = (-4, -1)$

Picturing Addition of Complex Numbers

Addition of complex numbers has a nice geometric interpretation in the complex plane. For instance, the sum of $3 + 7i$ and $2 - 4i$ is $5 + 3i$. As shown in the diagram at the right, the numbers $(3, 7)$, $(2, -4)$, their sum $(5, 3)$, and the origin $(0, 0)$ are the vertices of a parallelogram.

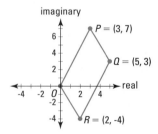

Objectives
C Represent complex numbers in different forms.
L Graph complex numbers.

Resources
From the *Teacher's Resource File*
■ Lesson Master 13-6
■ Answer Master 13-6
■ Assessment Sourcebook: Quiz for Lessons 13-4 through 13-6
■ Teaching Aids
    113 Warm-up
    123 Geometric Addition Theorem/Example 2

Additional Resources
■ Visuals for Teaching Aids 113, 123

Teaching Lesson **13-6**

Warm-up
Suppose * is an operation on ordered pairs, with $(a, b) * (c, d) = (a + c, b + d)$.
1. Calculate $(2, 5) * (7, -1)$. **(9, 4)**
2. Graph $(0, 0)$, $(2, 5)$, $(7, -1)$, and your answer to Question 1. **The points are vertices of a parallelogram.**
3. Generalize the result of Question 2. **$(0, 0)$, (a, b), (c, d), and $(a + c, b + d)$ are vertices of a parallelogram.**

Lesson 13-6 Overview

Broad Goals This is the first of three lessons in which the operations on complex numbers are pictured. Here addition and subtraction are discussed.

Perspective Just as there is a 1-1 correspondence between the set of real numbers and the points on a line, so there is a 1-1 correspondence between the set of complex numbers and the points of a plane. We associate the complex number $x + yi$ with

the point (x, y) or with the equivalent polar form $[r, \theta]$. The polar form has some nice advantages; the distance of the complex number $[r, \theta]$ from the origin is $|r|$, the absolute value of the number. To graph a point (x, y) in rectangular coordinates, we think of "going over x and up y." This process is similar to applying the translation $T_{x,y}$ to the origin. To add two complex numbers (a, b) and (c, d), we can think of applying

the translation $T_{c,d}$ to the first point. That is, we move the first point over c and up d. The result is the sum $(a + c, b + d)$. This addition is the same as vector addition of the vectors (a, b) and (c, d), as parroted in the Warm-up. The two addends, the sum, and the origin are vertices of a parallelogram.

Notes on Reading

Making Connections There are at least four analogies that you can make in this lesson between real numbers and complex numbers. (1) Real numbers are identified with points on a line, which is then sometimes called the *real number line.* Complex numbers are identified with points on a plane, which is then sometimes called the *complex plane.* (2) Real number addition can be done using arrows on a number line. The picture of complex number addition is identical, except it involves two dimensions. (**Teaching Aid 123** is provided.) (3) When x is a real number, $|x|$ is the distance of x from 0, and when $z = a + bi = (a, b)$ is a complex number, $|z| = \sqrt{a^2 + b^2}$ is the distance of z from $(0, 0)$. (4) If x and y are real numbers, then $|x - y|$ is the distance on a number line from x to y. If z and w are complex numbers, then $|z - w|$ is the distance between them in the complex plane. (See **Question 15.**)

Although there are many polar coordinates $[r, \theta]$ for a given complex number, in practice the preferred value of r is positive, and θ is usually in the interval $0 \le \theta < 2\pi$. This is similar to the preference of having a fraction in lowest terms.

Error Alert A common error is for students to put an i in the second coordinate of the complex number. That is, they will write (a, bi) for $a + bi$. Explain that the order of the coordinates tells which is the real part and which is the imaginary part, so no i is needed.

This is easy to verify. Because the slopes of the opposite sides of $OPQR$ are equal, the opposite sides are parallel and the quadrilateral is a parallelogram.

$$\text{slope of } \overline{OP} = \tfrac{7 - 0}{3 - 0} = \tfrac{7}{3}$$
$$\text{slope of } \overline{PQ} = \tfrac{3 - 7}{5 - 3} = \tfrac{-4}{2} = -2$$
$$\text{slope of } \overline{QR} = \tfrac{-4 - 3}{2 - 5} = \tfrac{-7}{-3} = \tfrac{7}{3}$$
$$\text{slope of } \overline{OR} = \tfrac{-4 - 0}{2 - 0} = \tfrac{-4}{2} = -2$$

This proves one instance of the following theorem. You are asked to prove the general case in the Questions.

Geometric Addition Theorem
If the complex numbers $a + bi$ and $c + di$ are not collinear with the origin in the complex plane, then their sum $(a + c) + (b + d)i$ is the fourth vertex of a parallelogram with consecutive vertices $a + bi$, 0, and $c + di$.

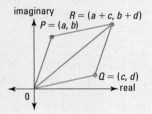

Example 2

Let $z = 8 + 6i$ and $w = 2 - 4i$. Represent geometrically the quantities $z + w$, $z - w$, $w - z$, and $-(z + w)$.

Solution

First perform the operations:
$$z + w = 10 + 2i$$
$$z - w = 6 + 10i$$
$$w - z = -6 - 10i$$
and
$$-(z + w) = -(10 + 2i).$$
Notice that $z - w$ is the opposite of $w - z$ and $-(z + w)$ is the opposite of $z + w$, as you would expect.

These complex numbers are graphed in the complex plane at the right. We have also graphed $-w$ and $-z$ to show how all these points are related.

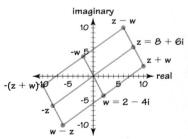

Optional Activities

After discussing the lesson, you might have students prove that the sum of a pair of conjugate complex numbers forms the fourth vertex of a rhombus with the other three vertices 0 and the two conjugates. [From the Geometric Addition Theorem, the four points form a parallelogram. We can either show that two consecutive sides are equal in length, or that the diagonals are perpendicular. If the conjugates are $a \pm bi$, then the length of the side from $(0, 0)$ to (a, b)

is $\sqrt{a^2 + b^2}$, which is equal to the length of the side from $(0, 0)$ to $(a, -b)$. Alternately, the slope of the diagonal from (a, b) to $(a, -b)$ is undefined, which means it is a vertical line. The slope of the diagonal from $(0, 0)$ to $(2a, 0)$ is zero, which means it is a horizontal line. Therefore, the two diagonals are perpendicular.]

Adapting to Individual Needs

Extra Help
Some students may not understand that complex numbers can be written in a variety of ways. Point out in **Example 3**, for instance, that $3 - 5i = (3, -5) \approx [\sqrt{34}, -59°]$. This is analogous to the many ways of writing a real number; for example, $18\tfrac{1}{3} = \tfrac{55}{3} \approx 18.33$.

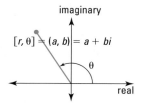

[r, θ] = (a, b) = a + bi

Graphing Complex Numbers in the Polar Coordinate Plane

Complex numbers can also be represented with polar coordinates. Let $[r, θ]$ with $r \geq 0$ be the polar coordinates for (a, b). Then from Lesson 13-4 you know that $r = \sqrt{a^2 + b^2}$ (because r is not negative) and $\tan θ = \frac{b}{a}$. There are usually two values of $θ$ between 0 and $2π$ which satisfy $\tan θ = \frac{b}{a}$. The correct value can be determined by examining the quadrant in which (a, b) is located.

Example 3

Find polar coordinates for the complex number $3 - 5i$.

Solution

Let $[r, θ]$ be polar coordinates for $3 - 5i = (3, -5)$.

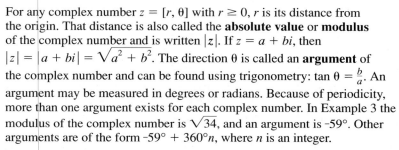

$$r = \sqrt{3^2 + (-5)^2} = \sqrt{34}$$

$$\tan θ = -\frac{5}{3}$$

Since $3 - 5i$ is in the 4th quadrant,

$$θ = \tan^{-1}\left(-\frac{5}{3}\right) \approx -59°.$$

Thus one pair of polar coordinates for (3, -5) is $\left[\sqrt{34}, -59°\right]$.

For any complex number $z = [r, θ]$ with $r \geq 0$, r is its distance from the origin. That distance is also called the **absolute value** or **modulus** of the complex number and is written $|z|$. If $z = a + bi$, then $|z| = |a + bi| = \sqrt{a^2 + b^2}$. The direction $θ$ is called an **argument** of the complex number and can be found using trigonometry: $\tan θ = \frac{b}{a}$. An argument may be measured in degrees or radians. Because of periodicity, more than one argument exists for each complex number. In Example 3 the modulus of the complex number is $\sqrt{34}$, and an argument is -59°. Other arguments are of the form $-59° + 360°n$, where n is an integer.

The form $[r, θ]$ for a complex number is called **polar form**. In the next lesson you will see that the polar form of complex numbers is very useful for describing the product or quotient of two complex numbers.

2b, 3b)

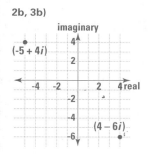

QUESTIONS

Covering the Reading

1. In a complex plane the horizontal axis is called the __a.__ axis, and the vertical axis is called the __b.__ axis.
   a) real   b) imaginary

In 2 and 3, a complex number is given. **a.** Rewrite each number as an ordered pair (a, b). **b.** Graph the number in the complex plane. b) See left.

2. $4 - 6i$ a) $(4, -6)$

3. $-5 + 4i$ a) $(-5, 4)$

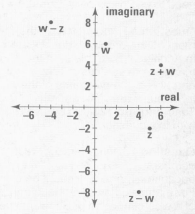

Additional Examples

1. At what point in the complex plane would each number be graphed?
   a. $3 - 7i$ (3, -7)
   b. $4i$ (0, 4)
   c. 8.21 (8.21, 0)

2. Let $z = 5 - 2i$ and $w = 1 + 6i$.
   a. Graph $z, w, z + w, z - w$, and $w - z$. $z = (5, -2), w = (1, 6),$
   $z + w = (6, 4),$
   $z - w = (4, -8),$ and
   $w - z = (-4, 8).$

   b. How are the graphs of these numbers related? **Sample: In the triangle with vertices $z + w, z - w$, and $w - z$, the midpoints of the three sides are z, w, and 0.**

3. Find polar coordinates for $-7 + 7i$. **Sample: $[7\sqrt{2}, \frac{3π}{4}]$**

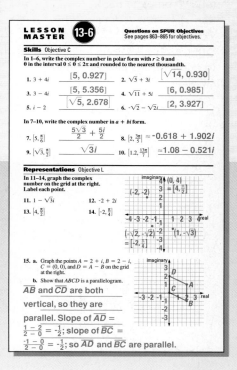

Adapting to Individual Needs

Challenge

Have students answer the following questions.

1. Suppose $a + bi$ is a complex number with absolute value r. Describe geometrically all other numbers in the complex plane with the same absolute value. [They are located on a circle centered at the origin with radius r.]

2. Let P be the graph of $a + bi$. Let O be the origin and Q be the graph of $a - bi$.

What is the measure of $\angle POQ$?
[$2 \tan^{-1}\left(\frac{b}{a}\right)$ if $a \neq 0$ and 180° if $a = 0$.]

835

Questions 7–8 In some cases, as in **Question 7**, the best students will be able to do is to estimate the argument of the number. In other cases, as in **Question 8**, the argument can be found exactly.

Question 9 Stress that the absolute value of a complex number is its distance from the origin. If students forget a formula for absolute value, they can easily reconstruct it. Also, they need to use distance in **Question 16**.

Question 13 You may wish to mention the property that is stated in Additional Example 2: In the triangle with vertices $z + w$, $z - w$, and $w - z$, the midpoints of the three sides are z, w, and 0. **Teaching Aid 123** can be used with this question.

Question 16 In general, for real numbers, $|u + v| \leq |u| + |v|$ because either u or v might be 0. For triangles, however, the length of a side cannot be 0. So, whenever u and v and 0 are not collinear, $|u + v| < |u| + |v|$.

Follow-up for Lesson 13-6

Practice

For more questions on SPUR Objectives, use **Lesson Master 13-6** (shown on page 835).

Assessment

Quiz A quiz covering Lessons 13-4 through 13-6 is provided in the *Assessment Sourcebook*.

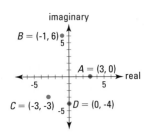

B = (-1, 6)
A = (3, 0)
C = (-3, -3)
D = (0, -4)

5b)

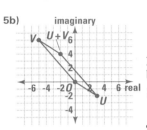

V   U+V
U

c) Let $W = U + V$. Then the slope of $\overline{OU} =$
$\frac{-2 - 0}{3 - 0} = -\frac{2}{3}$;
the slope of $\overline{UW} =$
$\frac{4 - -2}{-2 - 3} = -\frac{6}{5}$; the slope of $\overline{WV} =$
$\frac{6 - 4}{-5 - -2} = -\frac{2}{3}$; and the slope of $\overline{OV} =$
$\frac{6 - 0}{-5 - 0} = -\frac{6}{5}$.
Because the slopes of the opposite sides of OUWV are equal, the opposite sides are parallel, and OUVW is a parallelogram.

---

4. Write each complex number pictured at the left in $a + bi$ form.
   $A = 3 + 0i$, $B = -1 + 6i$, $C = -3 - 3i$, $D = 0 - 4i$
5. Let $U = 3 - 2i$, $V = -5 + 6i$, and $O = 0 + 0i$.
   a. Find $U + V$. $-2 + 4i$
   b. Graph U, V, and $U + V$ in the same coordinate plane. **See left.**
   c. Verify that U, O, V, and $U + V$ are vertices of a parallelogram. **See left.**
6. Prove the Geometric Addition Theorem. **See margin.**

In 7 and 8, give polar coordinates $[r, \theta]$ for each complex number, assuming $r \geq 0$ and $0 \leq \theta \leq 2\pi$.

7. $4 - 3i$ **[5, 5.64]**

8. $\frac{1}{2} + \frac{\sqrt{3}}{2}i$ $\left[1, \frac{\pi}{3}\right]$

9. How is the absolute value of the complex number $a + bi$ calculated? Find $\sqrt{a^2 + b^2}$.

In 10 and 11, a complex number is given. **a.** Find its absolute value.
b. Find its argument θ, if $r \geq 0$ and $0° \leq \theta < 360°$.

10. $7i$
    a) 7   b) 90°

11. $-3 + 6i$
    a) $3\sqrt{5} \approx 6.71$ b) $\approx 116.57°$

Applying the Mathematics

12. Name and graph four complex numbers with modulus 1. **See margin.**

13. Refer to Example 2.
    a. Prove that the largest quadrilateral pictured is a parallelogram.
    b. How many other parallelograms are determined by the complex numbers pictured? **8**
    a) **See margin.**

14. a. Draw the quadrilateral with vertices $P = 6 + i$, $Q = 6 - i$, $P + Q$, and $(0, 0)$. **See margin.**
    b. What special type of parallelogram is this? **rhombus**
    c. Determine the length of the longer diagonal of the quadrilateral. **12**

15. On the real number line, the distance between points with coordinates u and v is $|u - v|$. Determine whether the distance from $u = a + bi$ to $v = c + di$ in the complex plane is $|u - v|$. Justify your answer. **See margin.**

16. Consider $u = -3 + 4i$ and $v = -12i$. Evaluate.
    a. $|u| + |v|$ **17**
    b. $|u + v|$ $\sqrt{73} \approx 8.54$
    c. Use the Triangle Inequality to explain why $|u + v| < |u| + |v|$ in general. **See margin.**

Review

In 17–20, graph each equation in the polar plane. *(Lesson 13-5)* **See margin.**

17. $\theta = \frac{3\pi}{4}$

18. $r = 3\theta$, $0 \leq \theta \leq 4\pi$

19. $r = 2 \sin \theta$

20. $r = \sin 5\theta$

21. Give an equation in a rectangular coordinate system for the polar equation in Question 19. *(Lesson 13-4)*
    $x^2 + (y - 1)^2 = 1$

---

22. Find three other pairs of polar coordinates for the point $\left[-4, \frac{\pi}{6}\right]$.
(Lesson 13-4) **Samples:** $\left[-4, \frac{13\pi}{6}\right], \left[4, \frac{7\pi}{6}\right], \left[4, \frac{-5\pi}{6}\right]$

23. Give the coordinates of the image of (11, 6) under a rotation of θ about the origin. *(Lesson 11-4)* **(11 cos θ − 6 sin θ, 11 sin θ + 6 cos θ)**

24. Seven pairs of 16-year-old African American female twins took part in a study of the heights (in inches) and weights (in pounds) of identical twins. Here are the (height, weight) data and a scatterplot of the data for each twin in each pair.

Tamera and Tia Mowry are identical twins.

Pair	(Height, Weight)	(height, weight)
1	A = (68, 148)	a = (67, 137)
2	B = (65, 124)	b = (67, 126)
3	C = (63, 118)	c = (63, 126)
4	D = (66, 131)	d = (64, 120)
5	E = (62, 123)	e = (65, 124)
6	F = (62, 119)	f = (63, 130)
7	G = (66, 114)	g = (66, 104)

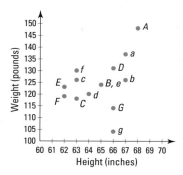

By calculating various statistics from the data, respond to the following questions.
a. Which pair do you think is most different on these variables?
b. Which pair do you think is most alike on these variables?
c. Defend your answers to parts **a** and **b**. *(Lessons 1-3, 1-7, 10-6)*
a) Sample: pair 4   b) Sample: pair 3

25. Give the complex conjugate. *(Lesson 9-6)*
a. −1 + 5i −1 − 5i **b.** 5i −5i **c.** −1   −1

26. Given $z_1 = 2 + i$ and $z_2 = 3 + 2i$, put in $a + bi$ form. *(Lesson 9-6)*
a. $z_1 z_2$ **4 + 7i**   **b.** $\frac{z_1}{z_2}$ $\frac{8}{13} - \frac{1}{13}i$

27. Two tracking stations are 30 miles apart. They measure the elevation angle of a weather balloon to be α and β, respectively. How high is a balloon sighted with $\alpha = 40°$ and $\beta = 70°$? *(Lesson 5-1)*
about 36 miles

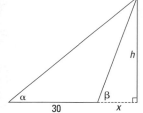

Exploration

28. Let $w = 1 + i$.
a. Write $w^0, w^2, w^3,$ and w^4 in $a + bi$ form.
b. Graph $w^0, w, w^2, w^3,$ and w^4 in the complex plane. **See margin.**
c. Describe the pattern that emerges in the graph of $(1 + i)^n$ for positive integers n. **The points lie on a spiral.**
a) $w^0 = 1 + 0i, w^2 = 0 + 2i, w^3 = -2 + 2i, w^4 = -4 + 0i$

24c) Calculate z-scores for the 14 heights and the 14 weights. Then pair 4 is the most different because the total difference of z-scores of D and d for height and weight is greatest; pair 3 is the most similar because the total difference of the z-scores for C and c is least.

Lesson 13-6   *The Geometry of Complex Numbers*   **837**

Additional Answers, pages 836–837

15. Yes, the distance from $u = a + bi$ to $v = c + di$ in the complex plane is $|u - v|$.
Proof:
$u - v = (a - c) + (b - d)i$, and
$|u - v| = \sqrt{(a - c)^2 + (b - d)^2}$,
which is the distance between the points (*a, b*) and (*c, d*).

16. c.
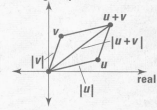

By the Geometric Addition Theorem, a parallelogram is formed with vertices (0, 0), u, v, and $u + v$. The diagonal from the origin forms two triangles with sides of length $|u + v|$, $|u|$ and $|v|$. By the Triangle Inequality, the length of one side of a triangle is less than the sum of the lengths of the other two sides. Therefore,
$|u + v| < |u| + |v|$.

17.
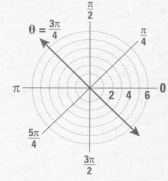

18–20, 28b. **See Additional Answers which begin on page T170 in this Teacher's Edition.**

---

14. a. imaginary
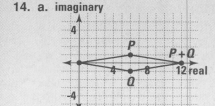

Setting Up Lesson 13-7
Do the In-class Activity on page 838.

In-class Activity

Resources

From the Teacher's Resource File
■ Answer Master 13-7

Additional Resources
■ Exploration 13-7

Students who have studied from UCSMP *Transition Mathematics* or UCSMP *Algebra* are familiar with the picturing of multiplication of positive and negative numbers by a size change. If a triangle is identified by its three vertices on a coordinate plane (*a*, *b*), (*c*, *d*), and (*e*, *f*), then multiplying each coordinate by a real number *k* results in a similar triangle with vertices (*ka*, *kb*), (*kc*, *kd*), and (*ke*, *kf*). The ratio of similitude is *k*.

Another way of thinking of this is that the original triangle has been transformed by the transformation S_k. When $k > 0$, the triangle and its image have the same tilt. When $k < 0$, the image is rotated 180°; it is "upside down."

Additional Answers

1.

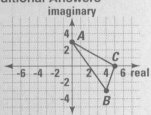

2. $A' = -6$, $B' = 6 + 8i$, $C' = 10i$

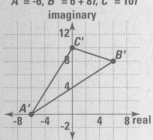

$A^* = -3 + 3i$, $B^* = 7 + i$, $C^* = 5 + 5i$

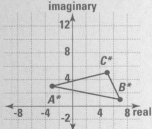

Work in pairs. Graph paper will make this easier.

1–3) See margin.

1 Graph $\triangle ABC$ in the complex plane with vertices $A = 3i$, $B = 4 - 3i$, and $C = 5$.

2 One of you should multiply each vertex by $2i$ to obtain A', B', and C', the vertices of an image $\triangle A'B'C'$. The other should multiply each vertex of $\triangle ABC$ by $1 + i$ to obtain A^*, B^*, and C^*, the vertices of a second image $\triangle A^*B^*C^*$. Each person should graph one of the images.

3 Find the lengths of all three sides of $\triangle ABC$ and of your image. Use these lengths to prove that $\triangle ABC$, $\triangle A'B'C'$, and $\triangle A^*B^*C^*$ are similar triangles.

4 Determine the ratio of similitude between $\triangle A'B'C'$ and $\triangle ABC$. Determine the ratio of similitude between $\triangle A^*B^*C^*$ and $\triangle ABC$. Try to determine how these ratios are related to the two complex numbers $2i$ and $1 + i$ that you used as multipliers. **For $\triangle A'B'C'$ and $\triangle ABC$, the ratio of similitude is 2, which is the modulus of $2i$. For $\triangle A^*B^*C^*$ and $\triangle ABC$, the ratio of similitude is $\sqrt{2}$, which is the modulus of $1 + i$.**

838

---

3. In $\triangle ABC$:
$AB = 2\sqrt{13}$, $BC = \sqrt{10}$, $AC = \sqrt{34}$

In $\triangle A'B'C'$:
$A'B' = 4\sqrt{13}$, $B'C' = 2\sqrt{10}$, $A'C' = 2\sqrt{34}$

In $\triangle A^*B^*C^*$:
$A^*B^* = 2\sqrt{26}$, $B^*C^* = 2\sqrt{5}$, $A^*C^* = 2\sqrt{17}$

$\triangle A'B'C' \sim \triangle ABC$ because the ratio of all pairs of corresponding sides is 2

$\triangle A^*B^*C^* \sim \triangle ABC$ because the ratio of all pairs of corresponding sides is $\sqrt{2}$.

$\triangle A'B'C' \sim \triangle A^*B^*C^*$ by transitivity.

Technology Connection
Materials: Explorations software

Students may use *Exploration 13-7, Geometric Transformations Using Complex Multiplication*, to do this In-Class Activity. Students draw a triangle in the complex plane by choosing 3 points for the vertices. They can use the computer to see the algebraic and geometric results of multiplying these points by a complex number. They can also find the distance between any two points in the complex plane.

You have now seen many ways of representing complex numbers.

z	single letter
$a + bi$	$a + bi$ form
(a, b)	rectangular coordinate form
$[r, \theta]$	polar coordinate form

You can convert from $a + bi$ or rectangular coordinate form to polar coordinate form using the relationships $r = \sqrt{a^2 + b^2}$ and $\tan \theta = \frac{b}{a}$. You can convert back using the relationships $a = r \cos \theta$ and $b = r \sin \theta$.

These conversions are useful because each form has advantages. The single letter form z is the shortest and helps shorten formulas such as the distance $|w - z|$ between two complex numbers w and z. In $a + bi$ form, operations with complex numbers can be performed as if the complex numbers are polynomials in i. In rectangular form, addition of complex numbers can be seen graphically as in finding the fourth vertex of a parallelogram.

In this lesson, we introduce the *trigonometric form* of a complex number. This form is related to the polar coordinate form and is quite useful for picturing multiplication, powers, and roots of complex numbers.

What Is the Trigonometric Form of a Complex Number?

Consider the complex number $z = a + bi$ with polar coordinates $[r, \theta]$, and with $r \geq 0$.

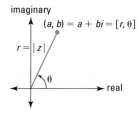

By a theorem of Lesson 13-4, $a = r \cos \theta$ and $b = r \sin \theta$. So

$$z = a + bi$$
$$= r \cos \theta + (r \sin \theta)i$$
$$= r(\cos \theta + i \sin \theta).$$

The expression $r (\cos \theta + i \sin \theta)$ is called the **trigonometric form of the complex number $a + bi$** because it uses the cosine and sine of the argument θ. Like polar form, the trigonometric form denotes a complex number in terms of r and θ, its absolute value and argument. But unlike polar form, a complex number in trigonometric form is still in the rectangular coordinate form $a + bi$. Because of this link between polar and rectangular coordinates, the trigonometric form of complex numbers is quite useful.

Objectives

B Perform operations with complex numbers in polar or trigonometric form.
C Represent complex numbers in different forms.
L Graph complex numbers.

Resources

From the *Teacher's Resource File*
■ Lesson Master 13-7
■ Answer Master 13-7
■ Teaching Aids
  114 Warm-up
  124 Product of Complex Numbers Theorem

Additional Resources
■ Visuals for Teaching Aids 114, 124

Warm-up

Consider the point (2, 3).
1. Find polar coordinates for this point. $\sqrt{13}$, tan⁻¹ 1.5] ≈ **[3.61, 56°]**
2. What complex number does this point represent? **2 + 3*i***
3. Square the complex number in Question 2, and graph it. **-5 + 12*i*, graphed as (-5, 12)**
4. Write polar coordinates for the complex number in Question 3. **[13, 113°]**

Lesson 13-7 Overview

Broad Goals This lesson begins by translating numbers from $a + bi$ form to trigonometric form and back. Then multiplication and division are pictured and described in this form.

Perspective To graph a point $[r, \theta]$ in polar coordinates, we can think of "turning [1, 0] an amount θ and then shooting out r times as far." This process is akin to applying the composite $S_r \circ R_\theta$ to [1, 0]. To multiply two complex numbers $[r, \theta]$ and $[s, \emptyset]$, think of applying the transformation $S_s \circ R_\emptyset$ to the first point. That is, rotate the first point $\emptyset$ and apply a size change of magnitude s. The result is the product $[rs, \theta + \emptyset]$. Thus multiplication of complex numbers in polar coordinates is precisely analogous to adding complex numbers in rectangular coordinates.

The two systems, however, present a difficulty; often we wish to both add and multiply complex numbers and we want to do this without having to convert from one system to the other. The trigonometric form $r(\cos \theta + i \sin \theta) = [r, \theta]$ resolves this difficulty. It exhibits r and θ and so the polar form ideas can be used, but it is a variant of $a + bi$ form which enables the rectangular coordinate ideas to be used.

After students have read this lesson, review the four ways they have had for writing complex numbers:

Form	Notation
binomial	$a + bi$
rectangular coordinate	(a, b)
polar coordinate	$[r, \theta]$
trigonometric	$r(\cos \theta + i \sin \theta)$

Continue the analogies with real numbers. Generally, real number addition and subtraction are easier if the real numbers are represented as decimals rather than fractions. Real number multiplication and division, however, are often easier with fractions. Similarly, complex number addition and subtraction are usually easier in $a + bi$ form or rectangular coordinate form, while complex number multiplication and division are easier in polar or trigonometric form.

Examples 1–2 cover translation from $a + bi$ form to trigonometric form and back.

Error Alert When converting from $a + bi$ form to trigonometric form, students may give the wrong value of θ if they do not start with a sketch to determine which quadrant the complex number is in.

Converting from $a + bi$ Form to Trigonometric Form

Example 1

Write the complex number $-2 - 2\sqrt{3}\,i$ in trigonometric form. Use a value of θ in the interval $0 \le \theta < 2\pi$.

Solution

The process is quite similar to that used in finding polar coordinates for a point. First sketch a graph.

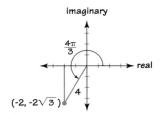

Let $-2 - 2\sqrt{3}i = a + bi$. Then $a = -2$ and $b = -2\sqrt{3}$.

$r = \sqrt{a^2 + b^2} = \sqrt{(-2)^2 + (-2\sqrt{3})^2} = \sqrt{4 + 12} = 4$

$\tan \theta = \frac{b}{a} = \frac{-2\sqrt{3}}{-2} = \sqrt{3}$

Since $-2 - 2\sqrt{3}i$ is in the third quadrant, $\theta = \pi + \frac{\pi}{3} = \frac{4\pi}{3}$.

So in polar coordinate form, $-2 - 2\sqrt{3}i = \left[4, \frac{4\pi}{3}\right]$.

Therefore, in trigonometric form, $-2 - 2\sqrt{3}i = 4\left(\cos \frac{4\pi}{3} + i \sin \frac{4\pi}{3}\right)$.

Consider again the number of Example 1. Since the sine and cosine have period 2π, $-2 - 2\sqrt{3}i = 4\left(\cos \left(\frac{4\pi}{3} + 2n\pi\right) + i \sin \left(\frac{4\pi}{3} + 2n\pi\right)\right)$, where n is an integer. In general, every complex number has infinitely many trigonometric forms.

Converting From Trigonometric Form to $a + bi$ Form

Example 2

Write the complex number $5\left(\cos \frac{2\pi}{3} + i \sin \frac{2\pi}{3}\right)$ in $a + bi$ form.

Solution

Distribute the 5 and simplify.

$$5\left(\cos \frac{2\pi}{3} + i \sin \frac{2\pi}{3}\right) = 5 \cos \frac{2\pi}{3} + i\left(5 \sin \frac{2\pi}{3}\right)$$

$$= -\frac{5}{2} + \frac{5\sqrt{3}}{2}\,i$$

Optional Activities

You might find this activity helpful when you discuss the examples. Students often write an incorrect argument when converting $a + bi$ into polar form, because they take the inverse tangent value their calculator gives as the answer. Ask them when they can use the inverse tangent value from their calculator "as is," and when (and how) they must change it. Have them give a reason for why this change is necessary. [When $a + bi$ is in the first or fourth quadrants, that is when $a \ge 0$, then students can use the inverse tangent value as is because the domain of tangent is restricted to the interval from -90° to 90° in order to make inverse tangent a function. When $a + bi$ is in the second or third quadrants, that is, when $a < 0$, students must add 180° to the calculator value in order to obtain the correct angle. The need to know the quadrant of the complex number indicates the importance of graphing.]

❶ Picturing Multiplication of Complex Numbers

The trigonometric form of complex numbers explains a nice geometrical property of complex number multiplication. Two instances were given in the In-class Activity on page 838, where three complex numbers A, B, and C were each multiplied by $2i$ and also by $1 + i$. Let us consider the multiplication by $2i$.

The graphs of $\triangle ABC$ and $\triangle A'B'C'$ are shown at the right. It appears that $\triangle A'B'C'$ is the image of $\triangle ABC$ under the composite of a size change of magnitude 2 and a rotation of 90°.

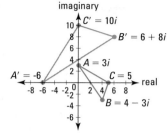

In trigonometric form, $2i = 2(\cos 90° + i \sin 90°)$. Thus the magnitudes of the transformations are the absolute value and argument of $2i$, respectively. That is, multiplication by $2i$ can be considered as the composite of a size change of magnitude 2 (its absolute value) and a rotation through 90° (its argument) around the origin.

In general, multiplying a complex number z_1 by the complex number $z_2 = [r_2, \theta_2] = r_2(\cos \theta_2 + i \sin \theta_2)$ applies to the graph of z_1 the composite of a size change of magnitude $|z_2|$ and a rotation θ_2 about the origin.

Product of Complex Numbers Theorem (Trigonometric Form)

If
$$z_1 = r_1(\cos \theta_1 + i \sin \theta_1) \text{ and}$$
$$z_2 = r_2(\cos \theta_2 + i \sin \theta_2),$$
then
$$z_1 z_2 = r_1 r_2(\cos (\theta_1 + \theta_2) + i \sin (\theta_1 + \theta_2)).$$

Proof

The proof applies, perhaps surprisingly, the sum formulas for the cosine and sine.

$$
\begin{aligned}
z_1 z_2 &= (r_1(\cos \theta_1 + i \sin \theta_1))(r_2(\cos \theta_2 + i \sin \theta_2)) \\
&= r_1 r_2(\cos \theta_1 + i \sin \theta_1)(\cos \theta_2 + i \sin \theta_2) \\
&= r_1 r_2(\cos \theta_1 \cos \theta_2 + i \cos \theta_1 \sin \theta_2 + i \sin \theta_1 \cos \theta_2 + i^2 \sin \theta_1 \sin \theta_2) \\
&= r_1 r_2((\cos \theta_1 \cos \theta_2 + i^2 \sin \theta_1 \sin \theta_2) + i(\cos \theta_1 \sin \theta_2 + \sin \theta_1 \cos \theta_2)) \\
&= r_1 r_2((\cos \theta_1 \cos \theta_2 - \sin \theta_1 \sin \theta_2) + i(\sin \theta_1 \cos \theta_2 + \cos \theta_1 \sin \theta_2)] \\
&= r_1 r_2(\cos (\theta_1 + \theta_2) + i \sin (\theta_1 + \theta_2))
\end{aligned}
$$

This is the trigonometric form for a complex number with absolute value $r_1 r_2$ and argument $\theta_1 + \theta_2$.

In polar coordinate form, the above theorem states that the product of the complex numbers $[r_1, \theta_1]$ and $[r_2, \theta_2]$ is $[r_1 r_2, \theta_1 + \theta_2]$.

Adapting to Individual Needs

Extra Help

Point out that while every complex number has infinitely many trigonometric forms, it is common practice to restrict θ to the interval $0 \le \theta \le 2\pi$. Unless a different interval is indicated, students should use this interval when they give the trigonometric form of a complex number.

---

❶ These paragraphs illustrate the geometry of complex number multiplication. The graphical representation of products of complex numbers is interesting, but time-consuming to draw. You might expect students to be able to explain the representation shown, but ask them to graph a product only once or twice (**Question 7c**). The fact that multiplication rotates a complex number will be applied in Lesson 13-8 when students examine the nth roots of a complex number.

The proof of the Product of Complex Numbers Theorem is provided on **Teaching Aid 124**.

Regarding the Product of Complex Numbers Theorem, the most important objective is that students be able to apply the theorem as in **Example 3** on page 842 and the Questions.

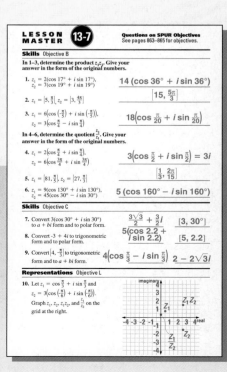

Additional Examples

1. Write $3 + 4i$ in trigonometric form. $\approx 5(\cos 53° + i \sin 53°)$
2. Write $2(\cos \frac{\pi}{4} + i \sin \frac{\pi}{4})$ in $a + bi$ form. $\sqrt{2} + \sqrt{2}\, i$
3. Consider $\triangle XYZ$ in the complex plane with $X = -3 - 6i$, $Y = 4i$, and $Z = 2 + i$.
   a. Multiply each vertex by $1 - i$ to obtain X', Y', and Z'. $X' = -9 - 3i$; $Y' = 4 + 4i$, and $Z' = 3 - i$;
   b. Describe the transformation that maps $\triangle XYZ$ onto $\triangle X'Y'Z'$. **The composite of a size change of magnitude $\sqrt{2}$ and a rotation of $-\frac{\pi}{4}$ with center at the origin.**
4. If $z = 4(\cos 25° + i \sin 25°)$ and $w = 0.75(\cos 30° + i \sin 30°)$, find zw. $3(\cos 55° + i \sin 55°)$
5. Using z and w from Additional Example 4, find $\frac{z}{w}$. $\frac{16}{3}(\cos (-5°) + i \sin (-5°))$

(Notes on Questions begin on page 844.)

Example 3

If $z_1 = 10i$ and $z_2 = 3(\cos 75° + i \sin 75°)$, find the product $z_1 z_2$ in trigonometric form.

Solution

In trigonometric form, $z_1 = 10(\cos 90° + i \sin 90°)$.
Now use the Product of Complex Numbers Theorem.
$$z_1 z_2 = 10 \cdot 3 \, (\cos (90° + 75°) + i \sin (90° + 75°))$$
$$= 30(\cos 165° + i \sin 165°)$$

Check

Multiplying by $z_2 = 3 (\cos 75° + i \sin 75°)$ should apply the composite of a size change of magnitude 3 and a rotation of 75° to the graph of the complex number $z_1 = 10 (\cos 90° + i \sin 90°)$. The graph below illustrates that this is so.

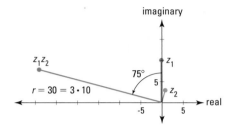

Picturing Division of Complex Numbers

Recall that to perform division of a number z by a complex number in $a + bi$ form, it was useful to multiply numerator and denominator of $\frac{z}{a + bi}$ by the complex conjugate $a - bi$. In trigonometric form, the conjugate of $r (\cos \theta + i \sin \theta)$ is $r (\cos \theta - i \sin \theta)$.

This result is needed to prove the following theorem, which you are asked to do in the Questions.

Division of Complex Numbers Theorem (Trigonometric Form)
If $\quad z_1 = r_1(\cos \theta_1 + i \sin \theta_1)$ and $\quad z_2 = r_2(\cos \theta_2 + i \sin \theta_2),$
then $\quad \frac{z_1}{z_2} = \frac{r_1}{r_2}(\cos (\theta_1 - \theta_2) + i \sin (\theta_1 - \theta_2)).$

Geometrically, division of the complex number $z_1 = [r_1, \theta_1]$ by the complex number $z_2 = [r_2, \theta_2]$ applies to z_1 the composite of a size change of magnitude $\frac{1}{|z_2|}$ and a rotation of $-\theta_2$ about the origin. So, in polar coordinate form, the above theorem states that the quotient $\frac{[r_1, \theta_1]}{[r_2, \theta_2]}$ is $\left[\frac{r_1}{r_2}, \theta_1 - \theta_2\right]$.

Adapting to Individual Needs

Challenge
Have students use the product theorem in this lesson to give a different proof for the identities below that were given in Lesson 11-6. If they need a hint, tell them to let $z = \cos \theta + i \sin \theta$.

$\sin 2\theta = 2 \cos \theta \sin \theta$
$\cos 2\theta = \cos^2 \theta - \sin^2 \theta$

[Let $z = r(\cos \theta + i \sin \theta)$ Then,
$z^2 = r^2(\cos \theta + i \sin \theta)^2$
$\quad = r^2(\cos^2 \theta + 2i \sin \theta \cos \theta - \sin^2 \theta)$
But by the Product of Complex Numbers Theorem,
$z^2 = r^2(\cos 2\theta + i \sin 2\theta)$
Thus $\cos 2\theta = \cos^2 \theta - \sin^2 \theta$
and $\sin 2\theta = 2 \cos \theta \sin \theta$].

Example 4

If $z_1 = 10\left(\cos\frac{\pi}{2} + i\sin\frac{\pi}{2}\right)$ and $z_2 = 2\left(\cos\frac{\pi}{3} + i\sin\frac{\pi}{3}\right)$, write $\frac{z_1}{z_2}$ in trigonometric form.

Solution

From the Division of Complex Numbers Theorem,

$$\frac{z_1}{z_2} = \frac{10}{2}\left(\cos\left(\frac{\pi}{2} - \frac{\pi}{3}\right) + i\sin\left(\frac{\pi}{2} - \frac{\pi}{3}\right)\right)$$
$$= 5\left(\cos\frac{\pi}{6} + i\sin\frac{\pi}{6}\right).$$

Check

Convert to $a + bi$ form.

$$z_1 = 10(0 + i(1)) = 10i$$
$$z_2 = 2\left(\frac{1}{2} + i\frac{\sqrt{3}}{2}\right) = 1 + \sqrt{3}i$$

Now compute the quotient by multiplying the numerator and denominator of $\frac{z_1}{z_2}$ by the conjugate of $1 + \sqrt{3}\,i$.

$$\frac{z_1}{z_2} = \frac{10i}{1 + \sqrt{3}\,i}$$
$$= \frac{10i(1 - \sqrt{3}\,i)}{(1 + \sqrt{3}\,i)(1 - \sqrt{3}\,i)}$$
$$= \frac{10i + 10\sqrt{3}}{4}$$
$$= \frac{5\sqrt{3} + 5i}{2}$$
$$= 5\left(\frac{\sqrt{3}}{2} + \frac{1}{2}i\right)$$
$$= 5\left(\cos\frac{\pi}{6} + i\sin\frac{\pi}{6}\right) \qquad \text{It checks.}$$

Note in Example 4 how using the trigonometric form greatly simplifies division of complex numbers. In the next lesson you will see how using the trigonometric form leads to beautifully simple ways to calculate powers and roots of complex numbers.

QUESTIONS

Covering the Reading

In 1–4, a complex number is given. **a.** Graph each number on the complex plane. **b.** Convert it to trigonometric form with $0° \leq \theta < 360°$. **See left.**

1. $3 + 3i$ **2.** $4\sqrt{3} - 4i$ **3.** -5 **4.** $-2 - 5i$

In 5 and 6, a complex number in trigonometric form is given. **a.** Graph each number on the complex plane. **b.** Convert to $a + bi$ form.

5. $3\left(\cos\frac{3\pi}{2} + i\sin\frac{3\pi}{2}\right)$ a) See left.   b) $0 - 3$

6. $2\left(\cos\left(-\frac{2\pi}{3}\right) + i\sin\left(-\frac{2\pi}{3}\right)\right)$ a) See left.   b) $-1 - \sqrt{3}i$

Side notes (left margin)

1a, 2a, 3a, 4a)

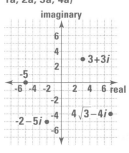

1b) $3\sqrt{2}(\cos 45° + i\sin 45°)$

2b) $8(\cos 330° + i\sin 330°)$

3b) $5(\cos 180° + i\sin 180°)$

4b) $\approx \sqrt{29}(\cos 248° + i\sin 248°)$

5a, 6a)

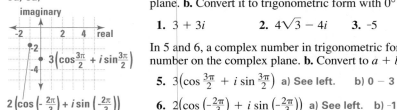

$3\left(\cos\frac{3\pi}{2} + i\sin\frac{3\pi}{2}\right)$

$2\left(\cos\left(-\frac{2\pi}{3}\right) + i\sin\left(-\frac{2\pi}{3}\right)\right)$

Practice

For more questions on SPUR Objectives, use **Lesson Master 13-7** (shown on page 841).

Assessment

Written Communication Have students **work in pairs**. Ask each partner to write a complex number in $a + bi$ form, and have each student convert both numbers to trigonometric form. Then Partner A should find the product while Partner B finds the quotient. Have students switch roles and repeat the activity. [Students give the trigonometric form of complex numbers and find products and quotients of numbers in this form.]

Extension

Students can use the ideas in this lesson to justify the following properties of complex number multiplication: In the set of complex numbers, excluding [0, 0°],
1. multiplication is closed.
2. multiplication is associative.
3. [1, 0°] is the multiplicative identity.
4. if $r \neq 0$, the multiplicative inverse of $[r, \theta]$ is $[\frac{1}{r}, -\theta]$.
5. multiplication is commutative.

Project Update Project 1, *Euler's Theorem*, on page 858, relates to the content of this lesson.

Question 7 You might wish to check **part a** by converting z_1 and z_2 each to $a + bi$ form and multiplying them in that form. (A calculator is helpful.)

Questions 8–10 Point out that the absolute value of z_1z_2 is the product of the absolute values of z_1 and z_2. This, too, is a generalization of a property held by real numbers.

Questions 14–15 The message of these questions is that the checks in $a + bi$ form require much more work than doing the problem in trigonometric form. That is another advantage of the trigonometric form.

Questions 25–26 Powers of binomials are calculated in the next lesson.

Question 27 The dimensions given here approximate those for many pencils.

Question 27 Science Connection An unusually pure deposit of graphite was discovered in Borrowdale, Cumberland, England, in 1564. Conrad Gesner, a German-Swiss naturalist, made the first pencil in 1565 by inserting graphite into a wooden cylinder. In 1779, Swedish chemist Carl W. Scherele showed that graphite was a form of carbon, not lead, but the name "lead pencil" stuck. Today's pencils usually use a mixture of graphite and clay, and sometimes also wax.

7c)

9a) $50\left(\cos \frac{5\pi}{4} + i \sin \frac{5\pi}{4}\right)$

b) 50

c) Sample: $\frac{5\pi}{4}$

11) $3\left(\cos \frac{\pi}{6} - i \sin \frac{\pi}{6}\right)$

14a) $6\left(\cos \frac{5\pi}{6} + i \sin \frac{5\pi}{6}\right)$

b) $\frac{z_1}{z_2} = \frac{-18 + 0i}{\frac{3\sqrt{3}}{2} + \frac{3}{2}i} =$

$\frac{-18\left(\frac{3\sqrt{3}}{2} - \frac{3}{2}i\right)}{\left(\frac{3\sqrt{3}}{2} + \frac{3}{2}i\right)\left(\frac{3\sqrt{3}}{2} - \frac{3}{2}i\right)} =$

$\frac{-27\sqrt{3} + 27i}{9} =$

$-3\sqrt{3} + 3i$, and

$6\left(\cos \frac{5\pi}{6} + i \sin \frac{5\pi}{6}\right) =$

$6\left(-\frac{\sqrt{3}}{2} + \frac{1}{2}i\right) =$

$-3\sqrt{3} + 3i$

18a) 15(cos 115° + i sin 115°)

---

7. a. Multiply $z_1 = 2(\cos 65° + i \sin 65°)$ by $z_2 = 4(\cos 40° + i \sin 40°)$, and express the result in trigonometric form. 8(cos 105° + i sin 105°)
  b. The composite of which two transformations maps z_1 to z_1z_2?
  c. Illustrate the multiplication with a diagram showing the appropriate size transformation and rotation. **See left.**
  b) S_4 and $R_{40°}$

In 8–10, two complex numbers z_1 and z_2 are given. **a.** Find z_1z_2. **b.** Give the absolute value of the product. **c.** Give an argument of the product. Use exact values if possible.

8. $z_1 = 3(\cos 150° + i \sin 150°)$, $z_2 = 2(\cos 60° + i \sin 60°)$
  a) 6(cos 210° + i sin 210°)   b) 6   c) Sample: 210°

9. $z_1 = 10\left(\cos \frac{11\pi}{4} + i \sin \frac{11\pi}{4}\right)$, $z_2 = 5\left(\cos \frac{\pi}{2} + i \sin \frac{\pi}{2}\right)$
  See left.

10. $z_1 = 2 + 3i$, $z_2 = -4 + i$
  a) -11 − 10i b) $\sqrt{221}$ c) Sample: ≈ 222.3°

In 11 and 12, write the conjugate of the complex number in the form given.

11. $3\left(\cos \frac{\pi}{6} + i \sin \frac{\pi}{6}\right)$ **See left.**   **12.** [5, 175°] [5, 185°]

13. a. Divide $z_1 = 12(\cos 220° + i \sin 220°)$ by $z_2 = 5(\cos 100° + i \sin 100°)$ and express the result in trigonometric form. $\frac{12}{5}$(cos 120° + i sin 120°)
  b. The composite of which two transformations maps z_1 to $\frac{z_1}{z_2}$?
  $S_{1/5}$ and $R_{-100°}$

In 14 and 15, two complex numbers z_1 and z_2 are given. **a.** Find the quotient $\frac{z_1}{z_2}$ and express the result in trigonometric form. **b.** Check your result by converting to $a + bi$ form.

14. $z_1 = 18(\cos \pi + i \sin \pi)$, $z_2 = 3\left(\cos \frac{\pi}{6} + i \sin \frac{\pi}{6}\right)$ **See left.**

15. $z_1 = [20, 300°]$, $z_2 = [5, 60°]$ **See margin.**

Applying the Mathematics

16. A complex number z has absolute value 7 and argument $\frac{2\pi}{3}$.
  a. Express z in polar coordinate form. $\left[7, \frac{2\pi}{3}\right]$
  b. Express z in $a + bi$ form. $-\frac{7}{2} + \frac{7\sqrt{3}}{2}i$

17. Prove the Division of Complex Numbers Theorem. (Hint: $r(\cos \theta - i \sin \theta)$ $= r \cos \theta - i(r \sin \theta) = r \cos (-\theta) + ir \sin (-\theta) = r (\cos (-\theta) + i \sin (-\theta))$). **See margin.**

18. The complex number $z = 3(\cos 40° + i \sin 40°)$ undergoes a transformation that multiplies its absolute value by 5 and rotates it 75° about the origin.
  a. What is the image of z under the transformation? **See left.**
  b. Identify the mathematical operation and the complex number that will accomplish the transformation.
  multiplication by 5(cos 75° + i sin 75°)

19. Let $z = 2(\cos 15° + i \sin 15°)$. **See margin.**
  a. Calculate z^2, z^3, z^4, and z^5. (Hint: Use the fact that $z^2 = z \cdot z$, $z^3 = z^2 \cdot z$, etc.)
  b. Look for a pattern in the results of part **a.** Use the pattern to predict what z^{10} should be.

Additional Answers

15. a. $4(\cos 240° + i \sin 240°)$

  b. $\frac{z_1}{z_2} = \frac{10 - 10\sqrt{3}\,i}{\frac{5}{2} + \frac{5\sqrt{3}}{2}i} = \frac{10 - 10\sqrt{3}\,i}{\frac{5}{2}(1 + \sqrt{3}\,i)}$

  $= \frac{4 - 4\sqrt{3}\,i}{1 + \sqrt{3}\,i} = \frac{(4 - 4\sqrt{3}\,i)(1 - \sqrt{3}\,i)}{(1 + \sqrt{3}\,i)(1 - \sqrt{3}\,i)}$

  $= \frac{-8 - 8\sqrt{3}\,i}{4} = -2 - 2\sqrt{3}\,i;$

  $4(\cos 240° + i \sin 240°)$

  $= 4\left(-\frac{1}{2} - \frac{\sqrt{3}}{2}i\right) = -2 - 2\sqrt{3}\,i.$

17. $\frac{z_1}{z_2} = \frac{r_1(\cos \theta_1 + i \sin \theta_1)}{r_2(\cos \theta_2 + i \sin \theta_2)} = \frac{r_1(\cos \theta_1 + i \sin \theta_1)(\cos \theta_2 - i \sin \theta_2)}{r_2(\cos \theta_2 + i \sin \theta_2)(\cos \theta_2 - i \sin \theta_2)}$

$= \frac{r_1}{r_2} \cdot \frac{(\cos \theta_1 + i \sin \theta_1)(\cos (-\theta_2) + i \sin (-\theta_2))}{(\cos^2 \theta_2 + \sin^2 \theta_2)}$

$= \frac{r_1}{r_2} \cdot \frac{(\cos \theta_1 \cos (-\theta_2) - \sin \theta_1 \sin (-\theta_2) + i \cos \theta_1 \sin (-\theta_2) + i \sin \theta_1 \cos (-\theta_2))}{1}$

$= \frac{r_1}{r_2}(\cos (\theta_1 - \theta_2) + i \sin (\theta_1 - \theta_2))$

21a)

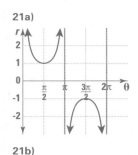

21b)

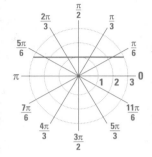

23a) $\begin{bmatrix} 0 & 4 & 5 \\ 3 & -3 & 0 \end{bmatrix}$

Review

20. What is the length of the diagonal $\overline{OT}$ of the parallelogram formed in the complex plane by the origin, $F = 3 - i$, $R = -1 - 2i$, and T? *(Lesson 13-6)*
$\sqrt{13}$

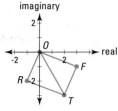

21. a. Graph $r = \csc \theta$ in rectangular coordinates.
b. Graph $r = \csc \theta$ in polar coordinates. *(Lessons 13-1, 13-5)*
a, b) See left.

22. a. Sketch a graph of $r = -\sin \theta$ in polar coordinates.
b. Prove that the graph is a circle. *(Lesson 13-5)*
a, b) See margin.

23. a. Represent $\triangle ABC$ of this lesson as a 2×3 matrix. **See left.**
b. Verify by matrix multiplication that $\triangle A'B'C'$ is the image of $\triangle ABC$ under a rotation of $90°$ and a size change of 2. *(Lesson 11-3)*
See margin.

24. A coin is tossed 35 times. If the coin is hypothesized to be fair, approximate each to the nearest 0.0001.
a. The probability of getting exactly 25 heads. **0.0053**
b. The probability of getting fewer than 10 heads. *(Lessons 8-9, 10-6)*
0.0030

In 25 and 26, expand using the Binomial Theorem. *(Lesson 8-8)*

25. $(a - b)^5$ $a^5 - 5a^4b + 10a^3b^2 - 10a^2b^3 + 5ab^4 - b^5$

26. $(2p + 3)^4$ $16p^4 + 96p^3 + 216p^2 + 216p + 81$

27. The wooden part of a pencil is a right, regular hexagonal prism with radius 3.5 mm and length 175 mm. The "lead" is a solid cylinder with diameter 2 mm running the length of the wood. What is the volume of wood in the pencil? *(Previous course, 5-3)* **about 5019.8 mm^3**

Exploration

28. Prove that $\triangle ABC$ and $\triangle A'B'C'$ in the lesson are similar triangles without using the lengths of the sides of the triangles. **Sample: $\triangle A'B'C'$ is the image of $\triangle ABC$ under the composite of a size change of magnitude 2 and a rotation $90°$, and both rotations and size changes preserve angle measure. So the angles of $\triangle ABC$ are equal in measure to the corresponding angles of $\triangle A'B'C'$. Thus $\triangle ABC$ is similar to $\triangle A'B'C'$.**

Additional Answers
22. a.

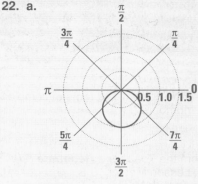

b. For $r \neq 0$,
$r = -\sin \theta \Leftrightarrow r = -\frac{y}{r}$
$\Leftrightarrow r^2 = -y \Leftrightarrow x^2 + y^2 = -y \Leftrightarrow x^2 + y^2 + y = 0$
$\Leftrightarrow x^2 + (y + \frac{1}{2})^2 = \frac{1}{4}$.
This is the equation of a circle with center $(0, -\frac{1}{2})$ and radius $\frac{1}{2}$. If $r = 0$, $x = y = 0$, so the origin is also included.

23. b.

$R_{90} = \begin{bmatrix} 0 & -1 \\ 1 & 0 \end{bmatrix}$ and
$S_2 = \begin{bmatrix} 2 & 0 \\ 0 & 2 \end{bmatrix}$ So,

$(S_2 \circ R_{90})(\triangle ABC) =$

$\begin{bmatrix} 2 & 0 \\ 0 & 2 \end{bmatrix} \cdot \begin{bmatrix} 0 & -1 \\ 1 & 0 \end{bmatrix} \begin{bmatrix} 0 & 4 & 5 \\ 3 & -3 & 0 \end{bmatrix}$

$= \begin{bmatrix} -6 & 6 & 0 \\ 0 & 8 & 10 \end{bmatrix}$

which is the matrix for $\triangle A'B'C'$.

19. a. $z^2 = 4(\cos 30° + i \sin 30°)$,
$z^3 = 8(\cos 45° + i \sin 45°)$,
$z^4 = 16(\cos 60° + i \sin 60°)$,
$z^5 = 32(\cos 75° + i \sin 75°)$
b. $z^n = 2^n(\cos (n \cdot 15°) + i \sin (n \cdot 15°))$
$z^{10} = 2^{10}(\cos 150° + i \sin 150°)$

Setting Up Lesson 13-8
Lesson 13-8 discusses and applies the pattern of **Question 19**.

Objectives

D Find powers and roots of complex numbers.

Resources

From the Teacher's Resource File
- Lesson Master 13-8
- Answer Master 13-8
- Teaching Aids
  114 Warm-up
  125 Graph for Example 1

Additional Resources
- Visuals for Teaching Aids 114, 125

Warm-up

1. Find the three solutions to
$x^3 - 1 = 0$. $1, -\frac{1}{2} + \frac{\sqrt{3}}{2}i, -\frac{1}{2} - \frac{\sqrt{3}}{2}i$
2. Square each of the non-real solutions and describe the result. **The square of either solution equals the other.**

Notes on Reading

Example 1 shows that the various powers of a complex number lie on a logarithmic spiral when plotted in the complex plane. This fact has no analogy with the real numbers. **Teaching Aid 125** shows the graphs for this example.

DeMoivre's Theorem

Gauss (1777–1855) was the first person to call the numbers you have been studying in the last two lessons "complex." He applied complex numbers to the study of electricity. To honor his work, a unit of electromagnetism is named after him. But during the century before Gauss, several mathematicians explored complex numbers and discovered many remarkable properties of them. This lesson presents a theorem about powers of complex numbers which is named after Abraham DeMoivre (1667–1754; his name is pronounced *de mwav'* or *dee moy'vree*).

Finding a Power of a Complex Number (Quickly)

Consider expanding $\left(2 + 2\sqrt{3}\,i\right)^4$. One way to do it is to use the Binomial Theorem.

$$\left(2 + 2\sqrt{3}\,i\right)^4 = 2^4 + 4 \cdot 2^3\left(2\sqrt{3}\,i\right)^1 + 6 \cdot 2^2\left(2\sqrt{3}\,i\right)^2 + 4 \cdot 2^1\left(2\sqrt{3}\,i\right)^3 + \left(2\sqrt{3}\,i\right)^4$$

$$= 16 + 64\sqrt{3}\,i + 24(-12) + 8\left(24\sqrt{3}\,(-i)\right) + 16 \cdot 9$$

$$= -128 - 128\sqrt{3}\,i$$

Another approach is to rewrite the number $2 + 2\sqrt{3}\,i$ in trigonometric form and use the theorems of the previous lesson. You may use the formulas or geometric inspection to find r and θ. We give all angles in degrees.

$$z = 2 + 2\sqrt{3}\,i$$
$$r = \sqrt{2^2 + (2\sqrt{3})^2} = 4$$
$$\theta = \tan^{-1}\left(\frac{2\sqrt{3}}{2}\right) = 60°$$

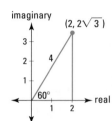

So $\qquad z = 4(\cos 60° + i \sin 60°)$.

Then $\qquad z^2 = 4(\cos 60° + i \sin 60°) \cdot 4(\cos 60° + i \sin 60°)$
$\qquad\qquad = 4^2(\cos 120° + i \sin 120°)$,

$\qquad z^3 = 4^2(\cos 120° + i \sin 120°) \cdot 4(\cos 60° + i \sin 60°)$
$\qquad\qquad = 4^3(\cos 180° + i \sin 180°)$,

and $\qquad z^4 = 4^3(\cos 180° + i \sin 180°) \cdot 4(\cos 60° + i \sin 60°)$
$\qquad\qquad = 4^4(\cos 240° + i \sin 240°)$
$\qquad\qquad = 256\left(-\frac{1}{2} - i\frac{\sqrt{3}}{2}\right)$
$\qquad\qquad = -128 - 128\sqrt{3}\,i.$

This second approach may seem tedious, but a simple pattern is developing. Note that for each value of n, $z^n = 4^n(\cos n \cdot 60° + i \sin n \cdot 60°)$. This result, generalized, is called *DeMoivre's Theorem*.

Lesson 13-8 Overview

Broad Goals In this lesson, students are expected to find powers and roots of complex numbers using DeMoivre's Theorem.

Perspective With complex numbers in polar form, $[r, \theta] \cdot [r, \theta] = [r^2, 2\theta]$, and it is not difficult to conjecture that $[r, \theta]^n = [r^n, n\theta]$. This is DeMoivre's Theorem, though it is more often given in trigonometric form: $[r(\cos \theta + i \sin \theta)]^n = r^n[\cos (n\theta) + i \sin (n\theta)]$. A rigorous proof requires mathematical induction

and is found in UCSMP *Precalculus and Discrete Mathematics*. DeMoivre's Theorem provides a formula for the *n*th power of any complex number. When the *n*th powers are graphed, they lie on a spiral.

The beauty of the geometry of complex numbers extends also to the *n*th roots of a number. If $[r, \theta]^n = z$, then so also does $[r, \theta + \frac{2\pi}{n}]^n = z$, so if $[r, \theta]$ is an *n*th root of z, another *n*th root is the image of the first

under a rotation of $\frac{2\pi}{n}$ about the origin. This process can be continued with $n - 1$ successive rotations finding all n *n*th roots, and so the *n*th roots are vertices of a regular *n*-gon centered at the origin. It is a wonderful result to have at the close of the year!

DeMoivre's Theorem

If $z = r(\cos\theta + i\sin\theta)$ and n is an integer,

then $z^n = r^n(\cos n\theta + i\sin n\theta)$.

In polar form, DeMoivre's Theorem states that if $z = [r, \theta]$, then $z^n = [r^n, n\theta]$ for all integers n. According to some historians, DeMoivre proved the theorem only for $r = 1$, but it is true for any r. The proof is beyond the scope of this course.

Graphing Powers of a Complex Number

Example 1

Let $z = 2\left(\cos\frac{\pi}{3} + i\sin\frac{\pi}{3}\right)$.

a. Find z^n for $n = 1, 2, 3, 4, 5, 6$, and 7.
b. Plot the powers in the complex plane.

Solution

a. Use DeMoivre's Theorem and convert to polar form for easy graphing.

$z^1 = 2\left(\cos\frac{\pi}{3} + i\sin\frac{\pi}{3}\right) \qquad = \left[2, \frac{\pi}{3}\right]$

$z^2 = 2^2\left(\cos 2\cdot\frac{\pi}{3} + i\sin 2\cdot\frac{\pi}{3}\right) = \left[4, \frac{2\pi}{3}\right]$

$z^3 = 2^3\left(\cos 3\cdot\frac{\pi}{3} + i\sin 3\cdot\frac{\pi}{3}\right) = \left[8, \pi\right]$

$z^4 = 2^4\left(\cos 4\cdot\frac{\pi}{3} + i\sin 4\cdot\frac{\pi}{3}\right) = \left[16, \frac{4\pi}{3}\right]$

$z^5 = 2^5\left(\cos 5\cdot\frac{\pi}{3} + i\sin 5\cdot\frac{\pi}{3}\right) = \left[32, \frac{5\pi}{3}\right]$

$z^6 = 2^6\left(\cos 6\cdot\frac{\pi}{3} + i\sin 6\cdot\frac{\pi}{3}\right) = \left[64, 2\pi\right]$

$z^7 = 2^7\left(\cos 7\cdot\frac{\pi}{3} + i\sin 7\cdot\frac{\pi}{3}\right) = \left[128, \frac{7\pi}{3}\right]$

b. The points are plotted at the left below. The smooth curve connecting them, shown below at the right, is called a *logarithmic spiral*.

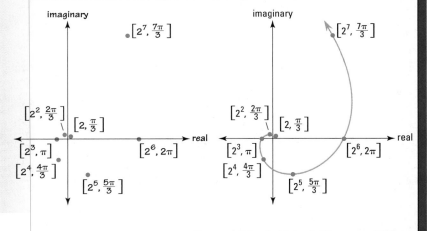

The application of DeMoivre's Theorem to finding roots of complex numbers on page 848 may take some time to discuss. You might wish to do either Additional Example 2 or **Question 4** as an example before discussing the general Roots of a Complex Number Theorem. Emphasize the equal spacing of roots around the origin in the complex plane; sketching roots can be a quick way to check calculations.

Error Alert Watch for students who confuse the patterns in the graphs of powers and roots of a complex number. The graph of consecutive powers lie on a logarithmic spiral that starts at the origin, while the graphs of n nth roots lie equally spaced on a circle centered at the origin.

History Connection Abraham DeMoivre (1667–1754) was born in France and settled in England. He is remembered for his work in probability theory and particularly for the theorem in this lesson.

The number of questions for this lesson may seem fewer than usual, but calculating roots takes time.

Additional Examples

1. Let $z = 1.5(\cos\frac{\pi}{4} + i\sin\frac{\pi}{4})$.

a. Calculate z^n for $n = 1, 2, 3, 4$, and 5. $z^1 = z$;
$z^2 = 2.25(\cos\frac{\pi}{2} + i\sin\frac{\pi}{2})$;
$z^3 = 3.375(\cos\frac{3\pi}{4} + i\sin\frac{3\pi}{4})$,
$z^4 = -5.0625$;
$z^5 = 7.59375(\cos\frac{5\pi}{4} +$
$i\sin\frac{5\pi}{4})$

(Additional Examples continue on page 848.)

Optional Activities

✎ **Writing** After discussing the lesson you might have students write a paragraph explaining how to find the nth roots of any complex number $a + bi$, as if explaining to a fellow student who missed the lesson in class. [Students should include the following steps in their paragraph: change the complex number to polar form by using $r = \sqrt{a^2 + b^2}$ and $\theta = \tan^{-1}\left(\frac{b}{a}\right)$ (adding 180° as necessary); apply the Roots of a Complex Number Theorem to find the absolute value of all the roots, $\frac{n}{r}$, and the positive argument of the first root, $\frac{\theta}{n}$ (when $k = 0$); use the addition of $k \cdot \frac{360°}{n}$ to find the arguments of the other roots; know that there should be n roots when finished, therefore use $k = 0, 1, 2, ..., n - 1$; plot the points on a complex plane and know they should form a regular n-gon centered at the origin, or n evenly spaced points on a circle of radius $\sqrt[n]{r}$.]

b. Plot these powers of z.
The points are $[1.5, \frac{\pi}{4}]$,
$[2.25, \frac{\pi}{2}]$, $[3.375, \frac{3\pi}{4}]$,
$[5.0625, \pi]$, and $[7.59375, \frac{5\pi}{4}]$

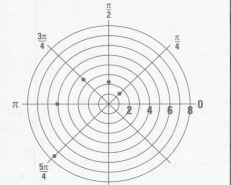

2. Find the 4th roots of $8\sqrt{3} + 8i$ and graph them in the polar coordinate system.
$2(\cos 7\frac{1}{2}° + i \sin 7\frac{1}{2}°)$,
$2(\cos 97\frac{1}{2}° + i \sin 97\frac{1}{2}°)$,
$2(\cos 187\frac{1}{2}° + i \sin 187\frac{1}{2}°)$,
$2(\cos 277\frac{1}{2}° + i \sin 277\frac{1}{2}°)$

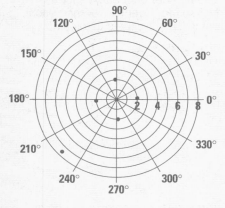

(Notes on Questions begin on page 850.)

Finding the *n*th Roots of a Complex Number

Two complex numbers in polar and trigonometric form are equal if and only if their absolute values are equal and their arguments differ by an integral multiple of 360°. With this knowledge and DeMoivre's Theorem, you can find roots of complex numbers.

Consider, for instance, a cube root z of the complex number 8i. By definition of cube root, $z^3 = 8i$.

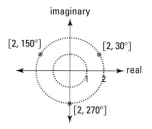

By examining the graph of 8i at the left, you can see that the argument of 8i is 90° and its absolute value is 8. So in trigonometric form, $8i = 8(\cos 90° + i \sin 90°)$. Substituting this and $z = r(\cos \theta + i \sin \theta)$ into $z^3 = 8i$ gives $(r(\cos \theta + i \sin \theta))^3 = 8(\cos 90° + i \sin 90°)$. Applying DeMoivre's Theorem, we get $r^3(\cos 3\theta + i \sin 3\theta) = 8(\cos 90° + i \sin 90°)$. For these complex numbers to be equal,
$$r^3 = 8 \quad \text{and} \quad \cos 3\theta + i \sin 3\theta = \cos 90° + i \sin 90°.$$
So $r = 2$ and $3\theta = 90° + 360n°$.
Thus $\theta = 30° + 120n°$, where *n* is an integer.
Therefore, the cube roots of 8i are of the form
$$z = 2(\cos (30° + 120n°) + i \sin (30° + 120n°)).$$

This solution may seem complicated, but actually there are only three distinct roots. For $n = 0$, 1, and 2, the roots are
$$2(\cos 30° + i \sin 30°) = \sqrt{3} + i,$$
$$2(\cos 150° + i \sin 150°) = -\sqrt{3} + i,$$
and $$2(\cos 270° + i \sin 270°) = -2i.$$
For any $n > 2$, you will find that these values are repeated.

These three roots of 8i are plotted below. Because they all have the same absolute value 2 and are 120° apart, they lie equally spaced around a circle with center at the origin and radius 2.

imaginary
[2, 150°]   [2, 30°]
                real
[2, 270°]

Generalizing the technique used to find the cube roots of 8i leads to the following theorem.

Roots of a Complex Number Theorem
Let *z* be any nonzero complex number and *n* be any positive integer. Then there are *n* distinct roots of $z^n = r(\cos \theta + i \sin \theta)$. They are
$$\sqrt[n]{r}\left(\cos\left(\frac{\theta}{n} + k\frac{360°}{n}\right) + i \sin\left(\frac{\theta}{n} + k\frac{360°}{n}\right)\right)$$
where $k = 0, 1, 2, ..., n - 1$.

Adapting to Individual Needs

Extra Help
Some students may need to be reminded that every real number is a complex number. As such, every nonzero real number has *n* complex *n*th roots which are the vertices of a regular polygon when $n \geq 2$.

Challenge
Have students answer the following.
1. Describe *r* and θ for the following roots of *i*.
   a. The two square roots $[r = 1; \theta = 45°$ and $225°]$
   b. The three cube roots $[r = 1; \theta = 30°, 150°, 270°]$
   c. The four fourth roots $[r = 1; \theta = 22.5°, 112.5°, 202.5°, 292.5°]$

   d. the *n* *n*th roots $[r = 1; \theta = \frac{90°}{n} + \frac{k\,360°}{n}$ where $k = 0, 1, 2, ..., n - 1]$
2. Describe *r* and θ for the *n* *n*th roots of -*i*. $[r = 1; \theta = \frac{270°}{n} + \frac{k\,360°}{n}$ where $k = 0, 1, 2, ..., n - 1]$

Graphing the *n*th Roots of a Complex Number

Example 2

Find the 5th roots of $16 + 16\sqrt{3}\,i$ and graph them in the polar coordinate system.

Solution

Calculate the absolute value and an argument of $16 + 16\sqrt{3}\,i$ or examine its graph to determine that $r = 32$ and $\theta = 60°$.

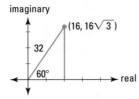

So in trigonometric form, $16 + 16\sqrt{3}\,i = 32(\cos 60° + i\sin 60°)$. Use the theorem above. The fifth roots are

$$\sqrt[5]{32}\left(\cos\left(\frac{60°}{5} + k\,\frac{360°}{5}\right) + i\sin\left(\frac{60°}{5} + k\,\frac{360°}{5}\right)\right)$$

$$= 2(\cos(12° + 72k°) + i\sin(12° + 72k°)),$$

where $k = 0, 1, 2, 3,$ and 4.

Thus the roots are $2(\cos 12° + i\sin 12°)$, $2(\cos 84° + i\sin 84°)$, $2(\cos 156° + i\sin 156°)$, $2(\cos 228° + i\sin 228°)$, and $2(\cos 300° + i\sin 300°)$. They are graphed below. Note that the 5 fifth roots of $16 + 16\sqrt{3}\,i$ are equally spaced on a circle centered at the origin with radius $32^{1/5} = 2$.

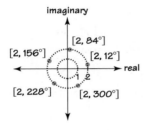

In general, for $n > 2$, the graphs of the *n*th roots of any nonzero complex number are vertices of a regular *n*-gon centered at the origin!

Practice

For more questions on SPUR Objectives, use **Lesson Master 13-8** (shown below).

Assessment

Written Communication Have students write a paragraph that (1) explains how to find the 2nd through *n*th powers and *n* *n*th roots of a complex number written in trigonometric form and (2) describes the related graphs. [Students explain how to find powers and roots of complex numbers in trigonometric form and interpret the related graphs.]

Extension

Technology On automatic graphers that will graph in parametric mode, the following instructions can be used to display the roots of a complex number graphically, and to determine the argument of each root through the trace feature. First set the calculator to parametric mode and degree mode. Explain to students that in parametric mode, *x* and *y* are given in terms of another variable *t*, which will be acting as an angle. Use the complex number in **Example 2** with students as an example.

(Follow Up continues on page 850.)

Enter $x = \sqrt[5]{16}\cos t$ and $y = \sqrt[5]{16}\sin t$. Set the Tmin to the positive argument of the first root, in this case to $\frac{60°}{5} = 12°$. Set the Tmax to $360° +$ Tmin, in this case to $372°$. Set the Tstep to $\frac{360°}{\text{number of roots}}$, in this case to $\frac{360°}{5}$ or $72°$. Press graph and a pentagon will appear. The calculator will draw in the sides of the pentagon unless the mode is set to dot (versus connected.) Students can trace to verify the arguments of the other roots.

Project Update Project 1, *Euler's Theorem*, on page 858, relates to the content of this lesson.

Notes on Questions

Question 4 A similar question is to graph the cube roots of 27. They too are vertices of an equilateral triangle centered at the origin. Since one vertex is known to be 3, the others can be determined geometrically.

Questions 10–11 Once one of the *n*th roots has been determined, the others can be determined by rotating the first root $\frac{2\pi}{n}$ about the origin.

Cartoonists use nth roots and other symbols to satirize advanced mathematics.

850

Covering the Reading

In 1 and 2, use DeMoivre's Theorem to find each power. Write your answer in trigonometric form.

1. $\left(3\left(\cos\frac{\pi}{5} + i\sin\frac{\pi}{5}\right)\right)^4$ 81 $(\cos\frac{4\pi}{5} + i\sin\frac{4\pi}{5})$

2. $\left(2\left(\cos\frac{4\pi}{7} + i\sin\frac{4\pi}{7}\right)\right)^3$ 8 $(\cos\frac{12\pi}{7} + i\sin\frac{12\pi}{7})$

3. Consider $z = 2\left(\cos\frac{\pi}{6} + i\sin\frac{\pi}{6}\right)$. a, b) See margin.
   a. Use DeMoivre's Theorem to calculate z^n for $n = 2$ to 6.
   b. Plot z^1, z^2, z^3, z^4, z^5, and z^6 in the complex plane.
   c. Describe the pattern in the graphs of the powers of z.
      They lie in a spiral.

4. a. Solve the equation $z^3 = 27(\cos 150° + i\sin 150°)$. See margin.
   b. Plot the solutions in the complex plane. See margin.
   c. Describe the graph in part **b**.
      They are the vertices of an equilateral triangle.

5. Find the 3 cube roots of $125(\cos 30° + i\sin 30°)$.
   5$(\cos 10° + i\sin 10°)$, 5$(\cos 130° + i\sin 130°)$, 5$(\cos 250° + i\sin 250°)$

6. Find the 4 fourth roots of $7\left(\cos\frac{4\pi}{5} + i\sin\frac{4\pi}{5}\right)$.
   See margin.

7. Find the square roots of -1. i, –i

Applying the Mathematics

In 8 and 9, use DeMoivre's Theorem to find each power in $a + bi$ form.

8. $(3i)^4$ 81 + 0i

9. $\left(-\sqrt{3} + i\right)^6$ -64 + 0i

In 10 and 11, write the roots in polar form and plot them in the complex plane.

10. the fourth roots of $8 + 8\sqrt{3}\,i$ [2, 15°], [2, 105°], [2, 195°], [2, 285°].
    See margin for graph.

11. the sixth roots of $64i$ [2, 15°], [2, 75°], [2, 135°], [2, 195°], [2, 255°], [2, 315°]. See margin for graph.

In 12 and 13, plot the solutions to each equation in the complex plane.

12. $z^3 = 8$ See margin.

13. $z^4 = -16$ See margin.

14. A ninth root of z is $2(\cos 30° + i\sin 30°)$. Find z in polar form.
    [512, 270°]

Review

15. Write $7(\cos 10° + i\sin 10°)$ in $a + bi$ form. *(Lesson 13-7)*
    7 cos 10° + 7 sin 10°i ≈ 6.89 + 1.22i

16. If $z_1 = 8(\cos 70° + i\sin 70°)$ and $z_2 = 5(\cos 155° + i\sin 155°)$, find $z_1 \cdot z_2$. *(Lesson 13-7)* 40 $(\cos 225° + i\sin 225°)$

17. a. Sketch a graph of $r = e^{\theta/3}$. a, b) See margin.
    b. Show that the points on the curve in part **a** satisfy the relationship $\ln r = k\theta$ for some constant k and identify k. *(Lessons 6-4, 13-5)*

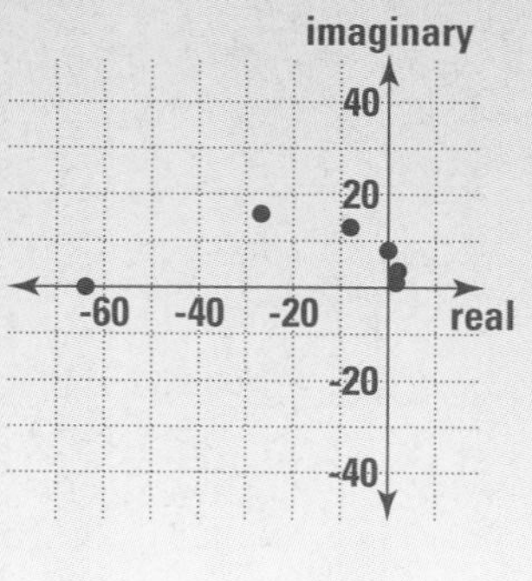

850

18) The graphs do not coincide. Counterexample:
Let $\alpha = \frac{\pi}{6}$. Then
$\sin^2 \alpha = \left(\sin \frac{\pi}{6}\right)^2 = \left(\frac{1}{2}\right)^2 = \frac{1}{4}$ and
$\frac{1}{2}(1 - \cos^2 \alpha) = \frac{1}{2}\left(1 - (\cos \frac{\pi}{6})^2\right) = \frac{1}{2}\left(1 - \frac{3}{4}\right) = \frac{1}{2}\left(\frac{1}{4}\right) = \frac{1}{8}$.

19) $-13x^2 + 34\sqrt{3}\,xy - 47y^2 + (128 - 12\sqrt{3})x + (-12 - 128\sqrt{3})y - 284 = 0$

20) $\begin{bmatrix} 2 & -1 & -1 \\ -1 & 2 & -1 \\ -1 & -1 & 2 \end{bmatrix}$

18. Prove or disprove: For all α, $\sin^2 \alpha = \frac{1}{2}(1 - \cos^2 \alpha)$. *(Lesson 13-2)*
See left.

19. Determine an equation of the hyperbola with major and minor axes of lengths 4 and 1, centered around the point $(3, -2)$, and whose major axis is rotated counterclockwise by $30°$ from the horizontal. *(Lesson 12-4)*
See left.

20. Find the product. $\begin{bmatrix} -1 & 0 & 1 \\ 0 & 1 & -1 \\ 1 & -1 & 0 \end{bmatrix} \cdot \begin{bmatrix} 1 & 2 & 3 \\ 2 & 3 & 1 \\ 3 & 1 & 2 \end{bmatrix}$ *(Lesson 11-1)* See left.

21. Evaluate $\lim\limits_{n \to \infty} \frac{n + 3}{4 - 2n}$. *(Lesson 8-2)* $-\frac{1}{2}$

Exploration

22. a. Graph the first ten terms of each sequence $a_n = z^n$. See below.
  i. $z = [1.25, 40°]$
  ii. $z = [1, 40°]$
  iii. $z = [0.9, 40°]$

b. Compare and contrast the three sets of points, and predict what happens for higher powers. The points in part i spiral outward, the points in part ii fall on a circle of radius 1 with center at the origin, and the points in part iii spiral inward. As the powers in part i increase, the absolute values of the terms increase, so the points continue to spiral farther and farther from the origin. Since $1^n = 1$ for every n, the absolute values of the terms in part ii are all 1, so the points will continue to fall on the circle. As n increases in part iii, the absolute values of the terms get smaller and smaller, so the points continue to spiral inward toward the origin.

22ai)
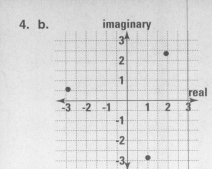

22aii)
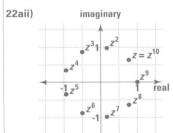

22aiii)
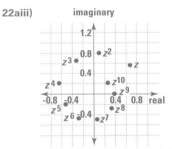

Lesson 13-8 *DeMoivre's Theorem* **851**

10.
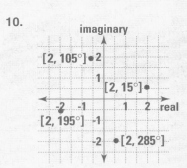

11.
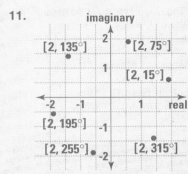

12.
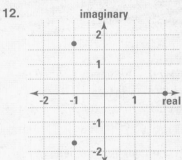

13.
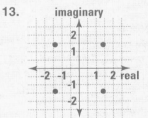

17. a.
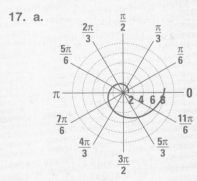

b. $r = e^{\frac{\theta}{3}} \Leftrightarrow \ln r = \ln e^{\frac{\theta}{3}} = \frac{\theta}{3} \ln e = \frac{\theta}{3}(1) = \frac{1}{3}\theta$, so $k = \frac{1}{3}$

4. b.
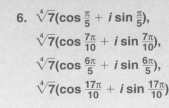

6. $\sqrt[4]{7}(\cos \frac{\pi}{5} + i \sin \frac{\pi}{5})$,
$\sqrt[4]{7}(\cos \frac{7\pi}{10} + i \sin \frac{7\pi}{10})$,
$\sqrt[4]{7}(\cos \frac{6\pi}{5} + i \sin \frac{6\pi}{5})$,
$\sqrt[4]{7}(\cos \frac{17\pi}{10} + i \sin \frac{17\pi}{10})$

Teaching Lesson **13-9**

Warm-up

Consider the sequence defined by $z_1 = \frac{i}{\sqrt{2}}$ and $z_n = (z_{n-1})^2 + \frac{i}{2}$.

1. Calculate the next five terms of this sequence.
$\frac{i}{2}, \frac{i-1}{2}, 0, \frac{i}{2}, \frac{-1+2i}{4}, \frac{-3+4i}{16}$

2. Do you think that the limit of this sequence is infinity? **No**

Notes on Reading

We close this book with this lesson for several reasons. The Mandelbrot Set is an example of a relatively recent development of mathematics, and hopefully students will appreciate that mathematics is a growing field of study—not a dead collection of numbers and algorithms to be memorized. The set is a result of the

---

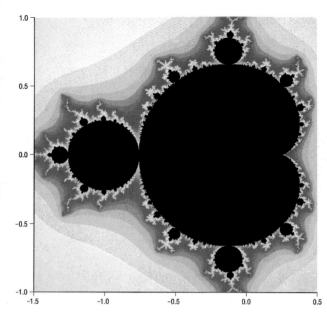

The last lesson ended with a geometrically beautiful result that has been known for about 200 years. This lesson discusses a geometric set that has been known only since 1980.

In recent years, a new field of mathematics has arisen, called *dynamical systems*, in which complex numbers play an important role. Some of the products of this field are beautiful computer-generated drawings which have won awards in art competitions. Among these are drawings involving the *Mandelbrot set* (named for Benoit Mandelbrot, a mathematician at IBM), which is a particular set of complex numbers plotted in the complex plane. Above is a graph of this set in part of the plane. Points colored black are in the Mandelbrot set. Points colored red or yellow are outside the set.

Determining Whether a Point Is in the Mandelbrot Set

Points in the Mandelbrot set are defined recursively. Let c be a fixed complex number, and consider this sequence of complex numbers starting with c.

$$\begin{cases} z_1 = c; \\ z_n = (z_{n-1})^2 + c \text{ for } n > 1. \end{cases}$$

The recursion squares the previous z value, adds c to the result, then repeats these two steps indefinitely. For many values of c, the limit of $|z_n|$ is infinity. Points in the Mandelbrot set are those values of c for which the limit of $|z_n|$ is not infinity.

Lesson 13-9 Overview

Broad Goals The purpose of this lesson is to explain how the Mandelbrot Set is constructed and to give pictures of this set in various windows in the complex plane. A computer program is given by which students can generate graphs themselves.

Perspective The mathematics of dynamical systems was first studied early in this century by French mathematicians. But only in recent years has the subject taken off,

because the computer has afforded the opportunity to analyze such systems in great detail. The Mandelbrot set is one of the important sets in this field, and its popularity is probably due more to the intriguing visual nature of the set than to its algebraic properties.

For instance, let $c = -1.5 - 1.0i$. Then the sequence begins with the following values.

$$z_1 = c = -1.5 - 1.0i, \text{ so } |z_1| \approx 1.80$$
$$z_2 = (-1.5 - 1.0i)^2 + (-1.5 - 1.0i) = -0.25 + 2i, \text{ so } |z_2| \approx 2.02$$
$$z_3 = (-0.25 + 2i)^2 + (-1.5 - 1.0i) = -5.4375 - 2i, \text{ so } |z_3| \approx 5.79$$

It can be shown that $|z_n|$ will go to infinity if and only if at some stage of the iteration $|z_n| > 2$. It also turns out that for most values of c which iterate to infinity, $|z_n|$ reaches 2 rather quickly. For these reasons, $c = -1.5 - 1.0i$ is discarded as not being part of the Mandelbrot set. Note that the point (-1.5, -1.0) is not colored black in the graph on page 852.

Examining Parts of the Mandelbrot Set

By varying the initial c and the size of the window, the Mandelbrot set can be studied to virtually any degree of detail. The three graphs below show the set as you zoom in on the region around the point $-0.55 + 0.62i$. Note how the "bump" on the original graph is very similar in shape to the original graph itself. For this reason, the Mandelbrot set is sometimes called "self-similar." In fact, however, most of the parts of the graph differ in some way.

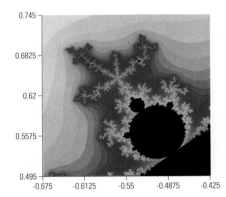

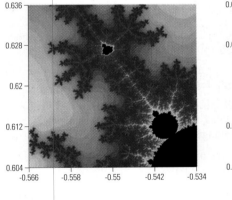

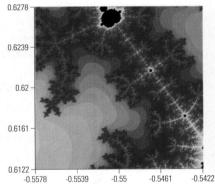

computer age—it could not have been studied so extensively without them. The set is an example of an application of a topic that students often think has few applications. And students at this level know enough mathematics and computer science to generate the set for themselves. Point this out to your students—they have successfully learned enough mathematics to study a topic which is at the cutting edge of mathematics research.

You will need to explain carefully how the Mandelbrot set is generated. The question is: Is a particular complex number c in the set or not? For this, we set up a sequence $z_1 = c$, $z_2 = z_1^2 + c$, $z_3 = z_2^2 + c$, $z_4 = z_3^2 + c$, and so on. Then we ask: Are the terms of this sequence bounded in the sense that they stay within a particular distance of the origin? If so, then c is in the Mandelbrot set. If not, then c is not in the set.

If you have access to a Macintosh computer, you might want to get a copy of a much faster and versatile graphics program called Super MANDELZOOM. It is available as a public domain item (a donation is suggested) from the developer Robert P. Munafo, 239 Clinton Road, Brookline, MA 02146. Send a two-sided (800K) disk with a self-addressed (two stamps) envelope. With Super MANDELZOOM, students have the ability to generate all the graphs that we have generated and we suggest that they do so. Students should not ignore the BASIC program or **Questions 1–8,** however, because the algorithm used in Super MANDELZOOM is the same. Making the graphs is one thing, understanding how they are created is where mathematics enters the picture.

If your library has back issues of *Scientific American*, it is worth the

Optional Activities

Activity 1 As an introduction to this lesson have available books on fractals so students can study the pictures. Fractals can also be found on the Internet. Students may be amazed to see fractals that look like coastlines, trees, lung cavities, and broccoli, as well as beautiful and abstract designs. See what other sets students discover. [The Julia set, for one, is related to the Mandelbrot set and is also widely seen.] Have students do some reading to find out why

fractals are being studied today, aside from their beauty. [To understand how weather patterns develop is one prominent application, as well as why small changes in a system may produce large effects.]

Activity 2 Technology Connection
In *Technology Sourcebook, Calculator Master 11,* students use a programmable calculator to enter and run a program that determines whether or not a point is in the Mandelbrot set.

effort to find the article by A. K. Dewdney in the August 1985 issue. It has beautiful full-color pictures of the set (the color comes by assigning different hues to values of z_n in different intervals). The August 1990 issue of *Scientific American* also includes color photos in an article on fractals by Hartmut Jürgens and others.

History Connection Bennoit B. Mandelbrot, born in 1924, discovered the set named after him while working at IBM. Julia Sets and Chaos Theory are some of the current mathematical research fields with connections to this set.

In the 1980s, John H. Hubbard, a mathematician at Cornell University, generated graphs of the Mandelbrot set using a computer. Hubbard's pioneer programs inspired many programs for drawing the Mandelbrot set. The pictures in this lesson were created with *The Beauty of Fractals Lab*, written by Thomas Eberhardt and Marc Parmet. This program makes use of sophisticated computing techniques and languages in order to increase the speed of the calculations and drawings. You can draw a small version of the set, however, using the following BASIC program.

```
10   REM MANDELZOOM
20   INPUT "ENTER THE REAL AND IMAGINARY PARTS OF C"; ACORNER,
     BCORNER
30   INPUT "ENTER THE SIZE OF THE VIEWING WINDOW"; SIZE
40   CLS
50   P = 50
60   DIM PIC(P,P)
70   GAP = SIZE / P
80   FOR J = 1 TO P
90       FOR K = 1 TO P
100          AC = ACORNER + J*GAP
110          BC = BCORNER + K*GAP
120          AZ = 0:BZ = 0: COUNT = 1
130          IF COUNT > 100 THEN 200
140              OLDAZ = AZ
150              AZ = AZ*AZ − BZ*BZ + AC
160              BZ = 2*OLDAZ*BZ + BC
170              MAGZ = SQR(AZ*AZ + BZ*BZ)
180              IF MAGZ > 2 THEN 210
190              COUNT = COUNT + 1: GO TO 130
200          PIC(J,K) = 1
210      NEXT K
220  NEXT J
230  FOR J = 1 TO P
240      FOR K = 1 TO P
250          IF PIC(J,K) = 1 THEN PSET (J,P−K)
260      NEXT K
270  NEXT J
```

The program has four major steps. (You do not need to understand every detail of the program.)

1. The program asks for the initial value of c and the size of the window in the complex plane (lines 20 and 30).

2. It scales the information from step (1) into "pixel-units" and creates an array PIC(J, K) for each pixel in the graph (lines 50–70). In this program, the rectangle is 50 pixels on a side (P = 50).

3. For every pixel with coordinates (AC, BC) in the viewing window, the program calculates $z_n = z_{n-1}^2 + c$ until $|z_n| > 2$ or $n = 100$, whichever comes first (lines 80–220). The bigger n is, the more accurate the graph, but the longer the time it takes to do the calculations. If $|z_n| \leq 2$ after

Adapting to Individual Needs

Extra Help
Point out to students that they can use the graph of the Mandelbrot set on page 852 to verify the results they get when they algebraically test whether or not a particular point is in the set. While this may not be practical for points very close to the boundary, it does work nicely for $c = -1.5 - 1.0i$, as discussed on page 853, and for **Questions 1–4**.

Challenge
If students are very familiar with programming their calculator, have them write a version of the BASIC program in this lesson that would fit their calculator.

100 iterations of the squaring process, then the pixel at PIC(J, K) is set to 1 (line 200). Lines 150–170 apply the mathematics of complex numbers you learned in Lesson 13-7. For $z = $ AZ $+$ BZi, the real part of z^2 is $(AZ)^2 - (BZ)^2$ and the imaginary part is 2(AZ)(BZ). The variable MAGZ is the absolute value of the new iteration of z.

4. Finally the graph is drawn (lines 230–270). If PIC(J, K) $= 1$, the point is in the set and the pixel is turned on (line 250).

(Note: this program is written to work on Macintosh computers running MS-BASIC. For other computers and other versions of BASIC there are slight variations. Run on one particular computer with $c = -2 - 1.25i$ and size $= 2.5$, MANDELZOOM took 28 seconds to produce the graph at left below. When run with P $= 200$ (line 50) and a maximum count of 200 rather than 100 (line 130), it took 14 minutes and produced the graph at the right.)

Using a BASIC program is obviously not the best way to graph the Mandelbrot set, but it shows how you can use the computing and mathematics skills you have studied in this text. With better programs and faster computers, you can apply the mathematics you know to generate gorgeous views like the ones below, centered at about $-0.76 + 0.26i$.

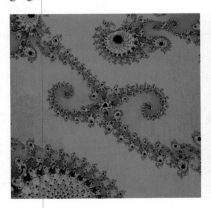 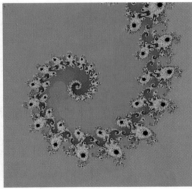

Question 1 You might try other real numbers to see if they are in the Mandelbrot set. For instance, if $z_1 = 1$, then $z_2 = 1^2 + 1 = 2$ and $z_3 = 2^2 + 1 = 5$, and clearly $|z_n|$ is growing without bound, so 1 is not in the set. But what if $z = 0.5$? What if $z = 0.2$? (If $0 \le z \le 0.25$, then the point is in the set.)

Additional Answers

11.

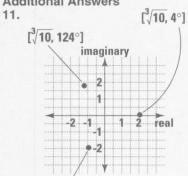

$[\sqrt[3]{10}, 124°]$

$[\sqrt[3]{10}, 4°]$

$[\sqrt[3]{10}, 244°]$

12.

$[1, 162°]$ $[1, 90°]$ $[1, 18°]$

$[1, 234°]$

$[1, 306°]$

1a) $z_1 = 0 + 0i,$
$z_2 = 0 + 0i,$
$z_3 = 0 + 0i$

b) Yes; $\lim_{n \to \infty} |z_n|$ is finite.

4) $|z_4| = \sqrt{9410} \approx 97.005;$
no

5b) $AZ = 0.202, BZ = 0.002, MAGZ \approx 0.202$

7)

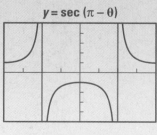

8a) It is probably in the set because the part of the graph near that point is black.

The boundary of a Mandelbrot set is an example of a *fractal*. Fractals can be generated by special functions embodying randomness. Thus, in a way, the Mandelbrot set is related to all the themes of this book—functions, statistics, and trigonometry. We hope you agree that it is a fitting subject for the last lesson of this book.

QUESTIONS

Covering the Reading

1. **a.** Calculate z_1, z_2, and z_3 in the Mandelbrot recursion for $c = 0 + 0i$.
   b. Is $c = 0 + 0i$ in the Mandelbrot set? Why or why not?

In 2–4, based on $|z_4|$, is the point in the Mandelbrot set?

2. $-1 + 0i$
$|z_4| = 0$; yes

3. $0 + 0.5i$
$|z_4| \approx 0.407$; yes

4. $1 + i$
See left.

5. Refer to the BASIC MANDELZOOM program in the lesson. Let ACORNER = 0.2, BCORNER = 0, and SIZE = 0.1 .
   a. Give the values of AC and BC the first time the computer executes lines 100 and 110. $AC = 0.202, BC = 0.002$
   b. Give the values of AZ, BZ, and MAGZ the first time the computer executes lines 150–170. See left.
   c. Will the computer turn on PIC(1, 1)? Yes

In 6–8, run the program MANDELZOOM for complex numbers $x + yi$ in the indicated viewing window.

6. Describe the graph a computer generates for $-0.5 \le x \le -0.49$, $0 \le y \le 0.01$. a square filling the entire viewing window

7. Draw a rough sketch of the graph a computer generates for $-1.5 \le x \le -0.9$, $-0.3 \le y \le 0.3$, $c = -1.5 - 0.3i$. See left.

8. **a.** Use the close-up views around $c = -0.5507 + 0.6259i$ to hypothesize whether c is actually in the set. See left.
   b. Test your hypothesis in part **a** by computing $|z_4|$ for this value of c. $|z_4| \approx 1.111$ and $|z_1| \approx 0.834$, so it seems that $|z_n|$ is close to 1 and that c is actually in the set.

Review

In 9 and 10, find each power. Write your answers in $a + bi$ form. *(Lesson 13-8)*

9. $\left(\frac{\sqrt{2}}{2} + \frac{\sqrt{2}}{2}i\right)^5$ $-\frac{\sqrt{2}}{2} - \frac{\sqrt{2}}{2}i$

10. $\left(1 + i\sqrt{3}\right)^6$ $64 + 0i$

In 11 and 12, write each root in trigonometric form and plot it in the complex plane. *(Lesson 13-8)* See margin for graphs.

11. the 3 cube roots of $10(\cos 12° + i \sin 12°)$ $\sqrt[3]{10}(\cos 4° + i \sin 4°)$, $\sqrt[3]{10}(\cos 124° + i \sin 124°)$, $\sqrt[3]{10}(\cos 244° + i \sin 244°)$

12. the 5 fifth roots of i
$\cos 18° + i \sin 18°$, $\cos 90° + i \sin 90°$, $\cos 162° + i \sin 162°$, $\cos 234° + i \sin 234°$, $\cos 306° + i \sin 306°$

Additional Answers, page 857

19. a.

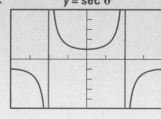

$y = \sec \theta$

$-\pi \le x \le \pi$, x-scale $= \frac{\pi}{4}$
$-5 \le y \le 5$, y-scale $= 1$

$y = \sec(\pi - \theta)$

$-\pi \le x \le \pi$, x-scale $= \frac{\pi}{4}$
$-5 \le y \le 5$, y-scale $= 1$

b. Let $\theta = 0$. Then $\sec \theta = \frac{1}{\cos 0} = 1$ and $\sec(\pi - \theta) = \frac{1}{\cos(\pi - \theta)}$ $= \frac{1}{\cos \pi} = -1$.
So $\sec \theta = \sec(\pi - \theta)$ is not an identity.

13a) $z_1 \approx \sqrt{11}(\cos 25.2° + i \sin 25.2°)$, $z_2 \approx \sqrt{11}(\cos 205.2° + i \sin 205.2°)$

b) $z_1 z_2 \approx 11$ $(\cos 230.4° + i \sin 230.4°)$, $\dfrac{z_1}{z_2} = 1(\cos(-180°) + i \sin(-180°)) = -1$

14a) $z_1 = 0 \left(\cos \dfrac{\pi}{6} + i \sin \dfrac{\pi}{6}\right)$, $z_2 = 2(\cos 0° + i \sin 0°)$

b) $z_1 z_2 = 0$, $\dfrac{z_1}{z_2} = 0$

16a)

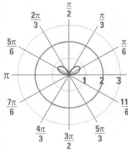

18a)

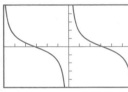

$-360° \le x \le 360°$, x-scale = 60°
$-5 \le y \le 5$, y-scale = 1

In 13 and 14, two complex numbers z_1 and z_2 are given. **a.** Express z_1 and z_2 in trigonometric form. **b.** Evaluate $z_1 \cdot z_2$ and $\dfrac{z_1}{z_2}$.   *(Lesson 13-7)* **See left.**

13. $z_1 = 3 + \sqrt{2}\,i$, $z_2 = -3 - \sqrt{2}\,i$

14. $z_1 = \left[0, \dfrac{\pi}{6}\right]$, $z_2 = [2, 0]$

15. Find $|z_1 z_2|$ when $z_1 = 112 - 15i$ and $z_2 = 0.01 + 4i$.   *(Lesson 13-7)*
   ≈ 452

16. The graph of $r = 2 \sin \theta \cos^2 \theta$ is called a *bifolium*.
   a. Sketch the bifolium for $0 \le \theta \le \pi$. **See left.**
   b. Graph $r = 2$ on the same axes as the graph in part **a**. Does $2 \sin \theta \cos^2 \theta = 2$ for any θ in $0 \le \theta \le \pi$?   *(Lesson 13-5)*
   See graph at left. No

17. A point $[r, \theta]$ has $\theta = -180°$.
   a. Where must this point be? **on the polar axis**
   b. Give a rectangular equation for all such points.   *(Lesson 13-4)*
   y = 0

In 18 and 19, a trigonometric equation is given. **a.** Use an automatic grapher to test whether the equation may be an identity. **b.** Prove your conclusion in part **a**.   *(Lessons 13-2, 13-3)*

18. $\dfrac{1 + \cos \alpha}{\sin \alpha} = \cot \dfrac{\alpha}{2}$ (Hint: $\cos \alpha = \cos\left(2 \cdot \dfrac{\alpha}{2}\right)$ and $\sin \alpha = \sin\left(2 \cdot \dfrac{\alpha}{2}\right)$.)
   a) See left.   **b) See below.**

19. $\sec \theta = \sec(\pi - \theta)$
   See margin.

Exploration

20. Explore the Mandelbrot set on intervals of your own choosing.
   Answers will vary.

18b) $\dfrac{1 + \cos \alpha}{\sin \alpha} = \dfrac{1 + \cos 2\left(\frac{\alpha}{2}\right)}{\sin 2\left(\frac{\alpha}{2}\right)} = \dfrac{1 + \cos^2\left(\frac{\alpha}{2}\right) - \sin^2\left(\frac{\alpha}{2}\right)}{2 \sin\left(\frac{\alpha}{2}\right) \cos\left(\frac{\alpha}{2}\right)} = \dfrac{2 \cos^2\left(\frac{\alpha}{2}\right)}{2 \sin\left(\frac{\alpha}{2}\right) \cos\left(\frac{\alpha}{2}\right)} =$

$\dfrac{\cos\left(\frac{\alpha}{2}\right)}{\sin\left(\frac{\alpha}{2}\right)} = \cot\left(\dfrac{\alpha}{2}\right)$ for $\alpha \ne n\pi$ where n is an integer.

Extension
If you have students that are interested in the program and have the patience to explore with it, suggest Project 3 on page 859 to them. Students with computers at home may be encouraged to run the program there for larger values of P and COUNT. If they discover special regions of the set they could print the screen and show the results to the class.

Project Update Project 3, *The Mandelbrot Set*, on page 859, relates to the content of this lesson.

Possible Responses, page 858
1. a. The sum of the first three terms $\approx .9800666667$. The value of the fourth term $\approx -8.8889 \times 10^{-8}$. Using a calculator we get $\cos(0.2) \approx .9800665778$. The difference between the estimate and the actual value is $.9800666667 - .9800665778 = 8.8859 \times 10^{-8}$, which is less than 8.8889×10^{-8}, the absolute value of the fourth term.

b. The sum of the first three terms $\approx .1986693333$. The value of the fourth term $\approx -2.54 \times 10^{-9}$. Using a calculator we get $\sin(0.2) \approx .1986693308$. The difference between the estimate and the actual value is $.198669333 - .198669331 = 2.50 \times 10^{-9}$, which is less than 2.54×10^{-9}, the absolute value of the fourth term.

c. The nth term of the series for $\cos x$ is $(-1)^{n-1} \dfrac{x^{2(n-1)}}{(2n-2)!}$. The formula for the nth term of the series for $\sin x$ is $(-1)^{n-1} \dfrac{x^{2n-1}}{(2n-1)!}$.

(Responses continue on page 858.)

Chapter 13 Projects

The projects relate chiefly to the content of the lessons of this chapter as follows:

Project	Lesson(s)
1	13-1, 13-2, 13-3, 13-6, 13-7, 13-8
2	13-4, 13-5
3	13-9

1 Euler's Theorem Students are asked to accept that the Taylor Series expansions for sine, cosine, and e^x are as given. We hope they find it interesting that $e^{ix} = \cos x + i \sin x$ in **part f**. **Part g** shows the fascinating relationship $e^{i\pi} = -1$ between the two transcendental numbers e and π, the imaginary number i, and the integer -1. In the form $e^{i\pi} + 1 = 0$ it involves the additive and multiplicative identities, the base of natural logs, and half the circumference of the unit circle. That such a simple formula involves so many basic numbers is one of the great results of mathematics.

2 Famous Polar Equations Most of the classic polar equations in this project were discovered in the 18th century. While Jakob Bernoulli is usually given credit for inventing the polar coordinate system because of a paper he wrote in 1691, there is evidence that Isaac Newton developed the system twenty years earlier. In *the Method of Fluxions and Infinite Series*, Newton introduced a coordinate system which located points by reference to a fixed point and a fixed line through that point—essentially the origin and polar axis. This project is difficult without a polar graphing option on an automatic grapher, but it is not impossible, since these ideas were discovered before calculators existed.

A project presents an opportunity for you to extend your knowledge of a topic related to the material of this chapter. You should allow more time for a project than you do for a typical homework question.

1 Euler's Theorem

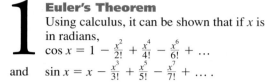

Using calculus, it can be shown that if x is in radians,

$$\cos x = 1 - \frac{x^2}{2!} + \frac{x^4}{4!} - \frac{x^6}{6!} + \dots$$

and $\sin x = x - \frac{x^3}{3!} + \frac{x^5}{5!} - \frac{x^7}{7!} + \dots$.

These series are sometimes the ones used in calculators to approximate values of sine and cosine.

a. Approximate $\cos 0.2$ using the first three terms of the appropriate series. Also, find the fourth term of the series. Show that the difference between your approximation and the calculator value of $\cos 0.2$ is less than the absolute value of the fourth term.

b. Repeat part **a** for $\sin 0.2$.

c. Give an explicit definition for the nth term of each series.

d. Use the series expansion for $\sin x$ and $\cos x$ to find series expansions for $\sin 2x$ and $\cos 2x$. Check your answers with a calculator.

e. In Lesson 6-4 you studied the following series expression for e^x.

$$e^x = 1 + x + \frac{x^2}{2!} + \frac{x^3}{3!} + \frac{x^4}{4!} + \dots$$

It can be proved that this series converges even if the exponent is a complex number. Find a series expansion for e^{ix}.

f. Use the result of part **e** to prove that $e^{ix} = \cos x + i \sin x$.

g. Use the result of part **f** to show that $i = e^{i \cdot \pi/2}$.

h. Find a complex number in the form $a + bi$ for $e^{i\pi}$. (The answer to this is known as *Euler's Theorem*, and is one of the most extraordinary results in mathematics.)

i. Find i^i. (It may surprise you that i^i is a real number.)

2 Famous Polar Equations

Explore some of the following classic polar equations with an automatic grapher. If the grapher does not have an option for entering equations in the form $r^2 = f(\theta)$, graph $r = \sqrt{f(\theta)}$ and $r = -\sqrt{f(\theta)}$ simultaneously. In all the equations, a may be any nonzero real number. Graph each equation a few times, with different values of a. Describe the patterns that you find.

a. Cardioids: $r = a(\cos \theta - 1)$

b. Cissoid of Diocles: $r = a \sin \theta \tan \theta$

c. Cochleoid (Ouija board curve): $r = \frac{a \sin \theta}{\theta}$

d. Folium of Descartes: $r = \frac{3a \sin \theta \cos \theta}{\sin^3 \theta + \cos^3 \theta}$

e. Strophoid: $r = a \cos 2\theta \sec \theta$

f. Lemniscate of Bernoulli: $r^2 = a^2 \cos 2\theta$; $r^2 = a^2 \sin 2\theta$

g. Lituus: $r^2 = \frac{a^2}{\theta}$

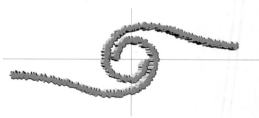

Responses begin on page 857

1. **d.** $\cos 2x = 1 - \frac{(2x)^2}{2!} + \frac{(2x)^4}{4!} - \frac{(2x)^6}{6!} + \dots + (-1)^{n-1} \frac{(2x)^{2(n-1)}}{(2n-2)!} + \dots$;

$\sin 2x = 2x - \frac{(2x)^3}{3!} + \frac{(2x)^5}{5!} - \frac{(2x)^7}{7!} + \dots + (-1)^{n-1} \frac{(2x)^{2n-1}}{(2n-1)!} + \dots$

e. $e^{ix} = 1 + ix + \frac{(ix)^2}{2!} + \frac{(ix)^3}{3!} + \frac{(ix)^4}{4!} + \dots = 1 + ix - \frac{x^2}{2!} - i\frac{(x)^3}{3!} + \frac{x^4}{4!} + \dots$

f. Group the real and imaginary parts of the expansion of e^{ix} to get

$e^{ix} = (1 - \frac{x^2}{2!} + \frac{x^4}{4!} - \frac{x^6}{6!} + \dots) + i(x - \frac{x^3}{3!} + \frac{x^5}{5!} - \frac{x^7}{7!} + \dots) = \cos x + i \sin x.$

g. From part f, $e^{i \cdot \frac{\pi}{2}} = \cos \frac{\pi}{2} + i \sin \frac{\pi}{2} = i.$

h. From part f, $e^{i\pi} = \cos \pi + i \sin \pi$

$= -1 + 0 \cdot i.$

i. From part g, $i^i = (e^{i \cdot \frac{\pi}{2}})^i$

$= e^{\frac{-\pi}{2}} \approx .208.$

3 The Mandelbrot Set

Use the BASIC MANDELZOOM program in Lesson 13-9. Experiment with the program. Leave P = 50 and try various values of c and SIZE. Remember to be patient—the program as written takes up to 45 minutes to run. You can speed it up by changing line 130 to 130 FOR COUNT = 1 TO 50, but this decreases detail and may give you a black square as the image.

a. Reproduce the 50 × 50 pixel Mandelbrot graph in the lesson. Let $c = -2 - 1.25i$, SIZE = 2.5.

b. The image to the right has $c = 0.26 + 0i$ and SIZE = 0.01, P = 100 and COUNT = 1 to 100. It took about $1\frac{1}{2}$ hours. Try a P = 50 version if you don't have time.

c. Look around the "neck" of the set. This is the area near $-0.76 + 0i$. (Do not expect results like the fancy drawings in the lesson.)

2. a. $r = a(\cos \theta - 1)$

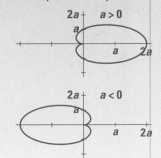

b. $r = a \sin \theta \tan \theta$

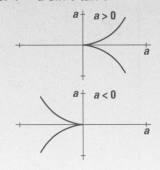

---

3 The Mandelbrot Set This project is for students who are interested in the Mandelbrot Set. There exists software that enables constructing the set. One such piece comes with the book *Fractals for the Macintosh*, by Jesse Jones (Wiate Group Press, 200 Tamal Plaza, Corte Madera, CA 94925). Students with such software should be encouraged to go beyond the project as written here.

2. c. $r = \dfrac{a \sin \theta}{\theta}$

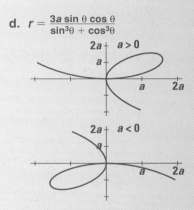

d. $r = \dfrac{3a \sin \theta \cos \theta}{\sin^3 \theta + \cos^3 \theta}$

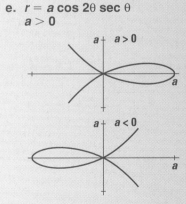

e. $r = a \cos 2\theta \sec \theta$
$a > 0$

(Responses continue on page 860.)

859

Summary

The Summary gives an overview of the entire chapter and provides an opportunity for students to consider the material as a whole. Thus, the Summary can be used to help students relate and unify the concepts presented in the chapter.

Vocabulary

Terms, symbols, and properties are listed by lesson to provide a checklist of concepts a student must know. Emphasize to students that they should read the vocabulary list carefully before starting the Progress Self-Test. If students do not understand the meaning of a term, they should refer back to the indicated lesson.

Additional responses, page 859

f. $r^2 = a^2 \cos 2\theta$

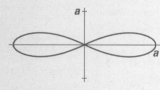

$r^2 = a^2 \sin 2\theta$

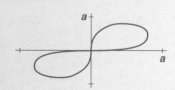

g. $r^2 = \dfrac{a^2}{\theta}$

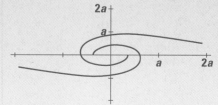

SUMMARY

Graphs can be used to test whether an equation is an identity: check if the graphs of the functions determined by the two sides of the proposed identity coincide. While the graphs cannot prove an identity, they can help in finding a counterexample. Some of the techniques of proving identities include: start with one side and rewrite it until it equals the other side; rewrite each side independently until equal expressions are obtained on both sides; begin with a known identity and derive equivalent statements until the proposed identity appears.

Many of identities involving circular functions hold only on restricted domains, excluding points where one or more of the functions in the identity are not defined. A point where a function is undefined is called a singularity. Singularities of functions show up as vertical asymptotes or missing single points on the graphs.

In a polar coordinate system, a point is identified by $[r, \theta]$, if and only if it is the image, under a rotation θ about the pole O, of the point on the polar axis with coordinate r. Every point has infinitely many polar coordinate representations. The four relations $x = r \cos \theta$, $y = r \sin \theta$, $r = \sqrt{x^2 + y^2}$, and $\tan \theta = \frac{y}{x}$ relate polar coordinates $[r, \theta]$ and rectangular coordinates (x, y).

Graphs of sets of points which satisfy equations involving r and θ include familiar figures, such as lines and circles, and beautiful spirals, rose curves, and other curves that do not have simple descriptions in terms of rectangular coordinates.

The complex number $a + bi$ is represented in rectangular coordinates as the point (a, b). It can also be represented in polar coordinates by the point $[r, \theta]$, where $r = \sqrt{a^2 + b^2}$ and $\tan \theta = \frac{b}{a}$. The trigonometric form of this number is $r(\cos \theta + i \sin \theta)$.

If $z = a + bi$, the absolute value of z is $|z| = \sqrt{a^2 + b^2}$. Addition of complex numbers $A = a + bi$ and $B = c + di$ where A, B, and the origin are not collinear, can be represented by a parallelogram in the complex plane with vertices at the origin, point A, point B, and the point $(a + c) + (b + d)i$. For $z_1 = r_1(\cos \theta_1 + i \sin \theta_1)$ and $z_2 = r_2(\cos \theta_2 + i \sin \theta_2)$, the product $z_1 z_2$ is equal to $|z_1 z_2| \cdot (\cos (\theta_1 + \theta_2) + i \sin (\theta_1 + \theta_2))$. This product is represented graphically as the image of z_1 under the composite of a size change with magnitude $|z_2|$ and a rotation with magnitude θ_2. Similarly, $\frac{z_1}{z_2} = \frac{|z_1|}{|z_2|} (\cos (\theta_1 - \theta_2) + i \sin (\theta_1 - \theta_2))$ is the image of z_1 under the composite of a size change of magnitude $\frac{1}{|z_2|}$ and a rotation of magnitude $-\theta_2$.

Repeated multiplications of a single complex number $z = r(\cos \theta + i \sin \theta)$ lead to DeMoivre's Theorem: For all postive integers n, $z^n = r^n(\cos n\theta + i \sin n\theta)$. Working backwards leads to a theorem for finding nth roots: If $z^n = r(\cos \theta + i \sin \theta)$ with $r > 0$, then $z = \sqrt[n]{r} \left(\cos \left(\frac{\theta}{n} + k \frac{360°}{n} \right) + i \sin \left(\frac{\theta}{n} + k \frac{360°}{n} \right) \right)$ where $k = 0, 1, 2, \ldots, n - 1$.

The Mandelbrot set is a recently-discovered, important, and intriguing graph of a set of complex numbers. Each number c in the set has the property that the sequence defined by

$\begin{cases} z_1 = c \\ z_n = (z_{n-1})^2 + c, n > 1 \end{cases}$ is bounded.

3. a. See the Mandelbrot graph on page 855.
   b. See graph on bottom of page 859.
   c. Answers will vary.

VOCABULARY

Below are the most important terms and phrases for this chapter. You should be able to give a general description and a specific example of each and a precise definition for those marked with an asterisk (*).

Lesson 13-1
*secant, sec
*cosecant, csc
*cotangent, cot
reciprocal trigonometric functions

Lesson 13-2
corollary

Lesson 13-3
singularity
removable singularity

Lesson 13-4
polar coordinate system
pole, polar axis
polar coordinates, $[r, \theta]$
polar grid

Lesson 13-5
rose curve, petal curve
Archimedan spiral
cardioid
logarithmic spiral

Lesson 13-6
Argand diagrams
complex plane
real axis, imaginary axis
Geometric Addition Theorem
*absolute value, modulus of a complex number
*argument of a complex number
polar form of a complex number

Lesson 13-7
*trigonometric form of a complex number
Product of Complex Numbers Theorem
Division of Complex Numbers Theorem

Lesson 13-8
DeMoivre's Theorem
Roots of a Complex Number Theorem

Chapter 13   *Summary and Vocabulary*   **861**

10. (Continued)
If we choose $r = -10$, possible choices for θ are $\frac{2\pi}{3}$ or $-\frac{4\pi}{3}$. Thus, $[10, -\frac{\pi}{3}]$, $[10, \frac{5\pi}{3}]$, $[-10, \frac{2\pi}{3}]$ and $[-10, -\frac{4\pi}{3}]$ are polar coordinate representations of $(5, -5\sqrt{3})$.

12. b. $\cos 120° + i \sin 120°$.

13. $3(\cos 65° + i \sin 65°)$, $3(\cos 155° + i \sin 155°)$, $3(\cos 245° + i \sin 245°)$, and $3(\cos 335° + i \sin 335°)$.

14. a. Sample:
$[1, \frac{\pi}{6}]$ and $[-1, -\frac{\pi}{6}]$.
b. Sample:

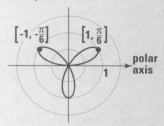

15. a. $15(\cos (-\frac{5\pi}{12}) + i \sin (-\frac{5\pi}{12}))$.
b. The absolute value of z_1 is multiplied by 5, which is a scale change of magnitude 5. $\frac{\pi}{12}$ is added to the argument, which is a rotation around the origin by an angle $\frac{\pi}{12}$.

16. b. The absolute value of z, is divided by 2, which is a size change of magnitude $\frac{1}{2}$. The argument is decreased by π, which is a rotation of $-\pi$ about the origin.

17. For all θ except where $\tan \theta$ is not defined, that is $\theta \neq \frac{\pi}{2} + n\pi$ for all integers n,
$(1 - \sin^2\theta)(1 + \tan^2\theta)$
$= (\cos^2\theta)(1 + \frac{\sin^2\theta}{\cos^2\theta})$
$= \cos^2\theta + \sin^2\theta = 1$.

18.

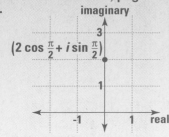

Additional Answers, page 862

9.

imaginary

$(2 \cos \frac{\pi}{2} + i \sin \frac{\pi}{2})$

3

1

-1   1   real

10. $r^2 = x^2 + y^2 = 5^2 + (-5\sqrt{3})^2 = 25 + 75$
$= 100 \Rightarrow r = \pm 10$. $\tan \theta = \frac{y}{x} = \frac{-5\sqrt{3}}{5}$
$= -\sqrt{3} \Rightarrow \theta = -\frac{\pi}{3} \pm n\pi$. The choice of values of θ and r depend on matching the angle to the quadrant. If we choose $r = 10$ then to match $(5, -5\sqrt{3})$ in the fourth quadrant $\theta = -\frac{\pi}{3}$ or $\theta = \frac{5\pi}{3}$.

(Continued at top of next column.)

Progress Self-Test

For the development of mathematical competence, feedback and correction, along with the opportunity to practice, are necessary. The Progress Self-Test provides the opportunity for feedback and correction; the Chapter Review provides additional opportunities and practice. We cannot overemphasize the importance of these end-of-chapter materials. It is at this point that the material "gels" for many students, allowing them to solidify skills and understanding. In general, student performance should be markedly improved after these pages.

Assign the Progress Self-Test as a one-night assignment. Worked-out *solutions* for all questions are in the Selected Answers section of the student book. Encourage students to take the Progress Self-Test honestly, grade themselves, and then be prepared to discuss the test in class.

Advise students to pay special attention to those Chapter Review questions (pages 863–865) that correspond to questions missed on the Progress Self-Test.

Additional Answers

3. a.

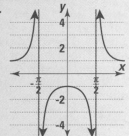

c. Sample: $x = -\frac{\pi}{2}$, $x = \frac{\pi}{2}$

PROGRESS SELF-TEST

3a, 3c, 5–10, 12b, 13–15, 16b, 17, 18) See margin.
Take this test as you would take a test in class. Then check the test yourself using the solutions at the back of the book.

In 1 and 2, evaluate without a calculator.

1. $\cot\left(-\frac{\pi}{6}\right)$ $-\sqrt{3}$ **2.** $\sec 405°$ $\sqrt{2}$

3. Consider the function $y = \sec(x - \pi)$.
  a. Sketch a graph of the function.
  b. State the period of the graph. 2π
  c. State equations of two of the asymptotes.

4. Give the apparent singularities of the function whose graph is shown below. $x = \frac{\pi}{2} + n\pi$ for all integers n

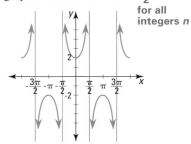

In 5 and 6, an automatic grapher shows the same graph for $f(x) = 2\cos^2 x \tan x$ and $g(x) = \sin 2x$.

5. *True or false.* This graph proves that the equation $2\cos^2 x \tan x = \sin 2x$ is an identity.

6. a. What values are not in the domain of the identity in Question 5?
  b. Prove that the equation in Question 5 is an identity without using the graphs.

In 7–9, plot on an appropriate coordinate system.

7. $[r, \theta] = [4, -185°]$

8. $-4 + 3i$

9. $2\left(\cos\frac{\pi}{2} + i\sin\frac{\pi}{2}\right)$

10. The rectangular coordinates of a point are $\left(5, -5\sqrt{3}\right)$. Find two pairs of polar coordinates $[r, \theta]$ that name this same point. Give θ in radians.

11. Expand $(3(\cos 20° + i\sin 20°))^4$ and write in $a + bi$ form. $\approx 14.07 + 79.77i$

---

12. Let $z = -\frac{1}{2} + \frac{\sqrt{3}}{2}i$. **a.** Write z in polar form. **[1, 120°]**
  b. Write z in trigonometric form.

13. Find the 4 fourth roots of $81(\cos 260° + i\sin 260°)$.

14. a. Give the coordinates of two points on the graph of $r = \sin 3\theta$.
  b. Trace the graph below and label on your copy the points you gave in part **a.**

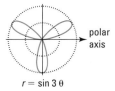

$r = \sin 3\theta$

In 15 and 16, two complex numbers z_1 and z_2 are given. **a.** Perform the indicated operation. **b.** Describe the effect of the operation on the absolute value and argument of z_1.

15. $z_1 = -3i$, $z_2 = 5\left(\cos\frac{\pi}{12} + i\sin\frac{\pi}{12}\right)$; find $z_1 z_2$.

16. $z_1 = [6, \pi]$, $z_2 = [2, \pi]$; find $\frac{z_1}{z_2}$. **a. [3, 0]**

17. Prove: For all θ for which both functions are defined, $(1 - \sin^2\theta)(1 + \tan^2\theta) = 1$.

18. Graph $r = 6\cos\theta$ in the polar coordinate system.

"We did the whole room over in fractals."

---

5. False.

6. a. Singularities occur where $\tan x$ **is not defined, that is, at** $\frac{\pi}{2} + n\pi$, **for all integers** n.
  b. $2\cos^2 x \tan x = 2\cos^2 x \cdot \frac{\sin x}{\cos x} = 2\cos x \sin x = \sin 2x$

7.

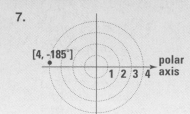

[4, -185°]

8.

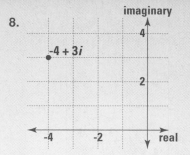

-4 + 3i

(*Additional Answers continue on page 861.*)

CHAPTER REVIEW

Questions on SPUR Objectives

SPUR stands for **S**kills, **P**roperties, **U**ses, and **R**epresentations. The Chapter Review questions are grouped according to the SPUR Objectives for this chapter.
17–22) See margin.

SKILLS DEAL WITH THE PROCEDURES USED TO GET ANSWERS.

Objective A: *Evaluate the reciprocal trigonometric functions.* *(Lesson 13-1)*

In 1–3, give exact values.

1. $\csc \frac{\pi}{2}$ **1**
2. $\cot\left(-\frac{\pi}{4}\right)$ **-1**
3. $\sec 390°$ $\frac{2\sqrt{3}}{3}$

In 4–6, evaluate to the nearest hundredth.

4. $\sec 28°$ **1.13**
5. $\csc 3.7$ **-1.89**
6. $\cot 237°$ **0.65**

Objective B: *Perform operations with complex numbers in polar or trigonometric form.* *(Lesson 13-7)*

In 7 and 8, determine $z_1 z_2$. Leave your answer in the form of the original numbers.

7. $z_1 = 5(\cos 32° + i \sin 32°)$, $z_2 = 3(\cos 157° + i \sin 157°)$ **15 (cos 189° + i sin 189°)**

8. $z_1 = [7, 0], z_2 = \left[1.3, \frac{\pi}{4}\right]$ $\left[9.1, \frac{\pi}{4}\right]$

In 9 and 10, given z_1 and $z_1 z_2$, determine z_2. Leave your answer in the form of the original numbers.

9. $z_1 = 9\left(\cos \frac{\pi}{5} + i \sin \frac{\pi}{5}\right)$,

$z_1 z_2 = 18\left(\cos \frac{\pi}{2} + i \sin \frac{\pi}{2}\right)$ **See right.**

10. $z_1 = \left[2, \frac{\pi}{6}\right], z_1 z_2 = \left[5, \frac{7\pi}{6}\right]$ $\left[\frac{5}{2}, \pi\right]$

In 11 and 12, a complex number is given. **a.** Give the absolute value. **b.** Give an argument.

11. $-10 + 12i$
a) $2\sqrt{61} \approx 15.62$
b) Sample: 129.8°

12. $\cos \frac{\pi}{3} + i \sin \frac{\pi}{3}$
a) 1
b) Sample: $\pi/3$

Objective C: *Represent complex numbers in different forms.* *(Lessons 13-6, 13-7)*

In 13–15, write the complex number in polar form. Use an argument θ in the interval $0° \leq \theta < 360°$.

13. $-\sqrt{3} + i$ **[2, 150°]**
14. $2 + 5i$ **See below.**

15. $\frac{1}{8}\left(\cos \frac{\pi}{5} + i \sin \frac{\pi}{5}\right)$ $\left[\frac{1}{8}, 36°\right]$

In 16 and 17, write the complex number in $a + bi$ form. **16) See below.**

16. $3(\cos(-120°) + i \sin(-120°))$ **17.** $\left[4, \frac{2\pi}{5}\right]$

18. Give two different representations of the complex number $[-2, 45°]$ in trigonometric form.

16) $-\frac{3}{2} - \frac{3\sqrt{3}}{2}i$

Objective D: *Find powers and roots of complex numbers.* *(Lesson 13-8)*

In 19 and 20, find z^n for the given z and n.

19. $z = \sqrt{2} + \sqrt{2}\,i, n = 5$
20. $z = 3(\cos 240° + i \sin 240°), n = 4$

In 21 and 22, find the indicated roots.

21. the 4 fourth roots of $256(\cos 12° + i \sin 12°)$
22. the 6 sixth roots of -2

9) $2\left(\cos \frac{3\pi}{10} + i \sin \frac{3\pi}{10}\right)$

14) $\left[\sqrt{29}, \tan^{-1}\left(\frac{5}{2}\right)\right] \approx [5.39, 68.2°]$

PROPERTIES DEAL WITH THE PRINCIPLES BEHIND THE MATHEMATICS.

Objective E: *Apply properties of the reciprocal trigonometric functions.* *(Lesson 13-1)*

In 23 and 24, consider the function $f(x) = \csc x$.

23. What is the period of f? **2π**

24. For what values is f undefined? $x = k\pi, k$ an integer

In 25 and 26, *true or false*.

25. $\sec \theta = \frac{1}{\csc \theta}$, for all θ. **False**

26. The function $f(x) = \cot x$ is an even function. **False**

Chapter 13   *Chapter Review*   **863**

Additional Answers, page 863

17. $4\cos\left(\frac{2\pi}{5}\right) + 4i \sin\left(\frac{2\pi}{5}\right) \approx 1.24 + 3.80i$

18. Samples: $2(\cos 225° + i \sin 225°)$,
$2(\cos(-135°) + i \sin(-135°))$

19. $z^5 = 32(\cos 225° + i \sin 225°)$
$= -16\sqrt{2} - 16\sqrt{2}\,i$

20. $z^4 = 81(\cos 240° + i \sin 240°)$

21. $4(\cos 3° + i \sin 3°)$,
$4(\cos 93° + i \sin 93°)$,
$4(\cos 183° + i \sin 183°)$,
$4(\cos 273° + i \sin 273°)$

22. $\sqrt[6]{2}(\cos 30° + i \sin 30°)$,
$\sqrt[6]{2}(\cos 90° + i \sin 90°)$,
$\sqrt[6]{2}(\cos 150° + i \sin 150°)$,
$\sqrt[6]{2}(\cos 210° + i \sin 210°)$,
$\sqrt[6]{2}(\cos 270° + i \sin 270°)$,
$\sqrt[6]{2}(\cos 330° + i \sin 330°)$

Chapter 13 Review

Resources
From the *Teacher's Resource File*
■ Answer Master for Chapter 13 Review
■ Assessment Sourcebook: Chapter 13 Test, Forms A–D Chapter 13 Test, Cumulative Form Comprehensive Test, Chapter 1-13

Additional Resources
■ Quiz and Test Writer

The main objectives for the chapter are organized in the Chapter Review under the four types of understanding this book promotes—Skills, Properties, Uses, and Representations.

Whereas end-of chapter material may be considered optional in some texts, in *UCSMP Functions, Statistics, and Trigonometry* we have selected these objectives and questions with the expectation that they will be covered. Students should be able to answer these questions with about 85% accuracy after studying the chapter.

You may assign these questions over a single night to help students prepare for a test the next day, or you may assign the questions over a two-day period. If you work the questions over two days, then we recommend assigning the *evens* for homework the first night so that students get feedback in class the next day, then assigning the *odds* the night before the test, because answers are provided to the odd-numbered questions.

It is effective to ask students which questions they still do not understand and use the day or days as a total class discussion of the material which the class finds most difficult.

Assessment

Evaluation The Assessment Sourcebook provides six forms of the Chapter 13 Test. Forms A and B present parallel versions in a short-answer format. Forms C and D offer performance assessment. The fifth test is Chapter 13 Test, Cumulative Form. About 50% of this test covers Chapter 13, 25% of it covers Chapter 12, and 25% of it covers earlier chapters. In addition to these tests, Comprehensive Test Chapters 1–13 gives roughly equal attention to all chapters covered thus far.

For information on grading, see *General Teaching Suggestions; Grading* in the *Professional Sourcebook*, which begins on page T20 in the Teacher's Edition.

Feedback After students have taken the test for Chapter 13 and you have scored the results, return the tests to students for discussion. Class discussion of the questions that caused trouble for the most students can be very effective in identifying and clarifying misunderstandings. You might want to have them write down the items they missed and work, either in groups or at home, to correct them. It is important for students to receive feedback on every chapter test, and we recommend that students see and correct their mistakes before taking a final exam.

27–32, 34, 36–38, 43) See margin.

Objective F: *Prove trigonometric identities.*
(Lessons 13-2, 13-3)

27. Prove the identity $(1 - \cos^2 x)(1 + \cot^2 x) = 1$ by starting with the left-hand side and rewriting it until the other side appears.

28. Prove that $\sin\left(\theta - \frac{\pi}{4}\right) = -\cos\left(\theta + \frac{\pi}{4}\right)$ for all θ by rewriting each side of the equation independently until equal expressions are obtained.

29. Prove that $\csc^2 x - \cot^2 x = 1$ for all $x \neq n\pi$, where n is an integer, starting with the Pythagorean Identity.

30. Prove: For all θ for which the equation is defined, $\frac{\sin \theta}{\cos \theta \cdot \tan \theta} = 1$.

Objective G: *Describe singularities of functions.*
(Lesson 13-3)

31. Explain why the restriction $x \neq n\pi$ (n an integer) is necessary for the identity in Question 29.

32. Consider the identity given in Question 30.
   a. Determine all the singularities of the functions mentioned in the equation.
   b. Give the biggest domain on which the identity holds.

33. a. Determine the singularities (if any) of the functions with the given equations.
   i. $f(x) = \frac{x^3 - 27}{x - 3}$ ii. $g(x) = \frac{x^3 - 27}{x^2 + 3x + 9}$
   b. *True or false.* The proposed identity is true for all real numbers x. Explain your answer.
   i. $\frac{x^3 - 27}{x - 3} = x^2 + 3x + 9$
   ii. $\frac{x^3 - 27}{x^2 + 3x + 9} = x - 3$

34. *True or false.* The functions $f(x) = \frac{1}{1 - \cos x}$ and $g(x) = \frac{1}{1 - \cos^2 x}$ have the same singularities. Explain your answer.

33ai) $x = 3$ aii) none
   bi) False, it is not true for $x = 3$.
   bii) True, the denominator is not zero for any real value of x.

USES DEAL WITH APPLICATIONS OF MATHEMATICS IN REAL SITUATIONS.

There are no objectives relating to uses in this chapter.

REPRESENTATIONS DEAL WITH PICTURES, GRAPHS, OR OBJECTS THAT ILLUSTRATE CONCEPTS.

Objective H: *Use an automatic grapher to test a proposed identity.*   *(Lessons 13-2, 13-3)*

35. *True or false.* Showing that the graphs of the functions on the two sides of a given equality in a single variable coincide when created by an automatic grapher proves that the equation is an identity. **False**

In 36–38, an equation is given.
a. Graph the functions related to the two sides of the proposed identity. b. Decide if a person should attempt to prove the identity. Explain your reasoning.

36. $\frac{x^2 - 4x - 5}{x + 1} = x - 5$

37. $\sin^2 x(1 + \tan^2 x) = \tan^2 x$

38. $\frac{\csc x}{\sec x} = \tan x$

Objective I: *Given polar coordinates of a point, determine its rectangular coordinates and vice versa.*   *(Lesson 13-4)*

In 39 and 40, convert from polar coordinates to rectangular coordinates.

39. $\left[4, \frac{3\pi}{2}\right]$ (0, -4)

40. $[-3, 85°] \approx$ (-0.26, -2.99)

In 41 and 42, give one pair of polar coordinates for each (x, y) pair.

41. (5, 2) **Sample:** $\approx$ [5.39, 21.8°]

42. (-2, -3) **Sample:** $\approx$ [3.61, 236.3°]

43. A point is located at $(-4\sqrt{3}, 4)$ in a rectangular coordinate system. Find three pairs of polar coordinates $[r, \theta]$ that name this same point. Assume θ is in radians.

Additional Answers

27. $(1 - \cos^2 x)(1 + \cot^2 x)$
   $= (\sin^2 x)\left(1 + \frac{\cos^2 x}{\sin^2 x}\right)$
   $= \sin^2 x + \cos^2 x$
   $= 1$ for all $x \neq n\pi$ for all integers n.

28. $\sin\left(\theta - \frac{\pi}{4}\right)$
   $= \sin \theta \cos \frac{\pi}{4} - \cos \theta \sin \frac{\pi}{4}$
   $= \frac{\sqrt{2}}{2} \sin \theta - \frac{\sqrt{2}}{2} \cos \theta$

   $-\cos\left(\theta + \frac{\pi}{4}\right)$
   $= -\left[\cos \theta \cos \frac{\pi}{4} - \sin \theta \sin \frac{\pi}{4}\right]$
   $= -\left[\frac{\sqrt{2}}{2} \cos \theta - \frac{\sqrt{2}}{2} \sin \theta\right]$
   $= \frac{\sqrt{2}}{2} \sin \theta - \frac{\sqrt{2}}{2} \cos \theta$

   So, $\sin\left(\theta - \frac{\pi}{4}\right) = -\cos\left(\theta + \frac{\pi}{4}\right)$.

45, 46, 49, 51–58b) See margin.

44. When the coordinates of P are written in polar form, $\theta = \frac{\pi}{6}$. When the coordinates of P are written in rectangular form, $x = 5$. Find the polar and rectangular coordinates for P.
$[10\sqrt{3}/3, \pi/6], (5, 5\sqrt{3}/3)$

Objective J: *Plot points in a polar coordinate system.* (Lesson 13-4)

In 45 and 46, plot $[r, \theta]$, where θ is in radians.

45. $\left[3, \frac{\pi}{6}\right]$

46. $[-2, 0]$

47. *Multiple choice.* Which polar coordinate pair does not name the same point as $[4, 250°]$? **b**
(a) $[4, -110°]$ (b) $[-4, 110°]$
(c) $[-4, 70°]$ (d) $[4, 610°]$

48. A point P has polar coordinates $\left[2, \frac{7\pi}{6}\right]$.
Give two pairs of polar coordinates for P where $r = -2$. **Sample: $[-2, \pi/6]$, $[-2, -11\pi/6]$**

Objective K: *Graph and interpret graphs of polar equations.* (Lesson 13-5)

49. Verify that $\left[2, \frac{2\pi}{3}\right]$ is on the graph of $r = 2 \cos 6\theta$.

50. Give the coordinates of two points on the graph of $r = \csc \theta$. **Sample: $[1, \pi/2]$, $\left[\sqrt{2}, \pi/4\right]$**

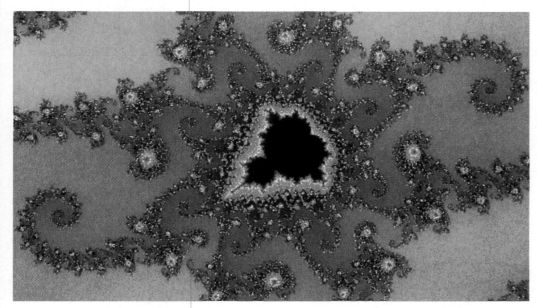

In 51 and 52, graph the equation in the polar coordinate system.

51. $r = 4 \sin \theta$

52. $r = 1 - \cos \theta$

In 53 and 54, a polar equation is given. **a.** Use an automatic grapher to graph the given equation. **b.** Verify the shape of the graph in part **a** by finding a rectangular coordinate equation for the relation.

53. $r = 4 \sec \theta$

54. $r = \frac{1}{3} \cos \theta$

Objective L: *Graph complex numbers.* (Lessons 13-6, 13-7)

In 55 and 56, graph in the complex plane.

55. $4 - 5i$

56. $8(\cos 130° + i \sin 130°)$

57. a. Graph the origin, $A = 3 + i$, $B = 1 - 3i$, and $A + B$ on one coordinate system.
b. Prove that the figure with vertices $(0, 0)$, A, B, and $A + B$ is a parallelogram.

58. Consider $z = 2(\cos 72° + i \sin 72°)$.
a. Graph z, z^2, z^3, z^4, and z^5 on one complex coordinate system.
b. Verify that z is a solution to $z^5 = 32$.

---

29. $\sin^2 x + \cos^2 x = 1 \Rightarrow 1 - \cos^2 x = \sin^2 x \Rightarrow \frac{1}{\sin^2 x} - \frac{\cos^2 x}{\sin^2 x} = \frac{\sin^2 x}{\sin^2 x} \Rightarrow \csc^2 x - \cot^2 x = 1$

30. $\frac{\sin \theta}{\cos \theta \cdot \tan \theta} = \frac{\sin \theta}{\cos \theta \cdot \frac{\sin \theta}{\cos \theta}} = \frac{\sin \theta}{\sin \theta} = 1$
for all $\theta \neq \frac{\pi}{2} + n\pi$ and $\theta \neq n\pi$ for all integers n.

31. Because of division by $\sin x$, the values for which $\sin x = 0$ must be excluded. These are $x = n\pi$ for all integers n.

32. a. $\theta = \frac{\pi}{2} + n\pi$ or $\theta = n\pi$ for all integers n
b. Sample: $0 < \theta < \frac{\pi}{2}$

34. False; $\frac{1}{1 - \cos x}$ has singularities when $\cos x = 1$, that is, when $x = n\pi$ and n is even. $\frac{1}{1 - \cos^2 x}$ has singularities when $\cos^2 x = 1 \Rightarrow \cos x = \pm 1$, that is, when $x = n\pi$, for all integers n.

---

36. a.
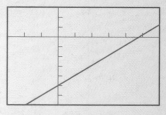
$-3 \leq x \leq 6$, x-scale $= 1$
$-7 \leq y \leq 3$, y-scale $= 1$
b. Yes, the graphs seem to coincide.

37. a.
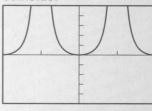
$-\pi \leq x \leq \pi$, x-scale $= \frac{\pi}{2}$
$-5 \leq y \leq 5$, y-scale $= 1$
b. Yes, the graphs seem to coincide.

38. a.
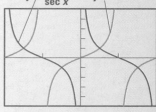
$-\pi \leq x \leq \pi$, x-scale $= \frac{\pi}{2}$
$-5 \leq y \leq 5$, y-scale $= 1$
b. No, the graphs do not seem to coincide.

43. Samples:
$[8, \frac{5\pi}{6}]$, $[8, -\frac{7\pi}{6}]$, $[-8, -\frac{\pi}{6}]$

45, 46.
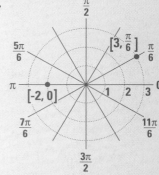

49. For $\theta = \frac{2\pi}{3}$, $r = 2 \cos 6\theta$
$= 2 \cos (6 \cdot \frac{2\pi}{3})$
$= 2 \cos (4\pi) = 2$

51–58. See Additional Answers which begin on page T170 in this Teacher's Edition.

Parent Functions and Their Graphs

Type of Function	Parent Function, f *	Graph of f	Inverse Function, f^{-1} †	Graph of f^{-1}
polynomial–constant	$f(x) = k$ domain: R range: $\{k\}$	for $k = 1$	none	
polynomial–linear	$f(x) = x$ domain: R range: R		$f^{-1}(x) = x$	
absolute value	$f(x) = |x|$ domain: R range: $R^{+} \cup \{0\}$		none	
greatest integer	$f(x) = \lfloor x \rfloor$ domain: R range: set of integers		none	

* R = set of real numbers, R^{+} = set of positive real numbers.

†   The domain and range of f^{-1} are the reverse of those for f except where indicated.

Type of Function	Parent Function, f *	Graph of f	Inverse Function, f^{-1} †	Graph of f^{-1}
polynomial– quadratic	$f(x) = x^2$ domain: R range: $R^+ \cup \{0\}$		$f^{-1}(x) = \sqrt{x}$ domain: $R^+ \cup \{0\}$ range: $R^+ \cup \{0\}$	
polynomial– cubic	$f(x) = x^3$ domain: R range: R		$f^{-1}(x) = \sqrt[3]{x}$	
polynomial of higher degree	$f(x) = x^n$ n an odd integer domain: R range: R	for $n = 5$	$f^{-1}(x) = \sqrt[n]{x}$	for $n = 5$
	$f(x) = x^n$ n an even integer domain: R range: $R^+ \cup \{0\}$	for $n = 6$	$f^{-1}(x) = \sqrt[n]{x}$ domain: $R^+ \cup \{0\}$ range: $R^+ \cup \{0\}$	for $n = 6$

Type of Function	Parent Function, f *	Graph of f	Inverse Function, f^{-1} †	Graph of f^{-1}
hyperbola	$f(x) = \frac{1}{x}$ domain: set of nonzero reals range: set of nonzero reals		$f^{-1}(x) = \frac{1}{x}$	
inverse-square	$f(x) = \frac{1}{x^2}$ domain: set of nonzero reals range: R^+		$f^{-1}(x) = \sqrt{\frac{1}{x}}$ domain: R^+ range: R^+	
exponential any base	$f(x) = b^x$ $b > 1$ domain: R range: R^+	for $b = 2$ 	$f^{-1}(x) = \log_b x$	for $b = 2$
	$f(x) = b^x$ $0 < b < 1$ domain: R range: R^+	for $b = 0.5$ 	$f^{-1}(x) = \log_b x$	for $b = 0.5$

868

Type of Function	Parent Function, f *	Graph of f	Inverse Function, f^{-1} †	Graph of f^{-1}
exponential base e	$f(x) = e^x$ domain: R range: R^+		$f^{-1}(x) = \ln x$	
circular–sine	$f(x) = \sin x$ domain: R range: $\{y: -1 \le y \le 1\}$		$f^{-1}(x) = \sin^{-1} x$ domain: $\{x: -1 \le x \le 1\}$ range: $\{y: \frac{\pi}{2} \le y \le \frac{\pi}{2}\}$	
circular–cosine	$f(x) = \cos x$ domain: R range: $\{y: -1 \le y \le 1\}$		$f^{-1}(x) = \cos^{-1} x$ domain: $\{x: -1 \le x \le 1\}$ range: $\{y: 0 \le y \le \pi\}$	
circular–tangent	$f(x) = \tan x$ domain: R except $\frac{\pi}{2} + n\pi$, n an integer range: R		$f^{-1}(x) = \tan^{-1} x$ domain: R range: $\{y: -\frac{\pi}{2} < y < \frac{\pi}{2}\}$	

Type of Function	Parent Function, f	Graph of f
reciprocal circular–cosecant	$f(x) = \csc x = \dfrac{1}{\sin x}$ domain: set of reals except $n\pi$, where n is an integer range: $\{y\colon y \geq 1 \text{ or } y \leq -1\}$	
reciprocal circular–secant	$f(x) = \sec x = \dfrac{1}{\cos x}$ domain: set of reals except $\dfrac{\pi}{2} + n\pi$, where n is an integer range: $\{y\colon y \geq 1 \text{ or } y \leq -1\}$	
reciprocal circular–cotangent	$f(x) = \cot x = \dfrac{1}{\tan x}$ domain: set of reals except $n\pi$, where n is an integer range: R	
normal	$f(x) = e^{-x^2}$ domain: R range: $\{y\colon 0 < y \leq 1\}$	

870

Programming Languages

COMMANDS

The BASIC commands used in this course, their translation into one calculator language, and examples of their use are given below.

LET... A value is assigned to a given variable. Most versions of BASIC allow you to omit the word LET in the assignment statement.

LET A = 5 $5 \to A$

The number 5 is stored in a memory location called A.

N = N + 2 $N + 2 \to N$

The value in the memory location called N is increased by 2 and then restored in the location called N. (N is replaced by $N + 2$.)

PRINT... The computer/calculator displays on the screen what follows the PRINT command. If what follows is a constant or variable, the value of that constant or variable is displayed. If what follows is in quotes, the quote is displayed exactly.

PRINT A   Disp A

The computer prints the number stored in memory location A.

PRINT "X = "A/B   Disp "X = ", A/B

Displayed is X = (value of A/B). Notice that the space after the equal sign in the quotes is transferred into a space after the equal sign in the displayed sentence. On some calculators, the display will place X = and the value on separate lines.

INPUT... The computer asks the user to give a value to the variable named, and stores that value.

INPUT X   Input X

When the program is run, the computer/calculator will prompt you to give it a value by displaying a question mark, and then will store the value you type in memory location X.

INPUT "HOW OLD"; AGE   Input "How Old", Age

The computer/calculator displays HOW OLD? and stores your response in memory location AGE.

REM... This command allows remarks to be inserted in a program. These may describe what the variables repesent, what the program does or how it works. REM statements are often used in long complex programs or programs others will use.

REM PYTHAGOREAN THEOREM

The statement appears when the LIST command is given, but it has no effect when the program is run. Some calculators have no corresponding command.

END This command causes a BASIC program to terminate. No BASIC program should have more than one END statement. In calculators, END statements are used to identify the ends of loops (see FOR on page 872) or conditionals (see IF . . . THEN . . . on page 872) and thus may appear more than once in a program.

END   End

| FOR . . .
NEXT . . .
STEP . . . | The FOR command assigns a beginning and ending value to a variable. The first time through the loop, the variable has the beginning value in the FOR command. When the program hits the line reading NEXT (or End), the value of the variable is increased by the amount indicated by STEP. The commands between FOR and NEXT (End) are then repeated. |

```
10 FOR N = 3 TO 10 STEP 2      :For(N,3,10,2)
20 PRINT N                     :Disp N
30 NEXT N                      :End
```

The program assigns 3 to N and then displays the value of N. On reaching NEXT, the program increases N by 2 (the STEP amount), and prints 5. The next N is 7, then 9, but 11 is too large, so the program executes the command after NEXT (End). The output from both programs is given here.

3
5
7
9

| IF . . . THEN . . . | The program performs the consequent (the THEN part) only if the antecedent (the IF part) is true. When the antecedent is false, the program *ignores* the consequent and goes directly to the next line of the program. |

```
IF X <= 100 THEN PRINT X       :If X ≤ 100
                               :Then:Disp X
                               :End
```

If the X value is less than or equal to 100, the computer/calculator displays the value stored in X. If the value of X is greater than 100, the value will not be printed.

| GOTO . . . | The program goes to whatever line of the program is indicated. GOTO statements are generally avoided because they interrupt program flow and make programs hard to interpret. Calculator programs typically do not have line numbers, and so GOTO statements are used in conjunction with a label. |

```
10 GOTO 50                     :Goto A
      .                              .
      .                              .
      .                              .
50 (Command)                   :Lbl A
                               :(Command)
```

The program goes to line 50 (label A) and executes that command.

FUNCTIONS

A large number of functions are built into most versions of BASIC and into all calculators. They are the same functions used outside of programming. Each function name must be followed by a variable or constant enclosed in parentheses. Here are some examples of the uses of functions in programs.

| ABS | The absolute value of the number that follows is calculated. |

```
LET A = ABS(-10)               abs(-10) → A
```

The program calculates $|-10| = 10$ and assigns the value 10 to memory location A.

| ATN | The arctangent or inverse tangent of the number or expression that follows is calculated. In BASIC and other computer programming languages, the result is always given in radians. In calculator programs, the result can be in either radians or degrees, depending on what mode the calculator is in. (Note: Some versions of BASIC do not include built-in functions for |

872

inverse sine and inverse cosine. But these can be created, since $\cos^{-1}x = \tan^{-1}\sqrt{\dfrac{1-x^2}{x^2}}$

over the domain $0 < x \le 1$ and $\sin^{-1}x = \tan^{-1}\sqrt{\dfrac{x^2}{1-x^2}}$ over the domain $0 \le x < 1$.)

LET P = ATN(1) $\tan^{-1}(1) \to P$

The program calculates $\tan^{-1}1 = \dfrac{\pi}{4}$ and stores the value 0.785398 in the memory location P.

EXP

The number e raised to the power or expression that follows is calculated.

LET J = EXP(2) $e^{\wedge}(2) \to J$

The program calculates e^2 and stores the value 7.389056 in the memory location J.

INT

The greatest integer less than or equal to the number that follows is calculated.

B = INT(N + .5) $\text{int}(N + .5) \to B$

The program adds .5 to the value of N, calculates $\lfloor N + .5 \rfloor$, and stores the result in B.

LOG or LN

The natural logarithm (logarithm to base e) of the number that follows is calculated.

LET J = LOG(6) $\ln(6) \to J$

The program calculates $\ln 6$ and assigns the value 1.791759469228 to memory location J. It may display only some of these decimal places.

RND(1)

A random number greater than 0 and less than 1 is generated. The argument of the RND function is always 1.

D = 2*RND(1) $2\,\text{rand} \to D$

The program generates a random number between 0 and 1 and stores twice the value in memory location D.

SIN
COS
TAN

The sine, cosine, or tangent of the number or expression that follows is calculated. In BASIC, the argument of these functions is always in radians. On most calculators, the argument can be in either degrees or radians, depending on the mode the calculator is in.

LET R = 5*SIN(0.7) $5\sin(0.7) \to R$

The program finds $5\sin 0.7$ and stores the value 3.221088 in the memory location R.

SQR

The square root of the number or expression that follows is calculated.

C = SQR(A*A + B*B) $\sqrt{}(A^{\wedge}2 + B^{\wedge}2) \to C$

The program calculates $\sqrt{A^2 + B^2}$ using the values stored in A and B and stores the result in C.

A Table of Random Numbers

row	col. 1	2	3	4	5	6	7	8	9	10	11	12	13	14
1	10480	15011	01536	02011	81647	91646	69719	14194	62590	36207	20969	99570	91291	90700
2	22368	46573	25595	85393	30995	89198	27982	53402	93965	34095	52666	19174	39615	99505
3	24130	48360	22527	97265	76393	64809	15179	24830	49340	32081	30680	19655	63348	58629
4	42167	93093	06423	61680	17856	16376	39440	53537	71341	57004	00849	74917	97758	16379
5	37570	39975	81837	16656	06121	91782	60468	81305	49684	60672	14110	06927	01263	54613
6	77921	06907	11008	42751	27756	53498	18602	70659	90655	15053	21916	81825	44394	42880
7	99562	72905	56420	69994	98872	31016	71194	18738	44013	48840	63213	21069	10634	12952
8	96301	91977	05463	07972	18876	20922	94595	56869	69014	60045	18425	84903	42508	32307
9	89579	14342	63661	10281	17453	18103	57740	84378	25331	12566	58678	44947	05585	56941
10	85475	36857	43342	53988	53060	59533	38867	62300	08158	17983	16439	11458	18593	64952
11	28918	69578	88231	33276	70997	79936	56865	05859	90106	31595	01547	85590	91610	78188
12	63553	40961	48235	03427	49626	69445	18663	72695	52180	20847	12234	90511	33703	90322
13	09429	93969	52636	92737	88974	33488	36320	17617	30015	08272	84115	27156	30613	74952
14	10365	61129	87529	85689	48237	52267	67689	93394	01511	26358	85104	20285	29975	89868
15	07119	97336	71048	08178	77233	13916	47564	81056	97735	85977	29372	74461	28551	90707
16	51085	12765	51821	51259	77452	16308	60756	92144	49442	53900	70960	63990	75601	40719
17	02368	21382	52404	60268	89368	19885	55322	44819	01188	65255	64835	44919	05944	55157
18	01011	54092	33362	94904	31272	04146	18594	29852	71585	85030	51132	01915	92747	64951
19	52162	53916	46369	58586	23216	14513	83149	98736	23495	64350	94738	17752	35156	35749
20	07056	97628	33787	09998	42698	06691	76988	13602	51851	46104	88916	19509	25625	58104
21	48663	91245	85828	14346	09172	30168	90229	04734	59193	22178	30421	61666	99904	32812
22	54164	58492	22421	74103	47070	25306	76468	26384	58151	06646	21524	15227	96909	44592
23	32639	32363	05597	24200	13363	38005	94342	28728	35806	06912	17012	64161	18296	22851
24	29334	27001	87637	87308	58731	00256	45834	15398	46557	41135	10367	07684	36188	18510
25	02488	33062	28834	07351	19731	92420	60952	61280	50001	67658	32586	86679	50720	94953
26	81525	72295	04839	96423	24878	82651	66566	14778	76797	14780	13300	87074	79666	95725
27	29676	20591	68086	26432	46901	20849	89768	81536	86645	12659	92259	57102	80428	25280
28	00742	57392	39064	66432	84673	40027	32832	61362	98947	96067	64760	64584	96096	98253
29	05366	04213	25669	26422	44407	44048	37937	63904	45766	66134	75470	66520	34693	90449
30	91921	26418	64117	94305	26766	25940	39972	22209	71500	64568	91402	42416	07844	69618
31	00582	04711	87917	77341	42206	35126	74087	99547	81817	42607	43808	76655	62028	76630
32	00725	69884	62797	56170	86324	88072	76222	36086	84637	93161	76038	65855	77919	88006
33	69011	65797	95876	55293	18988	27354	26575	08625	40801	59920	29841	80150	12777	48501
34	25976	57948	29888	88604	67917	48708	18912	82271	65424	69774	33611	54262	85963	03547
35	09763	83473	73577	12908	30883	18317	28290	35797	05998	41688	34952	37888	38917	88050
36	91567	42595	27958	30134	04024	86385	29880	99730	55536	84855	29080	09250	79656	73211
37	17955	56349	90999	49127	20044	59931	06115	20542	18059	02008	73708	83517	36103	42791
38	46503	18584	18845	49618	02304	51038	20655	58727	28168	15475	56942	53389	20562	87338
39	92157	89634	94824	78171	84610	82834	09922	25417	44137	48413	25555	21246	35509	20468
40	14577	62765	35605	81263	39667	47358	56873	56307	61607	49518	89656	20103	77490	18062

Standard Normal Distribution Table

This table gives the area under the standard normal curve to the left of a given positive number a.

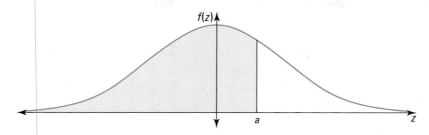

$P(z < a)$ for $a \geq 0$										
a	0	1	2	3	4	5	6	7	8	9
0.0	.5000	.5040	.5080	.5120	.5160	.5199	.5239	.5279	.5319	.5359
0.1	.5398	.5438	.5478	.5517	.5557	.5596	.5636	.5675	.5714	.5753
0.2	.5793	.5832	.5871	.5910	.5948	.5987	.6026	.6064	.6103	.6141
0.3	.6179	.6217	.6255	.6293	.6331	.6368	.6406	.6443	.6480	.6517
0.4	.6554	.6591	.6628	.6664	.6700	.6736	.6772	.6808	.6844	.6879
0.5	.6915	.6950	.6985	.7019	.7054	.7088	.7123	.7157	.7190	.7224
0.6	.7257	.7291	.7324	.7357	.7389	.7422	.7454	.7486	.7517	.7549
0.7	.7580	.7611	.7642	.7673	.7704	.7734	.7764	.7794	.7823	.7852
0.8	.7881	.7910	.7939	.7967	.7995	.8023	.8051	.8078	.8106	.8133
0.9	.8159	.8186	.8212	.8238	.8264	.8289	.8315	.8340	.8365	.8389
1.0	.8413	.8438	.8461	.8485	.8508	.8531	.8554	.8577	.8599	.8621
1.1	.8643	.8665	.8686	.8708	.8729	.8749	.8770	.8790	.8810	.8830
1.2	.8849	.8869	.8888	.8907	.8925	.8944	.8962	.8980	.8997	.9015
1.3	.9032	.9049	.9066	.9082	.9099	.9115	.9131	.9147	.9162	.9177
1.4	.9192	.9207	.9222	.9236	.9251	.9265	.9279	.9292	.9306	.9319
1.5	.9332	.9345	.9357	.9370	.9382	.9394	.9406	.9418	.9429	.9441
1.6	.9452	.9463	.9474	.9484	.9495	.9505	.9515	.9525	.9535	.9545
1.7	.9554	.9564	.9573	.9582	.9591	.9599	.9608	.9616	.9625	.9633
1.8	.9641	.9649	.9656	.9664	.9671	.9678	.9686	.9693	.9699	.9706
1.9	.9713	.9719	.9726	.9732	.9738	.9744	.9750	.9756	.9761	.9767
2.0	.9772	.9778	.9783	.9788	.9793	.9798	.9803	.9808	.9812	.9817
2.1	.9821	.9826	.9830	.9834	.9838	.9842	.9846	.9850	.9854	.9857
2.2	.9861	.9864	.9868	.9871	.9875	.9878	.9881	.9884	.9887	.9890
2.3	.9893	.9896	.9898	.9901	.9904	.9906	.9909	.9911	.9913	.9916
2.4	.9918	.9920	.9922	.9925	.9927	.9929	.9931	.9932	.9934	.9936
2.5	.9938	.9940	.9941	.9943	.9945	.9946	.9948	.9949	.9951	.9952
2.6	.9953	.9955	.9956	.9957	.9959	.9960	.9961	.9962	.9963	.9964
2.7	.9965	.9966	.9967	.9968	.9969	.9970	.9971	.9971	.9973	.9974
2.8	.9974	.9975	.9976	.9977	.9977	.9978	.9979	.9979	.9980	.9981
2.9	.9981	.9982	.9982	.9983	.9984	.9984	.9985	.9985	.9986	.9986
3.0	.9987	.9987	.9987	.9988	.9988	.9989	.9989	.9989	.9990	.9990

For specific details on the use of this table, see page 655.

Lesson 7-1 (pp. 426-432)

13. 50 **15. a.** 1 **b.** 0 **c.** $\frac{1}{4}$ **17.** $\frac{1}{6}$ **19. a.** ≈ 0.318 **b.** 326
21. a. 50% **b.** $\approx 18.95\%$ **23.** 55

Lesson 7-2 (pp. 433-439)
13. Sample: The temperature is above 90°; the temperature is
below 40°. **15. a.** 0.54 **b.** 0.83 **c.** 0.32 **d.** 0.44 **17. a** $\frac{25\pi}{484} \approx$
0.162 **b.** $1 - \frac{57\pi}{484} \approx 0.630$ **19. a.** 0.05 **b.** 0.45 **c.** 0.75 **d.** 0.65
21. 0.1 **23.** $y = -x^2 + 4x$

Lesson 7-3 (pp. 440-444)

11. $10! = 3,628,800$ **13.** 6 **15. a.** 20 **b.** $n = 9$, $r = 7$
17. $r + c - b$ **19. a** $\frac{1}{12} \approx 0.08$ **b** 11 to 1 **21. a.** $\frac{3\pi}{4}$

Lesson 7-4 (pp. 445-449)

13. 56 **15. a.** $10! = 3,628,800$ **b.** $2(6!\cdot4!) = 34,560$ **17. a.** 16
b. See below. 19. 32 **21.** 61,162,590 **23.** $\frac{2}{3}$ **25 a. See below.**
b. true

17. b.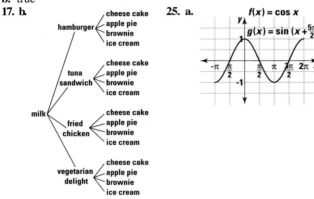

25. a.

Lesson 7-5 (pp. 450-456)

9. Yes; $P(A) = \frac{1}{2}$, $P(B) = \frac{3}{4}$, $P(A \cap B) = \frac{3}{8} = \frac{1}{2} \cdot \frac{3}{4}$ **11.** Sample:
We cannot answer this with certainty. If the relative frequencies
represent the probabilities that the lights stop the motorist, and all
the events are independent, then the probability of all happening
is $\frac{20}{50} \cdot \frac{22}{50} \cdot \frac{25}{50} \cdot \frac{19}{50} \cdot \frac{24}{50}$, or about .016. This would suggest that, on
the average, in 50 trips, about 0.8 times all the lights would come
on. That rounds out to 1, suggesting that the lights are operating
independently. **13. a.** ≈ 0.027 **b.** $\approx .0533$ **c.** $\approx .0789$ **15.** $6! = 720$
17. $n = 25$ and $r = 2$ or $n = 600$ and $r = 1$ **19.** 0.25 **21.** $\frac{3}{25} = 0.12$

Lesson 7-6 (pp. 457-463)

11. a. See above right. b. mean difference $= \frac{709}{360} \approx 1.97$
13. a. It represents a loss; it is negative because $1 must be paid
for the ticket. **b.** $\frac{122}{125} = 0.976$ **c.** $-\frac{25}{125} = -\$0.20$ or $-20¢$

15. a. $f(0) = -\frac{1}{4}\left|0 - \frac{3}{2}\right| + \frac{1}{2} = \frac{1}{8}$; $f(1) = -\frac{1}{4}\left|1 - \frac{3}{2}\right| + \frac{1}{2} = \frac{3}{8}$;
$f(2) = -\frac{1}{4}\left|2 - \frac{3}{2}\right| + \frac{1}{2} = \frac{3}{8}$; $f(3) = -\frac{1}{4}\left|3 - \frac{3}{2}\right| + \frac{1}{2} = \frac{1}{8}$

b. Substituting $x - \frac{3}{2}$ for x and $\dfrac{y - \frac{1}{2}}{-\frac{1}{4}}$ for y in $y = |x|$ results in

$\dfrac{y - \frac{1}{2}}{-\frac{1}{4}} = \left|x - \frac{3}{2}\right|$ or $y = -\frac{1}{4}\left|x - \frac{3}{2}\right| + \frac{1}{2}$. **17. a.** $\frac{31}{32} = 0.96875$

b. $\frac{10}{32} = 0.3125$ **c.** False **19.** $(n + 2)(n + 1) = n^2 + 3n + 2$
21. a. 1298 **b.** 740 **c.** Sample: median; the median is not
affected by the unusually high score of 6450. **d.** about 1813
e. It has a great effect. If that score is removed, the standard
deviation changes from about 1813 to 112.

11. a.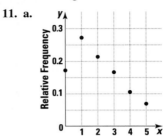

Lesson 7-7 (pp. 465-470)
9. a.–c. Designs will vary, but results should all approximate a
.300 batting average. **11. a. See below. b.** The relative
frequencies can be considered as the probability of randomly
choosing a family of the given size from all the families in the
village. **c.** $\frac{432}{87} \approx 4.97$ **13.** none of these (assumes the first
student has not been replaced) **15.** mutually exclusive (assumes
another possibility: "Kevin arrives exactly on time.") **17. a.** 0
b. $\frac{576}{27,907,200} \approx 2.1 \cdot 10^{-5}$ **19. a.** 0, 0, 1, 2 **b.** $\frac{1}{3} \le x < \frac{2}{3}$

11. a.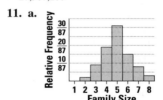

Lesson 7-8 (pp. 471–477)
15. Answers will vary. Note that the command "ROUND
(RAND, 3)" will provide 3 random digits on some calculators.
17. Answers will vary, but repeated valid simulations would
reveal that 102 nails would be adequate in most cases, and
103 nails in almost all cases. **19.** $\frac{5}{144} \approx 0.035$
21. a. $_8P_5 = 8 \cdot {_7P_4} = 8 \cdot 7 \cdot {_6P_3} = 56 \cdot {_6P_3}$
b. $_nP_r = n \cdot {_{n-1}P_{r-1}} = n \cdot (n - 1) \cdot {_{n-2}P_{r-2}} = (n^2 - n) \cdot {_{n-2}P_{r-2}}$

Chapter 7 Progress Self-Test (p. 481)

1. a. Each outcome can be represented by a pair of numbers, one for each spinner. So $S = \{(1, 1),(1, 2), (1, 3), (2, 1), (2, 2), (2, 3), (3, 1), (3, 2), (3, 3)\}$ **b.** Of the nine possible outcomes, three have sums greater than 4. Thus $P(\text{sum} > 4) = \frac{\text{number of outcomes in the event}}{\text{number of outcomes in the sample space}} = \frac{3}{9} = \frac{1}{3} \approx 0.33$. **2.** The two dice are independent of each other, and for each one the probability of showing an odd or even number is $\frac{1}{2}$. So, $P(\text{Odd on Red }and\text{ Even on Green}) = \frac{1}{2} \cdot \frac{1}{2} = \frac{1}{4} = 0.25$. **3.** By the Probability of a Union Theorem, $P(A \cup B) = P(A) + P(B) - P(A \cap B) = 0.6 + 0.8 - 0.5 = 0.9$. **4. a.** Since the six letters are different, by the Permutation Theorem, there are $6! = 720$ permutations. **b.** When A and T are fixed at the two ends, there are four letters (M, S, E, and R) left to permute in the middle. There are $4! = 24$ such arrangements.

5. $\frac{9!}{3!} = \frac{9 \cdot 8 \cdot \ldots \cdot 3 \cdot 2 \cdot 1}{3 \cdot 2 \cdot 1} = 9 \cdot 8 \cdot \ldots \cdot 4 = 60,480$

6. $_5P_3 = \frac{5!}{(5-3)!} = \frac{5!}{2!} = 5 \cdot 4 \cdot 3 = 60$ **7.** True, since $A = S$ (the sample space), and $P(S) = 1$. **8.** Let A be the event of scoring under 50 and B be the event of scoring between 50 and 100, inclusive. **a.** The events are mutually exclusive, and, since A and B cover all the possible scores, they are also complementary. **b.** The events are mutually exclusive, but, since $A \cup B \neq S$, they are not complementary. **9.** $_nP_4 = 56 _nP_2$; $\frac{n!}{(n-4)!} = 56 \cdot \frac{n!}{(n-2)!}$; $\frac{(n-2)!}{(n-4)!} = 56$; $\frac{(n-2)(n-3)(n-4)(n-5)\ldots(1)}{(n-4)(n-5)\ldots(1)} = 56$;

$(n-2)(n-3) = 56$; $n^2 - 5n + 6 = 56$; $n^2 - 5n - 50 = 0$; $(n-10)(n+5) = 0$; $n = 10$, the only positive solution. **10. a.** Random selection means that the weights of the bags are independent of each other. Each has a 0.25 probability of being underweight. So, $P(\text{all three bags are underweight}) = (0.25)^3 \approx 0.016$. **b.** Each bag has a 0.75 probability of not being underweight. So, $P(\text{none of the bags is underweight}) = (0.75)^3 \approx 0.42$. **11.** By the Multiplication Counting Principle, $N(\text{jeans}) \cdot N(\text{sneakers}) \cdot N(\text{sweatshirts}) = 3 \cdot 2 \cdot 5 = 30$. **12.** There are 15 different questions, 10 with two possible answers, 5 with four. So, by the Multiplication Counting Principle, $N(\text{answer sheets}) = 2^{10} \cdot 4^5 = 2^{20} = 1,048,576$. **13.** Designs will vary. Sample: A die thrown 100 times counting rolls of 1 and 2 as shots made, and 3, 4, 5 and 6 as shots not made. **14.** Answers will vary depending on table starting point but infections should number 2 to 4 of the 25 trials in most cases. **15.** Answers will vary, but random coordinates should be generated with the range 0 to $\frac{\pi}{2}$ for x, and 0 to 1 for y, and the area should be estimated by multiplying the resulting proportion of points below the line by $\frac{\pi}{2}$. The actual area is 1. **16. a.** Each value of $P(x)$ satisfies $0 \leq P(x) \leq 1$ and their sum is 1. **b. See right. c.** $\mu = \sum_{i=1}^{5} (x_i \cdot P(x_i)) = 1(.03) + 2(.47) + 3(.22) + 4(.05) + 5(.23) = 2.98$.

16. b.

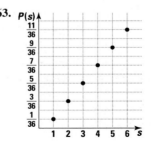

The chart below keys the **Progress Self-Test** questions to the objectives in the **Chapter Review** on pages 482-485 or to the **Vocabulary** (Voc.) on page 480. This will enable you to locate those **Chapter Review** questions that correspond to questions students missed on the **Progress Self-Test**. The lesson where the material is covered is also indicated on the chart.

Question	1	2	3	4	5	6	7	8	9	10
Objective	A, B	B	B	C	D	D	E	F	G	H
Lesson	7-1	7-1	7-2	7-4	7-3	7-4	7-1	7-2	7-4	7-5

Question	11	12	13	14	15	16
Objective	I	I	J	J	K	L
Lesson	7-3	7-3	7-7	7-7	7-8	7-6

Chapter 7 Review (pp. 482-485)

1. {HHH, HHT, HTH, HTT, THH, THT, TTH, TTT} **3.** True **5.** $\varnothing$ **7.** $\frac{1}{4} = 0.25$ **9.** $\frac{5}{12} \approx 0.417$ **11.** $\frac{2}{10} = 0.2$ **13.** 128 **15. a.** 720 **b.** 6 **17.** 5040 **19.** 21 **21.** 197,149,680 **23.** 5040 **25.** 0.77 **27.** False **29.** False **31.** mutually exclusive **33.** False **35.** c **37.** a, b **39.** $x = 8$ **41.** $n = 16$ **43.** $\frac{26}{257} \approx 0.1012$ **45.** 0.28 **47.** $4^{20} \approx 1.1 \times 10^{12}$ **49.** 120 **51.** $26^2 \cdot 10^4 = 6,760,000$ **53.** Answers may vary. Sample: Use 100 small pieces of paper numbered from 1 to 100. If a piece of paper is numbered less than 26, call it damaged; otherwise, call it undamaged. Randomly choose 16 pieces of paper from the 100, and record the number of pieces of paper numbered less than 26. Repeat that 5 times and get 5 samples. Our result shows the percentage of corn damaged in each sample as follows: .25, .375, .5625, .12, and .3125. **55.** Answers may vary. Sample: Choose a triple of digits from 000 to 999, and if it is from 000 to 324, John gets a hit; if it is from 325 to 999, he does not get a hit. Run it 10 times and

record the number of times with 4 or more hits. Repeat the above procedure a certain number of times (e.g., 10 times). Our result shows the estimated probability is .4. (The actual probability is .418.) **57.** Answers will vary, but should approximate 0.06. **59.** Estimate should be close to $\frac{10}{3}$. **61. a.** $P(0) = \frac{1}{6}$, $P(1) = \frac{1}{3}$, $P(2) = \frac{1}{3}$, $P(4) = \frac{1}{6}$ **b.** See below. **c.** $\frac{5}{3}$ **63.** See right.

65. $\frac{381}{85} \approx 4\frac{1}{2}$ years

61. b.

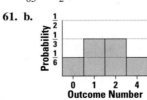

63.

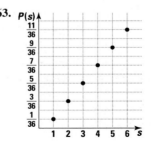

Lesson 8-1 (pp. 488-495)

13. a. $U_n = (2 \div 3) * U_{n-1}$ or $U_n = 36\left(\frac{2}{3}\right)^{n-1}$; U_nStart $= 36$; $_n$Start $= 1$ **b.** 36, 24, 16, 10.67, 7.11, 4.74, 3.16, 2.11, 1.40, 0.936, 0.624, 0.416, 0.277, 0.185, 0.123, 0.082, 0.055, 0.037, 0.024, 0.016 **15.** $3 \cdot (1.10)^5 \approx 4.8$ miles **17. a.** $O_n = n(n+2)$ **b.** $O_{100} = 10{,}200$ **19. a.** $-97, -93, -89, -85, -81, -77, -73, -69, -65, -61, -57, -53, -49, -45, -41, -37, -33, -29, -25, -21$

b. the 25th **21.** $x \approx 19.7$ **23. a.** Sample: $y = \frac{3x}{x+1}$ **See below.**
b. Sample: $y = 3$

23. a.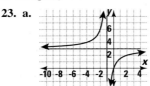

Lesson 8-2 (pp. 496-502)

15. a. exists; 0 **b.** does not exist **c.** does not exist **d.** exists; 0
e. If $|r| < 1$, $\lim_{n \to \infty} r^n = 0$. If $|r| > 1$, $\lim_{n \to \infty} r^n$ does not exist.
17. Step 2: Limit Property 4 Step 3: Limit Property 6 Step 4: Algebraic Definition of Division **19. a.** $x - y$ **b.** $52x - 47y$
21. a. $t_n = 5(3)^{n-1}$ **b.** $\log 5 \approx .70$, $\log 15 = 1.18$, $\log 45 \approx 1.65$, $\log 135 \approx 2.13$, $\log 405 \approx 2.61$ **c.** $t_n = 5 \cdot (3)^{n-1}$, so $\log t_n = \log(5 \cdot 3^{n-1}) = \log 5 + \log 3^{n-1} = \log 5 + (n-1)\log 3$. Therefore, the terms of $\log t_n$ form an arithmetic sequence with first term $\log 5$ and constant difference $\log 3$. **23. a.** $\sum_{i=1}^{4} a_i$
b. $\sum_{n=2}^{10} b_n$ **c.** $\sum_{j=1}^{n} m_j$

Lesson 8-3 (pp. 503-508)

11. 873,612 **13.** 78 **15.** 21 **17.** convergent; $\frac{1}{4}$ **19. a.** $\frac{\sqrt{3}}{2}, \frac{1}{2}, 0$, $-\frac{1}{2}, -\frac{\sqrt{3}}{2}$ **b.** neither **c.** $\lim_{n \to \infty} t_n$ does not exist
21. a. $\begin{cases} a_{1996} = 206.6 \\ a_n = 1.015a_{n-1} \text{ for } n > 1996 \end{cases}$ **b.** $206.6(1.015)^{14} \approx$ 254.5 million **c.** Samples: Immigration may increase. The birth rate may change.

Lesson 8-4 (pp. 509-514)

13. 4265.625 **15. a.** Samples: $1, 1, 1, 1, \ldots 1$; $c, c, c, \ldots, c$
b. Sample: $\frac{1(1-1^n)}{1-1}$ is not equal to the sum since the denominator is zero. **c.** Samples: n; cn **17.** about 62 ft **19. a.** $25{,}250$
b. $218{,}750$ **21.** 12 **23. a.** $(x, y) \to (x - 8, y + 5)$ **b.** $x = -8$, $y = 5$

Lesson 8-5 (pp. 516-522)

11. a. $1 + \frac{1}{2} + \frac{1}{3} + \frac{1}{4} + \frac{1}{5}$ **b. i.** 11 **ii.** 83 **c.** True
13. a. $|b| < 4$ **b.** $\frac{4b}{4-b}$ **15.** 420 ft **17. a.** ≈ 19.7 ft **b.** ≈ 268 ft
c. about 9 minutes **19.** 1092 **21.** 3 **23.** True

Lesson 8-6 (pp. 523-528)

13. n **15.** $_nP_r$ is larger. Sample: $\dfrac{_nP_r}{_nC_r} = \dfrac{\frac{n!}{(n-r)!}}{\frac{n!}{r!(n-r)!}} = r! > 1$,
so $_nP_r > {}_nC_r$. **17. a.** 20 **b.** $_nC_3 = \dfrac{n!}{3!(n-3)!}$ **19. a.** $_{52}C_5 =$ 2,598,960 hands **b.** $_{13}C_5 = 1287$ hands **c.** $\dfrac{1287}{2{,}598{,}960} \approx .0004952 \approx$ $0.0005 \approx \frac{1}{2000}$ **21. a.** 0.8 **b.** $0.8b$ **23.** $x = 23$

Lesson 8-7 (pp. 529-534)

11. 27, 1 **13.** Sample: the "hockey stick" pattern. In any shape as shown below, with any number of terms in the "handle" but only one in the "blade," the sum of the terms in the handle is equal to the term in the blade. For example, $1 + 3 + 6 + 10 = 20$.
See below. 15. $_{22}C_{11} = 705{,}432$ **17. a.** $\frac{27}{64}$ **b. i.** ≈ 2421.19 cm^3
ii. ≈ 2421.62 cm^3 **19.** 15 **21. a.** 96 units^3 **b.** 24π units^3
c. 8π units^3

13.

Lesson 8-8 (pp. 535-539)

11. True **13.** True **15.** $\frac{11}{16} = 68.75\%$ **17.** $2^n = (1+1)^n$

$$= \sum_{k=0}^{n} {}_nC_k(1)^{n-k}1^k$$
$$= \sum_{k=0}^{n} {}_nC_k$$

19. 210 **21. a.** permutation **b.** 94,109,400 **23.** $\dfrac{98}{161700} \approx$ 0.000606 **25.** 128

Lesson 8-9 (pp. 540-545)

11. a. 4 **b.** 3.5 **13. a.** $\frac{1}{3}$

b.

x	0	1	2	3	4
$P(x)$	0.198	0.395	0.296	0.099	0.012

c. See below. **d.** 0.111 **e.** 0.802 **15. a.** $(1-a)$ **b.** $(35)a^3(1-a)^4$
17. $a^6 + 12a^5b + 60a^4b^2 + 160a^3b^3 + 240a^2b^4 + 192ab^5 + 64b^6$
19. $\dfrac{1}{_{55}C_6} = \dfrac{1}{28989675} \approx 3.4 \times 10^{-8}$ **13. c.**
21. 0.220 **23.** 4475

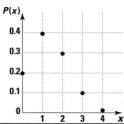

Chapter 8 Progress Self-Test (p. 550)

1. The sequence is neither geometric nor arithmetic. **2.** $g_1 = 0$; $g_2 = g_1 + 2^2 = 0 + 4 = 4$; $g_3 = g_2 + 3^2 = 4 + 9 = 13$; $g_4 = g_3 + 4^2 = 29$ **3.** $a_{15} = a_1 + (15-1)(d) = -12 + 14d$
4. $g_n = 9 \cdot \left(\frac{1}{3}\right)^{n-1}$, so $g_7 = 9 \cdot \left(\frac{1}{3}\right)^6 = \frac{1}{81}$ **5. a.** The employee's

salary is $(19{,}000)(1.05)$ during the second year, $(19{,}000)(1.05)^2$ during the third year, and $(19{,}000)(1.05)^3 \approx \$21{,}994.88$ during the fourth year. **b.** This is a geometric sequence, so the salary during the nth year is $S_n = \$19{,}000(1.05)^{n-1}$. **6. a.** See p. 895. Some initial values are: $a_1 = 3$, $a_2 = 3 - \frac{1}{2}(2) = 2$, $a_3 = 2 - \frac{1}{2}(3) =$

$\frac{1}{2}$, $a_4 = \frac{1}{2} - \frac{1}{2}(4) = -\frac{3}{2}$, ... **b.** As n grows large, the a_ns become larger negative numbers. So the sequence does not converge.
7. This is a geometric series with $g_1 = 75$ and $r = 0.70$. Then $S = \frac{g_1}{1-r} = \frac{75}{1-0.70} = 250$ cm. **8.** Using the sequence mode on a calculator, $\sum_{i=1}^{\infty} \frac{3}{i^3} = 3.606$ when rounded to three decimal places.
9. This is an arithmetic series with $a_1 = 100$, $d = 1$, so $S_n = n \cdot \frac{(a_1 + a_n)}{2}$. Then $100 + 101 + \ldots 200 = S_{101} = \frac{101}{2}(100 + 200) = 15{,}150$. **10.** This is a geometric series with $g_1 = 7 \cdot \frac{3}{4} = \frac{21}{4}$, $r = \frac{3}{4}$, and $n = 10$. Then, $S_{10} = \frac{g_1(1-r^{10})}{1-r} = \frac{\frac{21}{4}\left(1 - \left(\frac{3}{4}\right)^{10}\right)}{1 - \frac{3}{4}} \approx 19.8174$. **11.** The distances Lillian runs each day are given by an arithmetic sequence with $a_1 = 0.5$ and $a_{12} = 3.25$. For the twelfth partial sum, $S_{12} = \frac{12}{2}(0.5 + 3.25) = 22.5$ miles.

12. $_nC_2 = \frac{n!}{(n-2)!2!} = \frac{n(n-1)(n-2)!}{(n-2)!2} = \frac{n(n-1)}{2}$;
$_nC_{n-2} = \frac{n!}{(n-n+2)!(n-2)!} = \frac{n!}{2!(n-2)!} = \frac{n(n-1)}{2}$.
So $_nC_2 = {}_nC_{n-2} = \frac{n(n-1)}{2}$ **13. a.** $(x+y)^3 = x^3 + 3x^2y + 3xy^2 + y^3$

b. The coefficients are the terms in row 3 of Pascal's Triangle.
14. By the Binomial Theorem, the 4th term is $_{10}C_3(2c)^{10-3}(-b)^3 = \frac{10!}{3!7!}(2c)^7(-b)^3 = \frac{10 \cdot 9 \cdot 8}{3!}(2c)^7(-b)^3$, or choice d. **15.** Three out of 50 are chosen without respect to order. So $_{50}C_3 = \frac{50!}{3!47!} = \frac{50 \cdot 49 \cdot 48}{3!}$, or choice d. **16.** This is a binomial experiment with $p = 0.86$ and $n = 5$. Then $P(\text{at least 4 successes}) = P(4 \text{ successes}) + P(5 \text{ successes}) = {}_5C_4(0.86)^4(0.14) + {}_5C_5(0.86)^5 \approx 0.85$.
17. Sample:
In row 1, $_1C_0 = {}_1C_1 = 1$.
In row 3, $_3C_0 + {}_3C_2 = 1 + 3 = 3 + 1 = {}_3C_1 + {}_3C_3$.
In row 4, $_4C_0 + {}_4C_2 + {}_4C_4 = 1 + 6 + 1 = 4 + 4 = {}_4C_1 + {}_4C_3$.

6. a.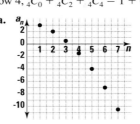

The chart below keys the **Progress Self-Test** questions to the objectives in the **Chapter Review** on pages 551-553 or to the **Vocabulary** (Voc.) on page 549. This will enable you to locate those **Chapter Review** questions that correspond to questions students missed on the **Progress Self-Test**. The lesson where the material is covered is also indicated on the chart.

Question	1	2	3	4	5	6	7	8	9	10
Objective	E	A	B	B	I	F	I	G	C	C
Lesson	8-1	8-1	8-1	8-1	8-1	8-2	8-5	8-5	8-3	8-4
Question	11	12	13	14	15	16	17			
Objective	I	H	D	D	J	K	L			
Lesson	8-3	8-7	8-8	8-8	8-6	8-9	8-7			

Chapter 8 Review (pp. 551-553)

1. a. 0, 2, 6, 12, 20 **b.** 132 **3. a.** 3, 6, 12, 24, 48 **b.** 6144
5. a. -749 **b.** $a_n = 84 - 17(n-1)$ **7.** $k_n = 22{,}000(0.8)^{n-1}$
9. 2358 **11.** 7,174,453 **13.** 18,900 **15.** $a^3 + 3a^2b + 3ab^2 + b^3$
17. $16x^4 - 160x^3 + 600x^2 - 1000x + 625$ **19.** $-12x^{11}y$
21. possibly arithmetic **23.** possibly arithmetic **25.** definitely geometric **27.** yes; 0 **29.** yes; 0 **31. a.** yes **b.** $\frac{3}{2}$ **33.** not convergent **35.** convergent; $\frac{5}{6}a$ **37. a.** when $b^2 < 1$ **b.** $\frac{a^3b^2}{1-b^2}$

39. $_nC_1 = \frac{n!}{1!(n-1)!} = \frac{n(n-1)!}{(n-1)!} = n$; $_nC_{n-1} = \frac{n!}{(n-1)!(n-n+1)!} = \frac{n(n-1)!}{(n-1)!} = n$ **41.** False **43. a.** 8 **b.** 50
45. a. \$692.67 **b.** about \$96,113 **47.** 286 **49. a.** 201,376
b. 4368 **51.** 1,058,400 **53.** $\approx .67232 \approx 67\%$ **55.** $\approx .73582 \approx 74\%$
57. True of every row; each is symmetric **59.** True in every row except row 1

Lesson 9-1 (pp. 556-562)

13. Sample: $x^3yz + xyz$ **15.** leading coefficient: c_n; degree: n. **17.** True

19. $t(n) + t(n+1) = \frac{1}{2}n(n+1) + \frac{1}{2}(n+1)(n+2)$
$= \frac{1}{2}(n+1)[n + (n+2)]$
$= \frac{1}{2}(n+1)(2n+2)$
$= \frac{1}{2}(n+1) \cdot 2(n+1)$
$= (n+1)^2 = s(n+1)$

21. a. Yearbook **b.** Sample: In general, drama clubs have a higher ineligibility rate than other activities. Half of the schools declared at least 30% of drama-club members ineligible, and at least one school declared all drama-club members ineligible. On the other hand, yearbook enjoys the lowest median ineligibility rate, with baseball a close second. Band and track are in the middle with median ineligibility rates of about 22% and 25%, respectively. Yearbook displays the widest diversity among many schools with $\frac{3}{4}$ of the schools declaring from 0% to 38% of the yearbook staff ineligible. In contrast, baseball has the least diversity among schools while having a median ineligibility rate only slightly higher than yearbook. Half of the schools declared from 10% to 20% of baseball players ineligible. **23.** $3x^2 + 14x + 15$ **25. a.** See p.896. **b.** See p.896.

25. a.    **25. b.**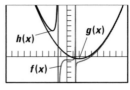

Lesson 9-2 (pp. 564-569)
9. a. $V = 4x^3 - 340x^2 + 7000x$ **b. See below.**
c. $x < 0$ or $35 < x < 50$; the side length of the square cannot be within these intervals because the volume must be positive.
d. $\approx (13.5, 42{,}377)$ **e.** ≈ 13.5 cm **f.** $\approx 42{,}377$ cm^3 **11. a.** ≈ 8 sec and ≈ 23 sec **b.** ≈ 3916 ft **c.** ≈ 31 sec **13. See below.** 1 relative minimum **15. See below.** 1 relative minimum **17. a.** r
b. $n - 1$ **19. a.** $A = (x + h)(y + h)$ **b.** $A = xy + xh + yh + h^2$
c. See below. 21. 6 **23.** $x = \dfrac{-b \pm \sqrt{b^2 - 4ac}}{2a}$ **25.** $(x - 6)(x - 5)$

9. b.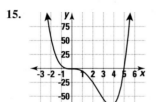
$-10 \leq x \leq 60$, x-scale $= 10$
$-20000 \leq y \leq 50000$, y-scale $= 10000$

13.
$-1 \leq x$

15.

19. c.

h^2	xh	h
yh	xy	y
h	x	

Lesson 9-3 (pp. 570-576)
11. a.

1	2	3	4	5	6
340	320	290	250	200	140

b. 2 **c.** $y = -5x^2 - 5x + 350$
d. $\begin{cases} t_0 = 350 \\ t_n = t_{n-1} - 10n, \text{ for integers } n > 0 \end{cases}$
13. a. $f(1) = a + b + c + d$
$f(2) = 8a + 4b + 2c + d$
$f(3) = 27a + 9b + 3c + d$
$f(4) = 64a + 16b + 4c + d$
$f(5) = 125a + 25b + 5c + d$
$f(6) = 216a + 36b + 6c + d$
b. 1st differences: $7a + 3b + c$, $19a + 5b + c$, $37a + 7b + c$, $61a + 9b + c$, $91a + 11b + c$
2nd differences: $12a + 2b$, $18a + 2b$, $24a + 2b$, $30a + 2b$
3rd differences: $6a$, $6a$, $6a$
15. No **17. a.** $750(1 + r)^2 + 750(1 + r) + 750$ **b.** $2359.73
19. a. $P = 62.5e^{0.017n}$ **b.** ≈ 66.9 million **c.** in the year 2024
21. a. $x = 0, x = 7$ **b.** $y = -9, y = \frac{7}{3}$ **c.** $z = -15, z = -8, z = 5$

Lesson 9-4 (pp. 577-583)
11. a. $q(a) = a + 5$, $r(a) = 5a + 15$ **b.** degree of remainder $= 1$, degree of divisor $= 2$ **c.** $(a^2 - 5)(a + 5) + (5a + 15) = (a^3 + 5a^2 - 5a - 25) + (5a + 15) = a^3 + 5a^2 - 10$

13. $x^2 + 3xy + y^2$ **15. a. See below. b.** The graphs of f and h are the same because $\dfrac{2x^4 - 8x^3 + 12}{x^2 - 2} = 2x^2 - 8x + 4 + \dfrac{-16x + 20}{x^2 - 2}$. g is very close to h for sufficiently large values of x because the remainder will become negligible (as x approaches positive or negative infinity, the denominator will become much larger than the numerator so the fraction will approach zero). f and h have asymptotes because both functions are undefined at $x = \sqrt{2}$ and $x = -\sqrt{2}$. g does not have these discontinuities. **17. a. See below.**
b. increasing: $-3.7 < x < -0.1$ or $x > 1.6$
  decreasing: $x < -3.7$ or $-0.1 < x < 1.6$
c. positive: $x < -5$ or $-1 < x < 1$ or $x > 2$
  negative: $-5 < x < -1$ or $1 < x < 2$
19. a. 7 **b.** $128a^7$ **c.** $-2187b^7$

15. a.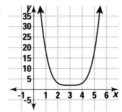
$-10 \leq x \leq 10$, x-scale $= 1$
$-50 \leq y \leq 100$, y-scale $= 10$

17. a.
$-6 \leq x \leq 4$, x-scale $= 1$
$-100 \leq y \leq 20$, y-scale $= 10$

Lesson 9-5 (pp. 584-589)
9. $(x + 2)$ and $(x - 1)$ **11.** $p = -2$ or $p = -5$
13. $f(x) = -(x + 8)(x)(x - 5)(x - 10) = -(x^4 - 7x^3 - 70x^2 + 400x)$
15. -972 **17.** $x^4 - 3x^3 + 9x^2 - 27x + 81$
19. a. 1st differences: 4   7   10
    2nd differences: 3   3
b. $p(n) = \frac{3}{2}n^2 - \frac{1}{2}n$ **c.** $p(5) = 35$,
$p(6) = 51$ **See right. 21. a.** 0.54
b. ≈ 0.45 **c.** 0.46 **d.** ≈ 0.19
e. ≈ 0.28

19. c.

Lesson 9-6 (pp. 590-595)
23. a. $(x - b)$ is a factor of $g(x)$ **b.** Yes **25. a.** $f(2 + i) = 0$
b. $f(2 - i) = 0$ **c.** $x^2 - 4x + 5 = (x - (2 + i))(x - (2 - i)) =$
$(x - 2 - i)(x - 2 + i)$ **27. a.** $-1 + 0i$ **b.** $w = \frac{1}{2} - \frac{\sqrt{3}}{2}i$;
$w^3 = -1 + 0i$ **c.** -1 **d.** -1 **29.** Samples:
$f(x) = (x - 2)(x - 4)\left(x + \frac{6}{5}\right) =$
   $x^3 - \frac{24}{5}x^2 + \frac{4}{5}x + \frac{48}{5}$
$g(x) = 10(x - 2)(x - 4)\left(x + \frac{6}{5}\right) =$
   $10x^3 - 48x^2 + 8x + 96$
$h(x) = x^2(x - 2)(x - 4)\left(x + \frac{6}{5}\right) =$
   $x^5 - \frac{24}{5}x^4 + \frac{4}{5}x^3 + \frac{48}{5}x^2$

31. a. $0 \leq P(x_i) \leq 1$ for all x_i
and $\sum_{i=1}^{8} P(x_i) = 1$ **b. See right.**
c. $\frac{109}{24} \approx 4.54$ **d.** Over a long period of time, the mean of the numbers the spinner lands on will approach $\frac{109}{24}$.

31. b.
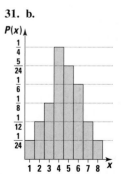

Lesson 9-7 (pp. 596-602)

15. $1, -1, i, -i$ **17.** $p(x) = (x - 3)(x - (1 - 2i))(x - (1 + 2i)) = x^3 - 5x^2 + 11x - 15$ **19. a.** Yes; a horizontal line crosses the graph at most 2 times, so the degree is greater than or equal to 2. **b.** Yes; a horizontal line crosses the graph at most 4 times, so the degree is greater than or equal to 4. **c.** No; the graph crosses the x-axis 6 times, so the degree is at least 6.

21. a. $w = 3 + 8i$ **b.** $6 + 0i$ **c.** $0 + 16i$ **d.** $73 + 0i$ **e.** $-\frac{55}{73} + \frac{48}{73}i$

23. $(2p + 3)(2p - 3)$ **25.** Multiply the quotient and divisor, then add the remainder. The result should equal the dividend.

27. a. $V(r) = 17\pi r^2 + \frac{2}{3}\pi r^3$ **b.** 3 **c.** $\frac{2}{3}\pi$ **d.** maximum ≈ 1597 m^3, minimum ≈ 537 m^3 **29. a, b.** Both will increase by 5%. **31.** True

Lesson 9-8 (pp. 603-607)

15. $7x^2(2y + x)(2y - x)$ **17.** $(2xy + 7z)(4x^2y^2 - 14xyz + 49z^2)$
19. a. $p(x) = x(x + 2)(x - 2)(x + 1)(x - 1)$, so the zeros are $-2, -1, 0, 1,$ and 2 **b. See below. 21.** True **23. a.** True **b.** False **c.** True **d.** True **e.** True **25. a.** $_{12}C_3 \cdot (0.36)^3(0.64)^9 \approx 0.18$ **b.** ≈ 0.32

19. b.

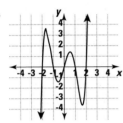

Lesson 9-9 (pp. 608-611)

7. a. $f(x) = x^2(2x - 5) + 3(2x - 5) = (x^2 + 3)(2x - 5) = (x + i\sqrt{3})(x - i\sqrt{3})(2x - 5)$ The zeros of f are $\frac{5}{2}, i\sqrt{3}$, and $-i\sqrt{3}$. **b. See below. 9.** $(x - z)(2x + y)$ **11.** Sample: $x^3 - x^2y^2 - xy + y^3 = 0$ **13.** $(x - 2)(x^2 + 2x + 4)$ **15.** $(6x^3 - yz^2)(6x^3 + yz^2)$

17. $\sqrt[3]{10}, -\frac{\sqrt[3]{10}}{2} + \frac{\sqrt{3}\sqrt[3]{10}}{2}i,$ $-\frac{\sqrt[3]{10}}{2} - \frac{\sqrt{3}\sqrt[3]{10}}{2}i$ **19. a.** $x = 0, \frac{1}{2}$

b. $x = -1, \frac{1}{2}, 1$ **c.** $\theta = \frac{\pi}{6} + 2\pi n, \frac{5\pi}{6} + 2\pi n, \frac{\pi}{2} + \pi n$ for n an integer

21. a. 10 **b.** r **c.** $\frac{8}{9}$ **23. a.** 3024 **b.** 336

7. b.

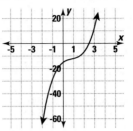

Lesson 9-10 (pp. 612-616)

9. $p(x) = (x + 1)^2(x^2 - x + 1)(x - 1)$; zeros are -1 (multiplicity 2), $1, \frac{1}{2} + \frac{\sqrt{3}}{2}i, \frac{1}{2} - \frac{\sqrt{3}}{2}i$ **11.** $\theta = \frac{\pi}{4}, \frac{3\pi}{4}, \frac{5\pi}{4},$ and $\frac{7\pi}{4}$ **13. a.** $2i$

b. $-24i, 48$ **c.** $3 \cdot 2^{100}$ **15. a.** $ax^3 - ax^2 - 2ax = f(x)$
b. $\frac{1}{2}x^3 - \frac{1}{2}x^2 - x = g(x)$ **c.** $\frac{1}{2}x^3 - \frac{1}{2}x^2 - x = g(x)$ is the specific case of $ax^3 - ax^2 - 2ax = f(x)$ for $a = \frac{1}{2}$.

17. a. $V(x) = x^3 - 2x^2 - 15x$ **b.** $S(x) = 6x^2 - 8x - 30$
c. $V(x)$: cubic centimeters; $S(x)$: square centimeters
19. mean $= 16.5$ oz; standard deviation $= 0.45$ oz

Chapter 9 Progress Self-Test (p. 621)

1.

1st differences	1		7		13		19		25		31
2nd differences		6		6		6		6		6	

Therefore, the function is a polynomial function of degree 2.
Let $f(x) = ax^2 + bx + c$.
$f(1)$: $-4 = a + b + c$
$f(2)$: $-3 = 4a + 2b + c$
$f(3)$: $4 = 9a + 3b + c$
Solving this system yields $a = 3, b = -8, c = 1$. So the equation is $y = 3x^2 - 8x + 1$.
2. See below right. $x \approx 1.42$
3.

$$
\begin{array}{r}
3x^3 - 13x^2 + 34x - 82 \\
x + 2 \overline{)\,3x^4 - 7x^3 + 8x^2 - 14x - 10} \\
\underline{3x^4 + 6x^3} \\
-13x^3 + 8x^2 \\
\underline{-13x^3 - 26x^2} \\
34x^2 - 14x \\
\underline{34x^2 + 68x} \\
-82x - 10 \\
\underline{-82x - 164} \\
154
\end{array}
$$

Therefore, $q(x) = 3x^3 - 13x^2 + 34x - 82$; $r(x) = 154$
4. $9x^2 - 3x - 2 = 9x^2 - 6x + 3x - 2 = 3x(3x - 2) + (3x - 2) = (3x - 2)(3x + 1)$ **5.** $t^6 + 1000y^3 = (t^2)^3 + (10y)^3 = (t^2 + 10y)(t^4 - 10t^2y + 100y^2)$ **6.** By the Factor Theorem, if $f(1) = 0$, then $x - 1$ is a factor of f. The choice is a. **7. a.** $2z + w = 2(2 + 5i) + (3 - i) = (4 + 3) + (2 \cdot 5 - 1)i = 7 + 9i$
b. $\frac{z}{w} = \frac{2 + 5i}{3 - i} = \frac{(2 + 5i)(3 + i)}{(3 - i)(3 + i)} = \frac{1}{10}(6 + 15i + 2i + 5 \cdot i^2) =$

$\frac{1}{10} + \frac{17}{10}i$ **8.** $-\frac{3}{2}$ **9.** 6 **10.** 3 **11.** It must have 7 zeros (counting multiplicities). Since complex zeros come in conjugate pairs, and the polynomial has an odd number of zeros, at least one of the roots must be real. **12.** Because i is a solution, $-i$ is also a solution. Divide $x^4 + 11x^2 + 10$ by $x^2 + 1$. From this, $x^4 + 11x^2 + 10 = (x^2 + 1)(x^2 + 10)$. So the solutions are $x = i, -i, \sqrt{10}i, -\sqrt{10}i$.
13. From the data, we can get the equation of the quadratic function $y = .06875x^2 - 1.0125x + 9.2$. Substitute $x = 16$ into the equation. We get the price $10.60.
14. From $x^2 + (x^2)^2 = (x^3)^2$, we have $x^6 - x^4 - x^2 = 0$, $x^2(x^4 - x^2 - 1) = 0$ Solve the equation. We get $x = 0$, or $x \approx 1.27$. As $x > 0$, $x \approx 1.27$. **15. a.** Observing the intersections of the part of the graph shown with the x-axis, there seems to be one real zero of multiplicity two and another real zero for a total of at least 3 real zeros. **b.** The graph crosses a horizontal line $y = d$ ($0 < d < t(0)$) three times. So the degree of $t(x)$ must be at least 3. **16.** $V = \pi r^2 \cdot 25 - \pi(r - .35)^2 \cdot 25 = 17.5\pi r - 3.0625\pi$ cubic meters

2.

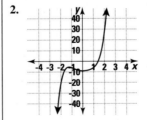

Question	1	2	3	4	5	6	7	8	9	10
Objective	A	B	C	D	D	G	E	F	F	G
Lesson	9-3	9-2	9-4	9-9	9-8	9-5	9-6	9-7	9-1	9-5

Question	11	12	13	14	15	16
Objective	H	H	I	J	K	J
Lesson	9-7	9-7	9-3	9-1	9-7	9-1

Chapter 9 Review (pp. 622-625)

1. a. 4 **b.** 5 **3. a.** No **5.** -1.62 **7.** Because $g(3) = 0$, by the Factor-Solution-Intercept Equivalence Theorem, 3 must be a t-intercept of the graph of g. **9.** $q(t) = 2t^3 - 9t + 1$; $r(t) = 27t + 8$
11. $q(x) = x^3 - 2x^2 + x - 1$; $r(x) = 0$ **13.** True
15. $(3t - u)(81t^4 + 27t^3u + 9t^2u^2 + 3tu^3 + u^4)$
17. $(z - 2)(z + 1 - \sqrt{3}i)(z + 1 + \sqrt{3}i)$
19. $(2x - 1)(10x + 1)$ **21. a.** $20 + 6i$ **b.** $-2 + 6i$ **c.** $107 - 102i$
d. $\frac{3}{4} + \frac{1}{2}i$ **23.** $\frac{14}{25} + \frac{27}{25}i$ **25.** 0 **27. a.** 7 **b.** 3 **c.** 0 **d.** -127 **e.** 7
29. False **31.** False **33.** True **35.** For all real a, $a = a + 0i$. The complex conjugate of $a + 0i$ is $a - 0i = a$. Thus every real number is equal to its complex conjugate. **37.** All four zeros must not be real. **39.** True. If $2 + i$ is a zero, then $2 - i$ must also be a zero because non-real zeros occur as conjugate pairs. If $1 + i$ were a zero, then $1 - i$ would also have to be a zero. But, since the polynomial is a cubic polynomial, it only has three zeros. The zeros must be $2 + i$, $2 - i$, and another zero which must be real.
41. a. $l = 510 - w$; $A(w) = w(510 - w)$ **b. i.** 41,000 ft^2
ii. 65,000 ft^2 **iii.** 63,000 ft^2 **c.** $l = 255$ ft, $w = 255$ ft

43. $V = \frac{1}{3}\pi r^2 h + \pi r^3$ **45. a.** $V = \frac{1}{3}\pi(25 - x^2)(x + 5) =$
$-\frac{1}{3}\pi x^3 - \frac{5}{3}\pi x^2 + \frac{25}{3}\pi x + \frac{125}{3}\pi$ **b.** 3 **c.** 4 inches **47.** 24 cm^2
49. a. See below. **b.** relative maximum: (-2.6, 0.4); relative minimum: (-1.4, -0.4) **c.** -3, -2, -1 **51. a.** See below.
b. relative maximum: (-1, 0); relative minimum: (0, -1)
c. -1 (multiplicity 2); 1 **53.** False; the equation $0.1x^5 - 2x^3 + x^2 - 27 = 0$ has exactly three real solutions.

49. a.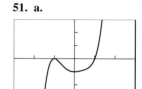
$-5 \leq x \leq 2$, **x-scale = 1**
$-4 \leq y \leq 8$, **y-scale = 1**

51. a.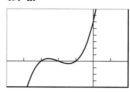
$-3 \leq x \leq 3$, **x-scale = 1**
$-3 \leq y \leq 3$, **y-scale = 1**

Lesson 10-1 (pp. 628–633)

9. a. 0.939 **b.** 0.103 **c.** 0.061 **11.** binomial
13. Sample: Use the command rand on a TI-83 to generate 20 random numbers x between 0 and 1. If $0 \leq x \leq 0.15$, the watermelon is large, if $0.15 < x \leq 0.5$, then the watermelon is small, if $0.5 < x \leq 1$, then the watermelon is medium. In our simulation, we obtained 3 large, 7 small, and 10 medium watermelons. **15.** $\approx 117.5°$

Lesson 10-2 (pp. 634–640)

7. a.

x	0	1	2	3	4
$P(x)$	0.316	0.422	0.211	0.047	0.004

b. See right. **c.** 1 **d.** $\frac{\sqrt{3}}{2} \approx .866$ **9.** 24 **11. a.** True **b.** False
13. a.

x	0	1	2	3	4	5	6	7	8	9	10
$P(x) \approx$	0.555	0.337	0.092	0.015	0.002	0	0	0	0	0	0

See right.
b. about 0.984 **c.** Sample: The mode would increase, the standard deviation decrease, and the graph become closer to bell-shaped. **d.** Sample: The mode would increase, the standard deviation increase, and the graph become closer to bell-shaped.
15. a. See right. **b.** $T(x, y) \rightarrow (-x, y)$ **c.** 0 **d.** 0 **17.** $\pm 3\sqrt{110}$
19. a. $540°$ **b.** Assume 4 angles are acute. Then their sum is less than $360°$ which implies the remaining angle is larger than $180°$. This implies the pentagon is not convex, which contradicts our assumption. Therefore, a pentagon cannot have 4 acute angles.

7. b.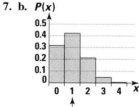

13. a.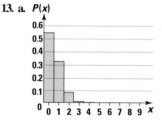

15. a.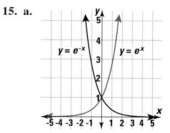

Lesson 10-3 <small>(pp. 641–647)</small>

7. $P\left(5 \text{ or more heads given the probability of heads is } \frac{1}{3}\right) \approx$
$0.213 > 0.05$. Thus, we cannot reject the null-hypothesis at the
0.05 level. **9.** mean $= 3\frac{1}{3}$; $\sigma = \frac{\sqrt{20}}{3}$ **11.** True
13. $2a^5(1 + 3bc^2)(1 - 3bc^2 + 9b^2c^4 - 27b^3c^6 + 81b^4c^8)$
15. a., c. **See below. b.** 0.258 **17. a.** 0.01 **b.** 0.64 **c.** 0.11

15. a., c.

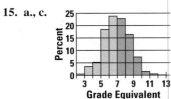

Grade Equivalent

Lesson 10-4 <small>(pp. 649–653)</small>

15. ≈ 0.96 **17.** Let $x =$ number of tails. $P(x \geq 8 \text{ or } x \leq 3) \approx .2266$
which is greater than 0.01, so the hypothesis cannot be rejected.
19. $x^4 + 2x^3 + 4x^2 + 8x + 16$ **21. a.** False, A and B might not be
mutually exclusive. **b.** True, by the definition of complementary

Lesson 10-5 <small>(pp. 654-661)</small>

13. ≈ 1.96 **15.** ≈ -0.67 **17.** The area under $y = e^{-x^2}$ is $\sqrt{\pi}$, while
the area under the standard normal curve is 1. **19.** $2x + 3 + 2h$
21. a. $0, \frac{3 \pm \sqrt{5}}{2}$ **b. See above right.** From the graph, zeros are
$0, \approx 2.62, \approx 0.38$. **23.** ≈ 0.166 **25. a.** $g(x) = -9x^2 - 12x + 5$
b. The axis of symmetry for the graph of g is $\frac{2}{3}$ units to the left of
the axis of symmetry for the graph of f. **c. see above right.**

21. b.

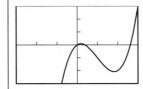

$-3 \leq x \leq 3$, x-scale = 1
$-3 \leq y \leq 3$, y-scale = 1

25. c.

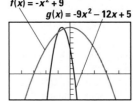

$f(x) = -x^2 + 9$
$g(x) = -9x^2 - 12x + 5$

$-5 \leq x \leq 5$, x-scale = 1
$-5 \leq y \leq 10$, y-scale = 1

Lesson 10-6 <small>(pp. 662-669)</small>

11. a. $z = \frac{t - 100}{4}$ **b.** $\mu = 0, \sigma = 1$ **13.** almost 0
15. Sample: **a.** 500 **b.** 0.05 **c.** between 228 and 272
17. ≈ 0.0038 **19.** $_{20}C_5 \cdot \ _{300}C_2 = 695{,}354{,}400$ **21.** ≈ 0.998

Lesson 10-7 <small>(pp. 671-679)</small>

15. No, the distribution for the small samples is skewed.
17. a. They are the same. **b.** The scores of the 45 games; these
scores are the population with a standard deviation σ. While
the 15 weekly averages are a subset consisting of 15 samples
of size 3 with a standard deviation $\sigma_{\bar{x}} = \frac{\sigma}{\sqrt{3}}$. **19. a.** ≈ 0
b. H_0: The students at Acme scored the same as the nation.
H_1: The students at Acme scored higher than the nation. Since
the $P\{z \geq 3.9\} \approx 0$, we reject the null hypothesis in favor of the
alternative. **21.** $\approx .901$ **23.** Sample: **a.** H_0: The baby has no
color preference between red and green. H_1: The baby prefers
red to green. **b.** (3 red, 1 green) and (4 red, 0 green) **c.** We
should accept the null hypothesis at the .05 level. **25. a.** $\approx 20°8'$
b. At that time the shadow will be near its shortest length and
thus its lowest price. **27.** $x = zs + m$

Lesson 10-8 <small>(pp. 680-686)</small>

9. a. $25\% \leq \mu \leq 31\%$ **b.** No **11. a.** $170 \leq \mu \leq 190$ **b.** No
13. False **15. a.** uniform distribution **b.** 54.5 **17.** about 14
19. b **21.** a **23.** d **25. a.** 112 **b.** geometric **27. a.** ≈ 0.028
b. ≈ 0.972

Chapter 10 Progress Self-Test <small>(p. 691)</small>

1. By the Binomial Probability Theorem, for each value of x,
$P(x \text{ of } 10 \text{ survive}) = _{10}C_x(0.89)^x(0.11)^{10-x}$. Evaluating this
expression for each possible value of x gives the following table:

x	$P(x \text{ of } 10 \text{ survive})$
0	2.6×10^{-10}
1	2.1×10^{-8}
2	7.6×10^{-7}
3	1.6×10^{-5}
4	2.3×10^{-4}
5	0.0023
6	0.015
7	0.071
8	0.214
9	0.385
10	0.312

These data are graphed in the histogram. **See p 900.**
2. The domain would increase; the range would "flatten" or
decrease; and the shape would approach a normal distribution.

3. $\mu = np = .2 \cdot 60 = 12$; $\sigma = \sqrt{npq} = \sqrt{60 \cdot .2 \cdot .8} = $
$\sqrt{9.6} \approx 3.1$ **4.** The mean resistance is 1500 ohms, because it is
the center of the distribution. The 99% confidence interval is
reported as 1500 ohms $\pm 5\%$, which gives a margin of error of
$\pm 5\% \times 1500 = \pm 75$ oms. From the table of the Standard Normal
Distribution, in order for the confidence level to be 99%, z, which
equals $\frac{\bar{x} - \mu_{\bar{x}}}{\sigma}$, must equal 2.5. Therefore, $\sigma = \frac{75}{2.57} \approx 29$ ohms.
5. Yes, $x = 0$, because $f(-x) = \frac{1}{2}e^{-(-x)^2} = \frac{1}{2}e^{-x^2} = f(x)$. **6.** False;
the standard normal curve has the equation $f(x) = \frac{1}{\sqrt{2\pi}}e^{\frac{-x^2}{2}}$.

7. Using the Standard Normal Distribution Table we get
$P(z < 1.3) = .9032$. **8.** $P(-1.5 < z < 1.5) = 1 - 2P(z < -1.5) = $
$1 - 2(1 - P(z < 1.5)) = 0.8664$, using the Standard Normal
Distribution Table. **9. a.** H_0: Average "normal" body temperature
is 98.6°F. H_1: Average "normal" body temperature is not 98.6°F.
b. $z = \frac{98.2 - 98.6}{\frac{.7}{\sqrt{130}}} \approx -6.52$, $P(z < -6.52) = 0 < 0.01$ Thus, we
reject the null hypothesis H_0 in favor of the alternative H_1 that

average "normal" body temperature is not 98.6°F. **10.** Using the Central Limit Theorem, we would expect a sample of 40 girls from this high school to have a mean height of about 170 cm with a standard deviation of about $\frac{7.2}{\sqrt{40}}$ cm, or 1.14 cm.

A sample mean of 180 cm is about 6 standard deviations from the population mean. A Standard Normal Distribution Table shows even 3.09 standard deviations from the mean to have a probability of less than 0.001. So the event is quite unusual. **11.** 1.96. We must find a value $a > 0$ such that $P(-a < z < a) = 0.95$. Since $P(-a < z < a) = P(z < a) - (1 - P(z < a)) = 2P(z < a) - 1 < 0.95 \Rightarrow 2P(z < a) < 1.95 \Rightarrow P(z < a) < = 0.975$. Using the Standard Normal Distribution Table, we see that the probability value 0.975 corresponds to the z-value $a = 1.96$. **12.** standard normal **13.** 0.0091. Let x be the number of miles a student travels to school. Then, because x is normally

distributed with a mean of 2.15 miles and a standard deviation of 0.36, the variable $z = \frac{x - 2.15}{0.36}$ has a standard normal distribution. So $P(x > 3) = 1 - P(x < 3) = 1 - P\left(z < \frac{3 - 2.15}{0.36} \approx 2.36\right) \approx 1 - 0.9909 = 0.0091$. **14.** 0.6424. $P(|z| < 0.92) = P(-0.92 < z < 0.92) = P(z < 0.92) - (1 - P(z < 0.92)) = -1 + 2P(z < 0.92) = -1 + 2(0.8212) = -1 + 1.6424 = 0.6424$.

1.

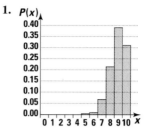

The chart below keys the **Progress Self-Test** questions to the objectives in the **Chapter Review** on pages 692-695 or to the **Vocabulary** (Voc.) on page 690. This will enable you to locate those **Chapter Review** questions that correspond to questions students missed on the **Progress Self-Test**. The lesson where the material is covered is also indicated on the chart.

Question	1	2	3	4	5	6	7	8	9	10
Objective	I	C	A	H	D	D	B	B	F	G
Lesson	10-1	10-1	10-2	10-8	10-4	10-4	10-5	10-5	10-3,10-7	10-7

Question	11	12	13	14
Objective	D	D	E	J
Lesson	10-5	10-6	10-6	10-5

Chapter 10 Review (pp. 692-695)

1. mean $= 36$, $\sigma = \sqrt{14.4} \approx 3.8$ **3.** $\mu = 10$, $\sigma = \sqrt{5} \approx 2.24$
5. 100 **7. a.** 0.7994 **b.** 0.7994 units^2 **9.** ≈ 0.1359 **11.** ≈ 0.0013
13. False **15.** True **17. a.** $f(-x) = e^{-(-x)^2} = e^{-x^2} = f(x)$
b. reflection symmetry over the y-axis **19.** False **21.** ≈ 0.35
23.
highly extroverted	score ≥ 49
extroverted	$42 \leq$ score ≤ 48
average	$29 \leq$ score ≤ 41
introverted	$22 \leq$ score ≤ 28
highly introverted	score < 22

25. c **27.** $P(\text{weight} > 27.8) \approx 0.0708 \geq 0.01$; the null hypothesis cannot be rejected at the 0.01 significance level. **29.** True
31. very close to zero **33.** 0.025 **35. a.** $0.624 \leq$ radius ≤ 0.626
b. about 864

37. a.
x	0	1	2	3	4
$p(x)$	$\frac{1}{16}$	$\frac{1}{4}$	$\frac{3}{8}$	$\frac{1}{4}$	$\frac{1}{16}$
b. See below.
39. See below. 41. Samples: It is continuous; $p(x) > 0$ for arbitrarily large values of x. **43.** ≈ 0.9772 **45.** ≈ 0.9544 **47.** $\frac{r}{2}$

37. b.
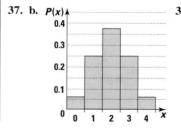

39.
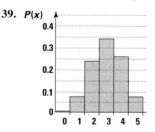

Lesson 11-1: (pp. 698–703)

15. $x = -2$ **17. a.** $\begin{bmatrix} 4 & 0 \\ 0 & 4 \end{bmatrix}$ **b.** $\begin{bmatrix} 0 & -8 \\ -8 & 0 \end{bmatrix}$ **19. a.** $\begin{bmatrix} 2860 \\ 2918 \\ 2640 \end{bmatrix}$ **b.** $2860

21. a. $\{0, 1, 2, 3, 4\}$
b.
b	0	1	2	3	4
$P(b)$	0.3164	0.4219	0.2109	0.0469	0.0039
c. See right.
23. $f(g(x)) = 9x^2 - 6x + 3$
25. a. v **b.** i **c.** ii **d.** iv
e. iii

21. c.
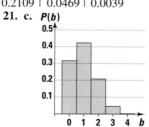

Lesson 11-2 (pp. 704–709)

9. a. $\begin{bmatrix} 0 & 1 \\ 1 & 0 \end{bmatrix}$ **b.** $\begin{bmatrix} 1 & 0 \\ 0 & 1 \end{bmatrix}$ **c.** the identity transformation

11. $\begin{bmatrix} 0 & 1 & 2 & 3 & 4 & 5 & 5 & 4 & 1 & 0 \\ 4 & 6 & 4 & 4 & 6 & 4 & -3 & -4 & -4 & -3 \end{bmatrix}$

13. a. $A' = \begin{bmatrix} 30 \\ -17 \end{bmatrix}$, $B' = \begin{bmatrix} 14 \\ -8 \end{bmatrix}$, $C' = \begin{bmatrix} -18 \\ 10 \end{bmatrix}$ **b.** Yes **c.** No

15. a. 3×4 **b.** 12 **17.** Product does not exist.

19. a. $\begin{bmatrix} -7 & -1 \\ -14 & -10 \end{bmatrix}$ **b.** $\begin{bmatrix} -7 & -1 \\ -14 & -10 \end{bmatrix}$ **c.** the Associative Property

21. $\theta = k\pi$ for all integers k

900

Lesson 11-3 (pp. 710–715)

13. **See below.** $u \circ t(\triangle ABC) = \begin{bmatrix} 28 & 30 & -110 \\ 0 & 3 & -18 \end{bmatrix}$

15. **a.** $r_x \circ r_{y=x} = \begin{bmatrix} 1 & 0 \\ 0 & -1 \end{bmatrix}\begin{bmatrix} 0 & 1 \\ 1 & 0 \end{bmatrix} = \begin{bmatrix} 0 & 1 \\ -1 & 0 \end{bmatrix}$ **b.** R_{270}

17. $\begin{bmatrix} 3 & -1 \\ 1 & 1 \end{bmatrix}$ **19.** $x = -2, y = 7$ **21.** d **23.** **a. b. See below.**
c. $S:(x, y) \to \left(\frac{x}{2}, \frac{y}{2}\right)$ **25.** $\frac{5\sqrt{3}}{4}$

13.

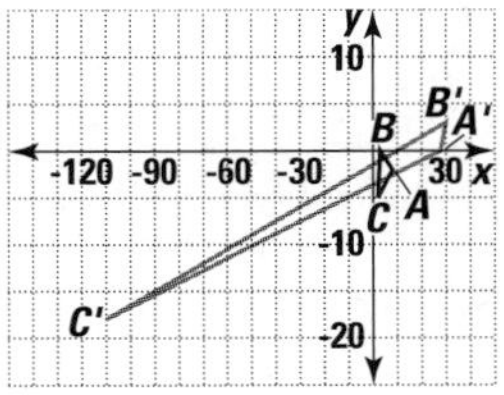

23 a,b.

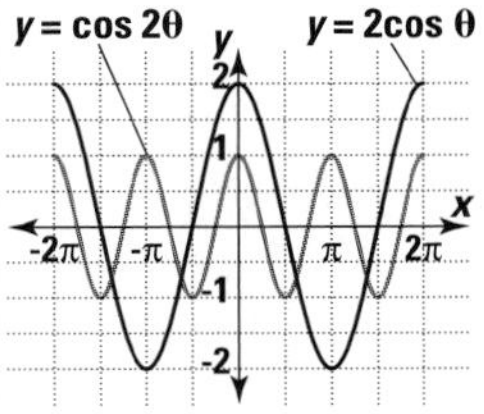

Lesson 11-4 (pp. 716–720)

11. **a.** $\begin{bmatrix} 0 & -4\sqrt{3} & -2\sqrt{3} \\ 0 & -4 & -6 \end{bmatrix}$ **b.** See below. **13.** **a.** A clockwise rotation of θ is equivalent to a counterclockwise rotation of $-\theta$.
So $R_{-\theta} = \begin{bmatrix} \cos(-\theta) & -\sin(-\theta) \\ \sin(-\theta) & \cos(-\theta) \end{bmatrix} = \begin{bmatrix} \cos\theta & \sin\theta \\ -\sin\theta & \cos\theta \end{bmatrix}$.

b. $\begin{bmatrix} \cos 90° & \sin 90° \\ -\sin 90° & \cos 90° \end{bmatrix} = \begin{bmatrix} 0 & 1 \\ -1 & 0 \end{bmatrix}$ **15.** **a.** Yes **b.** No **c.** Yes
d. No **17.** **a.** $y = x^2 - 2x + 1$ **b.** There is not a unique cubic function through three points. Sample: Using (0, 0) as a fourth point, the function containing these four points is $y = \frac{1}{3}x^3 + 2x^2 - \frac{7}{3}x$. **19.** False **21.** False **23.** a **25.** **a.** $c = 0.12n + 5$
b. $245

11. b.

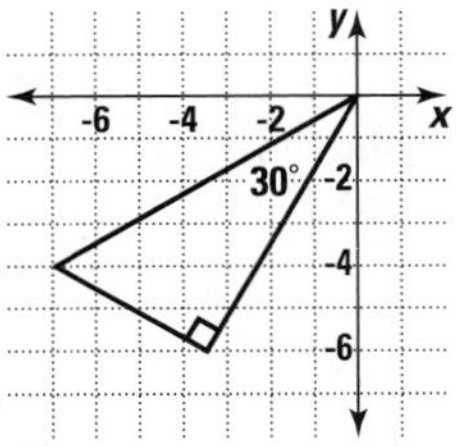

Lesson 11-5 (pp. 721-725)

11. $\frac{-\sqrt{2} - \sqrt{6}}{4}$ **13.** $\begin{bmatrix} \frac{\sqrt{6} - \sqrt{2}}{4} & -\frac{\sqrt{6} + \sqrt{2}}{4} \\ \frac{\sqrt{6} + \sqrt{2}}{4} & \frac{\sqrt{6} - \sqrt{2}}{4} \end{bmatrix}$

15. **a.** $g(x)$ **b.** **See below.** **c.** $f(x) = 2\sin\left(x + \frac{\pi}{6}\right) = 2\left(\sin x \cos\frac{\pi}{6} + \cos x \sin\frac{\pi}{6}\right) = 2\left(\frac{\sqrt{3}}{2}\sin x + \frac{1}{2}\cos x\right) = \sqrt{3}\sin x + \cos x = h(x)$ **17.** $\sin\left(x - \frac{\pi}{2}\right) = \sin\left(x + \left(-\frac{\pi}{2}\right)\right) = \sin x \cos\left(-\frac{\pi}{2}\right) + \cos x \sin\left(-\frac{\pi}{2}\right) = \sin x \cdot 0 + \cos x \cdot -1 = -\cos x$

19. **a.** $\frac{1 - 2\sqrt{6}}{6}$ **b.** $\frac{2\sqrt{6} - 1}{6}$ **c.** Sample: **See below.**

21. **a.** $P' = \begin{bmatrix} 2 & 12 & 16 & 6 \\ -1 & -1 & -4 & -4 \end{bmatrix}$ **b.** It is a scale change: $(x, y) \to (2x, -y)$ **23.** **a.** 15 **b.** Friday **c.** HR **d.** $52.80

25. **a.** 3 **b.** 4 **c.** True. There are four observable solutions to $g(x) = 0$, counting the double root twice. By the Factor Theorem, each solution c implies $(x - c)$ is a factor of g. **27.** c

15. b.

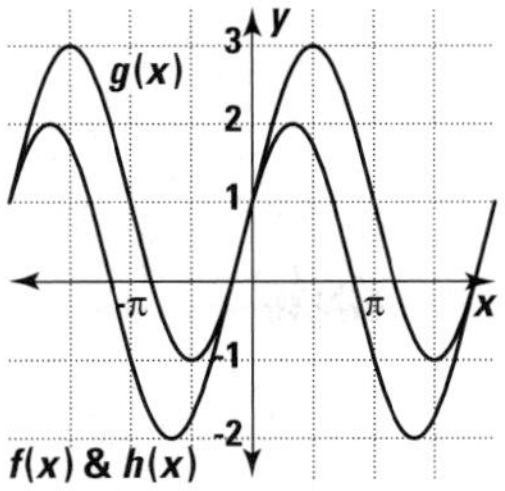

19. c.

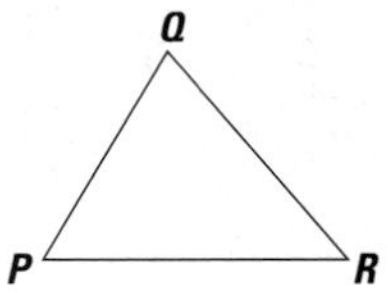

Lesson 11-6 (pp. 726–730)

13. **a.** $\frac{3}{5}$ **b.** $\frac{24}{25}$ **15.** $r_L = \begin{bmatrix} \cos(2 \cdot 0°) & \sin(2 \cdot 0°) \\ \sin(2 \cdot 0°) & -\cos(2 \cdot 0°) \end{bmatrix} = \begin{bmatrix} 1 & 0 \\ 0 & -1 \end{bmatrix} = r_x$ **17.** **a.** $\begin{bmatrix} \frac{1}{2} & \frac{\sqrt{3}}{2} \\ \frac{\sqrt{3}}{2} & -\frac{1}{2} \end{bmatrix}$ **b.** $\left(\frac{1}{2}, \frac{\sqrt{3}}{2}\right)$ **See below.**

19. **a.**
$$\begin{aligned} -\cos 2\theta &= \sin^2\theta - \cos^2\theta \\ + \quad 1 &= \sin^2\theta + \cos^2\theta \\ \hline 1 - \cos 2\theta &= 2\sin^2\theta \\ \frac{1 - \cos 2\theta}{2} &= \sin^2\theta \\ \sin\theta &= \pm\sqrt{\frac{1 - \cos 2\theta}{2}} \end{aligned}$$

b. $\sin\frac{\pi}{8} = \pm\sqrt{\frac{1 - \cos\frac{\pi}{4}}{2}} = \pm\sqrt{\frac{1 - \frac{\sqrt{2}}{2}}{2}} = \pm\sqrt{\frac{2 - \sqrt{2}}{4}} = \pm\frac{\sqrt{2 - \sqrt{2}}}{2}$. Since $\frac{\pi}{8}$ is in the first quadrant, $\sin\frac{\pi}{8} > 0$; therefore $\sin\frac{\pi}{8} = \frac{\sqrt{2 - \sqrt{2}}}{2}$. **21.** $\frac{\sqrt{2} - \sqrt{6}}{4}$ **23.** $\begin{bmatrix} -4 & 2 \\ 1 & 3 \end{bmatrix}$
25. from 240 to 292 days **27.** **a.** **See below.** **b.** iii

17. b.

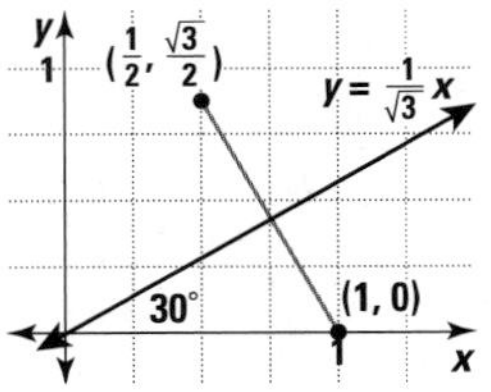

27. a.

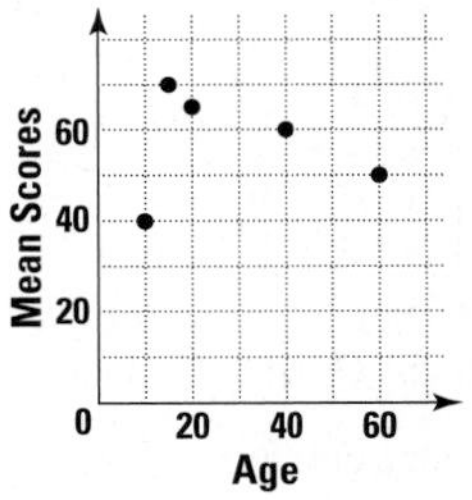

Lesson 11-7 (pp. 731–737)

17. **a.** True **b.** $-\det\begin{bmatrix} Y & Z \\ W & X \end{bmatrix}$ **c.** $\det\begin{bmatrix} W & X \\ Y & Z \end{bmatrix} = WZ - XY$ and $-\det\begin{bmatrix} Y & Z \\ W & X \end{bmatrix} = -(XY - WZ) = WZ - XY$ **19.** **a.** $\begin{bmatrix} 1 & 2 \\ 3 & -1 \end{bmatrix}\begin{bmatrix} x \\ y \end{bmatrix} = \begin{bmatrix} x + 2y \\ 3x - y \end{bmatrix}$ **b.** $\begin{bmatrix} \frac{1}{7} & \frac{2}{7} \\ \frac{3}{7} & -\frac{1}{7} \end{bmatrix}$ **c.** $\begin{bmatrix} x \\ y \end{bmatrix} = \begin{bmatrix} 5 \\ 3 \end{bmatrix}$ **d.** $x = 5, y = 3$
e. $x = -\frac{1}{2}, y = \frac{7}{3}$ **21.** **a.** 3 **b.** π **c.** Sample: $y = 3\sin(2x)$
d. $y = 3\sin(2x) = 3(2\sin x\cos x) = 6\sin x\cos x$ **23.** $\cos(3\theta)$
25. **a.** R_a **b.** r_x **27.** **a.** $M = \begin{bmatrix} 2 & 5 & 5 \\ -1 & -1 & -5 \end{bmatrix}$ **b.** **See p.902.**
c. $M' = \begin{bmatrix} 1 & 1 & 5 \\ -2 & -5 & -5 \end{bmatrix}$ **d.** **See p.902.** **e.** $\begin{bmatrix} -1 & -1 & -5 \\ 2 & 5 & 5 \end{bmatrix}$
29. **a.** $x = 729$ **b.** $x = 729.00$

27. b.

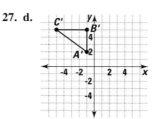

27. d.

Lesson 11-8 (pp. 738–744)

13. a. r_x **b.** $\begin{bmatrix} 1 & 0 \\ 0 & -1 \end{bmatrix}$ **c.** r_x **15.** If T_1 and T_2 are scale changes with $T_1: (x, y) \rightarrow \left(3x, \frac{1}{2}y\right)$ and $T_2: (x, y) \rightarrow \left(\frac{1}{3}x, 2y\right)$, then $T_1 \circ T_2 = I$, where I is the identity transformation. **17.** $\sin 3\theta = 3 \sin \theta - 4\sin^3\theta$

19. a. $\frac{\sqrt{2} - \sqrt{6}}{4}$ **b.** 1 **21. a.** $\begin{bmatrix} 3 & 5 \\ -1 & 4 \end{bmatrix}$ **b.** (0, 0) **c.** (8, 3)

Chapter 11 Progress Self-Test (p. 748)

1. Multiply the number of voters in each region by the percentage of people expected to vote Republican in that region and then add the three results; for example, .29(3.4) + .41(0.6) + .58(2.1) =

2.45 million **2.** $VP = \begin{bmatrix} 0.50 & 0.47 & 0.29 \\ 0.29 & 0.41 & 0.58 \\ 0.21 & 0.12 & 0.13 \end{bmatrix} \begin{bmatrix} 3.4 \\ 0.6 \\ 2.1 \end{bmatrix} =$

$\begin{bmatrix} 0.5 \cdot 3.4 + 0.47 \cdot 0.6 + 0.29 \cdot 2.1 \\ 0.29 \cdot 3.4 + 0.41 \cdot 0.6 + 0.58 \cdot 2.1 \\ 0.21 \cdot 3.4 + 0.12 \cdot 0.6 + 0.13 \cdot 2.1 \end{bmatrix} = \begin{bmatrix} 2.591 \\ 2.45 \\ 1.059 \end{bmatrix}$

3. To obtain the first row of VP, we multiplied the percentage of urban voters that are expected to vote Democrat by the total number of registered urban voters, added the percentage of rural voters that are expected to vote Democrat times the total number of rural voters, and then added the percentage of suburban voters that are expected to vote Democrat times the total number of suburban voters. Thus the entry in the first row is the total number of registered voters expected to vote Democrat. Similarly, the second and third rows represent the total number of voters expected to vote Republican and Independent, respectively.

4. $\begin{bmatrix} 5 & -1 \\ 2 & 0 \end{bmatrix}\begin{bmatrix} 3 & 8 \\ -1 & 1 \end{bmatrix} = \begin{bmatrix} 5 \cdot 3 + -1 \cdot -1 & 5 \cdot 8 + -1 \cdot 1 \\ 2 \cdot 3 + 0 \cdot -1 & 2 \cdot 8 + 0 \cdot 1 \end{bmatrix} = \begin{bmatrix} 16 & 39 \\ 6 & 16 \end{bmatrix}$

5. Since M is a 3×4 matrix and N is a $4 \times t$ matrix, MN is a $3 \times t$ matrix (the number of rows of M by the number of columns of N). Since $Z = 3 \times 5$ and $MN = Z$, then $t = 5$. **6.** $A = (0, 2)$, $B = (-3, 0)$, and $C = (4, -1)$ so the point matrix for $\triangle ABC$ is $\begin{bmatrix} 0 & -3 & -4 \\ 2 & 0 & -1 \end{bmatrix}$. **7.** $XM = \begin{bmatrix} -1 & 0 \\ 0 & 2 \end{bmatrix}\begin{bmatrix} 0 & -3 & -4 \\ 2 & 0 & -1 \end{bmatrix} =$

$\begin{bmatrix} -1 \cdot 0 + 0 \cdot 2 & -1 \cdot -3 + 0 \cdot 0 & -1 \cdot -4 + 0 \cdot -1 \\ 0 \cdot 0 + 2 \cdot 2 & 0 \cdot -3 + 2 \cdot 0 & 0 \cdot -4 + 2 \cdot -1 \end{bmatrix} = \begin{bmatrix} 0 & 3 & 4 \\ 4 & 0 & -2 \end{bmatrix}$

8. See below right. 9. a. The reflection $r_{y=x}: (x, y) \rightarrow (y, x)$ maps (1, 0) to (0, 1) and (0, 1) to (1, 0). Therefore, the matrix representing $r_{y=x}$ is $\begin{bmatrix} 0 & 1 \\ 1 & 0 \end{bmatrix}$. **b.** $\begin{bmatrix} 0 & 1 \\ 1 & 0 \end{bmatrix}\begin{bmatrix} 0 & 1 \\ 1 & 0 \end{bmatrix} = \begin{bmatrix} 1 & 0 \\ 0 & 1 \end{bmatrix}$, which is the identity matrix. So $r_{y=x} \circ r_{y=x} = I$. **10.** $R_{30°} =$

$\begin{bmatrix} \cos 30° & -\sin 30° \\ \sin 30° & \cos 30° \end{bmatrix} = \begin{bmatrix} \frac{\sqrt{3}}{2} & -\frac{1}{2} \\ \frac{1}{2} & \frac{\sqrt{3}}{2} \end{bmatrix}$, which is choice b.

11. a. r_x **b.** The matrix representing r_x is $\begin{bmatrix} 1 & 0 \\ 0 & -1 \end{bmatrix}$, and the matrix representing R_{180} is $\begin{bmatrix} -1 & 0 \\ 0 & -1 \end{bmatrix}$. So the matrix representing $R_{180} \circ r_x$ is $\begin{bmatrix} -1 & 0 \\ 0 & -1 \end{bmatrix}\begin{bmatrix} 1 & 0 \\ 0 & -1 \end{bmatrix} = \begin{bmatrix} -1 & 0 \\ 0 & 1 \end{bmatrix}$. **12.** $\triangle PQR$ is represented by the matrix $\begin{bmatrix} 0 & 1 & 0 \\ 0 & 0 & 1 \end{bmatrix}$, and the rotation R_θ is represented by the matrix $\begin{bmatrix} \cos \theta & -\sin \theta \\ \sin \theta & \cos \theta \end{bmatrix}$. So the image of $\triangle PQR$ is represented by the point matrix $\begin{bmatrix} \cos \theta & -\sin \theta \\ \sin \theta & \cos \theta \end{bmatrix}\begin{bmatrix} 0 & 1 & 0 \\ 0 & 0 & 1 \end{bmatrix} = \begin{bmatrix} 0 & \cos \theta & -\sin \theta \\ 0 & \sin \theta & \cos \theta \end{bmatrix}$

13. By the Subtraction Formula for Sine, $\sin (\alpha - \beta) = \sin \alpha \cos \beta - \cos \alpha \sin \beta$. So, $\sin 83° \cos 42° - \cos 83° \sin 42° = \sin (83° - 42°) = \sin 41°$. **14.** $\cos (\alpha + \beta) = \cos \alpha \cos \beta - \sin \alpha \sin \beta$. So, $\cos (\pi + \theta) = \cos \pi \cos \theta - \sin \pi \sin \theta = -1 \cdot \cos \theta - 0 \cdot \sin \theta = -\cos \theta$. **15.** Because A is acute, $\cos A = \sqrt{1 - \sin^2 A}$. $\sin 2A = 2 \sin A \cos A = 2 \sin A \left(\sqrt{1 - \sin^2 A}\right) = 2 \cdot 0.40 \cdot \sqrt{1 - (0.40)^2} \approx 0.733$. **16.** If $A = \begin{bmatrix} a & b \\ c & d \end{bmatrix}$, then $A^{-1} = \begin{bmatrix} \frac{d}{\det A} & -\frac{b}{\det A} \\ -\frac{c}{\det A} & \frac{a}{\det A} \end{bmatrix}$. For C, $\det C = 1 \cdot 5 - 3 \cdot -1 = 8$. So $C^{-1} = \begin{bmatrix} \frac{5}{8} & \frac{1}{8} \\ -\frac{3}{8} & \frac{1}{8} \end{bmatrix}$. **17.** $\det G = 3x \cdot 10 - 6 \cdot 5x = 30x - 30x = 0$. A matrix with a zero determinant has no inverse.

18. a. $\begin{bmatrix} 3 & -1 \\ 5 & -2 \end{bmatrix}\begin{bmatrix} x \\ y \end{bmatrix} = \begin{bmatrix} 6 \\ 11 \end{bmatrix}$

b. $\det\begin{bmatrix} 3 & -1 \\ 5 & -2 \end{bmatrix} = -1$, so $\begin{bmatrix} 3 & -1 \\ 5 & -2 \end{bmatrix}^{-1} = \begin{bmatrix} \frac{-2}{-1} & \frac{1}{-1} \\ \frac{-5}{-1} & \frac{3}{-1} \end{bmatrix} = \begin{bmatrix} 2 & -1 \\ 5 & -3 \end{bmatrix}$.

Multiplying both sides of the equation in part **a** on the left by the inverse gives

$\begin{bmatrix} 2 & -1 \\ 5 & -3 \end{bmatrix}\begin{bmatrix} 3 & -1 \\ 5 & -2 \end{bmatrix}\begin{bmatrix} x \\ y \end{bmatrix} = \begin{bmatrix} 2 & -1 \\ 5 & -3 \end{bmatrix}\begin{bmatrix} 6 \\ 11 \end{bmatrix}$;

$\begin{bmatrix} 1 & 0 \\ 0 & 1 \end{bmatrix}\begin{bmatrix} x \\ y \end{bmatrix} = \begin{bmatrix} 12 + -11 \\ 30 + -33 \end{bmatrix}$; $\begin{bmatrix} x \\ y \end{bmatrix} = \begin{bmatrix} 1 \\ -3 \end{bmatrix}$.

8.

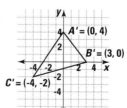

A' = (0, 4)
B' = (3, 0)
C' = (-4, -2)

The chart below keys the **Progress Self-Test** questions to the objectives in the **Chapter Review** on pages 749-751 or to the **Vocabulary** (Voc.) on page 747. This will enable you to locate those **Chapter Review** questions that correspond to questions students missed on the **Progress Self-Test.** The lesson where the material is covered is also indicated on the chart.

Question	1	2	3	4	5	6	7	8	9	10
Objective	F	A	F	A	D	I	I	I	C, G	G
Lesson	11-1	11-1	11-1	11-1	11-1	11-2	11-2	11-2	11-2,11-7	11-4

Question	11	12	13	14	15	16	17	18		
Objective	H	I	E	E	E	C	C	B		
Lesson	11-3	11-4	11-5, 11-6	11-5	11-6	11-7	11-7	11-7		

Chapter 11 Review (pp. 749–751)

1. c **3.** $[x - 21]$ **5.** $x = 5$ **7.** $x = \frac{3}{5}, y = \frac{3}{2}$ **9.** $x = 3, y = 2, z = 1$

11. $\begin{bmatrix} \cos 40° & \sin 40° \\ -\sin 40° & \cos 40° \end{bmatrix}$ **13.** a, e **15.** 5×2 **17.** Sample: a rotation about the origin, a reflection over a line containing the origin, and the identity transformation.

19. $\frac{\sqrt{6} - \sqrt{2}}{4}$ **21.** 0.96

23. $-\cos \theta$ **25.** $\sin 2A$ **27.** $\cos 50°$ **29.** By the derivation in **28.**, $\cos (\alpha + \beta) = \cos \alpha \cos \beta - \sin \alpha \sin \beta$. So, if $\alpha = \theta$ and $\beta = \theta$, $\cos (\theta + \theta) = \cos \theta \cos \theta - \sin \theta \sin \theta$; $\cos 2\theta = \cos^2\theta - \sin^2\theta$. Also, from the identity $\sin^2\theta + \cos^2\theta = 1$, $\sin^2\theta = 1 - \cos^2\theta$ and $\cos^2\theta = 1 - \sin^2\theta$. So, by substitution, $\cos 2\theta = 1 - 2 \sin^2\theta$, and $\cos 2\theta = 2 \cos^2\theta - 1$. **31.** \$10,900

33. a. \$491.76 **b.** True **35.** $\begin{bmatrix} 1 & 0 \\ 0 & \frac{1}{3} \end{bmatrix}$ **37.** a size change of magnitude 11 **39.** R_{180}

41. $\begin{bmatrix} -\frac{1}{2} & -\frac{\sqrt{3}}{2} \\ \frac{\sqrt{3}}{2} & -\frac{1}{2} \end{bmatrix}$ **43. a.** $\begin{bmatrix} 5 & 0 \\ 0 & -1 \end{bmatrix}$ **b.** $(5, -1)$

45. a counterclockwise rotation of 90°, followed by a reflection over the line $y = x$, followed by a counterclockwise rotation of 32°. **47. a.** $\begin{bmatrix} -1 & 0 \\ 0 & 1 \end{bmatrix}$ **b.** r_y

49. a. Sample: $\begin{bmatrix} 0 & 7 & 7 & 0 \\ 0 & -1 & 0 & 1 \end{bmatrix}$ **b. See below.**

51. $R_{-75} = \begin{bmatrix} \cos (-75°) & -\sin (-75°) \\ \sin (-75°) & \cos (-75°) \end{bmatrix} = \begin{bmatrix} \cos 75° & \sin 75° \\ -\sin 75° & \cos 75° \end{bmatrix}$

49. b.

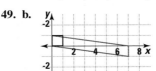

Lesson 12-1 (pp. 754–759)

11. True. The center of the circle is the location of both foci. The focal constant is twice the radius of the circle. **13. a.** There is no smallest focal constant, but it must be larger than 1 meter. **b.** As the focal constant gets larger, the ellipse looks more and more like a circle. **c.** There is no largest focal constant; it can be arbitrarily large as long as it is larger than 1 meter.

15. $\{x: B < x < D\}, \{x: x > F\}$ **17.** No **19.** False. Counterexample: $g(f(-2)) = ((-2)^6)^{\frac{1}{6}} = 2$, but $f(g(-2))$ is undefined.

21. $4ab$ **23.** $\sqrt{(a - x)^2 + (b - y)^2}$

Lesson 12-2 (pp. 760–767)

13. Dividing both sides of the equation $2x^2 + 3y^2 = 12$ by 12 gives the equation $\frac{x^2}{6} + \frac{y^2}{4} = 1$, which is an equation of an ellipse in standard form. **15. a.** $\frac{x^2}{100} + \frac{y^2}{49} = 1$ **b.** $\frac{(x - 3)^2}{100} + \frac{(y + 6)^2}{49} = 1$

17. a. Eccentricity $= \frac{c}{a}$, where $c^2 = a^2 - b^2$ **b.** greater **19.** ≈ 0.25

21. hyperbola **23.** $\approx 125°$ **25. a.** about 3971 megabytes **b.** 5000 megabytes

Lesson 12-3 (pp. 768–775)

11. Let $F_1 = (\sqrt{2}, 0)$, $F_2 = (-\sqrt{2}, 0)$, the focal constant $k = 2$, and $P = (1, 0)$. We have to show $|PF_1 - PF_2| = 2$, or, equivalently,

$(PF_1 - PF_2)^2 = 4$. $(PF_1 - PF_2)^2 =$
$\left(\sqrt{(1 - \sqrt{2})^2 + (0 - 0)^2} - \sqrt{(1 + \sqrt{2})^2 + (0 - 0)^2}\right)^2$
$= \left(\sqrt{(3 - 2\sqrt{2})} - \sqrt{(3 + 2\sqrt{2})}\right)^2 = 3 - 2\sqrt{2} -$
$2\sqrt{(3 - 2\sqrt{2})(3 + 2\sqrt{2})} + 3 + 2\sqrt{2} =$
$6 - 2\sqrt{9 - 8} = 4$

13. a. Dividing both sides of the equation $x^2 - 2y^2 = 2$ by 2 gives the equivalent equation $\frac{x^2}{2} - y^2 = 1$, which is the equation for a hyperbola in standard form, with $a = \sqrt{2}$ and $b = 1$.

b. foci: $(\sqrt{3}, 0), (-\sqrt{3}, 0)$; focal constant: $2\sqrt{2}$ **15. a.** (h, k)
b. $(a + h, k), (-a + h, k)$ **c.** $(\sqrt{a^2 + b^2} + h, k), (-\sqrt{a^2 + b^2} + h, k)$
d. $\frac{y - k}{b} = \frac{x - h}{a}, \frac{y - k}{b} = -\frac{(x - h)}{a}$ **17. a.** center: $(-2, 5)$

foci: $(\sqrt{21} - 2, 5), (-\sqrt{21} - 2, 5)$ **b.** major axis: 10 minor axis: 4
c. See below. **19.** about 8 **21.** $4a^2 + 2b^2$

17. c.

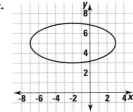

903

T147

Lesson 12-4 (pp. 776–783)

9. a. Sample: $y^2 - x^2 = 2k$ **b.** True **11.** An equation for the x-axis is $y = 0$. By the Graph Rotation Theorem, the image of the x-axis under R_θ has equation $-x \sin \theta + y \cos \theta = 0$. Solving for y yields $y = x \tan \theta$.

13. a. See below. **b.** $y = \frac{1}{6}x$, $y = -\frac{1}{6}x$

c. $\frac{y^2}{36} - x^2 = 1$

15. a. an equation which is true for all values in the domain of the variables **b.** Sample: $\cos^2\theta + \sin^2\theta = 1$ **c.** Sample: $\cos \theta + \sin \theta = 1$ **17.** a **19.** d

13. a.

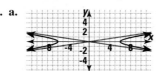

Lesson 12-5 (pp. 784–791)

15. Let $s = \sin \theta$ and $t = \cos \theta$.
$B'^2 - 4A'C' = (2(A - C)ts + B(t^2 - s^2))^2 -$
$4(At^2 - Bts + Cs^2)(As^2 + Bts + Ct^2) = 4(A - C)^2t^2s^2 +$
$4(A - C)B(t^2 - s^2)ts + B^2(t^2 - s^2)^2 - 4(A^2s^2t^2 - B^2s^2t^2 +$
$C^2s^2t^2 + AB(st^3 - s^3t) + AC(s^4 + t^4) + BC(s^3t - st^3)) =$
$4A^2t^2s^2 - 8ACt^2s^2 + 4AB(t^3s - ts^3) - 4BC(t^3s - ts^3) +$
$B^2t^4 - 2B^2t^2s^2 + B^2s^4 - 4A^2s^2t^2 + 4B^2s^2t^2 - 4C^2s^2t^2 -$
$4AB(st^3 - s^3t) - 4AC(s^4 + t^4) - 4BC(s^3t - st^3) =$

$B^2(t^2 + s^2)^2 - 4AC(t^2 + s^2)^2 = B^2(t^4 + 2t^2s^2 + s^4) -$
$4AC(t^4 + 2t^2s^2 + s^4) = B^2 - 4AC$

17. $x^2 - 2\sqrt{3}xy - y^2 = 2$ **19. a.** See below. **b.** $\frac{x^2}{25} + \frac{y^2}{4} = 1$

21. $-\cos \theta$

23. False; if $x = 0$, then $\sin\left(\frac{\pi}{2} - x\right) = \sin\left(\frac{\pi}{2}\right) = 1$, but $\sin\left(x - \frac{\pi}{2}\right) = \sin\left(0 - \frac{\pi}{2}\right) = \sin\left(-\frac{\pi}{2}\right) = -1$.

19. a.

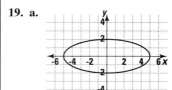

Lesson 12-6 (pp. 792–796)

11. hyperbola **13. a.** $y^2 - x^2 = -12$ **b.** True **15. a.** See below.

b. $\left(-\sqrt{33}, 0\right), \left(\sqrt{33}, 0\right)$ **c.** 10 **17.** 32,000 miles

15. a.

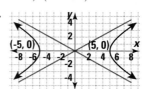

Chapter 12 Progress Self-Test (p. 801)

1. a. By taking the intersection of the cone with a plane while the angle formed by the cone's axis and the plane is greater than the angle between the axis and the rotating line. **b. See p. 905.**
2. The graph is an ellipse, the image of the unit circle under the stretch $(x, y) \to (5x, 9y)$. So the endpoints of its axes are (5, 0), (-5, 0), (0, 9), and (0, -9). **See p. 905. 3.** Dividing each side of the equation by 9 converts the equation into standard form $\frac{x^2}{9} - y^2 = 1$ The graph is a hyperbola with vertices (3, 0) and (-3, 0) and asymptotes $y = \pm\frac{1}{3}x$. **See p. 905. 4.** The graph is the translation image of the ellipse $\frac{x^2}{36} + \frac{y^2}{20}$ under the translation $(x, y) \to (x + 2, y - 1)$. The endpoints of the axes of the parent ellipse are (6, 0), (-6, 0), $\left(0, \sqrt{20}\right)$, and $(0, -\sqrt{20})$. So the endpoints of the axes of this ellipse are (8, -1), (-4, -1), $\left(2, \sqrt{20} - 1\right)$, and $\left(2, -\sqrt{20} - 1\right)$. **See p. 905. 5.** The hyperbola with foci $(c, 0)$ and $(-c, 0)$ and focal constant $2a$ has equation $\frac{x^2}{a^2} - \frac{y^2}{b^2} = 1$, where $b^2 = c^2 - a^2$. Here $c = 7$ and $2a = 10$ $\Rightarrow a = 5$. Thus $b^2 = 7^2 - 5^2 = 24$, so an equation for the hyperbola is $\frac{x^2}{25} - \frac{y^2}{24} = 1$. **6.** The ellipse should have the shape of the ellipse below, where the distance between the foci is 8 cm and the minor axis is 6 cm. **See p. 905. 7. a.** A hyperbola of the form $\frac{x^2}{a^2} - \frac{y^2}{b^2} = 1$ has asymptotes with equations $y = \frac{b}{a}x$ and $y = \frac{-b}{a}x$. Thus the hyperbola $\frac{x^2}{81} - \frac{y^2}{100} = 1$ has asymptotes $y = \frac{10}{9}x$ and $y = \frac{-10}{9}x$. **b.** The symmetry lines of a hyperbola are the axes of the hyperbola. One axis is the line through the foci, $x = 0$.

The other is the perpendicular bisector of the segment joining the foci, $y = 0$. **8.** By the Graph Rotation Theorem, find the image of $y = x^2 - 3x - 4$ under $R_{\pi/3}$ by replacing x with $x \cos \frac{\pi}{3} + y \sin \frac{\pi}{3} = \frac{1}{2}x + \frac{\sqrt{3}}{2}y$ and y with $-x \sin \frac{\pi}{3} + y \cos \frac{\pi}{3} = \frac{-\sqrt{3}}{2}x + \frac{1}{2}y$. This gives $\frac{-\sqrt{3}}{2}x + \frac{1}{2}y = \left(\frac{1}{2}x + \frac{\sqrt{3}}{2}y\right)^2 - 3\left(\frac{1}{2}x + \frac{\sqrt{3}}{2}y\right) - 4 = \frac{1}{4}x^2 + \frac{\sqrt{3}}{2}xy + \frac{3}{4}y^2 - \frac{3}{2}x - \frac{3\sqrt{3}}{2}y - 4$. Simplifying, $\frac{1}{4}x^2 + \frac{\sqrt{3}}{2}xy + \frac{3}{4}y^2 + \frac{-3 + \sqrt{3}}{2}x + \frac{-1 - 3\sqrt{3}}{2}y - 4 = 0$.
9. No; the asymptotes $y = \frac{\sqrt{30}}{2}x$ and $y = \frac{-\sqrt{30}}{2}x$ are not perpendicular, thus the hyperbola is not rectangular.
10. $64x^2 - 9y^2 - 576 = 0$ $A = 64, B = 0, C = -9, D = 0, E = 0, F = -576$ **11.** $B^2 - 4AC = (-6)^2 - 4 \cdot 2 \cdot 18 = 36 - 144 < 0$, so the graph of this equation is either an ellipse, a single point, or the null set. Substituting 0 for x we get $18y^2 + 6y - 110 = 0$. Solving using the quadratic formula gives $y = \frac{-1 \pm \sqrt{21}}{6}$. Since the points $\left(0, \frac{-1 + \sqrt{21}}{6}\right)$ and $\left(0, \frac{-1 - \sqrt{21}}{6}\right)$ are on the graph it cannot be a single point or the null set. Thus, the graph is an ellipse. **12.** $B^2 - 4AC = (-2)2 - 4 \cdot 9 \cdot 1 = 4 - 36 < 0$, so the graph of this equation is either an ellipse, a single point, or the null set. Substitute a value, call it a, for x to get the quadratic equation $y^2 - 2ay + (9a^2 - 4a + 22) = 0$. This equation has solution $\frac{2a \pm \sqrt{4a^2 - 4(9a^2 - 4a + 22)}}{2} = a \pm\sqrt{a^2 - 9a^2 + 4a - 22} = a \pm\sqrt{-8a^2 + 4a - 22}$. The value under the radical sign is always negative (this can be seen by graphing the parabola $y = -8x^2 + 4x - 22$), thus $9x^2 - 2xy + y^2 - 4x + 22 = 0$ is not defined for any value of x so its graph must be the null set.

13. The situation is illustrated at the right. The center of the orbit is the origin and the sun is at $(c, 0)$ where the unit is one million miles. The maximum and minimum distances from the sun will be achieved when Jupiter intersects the x-axis. From the given information $a - c = 460$ and $c - (-a) = 508$. Adding these equations gives $2a = 968$, so $a = 484$. Thus $c = 24$. So the second focus is $(-24, 0)$ and is 48 million miles from the sun. **See right.**

1. b.

2.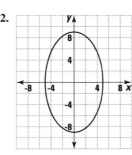

3.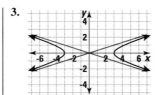

4.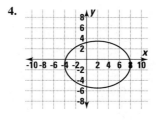

6.

13.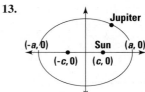

Jupiter

$(-a, 0)$ Sun $(a, 0)$

$(-c, 0)$ $(c, 0)$

The chart below keys the **Progress Self-Test** questions to the objectives in the **Chapter Review** on pages 802–803 or to the **Vocabulary** (Voc.) on page 800. This will enable you to locate those **Chapter Review** questions that correspond to questions students missed on the **Progress Self-Test**. The lesson where the material is covered is also indicated on the chart.

Question	1	2	3	4	5	6	7	8	9	10
Objective	E	G	G	H	A	D	D	B	D	C
Lesson	12-1	12-2	12-3	12-2	12-3	12-1	12-3	12-4	12-4	12-5

Question	11	12	13
Objective	I	I	F
Lesson	12-5	12-5	12-2

Chapter 12 Review (pp. 802–803)

1. $\frac{x^2}{64} + \frac{y^2}{289} = 1$ **3.** $\frac{x^2}{81} + \frac{4y^2}{49} = 1$ **5.** Sample: $5x^2 + 6xy + 5y^2 = 72$ **7.** Sample: $3x^2 + 2\sqrt{3}\,xy + y^2 + 2x - 2\sqrt{3}\,y - 32 = 0$
9. Sample: $y^2 - x^2 = 240$ **11.** $49x^2 + 25y^2 - 1225 = 0$ $A = 49$, $B = 0$, $C = 25$, $D = 0$, $E = 0$, $F = -1225$ **13.** $7xy - 8 = 0$ $A = 0$, $B = 7$, $C = 0$, $D = 0$, $E = 0$, $F = -8$ **15.** The ellipse should have the shape of the ellipse below with 6 cm between the foci and a minor axis of $2\sqrt{7} \approx 5.3$ cm. **See right. 17.** 2
19. No, because the asymptotes $y = \sqrt{2}x$ and $y = -\sqrt{2}x$ are not perpendicular. **21.** The cone is formed by rotating one of two intersecting, non-perpendicular lines about the other. **23. See right. 25.** 15,120,000 miles **27.** The endpoints of the axes of the ellipse are $(1, 0)$, $(-1, 0)$, $(0, 4)$, and $(0, -4)$. **See right. 29.** The vertices of the hyperbola are $\left(0, \pm\sqrt{40}\right)$ and its asymptotes have equations $y = \pm\frac{\sqrt{40}}{3}x$. **See p. 906. 31.** The hyperbola has vertices $(0, \pm 1)$ and the equations of its asymptotes are $y = \pm x$. **See p. 906. 33.** $\frac{x^2}{64} + \frac{y^2}{16} = 1$ **35.** The ellipse has center $(4, -2)$ and the endpoints of its axes are $(-1, -2)$, $(9, -2)$, $(4, 0)$, and $(4, -4)$. **See p. 906. 37.** The hyperbola has vertices $\left(\sqrt{20}, \sqrt{20}\right)$ and $\left(-\sqrt{20}, -\sqrt{20}\right)$. Its asymptotes are the x-axis and the y-axis. **See p. 906. 39.** the null set **41.** parabola

15.

23.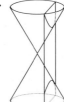

27.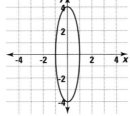

29.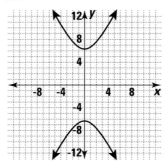

31.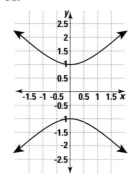

35.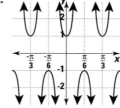

37.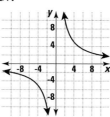

Lesson 13-1 (pp. 806–810)

13. $\frac{z}{x}$ **15.** $\frac{z}{x}$ **17.** $14 \cot 28° + 5 \approx$ **19. a.**
31 ft **19. a. See right. b.** $\frac{\pi}{3}$

21. $\cot(-x) = \frac{\cos(-x)}{\sin(-x)} = \frac{\cos x}{-\sin x} =$
$-\cot x$ **23.** -0.96 **25.** 18 to 29.8

27. a. $\theta = \frac{3\pi}{2}$ **b.** $\theta = \frac{3\pi}{2} + 2\pi n$
for all integers n **29.** $120°$

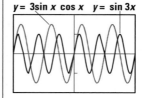

Lesson 13-2 (pp. 811–815)

7. $\sin x \cdot \cos x \cdot \tan x$ | $\frac{1}{\csc^2 x}$

$= \sin x \cdot \cos x \cdot \frac{\sin x}{\cos x}$ | $= \frac{1}{\frac{1}{\sin^2 x}}$

$= \sin^2 x$ | $= \sin^2 x$

So, $\sin x \cdot \cos x \cdot \tan x = \frac{1}{\csc^2 x}$ for $x \neq$, for all integers n.

9. a. $\sec x \tan x \cos x = \tan x$ **b.** $\sec x \tan x \cos x =$

$\frac{1}{\cos x} \cdot \cos x \cdot \tan x = \tan x$ **c.** for all x such that $x \neq \frac{\pi}{2} + n\pi$, for

all integers n **11. a. See above right.** **b.** Let $x = \frac{\pi}{3}$. Then $\sin$

$\left(3 \cdot \frac{\pi}{3}\right) = \sin \pi = 0$ and $3 \sin \frac{\pi}{3} \cos \frac{\pi}{3} = 3 \cdot \frac{\sqrt{3}}{2} \cdot \frac{1}{2} = \frac{3\sqrt{3}}{4}$. So, $\sin$

$3x \neq 3 \sin x \cos x$, for all x. **13. a. See above right.**

b. $\tan^2 x \cos^2 x$ | $1 - \cos^2 x$

$= \frac{\sin^2 x}{\cos^2 x} \cdot \cos^2 x$ | $= \sin^2 x$

$= \sin^2 x$

So, $\tan^2 x \cos^2 x = 1 - \cos^2 x$, for all x such that $x \neq + n\pi$ for
all integers n.

15. Begin with the Pythagorean Identity:
for all x, $\cos^2 x + \sin^2 x = 1$
$(\cos^2 x + \sin^2 x)(\cos^2 x - \sin^2 x) = \cos^2 x - \sin^2 x$
$\cos^4 x - \sin^4 x = \cos^2 x - \sin^2 x$
$\cos^4 x + \sin^2 x = \sin^4 x + \cos^2 x$

17. For all x, $\log x^3 + \log x^4 = \log(x^3 \cdot x^4) = \log x^7$, so it is
an identity. **19.** $\frac{a}{b}$ **21.** $-\frac{\pi}{2}$ **23.** $(4 \cos \theta, 4 \sin \theta)$

11. a.

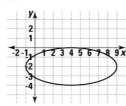

$y = 3\sin x \cos x$ $y = \sin 3x$

$-2\pi \leq x \leq 2\pi$, x-scale $= \pi$
$-2 \leq y \leq 2$, y-scale $= 1$

13. a.

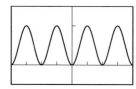

$-2\pi \leq x \leq 2\pi$, x-scale $= \frac{\pi}{2}$
$-0.5 \leq y \leq 1.5$, y-scale $= 1$

Lesson 13-3 (pp. 816–819)

11. a. See below. b. $x \neq \frac{n\pi}{2}$ for all integers n **c.** $\frac{1 + \cos 2x}{\sin 2x} = \cot x$

d. $\frac{1 + \cos 2x}{\sin 2x} = \frac{1 + 2\cos^2 x - 1}{2 \sin x \cos x} = \frac{2\cos^2 x}{2 \sin x \cos x} = \frac{\cos^2 x}{\sin x \cos x} =$

$\frac{\cos x}{\sin x} = \cot x$, for all x such that $x \neq \frac{n\pi}{2}$, for all integers n.

13. a. $x \neq \frac{n\pi}{2}$, for all integers n

b. $\csc^2 x \sin x$ | $\frac{\sec^2 x - \tan^2 x}{\sin x}$

$= \frac{1}{\sin^2 x} \cdot \sin x$ | $= \frac{1}{\sin x}$

$= \frac{1}{\sin x}$

So, $\csc^2 x \sin x = \frac{\sec^2 x - \tan^2 x}{\sin x}$ for all x such that $x \neq \frac{n\pi}{2}$,
for all integers n.

15. a. $\sqrt{17}$ **b.** $\frac{\sqrt{17}}{17}$ **c.** $-\frac{8}{17}$ **17.** False **19. a.** $(0.98)^{25} \approx 0.60$
b. ≈ 0.013 **c.** 24.5 units **d.** 0.7 **21. a.** 66 **b.** 4096 **23.** $t \approx 2448.6$

11. a.

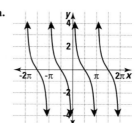

906

Lesson 13-4 (pp. 820–826)

15. a circle with radius 8 and center at the pole **17.** Samples: $\left[6, -\frac{\pi}{3}\right]$, $\left[-6, \frac{2\pi}{3}\right]$ **19. a.** south **b.** 10° W of N **c.** 40° E of S **d.** 20° W of S **21.** $\sin\left(\frac{\pi}{2} + x\right) = \sin\frac{\pi}{2}\cos x + \cos\frac{\pi}{2}\sin x = 1 \cdot \cos x + 0 \cdot \sin x = \cos x$ for all x **23. a.** 1 **b.** 25 **25.** center: (−1, −4), radius: 5 **27. a. b. See below.**

27. a, b.

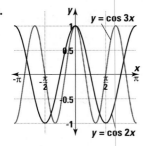

$y = \cos 3x$
$y = \cos 2x$

Lesson 13-5 (pp. 827–832)

9. See below. 11. See below. 13. a. $[1, 0]$, $\left[1.72, \frac{\pi}{4}\right]$, $\left[2.97, \frac{\pi}{2}\right]$, $\left[5.12, \frac{3\pi}{4}\right]$, $[8.82, \pi]$, $\left[15.21, \frac{5\pi}{4}\right]$, $\left[26.22, \frac{3\pi}{2}\right]$, $\left[45.19, \frac{7\pi}{4}\right]$ **b. See below. 15.** a, b, and c **17. a.** Not an identity. **See below.**
b. When $x = 30°$, $\tan 2x = \tan 60° = \sqrt{3}$ and $2\tan x = 2\tan 30° = 2 \cdot \frac{1}{\sqrt{3}} = \frac{2\sqrt{3}}{3}$. So $\tan 2x = 2\tan x$ is not an identity.
19. $9, -\frac{9}{2} + \frac{9\sqrt{3}}{2}i, -\frac{9}{2} - \frac{9\sqrt{3}}{2}i$

9.

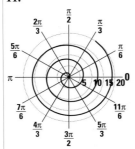

11.

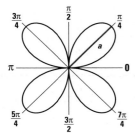

13. b.

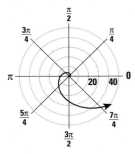

17. a.

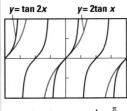

$y = \tan 2x$ $y = 2\tan x$

$-\pi \leq x \leq \pi$, x-scale $= \frac{\pi}{4}$
$-4 \leq y \leq 4$, y-scale $= 2$

Lesson 13-6 (pp. 833–837)

13. a. Let $A = z - w$, $B = z + w$, $C = w - z$, and $D = -(z + w)$. Then, the slope of $\overline{AB} = \frac{2 - 10}{10 - 6} = -2$; the slope of $\overline{BC} = \frac{-10 - 2}{-6 - 10} = \frac{3}{4}$; the slope of $\overline{CD} = \frac{-2 - -10}{-10 - -6} = -2$; the slope of $\overline{DA} = \frac{-10 - -2}{-6 - -10} = \frac{3}{4}$. Because the slopes of the opposite sides of $ABCD$ are equal, the opposite sides are parallel, and the quadrilateral is a parallelogram. **b.** 8 **15.** Yes, the distance from $u = a + bi$ to $v = c + di$ in the complex plane is $|u - v|$. Proof: $u - v = (a - c) + (b - d)i$, and $|u - v| = \sqrt{(a - c)^2 + (b - d)^2}$, which is the distance between the points (a, b) and (c, d). **17. See below. 19. See below.**
21. $x^2 + (y - 1)^2 = 1$ **23.** $(11\cos\theta - 6\sin\theta, 11\sin\theta + 6\cos\theta)$ **25. a.** $-1 - 5i$ **b.** $-5i$ **c.** -1 **27.** about 36 miles

17.

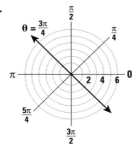

19.

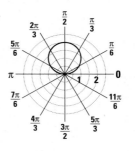

Lesson 13-7 (pp. 839–845)

17. $\frac{z_1}{z_2} = \frac{r_1(\cos\theta_1 + i\sin\theta_1)}{r_2(\cos\theta_2 + i\sin\theta_2)} = \frac{r_1(\cos\theta_1 + i\sin\theta_1)(\cos\theta_2 - i\sin\theta_2)}{r_2(\cos\theta_2 + i\sin\theta_2)(\cos\theta_2 - i\sin\theta_2)}$

$= \frac{r_1}{r_2} \cdot \frac{(\cos\theta_1 + i\sin\theta_1)(\cos(-\theta_2) + i\sin(-\theta_2))}{(\cos^2\theta_2 + \sin^2\theta_2)}$

$= \frac{r_1}{r_2} \cdot \frac{(\cos\theta_1\cos(-\theta_2) - \sin\theta_1\sin(-\theta_2) + i\cos\theta_1\sin(-\theta_2) + i\sin\theta_1\cos(-\theta_2))}{1}$

$= \frac{r_1}{r_2}(\cos(\theta_1 - \theta_2) + i\sin(\theta_1 - \theta_2))$

19. a. $z^2 = 4(\cos 30° + i\sin 30°)$, $z^3 = 8(\cos 45° + i\sin 45°)$, $z^4 = 16(\cos 60° + i\sin 60°)$, $z^5 = 32(\cos 75° + i\sin 75°)$ **b.** $z^n = 2^n(\cos(n \cdot 15°) + i\sin(n \cdot 15°))$. $z^{10} = 2^{10}(\cos 150° + i\sin 150°)$

21. a. See below. b. See below. 23. a. $\begin{bmatrix} 0 & 4 & 5 \\ 3 & -3 & 0 \end{bmatrix}$

b. $R_{90} = \begin{bmatrix} 0 & -1 \\ 1 & 0 \end{bmatrix}$ and $S_2 = \begin{bmatrix} 2 & 0 \\ 0 & 2 \end{bmatrix}$ So, $(S_2 \circ R_{90})(\triangle ABC) = \begin{bmatrix} 2 & 0 \\ 0 & 2 \end{bmatrix} \cdot \begin{bmatrix} 0 & -1 \\ 1 & 0 \end{bmatrix}\begin{bmatrix} 0 & 4 & 5 \\ 3 & -3 & 0 \end{bmatrix} = \begin{bmatrix} -6 & 6 & 0 \\ 0 & 8 & 10 \end{bmatrix}$, which is the matrix for $\triangle A'B'C'$. **25.** $a^5 - 5a^4b + 10a^3b^2 - 10a^2b^3 + 5ab^4 - b^5$ **27.** about 5019.8 mm^3

21. a.

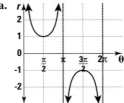

b.

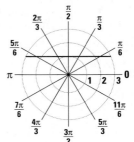

Lesson 13-8 (pp. 846–851)

9. $(2(\cos 150° + i \sin 150°))^6 = -64 + 0i$ **11.** $[2, 15°]$, $[2, 75°]$, $[2, 135°]$, $[2, 195°]$, $[2, 255°]$, $[2, 315°]$ **See below.**
13. See below. 15. $7 \cos 10° + 7 \sin 10° \, i \approx 6.89 + 1.22i$
17. a. See below.

b. $r = e^{\theta/3} \Leftrightarrow \ln r = \ln e^{\theta/3} = \frac{\theta}{3} \ln e = \frac{\theta}{3}(1) = \frac{1}{3}\theta$, so $k = \frac{1}{3}$

19. $-13x^2 + 34\sqrt{3}\, xy - 47y^2 + (128 - 12\sqrt{3})x +$

$(-12 - 128\sqrt{3})y - 284 = 0$ **21.** $-\frac{1}{2}$

11.

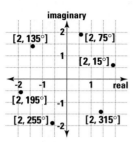

13.

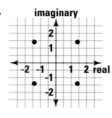

17. a.

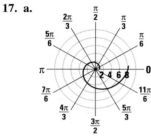

Lesson 13-9 (pp. 852–857)

9. $-\frac{\sqrt{2}}{2} - \frac{\sqrt{2}}{2} i$ **11.** $\sqrt[3]{10}\,(\cos 4° + i \sin 4°)$,

$\sqrt[3]{10}\,(\cos 124° + i \sin 124°)$, $\sqrt[3]{10}\,(\cos 244° + i \sin 244°)$

See below. 13. a. $z_1 \approx \sqrt{11}\,(\cos 25.2° + i \sin 25.2°)$,

$z_2 \approx \sqrt{11}\,(\cos 205.2° + i \sin 205.2°)$
b. $z_1 z_2 \approx 11(\cos 230.4° + i \sin 230.4°)$,

$\frac{z_1}{z_2} = 1(\cos(-180°) + i \sin(-180°)) = -1$

15. ≈ 452 **17. a.** on the polar axis **b.** $y = 0$ **19. a. See below.**

b. Let $\theta = 0$. Then $\sec \theta = \frac{1}{\cos 0} = 1$ and $\sec(\pi - \theta) =$

$\frac{1}{\cos(\pi - \theta)} = \frac{1}{\cos \pi} = -1$. So $\sec \theta = \sec(\pi - \theta)$ is not an identity.

11.

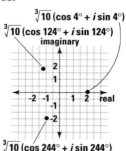

19. a.

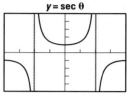

$y = \sec \theta$

$-\pi \le x \le \pi, \quad x\text{-scale} = \frac{\pi}{4}$
$-5 \le y \le 5, \quad y\text{-scale} = 1$

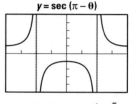

$y = \sec(\pi - \theta)$

$-\pi \le x \le \pi, \quad x\text{-scale} = \frac{\pi}{4}$
$-5 \le y \le 5, \quad y\text{-scale} = 1$

Chapter 13 Progress Self-Test (p. 862)

1. $\cot\left(-\frac{\pi}{6}\right) = \frac{\cos\left(-\frac{\pi}{6}\right)}{\sin\left(-\frac{\pi}{6}\right)} = \frac{\frac{\sqrt{3}}{2}}{-\frac{1}{2}} = -\sqrt{3}$ **2.** $\sec 405° = \frac{1}{\cos 405°} =$

$\frac{1}{\cos(405° - 360°)} = \frac{1}{\cos 45°} = \frac{1}{\frac{\sqrt{2}}{2}} = \frac{2}{\sqrt{2}} = \sqrt{2}$ **3. a. See p. 909.**

b. 2π **c.** Sample: $x = -\frac{\pi}{2}, x = \frac{\pi}{2}$ **4.** $x \ne \frac{\pi}{2} + n\pi$ for all integers n, as signaled by each vertical asymptote. **5.** False, a graph can only show the functions on a finite domain; a proof must show that the equation is an identity for all values for which the functions are defined. **6. a.** Singularities occur where

$\tan x$ is not defined, that is, at $\frac{\pi}{2} + n\pi$, for all integers n.

b. $2\cos^2 x \tan x = 2\cos^2 x \cdot \frac{\sin x}{\cos x} = 2 \cos x \sin x = \sin 2x$

7. See p. 909. 8. See p. 909. 9. See p. 909.
10. $r^2 = x^2 + y^2 = 5^2 + (-5\sqrt{3})^2 = 25 + 75 = 100 \Rightarrow r = \pm 10$.

$\tan \theta = \frac{y}{x} = \frac{-5\sqrt{3}}{5} = -\sqrt{3} \Rightarrow \theta = -\frac{\pi}{3} \pm n\pi$. The choice of values of θ and r depend on matching the angle to the quadrant. If we choose $r = 10$ then to match $(5, -5\sqrt{3})$ in the fourth quadrant $\theta = -\frac{\pi}{3}$ or $\theta = \frac{5\pi}{3}$. If we choose $r = -10$, possible choices for θ

are $\frac{2\pi}{3}$ or $-\frac{4\pi}{3}$. Thus, $\left[10, -\frac{\pi}{3}\right], \left[10, \frac{5\pi}{3}\right], \left[-10, \frac{2\pi}{3}\right]$ and $\left[-10, -\frac{4\pi}{3}\right]$

are polar coordinate representations of $(5, -5\sqrt{3})$.
11. By DeMoivre's Theorem, $(3(\cos 20° + i \sin 20°))^4 =$
$3^4(\cos 4 \cdot 20° + i \sin 4 \cdot 20°) = 81(\cos 80° + i \sin 80°) =$
$81 \cos 80° + 81\, i \sin 80° \approx 14.07 + 79.77i$.

12. a. $r^2 = a^2 + b^2 = \left(-\frac{1}{2}\right)^2 + \left(\frac{\sqrt{3}}{2}\right)^2 = \frac{1}{4} + \frac{3}{4} = 1 \Rightarrow r = \pm 1$.

$\tan \theta = \frac{b}{a} = \frac{\frac{\sqrt{3}}{2}}{-\frac{1}{2}} = -\sqrt{3}$. Since $\left(-\frac{1}{2}, \frac{\sqrt{3}}{2}\right)$ is in the second quadrant,

we can choose $r = 1$ and $\theta = 120°$ giving the polar form $[1, 120°]$.
b. $-\frac{1}{2} + \frac{\sqrt{3}}{2} i = r \cos \theta + i \sin \theta = \cos 120° + i \sin 120°$.
13. By the Roots of a Complex Number Theorem, the fourth roots

of $81(\cos 260° + i \sin 260°) = \sqrt[4]{81}\left(\cos\left(\frac{260°}{4} + k \cdot \frac{360°}{4}\right)\right) =$

$3(\cos(65° + 90°k) + i \sin(65° + 90°k))$ where $k = 0, 1, 2, 3$. Thus, the fourth roots are $3(\cos 65° + i \sin 65°)$, $3(\cos 155° + i \sin 155°)$, $3(\cos 245° + i \sin 245°)$, and $3(\cos 335° + i \sin 335°)$.
14. a. Sample: When $\theta = \frac{\pi}{6}$, $r = \sin\left(3 \cdot \frac{\pi}{6}\right) = \sin\left(\frac{\pi}{2}\right) = 1$.

When $\theta = -\frac{\pi}{6}$, $r = \sin\left(3 \cdot -\frac{\pi}{6}\right) = \sin\left(-\frac{\pi}{2}\right) = -1$. So two points

908

on the graph of $r = \sin 3\theta$ are $\left[1, \frac{\pi}{6}\right]$ and $\left[-1, -\frac{\pi}{6}\right]$. **b.** Sample:
See right. 15. a. Converting $z = -3i$ to trigonometric form gives
$z_1 = 3\left(\cos\left(-\frac{\pi}{2}\right) + i \sin\left(-\frac{\pi}{2}\right)\right)$. By the Product of Complex

Numbers Theorem, $z_1 z_2 = 3 \cdot 5\left(\cos\left(-\frac{\pi}{2} + \frac{\pi}{12}\right) + i \sin\left(-\frac{\pi}{2} + \frac{\pi}{12}\right)\right)$
$= 15\left(\cos\left(-\frac{5\pi}{12}\right) + i \sin\left(-\frac{5\pi}{12}\right)\right)$. **b.** The absolute value of z_1 is
multiplied by 5, which is a scale change of magnitude 5.
$\frac{\pi}{12}$ is added to the argument, which is a rotation around the origin
by an angle $\frac{\pi}{12}$. **16. a.** By the Division of Complex Numbers
Theorem, $\frac{z_1}{z_2} = \left[\frac{6}{2}, \pi - \pi\right] = [3, 0]$. **b.** Sample: The absolute
value of z_1 is divided by 2, which is a size change of magnitude $\frac{1}{2}$.
Then π is subtracted from the argument, which is a rotation
about the origin by an angle of $-\pi$. **17.** For all θ except
where $\tan \theta$ is not defined, that is $\theta \neq \frac{\pi}{2} + n\pi$ for all integers n,

$(1 - \sin^2\theta)(1 + \tan^2\theta) = (\cos^2\theta)\left(1 + \frac{\sin^2\theta}{\cos^2\theta}\right) = \cos^2\theta + \sin^2\theta = 1$.
18. See right.

3. a.

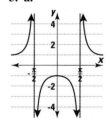

7.

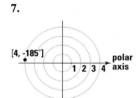

8.

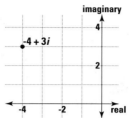

9.

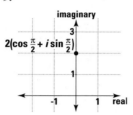

14. b.

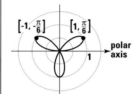

18.

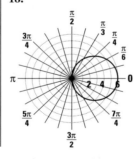

The chart below keys the **Progress Self-Test** questions to the objectives in the **Chapter Review** on pages 863–865 or to the **Vocabulary** (Voc.) on page 861. This will enable you to locate those **Chapter Review** questions that correspond to questions students missed on the **Progress Self-Test**. The lesson where the material is covered is also indicated on the chart.

Question	1	2	3	4	5	6	7	8	9	10
Objective	A	A	E	G	H	F, G	J	L	L	I
Lesson	13-1	13-1	13-1	13-3	13-2	13-2, 13-3	13-4	13-6	13-7	13-4

Question	11	12	13	14	15	16	17	18
Objective	C	D	D	K	B	B	F	K
Lesson	13-6, 13-7	13-8	13-8	13-5	13-7	13-7	13-2	13-5

1. 1 **3.** $\frac{2\sqrt{3}}{3}$ **5.** -1.89 **7.** $15(\cos 189° + i \sin 189°)$

9. $2\left(\cos \frac{3\pi}{10} + i \sin \frac{3\pi}{10}\right)$ **11. a.** $2\sqrt{61} \approx 15.62$ **b.** Sample: 129.8°

13. $[2, 150°]$ **15.** $\left[\frac{1}{8}, 36°\right]$ **17.** $4 \cos\left(\frac{2\pi}{5}\right) + 4i \sin\left(\frac{2\pi}{5}\right) \approx 1.24 +$

$3.80i$ **19.** $z^5 = 32(\cos 225° + i \sin 225°) = -16\sqrt{2} - 16\sqrt{2}i$

21. $4(\cos 3° + i \sin 3°)$, $4(\cos 93° + i \sin 93°)$,

$4(\cos 183° + i \sin 183°)$, $4(\cos 273° + i \sin 273°)$ **23.** 2π **25.** False

27. $(1 - \cos^2 x)(1 + \cot^2 x) = (\sin^2 x)\left(1 + \frac{\cos^2 x}{\sin^2 x}\right) = \sin^2 x + \cos^2 x = 1$

for all $x \neq n\pi$ for all integers n.

29. $\sin^2 x + \cos^2 x = 1 \Rightarrow 1 - \cos^2 x = \sin^2 x \Rightarrow \frac{1}{\sin^2 x} - \frac{\cos^2 x}{\sin^2 x} =$

$\frac{\sin^2 x}{\sin^2 x} \Rightarrow \csc^2 x - \cot^2 x = 1$ **31.** Because of division by $\sin x$,

the values for which $\sin x = 0$ must be excluded. These are

$x = n\pi$ for all integers n. **33. a. i.** $x = 3$ **ii.** none **b. i.** False,

it is not true for $x = 3$. **ii.** True, the denominator is not zero for

any real value of x. **35.** False **37. a. See below. b.** Yes, the

graphs seem to coincide. **39.** $(0, -4)$ **41.** Sample: $\approx [5.39, 21.8°]$

43. Samples: $\left[8, \frac{5\pi}{6}\right], \left[8, -\frac{7\pi}{6}\right], \left[-8, -\frac{\pi}{6}\right]$ **45. See below. 47.** b

49. For $\theta = \frac{2\pi}{3}$, $r = 2 \cos 6\theta = 2 \cos\left(6 \cdot \frac{2\pi}{3}\right) = 2 \cos(4\pi) = 2$

51. See right. 53. a. See right. b. For $\theta \neq \frac{\pi}{2} + n\pi$, where

n is an integer, $r = 4 \sec \theta = \frac{4}{\cos \theta} \Leftrightarrow r \cos \theta = 4 \Leftrightarrow x = 4$,

which is a line. **55. See right. 57. a. See right.**

b. Let $C = A + B = 4 - 2i$. The slope of $\overline{OA} = \frac{1 - 0}{3 - 0} = \frac{1}{3}$;

the slope of $\overline{BC} = \frac{-2 - -3}{4 - 1} = \frac{1}{3}$; the slope of $\overline{OB} = \frac{-3 - 0}{1 - 0} = -3$;

and the slope of $\overline{AC} = \frac{-2 - 1}{4 - 3} = -3$. Because the slopes of both

pairs of opposite sides of $OACB$ are equal, the opposite sides are

parallel and $OACB$ is a parallelogram.

37. a.

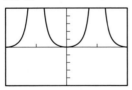

$-\pi \leq x \leq \pi$, x-scale $= \frac{\pi}{2}$

$-5 \leq y \leq 5$, y-scale $= 1$

45.

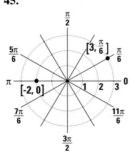

51.

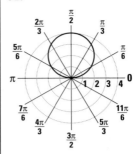

53. a.

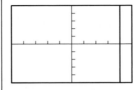

$-5 \leq x \leq 5$, x-scale $= 1$

$-5 \leq y \leq 5$, y-scale $= 1$

55.

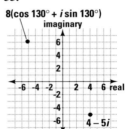

57. a.

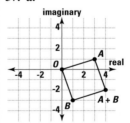

absolute value of a complex number, $|z|$ The distance of the graph of a complex number from the origin or pole. Also called *modulus*. (835)

acceleration due to gravity   The acceleration of a free-falling object toward another object caused by gravitational forces; on the surface of Earth equal to approximately 32 feet or 9.8 meters per second per second. (122)

Addition Counting Principle (General Form)   For any finite sets A and B, $N(A \cup B) = N(A) + N(B) - N(A \cap B)$. (435)

Addition Counting Principle (Mutually Exclusive Form)   If two finite sets A and B are mutually exclusive, then $N(A \cup B) = N(A) + N(B)$. (433)

Addition Formulas for the Cosine and Sine   For all real numbers α and β, $\cos(\alpha + \beta) = \cos \alpha \cos \beta - \sin \alpha \sin \beta$, and $\sin(\alpha + \beta) = \sin \alpha \cos \beta + \cos \alpha \sin \beta$. (722)

Alternate Formula for $_nP_r$ Theorem   The number of permutations of n objects taken r at a time is $_nP_r = \frac{n!}{(n-r)!}$. (446)

alternating harmonic sequence   The sequence $-1, \frac{1}{2}, -\frac{1}{3}, \frac{1}{4}, \ldots$ in which $c_n = \frac{(-1)^n}{n}$. (498)

alternative hypothesis, H_1   A hypothesis usually contrasted with the null hypothesis in an experiment. (643)

ambiguous case   The situation in which two noncongruent triangles each satisfy a given SSA condition. (329)

amplitude   One-half the difference between the maximum and minimum values of a sine wave. (272)

angle   The union of two rays (its **sides**) with the same endpoint (its **vertex**). (232)

angle of depression   An angle measured downward from a horizontal line. (311)

angle of elevation   An angle measured upward from a horizontal line. (312)

angle of incidence   The angle formed by the path of an object hitting a surface, and the ray perpendicular to the surface at the point of contact. (792)

angle of reflection   The angle of the path of a ray formed by the path of an object reflecting off a surface, and the ray perpendicular to the surface at the point of contact. (792)

Arccos function   See *inverse cosine function*.

Archimedean spiral   The graph of $r = k\theta$, for $\theta > 0$, in the polar plane. (832)

Arcsin function   See *inverse sine function*.

Arctan function   See *inverse tangent function*.

area under a curve   The area between the curve and the x-axis. (651)

Argand diagram   A graphical representation of the complex number $a + bi$ as (a, b) in the coordinate plane. (833)

argument of a complex number   For the complex number $[r, \theta]$, θ. (835)

argument of a function   The variable x of a function $f(x)$. (85)

arithmetic sequence   A sequence in which the difference between consecutive terms is constant. (490)

arithmetic series   An indicated sum of the terms of an arithmetic sequence. (503)

ascending order   Rank-ordered from lowest to highest value. (29)

astronomical unit (a.u.)   A unit of distance equal to the radius of Earth's orbit, with a value of approximately 93 million miles or 150 million kilometers. (758)

asymptote   A line that the graph of a function $y = f(x)$ approaches as the variable x approaches a fixed value or increases or decreases without bound. (108, 163)

asymptotes of a hyperbola   Lines to which the hyperbola's branches approach as they are farther and farther from its center. (771)

at random   See *randomly*.

automatic grapher   A calculator or computer software that can draw and display the graph of a relation. (160)

average   See *mean*.

average rate of change (between two points)   The slope of the line segment joining the points. (47)

axes of a hyperbola   The lines of symmetry for a hyperbola. (772)

axis of a cone   The fixed line in the procedure for generating a cone. (754)

axis of symmetry   In a plane, a reflecting line ℓ over which a figure can be mapped onto itself; in three-dimensional space, a line around which a figure can be rotated onto itself. Also called *line of symmetry*. (179)

back-to-back stemplot   A stemplot in which the stem is written in the center of the graph, with one set of leaves to the right of the stem and another set of leaves to the left. (14)

bar graph   A two-dimensional display of data in which one axis labels categories or variables and the other is a numerical scale typically with counts or percentages. (9)

base (of an exponential function)   The number b in the exponential function $f(x) = ab^x$. (106)

base (of a logarithmic function)   The number b in the logarithmic function $f(x) = \log_b x$. (383)

Basic Properties of Probability Theorem   Let S be the sample space associated with an experiment, and let $P(E)$ be the probability of E. Then $0 \leq P(E) \leq 1$; if $E = S$, then $P(E) = 1$; and if $E = \varnothing$, then $P(E) = 0$. (430)

bearing   An angle measured clockwise from due north. (315)

bell-shaped curve   See *normal curve*.

binomial   A polynomial with two terms. (558)

binomial coefficients   The coefficients in the series expansion of $(x + y)^n$; the combinations $_nC_k$. (536)

911

binomial distribution function   The function $B(k) = {}_nC_k \, p^k(1 - p)^{n-k}$, giving the probability of getting exactly k successes in n binomial trials, each of which has a probability p of success. (629)

binomial experiment   An experiment with a fixed number of independent trials, each with only two possible outcomes, often called *success* and *failure*, and each with the same probability of success. (540)

binomial probability distribution   The probability distribution generated from the probability of x successes in a binomial experiment. (542)

Binomial Probability Theorem   Suppose that in a binomial experiment with n trials the probability of success is p in each trial, and the probability of failure is q, where $q = 1 - p$. Then $P(\text{exactly } k \text{ successes}) = {}_nC_k \cdot p^k q^{n-k}$. (541)

Binomial Theorem   For any nonnegative integer n, $(x + y)^n = {}_nC_0 x^n + {}_nC_1 x^{n-1}y + {}_nC_2 x^{n-2}y^2 + \ldots + {}_nC_k x^{n-k}y^k + \ldots + {}_nC_n y^n = \sum_{k=0}^{n} {}_nC_k x^{n-k}y^k$. (536)

birthday problem   The problem of determining the probability that n people have n different birthdays. (478)

bivariate data   Data involving two variables. (81)

box plot   A visual representation of the five-number summary of a data set in which a box represents the part of the data from the first to the third quartile, with another line segment crossing the box at the set's median, and two segments protruding from the box (called **whiskers**) to represent the rest of the data. (31)

box-and-whiskers plot   See *box plot*.

cardioid   The graph of $r = a(\cos \theta - 1)$ or $r = a(\sin \theta - 1)$ in the polar plane. (832)

ceiling function   See *rounding-up function*.

census   A survey of an entire population; in the U.S., a survey, conducted every ten years, of the entire population of the United States. (6)

912

center of a hyperbola   The intersection of the hyperbola's axes, the midpoint of the segment joining its foci. (772)

center of an ellipse   The intersection of the ellipse's axes, the midpoint of the segment joining its foci. (762)

center of gravity of a data set   The point whose coordinates are the means of the corresponding coordinates of the points in the data set. (99)

center of symmetry for a figure   The center of a rotation under which the figure is mapped onto itself. (179)

central angle of a circle   An angle whose vertex is the center of the circle. (239)

Central Limit Theorem   Suppose random samples of size n are selected from a population with mean μ and standard deviation σ. Then, as n increases the following occur: The mean $\mu_{\bar{x}}$ of the distribution of sample means approaches μ; the standard deviation $\sigma_{\bar{x}}$ of the distribution of sample means approaches $\frac{\sigma}{\sqrt{n}}$; and the distribution of sample means approaches a normal curve with mean μ and standard deviation $\frac{\sigma}{\sqrt{n}}$. (673)

Change of Base Theorem   For all values of a, b, and c for which the logarithms exist, $\log_b a = \frac{\log_c a}{\log_c b}$. (406)

circle graph   A display of numerical data in which the total is represented by the entire circle and sectors of a circle represent parts of the total in proportion to their contribution to the total. Also called *pie chart*. (9)

circular functions   The trigonometric functions, when defined in terms of the unit circle. (267)

circular motion   Movement of a point around a circle. (288)

Circular Arc Length Formula   If s is the length of the arc of a central angle of θ radians in a circle of radius r, then $s = r\theta$. (240)

Circular Sector Area Formula   If A is the area of the sector formed by a central angle of θ radians in a circle of radius r, then $A = \frac{1}{2}\theta r^2$. (240)

cliometrics   The discipline of applying mathematics to history. (64)

cluster   In a frequency distribution of a set of data, a place where a relatively large number of data are near each other. (14)

coefficient   The numbers a_n, $a_{n-1}, \ldots a_0$ of the polynomial $a_n x^n + a_{n-1}x^{n-1} + \ldots a_1 x + a_0$; more generally, a constant factor of a variable term. (557)

column matrix   A matrix consisting of a single column. (699)

combination   A collection of objects in which the order of objects does not matter. (524)

combination of n things taken r at a time, ${}_nC_r$, $\binom{n}{r}$ A subset of r objects from a set of n objects. (525)

common logarithm   A logarithm with a base equal to 10. (384)

complementary events   Events that are mutually exclusive and whose union is the entire sample space. (437)

Complements Theorem   For all θ in radians, $\sin\left(\frac{\pi}{2} - \theta\right) = \cos \theta$ and $\cos\left(\frac{\pi}{2} - \theta\right) = \sin \theta$. (254)

complex conjugates   A pair of complex numbers in the form $a + bi$ and $a - bi$. (592)

complex number   The number of the form $a + bi$, where a and b are real numbers and $i = \sqrt{-1}$. (591)

complex plane   A coordinate plane for representing complex numbers. Also called *Argand diagram*. (833)

composite   The function $g \circ f$ defined by $(g \circ f)(x) = g(f(x))$, whose domain is the set of values of x in the domain of f for which $f(x)$ is in the domain of g. (202)

composition of functions   The binary operation that maps two functions g and f onto their composite $g \circ f$. (202)

compounded continuously   The limit of compounding interest as the number of compoundings grows larger and larger in a given time period. (392)

concave down   Said of an interval that is curving downwards, that is, its slope is continuously decreasing. (648)

concave up Said of an interval that is curving upwards, that is, its slope is continuously increasing. (648)

confidence interval An interval within which a certain specified percentage (usually 90%, 95%, or 99%) of outcomes from an experiment is expected to occur. (681)

conic section The intersection of a two-napped cone with a plane not containing the vertex of the cone: an ellipse, a parabola, or a hyperbola. (754)

Conjugate Zeros Theorem Let $p(x) = a_n x^n + a_{n-1} x^{n-1} + \ldots + a_1 x + a_0$ where $a_n, a_{n-1}, \ldots, a_1, a_0$ are all real numbers, and $a_n \neq 0$. If $z = a + bi$ is a zero of $p(x)$, then the complex conjugate of z, $a - bi$, is also a zero of $p(x)$. (599)

constant A variable whose values do not change in the course of a problem. (Previous course)

constant function Any function with an equation $f(x) = k$, where k is a fixed value. (Previous course)

continuous function A function that has no points of discontinuity in its domain. Informally, a function whose graph can be drawn without lifting the pencil off the paper. (129)

Continuous Change Model If a quantity p grows or decays continuously at an annual rate r, the amount $A(t)$ after t years is given by $A(t) = Pe^{rt}$. (392)

convergent sequence (to L) A sequence which has a finite limiting value L. If this value exists, the sequence is said to be *convergent to L*. (497)

convergent series A series in which the limit of the sequence of partial sums exists. (516)

corollary A theorem that can be quickly deduced from another theorem. (814)

correlation coefficient, r A measure of the strength of the linear relation between two variables. (91)

cosecant (csc) of a real number x For a real number x, $\csc x = \frac{1}{\sin x}$, when $\sin x \neq 0$. (806)

cosine (cos) of an acute angle θ in a right triangle $\frac{\text{leg adjacent to } \theta}{\text{hypotenuse}}$ (310)

cosine (cos) of a real number x The first coordinate of the image of the point (1, 0) under a rotation of magnitude x about the origin. (245)

cosine function The function that maps x onto $\cos x$ for all x in its domain. (266)

cotangent (cot) of a real number x For a real number x, $\cot x = \frac{\cos x}{\sin x}$, when $\sin x \neq 0$. (806)

cross section of a three-dimensional figure The intersection of a plane with the figure. Also called *section*. (754)

cube root For a number k, a number x that satisfies $x^3 = k$. (370)

cumulative binomial probability table A table that gives, for fixed n (number of trials) and p (probability of success), the probabilities for k or fewer successes. (633)

cumulative percentage curve See *percentile curve*.

cycle One period of a periodic function, such as a sine wave. (265)

data The plural of *datum*, the Latin word for fact; a piece of information. (6)

decreasing A function is decreasing on an interval if the segment connecting any two points on the graph of the function over that interval has negative slope. (47, 566)

deductive reasoning Reasoning adhering to strict principles of logic. (64)

default window The viewing window which is present in an automatic grapher until changed by the user. (160)

degenerate conic section The intersection of a cone and a plane containing the vertex of the cone; the graph of a quadratic relation that is not a conic section. (786)

degree A unit for measuring angles or rotations. (232)

degree of a polynomial In a polynomial with a single variable, the number n in the polynomial $a_n x^n + a_{n-1} x^{n-1} + \ldots + a_1 x + a_0$; in a polynomial in more than one variable, the largest sum of the exponents of the variables in any term. (557, 559)

DeMoivre's Theorem If $z = r(\cos \theta + i \sin \theta)$ and n is an integer, then $z^n = r^n(\cos n\theta + i \sin n\theta)$. (847)

dependent events Events A and B in which $P(A \cap B) \neq P(A) \cdot P(B)$. (452)

dependent variable The second variable in a relation. (82)

determinant, det A number associated with a matrix used to determine whether the matrix has an inverse. For the 2×2 matrix $\begin{bmatrix} a & b \\ c & d \end{bmatrix}$, $ad - bc$. (720)

deviation The difference of a value in a set from the set's mean. Also, see *error*. (54, 97)

dimensions of a matrix The numbers of rows and columns of the matrix. (698)

discontinuous function A function that has one or more points of discontinuity in its domain. (129)

discriminant of a quadratic equation For the equation $ax^2 + bx + c = 0$, the number $b^2 - 4ac$. (593)

discriminant of a quadratic relation For the relation $Ax^2 + Bxy + Cy^2 + Dx + Ey + F = 0$, the value of $B^2 - 4AC$. If the discriminant is less than zero, then the figure is an ellipse, a single point, or the null set. If greater, the figure is a hyperbola or a pair of lines. If it is equal to zero, the figure is a parabola, two parallel lines, a line, or the null set. (789)

disjoint The sets with no elements in common. Also called *mutually exclusive*. (433)

disk The union of a circle and its interior. (240)

divergent sequence A sequence with no finite limit. (497)

divergent series A series in which the sequence of partial sums does not have a finite limit. (516)

dividend The number or expression a when a is divided by b. (577)

Division of Complex Numbers Theorem If $z_1 = r_1(\cos \theta_1 + i \sin \theta_1)$ and $z_2 = r_2(\cos \theta_2 + i \sin \theta_2)$, then $\frac{z_1}{z_2} = \frac{r_1}{r_2}(\cos (\theta_1 - \theta_2) + i \sin (\theta_1 - \theta_2))$. (842)

913

GLOSSARY

divisor   The number or expression b when a is divided by b. (577)

domain   The set of first elements of ordered pairs of a function; more generally, the set of replacement values for a variable. (82)

dotplot   A graph of a frequency distribution in which the number of dots over each individual value is the frequency of that value. Also called *dot frequency diagram*. (15)

Double Angle Formulas   For all real numbers θ, $\sin 2\theta = 2\sin\theta\cos\theta$ and $\cos 2\theta = \cos^2\theta - \sin^2\theta = 2\cos^2\theta - 1 = 1 - 2\sin^2\theta$. (726)

doubling time   The time it takes a quantity to grow to double its original amount, usually applied to exponential growth situations. (114)

e $\lim\limits_{n\to\infty}\left(1 + \dfrac{1}{n}\right)^n \approx 2.718$; the base of natural logarithms. (390)

eccentricity of a conic   The ratio $\dfrac{c}{a}$ for a conic section, where c is the distance from the center of the conic to a focus, and a is one-half the focal constant. (798)

element   An object in an array. A member of a set. (698)

ellipse   The set of all points P such that $PF_1 + PF_2 = k$ and $k > F_1F_2$, where F_1 and F_2 are points (the **foci,** singular **focus**) and k is the **focal constant.** (756)

ellipsoid   The three-dimensional surface formed by rotating an ellipse about one of its axes. (793)

elliptic paraboloid   The quadric surface formed by the equation $z = \dfrac{x^2}{a^2} + \dfrac{y^2}{b^2}$. (798)

end behavior of a sequence   The description of what happens to the values t_n of a sequence as n gets very large. (497)

error (in a prediction)   The difference between the observed and the expected value of a variable. Also called *deviation*. (97)

even function   A function f such that for all x in its domain, $f(-x) = f(x)$. (181)

event   Any subset of the sample space of an experiment. (427)

expected value   A value predicted by a mathematical model. Also called *predicted value*. (97)

expected value of a probability distribution   See *mean of a probability distribution*.

experiment   A situation that has several possible outcomes. (426)

explicit formula for a sequence   A formula which gives the nth term of the sequence in terms of n. (488)

exponent   The number n in the expression r^n. (Previous course)

exponential decay   A situation that can be modeled by $f(x) = ab^x$ with base $0 < b < 1$. (108)

exponential decay curve   The graph of an exponential decay function. (108)

exponential decay function   An exponential function $f(x) = ab^x$ with $a > 0$ and $0 < b < 1$. (108).

exponential equation   An equation to be solved for a variable in an exponent. (403)

exponential function   The exponential function with base b is a function with a formula of the form $f(x) = ab^x$, where $a \ne 0$, $b > 0$, and $b \ne 1$. (106)

exponential growth curve   The graph of an exponential growth function. (106)

exponential growth function   An exponential function with a base greater than one and a leading coefficient greater than zero. (106)

exponential model   A mathematical model of a situation in the form of an exponential function. (112)

exponential regression   The method of fitting an exponential function to a set of data. (114)

extrapolation   Estimating a value beyond known values of data. (100)

extrema of functions   The extreme values for a function, classified as either *maxima* or *minima*. (564)

f^{-1}   See *inverse function*.

Factor Theorem   For any polynomial $f(x)$, a number c is a solution to $f(x) = 0$ if and only if $(x - c)$ is a factor of $f(x)$. (585)

Factor-Solution-Intercept Equivalence Theorem   For any polynomial f, the following are logically equivalent statements: $(x - c)$ is a factor of f; $f(c) = 0$; c is an x-intercept of the graph of $y = f(x)$; c is a zero of f; the remainder when $f(x)$ is divided by $(x - c)$ is 0. (585)

failure (binomial)   See *binomial experiment*.

fair experiment   An experiment in which all outcomes of the sample space are equally likely. Also called *unbiased experiment*. (428)

Federalist, The   Essays written between 1787 and 1788 by James Madison, Alexander Hamilton, and John Jay under the collective pen name "Publius" to persuade the citizens of the state of New York to ratify the U.S. Constitution. (62)

finite series   A series where the number of terms added is finite. (503)

first (lower) quartile   In a data set, the median of the numbers less than the set's median. (30)

five-number summary   The three quartiles, the maximum, and the minimum of a data set. (30)

floor function   See *greatest integer function*.

focal constant of a hyperbola   See *hyperbola*.

focal constant of an ellipse   See *ellipse*.

focus (foci) of a hyperbola   See *hyperbola*.

focus (foci) of an ellipse   See *ellipse*.

Formula for $_nC_r$ Theorem   For all whole numbers n and r, with $r \le n$, $_nC_r = \dfrac{n!}{(n-r)!r!}$. (525)

Formula for $_nP_r$ Theorem   The number of permutations of n objects taken r at a time is $_nP_r = n(n-1)(n-2)\cdot\ldots\cdot(n-r+1)$. (446)

frequency   The number of times an item of an event occurs. The number of cycles in a period of a periodic function. (15, 275)

frequency distribution   A function that maps events onto their frequencies. (15)

914

frequency histogram   A histogram that displays the number of values that fall into each interval of the histogram. (39)

function   A set of ordered pairs (x, y) in which each value of x is paired with exactly one value of y. A correspondence between two sets A and B in which each element of A corresponds to exactly one element of B. (82, 83)

function notation   The notation $f(x)$ for the value of a function f when the value of the independent variable is x. (85)

Fundamental Theorem of Algebra If $p(x)$ is any polynomial of degree $n \geq 1$ with complex coefficients, then $p(x) = 0$ has at least one complex zero. (597)

Galton board   See *quincunx*.

general form of a quadratic relation in two variables   The form $Ax^2 + Bxy + Cy^2 + Dx + Ey + F = 0$ where at least one of A, B, and C is not zero. (784)

general solution to a trigonometric equation   A solution to an equation for all real numbers for which the variable is defined. (346)

geometric sequence   A sequence in which the ratio of consecutive terms is constant. (491)

geometric series   An indicated sum of the terms of a geometric sequence. (510)

Geometric Addition Theorem   If the complex numbers $a + bi$ and $c + di$ are not collinear with the origin in the complex plane, then their sum $(a + c) + (b + d)i$ is the fourth vertex of a parallelogram with consecutive vertices $a + bi$, 0, and $c + di$. (834)

gradient (grad)   A unit for measuring angles. 100 grads = 90 degrees. (237)

Graph Rotation Theorem In a relation described by a sentence in x and y, replacing x by $x \cos \theta + y \sin \theta$ and y by $-x \sin \theta + y \cos \theta$ yields the same graph as applying the rotation of magnitude θ about the origin to the graph of the original equation. (778)

Graph Scale-Change Theorem In a relation described by a sentence in x and y, replacing x by $\frac{x}{a}$ and y by $\frac{y}{b}$ in the sentence yields the same graph as applying the scale change $(x, y) \rightarrow (ax, by)$ to the graph of the original relation. (188)

Graph-Standardization Theorem   In a relation described by a sentence in x and y, replacing x by $\frac{x - h}{a}$ and y by $\frac{y - k}{b}$ in the sentence yields the same graph as applying the scale change $(x, y) \rightarrow (ax, by)$, where $a \neq 0$ and $b \neq 0$, followed by applying the translation $(x, y) \rightarrow (x + h, y + k)$ to the graph of the original relation. (286)

Graph Translation Theorem   In a relation described by a sentence in x and y, replacing x by $x - h$ and y by $y - k$ in the sentence yields the same graph as applying the translation $(x, y) \rightarrow (x + h, y + k)$ to the graph of the original relation. (169)

great circle   A circle on a sphere that has the same center as the sphere. (353)

greatest integer function, $\lfloor \ \rfloor$ The function f such that $f(x)$ is the greatest integer less than or equal to x. Also called the *rounding-down function* or the *floor function*. (129)

Greenwich meridian   See *prime meridian*.

grouping   A technique used to factor polynomials which contain groups of terms with common factors. (608)

growth factor   In an exponential growth situation, the base of the exponential function. (112)

growth rate   The factor by which a quantity changes during a given time period. (106)

Half Angle Formulas   For all θ, $\cos \theta = \pm \sqrt{\frac{1 + \cos 2\theta}{2}}$ and $\sin \theta = \pm \sqrt{\frac{1 - \cos 2\theta}{2}}$. The sign is determined by the quadrant in which θ lies. (729)

half-life   The time it takes a quantity to decay to half its original amount, usually applied to exponential decay situations. (114)

Half-Turn Theorem   For all θ in radians, $\cos(\pi + \theta) = -\cos \theta$, $\sin(\pi + \theta) = -\sin \theta$, and $\tan(\pi + \theta) = \tan \theta$. (255)

harmonic sequence   The sequence of the reciprocals of the positive integers. (497)

histogram   A bar graph in which the range of values of a numerical variable are broken into non-overlapping intervals of equal width, and side-by-side bars display the number of values that fall into each interval. (39)

homogeneous form   The increasing of the dimension of a point or matrix in order for it to be treated. For the point (x, y) the homogenous form is $(x, y, 1)$. For the 2×2 transformation matrix $\begin{bmatrix} a & b \\ c & d \end{bmatrix}$ the homogenous form is $\begin{bmatrix} a & b & 0 \\ c & d & 0 \\ 0 & 0 & 1 \end{bmatrix}$. (739)

homogeneous population   A population in which members are very similar on some measure. (60)

horizontal scale change   A transformation that maps (x, y) to (ax, y) for all (x, y), where $a \neq 0$. (188)

horizontal scale factor   The number a in the transformation that maps (x, y) to (ax, by). (188)

hyperbola   The set of all points P such that $|PF_1 - PF_2| = k$ and $k < F_1F_2$ where F_1 and F_2 are points (the **foci,** singular **focus**) and k is the **focal constant.** (769)

hypothesis   In statistics, a statement to be tested. (642)

hypothesis testing   The process of using statistics to find if a given hypothesis fits a situation within a given significance level. (643)

identity   An equation that is true for all values of the variable(s) for which the expressions are defined. (251)

identity function, *I*   A function that maps each element in its domain onto itself, that is, $I(x) = x$ for all x. (211)

identity transformation   The transformation I with $I(P) = P$ for all points P. (731)

915

image The result of a transformation. (167, 173)

imaginary axis The vertical axis (axis of second coordinates) in a complex plane. (833)

imaginary numbers The number $i = \sqrt{-1}$ and its nonzero real-number multiples. (590)

imaginary part of a complex number The real number b in the complex number $a + bi$. (591)

impressionistic model A model where no theory exists that explains why the model fits the data. Also called *non-theory based model*. (125)

in-phase circuit An alternating current circuit in which the voltage and current flow coincide. (280)

increasing function A function is increasing on an interval if the segment connecting any two points on the graph of the function over that interval has positive slope. (47, 566)

independent events Events A and B such that $P(A \cap B) = P(A) \cdot P(B)$. (451)

independent variable The first variable in a relation. (82)

index A variable indicating the position of a number in an ordered list or sequence. (21)

inductance Property of an alternating current circuit created when the current flow lags behind the voltage. (280)

inferential reasoning Reasoning based on principles of probability. (64)

infinite series An indicated sum of the terms of an infinite sequence. (503, 516)

infinity, ∞ The limit of a sequence whose terms after a given point become larger than any fixed number one might choose; greater than any given number. (497)

inflection point A point on a graph where the graph changes concavity. (648)

initial side (of an angle) The side of an angle from which the angle is considered to have been generated, and from which the angle is measured. (232)

initial value In a function f modeling a situation, the value $f(0)$. (112)

interest rate In an investment, the percent by which the principal is multiplied to obtain the interest paid to the investor. (391)

International Date Line The meridian which is 180° W (and 180° E) of the prime meridian. (354)

interpolation Estimating a value between known values of data. (100)

interquartile range (IQR) The difference between the third quartile and the first quartile. (30)

intersection, $A \cap B$ The set of elements that are in both set A and set B. (433)

invariant Unchanged by a particular transformation. (176)

inverse cosine function, $\cos^{-1}$, Arccos The function $y = \cos^{-1} x =$ Arccos x, if and only if $x = \cos y$ and $0 \leq y \leq \pi$. (322)

inverse function, f^{-1} The function which is the inverse of the function f. (210)

inverse matrices Two matrices whose product is the identity matrix for matrix multiplication. (732)

inverse of a function The relation formed by switching the coordinates of the ordered pairs of a given function. (208)

inverse sine function, $\sin^{-1}$, Arcsin The function $y = \sin^{-1} x =$ Arcsin x if and only if $x = \sin y$ and $-\frac{\pi}{2} \leq y \leq \frac{\pi}{2}$. (335)

inverse tangent function, $\tan^{-1}$, Arctan The function $y = \tan^{-1} x =$ Arctan x if and only if $x = \tan y$ and $-\pi < y < \pi$. (340)

inverse transformation If P is a point and $T(P) = Q$, then the inverse transformation T^{-1} is such that $T^{-1}(Q) = P$. (731)

Inverse Function Theorem Two functions f and g are inverse functions if and only if $f(g(x)) = x$ for all x in the domain of g, and $g(f(x)) = x$ for all x in the domain of f. (211)

Inverse of a 2 × 2 Matrix Theorem

If $ad - bc \neq 0$, then $\begin{bmatrix} a & b \\ c & d \end{bmatrix}^{-1} = \begin{bmatrix} \frac{d}{ad-bc} & \frac{-b}{ad-bc} \\ \frac{-c}{ad-bc} & \frac{a}{ad-bc} \end{bmatrix}$. (734)

isometry A composite of translations, rotations, and reflections; a distance-preserving transformation. (780)

latitude A measure of the extent to which a point is north of south of the equator determined by the angle subtended at the center of the earth by an arc on a line of longitude. (354)

Law of Cosines In any triangle ABC, $c^2 = a^2 + b^2 - 2ab \cos C$. (316)

Law of Sines In any triangle ABC, $\frac{\sin A}{a} = \frac{\sin B}{b} = \frac{\sin C}{c}$. (328)

leading coefficient (of a polynomial) The coefficient of the term of the highest degree a polynomial. (557)

leaf The digits with lower place value in a stemplot, typically listed in a row originating from their respective stems. (13)

limit of a sequence, $\lim_{n \to \infty} s_n$ A number to which the terms of a sequence approach as their position increases (or decreases). Also called a *limiting value*. (496)

line graph The graph of a set of ordered pairs (x, y) connected by segments in order of the values of x. (46)

line of best fit The line that fits a set of data points with the smallest value for the sum of the squares of the deviations (vertical distances) from the data points to the line. Also called *regression line* or *least-squares line*. (97)

line of symmetry See *axis of symmetry*.

linear function A function with an equation of the form $y = mx + b$, where m and b are constants. (89)

linear regression The method of finding a line of best fit to a set of points. (88, 90)

linearity A relation's degree of correlation to a linear model. (93)

ln See *natural logarithm*.

logarithm (log) Let $b > 0$ and $b \neq 1$. Then y is the logarithm of x to the base b, written $y = \log_b x$, if and only if $b^y = x$. (383)

916

logarithm function (with base b)
The function which maps x onto $\log_b x$. (385)

logarithmic transformation A transformation under which a variable x is replaced by $\log_b x$. (412)

Logarithm of 1 Theorem For any base b, $\log_b 1 = 0$. (398)

Logarithm of a Power Theorem For any base b, and for any positive real number x, and any real number p, $\log_b x^p = p \log_b x$. (399)

Logarithm of a Product Theorem For any base b, and for any positive real numbers x and y, $\log_b(xy) = \log_b x + \log_b y$. (398)

Logarithm of a Quotient Theorem For any base b and for any positive real numbers x and y, $\log_b \frac{x}{y} = \log_b x - \log_b y$. (399)

logarithmic spiral The polar graph of $r = ka^\theta$, where $a > 0$. (832)

longitude The number of degrees that a meridian is E or W of the prime meridian, used as a coordinate of a location on Earth. (354)

lower quartile See *first quartile*.

major axis of an ellipse The longer of the two axes of a noncircular ellipse, the axis containing the foci. (762)

Mandelbrot set The set of complex numbers c for which the limit of the sequence defined by
$$\begin{cases} z_1 = c \\ z_n = (z_{n-1})^2 + c \text{ for } n > 1 \end{cases}$$
is not infinity. (852)

MANDELZOOM A computer program for generating graphs of the Mandelbrot set. (854)

margin of error Half the length of a confidence interval. (681)

mathematical model A mathematical description of a real situation, often involving some simplifications and assumptions about that situation. (81)

Matrices for Reflections Theorem The matrix for r_x, reflection over the x-axis, is $\begin{bmatrix} 1 & 0 \\ 0 & -1 \end{bmatrix}$. The matrix for r_y, reflection over the y-axis, is $\begin{bmatrix} -1 & 0 \\ 0 & 1 \end{bmatrix}$. The matrix for $r_{y=x}$, reflection over the line $y = x$, is $\begin{bmatrix} 0 & 1 \\ 1 & 0 \end{bmatrix}$. (705)

Matrices for Rotations Theorem The matrix for R_{90}, the rotation of 90° around the origin, is $\begin{bmatrix} 0 & -1 \\ 1 & 0 \end{bmatrix}$. The matrix for R_{180}, the rotation of 180° around the origin, is $\begin{bmatrix} -1 & 0 \\ 0 & -1 \end{bmatrix}$. The matrix for R_{270}, the rotation of 270° around the origin, is $\begin{bmatrix} 0 & 1 \\ -1 & 0 \end{bmatrix}$. (712)

matrix A rectangular arrangement of objects into m rows and n columns. (698)

Matrix Basis Theorem Suppose T is a transformation represented by a 2×2 matrix. If $T(1, 0) = (x_1, y_1)$ and $T(0, 1) = (x_2, y_2)$ then T has the matrix $\begin{bmatrix} x_1 & x_2 \\ y_1 & y_2 \end{bmatrix}$. (713)

matrix multiplication An operation on an $m \times n$ matrix A and an $n \times p$ matrix B whose result is the product matrix $A \cdot B$, an $m \times p$ matrix whose element in row i and column j is the sum of the products of elements in row i of A and corresponding elements in column j of B. (700)

matrix representing a transformation A matrix M such that whenever F, a matrix for a geometric figure, is multiplied by M, the product is a matrix for the image of F under the transformation T. (705)

maximum The largest value in a set. (14)

maximum value of a function The largest value in a function's range. (120, 564)

mean The sum of the elements of a numerical data set divided by the number of items in the data set. Also called *average*. (19, 22)

Mean of a Binomial Distribution Theorem The mean μ of a binomial distribution with n trials and probability p of success on each trial is given by $\mu = np$. (636)

mean of a probability distribution For the probability distribution $\{(x_1, P(x_1)), (x_2, P(x_2)), \ldots, (x_n, P(x_n))\}$, the number $\mu = \sum_{i=1}^{n} (x_i \cdot P(x_i))$. Also called *expected value of a probability distribution*. (459)

measure of an angle A number that represents the size and direction of rotation used to generate an angle. (232)

measure of center A statistic describing a typical value of a numerical data set. Measures of center include the *mean* and *median*, and sometimes the *mode*. Also called *measure of central tendency*. (24)

measure of central tendency See *measure of center*.

measure of spread A statistic that describes how far data are from a center of a distribution. (54)

median The middle value of a set of data placed in ascending or descending order. The median of a set with an even number of elements is the mean of the two middle values. (19, 22)

meridian A semicircle of a great circle on the surface of Earth from the north pole to the south pole. Also called *line of longitude*. (354)

method of least squares The process of finding the line of best fit. (97)

middle quartile See *second quartile*.

minimum The smallest value in a set. (14)

minimum value of a function The smallest value in a function's range. (120, 544)

minor axis of an ellipse The shorter of the two axes of a non-circular ellipse. (762)

minute (of a degree) A unit for measuring angles. 60 minutes = 1 degree. (312)

mode The item(s) with the greatest frequency in a data set. (19, 24)

modulus See *absolute value of a complex number*.

monomial A polynomial with one term. (558)

917

Monte Carlo method The method of using random numbers and related probabilities to simulate events for the purpose of solving a problem. (465)

Multiplication Counting Principle Let A and B be any finite sets. The number of ways to choose one element from A and then one element from B is $N(A) \cdot N(B)$. (440)

multiplicity of a zero For a zero r of a polynomial, the highest power of $(x - r)$ that appears as a factor of that polynomial. (597)

mutually exclusive See *disjoint*.

n factorial, n! For a positive integer n, the product of the positive integers from 1 to n. In symbols, $n! = n \cdot (n - 1) \cdot (n - 2) \cdot (n - 3) \cdot \ldots \cdot 3 \cdot 2 \cdot 1$. $0! = 1$. (442)

nappe One of the two halves of a generated cone, consisting of the points that lie on one side of the cone's vertex. (754)

natural logarithm, ln The logarithm to the base e, written $\ln x$. (394)

natural logarithm function The function that maps x to $\ln x$. (394)

$_nC_r$ See *Formula for $_nC_r$ Theorem*.

Negative Exponent Theorem For all $x \neq 0$ and n for which x^n is defined, $x^{-n} = \frac{1}{x^n}$. (378)

negative relation A relation between two variables where the larger values of the one variable are associated with smaller values of the other. (91)

non-theory-based model See *impressionistic model*.

normal curve The graph of a normal distribution. (649)

normal distribution The continuous function that the binomial distribution approaches as n, the number of trials, increases without bound. (649)

not A The complement of an event A, that is, the set of outcomes of the sample space that are not in A. (437)

nth partial sum The sum of the first n terms of a sequence. (510)

nth root, $\sqrt[n]{x} = k$ if and only if $k^n = x$ where n is an integer ≥ 2. If $x \geq 0$, $\sqrt[n]{x} = x^{\frac{1}{n}}$. (372)

nth root function A function with an equation of the form $y = x^{1/n}$, where n is an integer with $n \geq 2$. (372)

nth roots of unity The zeros of $x^n - 1$. (601)

null hypothesis, H_0 The main hypothesis used in hypothesis testing of a situation. (643)

Number of Zeros of a Polynomial Theorem A polynomial of degree $n \geq 1$ with complex coefficients has exactly n complex zeros, if multiplicities are counted. (598)

oblate spheroid See *spheroid*.

observed values Data collected from sources such as experiments or surveys. (97)

odd function A function f such that for all x in its domain, $f(-x) = -f(x)$. (181)

1.5 X IQR criterion A criterion under which those elements of a data set greater than 1.5 X IQR plus the third quartile or less than the first quartile minus 1.5 X IQR are considered to be outliers. (33)

ogive See *percentile curve*.

one-to-one function A function in which no two domain values correspond to the same range value. (213)

Opposites Theorem For all θ, $\cos(-\theta) = \cos\theta$, $\sin(-\theta) = -\sin\theta$, and $\tan(-\theta) = -\tan\theta$. (252)

oscilloscope An instrument for representing the oscillations of varying voltage or current on the fluorescent screen of a cathode-ray tube. (231)

out-of-phase circuit An alternating current circuit in which the current flow lags behind the voltage. (280)

outcome A possible result of an experiment. (426)

outlier An element of a set of numbers which is very different from most or all of the other elements. (14)

overlapping sets Two sets that are not disjoint. (433)

parabola The graph of a quadratic function. The intersection of a plane and a cone, where the plane is parallel to an edge of the cone, but does not intersect the cone's vertex. (120, 754)

paraboloid The three-dimensional surface formed by rotating a parabola about its axis. (794)

parameters of the binomial distribution The numbers n (number of trials) and p (probability of success) in the binomial distribution function $B(k) = {_nC_x} p^k (1 - p)^{n-k}$. (629)

parent function A simple form or the simplest form of a class of functions, from which other members of the class can be derived by transformations. (162, Appendix A)

partial sum See *nth partial sum*.

Pascal's Triangle The values of $_nC_r$ arranged in an array in the form of a triangle; the $(r + 1)$st term in row n of Pascal's Triangle is $_nC_r$. (529)

pentagonal numbers The sequence of numbers 1, 5, 12, 22, ..., each of which represents the number of dots in pentagonal arrays and sharing a single vertex. (589)

percentile The pth percentile of a set of numbers is the value in the set such that p percent of the numbers are less than or equal to that value. (31)

percentile curve A curve in which each ordered pair (x, y) represents the percent y of the data in the set that are less than x. Also called a *cumulative percentage curve* or *ogive*. (687)

perfect correlation A correlation coefficient of 1 or -1; a situation in which all data points lie on the same line. (91)

periodic function A function f in which there is a positive real number p such that $f(x + p) = f(x)$ for all x. The smallest positive value of p is the **period** of the function. (268)

Periodicity Theorem For all θ, and for every integer n, $\sin(\theta + 2\pi n) = \sin\theta$, $\cos(\theta + 2\pi n) = \cos\theta$, and $\tan(\theta + \pi n) = \tan\theta$. (268)

permutation Each different arrangement of a set of objects. (445)

918

permutation of *n* objects taken *r* at a time, $_nP_r$ An arrangement of *r* objects from a set of *n* objects. (446)

Permutation Theorem The are *n*! permutations of *n* different elements. (445)

petal curve See *rose curve*.

phase shift The least positive or the greatest negative horizontal translation that maps the graph of a circular function onto a given sine wave. (278)

pie chart See *circle graph*.

point matrix The matrix $\begin{bmatrix} a \\ b \end{bmatrix}$, when it represents the point (*a*, *b*). (704)

point of discontinuity A value of *x* for which a function is not continuous. (129, 163)

point-symmetric figure A figure that has 180° rotation-symmetry. (179)

polar axis A ray, usually horizontal and drawn to the right, through the pole of a polar coordinate system, from which magnitudes of rotations are measured. (820)

polar coordinate system A coordinate system in which a point is identified by a pair of numbers [*r*, θ], where |*r*| is the distance of the point from a fixed point (the pole), and θ is a magnitude of rotation from the polar axis. (820)

polar coordinates, [*r*, θ] The description of a point in a polar coordinate system. (820)

polar form of a complex number The description of a complex number using polar coordinates. (835)

polar grid A grid of rays and concentric circles radiating from a central point, used for plotting points and sketching curves in the polar plane. (822)

pole See *polar coordinate system*.

polynomial A sum of multiples of nonnegative integer powers of a variable or variables. (555)

polynomial function A function whose rule can be written as a polynomial. (557)

polynomial in *x* An expression of the form $a_n x^n + a_{n-1} x^{n-1} + a_{n-2} x^{n-2} + \ldots + a_1 x + a_0$ where *n* is a nonnegative integer and $a_n \neq 0$. Also called *the general form of a polynomial in one variable*. (557)

Polynomial Difference Theorem The function $y = f(x)$ is a polynomial function of degree *n* if and only if, for any set of *x*-values that form an arithmetic sequence, the *n*th differences of corresponding *y*-values are equal and nonzero. (571)

population The set of all individuals or objects to be studied. (6)

population standard deviation, σ See *standard deviation*.

population variance, σ^2 See *variance*.

position of a term in a sequence The domain value of a term in the sequence. (488)

positive relation A relation between two variables where larger values of one variable are associated with larger values of the other. (91)

power function A function *f* with an equation of the form $y = ax^n$, where *n* is an integer greater than 1. (181)

predicted values See *expected value*.

preimage The domain or set of domain values of a transformation. (167)

prime meridian The meridian through Greenwich, England, from which all other meridians are measured. (354)

probability A number which indicates the measure of certainty of an event. (425)

probability distribution A function which maps each value of a random variable onto its probability. (457)

probability of an event, *P(E)* If *E* is an event in a finite sample space *S*, and each outcome in *S* is equally likely, then the probability that *E* occurs, denoted *P(E)*, is given by $P(E) = \dfrac{\text{number of outcomes in the event}}{\text{number of outcomes in the sample space}}$. (428)

probability theory The branch of mathematics that studies chance. (426)

Probability of the Union of Mutually Exclusive Events Theorem If *A* and *B* are mutually exclusive events in the same finite sample space, then $P(A \cup B) = P(A) + P(B)$. (433)

Probability of a Union of Events Theorem (General Form) If *A* and *B* are any events in the same finite sample space, then $P(A \text{ or } B) = P(A \cup B) = P(A) + P(B) - P(A \cap B)$. (435)

Probability of Complements Theorem If *A* is any event, then $P(\text{not } A) = 1 - P(A)$. (437)

product matrix See *matrix multiplication*.

Product of Complex Numbers Theorem (Trigonometric Form) If $z_1 = r_1(\cos \theta_1 + i \sin \theta_1)$ and $z_2(\cos \theta_2 + i \sin \theta_2)$, then $z_1 z_2 = r_1 r_2(\cos (\theta_1 + \theta_2) + i \sin (\theta_1 + \theta_2))$. (841)

prolate spheroid See *spheroid*.

pseudo-random numbers Numbers generated by an algorithm (such as a computer program) that are very nearly, but not quite, random. (471)

Pythagorean identity For every θ, $\cos^2 \theta + \sin^2 \theta = 1$. (251)

quadratic function A function of the form $f(x) = ax^2 + bx + c$ where $a \neq 0$. (565)

quadratic models A quadratic function used to estimate data in a set. (120)

quadratic regression A method of finding an equation for the best-fitting parabola through a set of points. (123)

quadratic relation The set of ordered pairs (*x*, *y*) satisfying an equation of the form $Ax^2 + Bxy + Cy^2 + Dx + Ey + F = 0$, where at least one of *A*, *B*, and *C* is not zero. (753)

quadric surfaces Three-dimensional surfaces formed by the revolution of conics, all of which satisfy the general equation $Ax^2 + By^2 + Cz^2 + Dxy + Exz + Fyz + Gx + Hy + Iz + J = 0$. (798)

quartiles The three values which divide an ordered set into four subsets of approximately the same size. See *first (lower) quartile*, *second (middle) quartile*, and *third (lower) quartile*. (30)

919

quincunx A device, invented by Sir Francis Galton, used to illustrate binomial experiments, consisting of a box in which balls striking an array of pins form, at the bottom of the box, a normal distribution. Also called *Galton board*. (687)

quotient The answer to a division problem. For polynomials, the polynomial $q(x)$ when $f(x)$ is divided by $d(x)$, where $f(x) = q(x)d(x) + r(x)$, and either $r(x) = 0$ or the degree of $r(x)$ is less than the degree of $d(x)$. (579)

radian A unit for measuring an angle or the magnitude of a rotation. 2π radians $= 360°$. (233)

radical The symbol $\sqrt{}$ used to denote square roots or nth roots. (372)

rand A function on some calculators that automatically generates pseudo-random numbers. (472)

random numbers A set of numbers such that each number has the same probability of occurring, each pair of numbers has the same probability of occurring, each trio of numbers has the same probability of occurring, and so on. (466)

random variable A variable whose values are numbers determined by the outcome of an experiment. (457)

randomly A property of sampling a population so that every member of the population has an equal chance of being chosen. Also referred to as *at random*. (7)

range The difference between the highest and lowest values in a set. The set of values of the dependent variable in a function. (14, 82)

rank ordered Sequenced in order on some scale. (29)

Rational Exponent Theorem For all positive integers m and n, and all real numbers $x \geq 0$, $x^{m/n} = (x^{1/n})^m = (\sqrt[n]{x})^m$ and $x^{m/n} = (x^m)^{1/n} = \sqrt[n]{x^m}$. (377)

rational power function A function f with an equation of the form $f(x) = ax^{m/n}$, where m and n are nonzero integers and $a \neq 0$. (379)

raw data Data that has not been transformed or statistically manipulated. (216)

real axis The horizontal axis (axis of first coordinates) in a complex plane. (833)

real part of a complex number The real number a in the complex number $a + bi$. (591)

reciprocal trigonometric functions The secant, cosecant, and cotangent functions. (806)

rectangular hyperbola A hyperbola whose asymptotes are perpendicular to one another. (780)

recursive formula A formula for a sequence in which the first term or the first few terms are given, and then the nth term is expressed using the preceding term(s). (489)

Reflecting Property of an Ellipse Theorem If P is a point on an ellipse with foci F_1 and F_2, then $\overrightarrow{PF_1}$ and form $\overrightarrow{PF_2}$ equal angles with the line tangent to the ellipse at P. (794)

reflection-symmetric figure A figure that can be mapped onto itself by a reflection over some line ℓ. (179)

regression line See *line of best fit*.

relation A set of ordered pairs. (82)

relative extrema Relative maxima or relative minima. (564)

relative frequency The ratio of the number of times an event occurred to the number of times it could have occurred. (39, 430)

relative frequency distribution A function mapping events onto their relative frequencies. (39)

relative frequency histogram A histogram that displays the percent of values that fall into each interval of the histogram. (39)

relative maximum A point or value at which a function has a maximum on a specified interval. (564)

relative minimum A point or value at which a function has a minimum on a specified interval. (565)

remainder (in polynomial division) The polynomial $r(x)$ when $f(x)$ is divided by $d(x)$ and $f(x) = q(x)d(x) + r(x)$. Either $r(x) = 0$ or the degree of $r(x)$ is less than the degree of $d(x)$. (579)

Remainder Theorem If a polynomial $f(x)$ is divided by $x - c$, then the remainder is $f(c)$. (580)

removable singularity A point of discontinuity of a function that can be "removed" by adding a single point to the function. (817)

rescaling See *scaling*.

residual The difference between the observed value and a value predicted by a model. (134)

revolution A unit for measuring rotations. 1 revolution (counterclockwise) $= 360°$. (232)

root function A function that maps x onto some root of x, such as its square root. (370)

root of a polynomial function For the polynomial function $f(x) = a_n x^n + a_{n-1} x^{n-1} + \ldots + a_1 x + a_0$, any value of x such that $f(x) = 0$. Also called *zero* of the function. (565)

Roots and Coefficients of Polynomials Theorem For the polynomial equation $x^n + a_1 x^{n-1} + a_2 x^{n-2} + \ldots + a_{n-1} x + a_n = 0$, the sum of the roots is $-a_1$, the sum of the products of the roots two at a time is a_2, the sum of the roots three at a time is $-a_3, \ldots$, and the product of all of the roots is $\begin{cases} a_n, \text{ if } n \text{ is even,} \\ -a_n, \text{ if } n \text{ is odd} \end{cases}$. (614)

Roots of a Complex Number Theorem For any positive integer n, the n distinct roots of $z^n = r(\cos\theta + i\sin\theta), r > 0$, are
$$z = \sqrt[n]{r}\left[\cos\left(\frac{\theta}{n} + k\frac{360°}{n}\right) + i\sin\left(\frac{\theta}{n} + k\frac{360°}{n}\right)\right]$$
where $k = 0, 1, 2, \ldots, n - 1$. (848)

rose curve The graph of the polar equation $r = a\sin b\theta$ or $r = a\cos b\theta$, where b is a positive integer and $a \neq 0$. Also called *petal curve*. (829)

Rotation Matrix Theorem The matrix for R_θ, the rotation of magnitude θ about the origin, is $\begin{bmatrix} \cos\theta & -\sin\theta \\ \sin\theta & \cos\theta \end{bmatrix}$. (716)

rotation-symmetric figure A figure that can be mapped onto itself under a nonzero rotation. (179)

rounding-down function See *greatest integer function*.

rounding-up function, ⌈ ⌉ The function which pairs each number x with the smallest integer greater than or equal to x. Also called *ceiling function*. (130)

row matrix A matrix consisting of a single row. (699)

rubberband transformation A transformation that is the composite of scale changes and translations. (286)

Rule of 72 The formula $t = \frac{72}{r}$, used to estimate the length of time t it takes to double an investment at an interest rate of $r\%$. (408)

sample The subset of a population that is studied in an experiment. (6)

sample space The set of all possible outcomes of an experiment. (426)

sample standard deviation, s See *standard deviation*.

sample variance, s^2 See *variance*.

sampling distribution A distribution of the means of samples from the same population. (671)

SAS Area Formula for a Triangle The area of any triangle is one-half the product of the lengths of any two sides and the sine of their included angle. (328)

scale change (of data) A transformation that maps each data value x_i in a set of data $\{x_1, x_2, \ldots, x_n\}$ to ax_i, where a is a nonzero constant. (194)

scale change (in the plane) The transformation that maps (x, y) to (ax, by), where $a \neq 0$ and $b \neq 0$ are constants. (188)

scale factor The nonzero constant by which each data value is multiplied in a scale change. (194)

scale image The result of a scale change, or the point it represents. (194)

scaling Applying a scale change to a data set. Also called *rescaling*. (194)

scatterplot A graph of a finite set of ordered pairs in the coordinate plane. (46)

secant (sec) of a real number For any real number x, $\sec x = \frac{1}{\cos x}$, for $\cos x \neq 0$. (806)

second (middle) quartile The median of a set of data. (30)

second (of a degree) A unit for measuring angles. 60 seconds = 1 minute, and 3600 seconds = 1 degree. (312)

section See *cross section*.

sector (of a circle) A part of the circle's disk that is on or in the interior of a given central angle. (240)

Selections with Replacement Theorem Let S be a set with n elements. Then there are n^k possible arrangements of k elements from S with replacement. (441)

Selections without Replacement Theorem Let S be a set with n elements. Then there are $n!$ possible arrangements of the n elements without replacement. (442)

sequence A function whose domain is a set of consecutive integers greater than or equal to a fixed integer k. (488)

sequence of partial sums The sequence whose nth term is the sum of the first n terms of a given sequence. (516)

series An indicated sum of the terms of a sequence. (503)

sides (of an angle) See *angle*.

Σ (sigma) A symbol for sum. (21)

Σ (sigma-notation) See *summation notation*. (21)

significance level The level of probability (often 0.05 or 0.01) that is chosen to test a hypothesis. (643)

similar figures Figures in which one is the image of the other under a composite of reflections, rotations, translations, and/or size changes. (221)

simulation An experimental model of a situation that attempts to capture all aspects of the situation that affect the outcomes. (465)

sine function The function that maps x onto $\sin x$ for all x in its domain. (265)

sine (sin) of an acute angle θ in a right triangle $\frac{\text{leg opposite } \theta}{\text{hypotenuse}}$. (310)

sine (sin) of a real number x The second coordinate of the image of the point $(1, 0)$ under a rotation of magnitude x about the origin. (245)

sine wave The graph of the image of the sine or cosine function, under a composite of translations and scale changes. (231, 272)

singularity An isolated value for which a function is undefined. (816)

sinusoidal Varying in the manner of a sine wave of the sine function. (231)

size change A scale change in which the scale factors are equal; a transformation that maps (x, y) to (kx, ky), where k is a nonzero constant. (188)

slope For the segment joining (x_1, y_1) and (x_2, y_2), the number $(y_2 - y_1)/(x_2 - x_1)$. (47)

spherical triangle A triangle on a sphere whose sides are arcs of great circles of that sphere. (356)

Spherical Law of Cosines If ABC is a spherical triangle with sides a, b, and c, then $\cos c = \cos a \cos b + \sin a \sin b \cos c$. (356)

spheroid A three-dimensional figure formed by the equation $\frac{x^2}{a^2} + \frac{y^2}{b^2} + \frac{z^2}{c^2} = 1$, where at least two of a, b and c are equal. A **prolate spheroid** is formed by rotating an ellipse about its major axis. An **oblate spheroid** is created by rotating an ellipse about its minor exis. (798)

spread An indication of how the value of data in a set vary. (29)

square matrix A matrix with the same number of rows as columns. (735)

square numbers The values of the function $s(n) = n^2$, where n is an integer. (561)

square root A solution to an equation of the form $x^2 = k$. (370)

standard deviation The square root of the sample variance (s) or the population variance (σ). (54, 57)

921

standard form equation for a hyperbola   The hyperbola with foci $(c, 0)$ and $(-c, 0)$ and focal constant $2a$ has equation $\frac{x^2}{a^2} - \frac{y^2}{b^2} = 1$, where $b^2 = c^2 - a^2$. (770)

standard form equation for an ellipse   The ellipse with foci $(c, 0)$ and $(-c, 0)$ and focal constant $2a$ has equation $\frac{x^2}{a^2} + \frac{y^2}{b^2} = 1$, where $b^2 = a^2 - c^2$. (761)

standard normal curve   The graph of the function $f(x) = \frac{1}{\sqrt{2\pi}}e^{-x^2/2}$. (651)

standard normal distribution   The probability distribution represented by the standard normal curve. (651)

standard score   See *z-score*.

Standard Normal Distribution Table   A table that gives the area under the standard normal curve to the left of a given positive number a. (655, 875)

standardized data   Data that has been transformed into *z*-scores. (216)

standardizing a variable   The process of transforming a variable's data values into *z*-scores. (216)

statistical inference   Judgments using probabilities derived from statistical tests. (683)

statistics   The branch of mathematics dealing with the collection, organization, analysis, and interpretation of information, usually numerical information. (6)

statistics utility   A graphics calculator with statistics capability or statistics software for use on a computer. (19)

stemplot   A display of numerical data in which digits with higher place values are listed in a column as **stems** while digits with lower place values, called **leaves**, are listed in rows originating from their respective stems. Also called *stem-and-leaf diagram*. (13)

step function   A function whose graph resembles a series of steps. (128)

stretch   A vertical or horizontal scale change with magnitude > 1. (187, 188)

strictly decreasing   Said of a function that decreases across an interval, or across its entire domain. (108)

strictly increasing   Said of a function that increases across an interval, or across its entire domain. (108)

strong relation   A relation for which the data in a data set falls close to a line (or another specified curve). (91)

success (binomial)   See *binomial experiment*.

sum of an infinite series, S_∞, $\sum\limits_{i=1}^{\infty} a_i$ The limit of the sequence of partial sums $S_n = \sum\limits_{i=1}^{n} a_i$ of the series, provided the limit exists and is finite. (516)

summation notation   The use of the symbol Σ to represent a summation. Also called *sigma-notation* or Σ-*notation*. (21)

Sums and Differences of Cubes Theorem   For all x and y, $x^3 + y^3 = (x + y)(x^2 - xy + y^2)$ and $x^3 - y^3 = (x - y)(x^2 + xy + y^2)$. (604)

Sums and Difference of Odd Powers Theorem   For all x and y and for all odd positive integers n, $x^n + y^n = (x + y)(x^{n-1} - x^{n-2}y + x^{n-3}y^2 - \ldots - xy^{n-2} + y^{n-1})$ and $x^n - y^n = (x - y)(x^{n-1} + x^{n-2}y + x^{n-3}y^2 + \ldots + xy^{n-2} + y^{n-1})$. (605)

Supplements Theorem   For all θ in radians, $\sin(\pi - \theta) = \sin\theta$, $\cos(\pi - \theta) = -\cos\theta$, and $\tan(\pi - \theta) = -\tan\theta$. (253)

survey   A gathering of facts or opinions through an interview or questionnaire; to gather such facts. (6)

symmetric to the origin   A relation such that if (x, y) is on its graph then so is $(-x, -y)$. (180)

symmetric with respect to the *y*-axis   A relation such that, for each point (x, y) on its graph, the point $(-x, y)$ is on the graph. (179)

symmetric with respect to the *x*-axis   A relation such that, for each point (x, y) on its graph, the point $(x, -y)$ is on the graph. (180)

symmetry to a point P   See *point symmetry*.

table of random numbers   A listing of (pseudo-)random numbers used to simulate random situations. (466, Appendix C)

tangent function   The function that maps x onto $\tan x$ for all x in its domain. (267)

tangent (tan) of a real number x   For all real numbers x, $\frac{\sin x}{\cos x}$, if $\cos x \neq 0$. (246)

tangent (tan) of an acute angle in a right triangle $\frac{\text{leg opposite the angle}}{\text{leg adjacent to the angle}}$ (310)

term   An element in the range of a sequence. (488)

tessellation   A covering of the plane with congruent regions that overlap only on their boundaries. Also spelled *tesselation*. (546)

tetrahedral array   A three-dimensional array made up of layers of points arranged in triangular arrays. (570)

tetrahedral numbers   The values $T(n)$ of the sequence defined by
$$\begin{cases} T(1) = 1; \\ T(n) = T(n-1) + t(n), \text{ for all} \end{cases}$$
integers $n > 1$, where $t(n)$ is the nth triangular number. (570)

theory-based model   A model based on a concrete theory that explains why the model should fit the data. (120)

third (upper) quartile   In a data set, the median of the numbers greater than the set's median. (30)

time-series data   A function with a finite domain in which the independent variable is time. (46)

transformation   A one-to-one correspondence between sets of points. (159)

translation (in the plane)   A transformation that maps each point (x, y) to $(x + h, y + k)$, where h and k are constants. (168)

translation (of data)   A transformation that maps each x_i of a data set to $x_i + h$, where h is some constant. (173)

translation image   The result of a translation. (167, 173)

922

tree diagram   A method of graphically presenting the possible outcomes of a sample space by using a network of branches, resembling a tree. (440)

trial   One of the instances of an experiment. (465, 540)

triangular numbers   The values of the sequence $t(n) = \frac{n(n + 1)}{2}$. (561)

trigonometric equation   An equation in which the variable to be found is in an argument of a trigonometric function. (346)

trigonometric form of a complex number   The form $r(\cos \theta + i \sin \theta)$ of the complex number $a + bi$. (840)

trigonometric functions   The sine, cosine, tangent, cotangent, secant, and cosecant functions and their offspring. Also called *circular functions*. (309)

trigonometry   The branch of mathematics that deals with the study of the circular functions, and the relations between sides and angles of triangles using these functions. (309)

trinomial   A polynomial with three terms. (558)

2 × 2 Identity Matrix   The matrix $\begin{bmatrix} 1 & 0 \\ 0 & 1 \end{bmatrix}$, which maps any point (x, y) to itself. (705)

unbiased   See *fair*.

union, $A \cup B$ The set of all elements that are either in set A or set B, or in both. (433)

unit circle   The circle with center at the origin and radius 1. (245)

univariate data   Data involving a single variable. (81)

upper quartile   See *third quartile*.

variable (in statistics)   A characteristic of a person or thing which can be classified, counted, ordered, or measured. (6)

variance, s^2, σ^2   In a data set, the sum of the squared deviations of the data from the mean divided by one less than the number of elements in the set (sample variance s^2) or by the number of elements in the set (population variance σ^2). (56, 57)

variance of a probability distribution   For a probability distribution $\{(x_i, P(x_i)\}$ with n outcomes and mean μ,
$$\sigma^2 = \sum_{i=1}^{n} x_i^2 \cdot P(x_i)) - \mu^2.\ (636)$$

Variance and Standard Deviation of a Binomial Distribution Theorem   In a binomial distribution with n trials, probability p of success and probability q of failure on each trial, the variance $\sigma^2 = npq$, and the standard deviation $\sigma = \sqrt{npq}$. (637)

Venn diagram   A method of displaying unions and intersections of sets, using circles. (433)

vertex (of a cone)   The point of intersection of the two lines used in the generation of a cone. (754)

vertex (of an angle)   See *angle*.

vertical line test   A test to determine whether a set of ordered pairs in the coordinate plane is a function; if there exists a vertical line that intersects the set in more that one point, then the set is not a function. (84)

vertical scale change   A transformation that maps (x, y) to (x, by), where $b \neq 0$ is a constant. (187)

vertical scale factor   The number b in the transformation that maps (x, y) to (ax, by). (188)

vertices of a hyperbola   The points where a hyperbola intersects the axis that contains the foci. (772)

vector processor   A high-speed computer processor designed to multiply a matrix row and a matrix column in one step. (741)

viewing window   The subset of the coordinate plane that appears on the screen of an automatic grapher. Also called *viewing rectangle*. (160)

weak relation   A relation for which, although a linear trend can be seen, many points are not very close to the line (or another specified curve). (92)

whispering gallery   An ellipsoidal room where whispers from one focus can be heard at the other focus even though the two foci are quite far apart. (793)

window   See *viewing window*.

world coordinates   Coordinate systems which are used for representing three-dimensional objects. (741)

yield   The actual percentage accrued to the principal in an investment annually, given by $\left(1 + \frac{r}{n}\right)^n$, where r is the annual interest rate and n is the number of compoundings per year. (391)

z-score   The value $z = \frac{x - \bar{x}}{s}$ for a member x of a data set with mean $\bar{x}$ and standard deviation s. (216)

Zero Exponent Theorem   If b is an nonzero real number, $b^0 = 1$. (378)

zero of a function   For a function f, a value of x such that $f(x) = 0$. (565)

923

Algebra

$\approx$	is approximately equal to
$\pm$	positive or negative
e	the base of the natural logarithms $\approx 2.71828\ldots$
π	pi
∞	infinity
!	factorial
$\lvert x \rvert$	absolute value of x
$\sqrt{x}$	positive square root of x
$\sqrt[n]{x}$	nth root of x
$a + bi$	complex number
(a, b)	rectangular coordinates; rectangular form of a complex number
$[r, \theta]$	polar coordinates; polar form of a complex number
$r(\cos\theta + i\sin\theta)$	trigonometric form of a complex number
$\bar{z}$	complex conjugate of a complex number
$\lvert z \rvert$	modulus of a complex number
i	imaginary unit, $\sqrt{-1}$
$\begin{bmatrix} a & b \\ c & d \end{bmatrix}$	2×2 matrix

Functions and Sequences

$\lim\limits_{n \to \infty} a_n$	limit of sequence a as n approaches infinity
a_n	nth term of sequence a
$\sum\limits_{i=1}^{n} x_i$	summation notation; the sum $x_1 + x_2 + \ldots + x_n$
S_∞	sum of the infinite series S
$\log x$	common logarithm of x
$\log_b x$	logarithm of x to the base b
$\ln x$	natural logarithm of x
$\lfloor x \rfloor$	greatest integer function of x, or floor function of x
$\lceil x \rceil$	ceiling function of x
f^{-1}	inverse function of f
$f \circ g$	composite of functions f and g
$x \to \infty$	x approaches infinity

Geometry

$\overleftrightarrow{AB}$	line through A and B
$\overrightarrow{AB}$	ray from A passing through B
$\overline{AB}$	segment with endpoints A and B
AB	distance from A to B

$\angle ABC$	angle ABC
$\mathrm{m}\angle ABC$	measure of angle ABC
$\triangle ABC$	triangle with vertices A, B, and C
$ABCD$	polygon with vertices A, B, C, and D
$/\!/$	is parallel to
$\cong$	is congruent to
$\sim$	is similar to
$T_{h,k}$	translation of h units horizontally and k units vertically
$S_{a,b}$	scale change with horizontal magnitude a and vertical magnitude b
S_a	size change of magnitude a
R_θ	rotation of magnitude θ
r_x	reflection over the x-axis
r_y	reflection over the y-axis
$r_{y=x}$	reflection over the line $y = x$
r_ℓ	reflection over line ℓ

Probability

$_nP_r$	number of permutations of n elements taken r at a time
$_nC_r$ or $\binom{n}{r}$	number of combinations of n elements taken r at a time
$A \cup B$	union of sets A and B
$A \cap B$	intersection of sets A and B
$N(A)$	number of elements of set A
$P(E)$	probability of event E

Statistics

$\bar{x}$	mean of a data set or of a sample
s	standard deviation of a data set or of a sample
s^2	variance of a data set or of a sample
μ	Greek letter mu, mean of a population, or expected value of a probability distribution
σ	Greek letter sigma, standard deviation of a population or of a probability distribution
σ^2	variance of a population or of a probability distribution
$\mu_{\bar{x}}$	mean of the distribution of sample means
$\sigma_{\bar{x}}$	standard deviation of the distribution of sample means
r	correlation coefficient
$B(k)$	binomial distribution function
H_0	null hypothesis
H_1	alternative hypothesis

934

Acknowledgments

Unless otherwise acknowledged, all photographs are the property of Addison Wesley Educational Publishers, Inc. Page abbreviations are as follows: (t) top, (c) center, (b) bottom, (l) left, (r) right.

ix Randy Faris/Westlight vi(r) Superstock, Inc. vi(l) Superstock, Inc. vii(r) Japack/Westlight vii(l) Superstock, Inc. viii Curtis Martin/Photographic Resources x Japack/Westlight 4-5(b) Paolo Koch/Photo Researchers 4(t&bl) Superstock, Inc. 4-5(c) Superstock, Inc. 5(tr) Centers for Disease Control 5(tl) Superstock, Inc. 6 John Olson/Stock Market 7 Stephen Frisch/Stock Boston 11 Christopher Brown/Stock Boston 15 King Features Syndicate 21 Richard Laird/FPG International Corp. 26 United Feature Syndicate 30 David Young-Wolff/PhotoEdit 35 James Porto/FPG International Corp. 39 Bob Daemmrich/Image Works 42 Tom Stewart/Stock Market 46 Miro Vintoniv/Stock Boston 54 Tom Strattman/AP/Wide World 61(t) The Byron Collection/Museum of the City of New York 62 Signing of the Constitution, National Historical Park Collections, Eastern National Parks & Monuments Association 64 Erich Lessing/Art Resource 65(b) James Monroe Memorial Library 65(c) Rare Book Room/New York Public Library, Astor, Lenox & Tilden Foundations 65(t) Independence Historic Park Collection/Eastern National Parks & Monuments Association 66 Joel Sartore/Grant Heilman Photography 67(all) Superstock, Inc. 68(all) Superstock, Inc. 69(tr&b) Superstock, Inc. 80-81(all) Superstock, Inc. 82 Richard Ellis/Sygma 89 Superstock, Inc. 95 Joseph Thorn 96 NASA 97 Zoom/Allsport 102 Mike Powell/Allsport 105 Superstock, Inc. 106 Bachmann/Stock Boston 109 Ted Wood/Tony Stone Images 112 Phil Degginger/Tony Stone Images 113 Dr. Jeremy Burgess/SPL/Photo Researchers 114 Corbis/Bettmann 121 John Moore 124 Robert Maier/Animals Animals 127(b) D. R. Specker/Animals Animals 130(b) Cameramann International, Ltd. 130(t) George Hunter/Tony Stone Images 132 John Livzey/Tony Stone Images 134 Superstock, Inc. 140 Peter Correz/Tony Stone Images 141 UPI/Corbis-Bettmann 148 Warren Morgan/Westlight 149(l) Orion Press/Westlight 149(tr, tc, br) Superstock, Inc. 158-159(l) Superstock, Inc. 158-159(c) Carol Barrington/TexStock Photo Inc. 158(b, tl), 159(b) Superstock, Inc. 160 State Road Commission of Utah 163 Fletcher/Bhylis/Photo Researchers 165 Harvey Lloyd/Stock Market 167 Pal Hermansen/Tony Stone Images 172 Ken Biggs/Tony Stone Images 173 Tony Duffy/Allsport 174 Bachmann/Stock Boston 180 N. Corraro/Sygma 187 Superstock, Inc. 193 Joe Cornish/Tony Stone Images 197 AP/Wide World 201(tl, tr, tcr, tcl, b) John Fitzgerald Kennedy Library 201(cr) AP/Wide World 201(cl) Frank J. Scherschel 207 James King-Holmes/SPL/Photo Researchers 213 Sidney Harris 214 AP/Wide World 215 Jack Manning/New York Times 219 Superstock, Inc. 221(b) Randy Faris/Westlight 221(t) Daniel J. Cox/Tony Stone Images 224 Superstock, Inc. 227 Steve Curtis 230(b) Japack/Westlight 230-231(t&c) Superstock, Inc. 230(cl) Leo de Wys, Inc. 231(b) Superstock, Inc. 231(r&cc) Cameramann International, Ltd. 234 Steve Elmore/Stock Market 236 Raj Kamal/Earth Scenes 237 NASA 239 Vandystadt/Allsport 241 Mike Andrews/Earth Scenes 249 Superstock, Inc. 251 Scala/Art Resource 257, 262, 271 Superstock, Inc. 272 Cameramann International, Ltd. 275, 276 Richard Megna/Fundamental Photographs 278 Joe Sohm/Stock Market 280 Cameramann International, Ltd. 284 Nancy Sefton/Photo Researchers 292 Chuck Pefley/Tony Stone Images 295 NASA 297 Chris Arend/AlaskaStock 299 Superstock, Inc. 300(b) Aaron Jones Studios/Tony Stone Images 300(t) Joerg Hardtke/Tony Stone Images 305 Cameramann International, Ltd. 308-309(br), 308(bl&c) Superstock, Inc. 308(t) R. Ian Loyd/Westlight 309(t) Curtis Martin/Photographic Resources 310 Gary Braasch/Tony Stone Images 313 Carolyn A. McKeone/Photo Researchers 316 Stephen Dunn/Allsport 327 Tom Bean/Tony Stone Images 334 NASA 339 Tom Stewart/Stock Market 341 Joe Towers/Check Six 343 Joseph Nettis/Stock Boston 344 Larry Ulrich/Tony Stone Images 346 Kevin Horan/Tony Stone Images 351 Chad Slattery/Tony Stone Images 353 Robert Llewellyn 358 Anthony Cassidy/Tony Stone Images 360(b) Charles D. Winters/Photo Researchers 360(tr) Scott Camazine/Photo Researchers 360(tl), 361(b) Superstock, Inc. 361(t) Westlight 368-369(t), 368(tl), 369(b) Superstock, Inc. 368-369(c) Ralph Clevenger/Westlight 368(b) Dennis Degnan/Westlight 374 Mel Lindstrom/Tony Stone Images 381 Mark C. Burnett/Photo Researchers 383 Courtesy, IBM Corporation 388 Everett Collection, Inc. 393 Mark Petersen/Tony Stone Images 394, 395 NASA 399 AP/Wide World 402 Russell D. Curtis/Photo Researchers 405 P. Plailly/Eurelios/SPL/Photo Researchers 408 Private Collection 409 Renee Lynn/Photo Researchers 411 J. H. Robinson/Photo Researchers

415 F. Stuart Westmorland/Photo Researchers 416, 417 Superstock, Inc. 424(c&br), 425(c) Superstock, Inc. 424(bl) Robert Landau/Westlight 424(t) Myron Taplin/Tony Stone Images 426 Michael Orton/Tony Stone Images 427 Bob Shaw/Stock Market 434 Peter Kiar/University of Chicago 439 Jonathan Daniel/Allsport 441 ©1968 United Feature Syndicate, Inc. Reprinted by permission of UFS, Inc. 441 United Feature Syndicate 443 John Margolies/Esto Photographics Inc. 444 Thomas Sennett/Magnum Photos 447 Everett Collection, Inc. 453 Joe Towers/Check Six 455 Hamman/Heldring/Animals Animals 457 Penny Gentieu/Tony Stone Images 461 Sygma 464 Gerard LACZ/Animals Animals 466 Lawrence Migdale/Tony Stone Images 469 Art Wolfe/Tony Stone Images 470 Bob Daemmrich/Stock Boston 478(all) Superstock, Inc. 483 Richard During/Tony Stone Images 485 David Lissman/Image Works 486-487(all) Superstock, Inc. 488 Bruce Iverson 492 Courtesy, Ford Motor Company 494 Lori Adamski Peek/Tony Stone Images 496 Lucia Eames dba Eames Office, ©1961, 1997, www.eamesoffice.com 504 Walter Sanders, Courtesy Stadtisches Museum, Brunswick, Germany 512 Kunsthistorisches Museum, Art History Museum, Burgring 5 A-101, Vienna, Austria 513 Jon Feingersh/Stock Boston 520 Cameramann International, Ltd. 521 Tom Carroll/FPG International Corp. 522 J. Sneesby/B. Wilkins/Tony Stone Images 524 Ulrike Welsch/PhotoEdit 525 Lawrence Migdale/Stock Boston 528 Reprinted with permission, The Chicago Sun-Times ©1996 530 Hand-colored by Cheryl Kucharzak 534(b) Kathi Lamm/Tony Stone Images 536 Corbis-Bettmann Archive 539 John Lawrence/Tony Stone Images 540 Hank Morgan/SS/Photo Researchers 540(inset) Dr. Gopal Murti/SPL/Photo Researchers 543 Robert Mizono 544 Cameramann International, Ltd. 546 Courtesy, Bausch & Lomb, Hand-colored by Cheryl Kucharzak 554-555(all) Superstock, Inc. 556 Comstock Inc. 558, 562 Superstock, Inc. 569 Walter Chandoha 576(t) Superstock, Inc. 589 Andrea Renault/Globe Photos, Inc. 602 Larry Lefever/Grant Heilman Photography 607 Charles Gupton/Stock Boston 611 Mark Gamba/Stock Market 616 Walter Chandoha 626(b) Bill Ross/Westlight 626(tl) Superstock, Inc. 626-627(c) Doug Wilson/Westlight 626-627(tr) Randy Faris/Westlight 627(b) Walter Hodges/Westlight 631 Doug Pensinger/Allsport 634 Jose More/©1996 Copyrighted, The Chicago Tribune. All Rights Reserved. 637 Kevin R. Morris/Tony Stone Images 639 Globe Photos, Inc. 645 Robert Maier/Animals Animals/Earth Scenes 646 Focus on Sports, Inc. 647 Superstock, Inc. 648 David McGlynn/FPG International Corp. 651 Eastern National Park and Monument Association/Independence National Historical Park Collection 666 Brent Jones 678 Laura Dwight 679 By permission of Johnny Hart and Creators Syndicate, Inc. 681 University of California, Berkeley 686 Superstock, Inc. 688 Jim Richardson/Westlight 694 Superstock, Inc. 696-697(b), 696(tl) Superstock, Inc. 696-697(tr) Photri, Inc. 696(b) W. Cody/Westlight 697(b) Ron Watts/Westlight 701 Stephen Crowley/New York Times 703(t) Dawn Murray 706 Superstock, Inc. 714 Paul Griffin/Stock Boston 720 Everett Collection, Inc. 721 Berenguier/Jerrican/Photo Researchers 725 Bob Daemmrich/Stock Boston 729 Focus on Sports, Inc. 730 David M. Grossman/Photo Researchers 738 Courtesy Evans and Sutherland 742 STAR WARS ™ © Lucasfilm Ltd. 1997. All Rights Reserved. 745 Focus on Sports, Inc. 752-753(c) Superstock, Inc. 752-753(br) Michael Busselle/Tony Stone Images 752(bl) Branson Reynolds/Index Stock Photography, Inc. 752(tl), 753(t) Superstock, Inc. 757 Corbis-Bettmann 759 Ronald Sheridan/Ancient Art & Architecture Collection 763 Sidney Harris 764 Vivian Hoette 765 Lawrence Sromovsky, University of Wisconsin-Madison, NASA 766 Galleria Borghese, Rome, Italy/Art Resource 767 NASA 782 National Portrait Gallery, London 792 Ralph Cowan/FPG International Corp. 793 Museum of Science and Industry, Chicago 795 Eduardo Garcia/FPG International Corp. 796 NASA 801(b) Erich Lessing/Art Resource 801(t) HST Comet Team/NASA 804-805(tr) Bill Ross/Westlight 804(b) Stock Connection 804-805(c) Allen Prier/Panoramic Images 804(tl) The Dickmans/Westlight 805(b) Orion Press/Westlight 807 Michael Newman/PhotoEdit 809 A. Ramey/PhotoEdit 817 L. Ferrarese, Johns Hopkins University/NASA 819 Bob Daemmrich/Tony Stone Images 826 Joe Towers/Hall, George/Check Six 829(all) Walter Chandoha 830, 832 Superstock, Inc. 837 Everett Collection, Inc. 859 From THE BEAUTY OF FRACTALS by Peitgen & Richter, ©1986, Springer-Verlag, Berlin, Heidelberg 862 Sidney Harris 865 From THE BEAUTY OF FRACTALS by Peitgen & Richter, ©1986 Springer-Verlag, Berlin, Heidelberg

CHAPTER 12 REVIEW, pp. 802–803

27. The endpoints of the axes of the ellipse are (1, 0), (-1, 0), (0, 4), and (0, -4).

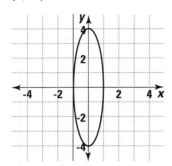

28. The vertices of the hyperbola are (1, 0), and (-1, 0), and its asymptotes have equations $y = \pm 4x$.

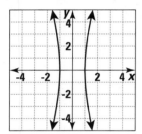

29. The vertices of the hyperbola are $(0, \pm\sqrt{40})$ and its asymptotes have equations $y = \pm\frac{\sqrt{40}}{3}x$.

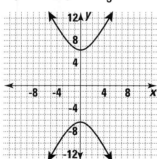

30. The endpoints of the axes of the ellipse are $(\pm 7, 0)$ and $(0, \pm\sqrt{20})$.

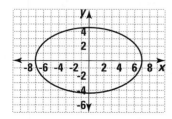

31. The hyperbola has vertices (0, ±1) and the equations of its asymptotes are $y = \pm x$.

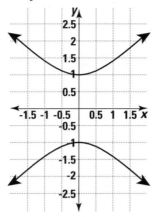

32. The vertices of the hyperbola are $(\pm 10, 0)$; the equations of its asymptotes are $y = \pm\frac{3}{10}x$.

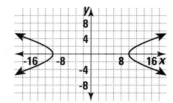

35. The ellipse has center (4, -2) and the endpoints of its axes are (-1, -2), (9, -2), (4, 0), and (4, -4).

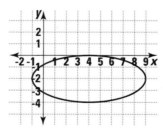

36. The hyperbola has center (-8, 3), vertices (-12, 3) and (-4, 3), and asymptotes with equations $y - 3 = \pm\frac{1}{4}(x + 9)$ or $y = \frac{1}{4}x + 5$ and $y = -\frac{1}{4}x + 1$.

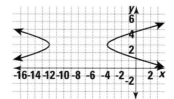

37. The hyperbola has vertices $(\sqrt{20}, \sqrt{20})$ and $(-\sqrt{20}, -\sqrt{20})$. Its asymptotes are the x-axis and the y-axis.

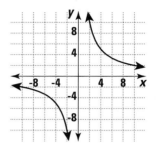

38.

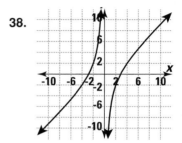

LESSON 13-3, p. 818

8. a. $y = \frac{\tan x}{\sec x}$ $y = \csc x$

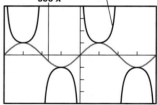

$-2\pi \le x \le 2\pi$, x-scale $= \frac{\pi}{2}$

$-4 \le y \le 4$,   y-scale $= 1$

b. Not an identity

9. a.

$-2\pi \le x \le 2\pi$,   x-scale $= \frac{\pi}{2}$

$-1.5 \le y \le 1.5$,   y-scale $= 1$

9. b. $\sin 2x$ | $\dfrac{2\tan x}{1+\tan^2 x}$

$= 2\sin x \cos x$ | $= \dfrac{2\frac{\sin x}{\cos x}}{\sec^2 x}$

| $= \dfrac{2\frac{\sin x}{\cos x}}{\frac{1}{\cos^2 x}}$

| $= 2\dfrac{\sin x}{\cos x}\cdot\cos^2 x$

| $= 2\sin x \cos x$

So, $\sin 2x = \dfrac{2\tan x}{1+\tan^2 x}$ for all x such that $x \neq \dfrac{\pi}{2}+n\pi$, for all integers n.

10. a.

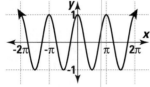

b. $x \neq \dfrac{\pi}{2}+n\pi$ for all integers n

c. $\dfrac{1-\tan^2 x}{1+\tan^2 x}=\cos 2x$

d. $\dfrac{1-\tan^2 x}{1+\tan^2 x}=\dfrac{1-\frac{\sin^2 x}{\cos^2 x}}{\sec^2 x}=\dfrac{1-\frac{\sin^2 x}{\cos^2 x}}{\frac{1}{\cos^2 x}}$

$=\cos^2 x\left(1-\dfrac{\sin^2 x}{\cos^2 x}\right)$

$=\cos^2 x - \sin^2 x = \cos 2x,$
for all x such that $x \neq \dfrac{\pi}{2}+n\pi$, for all integers n.

11. a.

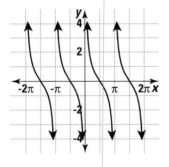

b. $x \neq \dfrac{n\pi}{2}$ for all integers n

c. $\dfrac{1+\cos 2x}{\sin 2x}=\cot x$

d. $\dfrac{1+\cos 2x}{\sin 2x}$

$=\dfrac{1+2\cos^2 x - 1}{2\sin x \cos x}=\dfrac{2\cos^2 x}{2\sin x \cos x}$

$=\dfrac{\cos^2 x}{\sin x \cos x}=\dfrac{\cos x}{\sin x}=\cot x,$ for

all x such that $x \neq \dfrac{n\pi}{2}$, for all integers n.

12. b. $\tan x + \cot x$ | $\sec x \csc x$

$=\dfrac{\sin x}{\cos x}+\dfrac{\cos x}{\sin x}$ | $=\dfrac{1}{\cos x}\cdot\dfrac{1}{\sin x}$

$=\dfrac{\sin^2 x}{\sin x \cos x}$ |

$+\dfrac{\cos^2 x}{\sin x \cos x}$ | $=\dfrac{1}{\sin x \cos x}$

$=\dfrac{\sin^2 x + \cos^2 x}{\sin x \cos x}$ |

$=\dfrac{1}{\sin x \cos x}$ |

So, $\tan x + \cot x = \sec x \csc x$ for all x such that $x \neq \dfrac{n\pi}{2}$, for all integers n.

13. b. $\csc^2 x \sin x$ | $\dfrac{\sec^2 x - \tan^2 x}{\sin x}$

$=\dfrac{1}{\sin^2 x}\cdot\sin x$ | $=\dfrac{1}{\sin x}$

$=\dfrac{1}{\sin x}$ |

So, $\csc^2 x \sin x = \dfrac{\sec^2 x - \tan^2 x}{\sin x}$ for all x such that $x \neq \dfrac{n\pi}{2}$, for all integers n.

14. a.

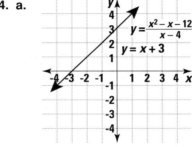

$y=\dfrac{x^2-x-12}{x-4}$

$y=x+3$

d. $\dfrac{x^2-x-12}{x-4}=\dfrac{(x-4)(x+3)}{x-4}$
$= x+3$, for all x such that $x \neq 4$.

16. a.

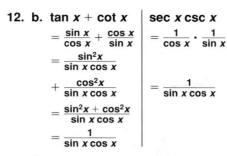

$\dfrac{x^2}{16}-\dfrac{y^2}{9}=1$

$\dfrac{x^2}{16}+\dfrac{y^2}{9}=1$

From the graphs, the solutions are (4, 0) and (-4, 0).

16. b.

$\dfrac{x^2}{16}-\dfrac{y^2}{9}=1$

$+\dfrac{x^2}{16}+\dfrac{y^2}{9}=1$

$\overline{\dfrac{2x^2}{16}=2}$

Therefore, $x^2 = 16$. That is, $x = 4$ or $x = -4$. From $\dfrac{(\pm 4)^2}{16}+\dfrac{y^2}{9}=1$, $y^2 = 0$. So $y = 0$. Thus, the solutions are (4, 0) and (-4, 0).

LESSON 13-6, pp. 836–837

18.

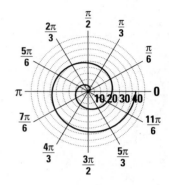

19.

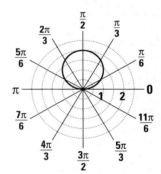

20.

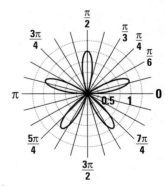

28. b.

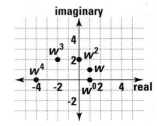

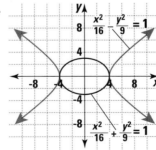

51.

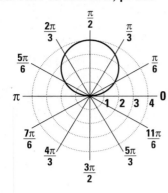

52.

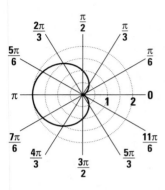

53. a.

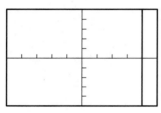

$-5 \leq x \leq 5,$ x-scale $= 1$
$-5 \leq y \leq 5,$ y-scale $= 1$

b. For $\theta \neq \frac{\pi}{2} + n\pi$, where n is an integer, $r = 4 \sec \theta = \frac{4}{\cos \theta}$
$\Leftrightarrow r \cos \theta = 4 \Leftrightarrow x = 4$, which is a line.

54. a.

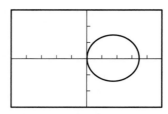

$-0.5 \leq x \leq 0.5,$ x-scale $= 0.1$
$-0.3 \leq y \leq 0.3,$ y-scale $= 0.1$

b. $r = \frac{1}{3} \cos \theta \Rightarrow r = \frac{1}{3} \cdot \frac{x}{r}$
$\Rightarrow r^2 = \frac{x}{3} \Rightarrow x^2 + y^2 = \frac{x}{3}$
$\Rightarrow x^2 - \frac{x}{3} + y^2 = 0$
$\Rightarrow \left(x - \frac{1}{6}\right)^2 + y^2 = \frac{1}{36}$

It is a circle with center $\left(\frac{1}{6}, 0\right)$ and radius $\frac{1}{6}$.

55, 56.

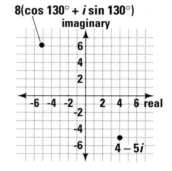

57. a.

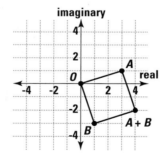

57. b. Let $C = A + B = 4 - 2i$.
The slope of $\overline{OA} = \frac{1 - 0}{3 - 0} = \frac{1}{3}$;
the slope of $\overline{BC} = \frac{-2 - -3}{4 - 1} = \frac{1}{3}$;
the slope of $\overline{OB} = \frac{-3 - 0}{1 - 0} = -3$;
and the slope of $\overline{AC} = \frac{-2 - 1}{4 - 3} = -3$.

Because the slopes of both pairs of opposite sides of $OACB$ are equal, the opposite sides are parallel and $OACB$ is a parallelogram.

58. a.

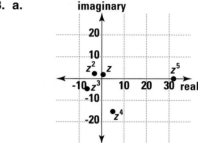

b. $z^5 = [2(\cos 72° + i \sin 72°)]^5$
$= 2^5(\cos 5 \cdot 72°$
$+ i \sin 5 \cdot 72°)$
$= 32(\cos 360° + i \sin 360°)$
$= 32(1 + i \cdot 0) = 32$

INDEX

NOTES   NOTES